GROWTH

including

Reproduction and Morphological Development

GROWTH

including

Reproduction and Morphological Development

COMPILED AND EDITED BY

Philip L. Altman and Dorothy S. Dittmer

PREPARED UNDER THE AUSPICES OF THE Committee on Biological Handbooks

Federation of American Societies for Experimental Biology
WASHINGTON, D. C.

MADE IN THE UNITED STATES OF AMERICA

Library of Congress Catalog Card Number: 62-21069

FOREWORD

GROWTH is the second of the Biological Handbooks to be issued under the general direction of the Committee on Biological Handbooks of the Federation of American Societies for Experimental Biology. This volume continues a series of handbooks prepared under the auspices of the National Academy of Sciences - National Research Council, the first of which was published in 1952.

This handbook presents comprehensive data on various aspects of normal growth, specifically compiled for reference purposes and critically evaluated. It contains verifiable data collected from the world literature together with references for those who wish a more comprehensive treatment of some particular item. Because of the limits of time, budget, and human frailty there will undoubtedly be omissions and errors which, we hope, will be brought to our attention for correction in future volumes.

The Committee on Biological Handbooks has the responsibility for the selection of fields to be covered during any particular period of time and guidance on the nature of the final product. For each book an Advisory Committee meets as often as is necessary in order to determine what should be included, and what should be excluded from the volume. They also make suggestions as to authorities in particular fields who should be asked to contribute their services. Original tables are sent in by one or more contributors. When necessary, these are integrated by the staff and sent to two or more reviewers for critical evaluation. With the aid of Committee and Advisory Committee members, the staff have been able to obtain remarkable cooperation in this and in previous volumes.

From the material contributed, the staff compile the data into tables that conform to our standards, and after review they compose and edit these. Because of the nature of the study it has been found more efficient to have composition, editing, indexing, and preparation of camera-ready copy done entirely within the office of Biological Handbooks.

On behalf of the Committee on Biological Handbooks, acknowledgement is made to numerous scientists who have been so liberal with their time and advice. The Committee also wishes to thank the National Institutes of Health, the National Science Foundation, and the Aeronautical Systems Division of the United States Air Force for the generous support and cooperation which have made possible the production of this book. Participation in this undertaking was fulfilled under National Institutes of Health Grant No. GM 06553, National Science Foundation Grant No. NSF-G21794, and Air Force Contract No. AF 33(616)-6773.

Washington, D.C.
October 1, 1962

Raymund L. Zwemer

. . . .

CONTRIBUTORS AND REVIEWERS

Abbott, R. Tucker
Afzelius, Björn A.
Aldrich, Frederick A.
Allen, George S.
Allen, Gordon
Allen, M. B.
Almquist, J. O.
Altland, Paul D.
Alvarez, Walter C.
Anderson, Lewis E.
Andrewartha, H. G.
Anson, Barry J.
Arey, Leslie B.
Arimoto, Kunitaro
Armer, Sister Joseph Marie
Asdell, S. A.
Asmundson, V. S.
Atlas, Meyer
Austin, Mary L.
Avery, James K.

Barratt, R. W.
Barrows, Charles H.
Bartelmez, George W.
Barton, Lela V.
*Bast, T. H.
Bateman, Angus J.
Bayley, Nancy
Beal, James A.
Beatty, R. A.
Beneke, E. S.
Bennett, W. F.
Biesele, John J.
Bishop, Harlow
Bishopp, Fred C.
Bittner, John J.
Blair, Albert P.
Blandau, Richard J.
Bold, Harold C.
Bookhout, C. G.
Böving, Bent G.
Boyd, Edith
Brase, Karl D.
Brown, James W.
Brown, Relis B.
Bruner, D. W.
Bumgardner, Harvey L.
Burns, George W.
Butler, L.
Butzel, Henry M., Jr.

Cable, Louella E.
Cagle, Fred R.
Calder, D. M.
Calhoun, John B.
Caplin, Samuel M.
Carlander, Kenneth D.
Carmichael, Leonard
Carriker, Melbourne R.
Castle, W. E.
Cave, Marion S.
Chang, M. C.
Chase, Samuel W.
Chen, T. T.
Chester, K. Starr

Clark, Clarence F.
Clark, Eliot R.
*Clark, Herbert C.
Cole, LaMont C.
Cooke, Wm. Bridge
Cooper, J. P.
Corliss, John O.
Cornman, Ivor
Craft, W. A.
Craigie, J. H.
Crandall, Lee S.
Crown, R. M.
Crum, Howard A.
Cutkomp, Laurence K.

D'Amato, Francesco
Damon, Albert
Darlington, C. D.
Darnell, Rezneat M.
Davis, David E.
Davis, Hallowell
Delisle, Albert L.
Dittmer, Howard J.
Downs, R. J.
DuBois, R. Callery
*Duca, Charles J.
Duggan, T. L.
Duggins, Oliver H.
Duke, Kenneth L.
Dupre, Margaret V.

Eakin, Robert E.
Eaton, Orson N.
Ehret, Charles F.
Eichbaum, Francisco W.
Elliott, F. I.
Emlen, John T., Jr.
*Engle, Earl T.
Erickson, Ralph O.
Evans, Titus C.
Ewing, K. P.

*Farris, Edmond J.
Firket, Henri
Fitch, Henry S.
Fitch, John E.
Fortmann, Henry R.
Foster, Adriance S.
Franzén, Åke

Gardner, Theodore R.
Gardner, William U.
Garn, Stanley M.
*Garner, W. W.
Gifford, Warren
Glass, Bentley
Glinos, André D.
Glucksmann, A.
Goodnight, Clarence J.
Gordon, Morris A.
Graham, John B.
Green, Margaret C.
Gresson, R. A. R.
Greulach, Victor A.
Grigsby, B. H.

Grove, Robert D.
Gruenwald, Peter

Haeussler, G. J.
Hagen, Charles W., Jr.
Hamilton, Howard L.
Hammond, John
Hansberry, Roy
Hansch, Corwin
Hanson, Earl D.
Hardy, Ross
Harrar, E. S.
Harrison, R. J.
Hartman, Olga
Hartweg, Norman
Hathaway, Milicent L.
Hayflick, Leonard
Henderson, Earl W.
Herrington, L. P.
Hertig, Arthur T.
Hesse, Claron O.
Heston, W. E.
Hetzer, Herbert O.
Hewitt, Harold B.
Heyner, Susan
Hickey, Joseph J.
Hines, Marion
Hoffman, Joseph Gilbert
Hollander, Franklin
Hooker, Davenport
Hoskins, W. M.
Hughes, Arthur
Hull, Fred H.
Hurme, V. O.
Hutt, F. B.

Irwin, M. R.
Isaac, Leo A.

Jennison, Marshall W.
Johnson, B. Connor
Johnson, Elton L.
Johnstone, Donald B.
Josephson, Horace R.
Justice, O. L.

Kampmeier, Otto F.
Karling, John S.
Karpinos, Bernard D.
Katz, Max
Kellogg, Remington
Kemp, Norman E.
Kendeigh, S. Charles
Kibler, H. H.
Kikkawa, H.
Kinman, Murray L.
Knipling, E. F.
Knobloch, Irving W.
Koch, Robert M.
Kollros, Jerry J.
Kramer, Paul J.
*Kratz, William A.
Kraybill, H. F.
Krogman, W. M.
Kurnick, N. B.

*Deceased

Larsen, Sigurd
Latimer, Homer B.
Latyszewski, M.
Law, Lloyd W.
Lawrence, Merle
Leblond, C. P.
Lees, A. D.
Legates, J. E.
Lewin, Ralph A.
Light, Amos E.
Lindquist, A. W.
Little, Elbert L., Jr.
Lochhead, John H.
Loosanoff, Victor L.
Low, Frank N.
*Low, Seth H.
Lowry, R. J.
Ludwig, Daniel
Lush, Jay L.

McCartney, Morley G.
MacConnachie, H. F.
Machlis, Leonard
McKenzie, Fred F.
MacLeod, Donald M.
McQuilkin, William E.
Mahlstede, John P.
Mainland, Gordon B.
Makino, Sajiro
Manville, Richard H.
Marsland, Douglas A.
Martin, G. W.
Mayer, Dennis T.
Mayr, Ernst
Medcof, J. C.
Meredith, Howard V.
Meyer, Marion P.
Migdalski, Edward C.
Mills, Clarence A.
Moment, Gairdner B.
Moorhead, P. S.
Morris, Melvin S.
Morrison, Peter R.
Morton, Newton E.
Mosby, Henry S.
Moser, Hermann A.
Mossman, Harland W.
Motokawa, K.
Muir, Robert M.
Myers, Earl H.

Neel, James V.
Neill, Catherine A.
Nice, Margaret Morse
Noback, Charles R.
Nordskog, A. W.
Novitski, E.

*O'Connor, R. J.
Olive, Lindsay S.
Oman, Paul W.
Osgood, Edwin E.

Parker, J. R.
Patten, Bradley M.
Patten, John A.
Pauley, Scott S.
Pease, Daniel C.
Pett, L. Bradley
Pfeiffer, Norma E.
Poole, Charles F.
Porter, B. A.
Potts, Carl G.
Powers, E. Lawrence
Prescott, John H.
Pritham, Gordon H.

*Quiring, Daniel P.

Ramsey, Elizabeth M.
Raper, John R.
Rawitscher-Kunkel, Erika
Reed, T. Edward
Rehder, Harald A.
Reyer, Randall W.
Reynolds, Albert E.
Rhoades, M. M.
Richards, A.
Richards, A. Glenn
Richards, Oscar W.
Rick, Charles M.
Ricker, William Edwin
Riesen, Austin H.
Riley, Edgar F.
Ritcher, Paul O.
Roberts, R. H.
Robinson, Florence B.
Rockstein, Morris
Rogers, C. B. W.
Rollin, S. F.
Rossetti, Victoria
Rothschild, Lord
Rowlands, I. W.
Rudolf, Paul O.
Rusoff, Louis L.
Russell, Jane A.
Rytand, D. A.

Sacher, George A.
St. Amand, W.
Sawin, Paul B.
Sax, Karl
Schachter, Joseph
Schmidt-Nielsen, Knut
Schreider, Eugène
Schull, William J.
Schultz, Adolph H.
Scott, J. P.
Scott, Roland B.
Sellmer, George P.
Sendroy, Julius, Jr.
Shaw, Charles E.
Shelton, Maurice
Shettles, Landrum B.
Shuster, Carl N., Jr.
Silva, P. C.
Singer, Ronald
Skreb, Nikola
Skutch, Alexander F.
Slate, George L.
Smith, Arthur H.
Smith, Homer W.
Smith, Paul G.
Snell, George D.
Soost, Robert K.
Sorokin, Constantine
Spiegelman, Mortimer
Sprague, G. F.
Staats, Joan
Steere, William C.
Stein, Janet R.
*Steinbauer, George P.
Stephen, R. C.
Stokes, J. L.
Stonaker, H. H.
Strickland, W. N.
Stringfield, G. H.
Strong, R. M.
Struckmeyer, Burdean E.
Stuart, Harold C.
Swallen, Jason R.
Swett, Walter W.
Szybalski, Waclaw

Tanner, Vasco M.
Templeton, George S.
Terrill, Clair E.
Thimann, Kenneth V.
Thornton, C. S.
Thornton, M. K.
Tietze, Christopher
Torrey, Theodore W.
Towers, Bernard
Turrell, Franklin M.

Van Demark, N. L.
Vandenberg, Steven G.
Van Liere, Edward J.
van Wagenen, Gertrude
Venge, Ole
Venzke, Walter G.
von Bonin, Gerhardt

Wadley, F. M.
Wadsworth, James R.
Walker, Henry
Walker, Richard B.
Warren, Katherine Brehme
Weagley, John L.
Webster, Stewart H.
Weintraub, Robert L.
Wetmore, Ralph H.
Wherry, Edgar T.
Whiting, P. W.
Wichterman, Ralph
Wilkes, A.
*Williams, Bert C.
Wimsatt, William A.
*Winters, L. M.
Witschi, Emil
Wolf, Frederick A.
Wright, Philip L.
Wright, Sewall
Wyman, Donald

Zechel, Gustav
Zucker, Lois M.
Zucker, Theodore F.

*Deceased

INTRODUCTION

This handbook, compiled for reference purposes, offers quantitative data on growth, reproduction, and development, arranged in 13 sections for the convenience of the user. The material is organized in the form of tables, graphs, diagrams, and charts. Most of the tables have been prepared especially for the Biological Handbooks Series from various collections of data and from the current literature. Contents of the volume have been authenticated by 372 leading investigators in the fields of biology and medicine. The review process to which the tables have been subjected was designed to eliminate, insofar as possible, material of questionable validity and errors of transcription.

An explanatory headnote, serving as an introduction to the subject matter, may precede a table. More frequently, tables are prefaced by a short headnote containing such important information as units of measurement, abbreviations, definitions, and estimate of the range of variation. To interpret the data, reading of the related headnote is essential.

The main conventions used throughout the handbook have been adapted from the *Style Manual for Biological Journals*, published in 1960 for the Conference of Biological Editors by the American Institute of Biological Sciences. The terminology has been checked against *Webster's Third New International Dictionary*, published in 1961 by G. & C. Merriam Company. On the advice of taxonomists, the use of scientific names has prevailed for the organisms appearing in this volume. In most of the tables animals have been listed in descending phylogenetic order, and plants in ascending order. For a few tables the contributors urged that an alphabetical arrangement be employed, and their wishes have been honored.

Appended to the tables are the names of the contributors, and a list of the literature citations arranged in alphabetical sequence. The reference abbreviations conform to the *List of Periodicals abstracted by Chemical Abstracts*, and the 1957-1960 supplements thereto, published by the Chemical Abstracts Service.

It is suggested that the table of contents be used in conjunction with the index: the table of contents to determine the scope of the data for a particular topic, and the index to locate data for a specific organism. To facilitate identification, the index includes the taxonomic order for vertebrates and invertebrates, and the family for plants. Common names of organisms appear in the index only when no scientific name has been specified.

. . . .

Values are generally presented as a mean and the lower and upper limit of the range of individual values about the mean. This range may be estimated in several ways, the method depending on the information available. Letter designations (a, b, c, d) identify types of ranges in descending order of accuracy.

(a) When the group of values is relatively large, a 95% range is derived by curve fitting. A recognized type of normal frequency curve is fitted to a group of measured values, and the extreme 2.5% of the area under the curve at each end is excluded (see illustration).

(b) When the group of values is too small for curve fitting, as is usually the case, a 95% range is estimated by a simple statistical calculation. Assuming a normal symmetrical distribution, the standard deviation is multiplied by a factor of 2, then subtracted from and added to the mean to give the lower and upper range limits.

(c) A less dependable, but commonly applied, procedure takes as range limits the lowest value and the highest value of the reported sample group of measurements. It underestimates the 95% range for small samples and overestimates for larger sample sizes, but may be used in preference to the preceding method where there is marked asymmetry in the position of the mean within the sample range.

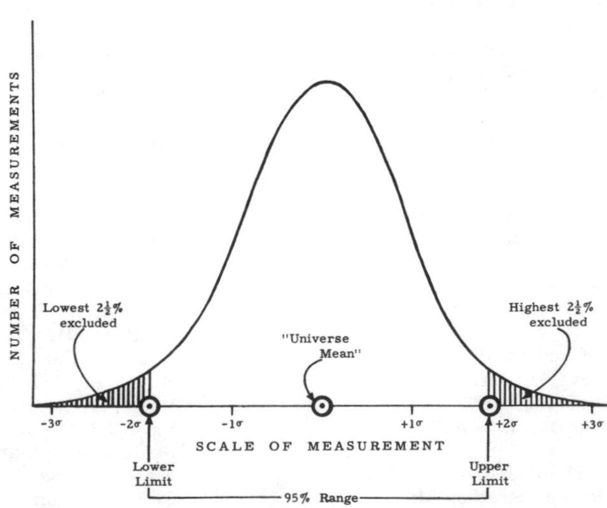

(d) Another estimate of the lower and upper limits of the range of variation is based on the judgment of an individual experienced in measuring the quantity in question. The trustworthiness of such limits should not be underestimated.

CONTENTS

I. CHROMOSOME NUMBERS

II. LINKAGE GROUPS, HERITABILITY, AND HYBRIDIZATION

III. CELLS AND TISSUES

IV. VERTEBRATE REPRODUCTION

V. INVERTEBRATE REPRODUCTION

VI. PLANT REPRODUCTION

VII. PRENATAL VERTEBRATE DEVELOPMENT

VIII. POSTNATAL VERTEBRATE DEVELOPMENT

IX. PLANT DEVELOPMENT AND COMPARATIVE MORPHOLOGY

X. COMPARATIVE ANIMAL MORPHOLOGY

XI. SEX RATIOS AND LIFE SPANS

XII. ENVIRONMENTAL FACTORS AND GROWTH

XIII. GROWTH REGULATORS AND INHIBITORS

APPENDIXES

GROWTH

including

Reproduction and Morphological Development

I. CHROMOSOME NUMBERS

1. CHROMOSOME NUMBERS: VERTEBRATES

For additional information, consult reference 51. Diploid (column D): s = spermatogonium, o = oogonium, m = somatic cell. Haploid (column E): ♂(I) = primary spermatocyte, ♂(II) = secondary spermatocyte, ♀(I) = primary oocyte, ♀(II) = secondary oocyte. Classification adapted from Lord Rothschild, *A Classification of Living Animals*, 1961.

	Order	Family	Species	Chromosome Number		Sex Type	Reference
				Diploid	Haploid		
	(A)	(B)	(C)	(D)	(E)	(F)	(G)
			Mammalia				
1	Primates	Hominidae	*Homo sapiens*	46s, o, m	23♂(I, II)	X-Y♂	122
2		Pongidae	*Hylobates hoolock*	44	...	...	11
3			*Pan troglodytes*	48	...	X-Y♂	138
4		Cercopithecidae	*Cercopithecus mona*	66	...	...	4
5			*Erythrocebus patas*	54	...	X-Y♂	12
6			*Macaca mulatta*	42	...	X-Y♂	12
7			*Papio sphinx*	42	...	...	4
8			*Presbytis entellus*	50	...	X-Y♂	52
9		Callithricidae	*Callithrix chrysoleucus*	46	...	X-Y♂	5
10			*Leontocebus illigeri*	46	...	X-Y♂	5
11		Cebidae	*Ateles belzebuth*	34	...	X-Y♂	11
12			*Callimico goeldii*	48	...	...	5
13			*Cebus apella*	54	...	X-Y♂	4,11
14		Lorisidae	*Galago senegalensis*	38	...	X-Y♂	11
15			*Nycticebus coucang*	50	...	...	4
16		Lemuridae	*Lemur macaco*	44	...	X-Y♂	11
17	Artiodac-tyla	Bovidae	*Bison bonasus*	60m	...	...	70
18			*Bos taurus*	60m	...	X-Y♂	40,103
19			*Bubalus buffelus*	48s	24♂(I, II)	X-Y♂	40,41
20			*Capra hircus*	60s	30♂(I, II)	X-Y♂	40,41
21			*Ovis aries*	54m	...	X-Y♂	70
22		Cervidae	*Rangifer phylarchus*	72s	36♂(I, II)	X-Y♂	41,48
23		Tayassuidae	*Pecari tajacu*	30s	15♂(I, II)	...	28
24		Suidae	*Sus scrofa*	40s	20♂(I, II)	X-Y♂	39,41
25	Perisso-dactyla	Equidae	*Equus asinus*	62	...	X-Y♂	90
26			*E. caballus*	64m	...	X-Y♂	103
27			*E. mulus*	63m	...	...	90
28	Carnivora	Otariidae	*Callorhinus alascanus*	30s	15♂(I, II)	X-Y♂	112
29		Felidae	*Felis bengalensis*	38s	19♂(I)	X-Y♂	120
30			*F. catus*	38m	...	X-Y♂	3
31		Mustelidae	*Martes foina*	38s	19♂(I)	...	16
32			*Mustela sibirica itatsi*	38s	19♂(I, II)	X-Y♂	43
33			*M. vison*	30	...	...	109
34			*Putorius furo*	34s	...	X-Y♂	27
35		Canidae	*Canis aureus*	74	...	...	68
36			*C. familiaris*	78m	...	X-Y♂	3
37			*Fennecus zerda*	64	...	...	68
38			*Nyctereutes viverrinus*	42s	21♂(I, II)	X-Y♂	71
39			*Vulpes ruppelli*	40	...	...	68
40			*V. vulpes*	38s	19♂(I)	X-Y♂	41,43
41	Cetacea	Phocaenidae	*Phocaena dalli*	44s	22♂(I, II)	X-Y♂	46
42	Rodentia	Capromyidae	*Myocastor coypus*	42s	21♂(I, II)	X-Y♂	43
43		Chinchillidae	*Chinchilla laniger*	64s	32♂(I)	...	53
44		Caviidae	*Cavia cobaya*	64m	...	X-Y♂	3
45		Erethizontidae	*Erethizon dorsatum*	34s	17♂(I)	...	53
46		Hystricidae	*Hystrix cristata*	64s	32♂(I)	...	53
47		Gliridae	*Eliomys quercinus*	52s	26♂(I, II)	X-Y♂	97
48			*Glis glis*	62s	31♂(I)	X-Y♂	97
49			*Muscardinus avellanarius*	48s	24♂(I)	X-Y♂	97
50		Muridae	*Apodemus agrarius*	48s	24♂(I, II)	X-Y♂	47,49
51			*Micromys minutus*	68s	34♂(I)	X-Y♂	39
52			*Mus musculus*	40s	20♂(I, II)	X-Y♂	36
53			*Rattus norvegicus*	42m	...	X-Y♂	57
54			*R. rattus*	42s	21♂(I, II)	X-Y♂	37,38

continued

1. CHROMOSOME NUMBERS: VERTEBRATES

	Order	Family	Species	Chromosome Number		Sex Type	Reference
				Diploid	Haploid		
	(A)	(B)	(C)	(D)	(E)	(F)	(G)
			Mammalia				
55	Rodentia	Cricetidae	*Arvicola amphibius*	36	....	....	69
56			*Clethrionomys glareolus*	56s	28♂(I, II)	X-Y♂	97
57			*Cricetulus triton*	30♀m	15♀(I)	X-X♀	47
58			*Cricetus cricetus*	22s	....	....	67
59			*Meriones unguiculatus*	44m	....	....	3
60			*Mesocricetus auratus*	44m	....	....	3
61			*Microtus pennsylvanicus*	46	....	....	67
62			*Neotoma floridana*	52s	....	X-Y♂	13
63			*Ondatra zibethica*	54s	....	....	54
64			*Peromyscus maniculatus*	48s	24♂(I)	X-Y♂	54
65			*P. truei*	48s	24♂(I)	....	54
66			*Sigmodon hispidus*	54s	....	X-Y♂	13
67		Heteromyidae	*Perognathus fallax*	44s	....	X-Y♂	13
68		Sciuridae	*Citellus columbianus*	32s	....	X-Y♂	129
69			*Cynomys ludovicianus*	52s	....	....	54
70			*Glaucomys volans*	52s	....	X-Y♂	13
71			*Marmota flaviventris*	42s	....	....	54
72			*Sciurus vulgaris*	40s	....	X-Y♂	75
73			*Tamiasciurus hudsonicus*	28s	....	X-Y♂	66
74	Lagomorpha	Leporidae	*Oryctolagus cuniculus*	44s	22♂(I)	X-Y♂	41,66
75	Edentata	Dasypodidae	*Dasypus novemcinctus*	60m	....	X-O♂?	93,94
76	Chiroptera	Vespertilionidae	*Barbastella barbastella*	32s	16♂(I)	X-X♂	8
77			*Myotis myotis*	44s	22♂(I)	X-Y♂	8
78			*Pipistrellus tralatitus*	26	....	....	119
79			*Plecotus auritus*	32s	16♂(I)	X-Y♂	8
80		Rhinolophidae	*Rhinolophus ferrum-equinum*	29	....	....	45
81		Pteropodidae	*Pteropus dasymallus*	38s	19♂(I, II)	X-Y♂	45
82	Insectivora	Talpidae	*Talpa europaea*	34s	17♂(I)	X-Y♂	7,8
83		Soricidae	*Crocidura russula*	42s	21♂(I)	X-Y♂	7,8
84			*Sorex araneus*	23s	11♂(I); 11, 12♂(II)	X_1X_2-Y♂	7,8
85		Macroscelididae	*Elephantulus myurus*	14s	7♂(I), 7♀(I)	X-Y♂, X-X♀	9
86		Erinaceidae	*Erinaceus europaeus*	48s	24♂(I)	X-Y♂	7,8
87	Marsupialia	Macropodidae	*Bettongia penicillata*	28s	....	X-Y♂	14
88			*Macropus giganteus*	22s	11♂(I)	X-Y♂	6
89			*Potorous tridactylus*	12s, ♀m	6♂(I, II)	X-Y♂, X-X♀	2
90		Phalangeridae	*Petaurus breviceps*	22s	....	X-Y♂	14
91			*Phascolarctos cinereus*	16s	8♂(II)	X-Y♂	26
92			*Pseudocheirus peregrinus*	20s	10♂(I)	X-Y♂	26
93			*Trichosurus vulpecula*	20s	10♂(I, II)	X-Y♂	26
94		Peramelidae	*Isoodon obesulus*	14s	7♂(I)	X-Y♂	14
95		Dasyuridae	*Dasyurus viverrinus*	14s	7♂(I)	X-Y♂	15
96		Didelphidae	*Didelphis virginiana*	22s, m	11♂(I, II)	X-Y♂	92
			Aves				
97	Passeriformes	Fringillidae	*Emberiza elegans*	84s	42♂(I)	....	123
98		Ploceidae	*Passer domesticus*	54-60s, m	23♂(I)?	X-X♂, X-O♀	98
99		Turdidae	*Turdus merula*	60-85s, o, m	....	X-X♂, X-O♀	124
100		Corvidae	*Pica pica*	82s, 81o	....	X-O♀	118
101	Cuculiformes	Cuculidae	*Cuculus canorus*	72s	36♂(I)	....	133
102	Psittaciformes	Psittacidae	*Melopsittacus undulatus*	58s	29♂(I)	....	133
103	Columbiformes	Columbidae	*Columba livia domestica*	80s, 79o	40♂(I)	X-X♂, X-O♀	137
104			*Streptopelia decaocto*	76s, 75o	38♂(I)	X-X♂, X-O♀	137
105	Charadriiformes	Alcidae	*Brachyramphus marmoratus*	50s	25♂(I)	....	86
106			*Lunda cirrhata*	50s	25♂(I)	....	86
107		Laridae	*Larus crassirastris*	64s	....	....	123
108			*Sterna albifrons*	66s	33♂(I)	....	86
109		Charadriidae	*Charadrius dubius*	78s	39♂(I)	....	133
110	Gruiformes	Rallidae	*Fulica atra*	86s, 85o	....	X-O♀	135
111	Galliformes	Meleagrididae	*Meleagris gallopavo*	82s, 81o	41♂(I)	X-X♂, X-O♀	134
112		Numididae	*Numida meleagris*	76s, 75o	38♂(I)	X-X♂, X-O♀	134

continued

1. CHROMOSOME NUMBERS: VERTEBRATES

	Order	Family	Species	Chromosome Number Diploid	Chromosome Number Haploid	Sex Type	Reference
	(A)	(B)	(C)	(D)	(E)	(F)	(G)
			Aves				
113	Galliformes	Phasianidae	*Bambusicola thoracica*	78s	...	...	133
114			*Chrysolophus amherstiae*	82s	41♂(I)	X-X♂, X-O♀	131
115			*Coturnix coturnix*	78s	39♂(I)	...	88
116			*Gallus domesticus*	78s, 77o	39♂(I)	X-X♂, X-O♀	131,132
117			*Gennaeus swinhoii*	82s, 81o	41♂(I)	X-X♂, X-O♀	134
118			*Phasianus colchicus*	82s, 81o	41♂(I)	X-X♂, X-O♀	131
119			*Syrmaticus soemmerringii*	82s	41♂(I)	X-X♂, X-O♀	131
120	Falconiformes	Falconidae	*Cerchneis tinnunculus*	37m	...	...	111
121	Anseriformes	Anatidae	*Aix sponsa*	80s	40♂(I)	...	136
122			*Anas platyrhynchos*	80s	40♂(I)	...	136
123			*Anser albifrons*	82s	41♂(I)	...	136
124			*Aythya fuligula*	80s	...	...	136
125			*Branta bernicla*	84s	42♂(I)	...	136
126			*Cairina moschata*	80s, 79o	40♂(I)	X-X♂, X-O♀	130
127			*Cygnus cygnus*	80s	...	...	136
128			*Mergus serrator*	80s	...	...	136
129			*Tadorna rutila*	44-46m	...	...	111
130	Ciconiiformes	Ardeidae	*Ardea cinerea*	76s	38♂(I)	...	135
131			*Egretta garzetta*	76s	38♂(I)	...	135
132			*Nycticorax nycticorax*	76s	38♂(I)	...	135
133	Pelecaniformes	Phalacrocoracidae	*Phalacrocorax carbo*	70s	35♂(I)	...	86
134	Procellariiformes	Hydrobatidae	*Oceanodroma leucorhoa*	74s, 73o	37♂(I)	X-X♂, X-O♀	86,89
135	Podicipediformes	Podicipedidae	*Podiceps ruficollis*	80s, 79o	...	X-O♀	135
			Reptilia				
136	Serpentes	Crotalidae	*Ancistrodon acutus*	36s	18♂(I)	X-X♂	79
137			*Trimeresurus flavoviridis*	36s	...	...	58,73
138		Viperidae	*Vipera aspis*	42s	21♂(I)	X-X♂	61,64
139			*V. berus*	36s	18♂(I, II)	...	58
140		Hydrophidae	*Laticauda semifasciata*	38s	19♂(I, II)	X-X♂	79
141		Elapidae	*Bungarus multicinctus*	36s	18♂(I, II)	X-X♂	79
142			*Naja naja*	38s	19♂(I, II)	X-X♂	79
143		Colubridae	*Coronella austriaca*	36s	18♂(I)	X-X♂	61
144			*Dinodon rufozonatum*	46s	23♂(I, II)	X-X♂	79
145			*Elaphe quadrivirgata*	36s	18♂(I, II)	X-X♂	79
146			*Natrix tigrina*	40s	20♂(I, II)	X-X♂	77
147			*Thamnophis butleri*	37s	18♂(I)	XX-Y♂?	121
148			*Zaocys nigromarginatus*	36s	...	X-X♂	79
149	Sauria	Varanidae	*Varanus gouldi*	40s	20♂(I, II)	X-X♂	60,61
150		Helodermatidae	*Heloderma suspectum*	38s	19♂(I, II)	X-X♂	60,61
151		Anniellidae	*Anniella pulchra*	24s	...	X-X♂	60,61
152		Anguidae	*Anguis fragilis*	44s, o	22♂(I)	X-Y♀?	59
153			*Gerrhonotus scincicauda*	44, 45s	22♂(I)	X-X♂	60,61
154			*Ophisaurus ventralis*	30s	15♂(I)	X-X♂	60,61
155		Amphisbaenidae	*Rhineura floridana*	46s	23♂(I, II)	X-X♂	63,64
156			*Trogonophis wiegmanni*	36s	18♂(I, II)	X-X♂	60,62
157		Lacertidae	*Lacerta viridis*	38s	19♂(I, II)	X-X♂	61
158			*L. vivipara*	36s, 35o	18♂(I, II)	X-X♂, X-O♀	84,85
159			*Takydromus smaragdinus*	38s	19♂(I, II)	...	82
160		Teiidae	*Ameiva surinamensis*	50s	25♂(I)	X-X♂	64
161			*Cnemidophorus sexlineatus*	46s	23♂(I, II)	X-X♂	64
162			*Tupinambis teguixin*	36s	18♂(I, II)	X-X♂	64
163		Gerrhosauridae	*Gerrhosaurus flavigularis*	36s	18♂(I, II)	X-X♂	64
164		Scincidae	*Eumeces elegans*	26s	...	...	58,73
165			*Mabuya macularia*	32s	16♂(I)	...	56
166			*Scincus officinalis*	32s	16♂(I, II)	X-X♂	61
167		Xantusidae	*Xantusia henshawi*	42s	21♂(I)	X-X♂	60,61
168		Iguanidae	*Anolis carolinensis*	36s	18♂(I, II)	X-X♂	61
169			*Crotaphytus collaris*	36-38s	18?♂(I)	XX-O♂?	91
170			*Sceloporus spinosus*	22s	11♂(I)	XX-O♂?	91

continued

1. CHROMOSOME NUMBERS: VERTEBRATES

	Order	Family	Species	Chromosome Number		Sex Type	Reference
				Diploid	Haploid		
	(A)	(B)	(C)	(D)	(E)	(F)	(G)
			Reptilia				
171	Sauria	Chamaeleonidae	*Chamaeleon vulgaris*	24s, o	....	X-Y♀?	65
172		Agamidae	*Agama stellio*	36s	18♂(I, II)	X-X♂	61
173			*Calotes versicolor*	34s, 33o	17♂(I)	X-X♂, X-O♀	55
174			*Sitana ponticeriana*	46s, 45o	23♂(I)	X-X♂, X-O♀	55
175			*Uromastix hardwicki*	34s	....	....	55
176		Gekkonidae	*Eublepharis variegatus*	32s	16♂(I, II)	X-Y♀?	63, 64
177			*Gekko japonicus*	38s	19♀(I, II)	X-O♀	76, 78
178			*Hemidactylus frenatus*	46s	23♂(I)	....	58, 73
179			*Tarentola mauritanica*	42s	21♂(I, II)	X-X♂	61
180	Crocodylia	Alligatoridae	*Alligator mississipiensis*	32s	16♂(I)	....	100
181	Chelonia	Trionychidae	*Amyda japonica*	64s, 63o	32♂(I, II), 31+X♀(I)	X-X♂, X-O♀	87
182		Chelonidae	*Caretta caretta*	58s, 57o	....	X-X♂, X-O♀	80
183			*Chelonia japonica*	56s, 55o	....	X-X♂, X-O♀	89
184		Testudinidae	*Testudo graeca*	54-60s	....	....	61
185		Emydidae	*Clemmys mutica*	52s	26♂(I)	X-X♂	80
186			*Cyclemys flavomarginata*	52s	26♂(I, II)	X-X♂	80
187			*Emys orbicularis*	50s	25♂(I)	X-X♂	61
188			*Geoemyda spengleri*	52s	26♂(I)	X-X♂	80
189		Kinosternidae	*Sternotherus odoratus*	50s	25♂(I, II)	....	99
190	Rhynchocephalia	Rhynchocephalidae	*Sphenodon punctatus*	36s	18♂(I, II)	....	25
			Amphibia				
191	Gymnophiona	Caeciliidae	*Ichthyophis glutinosus*	42s, ♂m	21♂(I, II)	....	108
192			*Uraeotyphlus narayani*	36s	18♂(I, II)	....	107
193	Salientia	Rhacophoridae	*Rhacophorus schlegelii*	26s	13♂(I, II)	....	29
194		Ranidae	*Rana catesbeiana*	26s	13♂(I, II)	....	44
195			*R. pipiens*	26s	13♂(I)	....	96
196			*R. temporaria*	26s, m	13♂(I, II)	....	42
197		Hylidae	*Hyla arborea*	24s	12♂(I, II)	....	21, 126
198			*H. cinerea*	24s	12♂(I)	....	21, 126
199			*H. versicolor*	24s	12♂(I)	....	21, 126
200		Bufonidae	*Bufo arenarum*	22s	11♂(I, II)	....	101, 102
201			*B. calamita*	22s	11♂(I)	....	126, 127
202			*B. viridis*	22s, o	11♂(I, II)	....	114
203		Pelobatidae	*Pelobates fuscus*	26s	13♂(I)	....	126, 127
204		Discoglossidae	*Alytes obstetricans*	36s	18♂(I)	....	127
205			*Bombina bombina*	24s	12♂(I)	....	127
206			*Discoglossus pictus*	28s	....	....	126, 127
207		Pipidae	*Xenopus laevis*	36s	....	....	126, 127
208	Caudata	Proteidae	*Proteus anguinus*	18s	9♂(I, II)	....	113
209		Plethodontidae	*Aneides lugubris*	28s	14♂(I)	....	110
210			*Batrachoseps attenuatus*	24s	12♂(I, II)	....	17
211			*Desmognathus fuscus*	24s	12♂(I)	....	74
212			*Eurycea bislineata*	28m	....	....	18
213			*Plethodon cinereus*	24s	12♂(I)	....	74
214		Salamandridae	*Pleurodeles waltl*	24s	12♂(I)	....	126
215			*Salamandra salamandra*	24s	12♂(I)	....	127
216			*Triturus cristatus*	24s	12♂(I)	....	126
217			*T. viridescens*	22m	....	....	19
218			*T. vulgaris*	24s	12♂(I)	....	126
219			*Tylototriton andersoni*	24s	12♂(I, II)	....	50
220		Ambystomidae	*Ambystoma mexicanum*	28s	....	....	126
221			*A. tigrinum*	28s	14♂(I)	X-O♂	10
222		Cryptobranchidae	*Cryptobranchus alleganiensis*	62s	31♂(I, II)	....	31
223			*Megalobatrachus japonicus*	64s	32♂(I, II)	....	24
224		Hynobiidae	*Hynobius kimurai*	60s	....	....	104
225			*H. nebulosus*	56s	28♂(II)	....	104
226			*Pachypalaminus boulengeri*	56s	....	....	104
			Pisces				
227	Dipneusti	Protopteridae	*Protopterus annectans*	34s	17♂(I)	....	126
228		Lepidosirenidae	*Lepidosiren paradoxa*	38m	19♂(I)	....	1

continued

1. CHROMOSOME NUMBERS: VERTEBRATES

	Order	Family	Species	Chromosome Number		Sex Type	Reference
				Diploid	Haploid		
	(A)	(B)	(C)	(D)	(E)	(F)	(G)
			Pisces				
229	Dipneusti	Ceratodontidae	*Ceratodus forsteri*	32-38m	....	....	126
230	Scleroparei	Cottidae	*Cottus bairdi*	36-38s	18♂(I)	....	23
231	Percomorphi	Atherinidae	*Menidia notata*	36m	....	....	72
232		Anabantidae	*Betta splendens*	42s	21♂(I, II)	X-X♂?	117
233		Pholidae	*Pholis pictus*	46s	....	....	33
234		Gobiidae	*Tridentiger obscurus*	44s	22♂(I)	....	83
235		Labridae	*Ctenolabrus adspersus*	38-48m	....	....	95
236		Percidae	*Lucioperca lucioperca*	24m	....	....	116
237			*Perca fluviatilis*	28m	....	....	116
238	Microcyprini	Poeciliidae	*Gambusia holbrooki*	36s	18♂(I, II)	....	22
239			*Heterandria formosa*	46s	23♂(I)	....	125
240			*Lebistes reticulatus*	46s, o	23♂(I, II), 23♀(I)	X-Y♂?	128
241			*Mollienisia sphenops*	46s	23♂(I)	....	125
242			*Phallichthys pittieri*	46s	23♂(I)	....	125
243			*Platypoecilus maculatus*	48s	24♂(I)	....	125
244			*Xiphophorus hellerii*	48s	24♂(I)	....	125
245		Cyprinodontidae	*Fundulus heteroclitus*	45m	....	....	95
246	Ostariophysi	Cobitidae	*Barbatula oreas*	48s	24♂(I, II)	....	35
247			*Misgurnus anguillicaudatus*	52s	26♂(I, II)	....	33,35
248		Cyprinidae	*Acheilognathus lanceolata*	50s	25♂(I, II)	....	34
249			*Carassius auratus*	94s	47♂(I, II)	....	30,35
250			*Cyprinus carpio*	104s	52♂(I, II)	....	30,34
251			*Pseudorasbora parva*	50s	25♂(I, II)	....	34
252			*Pungtungia hilgendorfi*	50s	....	....	81
253			*Tribolodon hakuensis*	50s	25♂(I, II)	....	34
254			*Zacco platypus*	50s	....	....	81
255	Haplomi	Esocidae	*Esox lucius*	18m	....	....	116
256	Isospondyli	Osmeridae	*Osmerus eperlanus*	58m	....	....	115
257		Thymallidae	*Thymallus thymallus*	102m	....	....	115
258		Coregonidae	*Coregonus albula*	80m	....	....	115
259		Salmonidae	*Oncorhynchus keta*	72s	....	....	33
260			*Salmo salar*	60m	30♂(I)	....	115
261			*S. trutta*	80m	40♂(I)	....	115
262			*Salvelinus alpinus*	80m	....	....	115
263			*S. fontinalis*	84m	....	....	115
			Chondrichthyes				
264	Batoidei	Rajidae	*Raja macrorhynchus*	24s	12♂(I, II)	....	20
265			*R. meerdervoortii*	104s	52♂(I, II)	....	32
266	Selachii	Squalidae	*Squalus suckleyi*	62s	31♂(I, II)	....	32
			Agnatha				
267	Myxini	Myxinidae	*Myxine glutinosa*	ca. 52s, m	26♂(I, II)	....	105,106

Contributor: Makino, Sajiro

References: [1] Agar, W. E. 1912. Quart. J. Microscop. Sci. 58:285. [2] Altmann, S. C. A., and M. E. W. Ellery. 1925. Ibid. 69:463. [3] Awa, A., M. Sasaki, and S. Takayama. 1959. Japan. J. Zool. 12:257. [4] Bender, M. A., and L. E. Mettler. 1958. Science 128:186. [5] Bender, M. A., and L. E. Mettler. 1960. Cytologia (Tokyo) 25:400. [6] Binder, S. 1927. Z. Zellforsch. u. mikroskop. Anat. 5:293. [7] Bovey, R. 1949. Experientia 5:72. [8] Bovey, R. 1949. Rev. suisse zool. 56:371. [9] Brenner, S. 1946. S. African J. Med. Sci. 11(biol. suppl.):71. [10] Carrick, R. 1934. Trans. Roy. Soc. Edinburgh 58:63. [11] Chu, E. H. Y., and M. A. Bender. 1961. Science 133:1399. [12] Chu, E. H. Y., and N. H. Giles. 1957. Am. Naturalist 91:273. [13] Cross, J. C. 1931. J. Morphol. 52:373. [14] Drummond, F. H. 1933. Quart. J. Microscop. Sci. 76:1. [15] Drummond, F. H. 1938. Cytologia (Tokyo) 8:343. [16] Ehrlich, I. 1949. Rev. suisse zool. 56:621. [17] Eisen, G. 1900. J. Morphol. 17:1. [18] Fankhauser, G. 1939. J. Heredity 30:379. [19] Fankhauser, G. 1941. J. Morphol. 68:161. [20] Farmer, J. B., and J. E. S. Moore. 1904. Quart. J. Microscop. Sci. 48:489. [21] Galgano, M. 1933. Arch. ital. anat. embriol. 32:171. [22] Geiser, S. W. 1924. Biol. Bull. 47:175. [23] Hann, H. W. 1927.

continued

J. Morphol. 43:427. [24] Iriki, S. 1932. Science Repts. Tokyo Bunrika Daigaku, B, 1:91. [25] Keenan, R. D. 1932. J. Anat. 67:1. [26] Koller, P. C. 1936. J. Genet. 32:451. [27] Koller, P. C. 1936. Proc. Roy. Soc. (London), B, 121:192. [28] Krallinger, H. F. 1936. Z. Zellforsch. u. mikroskop. Anat. 24:1. [29] Makino, S. 1932. Proc. Imp. Acad. (Tokyo) 8. [30] Makino, S. 1934. Japan. J. Genet. 9:100. [31] Makino, S. 1935. J. Morphol. 58:573. [32] Makino, S. 1937. Cytologia (Tokyo), Fujii jubilaei vol. (2):867. [33] Makino, S. 1937. Zool. Mag. (Japan) 49. [34] Makino, S. 1939. Cytologia (Tokyo) 9:430. [35] Makino, S. 1941. Ibid. 12:96. [36] Makino, S. 1941. J. Fac. Sci. Hokkaido Imp. Univ., VI, 7:305. [37] Makino, S. 1942. Japan. J. Genet. 18(2):48. [38] Makino, S. 1943. J. Fac. Sci. Hokkaido Imp. Univ., VI, 7:19. [39] Makino, S. 1943-44. Cytologia (Tokyo) 13:170. [40] Makino, S. 1943-44. Ibid. 13:247. [41] Makino, S. 1944. Zool. Mag. (Japan) 56:8. [42] Makino, S. 1946. Kromosomo (Tokyo) 2:79. [43] Makino, S. 1947. J. Fac. Sci. Hokkaido Univ., VI, 9:345. [44] Makino, S. 1947. Kromosomo (Tokyo) 3-4:137. [45] Makino, S. 1948. Biol. Bull. 94:275. [46] Makino, S. 1948. Chromosoma 3:220. [47] Makino, S. 1949. Cytologia (Tokyo) 15:153. [48] Makino, S. 1949. Japan. J. Zootech. Sci. 19. [49] Makino, S. 1950. Iden no Sogo Kenkyu 1:79. [50] Makino, S. 1950. Kromosomo (Tokyo) 6. [51] Makino, S. 1951. An atlas of the chromosome numbers in animals. Ed. 2. Iowa State College Press, Ames. [52] Makino, S. 1952. Cytologia (Tokyo) 16:288. [53] Makino, S. 1953. Experientia 9:213. [54] Makino, S. 1953. Science 118:630. [55] Makino, S., and J. J. Asana. 1948. Chromosoma 3:208. [56] Makino, S., and J. J. Asana. 1950. Iden no Sogo Kenkyu 1. [57] Makino, S., and T. C. Hsu. 1954. Cytologia (Tokyo) 19:23. [58] Makino, S., and E. Momma. 1949. Ibid. 15:153. [59] Margot, A. 1946. Rev. suisse zool. 53:555. [60] Matthey, R. 1931. Bull. soc. vaudoise sci. nat. 57:269. [61] Matthey, R. 1931. Rev. suisse zool. 38:117. [62] Matthey, R. 1932. Arch. zool. exptl. et gén. 74:193. [63] Matthey, R. 1932. Compt. rend. soc. biol. 110:273. [64] Matthey, R. 1933. Rev. suisse zool. 40:281. [65] Matthey, R. 1943. Arch. Julius Klaus-Stift. Vererbungsforsch. Sozialanthropol. u. Rassenhyg. 18:1. [66] Matthey, R. 1949. Les chromosomes des vertébrés. Rouge, Lausanne. [67] Matthey, R. 1951. Experientia 7:340. [68] Matthey, R. 1954. Mammalia 18:225. [69] Matthey, R. 1956. Chromosoma 7:670. [70] Melander, Y. 1959. Hereditas 45:649. [71] Minouchi, O. 1929. Cytologia (Tokyo) 1:88. [72] Moenkhaus, W. J. 1904. Am. J. Anat. 3:29. [73] Momma, E. 1948. Zool. Mag. (Japan) 58. [74] Montgomery, T. H., Jr. 1903. Biol. Bull. 4:259. [75] Muldal, S. 1949. John Innes Hort. Inst. Ann. Rept. 39:21. [76] Nakamura, D. 1931. Proc. Imp. Acad. (Tokyo) 7. [77] Nakamura, K. 1928. Mem. Coll. Sci. Kyoto Imp. Univ., B, 4:1. [78] Nakamura, K. 1932. Cytologia (Tokyo) 3:156. [79] Nakamura, K. 1935. Mem. Coll. Sci. Kyoto Imp. Univ., B, 10:341. [80] Nakamura, K. 1949. Kromosomo (Tokyo) 5. [81] Nogusa, S. 1943. Japan. J. Genet. 19:282. [82] Nogusa, S. 1944. Ibid. 20(3):76. [83] Nogusa, S. 1950. Ibid. 25:222. [84] Oguma, K. 1934. Arch. biol. (Liège) 45:27. [85] Oguma, K. 1934. Zool. Mag. (Japan) 46. [86] Oguma, K. 1937. J. Fac. Sci. Hokkaido Imp. Univ., VI, 5. [87] Oguma, K. 1937. J. Genet. 34:247. [88] Oguma, K. 1938. Ann. Zool. (Japan) 17. [89] Oguma, K. 1942. Kaibogaku Zasshi 20. [90] Ohno, S., and J. M. Trujillo. 1962. J. Heredity 63. [91] Painter, T. S. 1921. J. Exptl. Zool. 34:281. [92] Painter, T. S. 1924. Ibid. 39:197. [93] Painter, T. S. 1925. Am. Naturalist 59:385. [94] Painter, T. S. 1925. Science 61:423. [95] Pinney, E. 1918. J. Morphol. 31:225. [96] Porter, K. R. 1941. Biol. Bull. 80:238. [97] Renaud, P. 1938. Rev. suisse zool. 45:349. [98] Riley, G. M. 1938. Cytologia (Tokyo) 9:165. [99] Risley, P. L. 1936. Ibid. 7:232. [100] Risley, P. L. 1942. Anat. Record 84:513. [101] Saez, F. A., P. Rojas, and E. de Robertis. 1936. Inst. museo univ. nacl. La Plata 2. [102] Saez, F. A., P. Rojas, and E. de Robertis. 1936. Z. Zellforsch. u. mikroskop. Anat. 24:727. [103] Sasaki, M. S., and S. Makino. 1962. J. Heredity 53. [104] Sato, I. 1936. J. Sci. Hiroshima Univ., B, 4:143. [105] Schreiner, A., and K. E. Schreiner. 1904. Anat. Anz. 24:561. [106] Schreiner, A., and K. E. Schreiner. 1904. Arch. biol. (Liège) 21:183. [107] Seshachar, B. R. 1939. Cellule 48:61. [108] Seshachar, B. R. 1939. Cytologia (Tokyo) 10:15. [109] Shiota, G., and M. S. Sasaki. 1962. Zool. Mag. (Japan) 71. [110] Snook, H. J., and J. A. Long. 1914. Univ. Calif. (Berkeley) Publs. zool. 11:511. [111] Sokolovskaja, I. I. 1940. Trudy Inst. Genet. 13:283. [112] Starks, D. J. 1928. Am. J. Anat. 40:471. [113] Stieve, H. 1920. Arch. mikroskop. Anat. u. Entwicklungsmech. 93(2):141. [114] Stohler, R. 1928.

continued

1. CHROMOSOME NUMBERS: VERTEBRATES

Z. Zellforsch. u. mikroskop. Anat. 7:400. [115] Svärdson, G. 1945. Medd. Statens Und. Försöksanstalt Sötvatt.-fisk. 23. [116] Svärdson, G., and T. Wickbom. 1939. Hereditas 25:472. [117] Svärdson, G., and T. Wickbom. 1942. Ibid. 28:212. [118] Suzuki, K. 1949. Japan. J. Genet. 24:90. [119] Takayama, S. 1959. Ibid. 34:107. [120] Tateishi, S. 1941. Kagaku (Taiwan) 9. [121] Thatcher, L. E. 1922. Science 56:372. [122] Tjio, J. H., and A. Levan. 1956. Hereditas 42:1. [123] Udagawa, T. 1954. Annotat. Zool. Japon. 27:91. [124] Unger, H. 1936. Z. Zellforsch. u. mikroskop. Anat. 25:476. [125] Wickbom, T. 1943. Hereditas 29:1. [126] Wickbom, T. 1945. Ibid. 31:241. [127] Wickbom, T. 1949. Ibid. 35:33. [128] Winge, Ö. 1923. J. Genet. 13:201. [129] Wodsedalek, J. E. 1929. Anat. Record 44:234. [130] Yamashina, Y. 1943. Japan. J. Genet. 19:209. [131] Yamashina, Y. 1943. J. Fac. Sci. Hokkaido Imp. Univ., VI, 8:307. [132] Yamashina, Y. 1944. Cytologia (Tokyo) 13:270. [133] Yamashina, Y. 1946. Kromosomo (Tokyo) 1. [134] Yamashina, Y. 1946. Seibutsu 1. [135] Yamashina, Y. 1950. Kromosomo (Tokyo) 6. [136] Yamashina, Y. 1951. Iden no Sogo Kenkyu 2. [137] Yamashina, Y., and S. Makino. 1946. Seibutsu 1. [138] Young, W. J., et al. 1960. Science 131:1672.

2. CHROMOSOME NUMBERS: INVERTEBRATES

Part I: INSECTS

For additional information, consult reference 105. Diploid (column C): s = spermatogonium, o = oogonium, m = somatic cell. Haploid (column D): ♂(I) = primary spermatocyte, ♂(II) = secondary spermatocyte, ♀(I) = primary oocyte, ♀(II) = secondary oocyte. Classification adapted from Borror and DeLong, *An Introduction to the Study of Insects*, 1954.

	Family	Species	Chromosome Number		Sex Type	Reference
			Diploid	Haploid		
	(A)	(B)	(C)	(D)	(E)	(F)
			Hymenoptera			
1	Apidae	*Apis mellifera*	16o	16♂(I, II)	...	41,42
2		*Xylocopa violacea*	16s	16♂(I, II)	...	56
3	Braconidae	*Habrobracon juglandis*	20o	10♀(I)	...	188
4	Cynipidae	*Andricus collaris*	10s, 20o	...	...	39
5		*Biorrhiza pallida*	10s, 20♀m	10♂(II)	...	39
6		*Cynips kollari*	20o, 20♀m	10♀(I)	...	66
7		*Diastrophus nebulosus*	20♀ m	...	...	62
8		*Neuoterus baccarum*	10s, ♂m; 20♀m	10♀(I), 10♂(II)	...	39,40
9		*Rhodites rosae*	18♀m	9♀(I)	...	66
10		*Trigonaspis megaptera*	10s	10♂(II)	...	39
11		*Xestophanes potentillae*	10s	10♂(II)	...	39
12	Diprionidae	*Diprion similis*	14s, 28o	14♂(II), 14♀(I)	...	183
13		*Neodiprion sertifer*	7♂m, 14♀m	7♂(II)	...	183
14	Eulophidae	*Melittobia chalybii*	5♂m, 10♀m	5♂(I), 5♀(I, II)	...	166
15	Formicidae	*Formica sanguinea*	ca. 48m	24♀(I, II)	...	165
16		*Lasius flava*	24♀m	11♀(I)	...	66
17	Ichneumonidae	*Aenoplex smithii*	13s, 26o	...	...	93
18		*Nemeritis canescens*	22o	11♀(I, II)	...	187
19		*Orthopelma luteolator*	22♀m	11♀(I)	...	66
20	Siricidae	*Sirex cyaneus*	16♀m	8♂(II)	...	149
21	Tenthredinidae	*Allantus calceatus*	8s, 16o	...	...	162
22		*Cladius pectinicornis*	6s, 6-8♂m	6♂(II)	...	162
23		*Pteronidea ribesii*	8s, 16o	8♂(I, II)	...	162
24		*Thrinax macula*	7s; 14o, ♀m	7♂(II), 14♀(I)	...	150
25	Vespidae	*Polistes fadwigae*	9s; 8o, ♀m	9♂(II)	...	101
26		*P. snelleni*	13s, 26o	13♂(II)	...	101
			Siphonaptera			
27	Hystrichopsyllidae	*Leptopsylla musculi*	22s	11♂(I)	X-Y♂?	74,75
28	Pulicidae	*Ctenocephalides canis*	14♂m	...	...	82,83

continued

2. CHROMOSOME NUMBERS: INVERTEBRATES

Part I: INSECTS

	Family	Species	Chromosome Number		Sex Type	Reference
			Diploid	Haploid		
	(A)	(B)	(C)	(D)	(E)	(F)
			Diptera			
29	Anthomyiidae	*Ophrya leucostoma*	12s	6♂(I)	....	120
30		*Pegomyia geniculata*	12♀m	....	....	52
31	Asilidae	*Asilus lecythus*	14s	7♂(II)	X-Y♂	120
32		*Erax rufilabris*	10s	5♂(II)	....	120
33		*Leptogaster badius*	10s	5♂(II)	X-Y♂	120
34	Bibionidae	*Bibio bortulanus*	10m	....	X-Y♂	64
35	Bombyliidae	*Anthrax sinuosa*	18s	9♂(II)	X-Y♂	120
36	Calliphoridae	*Calliphora erythrocephala*	12s, o	6♂(I, II)	X-Y♂	79
37		*Lucilia caesar*	12s	6♂(I, II)	X-Y♂	79
38		*Phormia regina*	12s	6♂(I, II)	X-Y♂	120
39	Cecidomyiidae	*Miastor americana*	48s, o; 12♀m	....	....	67
40		*Phytophaga destructor*	8♂, ♀m	....	....	119
41	Chironomidae	*Chironomus* sp.	8s	....	....	172,173
42	Culicidae	*Aedes albopictus*	6s, o	....	X-Y♂	179
43		*Anopheles punctipennis*	6s, o	3♂(I, II)	X-Y♂	196
44		*Choaborus plumicornis*	8s, m	4♂(I, II)	X-Y♂	52,53
45		*Culex pipiens*	6s, o, m	3♂(I)	....	125
46	Drosophilidae	*Drosophila affinis*	10m	....	X-Y♂	197
47		*D. ananassae*	8s, o, m	....	X-Y♂	86
48		*D. hydei*	12m	....	X-Y♂	63
49		*D. melanogaster*	8s, o	4♀(I)	X-Y♂	59
50		*D. prosaltans*	6m	....	....	20
51		*D. pseudoobscura*	10s, o, m	5♂(I)	X-Y♂	38
52		*D. virilis*	12s, o	5♂(I, II)	X-Y♂	120,121
53		*D. willistoni*	6s, m	3♂(I)	X-Y♂	121
54	Dryomyzidae	*Neuroctena analis*	12s	6♂(II)	....	120
55	Ephydridae	*Scatophila unicornis*	13♂m, 14♀m	7♂(I); 6, 7♂(II)	X-Y♂	63
56	Hippoboscidae	*Melophagus ovinus*	18s	9♂(I, II)	X-Y♂	26
57		*Olfersia bisulcata*	8s	4♂(I)	X-Y♂	27,28
58	Lauxaniidae	*Physegenua vittata*	12s	....	....	120
59	Muscidae	*Musca domestica*	12s, o	6♂(I, II)	X-Y♂	193
60	Mycetophilidae	*Brachypeza radiata*	12m	6♂(I)	X-Y♂	97
61		*Fungivora blanda*	8o, ♀m	4♂(I, II)	X-Y♂	53
62		*Rhymosia fenestralis*	8m	4♂(I, II)	X-Y♂	97
63	Otitidae	*Camptoneura picta*	12s	6♂(I)	....	120
64		*Chaetopsis fulvifrons*	8s	4♂(I)	....	120
65	Ptychopteridae	*Liponeura cinerasceus*	10s	....	X-Y♂	220
66	Sarcophagidae	*Sarcophaga carnaria*	12s	6♂(I, II)	X-Y♂	79
67	Sciaridae	*Sciara coprophila*	10s, o; 7♂m; 8♀m	6♂(I, II), 5♀(I, II)	....	122,123
68	Sciomyzidae	*Tetanocera sparsa*	12s, o	6♂(I, II)	X-Y♂	192,193
69	Scopeumatidae	*Scatophaga stercoraria*	12s	6♂(I, II)	X-Y♂	79
70	Simuliidae	*Simulium* sp.	6m	....	X-Y♂	146
71	Stratiomyidae	*Ptecticus trivittatus*	16s	....	X-Y♂	120
72	Syrphidae	*Eristalis bastardi*	12s	6♂(I)	X-Y♂	120
73		*Mesogramma marginata*	12s	6♂(I)	X-Y♂	120
74		*Sphaerophoria scripta*	8s	4♂(I, II)	....	79
75	Tachinidae	*Phorocera hamata*	12♂m	6♂(I)	X-Y♂	184
76	Tipulidae	*Dicranomyia trinotata*	6s	3♂(I)	....	219
77		*Tipula paludosa*	8s, o	....	....	8
78	Trypetidae	*Anastrepha ludens*	10s	5♂(I)	....	47
79		*Tephritis arnicae*	11s	6♂(I); 5, 6♂(II)	X-O♂	79
			Lepidoptera			
80	Arctiidae	*Phragmatobia fuliginosa*	56s, 58o	28♂(I, II); 28♀(I); 28, 29♀(II)	Z-2W♀	170
81	Bombycidae	*Bombyx mori*	56s	28♂(I, II)	....	138
82	Geometridae	*Abraxas grossulariata*	56s, 56o	28♂(I, II), 28♀(I, II)	X-X♂, X-O♀	44
83		*Biston hirtaria*	28s, o	14♂(I)	....	60
84		*Nyssia zonaria*	ca. 112s	56♂(I, II), 50-60♀(I)	....	44
85	Lasiocampidae	*Dendrolimus spectabilis*	60s	30♂(I, II)	....	103
86	Liparidae	*Lymantria dispar*	62s, o	31♂(I, II), 31♀(I)	....	168
87		*Orgyia thyellina*	22s	11♂(I, II)	....	29

continued

2. CHROMOSOME NUMBERS: INVERTEBRATES

Part I: INSECTS

	Family	Species	Chromosome Number		Sex Type	Reference
			Diploid	Haploid		
	(A)	(B)	(C)	(D)	(E)	(F)
		Lepidoptera				
88	Lycaenidae	*Lycaeides idas*	19-24s	9-13♂(I)	....	205
89	Papilionidae	*Papilio podalirius*	54-58s	....	....	78
90		*P. rutilus*	28s	28♂(I, II)	....	132
91	Phalaenidae	*Dicranura erminea*	56s	28♂(I, II)	....	49
92		*D. vinula delavoiei*	62m	30♀(I)	....	49
93		*D. vinula fennica*	42m	21♂(I, II), 21♀(I, II)	....	49
94		*Pygaera curtula*	48m	29♂(I, II), 29♀(I)	....	48
95		*P. pigra*	46s, m	23♂(I, II), 23♀(I)	....	48
96	Pieridae	*Pieris brassicae*	30s, o	15♂(I, II), 15♀(I)	....	43
97	Psychidae	*Fumea casta*	62s, 61o	31♂(I, II), 30,31♀	X-X♂, X-O♀	169
98		*Solenobia triquetrella*	62♀m	31♀(I)	....	171
99		*Talaeporia tubulosa*	60♂m, 59♀m	30♂(I, II); 30♀(I); 29, 30♀(II)	X-X♂, X-O♀	169
100	Pyralidae	*Chiro simplex*	58s	29♂(I, II)	....	95
101	Saturniidae	*Philosamia cynthia*	26s, o, ♀m	13♂(I, II), 13♀(I, II)	....	33
102		*P. cynthia pryeri*	28s	14♂(I, II)	....	77
103		*P. cynthia walkeri*	26s	13♂(I, II)	....	77
104		*Telea polyphemus*	60s	30♂(I, II)	....	25
105	Sphingidae	*Deilephila euphorbiae*	28s	28♂(I, II)	....	14
106	Tischeriidae	*Tischeria angusticolella*	42s, o	21♂(I, II), 21♀(I)	....	92
		Trichoptera				
107	Hydropsychidae	*Hydropsyche pellucidula*	30s	15♂(I)	....	154
108	Limnephilidae	*Chaetopteryx villosa*	60s	30♂(I, II)	....	154
109		*Halesus tesselatus*	42s	21♂(I, II)	....	154
110		*Limnephilus affinis*	12s	6♂(I)	....	154
111		*L. lunatus*	26s, 25o	13♂(I, II)	X-X♂, X-O♀	89
112		*Platyphylax designatus*	55-60o	30♂(I, II)	....	100
113		*Stenophylax stellatus*	60s	30♀(I)	....	57
114	Psychomyiidae	*Plectrocnemia conspersa*	26s	13♂(I, II)	....	154
		Mecoptera				
115	Panorpidae	*Panorpa japonica*	46o	....	X-X♀	85
		Coleoptera				
116	Buprestidae	*Agrilus anxius*	22s, o	11♂(I, II)	X-Y♂	185
117		*Julodis whithilli*	24s	12♂(I, II)	X-O♂	7
118		*Sternocera laevigata*	26s	13♂(I, II)	X-O♂	7
119	Cantharidae	*Photinus pennsylvanicus*	19s, ♂m; 20o	10♂(I, II)	X-O♂	194
120	Carabidae	*Anthia sexguttata*	35s	18♂(I); 17, 18♂(II)	X-O♂	7
121		*Chalenius pallipes*	37s	19♂(I); 18, 19♂(II)	X-O♂	230
122		*Palatinus* sp.	37s	19♂(I); 18, 19♂(II)	X-O♂	230
123	Cerambycidae	*Pterolophia caudata*	20s	10♂(I, II)	X-Y♂	230
124		*Tetraopes tetraophthalmus*	20s	10♂(I, II)	X-Y♂	194
125	Chrysomelidae	*Agelastica caerulae*	24s	12♂(I, II)	X-Y♂	223
126		*Chelymorpha argus*	22s	11♂(I, II)	X-Y♂	191
127		*Chrysomela exanthematica*	23s	12♂(I)	X-O♂	223
128		*Coptocycla aurichalcea*	22s	11♂(I, II)	X-Y♂	137
129		*Diabrotica vittata*	21s	11♂(I); 10, 11♂(II)	X-Y♂	193
130		*Haltica chalybea*	22s	11♂(I)	X-Y♂	194
131		*Lema trilineata*	32s	16♂(II)	X-Y♂	194
132		*Leptinotarsa signaticolis*	34s	17♂(I); 16, 17♂(II)	2X-O♂?	211
133		*Luperodes praeustus*	32s, o	16♂(I)	X-O♂	223,230
134		*Melasoma populi*	32s	16♂(I, II)	X-Y♂	230
135	Cicindelidae	*Cicindela primeriana*	20s	10♂(I, II)	X-Y♂	191
136	Coccinellidae	*Adalia bipunctata*	20s	10♂(I, II)	X-Y♂	191
137		*Calvia 14-guttata*	20s	10♂(I, II)	X-Y♂	223
138		*Coccinella bruckii*	18s	9♂(I, II)	X-Y♂	223
139		*Epilachna pustulosa*	20s	10♂(I, II)	X-Y♂	227
140		*Harmonia axyridis*	16s	8♂(I, II)	X-Y♂	223
141		*Hippodamia tredecimpunctata*	20s, o, ♀m	10♂(I, II)	X-Y♂	223,230
142		*Synonycha grandis*	20s, o	10♂(I, II)	X-Y♂	223,225

continued

2. CHROMOSOME NUMBERS: INVERTEBRATES

Part I: INSECTS

	Family	Species	Chromosome Number: Diploid	Chromosome Number: Haploid	Sex Type	Reference
	(A)	(B)	(C)	(D)	(E)	(F)
		Coleoptera				
143	Curculionidae	*Calendra oryzae*	12o, ♀m	....	....	204
144		*Otiorhynchus arcticus*[1]	22s	11♂(I, II), 11♀(I)	X-Y♂	198,199
145		*O. gemmatus*[2]	33♀m	33♀(I)	....	201
146		*O. scaber*[3]	44♀m	42-44♀(I)	....	198,199, 201
147		*Polydrosus pilosus*	22s, o	11♂(I, II)	X-X♀	198,199
148	Dytiscidae	*Dytiscus circumcinctus*	38s	19♂(I, II)	X-Y♂	164
149	Elateridae	*Limonius griseus*	17s	9♂(I); 8, 9♂(II)	X-O♂	191
150	Hydrophilidae	*Hydrophilus piceus*	30s, ♂m	15♂(I, II)	....	1
151		*Hydrous acuminatus*	30s	15♂(I, II)	X-Y♂	7
152	Melandryidae	*Penthe obliquata*	16s	8♂(II)	X-Y♂	194
153	Meloidae	*Epicauta cinerea*	20s	10♂(I, II)	X-Y♂	194
154		*Meloe* sp.	20s	10♂(I, II)	X-Y♂	7
155	Mylabridae	*Acanthoscelides obtectus*	20♀m	10♂(I)	....	15
156		*Bruchus quadrimaculatus*	19s, 20m	10♂(I); 9, 10♂(II)	X-O♂	13
157	Passalidae	*Passalus cornutus*	ca. 26s	13♂(I)	X-Y♂	174
158	Scarabaeidae	*Anomala rufocuprea*	18s	9♂(I, II)	X-Y♂	228
159		*Cotalpa lanigera*	20s	10♂(I, II)	X-Y♂	175
160		*Euphoria inda*	20s	10♂(I, II)	X-Y♂	191
161		*Lachnosterna delata*	20s	10♂(I, II)	X-Y♂	175
162		*Pelidnota punctata*	20s	10♂(I, II)	X-Y♂	175
163		*Phaneus carnifex*	12s	6♂(I)	....	61
164		*Popillia japonica*	18s	9♂(I, II)	X-Y♂	228
165	Silphidae	*Necrophorus sayi*	13s	7♂(I); 6, 7♂(II)	X-O♂	194
166		*Silpha americana*	40s	20♂(I, II)	X-Y♂	191
167	Silvanidae	*Oryzaephilus surinamensis*	ca. 13-14s	7♂(I, II)	....	116
168	Staphylinidae	*Listotrophus cingulatus*	26s	13♂(I, II)	X-Y♂	194
169	Tenebrionidae	*Blaps gigas*	35s, 38o	....	XX-Y♂	58
170		*Tenebrio molitor*	20s, o, ♀m	10♂(I, II)	X-Y♂, X-X♀	191
		Neuroptera				
171	Ascalaphidae	*Ascalaphus libelluloides*	22o, ♀m	11♂(I, II)	X-Y♂	134
172		*Glyptobasis dentifera*	22s	....	X-Y♂	2
173		*Hybris subjacens*	22s	11♂(I, II)	X-Y♂	76
174		*Ogcogaster segmentator*	22s	....	X-Y♂	2
175	Chrysopidae	*Chrysopa aspersa*	12s, o	6♂(I)	X-Y♂	134,135
176		*C. flava*	14s	7♂(I)	X-Y♂	135
177		*C. septempunctata cognata*	10s, o	5♂(I, II)	X-Y♂	80
178	Coniopterygidae	*Semidalis albata*	18o	....	....	85
179	Corydalidae	*Chauliodes japonicus*	20s, o	....	X-Y♂	73
180	Hemerobiidae	*Hemerobius stigma*	14s	7♂(I, II)	X-Y♂	90
181	Mantispidae	*Mantispa styriaca*	18s	9♂(I, II)	X-Y♂	134
182	Myrmeleontidae	*Creagris plumbea*	18s	9♂(I, II)	X-Y♂	135
183		*Macronemurus appendiculatus*	16s	8♂(I, II), 8♀(I)	X-Y♂	134
184		*Morter hyalinus*	14s	7♂(I, II)	X-Y♂	135
185		*Myrmeleon europaeus*	14s, o, m	7♂(I, II)	X-Y♂	134
186		*Neuroleon* sp.	16s	8♂(I, II)	X-Y♂	2
187		*Palpares pardus asani*	26s	13♂(I)	X-Y♂	104
188	Raphidiidae	*Raphidia nigricollis*	24s, ♀m	12♂(I)	X-Y♂	135
189	Sialidae	*Protohermes grandis*	23s	....	X-Y♂?	73
190	Sisyridae	*Sisyra fuscata*	14s	....	X-Y♂	91
		Homoptera				
191	Aleyrodidae	*Aleurodes proletella*	13♂m, 26-28♀m	13♀(I, II)	Parth.	203
192		*Trialeurodes vaporariorum*	22o, ♀m	11♀(I, II)	....	203
193	Aphididae	*Aphis oenothera*	10s, m	5♂(I); 4, 5♂(II); 5♀(I)	X-O♂	195
194		*Hyalopterus pruni*	9s, 10♀m	5♂(I, II)	X-O♂	176
195		*Macrosiphum solanifolii*	9s, ♂m; 10♀m	5♂(I); 4, 5♂(II); 10♀(I)	X-O♂	96

/1/ $2n$ bisexual species. /2/ $3n$ parthenogenetic species. /3/ $4n$ parthenogenetic species.

continued

2. CHROMOSOME NUMBERS: INVERTEBRATES

Part I: INSECTS

	Family	Species	Chromosome Number		Sex Type	Reference
			Diploid	Haploid		
	(A)	(B)	(C)	(D)	(E)	(F)
		Homoptera				
196	Aphididae	*Myzus linderae*	11s, 12o	6♂(I); 5, 6♂(II)	X-O♂	178
197		*Pemphigus pyriformis*	20♀m	20♀(I)	Parth.	206
198		*Phyllaphis coweni*	5s, 6o	3♂(I); 2, 3♂(II)	X-O♂	129
199		*Schizoneura subelliptica*	12♀m	12♀(I)	Parth.	206
200	Cercopidae	*Aphrophora coctalis*	30s	15♂(I, II)	X-Y♂	124
201		*Clastoptera obtusa*	15s	8♂(I); 7, 8♂(II)	X-O♂	10
202		*Philaenus lineatus*	29s	15♂(I); 14, 15♂(II)	X-O♂	12
203	Cicadidae	*Cicada septemdecim*	19s, 20o	10♂(I); 9, 10♂(II)	X-O♂	175
204	Coccidae	*Aonidiella aurantii*	8♀m	....	....	37
205		*Lecanium hemisphaericum*	16s, ♀m	8♀(I, II)	....	198
206		*Llaveia oaxacoensis*	5s, ♂m; 6o, ♀m	3♂(I, II)	X-O♂	71
207		*Matsucoccus gallicola*	34s, 40♀m	14, 20♂(II)	6X-O♂	71
208		*Pseudococcus acericola*	12s, o	12♂(I, II), 6♀(I, II)	....	69
209	Fulgoridae	*Amphiscepa bivittata*	25s	13♂(I); 12, 13♂(II)	X-O♂	10
210		*Poeciloptera pruinosa*	27s, 28♀m	14♂(I); 13, 14♂(II)	X-O♂	10
211	Membracidae	*Campylenchia curvata*	19s	10♂(I); 9, 10♂(II)	X-O♂	10
212		*Enchenopa binotata*	20s, o	10♂(I, II)	X-Y♂	94
213		*Thelia bimaculata*	21s, 22o	11♂(I)	....	94
214	Phylloxeridae	*Phylloxera fallax*	10s, o, ♀m	6♂(I); 4, 6♂(II); 6♀(I;II)	2X-O♂?	129
215	Psylliidae	*Chermes pectinata*	20♀m	10♂(I;II), 10♀(I)	....	51
		Hemiptera				
216	Belostomadidae	*Belostoma flumineum*	24s	13♂(I), 12♂(II)	X-Y♂	21
217		*Benacus griseus*	28s	15♂(I), 14♂(II)	....	21
218		*Lethocerus americanus*	8s	5♂(I), 4♂(II)	X-Y♂	21, 22
219	Cimicidae	*Cimex lectularius*	30-34s, 33-41o	18-21♂(I)	4X...7X-Y♂	32
220	Coreidae	*Acanthocoris sordidus*	24s	12♂(I, II)	XX-O♂	224
221		*Anasa tristis*	21s, 22o	11♂(I, II)	X-O♂	217
222		*Leptoglossus stigma*	21s	11♂(I, II)	X-O♂	35
223	Coriscidae	*Alydus calcaratus*	13s	7♂(I)	X-O♂	158
224		*Coriscus calcaratus*	13s	8♂(I)	X-O♂	163
225		*Protenor belfragei*	13s, 14o	7♂(I, II)	X-O♂	217
226	Corixidae	*Callicorixa caledonica*	24s	....	X-Y♂	180
227		*Corixa punctata*	24s	....	X-Y♂	180
228	Corizidae	*Corizus* sp.	13s	7♂(I, II)	X-O♂	229
229		*Harmostes reflexulus*	13s, 14o	....	X-O♂, X-X♀	214
230		*Jadera sanguinolenta*	13s	7♂(I)	X-O♂	35
231		*Leptocoris trivittatus*	13s	7♂(I)	X-O♂	222
232	Gerridae	*Gerris lateralis*	21s, 22o	11♂(I)	X-O♂	54
233	Hydrometridae	*Hydrometra lacustris*	11s	12♂(I, II)	....	212
234		*Hygotrechus* sp.	21s	11♂(I, II)	X-O♂	128
235	Lygaeidae	*Aphanus japonicus*	17s	11♂(I), 7♂(II)	4X-Y♂	224
236		*Eremocoris erraticus*	20s	10♂(I), 9♂(II)	X-Y♂	207
237		*Geocoris ater*	20s	11♂(I), 10♂(II)	X-Y♂	207
238		*Ligirocoris silvestris*	16s, o	9♂(I), 8♂(II), 8♀(I, II)	X-Y♂	207
239		*Lygaeus equestris*	14s	8♂(I), 7♂(II)	X-Y♂	224
240		*Macrodema micropterum*	18o	10♂(I), 9♂(II), 9♀(I)	X-Y♂	207
241		*Nysius jacobeae*	14s, o	8♂(I), 7♂(II), 7♀(I)	X-Y♂	207
242		*Oncopeltus fasciatus*	16s, o	9♂(I), 8♂(II)	X-Y♂	218
243		*Rhyparochromus chiragra*	14s	8♂(I), 7♂(II), 7♀(I)	XX-Y♂	207
244		*Stygnocoris fuligineus*	16s, o	9♂(I), 8♂(II), 8♀(I)	X-Y♂	207
245	Mesoveliidae	*Mesovelia furcata*	35s	....	4X-Y♂	46
246	Miridae	*Adelphocoris lineolatus*	17s	8♂(I)	X-O♂	163
247		*Calocoris rapidus*	30s	16♂(I); 15, 16♂(II)	2X-O♂	128
248		*Lygus pratensis*	ca. 35s	19♂(I); 17, 18♂(II)	....	128
249	Naucoridae	*Naucoris cimicoides*	51s	26♂(I, II)	X-O♂	189
250	Nepidae	*Nepa cinerea*	35s, 36o	18♂(I); 17, 18♂(II)	X-O♂	186
251		*Ranatra chinensis*	46s	24♂(I), 23♂(II)	X-Y♂	177
252	Notonectidae	*Notonecta maculata*	24s	13♂(I), 12♂(II)	X-Y♂	155

continued

2. CHROMOSOME NUMBERS: INVERTEBRATES

Part I: INSECTS

	Family	Species	Chromosome Number		Sex Type	Reference
			Diploid	Haploid		
	(A)	(B)	(C)	(D)	(E)	(F)
			Hemiptera			
253	Pentatomidae	*Aelia accuminata*	14s	8♂(I), 7♂(II)	X-Y♂	163
254		*Banasa dimidiata*	16s, o	9♂(I), 8♂(II)	X-Y♂	215
255		*Coptosoma biguttula*	14s	8♂(I), 7♂(II)	X-Y♂	229
256		*Cosmopelpa carnifex*	16s	9♂(I), 8♂(II)	X-Y♂	128
257		*Dolycoris baccarum*	14s	8♂(I), 7♂(II)	X-Y♂	136,163
258		*Eusarcoris lewisi*	14s	8♂(I), 7♂(II)	X-Y♂	224,226
259		*Euschistus crassus*	12s, o	7♂(I), 6♂(II)	X-Y♂	50
260		*Graphosoma rubrolineatum*	14s	8♂(I), 7♂(II)	X-Y♂	229
261		*Halyomorpha picus*	14s	8♂(I), 7♂(II)	X-Y♂	224,226
262		*Palomena angulosa*	16s, o	9♂(I), 8♂(II)	X-Y♂	224,226
263		*Pentatoma senilis*	6s, o	3♂(I, II)	X-Y♂	167
264		*Perrilus confluens*	14s	8♂(I), 7♂(II)	X-Y♂	128
265		*Podisus spinosus*	16s	9♂(I), 8♂(II)	X-Y♂	128
266		*Thyanta calceata*	27s, 28o	15♂(I)	X_1X_2-Y♂	217
267	Pyrrhocoridae	*Dysdercus ruficollis*	13s	7♂(I, II)	X-O♂	36
268		*Largus cinctus*	11s, 12o	....	X-O♂	216
269	Reduviidae	*Apiomeris crassipes*	24s	13♂(I), 12♂(II)	X-Y♂	148
270		*Diplacodus exsanguis*	26♂, ♀m	14♂(I), 13♂(II)	X-Y♂	147
271		*Pselliodes cinctus*	28s, 30o	16♂(I, II)	XXX-Y♂	55
272	Velidae	*Velia currens*	25s	13♂(I)	X-O♂	156
			Anoplura			
273	Haematopinidae	*Haematopinus asini*	9s	....	....	16
274		*Linognathus tenuirostris*	14o, ♀m	....	....	159
275	Pediculidae	*Pediculus capitis*	12m	....	....	45
			Mallophaga			
276	Philopteridae	*Goniodes slylifer*	12s, 24o	....	....	153
277		*Lipeurus baculus*	12♀m	....	....	159
			Psocoptera			
278	Psocidae	*Ceratipsocus venosus*	17s	9♂(I); 8, 9♂(II)	X-O♂	11
			Embioptera			
279	Oligotomidae	*Oligotoma japonica*	19s, 20o	....	X-O♂	84
280		*O. saundersii*	21s, 22♀m	....	X-O♂	65
			Dermaptera			
281	Forficulidae	*Forficula auricularia*	24s	12♂(I, II)	X-Y♂	118
282	Labiduridae	*Anisolabis annulipes*	25s	12♂(I); 12, 13♂(II)	X_1X_2-Y♂	130
283		*Labidura riparia*	14s, ♀m	7♂(I, II)	X-Y♂, X-X♀	3
284	Labiidae	*Labia minor*	14s, o	7♂(I, II)	X-Y♂, X-X♀	130
			Plecoptera			
285	Isoperlidae	*Isoperla grammatica*	26s	12, 14♂(II)	X_1X_2-O♂	110
286	Perlidae	*Acroneuria jezoensis*	25s, 26♀m	13♂(I); 12, 13♂(II)	X-O♂	72
287		*Perla maxima*	19s	9, 10♂(II)	X-O♂	110
288	Perlodidae	*Isogenus fontium*	26s	13♂(I); 12, 14♂(II)	X_1X_2-O♂	110
289		*Perlodes microcephala*	27s	13♂(I); 12, 15♂(II)	$X_1X_2X_3$-O♂	110
			Isoptera			
290	Hodotermitidae	*Termopsis angusticollis*	52s	26♂(I, II)	....	190
291	Kalotermitidae	*Zootermopsis angusticollis*	52♀m	....	....	99
			Orthoptera			
292	Acrididae	*Acrida exaltata*	23s	12♂(I); 11, 12♂(II)	X-O♂	6
293		*Atractomorpha ambigua*	19s	10♂(I); 9, 10♂(II)	X-O♂	127
294		*Brachystola magna*	23s	12♂(I); 11, 12♂(II)	X-O♂	18
295		*Camnula pellucida*	23s	12♂(I); 11, 12♂(II)	X-O♂	19
296		*Chorthippus bicolor*	17s	9♂(I); 8, 9♂(II)	X-O♂	127
297		*Chortophaga viridifasciata*	23s	....	X-O♂	24
298		*Circotettix undulatus*	21s	11♂(I)	X-O♂	210

continued

2. CHROMOSOME NUMBERS: INVERTEBRATES

Part I: INSECTS

	Family	Species	Chromosome Number Diploid	Chromosome Number Haploid	Sex Type	Reference
	(A)	(B)	(C)	(D)	(E)	(F)
		Orthoptera				
299	Acrididae	*Dissosteira* sp.	23s	12♂(I); 11, 12♂(II)	X-O♂	112
300		*Gomphocerus sibericus*	17s	9♂(I)	X-O♂	115
301		*Hesperotettix pratensis*	22s	12♂(I); 11♂(II)	X-O♂	113
302		*Locusta migratoria*	23s	12♂(I); 11, 12♂(II)	X-O♂	221
303		*L. viridissima*	29s, 30o	15♂(I); 14, 15♂(II)	X-O♂	126
304		*Mecostethus lineatus*	23s	12♂(I)	X-O♂	114
305		*Melanoplus differentialis*	24♀m	12♀(I, II)	Parth.	181
306		*Melanoplus femur-rubrum*	23s	12♂(I)	X-O♂	209
307		*Mermiria bivittata*	22s, ♀m	11♂(I, II)	X-O♂	113
308		*Miramella dairisama*	21s	11♂(I); 10, 11♂(II)	X-O♂	127
309		*Oxya intricata*	23s	12♂(I); 11, 12♂(II)	X-O♂	127
310		*Podisma sapporoensis*	23s	12♂(I); 11, 12♂(II)	X-O♂	127
311		*Schistocerca gregaria*	23s	12♂(I)	X-O♂	30
312		*Stauroderus bicolor*	17s	9♂(I)	X-O♂	31
313		*Stenobothrus bicolor*	17s	9♂(I); 8, 9♂(II)	X-O♂	117
314		*Syrbula acuticornis*	23s	12♂(I); 11, 12♂(II)	X-O♂	160
315		*Teratodes monticolis*	23s	12♂(I); 11, 12♂(II)	X-O♂	6
316		*Traulia ornata*	23s	12♂(I); 11, 12♂(II)	X-O♂	127
317		*Trimerotropis* sp.	23s	12♂(I); 11, 12♂(II)	X-O♂	210
318		*Zarytes squalina*	19s	10♂(I); 9, 10♂(II)	X-O♂	157
319	Blattidae	*Blabera fusca*	73s	37♂(I); 36, 37♂(II)	X-O♂	200
320		*Blatta germanica*	23s, 24o	12♂(I); 11, 12♂(II)	X-O♂	208
321		*B. orientalis*	47s, 48♀m	24♂(I); 23, 24♂(II)	X-O♂	200
322		*Leucophaea maderae*	23s, 24o	11, 12♂(II)	X-O♂	131
323		*Loboptera decipiens*	33s	17♂(I); 16, 17♂(II)	X-O♂	200
324		*Periplaneta americana*	33s, 34♀m	17♂(I); 16, 17♂(II)	X-O♂	200
325		*Pycnoscelus surinamensis*	37s, 38o	19♂(I); 18, 19♂(II)	X-O♂	107
326	Gryllacridae	*Eremus testaceus*	17s	....	X-O♂	142
327	Gryllidae	*Acheta campestis*	29s	....	X-O♂	141
328		*Apithes agitator*	13s	....	....	9
329		*Endecous cavernicola*	19s	10♂(I); 9, 10♂(II)	X-O♂	34
330		*Gryllodes* sp.	21s	11♂(I); 10, 11♂(II)	X-O♂	34
331		*Gryllus assimilis*	29s	15♂(I); 14, 15♂(II)	X-O♂	34
332		*Liphoplus annulipedus*	14s	....	X-O♂	202
333		*Madasumma hibinonis*	15s	....	X-O♂	141
334		*Nemobius* sp.	17s	....	X-O♂	142
335		*Oecanthus longicauda*	20s	10♂(I, II)	X-Y♂	102
336		*Scapsipedus* sp.	21s	....	X-O♂	144
337	Grylloblattidae	*Galloisiana nipponensis*	30s	....	X-Y♂	133
338	Gryllotalpidae	*Gryllotalpa africana*	23s	12♂(I)	X-O♂	141
339	Mantidae	*Choeradodis rhombicollis*	31s	15♂(I); 15, 16♂(II)	X_1X_2-Y♂	68
340		*Creobroter laevicolis*	27s	14♂(I)	X-O♂	140
341		*Hierodula patellifera*	27s	13♂(I); 13, 14♂(II)	X_1X_2-Y♂	140
342		*Mantis religiosa*	27s	13♂(I); 13, 14♂(II)	X_1X_2-Y♂	88
343		*Stagmomantis carolina*	27s	13♂(I); 13, 14♂(II)	X_1X_2-Y♂	68
344		*Tenodera sinensis*	27s	13♂(I); 13, 14♂(II)	X_1X_2-Y♂	88
345		*Toxomantis sinensis*	27s	14♂(I)	X-O♂	140
346	Phasmatidae	*Bostra* sp.	35s	18♂(I); 17, 18♂(II)	X-O♂	70
347		*Carausius juvenilis*	41s	20, 21♂(II)	X-O♂	17
348		*Isagoras* sp.	47s	24♂(I); 23, 24♂(II)	X-O♂	70
349		*Oncotophasma* sp.	41s	21♂(I); 20, 21♂(II)	X-O♂	70
350		*Pseudophasma menius*	23s	12♂(I); 11, 12♂(II)	X-O♂	70
351	Tetrigidae	*Acridium granulatus*	13s, ♂m; 14♀m	7♂(I); 6, 7♂(II)	X-O♂	161
352		*Paratettix cucculatus*	13s	7♂(I)	X-O♂	160
353		*Tettigidea parvipennis*	13s, ♂m; 14o	7♂(I); 6, 7♂(II)	X-O♂	161
354	Tettigoniidae	*Amblycorypha rotundifolia*	33s	17♂(I); 16, 17♂(II)	X-O♂	151
355		*Anabrus* sp.	33s	17♂(I); 16, 17♂(II)	....	112
356		*Conocephalus* sp.	33s	17♂(I); 16, 17♂(II)	X-O♂	34
357		*Ephippigera vitium*	29s	15♂(I)	X-O♂	106
358		*Hexacentrus mundus*	31s	16♂(I); 15, 16♂(II)	X-O♂	5
359		*Holochlora* sp.	31s	16♂(I); 15, 16♂(II)	X-O♂	5
360		*Homoeocoryphus lineosus*	25s	....	X-O♂	142

continued

2. CHROMOSOME NUMBERS: INVERTEBRATES

Part I: INSECTS

	Family	Species	Chromosome Number		Sex Type	Reference
			Diploid	Haploid		
	(A)	(B)	(C)	(D)	(E)	(F)
			Orthoptera			
361	Tettigoniidae	*Meconema albicornis*	31s	....	X-O♂	143
362		*Mecopoda elongata*	27s	14♂(I); 13, 14♂(II)	X-O♂	5
363		*Microcentrum* sp.	33s	17♂(I); 16, 17♂(II)	X-O♂	111
364		*Odontura maroccana*	27s	....	X-O♂	108
365		*Orchelimum concinnum*	33s, 34o	....	X-O♂	87
366		*Saga cappadocica*	31s	16♂(I); 15, 16♂(II)	X-O♂	109
367		*Scudderia* sp.	31s	16♂(I); 15, 16♂(II)	X-O♂	34
368		*Xiphidiopsis suzukii*	31s	....	X-O♂	143
369	Tridactylidae	*Tridactylus japonicus*	13s	7♂(I)	X-O♂	141
			Odonata			
370	Aeshnidae	*Aeshna crenata*	27s, 28o	14♂(I, II)	X-O♂	145
371		*Anax junius*	27s	14♂(I, II)	X-O♂	98
372		*Ictinus rapax*	23s	12♂(I, II)	X-O♂	4
373	Coenagrionidae	*Ceriagrion rubiae*	27s	14♂(I, II)	X-O♂	4
374	Cordulegastridae	*Cordulegaster annulatus*	26♀m	13♂(I)	....	145
375	Lestidae	*Lestes sponsa*	25s	13♂(I, II)	X-O♂	84
376	Libellulidae	*Brachythemis contaminata*	25s	13♂(I, II)	X-O♂	4
377		*Crocothemis servilia*	25s	13♂(I, II)	X-O♂	4
378		*Diplacodes trivialis*	25s	13♂(I, II)	X-O♂	4
379		*Libellula basalis*	25s	13♂(I, II)	X-O♂	182
380		*Orethetrum sabina*	25s	13♂(I, II)	X-O♂	4
381		*Pantala flavescens*	25s	13♂(I, II)	X-O♂	4
382		*Somatochlora pedemontanum*	25s	13♂(I, II)	X-O♂	139
383		*Tramea limbata*	25s	13♂(I, II)	X-O♂	4
384		*Trithemis pallidinervis*	25s	13♂(I, II)	X-O♂	4
385	Petaluridae	*Tachopteryx pryeri*	17s	9♂(I, II)	X-O♂	81
			Ephemeroptera			
386	Ephemeridae	*Ephemera danica*	11s	....	X-O♂	220
387	Siphlonuridae	*Ameletus costalis*	18s, o, ♀m	9♂(I, II)	X-Y♂	76
			Collembola			
388	Poduridae	*Anurida maritima*	8o	....	....	23
389		*Podura aquatica*	8o	....	....	213
			Thysanura			
390	Lepismatidae	*Thermobia domestica*	34s, 36o	18♂(I); 16, 18♂(II)	X_1X_2-O♂, X_1X_1-X_2X_2♀	152

Contributor: Makino, Sajiro

References: [1] Arnold, G. 1908-09. Arch. Zellforsch. 2:181. [2] Asana, J. J., and H. Kichijo. 1936. J. Fac. Sci. Hokkaido Imp. Univ., VI, 5. [3] Asana, J. J., and S. Makino. 1934. J. Morphol. 56:361. [4] Asana, J. J., and S. Makino. 1935. J. Fac. Sci. Hokkaido Imp. Univ., VI, 4. [5] Asana, J. J., S. Makino, and H. Niiyama. 1938. Ibid., VI, 6. [6] Asana, J. J., S. Makino, and H. Niiyama. 1939. Japan. J. Genet. 15:251. [7] Asana, J. J., S. Makino, and H. Niiyama. 1942. Cytologia (Tokyo) 12:187. [8] Bauer, H. 1931. Z. Zellforsch. u. mikroskop. Anat. 14:138. [9] Baumgartner, W. J. 1917. Anat. Record 11:495. [10] Boring, A. M. 1907. J. Exptl. Zool. 4:469. [11] Boring, A. M. 1913. Biol. Bull. 24:125. [12] Boring, A. M., and R. H. Fogler. 1915. Ibid. 29:312. [13] Brauer, A. 1928. J. Morphol. 46:217. [14] Buder, J. E. 1917. Arch. Zellforsch. 14:26. [15] Bushnell, R. J. 1936. J. Morphol. 60:221. [16] Cannon, H. G. 1922. Quart. J. Microscop. Sci. 66:213. [17] Cappe de Baillon, P., M. Favrelle, and G. de Vichet. 1938. Bull. biol. France et Belg. 72:167. [18] Carothers, E. E. 1913. J. Morphol. 24:287. [19] Carroll, M. 1920. Ibid. 34:375. [20] Cavalcanti, A. G. L. 1948. Genetics 33:529. [21] Chickering, A. M. 1927. J. Morphol. 44:541. [22] Chickering, A. M.

continued

1931. Papers Mich. Acad. Sci. 15:357. [23] Claypole, A. M. 1898. J. Morphol. 14:219. [24] Coleman, L. C. 1943. Genetics 28:2. [25] Cook, M. H. 1910. Proc. Phila. Acad. Nat. Sci. 62:294. [26] Cooper, K. W. 1941. Proc. Natl. Acad. Sci. U. S. 27:109. [27] Cooper, K. W. 1944. Genetics 29:537. [28] Cooper, K. W. 1944. Proc. Natl. Acad. Sci. U. S. 30:50. [29] Cretschmar, M. 1928. Z. Zellforsch. u. mikroskop. Anat. 7:290. [30] Csik, L., and P. C. Koller. 1939. Chromosoma 1:191. [31] Darlington, C. D. 1936. J. Genet. 33:465. [32] Darlington, C. D. 1939. Ibid. 39:101. [33] Dederer, P. H. 1928. J. Morphol. 45:599. [34] De Toledo Piza, S. 1945. Anais escola super. agr. "Luis de Queiroz" Univ. São Paulo (2). [35] De Toledo Piza, S. 1946. Ibid (6). [36] De Toledo Piza, S. 1947. Ibid. (4). [37] Dickson, R. C. 1941. Hilgardia 13:513. [38] Dobzhansky, T., and P. C. Koller. 1939. Genetics 24:97. [39] Dodds, K. S. 1938. Genetica (Haag) 20:67. [40] Dodds, K. S. 1939. Ibid. 21:177. [41] Doncaster, L. 1906. Anat. Anz. 29:490. [42] Doncaster, L. 1907. Ibid. 31:168. [43] Doncaster, L. 1912. Proc. Cambridge Phil. Soc. 16:491. [44] Doncaster, L. 1914. J. Genet. 4:1. [45] Doncaster, L., and H. G. Cannon. 1920. Quart. J. Microscop. Sci. 64:303. [46] Ekblom, T. 1941. Chromosoma 2:12. [47] Emmart, E. W. 1935. Proc. Entomol. Soc. Wash. 37:119. [48] Federley, H. 1930. Z. Zellforsch. u. mikroskop. Anat. 12:772. [49] Federley, H. 1943. Hereditas 29:205. [50] Foot, K., and E. C. Strobell. 1912. Arch. Zellforsch. 12:485. [51] Frolowa, S. 1924. Z. Zellforsch. u. mikroskop. Anat. 1:29. [52] Frolowa, S. 1929. Ibid. 8:542. [53] Frolowa, S. 1929. Ibid. 9:66. [54] Geitler, L. 1937. Ibid. 26:641. [55] Goldsmith, W. M. 1916. Biol. Bull. 31:121. [56] Granata, L. 1913. Monit. zool. ital. 24:31. [57] Gresson, R. A. R. 1935. Proc. Roy. Soc. Edinburgh, B, 53:322. [58] Guénin, H. A. 1949. Rev. suisse zool. 56:336. [59] Guyénot, E., and A. Naville. 1929. Cellule 39:25. [60] Harrison, J. W. H., and L. Doncaster. 1914. J. Genet. 3:229. [61] Hayden, M. A. 1925. J. Morphol. 40:261. [62] Hegner, R. W. 1915. Ibid. 26:495. [63] Heitz, E. 1933. Z. Zellforsch. u. mikroskop. Anat. 20:237. [64] Heitz, E., and H. Bauer. 1933. Ibid. 17:67. [65] Hirai, H. 1948. Japan. J. Genet. 23:15. [66] Hogben, L. T. 1920. Proc. Roy. Soc. (London), B, 91:268. [67] Huettner, A. F. 1934. Anat. Record 60(suppl):80. [68] Hughes-Schrader, S. 1943. Biol. Bull. 85:265. [69] Hughes-Schrader, S. 1944. Ibid. 87:167. [70] Hughes-Schrader, S. 1947. Chromosoma 3:52. [71] Hughes-Schrader, S. 1948. Advances in Genet. 2:127. [72] Itoh, H. 1933. Cytologia (Tokyo) 4:427. [73] Itoh, H. 1933. Zool. Mag. (Japan) 45. [74] Karnkowska, Z. 1932. Bull. soc. vaudoise sci. nat. 57:591. [75] Karnkowska, Z. 1932. Compt. rend. soc. biol. 110:670. [76] Katayama, H. 1939. Japan. J. Genet. 15:75. [77] Kawaguchi, E. 1937. Cytologia (Tokyo), Fujii jubilaei vol. (2):1023. [78] Kernewitz, B. 1915. Arch. Naturgeschichte, A, 81(1):1. [79] Keuneke, W. 1924. Z. Zellforsch. u. mikroskop. Anat. 1:357. [80] Kichijo, H. 1935. Zool. Mag. (Japan) 47. [81] Kichijo, H. 1939. Japan. J. Genet. 15(5):287. [82] Kichijo, H. 1941. Botany Zool. (Tokyo) 9. [83] Kichijo, H. 1941. Japan. J. Genet. 17:122. [84] Kichijo, H. 1942. Ibid. 18:196. [85] Kichijo, H. 1943. Nagasaki Igakkai Zasshi 21. [86] Kikkawa, H. 1938. Genetica (Haag) 20:458. [87] King, R. L. 1924. Science 60:362. [88] King, R. L. 1931. J. Morphol. 52:525. [89] Klingstedt H. 1928. Mem. Soc. Fauna Flora Fennica 4. [90] Klingstedt, H. 1933. Ibid. 10. [91] Klingstedt, H. 1937. Nature 139:468. [92] Knaben, N. 1934. Z. Zellforsch. u. mikroskop. Anat. 21:604. [93] Koonz, C. H. 1936. Biol. Bull. 71:375. [94] Kornhauser, S. I. 1914. Arch. Zellforsch. 12:241. [95] Kurihara, A. 1929. J. Coll. Agr. Tokyo Imp. Univ. 10. [96] Lawson, C. A. 1936. Biol. Bull. 70:288. [97] Le Calvez, J. 1947. Chromosoma 3:137. [98] Lefevre, G., and C. McGill. 1908. Am. J. Anat. 7:469. [99] Light, S. F. 1938. Anat. Record 72(suppl.):102. [100] Lutman, B. F. 1910. Biol. Bull. 19:55. [101] Machida, S. 1934. Proc. Imp. Acad. (Tokyo) 10. [102] Makino, S. 1932. J. Fac. Sci. Hokkaido Imp. Univ., VI, 2. [103] Makino, S. 1933. Proc. Imp. Acad. (Tokyo) 9. [104] Makino, S. 1948. Cytol. Genet., Oguma commem. vol. (1). [105] Makino, S. 1951. An atlas of the chromosome numbers in animals. Ed. 2. Iowa State College Press, Ames. [106] Matthey, R. 1947. Scientia Genet. (Turin) 3:23. [107] Matthey, R. 1948. Arch. Julius Klaus-Stift. Vererbungsforsch. Sozialanthropol. u. Rassenhyg. 23:517 [108] Matthey, R. 1948. Rev. suisse zool. 55:45. [109] Matthey, R. 1950. Arch. Julius Klaus-Stift. Vererbungsforsch. Sozialanthropol. u. Rassenhyg. 25:607. [110] Matthey, R., and J. Aubert. 1947.

continued

Bull. biol. France et Belg. 81:202. [111] McClung, C. E. 1902. Univ. Kansas Sci. Bull. 1:185. [112] McClung, C. E. 1914. J. Morphol. 25:651. [113] McClung, C. E. 1917. Ibid. 29:519. [114] McClung, C. E. 1928. Z. Zellforsch. u. mikroskop. Anat. 7:756. [115] McClung, C. E. 1930. Acta Congr. Intern. Biol. Montevideo 7. [116] McMullen, D. B. 1928. Am. Naturalist 62:435. [117] Meek, C. F. U. 1913. Proc. Roy. Soc. (London), B, 203:1. [118] Meek, C. F. U. 1915. Quart. J. Microscop. Sci. 61:1. [119] Metcalfe, M. E. 1935. Ibid. 77:585. [120] Metz, C. W. 1916. J. Exptl. Zool. 21:213. [121] Metz, C. W. 1926. Z. Zellforsch. u. mikroskop. Anat. 4:1. [122] Metz, C. W. 1938. Am. Naturalist 72:485. [123] Metz, C. W. 1938. Carnegie Inst. Wash. Publ. 501:275. [124] Misra, A. B. 1937. J. Fac. Sci. Hokkaido Imp. Univ., VI, 5. [125] Moffett, A. A. 1936. Cytologia (Tokyo) 7:184. [126] Mohr, O. L. 1916. Arch. biol. (Liège) 29:579. [127] Momma, E. 1943. J. Fac. Sci. Hokkaido Imp. Univ. 9:59. [128] Montgomery, T. H., Jr. 1906. Trans. Am. Phil. Soc. 21:97. [129] Morgan, T. H. 1915. J. Exptl. Zool. 19:285. [130] Morgan, W. P. 1928. J. Morphol. 46:241. [131] Morse, M. 1909. Arch. Zellforsch. 3:483. [132] Munson, J. P. 1907. Proc. Boston Soc. Nat. Hist. 33:43. [133] Nakamura, K. 1946. Kromosomo (Tokyo) 1. [134] Naville, A., and J. de Beaumont. 1933. Arch. anat. microscop. (Paris) 29:199. [135] Naville, A., and J. de Beaumont. 1936. Ibid. 32:271. [136] Nishimura, Y. 1935. Manshu Seibutsugaku Kaiho (1). [137] Nowlin, W. N. 1906. J. Exptl. Zool. 3:583. [138] Oguma, K. 1919. Zool. Mag. (Japan) 31. [139] Oguma, K. 1930. J. Fac. Sci. Hokkaido Imp. Univ., VI, 1. [140] Oguma, K. 1946. Kromosomo (Tokyo) 1. [141] Ohmachi, F. 1935. Bull. Mie Univ. Fac. Agr. 5. [142] Ohmachi, F. 1935. Zool. Mag. (Japan) 47. [143] Ohmachi, F. 1943. Ibid. 55. [144] Ohmachi, F. 1944. Japan. J. Genet. 20:86. [145] Oksala, T. 1939. Hereditas 25:132. [146] Painter, T. S., and A. B. Griffen. 1937. Genetics 22:612. [147] Payne, F. 1909. Biol. Bull. 16:119. [148] Payne, F. 1912. J. Morphol. 23:331. [149] Peacock, A. D., and R. A. R. Gresson. 1931. Proc. Roy. Soc. Edinburgh, B, 51:97. [150] Peacock, A. D., and A. R. Sanderson. 1939. Trans. Roy. Soc. Edinburgh 59:647. [151] Pearson, N. E. 1929. J. Morphol. 47:531. [152] Perrot, J. L. 1933. Z. Zellforsch. u. mikroskop. Anat. 18:573. [153] Perrot, J. L. 1934. Quart. J. Microscop. Sci. 76:353. [154] Pkakadze, G. 1930. Arch. russ. anat. histol. et embryol. 9. [155] Poisson, R. 1927. Arch. zool. exptl. et gén. 66(2):23. [156] Poisson, R. 1936. Ibid. 78(4):133. [157] Ramachandra Rao, T. 1937. J. Morphol. 61:223. [158] Reuter, E. 1930. Acta Zool. Fennica 9:1. [159] Ries, E. 1932. Z. Zellforsch. u. mikroskop. Anat. 16:314. [160] Robertson, W. R. B. 1916. J. Morphol. 27:179. [161] Robertson, W. R. B. 1931. Ibid. 51:119. [162] Sanderson, A. R. 1932. Genetica (Haag) 14:321. [163] Schachow, S. D. 1932. Anat. Anz. 75:1. [164] Schäfer, F. 1907. Zool. Jahrb. 23:535. [165] Schleip, W. 1908. Ibid. 26:651. [166] Schmieder, R. G. 1938. Biol. Bull. 74:256. [167] Schrader, F. 1940. J. Morphol. 67:123. [168] Seiler, J. 1914. Arch. Zellforsch. 13:159. [169] Seiler, J. 1924. Z. induktive Abstammungs.- u. Vererbungslehre 31:1. [170] Seiler, J. 1925. Arch. Julius Klaus-Stift. Vererbungsforsch. Sozialanthropol. u. Rassenhyg. 1:63. [171] Seiler, J. 1942. Ibid. 17:513. [172] Sengün, A. 1948. Commun. Univ. Ankara 1. [173] Sengün, A, and C. Kosswig. 1948. Chromosoma 3:195. [174] Shaffer, E. L. 1917. Biol. Bull. 32:407. [175] Shaffer, E. L. 1920. Ibid 38:83. [176] Shibata, B. 1941. Oyo Dobutsugaku Zasshi 13:162. [177] Shikato, T. 1947. Japan. J. Genet. 22:94. [178] Shinji, O. 1941. Oyo Dobutsugaku Zasshi 13:163. [179] Sinoto, Y., and K. Suzuki. 1943. Igaku to Seibutsugaku 3:175. [180] Slack, H. D. 1938. Proc. Roy. Soc. Edinburgh, B, 58:192. [181] Slifer, E. H., and R. L. King. 1934. J. Morphol. 56:593. [182] Smith, E. A. 1916. Biol. Bull. 31:269. [183] Smith, S. G. 1941. Sci. Agr. 21:245. [184] Smith, S. G. 1944. Ibid. 24:491. [185] Smith, S. G. 1949. Evolution 3:344. [186] Spaul, E. A. 1922. J. Roy. Microscop. Soc. 3:237. [187] Speicher, B. R. 1937. J. Morphol. 61:453. [188] Speicher, K. G., and B. R. Speicher. 1938. Biol. Bull. 74:247. [189] Steopoe, I. 1929. Compt. rend. soc. biol. 102:116. [190] Stevens, N. M. 1906. Carnegie Inst. Wash. Publ. 36(1). [191] Stevens, N. M. 1906. Ibid. 36(2). [192] Stevens, N. M. 1908. J. Exptl. Zool. 5:359. [193] Stevens, N. M. 1908. Ibid. 5:453. [194] Stevens, N. M. 1909. Ibid. 6:101. [195] Stevens, N. M. 1910. Biol. Bull. 18:72. [196] Stevens, N. M. 1911. Ibid. 20:109. [197] Sturtevant, A. H., and T. Dobzhansky. 1936. Am. Naturalist 70:574. [198] Suomalainen, E. 1940. Ann. Acad. Sci. Fennicae, A(4), 5.

continued

2. CHROMOSOME NUMBERS: INVERTEBRATES

Part I: INSECTS

[199] Suomalainen, E. 1940. Hereditas 26:51. [200] Suomalainen, E. 1946. Ann. Acad. Sci. Fennicae, A(4), 10. [201] Suomalainen, E. 1948. Ann. Entomol. Fennicae 14(suppl.):206. [202] Tateishi, S. 1932. Zool. Mag. (Japan) 44. [203] Thomsen, M. 1927. Z. Zellforsch. u. mikroskop. Anat. 5:1. [204] Tiegs, O. W., and F. V. Murray. 1938. Quart. J. Microscop. Sci. 80:159. [205] Valle, A. 1948. Experientia 4:388. [206] Von Baehr, W. B. 1909. Arch. Zellforsch. 3:269. [207] Von Pfaler-Collander, E. 1941. Acta Zool. Fennica 30:1. [208] Wassilieff, A. 1907. Arch. mikroskop. Anat. u. Entwicklungsmech. 70:1. [209] White, M. J. D. 1940. J. Genet. 40:303. [210] White, M. J. D. 1949. Genetics 34:537. [211] Wieman, H. L. 1910. J. Morphol. 21:135. [212] Wilke, G. 1913. Arch. Zellforsch. 10:203. [213] Willem, V. 1900. Mém. couron. acad. méd. belg. 58(3). [214] Wilson, E. B. 1906. J. Exptl. Zool. 3:1. [215] Wilson, E. B. 1907. Biol. Bull. 12:303. [216] Wilson, E. B. 1909. J. Exptl. Zool. 6:69. [217] Wilson, E. B. 1911. J. Morphol. 22:71. [218] Wilson, E. B. 1912. J. Exptl. Zool. 13:345. [219] Wolf, E. 1941. Chromosoma 2:192. [220] Wolf, E. 1946. Z. Naturforsch. 1:108. [221] Wu, J. S. 1938. Cytologia (Tokyo) 9:334. [222] Yocum, H. B. 1923. J. Morphol. 37:287. [223] Yosida, T. 1944. Japan. J. Genet. 20:107. [224] Yosida, T. 1946. Kromosomo (Tokyo) 2-3. [225] Yosida, T. 1926. Seibutsu 1. [226] Yosida, T. 1947. Kromosomo (Tokyo) 3-4. [227] Yosida, T. 1948. Matsumushi 2. [228] Yosida, T. 1949. Trans. Sapporo Nat. Hist. Soc. 18:43. [229] Yosida, T. 1950. Iden no Sogo Kenkyu 1:85. [230] Yosida, T. 1951. Kromosomo (Tokyo) 9.

Part II: INVERTEBRATES OTHER THAN INSECTS

For additional information, consult reference 68. Diploid (column D): s = spermatogonium, o = oogonium, m = somatic cell. Haploid (column E): ♂(I) = primary spermatocyte, ♂(II) = secondary spermatocyte, ♀(I) = primary oocyte, ♀(II) = secondary oocyte. Classification adapted from Lord Rothschild, *A Classification of Living Animals*, 1961.

	Class and Sub-class	Order	Species	Chromosome Number: Diploid	Chromosome Number: Haploid	Sex Type	Reference
	(A)	(B)	(C)	(D)	(E)	(F)	(G)
			Echinodermata				
1	Asteroidea	Forcipulata	*Asterias amurensis*	30s	15♂(I)	....	101
2			*A. forbesii*	36m	18♂(I, II)	....	52
3		Spinulosa	*Henricia nipponica*	54s	27♂(I)	....	101
4	Echinoidea	Spatangoida	*Echinocardium mediterraneum*	42m	21♀(I)	....	156
5		Clypeasteroida	*Clypeaster rosaceus*	44m	....	X-Y?	32
6		Echinoida	*Echinus acutus*	38m	....	....	24
7			*Strongylocentrotus intermedius*	50s	25♂(I)	....	101
8		Temnopleuroida	*Toxopneustes variegatus*	36m	....	X-Y?	43
9			*Tripneustes esculentus*	32-34m	....	....	141
10		Arbacioida	*Arbacia punctulata*	ca. 40m	....	....	140
11	Holothuroidea	Aspidochirota	*Stichopus regalis*	28-36s	16-18♂(I)	....	28
			Arthropoda				
12	Tardigrada	Eutardigrada	*Macrobiotus lacustris*	10m	5♀(I, II)	....	158
13	Pentastomida	Porocephalida	*Porocephalus armillatus*	20o	10♀(I)	....	153
14	Arachnida	Acari	*Argas columbarum*	26s, o	13♂(I)	X-Y♂, X-X♀	107
15			*Gamasus brevicornis*	12s	6♂(I)	....	133
16			*Ixodes ricinus*	28s	....	....	102
17			*Pediculopsis graminum*	6m	3♀(I)	....	18
18		Araneae	*Agelena opulenta*	44s	23♂(I); 21,23♂(II)	X_1X_2-O♂	137
19			*Araneus foliatus*	24s	13♂(I)	X_1X_2-O♂	36

continued

2. CHROMOSOME NUMBERS: INVERTEBRATES

Part II: INVERTEBRATES OTHER THAN INSECTS

	Class and Sub-class	Order	Species	Chromosome Number		Sex Type	Reference
				Diploid	Haploid		
	(A)	(B)	(C)	(D)	(E)	(F)	(G)
	Arthropoda						
20	Arachnida	Araneae	*Argiope amoena*	24s	13♂(I); 11,13♂(II)	X_1X_2-O♂	137
21			*Ariamnes cylindrogaster*	22s	12♂(I); 10,12♂(II)	X_1X_2-O♂	137
22			*Clubiona japonicola*	20s	11♂(I); 9,11♂(II)	X_1X_2-O♂	137
23			*Cyclosa octotuberculata*	24s, 26o	13♂(I)	X_1X_2-O♂	136, 137
24			*Dolomedes pallitarsus*	28s	15♂(I); 13,15♂(II)	X_1X_2-O♂	137
25			*Drapetisca socialis*	24s	13♂(I)	X_1X_2-O♂	36
26			*Epeira scolopetaria*	23s	12♂(I); 11,12♂(II)	X-O♂	6
27			*Heptathela kimurai*	80s	40♂(I)	X_1X_2-O♂	136, 137
28			*Heteropoda venatoria*	41s, 44o, ♀m	22♂(I); 19,22♂(II)	$X_1X_2X_3$-O♂	138
29			*Icius elongatus*	28s	15♂(I); 13,15♂(II)	X_1X_2-O♂	137
30			*Lycosa T-insignita*	28s	15♂(I); 13,15♂(II)	X_1X_2-O♂	137
31			*Misumea tricuspidata*	24s	12♂(I)	X_1X_2-O♂	136
32			*Misumena tricuspidata*	23s	12♂(I); 11,12♂(II)	X-O♂	137
33			*Oxyopes ramosus*	21s	11♂(I); 10,11♂(II)	X-O♂	36
34			*Philodromus roseus*	28s	15♂(I); 13,15♂(II)	X_1X_2-O♂	137
35			*Plexippus paykulli*	28s	15♂(I); 13,15♂(II)	X_1X_2-O♂	137
36			*Schizocosa crassipes*	22s	12♂(I); 10,12♂(II)	X_1X_2-O♂	37
37			*Tegenaria atrica*	42s	22♂(I)	X_1X_2-O♂	116
38			*Tetragnatha japonica*	24s	13♂(I); 11,13♂(II)	X_1X_2-O♂	136, 137
39			*Theridion tepidariorum*	24m	12♀(I, II)	....	79
40			*Trochosa ruricola*	26s, 28o	14♂(I); 12,14♂(II) 14♀(I)	X_1X_2-O♂	36
41			*Xysticus ephippiatus*	23s	12♂(I); 11,12♂(II)	X-O♂	137
42		Opiliones	*Gagrellopsis nodulifera*	16s	8♂(I, II)	....	142
43			*Gagrellula ferruginea*	22s	11♂(I, II)	....	135
44			*Liobunum japonicum*	20s	10♂(I, II)	....	135
45			*Melanopa* sp.	20s	10♂(I, II)	....	135
46			*Metagagrella* sp.	20s	10♂(I, II)	....	135
47			*Mitopus morio*	32s	16♂(I, II)	....	132
48			*Nemastoma lugubre*	16s	....	....	132
49			*Oligolophus aspersus*	20s	10♂(I, II)	....	135
50			*Opilio parietinum*	24s	12♂(I, II)	....	132
51		Pseudoscorpiones	*Chelanops cyrneus*	61-62s	31♂(I)	X_1X_2-O♂	131
52			*Obisium muscorum*	67-68s	34♂(I)	X_1X_2-O♂	131
53		Scorpiones	*Ananteris balzani*	12m	....	....	22
54			*Buthus martensii*	24s	12♂(I, II)	....	120
55			*Centrurus exilicauda*	26s	13♂(I)	....	163
56			*Hadrurus hirsutus*	ca. 100s	ca. 50♂(I)	....	163
57			*Isometrus maculatus*	12s	....	....	22
58			*Tityus bahiensis*	10s, ♀m	5♂(I, II)	....	23
59			*T. trivittatus*	14s, ♀m	....	....	23
60			*Vejovis boreus*	ca. 100s	ca. 50♂(I)	....	163
61	Merostomata	Xiphosura	*Tachypleus tridentatus*	26s	13♂(I, II)	....	106
	Crustacea						
62	Malacostraca	Decapoda	*Cambaroides japonicus*	196s	98♂(I, II)	....	86
63			*Cambarus clarkii*	200s	100♂(I, II)	....	95
64			*Eriocheir japonicus*	148s	74♂(I, II)	X-Y♂	89
65			*Eupagurus ochotensis*	254s	127♂(I, II)	....	100
66			*Gebia major*	82s, o	41♂(I)	....	105
67			*Hemigrapsus sanguincus*	128s	64♂(I, II)	X-Y♂	92
68			*Macrocheira kampferi*	106s	53♂(I, II)	....	93
69			*Matuta lunaris*	94s	47♂(I, II)	....	96
70			*Nephrops japonicus*	164s	82♂(I, II)	....	93
71			*Nephropsis carpenteri*	152s	76♂(I, II)	....	93
72			*Ovalipes punctatus*	103s	52♂(I); 51,52♂(II)	X-O♂	94
73			*Panulirus japonicus*	140s	70♂(I, II)	....	89, 90
74			*Paralithodes camtschatica*	208s	104♂(I, II)	....	87, 88
75			*Penaeus japonicus*	92s	46♂(I, II)	....	98
76			*Plagusia dentipes*	106s	53♂(I, II)	X-Y♂	89, 91
77			*Ranina ranina*	106s	53♂(I, II)	....	96
78			*Scylla serrata*	106s	53♂(I, II)	....	96

continued

2. CHROMOSOME NUMBERS: INVERTEBRATES

Part II: INVERTEBRATES OTHER THAN INSECTS

	Class and Sub-class	Order	Species	Chromosome Number		Sex Type	Reference
				Diploid	Haploid		
	(A)	(B)	(C)	(D)	(E)	(F)	(G)
			Arthropoda				
	Crustacea						
79	Malacostraca	Decapoda	*Telmessus cheiragonus*	124s	62♂(I, II)	....	96
80			*Telphusa fluviatilis*	78s	39♂(I)	2X-O♂	20
81		Stomatopoda	*Squilla oratoria*	48s	24♂(I, II)	....	59
82		Amphipoda	*Gammarus annandalei*	54s	27♂(I)	X-Y♂	87,99
83			*G. chevreuxi*	26s	13♂(I)	X-Y♂	109
84			*G. pulex*	52s	26♂(I)	....	113
85		Isopoda	*Anilocra mediterranea*	12s, o	6♂(I)	....	13
86			*Armadillidium vulgare*	54s	27♂(I, II)	....	55
87			*Asellus aquaticus*	16s	8♂(I), 8♀(I)	....	145,146
88			*Epipenaeon japonica*	14m	....	....	44
89			*Ligia exotica*	72s	36♂(I, II)	....	55
90			*Oniscus asellus*	32s	16♂(I)	....	85
91			*Porcellio scaber*	56s	28♂(I, II)	....	48
92			*Proasellus meridianus*	16s	8♂(I)	....	145
93			*Trichoniscus biformatus*	16s	8♂(I)	....	146
94	Cirripedia	Thoracica	*Lepas anatifera*	26s, o	13♂(I), 13♀(I)	....	164
95			*Scalpellum scalpellum*	32s, o	16♂(I), 16♀(I)	....	62
96			*Tetraclita squamosa*	32s	16♂(I)	....	51
97	Copepoda	Caligoida	*Laemargus muricatus*	16s, o	8♂(I, II)	....	71
98			*Pandarus sinuatus*	16s, o	8♂(I,II), 8♀(I,II)	....	71,72
99		Harpacticoida	*Canthocamptus staphylinus*	24o	12♀(I)	....	35
100		Cyclopoida	*Cyclops bicuspidatus*	18m	9♀(I)	....	11
101			*C. gracilis*	6m	3♀(I, II)	....	69
102			*C. insignis*	22m	11♀(I)	....	11
103		Calanoida	*Anomalocera patersonii*	16o, 32m	16♀(I, II)	....	150
104			*Calanus finmarchicus*	34s	17♂(I)	....	41
105			*Diaptomus castor*	34s	17♂(I), 17♀(I)	....	41
106			*Heterocope weismanni*	32s	16♂(I)	....	41,42
107	Ostracoda	Podocopa	*Cypris fuscata*	24m	24♀(I)	....	123
108			*Notodromas monacha*	16m	8♂(I, II)	....	124
109	Branchiopoda	Cladocera	*Daphnia magna*	20s, m	10♀(I)	....	80
110			*D. pulex*	24m	12♀(I)	Parth.	80
111			*Moina rectirostria*	30s, ♀m	15♂(I,II), 15♀(I,II)	....	152
112			*Polyphemus pediculus*	8s, m	8♀(I)	....	63
113		Anostraca	*Artemia salina*	42m	21♀(I, II)	Bisexual	3
114				84m	84♀(I)	Parth.	3
115			*Branchipus grubii*	24o, m	12♀(I, II)	....	10
116			*Chirocephalus* sp.	23s, 21-23m	....	....	127
	Chilopoda						
117	Anamorpha	Scutigeromorpha	*Scutigera forceps*	37s	19♂(I); 18,19♂(II)	X-O♂	74
118	Epimorpha	Scolopendromorpha	*Scolopendra subspinipes mutilans*	28s	14♂(I, II)	....	104
	Diplopoda						
119	Pselaphognatha	Polyxenida	*Polyxenus* sp.	ca. 16s	8♂(I, II)	....	130
120	Onychophora		*Peripatus* sp.	28s, o, m	14♂(I, II)	....	77
			Annelida				
121	Archiannelida		*Dinophilus apatris*	20m	10♂(I,II), 10♀(I,II)	....	84
122	Hirudinea	Gnathobdellida	*Nephelis vulgaris*	16o	8♀(I)	....	53
123		Rhynchobdellida	*Glossosiphonia complanata*	26s	13♂(I, II)	....	161
124			*Hemiclepsis marginata*	32s, m	16♂(II)	....	161
125	Oligochaeta		*Allolobophora chloratica*	32m	....	....	81
126			*A. nocturna*	36m	....	....	81
127			*Eisenia foetida*	22m	....	....	81
128			*Eiseniella tetraedra*	72m	....	....	81
129			*Enchytraeus humicultor*	32s, o	16♀(I)	....	147

continued

2. CHROMOSOME NUMBERS: INVERTEBRATES

Part II: INVERTEBRATES OTHER THAN INSECTS

	Class and Sub-class	Order	Species	Chromosome Number Diploid	Chromosome Number Haploid	Sex Type	Reference
	(A)	(B)	(C)	(D)	(E)	(F)	(G)
			Annelida				
130	Oligochaeta		*Fredericia hegemon*	64s, o	32♀(I)	....	147
131			*Lumbricus terrestris*	36m	....	....	81
132			*Octolasium cyanoum*	114m	....	....	81
133			*Tubifex bavaricus*	20o, m	....	....	108
134	Myzostomaria		*Myzostoma glabrum*	24m	12♀(I, II)	....	162
135	Polychaeta		*Chaetopterus pergamentaceous*	18m	9♀(I, II)	....	73
136			*Laonice conchylega*	6m	6♂(I), 3♂(II)	....	19
137			*Ophryotrocha gracilis*	10s, o, m	5♂(I,II), 5♀(I,II)	....	47
138			*Sabellaria spinulosa*	8s, m	8♂(I), 4♂(II), 8♀(I), 4♀(II)	....	19
139			*Saccocirrus major*	18s, o, m	9♂(I,II), 9♀(I,II)	....	151
140			*Tomopteris elegans*	10o	5♀(I)	....	128
			Mollusca				
	Gastropoda						
141	Pulmonata	Stylommatophora	*Bradybaena similaris*	58s	29♂(I)	....	50
142			*Euhadra eoa*	56s	28♂(I)	....	50
143			*Fruticicola sieboldiana*	58s	29♂(I, II)	....	50
144			*Helix aspersa*	54s	27♂(I)	....	112
145			*H. hortensis*	48s	24♂(I, II)	....	58
146			*H. pomatia*	54s	27♂(I), 27♀(I)	....	112
147			*Incillaria fruhstorferi*	48s	24♂(I)	....	50
148			*Limax cinereo-niger*	16s	8♂(I)	....	149
149			*Mesodon thyroidus*	58s	29♂(I)	....	46
150			*Stenotrema hirsutum*	58s	29♂(I)	....	46
151			*Succinea horticola*	34s	17♂(I)	....	49
152			*Triodopsis dentifera*	58s	29♂(I)	....	46
153		Basommatophora	*Lymnaea japonica*	36s	18♂(I)	....	50
154			*Melampus boholensis*	16s	8♂(I)	....	60
155	Opisthobranchia	Acoela	*Doris bifida*	32m	16♀(I, II)	....	129
156			*Pleurophyllidea californica*	20-24m	10-12♀(II)	....	67
157		Pteropoda	*Creseis acicula*	20s, o, m	10♂(I,II), 10♀(I,II)	....	167
158			*Limacina retroversa*	24s, m	12♂(I, II)	....	45
159		Pleurocoela	*Aplysia punctata*	24m	....	....	14, 15
160	Prosobranchia	Mesogastropoda	*Bythinia tentaculata*	34s	17♂(I, II)	....	1
161			*Campeloma rufum*	12o	12♀(I, II)	....	70
162			*Carinaria mediterrania*	32m	16♀(I, II)	....	9
163			*Crepidula plana*	60m	30♀(I, II)	....	17
164			*Goniobasis laqueata*	36s	18♂(I)	....	165
165			*Paludina vivipara*	14o, m	7♀(I)	....	114
166			*Pterotrachea mutica*	32m	16♀(I, II)	....	9
167			*Valvata tricarinata*	18s	9♂(I)	....	31
168			*Viviparus viviparus*	34s	17♂(I)	....	1
			Aschelminthes				
	Nematoda						
169	Phasmidia	Rhabditida	*Ascaris lumbricoides*	43s; 48o; 43, 48m	24♂(I); 19,24♂(II); 24♀(I,II)	$X_1 \ldots X_5$-O♂	159
170			*A. megalocephala* (bivalens)	4s, o, m	2♂(I,II), 2♀(I,II)	....	144
171			*A. megalocephala* (univalens)	2s, o, m	1♂(I,II), 1♀(I,II)	....	125
172			*Belascaris mystax*	18s, m; 18-20o	9♂(I,II), 9♀(I,II)	X-O♂	159
173			*Filaria papillosa*	11, 12m	6♀(I, II)	....	75
174			*Ganguleterakis spumosa*	10s, 12o, 20-24m	6♂(I); 4,6♂(II); 6♀(I, II)	X_1X_2-O♂	159
175			*Heterakis papillosa*	9s, 10o, 18-20m	5♂(I); 4, 5♂(II); 5♀(I, II)	X-O♂	159
176			*Rhabditis aspera*	13s, 14o, 13-14m	7♂(I); 6, 7♂(II); 7♀(I, II)	X-O♂	61
177			*R. monohystera*	20o, m	10♀(I)	....	5

continued

2. CHROMOSOME NUMBERS: INVERTEBRATES

Part II: INVERTEBRATES OTHER THAN INSECTS

	Class and Sub-class	Order	Species	Chromosome Number		Sex Type	Reference
				Diploid	Haploid		
	(A)	(B)	(C)	(D)	(E)	(F)	(G)
			Aschelminthes				
178	Nematoda Phasmidia	Rhabditida	*Sclerostomum edentatum*	11s, 12o	6♂(I); 5,6♂(II); 6♀(I,II)	X-O♂	64
179			*Strongylus paradoxus*	11s; 12o; 11, 12m	6♂(I); 5, 6♂(II)	X-O♂	61
180	Nemato-morpha	Gordioidea	*Gordius tolosanus*	4s, o	2♀(I)	....	148
181			*Paragordius varius*	14m	7♀(I, II)	....	78
182	Rotifera	Monogononta	*Asplanchna intermedia*	24s, ♂m	12♂(I)	....	139
			Nemertina				
183	Anopla	Heteronemer-tina	*Cerebratulus lacteus*	36-38m	18-19♀(I)	....	166
184			*Lineus ruber*	16m	8♀(I)	....	103
			Platyhelminthes				
185	Trematoda	Digenea	*Brachycoelium salamandrae*	20s, o, m	10♂(I), 10♀(I)	....	154
186			*Cryptocotyle lingua*	12s, o, m	6♂(I)	....	12
187			*Distomum turgidum*	16m	9♀(I, II)	....	65
188			*Fasciola hepatica*	12o, m	6♀(I, II)	....	121
189			*Paragonimus kellicotti*	16s	8♂(I)	....	16
190			*Parorchis acanthus*	22s	11♂(I), 11♀(I, II)	....	115
191			*Pneumonoeces medioplexus*	22s, o, m	11♂(I,II), 11♀(I,II)	....	110
192			*Schistosoma haematobium*	14s	8♂(I); 6, 8♂(II); 8♀(II)	X_1X_2-O♂	66
193			*Zoogonus mirus*	11-14o, m	6-7♀(I), 6♀(II)	....	160
194		Monogenea	*Gyrodactylus elegans*	12s, m	6♀(I, II)	....	33
195			*Polystoma integerrimum*	20m	10♀ (I, II)	....	76
196	Turbellaria	Polycladida	*Cycloporus papillosus*	16m	8♀(I, II)	....	29, 30
197			*Leptoplana tremellaris*	16m	8♀(I, II)	....	29
198			*Prostheceraeus vittatus*	12m	6♀(I, II)	....	155
199			*Prosthiostomum siphunculus*	16m	8♀(I, II)	....	30
200			*Thysanozoon brocchi*	18m	9♀(I, II)	....	126
201		Tricladida	*Bdelloura candida*	12s, o	6♂(I, II), 6♀(I)	....	111
202			*Curtisia foremanii*	12s, o	6♂(I, II), 6♀(I)	....	111
203			*Dendrocoelum lacteum*	16s, o	8♂(I, II), 8♀(I)	....	2
204			*Planaria gonocephala*	16s, o	8♂(I, II), 8♀(I)	....	122
205			*Procerodes gerlachei*	12s, m	6♂(I, II)	....	8
206		Alloeocoela	*Bothrioplana semperi*	20-30	....	....	118
207			*Geocentrophora applantus*	20-30	....	....	118
208			*Monocelis fusca*	6s	3♂(I)	....	118
209			*Plagiostomum stellatum*	10s	5♂(I)	....	118
210			*Prorhynchus stagnalis*	20-30	....	....	118
211		Rhabdocoela	*Amphibolella virginiana*	4s	2♂(I)	....	56
212			*Castrada virginiana*	6s	3♂(I)	....	57
213			*Castrella truncata*	4s	2♂(I)	....	118
214			*Catenula virginiana*	20-40	....	....	118
215			*Dalyellia virginiana*	4s	2♂(I)	....	117
216			*Gyratrix hermaphroditus*	4s	2♂(I)	....	118
217			*Macrostomum beaufortensis*	6s	3♂(I)	....	27
218			*Mesostoma ehrenbergii*	10o	5♀(I, II)	....	157
219			*Microstomum bispiralis*	16s	8♂(I)	....	134
220			*Paravortex gemmellipara*	8m	4♀(II)	....	4
221			*Phaenocora jucunda*	12s, ♂m	6♂(I, II)	....	21
222			*Polycystis goetti*	16s	8♂(I)	....	118
223			*Prorhynchella minuta*	4s	2♂(I)	....	119
224			*Typhloplana viridata*	6s	3♂(I)	....	118
225		Acoela	*Aphanostoma diversicolor*	20-30	....	....	118
226			*Convoluta* sp.	20-30	....	....	118
			Cnidaria				
227	Scyphozoa	Semaeosto-mae	*Aurelia flavedula*	18-20m	9-10♀(I)	....	38
228	Hydrozoa	Trachymedu-sae	*Aglantha digitalis*	16o	8♀(I, II)	....	40

continued

2. CHROMOSOME NUMBERS: INVERTEBRATES

Part II: INVERTEBRATES OTHER THAN INSECTS

	Class and Sub-class	Order	Species	Chromosome Number		Sex Type	Reference
				Diploid	Haploid		
	(A)	(B)	(C)	(D)	(E)	(F)	(G)
			Cnidaria				
229	Hydrozoa	Limnomedusae	*Gonionemus murbachii*	24-25s ca. 24o, m	ca. 12♂(I, II)	....	7
230		Thecata	*Aequorea forskalea*	12m	6♀(II)	....	34
231			*Campanularia fleuxuosa*	20m	10♀(I)	....	39
232			*Obelia geniculata*	34o	17♀(I)	X-Y♀?	26
233		Athecata	*Hydra circumcincta*	30m	15♂(I)	....	97
234			*H. vulgaris attenuata*	32s, o, m	16♂(I)	....	97
235			*Pelmatohydra oligactis*	30m	....	....	97
			Porifera				
236	Demospongiae	Haploscleri-na	*Reniera simulans*	16m	8♂(I)	....	143
237			*Spongilla lacustria*	10-12m	....	....	82,83
238	Calcarea	Syconosa	*Grantia compressa*	26m	13♂(I), 13♀(I)	....	25
239			*Sycandra raphanus*	16m, 8o	8♀(I, II)	....	54
240			*Sycon ciliatum*	26m	13♀(I)	....	25

Contributor: Makino, Sajiro

References: [1] Ankel, W. E. 1924. Z. Zellforsch. u. mikroskop. Anat. 1:85. [2] Arnold, G. 1909. Arch. Zellforsch. 3:431. [3] Artom, C. 1928. Compt. rend. soc. biol. 99(suppl.):29. [4] Ball, S. C. 1916. J. Morphol. 27:453. [5] Belar, K. 1924. Z. Zellforsch. u. mikroskop. Anat. 1:1. [6] Berry, E. H. 1906. Biol. Bull. 11:193. [7] Bigelow, H. B. 1907. Bull. Museum Comp. Zool. Harvard Univ. 48:287. [8] Böhmig, L. 1907. Arch. biol. (Liège) 23:1. [9] Boveri, T. 1890. Jena. Z. Naturw. 17:314. [10] Brauer, A. 1894. Arch. mikroskop. Anat. u. Entwicklungsmech. 43:162. [11] Braun, H. 1909. Arch. Zellforsch. 3:449. [12] Cable, R. M. 1934. Quart. J. Microscop. Sci. 76:573. [13] Callan, H. G. 1940. Ibid. 82:327. [14] Carazzi, D. 1905. Arch. ital. anat. embriol. 4:231. [15] Carazzi, D. 1905. Ibid. 4:459. [16] Chen, P.-D. 1937. Trans. Am. Microscop. Soc. 56:208. [17] Conklin, E. G. 1902. J. Phila. Acad. Nat. Sci., Ser. 2, 12:12. [18] Cooper, K. W. 1939. Chromosoma 1:51. [19] De Horne, A. 1911. Arch. zool. exptl. et gén. 9(1):1. [20] Delpino, I. 1935. Arch. zool. ital. 21:19. [21] De Martiis, L. C. 1922. Arch. Zellforsch. 16:249. [22] De Toledo Piza, S. 1947. Anais escola super. agr. "Luis de Queiroz" Univ. São Paulo 4. [23] De Toledo Piza, S. 1948. Rev. Agr. (São Paulo) 46. [24] Doncaster, L., and J. Gray. 1913. Quart. J. Microscop. Sci. 58:483. [25] Dubosq. O., and O. Tuzet. 1937. Arch. zool. exptl. et gén. 79(2):157. [26] Faulkner, G. H. 1929. Quart. J. Microscop. Sci. 73:225. [27] Ferguson, F. F. 1937. Zool. Anz. 120:230. [28] Field, G. W. 1895. J. Morphol. 11:235. [29] Francotte, H. 1897. Mém. couron. acad. méd. belg. 55(3). [30] Francotte, P. 1898. Arch. zool. exptl. et gén. 6:189. [31] Furrow, C. L. 1935. Z. Zellforsch. u. mikroskop. Anat. 22:282. [32] Gardiner, M. S. 1927. J. Morphol. 43:547. [33] Gille, K. 1914. Arch. Zellforsch. 12:414. [34] Häcker, V. 1892. Arch. mikroskop. Anat. u. Entwicklungsmech. 40:243. [35] Häcker, V. 1895. Ibid. 45:200. [36] Hackman, W. 1948. Acta Zool. Fennica 54:1. [37] Hard, W. L. 1939. J. Morphol. 65:121. [38] Hargitt, G. T. 1910. Ibid. 21:593. [39] Hargitt, G. T. 1913. Ibid. 24:383. [40] Hargitt, G. T. 1917. Ibid. 28:593. [41] Heberer, G. 1932. Z. wiss. Zool. 142:191. [42] Heberer, G. 1938. Biol. Zentr. 58:343. [43] Heffner, B. 1910. Biol. Bull. 19:195. [44] Hiraiwa, Y. K. 1936. J. Sci. Hiroshima Univ., B(1), 4:101. [45] Hsiao, S. C. T. 1939. Biol. Bull. 76:7. [46] Husted, L., and P. R. Burch. 1946. Am. Naturalist 80:410. [47] Huth, W. 1933. Z. Zellforsch. u. mikroskop. Anat. 20:309. [48] Imai, G., and S. Makino. 1940. Japan. J. Genet. 16:75. [49] Inaba, A. 1945. Japan. J. Malacol. 14. [50] Inaba, A. 1950. Japan. J. Genet. 25:222. [51] Iwasa, M. 1932. Zool. Mag. (Japan) 44. [52] Jordan, H. E. 1908. Papers Tortugas Lab. Carnegie Inst. Wash. 1:1. [53] Jörgensen, M. 1908. Arch. Zellforsch. 2:279. [54] Jörgensen, M. 1910. Ibid. 4:163. [55] Kato, K. 1949. Cytol. Genet., Oguma commem. vol. (2).

continued

2. CHROMOSOME NUMBERS: INVERTEBRATES

Part II: INVERTEBRATES OTHER THAN INSECTS

[56] Kepner, W. A., and T. K. Ruebush. 1937. Zool. Anz. 118:103. [57] Kepner, W. A., T. K. Ruebush, and F. F. Ferguson. 1937. Ibid. 119:307. [58] Kleinert, M. 1909. Jena. Z. Naturw. 38:445. [59] Komai, T. 1920. J. Morphol. 34:307. [60] Kowslowsky, F. 1933. Jena. Z. Naturw. 68:117. [61] Kröning, F. 1923. Arch. Zellforsch. 17:63. [62] Krüger, P. 1920. Z. induktive Abstammungs.- u.Vererbungslehre 24:105. [63] Kühn, A. 1908. Arch. Zellforsch. 1:538. [64] Kühtz, K. 1913. Arch. mikroskop. Anat. u. Entwicklungsmech. 83:191. [65] Levy, F. 1914. Ibid. 85(2):125. [66] Lindner, E. 1914. Arch. Zellforsch. 12:516. [67] MacFarland, F. M. 1897. Zool. Jahrb. 10:227. [68] Makino, S. 1951. An atlas of the chromosome numbers in animals. Ed. 2. Iowa State College Press, Ames. [69] Matscheck, H. 1910. Arch. Zellforsch. 5:36. [70] Mattox, N. T. 1937. Z. Zellforsch. u. mikroskop. Anat. 27:455. [71] McClendon, J. F. 1906. Biol. Bull. 12:37. [72] McClendon, J. F. 1910. Arch. Zellforsch. 5:229. [73] Mead, A. D. 1898. J. Morphol. 14:181. [74] Medes, G. 1905. Biol. Bull. 9:156. [75] Meves, F. 1915. Arch. mikroskop. Anat. u. Entwicklungsmech. 87:611. [76] Minouchi, O. 1936. Z. Zellforsch. u. mikroskop. Anat. 24:85. [77] Montgomery, T. H., Jr. 1900. Zool. Jahrb. 14:277. [78] Montgomery, T. H., Jr. 1904. Proc. Phila. Acad. Nat. Sci. 56:738. [79] Montgomery, T. H., Jr. 1907. Zool. Jahrb. 25:237. [80] Mortimer, C. H. 1935. Naturwissenschaften 23:476. [81] Muldal, S. 1949. John Innes Hort. Inst. Ann. Rept. 39:21. [82] Müller, K. 1911. Wilhelm Roux' Arch. Entwicklungsmech. Organ. 32:397. [83] Müller, K. 1911. Ibid. 32:557. [84] Nachtsheim, H. 1919. Arch. mikroskop. Anat. u. Entwicklungsmech. 93(2):17. [85] Nichols, M. L. 1909. J. Morphol. 20:461. [86] Niiyama, H. 1934. J. Fac. Sci. Hokkaido Imp. Univ., VI, 3. [87] Niiyama, H. 1935. Japan. J. Genet. 11:34. [88] Niiyama, H. 1935. J. Fac. Sci. Hokkaido Imp. Univ., VI, 4. [89] Niiyama, H. 1936. Ibid., VI, 5. [90] Niiyama, H. 1936. Japan. J. Genet. 12:53. [91] Niiyama, H. 1937. Ibid. 13:37. [92] Niiyama, H. 1938. Ibid. 14:34. [93] Niiyama, H. 1939. Ibid. 15:290. [94] Niiyama, H. 1940. Ibid. 16:257. [95] Niiyama, H. 1941. Ibid. 17:304. [96] Niiyama, H. 1942. Zool. Mag. (Japan) 54:302. [97] Niiyama, H. 1944. Cytologia (Tokyo) 13:204. [98] Niiyama, H. 1948. Cytol. Genet., Oguma commem. vol. (1). [99] Niiyama, H. 1950. Ann. Zool. (Japan) 23. [100] Niiyama, H. 1950. Kromosomo (Tokyo) 6. [101] Niiyama, H., and S. Makino. 1947. J. Fac. Sci. Hokkaido Univ., VI, 9(3):225. [102] Nordenskiöld, E. 1920. Parasitology 12:159. [103] Nusbaum, J., and M. Oxner. 1913. Z. wiss. Zool. 107:78. [104] Ogawa, K. 1950. Zool. Mag. (Japan) 59:142. [105] Oka, T. 1941. J. Fac. Sci. Imp. Univ. Tokyo, IV, 5. [106] Okada, A. 1938. J. Sci. Hiroshima Univ., B(1), 6:37. [107] Oppermann, E. 1935. Z. mikroskop.-anat. Forsch. 37:538. [108] Oschmann, A. 1914. Arch. Zellforsch. 12:299. [109] Palmer, R. 1926. Quart. J. Microscop. Sci. 70:541. [110] Pennypacker, M. I. 1936. Arch. biol. (Liège) 47:309. [111] Pennypacker, M. I. 1938. J. Morphol. 63:421. [112] Perrot, J.-L., and M. Perrot. 1938. Compt. rend. 207:1005. [113] Poisson, R., and J. Le Calvez. 1948. Ibid. 227:228. [114] Popoff, M. 1908. Biol. Zentr. 28:555. [115] Rees, G. 1939. Parasitology 31:417. [116] Revell, S. H. 1947. Heredity 1:337. [117] Ruebush, T. K. 1937. Zool. Anz. 119:237. [118] Ruebush, T. K. 1938. Ibid. 122:321. [119] Ruebush, T. K. 1939. Ibid. 127:204. [120] Sato, I. 1940. J. Sci. Hiroshima Univ., B(1), 8:1. [121] Schellenberg, A. 1911. Arch. Zellforsch. 6:443. [122] Schleip, W. 1907. Zool. Jahrb. 24:129. [123] Schleip, W. 1909. Arch. Zellforsch. 2:390. [124] Schmalz, J. 1912. Ibid. 8:407. [125] Schneider, C. C. 1891. Arb. zool. Inst. Wien 9:179. [126] Schockaert, R. 1905. Cellule 22:5. [127] Selipova, L. 1930. Bull. acad. sci. U.R.S.S., Ser. biol., (5):437. [128] Senna, A. 1910. Arch. ital. anat. embriol. 9:299. [129] Smallwood, W. M. 1905. Morphol. Jahrb. 33:87. [130] Sokoloff, J. 1914. Zool. Anz. 44:558. [131] Sokolow, I. 1926. Z. Zellforsch. u. mikroskop. Anat. 3:615. [132] Sokolow, I. 1929. Ibid. 10:164. [133] Sokolow, I. 1934. Ibid. 21:42. [134] Stirewalt, M. A. 1937. Zool. Anz. 119:314. [135] Suzuki, S. 1941. Zool. Mag. (Japan) 53:101. [136] Suzuki, S. 1949. Ibid. 58. [137] Suzuki, S. 1950. Ibid. 59:57. [138] Suzuki, S., and A. Okada. 1950. J. Sci. Hiroshima Univ., B(1), 11. [139] Tauson, A. 1927. Z. Zellforsch. u. mikroskop. Anat. 4:652. [140] Tennent, D. H. 1912. J. Exptl. Zool. 12:391. [141] Tennent, D. H. 1912. J. Morphol. 23:17. [142] Tomohiro, M. 1940. J. Sci. Hiroshima Univ., B(1), 7:157. [143] Tuzet, O. 1930. Compt. rend. soc. biol. 103:970. [144] Van Beneden, E., and A. Neyt. 1887. Bull. acad. roy. sci. Belg., III, 14:215. [145] Vandel, A.

continued

2. CHROMOSOME NUMBERS: INVERTEBRATES

Part II: INVERTEBRATES OTHER THAN INSECTS

1938. Compt. rend. 206:621. [146] Vandel, A. 1947. Bull. biol. France et Belg. 81:154. [147] Vejdovsky, F. 1907. Sitzber. kgl. böhm. Ges. Wiss. math.-naturw. Kl. (1). [148] Vejdovsky, F. 1912. Ibid. (7). [149] Vom Rath, O. 1892. Arch. mikroskop. Anat. u. Entwicklungsmech. 40:102. [150] Vom Rath, O. 1895. Ibid. 46:168. [151] Von Baehr, W. B. 1913. Zool. Anz. 43:10. [152] Von Dehn, M. 1948. Chromosoma 3:167. [153] Von Haffner, K. 1922. Zool. Anz. 54:170. [154] Von Kemnitz, G. A. 1913. Arch. Zellforsch. 10:470. [155] Von Klinckowström, A. 1897. Arch. mikroskop. Anat. u. Entwicklungsmech. 48:587. [156] Von Ubisch, M. 1923. Arch. Zellforsch. 17:261. [157] Von Voss, H. 1914. Ibid. 12:159. [158] Von Wenck, W. 1914. Zool. Jahrb. 37:465. [159] Walton, A. C. 1924. Z. Zellforsch. u. mikroskop. Anat. 1:167. [160] Wassermann, F. 1913. Arch. mikroskop. Anat. u. Entwicklungsmech. 83:1. [161] Wendrowsky, V. 1928. Z. Zellforsch. u. mikroskop. Anat. 8:153. [162] Wheeler, W. M. 1897. Arch. biol. (Liège) 15:1. [163] Wilson, E. B. 1931. J. Morphol. 52:429. [164] Witschi, E. 1935. Biol. Bull. 68:263. [165] Woodard, T. M. 1935. J. Morphol. 57:1. [166] Yatsu, N. 1909. Ibid. 20:353. [167] Zarnick, B. 1911. Verhandl. deut. zool. Ges. 21:205.

3. CHROMOSOME NUMBERS: ALGAE

Many of the chromosome numbers are of doubtful accuracy since the small size of the chromosomes presents technical difficulties in determining exact counts. In some of the early literature it is impossible to determine whether the investigator was dealing with the haploid or diploid generation; in such cases the count has been assigned to the "*n*" or "2*n*" column on the basis of the best information available at present. Previous comprehensive chromosome lists of algae have been consulted in preparation of this table [20, 33, 71, 179, 262-265]. Classification adapted from Engler, *Syllabus der Pflanzenfamilien,* I Band, 1954.

<table>
<tr><th rowspan="2"></th><th rowspan="2">Family and Species</th><th colspan="2">Chromosome Number[1]</th><th rowspan="2">Reference</th></tr>
<tr><th>Haploid</th><th>Diploid</th></tr>
<tr><td></td><td>(A)</td><td>(B)</td><td>(C)</td><td>(D)</td></tr>
<tr><td></td><td colspan="4">Euglenophyta</td></tr>
<tr><td></td><td>Euglenaceae</td><td></td><td></td><td></td></tr>
<tr><td>1</td><td>Entosiphon sulcatum</td><td>20± 2</td><td>..........</td><td>143</td></tr>
<tr><td>2</td><td>Euglena agilis</td><td>ca.14</td><td>..........</td><td>11</td></tr>
<tr><td>3</td><td>E. gracilis</td><td colspan="2">ca.45</td><td>145</td></tr>
<tr><td>4</td><td>E. leucops</td><td>22-25</td><td>..........</td><td>79</td></tr>
<tr><td>5</td><td>E. spirogyra</td><td colspan="2">86</td><td>145</td></tr>
<tr><td>6</td><td>E. viridis</td><td colspan="2">42</td><td>145</td></tr>
<tr><td>7</td><td>Eutreptia lanowii</td><td colspan="2">90</td><td>145</td></tr>
<tr><td>8</td><td>Hyalophacus ocellatus</td><td colspan="2">92</td><td>145</td></tr>
<tr><td>9</td><td>Lepocinclis ovum buetschlii</td><td colspan="2">ca.34</td><td>145</td></tr>
<tr><td>10</td><td>Menoidium cultellus</td><td colspan="2">ca.15</td><td>145</td></tr>
<tr><td>11</td><td>Phacus pusillus</td><td colspan="2">42</td><td>145</td></tr>
<tr><td>12</td><td>Trachelomonas bulla</td><td colspan="2">ca.25</td><td>145</td></tr>
<tr><td>13</td><td>T. grandis</td><td colspan="2">40-60</td><td>145</td></tr>
<tr><td></td><td>Astasiaceae</td><td></td><td></td><td></td></tr>
<tr><td>14</td><td>Astasia dangeardi</td><td>12</td><td>..........</td><td>144</td></tr>
<tr><td>15</td><td>A. klebsii</td><td colspan="2">ca.18</td><td>145</td></tr>
<tr><td>16</td><td>Distigma proteus</td><td>16</td><td>..........</td><td>144</td></tr>
<tr><td></td><td>Peranemaceae</td><td></td><td></td><td></td></tr>
<tr><td>17</td><td>Peranema trichophorum</td><td>ca.32</td><td>..........</td><td>16</td></tr>
<tr><td>18</td><td></td><td colspan="2">ca.177</td><td>145</td></tr>
<tr><td></td><td>Colaciaceae</td><td></td><td></td><td></td></tr>
<tr><td>19</td><td>Colacium mucronatum</td><td colspan="2">ca.35</td><td>145</td></tr>
<tr><td></td><td colspan="4">Pyrrophyta</td></tr>
<tr><td></td><td>Chloromonadaceae</td><td></td><td></td><td></td></tr>
<tr><td>20</td><td>Anisonema viride</td><td>ca.30</td><td>..........</td><td>50</td></tr>
<tr><td></td><td>Pronoctilucaceae</td><td></td><td></td><td></td></tr>
<tr><td>21</td><td>Oxyrrhis marina</td><td>ca.40</td><td>..........</td><td>78</td></tr>
<tr><td></td><td>Noctilucaceae</td><td></td><td></td><td></td></tr>
<tr><td>22</td><td>Noctiluca miliaris</td><td>10</td><td>..........</td><td>111</td></tr>
<tr><td></td><td>Blastodiniaceae</td><td></td><td></td><td></td></tr>
<tr><td>23</td><td>Collozoum inerme</td><td>6</td><td>..........</td><td>193</td></tr>
<tr><td></td><td>Glenodiniaceae</td><td></td><td></td><td></td></tr>
<tr><td>24</td><td>Glenodinium pulvisculus</td><td>.........</td><td>ca.60</td><td>131</td></tr>
<tr><td></td><td colspan="4">Chrysophyta</td></tr>
<tr><td></td><td>Vaucheriaceae</td><td></td><td></td><td></td></tr>
<tr><td>25</td><td>Vaucheria geminata</td><td>5</td><td>.........</td><td>173</td></tr>
<tr><td>26</td><td></td><td>ca.7</td><td>.........</td><td>75</td></tr>
<tr><td>27</td><td>V. sessilis</td><td>7-10</td><td>.........</td><td>80</td></tr>
<tr><td></td><td>Ochrosphaeraceae</td><td></td><td></td><td></td></tr>
<tr><td>28</td><td>Ochrosphaera neopolitana</td><td>6</td><td>.........</td><td>234</td></tr>
<tr><td></td><td>Ochromonadaceae</td><td></td><td></td><td></td></tr>
<tr><td>29</td><td>Ochromonas granularis</td><td>2</td><td>.........</td><td>36</td></tr>
<tr><td></td><td>Coscinodiscaceae</td><td></td><td></td><td></td></tr>
<tr><td>30</td><td>Coscinodiscus apiculatus</td><td>8</td><td>16</td><td>215</td></tr>
<tr><td>31</td><td>C. biconicus</td><td>5-6</td><td>8-10</td><td>94</td></tr>
<tr><td>32</td><td>Cyclotella sp.</td><td>15-18</td><td>.........</td><td>64</td></tr>
<tr><td>33</td><td>C. meneghiniana</td><td>32-34</td><td>60+</td><td>114</td></tr>
<tr><td>34</td><td>Melosira arenaria</td><td>.......</td><td>30-40</td><td>280</td></tr>
<tr><td>35</td><td>M. varians</td><td>6</td><td>ca.11</td><td>195</td></tr>
<tr><td>36</td><td></td><td>22,25,27</td><td>.........</td><td>283</td></tr>
<tr><td></td><td>Chaetoceraceae</td><td></td><td></td><td></td></tr>
<tr><td>37</td><td>Chaetoceras boreale</td><td>11-12</td><td>.........</td><td>194</td></tr>
</table>

/1/ Uncertain whether *n* or 2*n* when centered between columns B and C.

continued

3. CHROMOSOME NUMBERS: ALGAE

	Family and Species	Chromosome Number[1]		Reference
		Haploid	Diploid	
	(A)	(B)	(C)	(D)
	Chrysophyta			
	Biddulphiaceae			
38	*Biddulphia mobiliensis*	....	ca.20	245
39	*B. rhombus*	ca.25	....	284
40	*B. sinensis*	16-18	32-36	216
41	*Triceratium dubium*	....	ca.26-30	245
	Anaulaceae			
42	*Terpsinoe musica*	....	ca.28	245
	Fragilariaceae			
43	*Centronella reicheltii*	6	....	136
	Achnanthaceae			
44	*Achnanthes inflata*	....	ca.12-16	245
45	*Cocconeis placentula*	....	28	55
46	*Rhoicosphenia curvata*	8	16	273
	Naviculaceae			
47	*Anomoeoneis sculpta*	14	....	274
48	*Navicula halophila*	24-26	48-52	307
49	*N. peregrina*	....	8	132
50	*N. radiosa*	....	ca.16	63
51	*Pleurosigma angulatum*	....	ca.40	245
	Cymbellaceae			
52	*Cymbella cistula*	18	....	279
53	*C. lacustris*	ca.9-10	....	275
54	*C. lanceolata*	20	....	54
55	*C. prostrata*	ca.18-20	....	275
56	*Gomphonema geminatum*	ca.14	....	166
57	*G. olivaceum*	ca.18-20	....	275
	Epithemiaceae			
58	*Epithemia zebra saxonica*	4?	....	58
	Nitzschiaceae			
59	*Nitzschia subtilis*	15-17	....	56
	Surirellaceae			
60	*Surirella saxonica*	64-65	128-130	120
	Chlorophyta			
	Polyblepharidaceae			
61	*Polytomella agilis*	5	....	36,37
62	*P. citri*	9	....	122
	Chlamydomonadaceae			
63	*Carteria cordiformis*	12	....	29
64	*C. crucifera*	9	....	6
65	*Chlamydomonas chlamydogama*	8	....	17
66	*C. dilli*	10	....	192
67		ca.10	....	29
68	*C. dysosmos*	16± 1	....	213
69	*C. eugametos*	8	....	17
70		10	....	84
71		36± 4	....	213
72	*C. microhalophila*	16± 1	....	13
73	*C. moewusii*	8	....	17
74		36± 2	....	213
75	*C. monadina*	ca.30	....	29
76	*C. nasuta*	8	....	123
77	*C. paupera*	10	....	84
78	*C. reinhardti*	8	....	17
79		18± 2	....	213
80	*C. variabilis*	10	....	29
81	*Chlorogonium elongatum*	10	....	81
82	*C. euchlorum*	ca.10	....	29
83	*Parapolytoma satura*	8	....	115
84	*Platymonas tetrathela*	10-12	....	304
	Chlamydomonadaceae			
85	*Polytoma pascheri*	8	....	167
86	*P. uvella*	4, 8	....	45,46
87		ca.6	....	31
88		8	....	167,205
	Haematococcaceae			
89	*Haematococcus pluvialis*	20-30	....	44
90		32	....	204
	Phacotaceae			
91	*Phacotus lenticularis*	ca.6-8	....	29
	Volvocaceae			
92	*Eudorina elegans*	10	....	82
93		12	....	21
94	*E. illinoisensis*	10	....	98
95	*E. indica*	10	....	38
96	*E. unicocca?*	7	....	21
97	*Gonium* sp.	ca.17	....	21
98	*G. pectorale*	17	....	21,241
99	*Pandorina morum*	12	....	26
100		ca.12	....	30
101	*Pleodorina californica*	14	....	21
102	*P. illinoisensis*	ca.12	....	163
103	*Volvox africanus*	13	....	21
104	*V. aureus*	12	....	303
105		14	....	21
106	*V. barberi*	5	....	21
107	*V. carteri*	ca.22	....	164,165
108	*V. globator*	5	....	21
109	*V. merrilli*	5	....	21
110	*V. powersii*	15	....	21
111	*V. rousseletii*	5	....	21
112	*V. spermatosphaera*	13	....	21
113	*V. tertius*	13	....	21
114	*V. weismannia*	14	....	21
115	*Volvulina steinii*	7	....	240
116		7,8	....	21
	Astrephomenaceae			
117	*Astrephomene gubernaculifera*	4,6,7,8	....	240,306
	Spondylomoraceae			
118	*Chlamydobotrys gracilis*	ca.8	....	217
119	*Spondylomorum quaternarium*	ca.6-8	....	243
	Tetrasporaceae			
120	*Tetraspora lubrica*	13	....	160
	Chaetopeltidaceae			
121	*Chaetopeltis orbicularis*	8	....	281
	Chlorococcaceae			
122	*Chlorochytrium grande*	ca.7	....	15
123	*C. lemnae*	6	....	139
124	*Kentrosphaera willei*	20-24	....	203
	Eremosphaeraceae			
125	*Eremosphaera viridis*	ca.80	....	154
	Protosiphonaceae			
126	*Protosiphon botryoides*	ca.12	....	14
	Oocystaceae			
127	*Oocystis crassa marssonii*	8	....	267
128	*Rhopalocystis oleifera*	8	....	260
	Hydrodictyaceae			
129	*Hydrodictyon africanum*	19± 1	....	199
130	*H. patenaeforme*	19± 1	....	199
131	*H. reticulatum*	18		212
132		19± 1	....	199

/1/ Uncertain whether *n* or 2*n* when centered between columns B and C.

continued

3. CHROMOSOME NUMBERS: ALGAE

No.	Family and Species (A)	Chromosome Number[1] Haploid (B)	Chromosome Number[1] Diploid (C)	Reference (D)
	Chlorophyta			
	Ulotrichaceae			
133	*Hormidium barlowi*	22-24		212
134	*H. crenulatum*	44-48		212
135	*Ulothrix rorida*	5	....	147
136	*U. subtilissima*	14		211,212
137	*U. variabilis*	7-8	....	277
138	*U. zonata*	4	....	76,221
139		10	....	211,212
140	*Uronema barlowi*	18	....	209
141	*U. confervicolum*	16	....	209
142	*U. gigas*	18	....	209
143	*U. terrestre*	16	....	211,212
	Microsporaceae			
144	*Microspora aequabilis*	24		212
145	*M. amoena*	8-12	....	282
146		18,20,32		211,212
147	*M. loefgrenii*	14-16	....	134
148		18		212
149	*M. stagnorum*	9	....	278
150		16		212
151	*M. tumidula*	16		212
	Cylindrocapsaceae			
152	*Cylindrocapsa involuta*	16-18		212
	Ulvaceae			
153	*Enteromorpha compressa*	9-10	....	212
154	*E. compressa lingulata*	10	20	200,201
155	*E. intermedia*	ca.16		212
156	*E. linza*	ca.12		182
157	*E. ramulosa*	ca.12		212
158	*Monostroma latissimum*	ca.10	....	18
159	*Ulva lactuca*	10	....	212
160		ca.10	....	18
161		13	26	51,52
162		....	ca.25	146
163	*U. linza*	....	ca.24-25	146
164	*U. pertusa*	13	....	299
	Prasiolaceae			
165	*Prasiola japonica*	3	....	53
166	*P. stipitata*	12-14		212
	Sphaeropleaceae			
167	*Sphaeroplea annulina*	5	....	189
168		16		210,212
169		19-20	....	69
170	*S. annulina crassisepta*	16		212
	Chaetophoraceae			
171	*Draparnaldia glomerata*	8	....	49
172	*D. plumosa*	18		212
173	*Draparnaldiopsis indica*	4	8	237
174	*Stigeoclonium amoenum*	5	10	238
175	*S. farctum*	5	....	238
	Cladophoraceae			
176	*Chaetomorpha area*	ca.10	ca.20	83
177		10-12	20-24	130
178		18		239
179	*C. area linum*	18	36	239
180	*C. capillaris*	18	36	239
181	*C. henningsii*	18		239
182	*C. linum*	18,36		239
183	*C. melagonium*	18		239
184	*Cladophora alpina*	24	....	61
185	*C. crispata*	24		239
186	*C. crystallina*	12	....	227
	Cladophoraceae			
187	*Cladophora flavescens*	12	24	90,92
188	*C. flexicaulis*	12	....	61
189	*C. flexuosa*	12	24	239
190	*C. fracta*	12	....	61
191	*C. fracta normalis*	24		239
192	*C. glomerata*	32	....	149
193		68		269
194		48	96	219,228, 230,231
195		48,96		239
196	*C. glomerata callicoma*	48		239
197	*C. glomerata genuina*	72		61,239
198	*C. glomerata kuetzingiana*	48		239
199	*C. gracilis*	....	24	224
200	*C. hutchinsiae*	12	24	239
201	*C. linneae*	12	24	239
202	*C. pellucida*	ca.16	ca.33	51
203		ca.18	....	239
204	*C. refracta*	12		239
205	*C. rupestris*	24		239
206	*C. suhriana*	6+1,6	....	222
207		12	....	61
208	*C. utriculosa*	12	....	227
209	*Pithophora kewensis*	24+	....	61
210	*Rhizoclonium* sp.	ca.30		197
211	*R. hieroglyphicum*	24	....	61
212		24		239
213	*R. hookeri*	18		239
214	*R. implexum*	24		239
215	*R. profundum*	ca.48		239
216	*R. riparium*	18	36	239
217	*R. riparium validum*	12	24	239
218	*R. sulfuratum*	48		239
219	*R. tortuosum*	24		239
220	*Urospora mirabilis*	4	....	116
	Oedogoniaceae			
221	*Oedogonium* spp.	9,13,17, 18,19	....	268
222	*O. cardiacum*	19	....	85
223	*O. cyathigerum*	19	....	271
224	*O. grande*	13	....	185
225	*O. pachyandrum*	15	....	135
226		17	....	268
	Mesotaeniaceae			
227	*Cylindrocystis brebissonii*	ca.20	....	124
228		ca.80	....	126,127
229	*Mesotaenium caldariorum*	8-10	....	27
230	*Netrium digitus*	ca.30	....	133
231		32	....	153
232		ca.122, ca.172-182,592	....	126,127
	Zygnemataceae			
233	*Spirogyra* sp.	24	....	248
234	*S. britannica*	10	....	70
235	*S. crassa*	12	....	57,59,68
236	*S. ellipsospora?*	70	....	68
237	*S. majuscula*	34-36	....	60
238	*S. mirabilis*	8	....	27
239	*S. subechinata*	4	....	70
240	*S. submargaritata*	38	....	70
241	*S. triformis*	6	....	68

/1/ Uncertain whether *n* or 2*n* when centered between columns B and C.

continued

3. CHROMOSOME NUMBERS: ALGAE

	Family and Species	Chromosome Number[1]		Reference
		Haploid	Diploid	
	(A)	(B)	(C)	(D)
	Chlorophyta			
	Zygnemataceae			
242	*Zygnema normani*	10	....	184
	Mougeotiaceae			
243	*Mougeotia* sp.	12	....	196,276
244	*Mougeotiopsis calospora*	16-18		212
	Gonatozygaceae			
245	*Gonatozygon monotaenium*	ca.34	....	126,127
	Desmidiaceae			
246	*Closterium acerosum*	60	....	272
247		ca.60	....	126,127
248	*C. ehrenbergii*	60+	....	272
249	*C. moniliferum*	ca.66	....	126,127
250	*Cosmarium botrytis*	18,26,94?	....	127
251		30+	....	121
252	*C. cucumis*	44,52	....	126,127
253	*C. subtumidum*	24	....	126,127
254	*Desmidium swartzii*	ca.28	....	126,127
255	*Hyalotheca dissiliens*	ca.12	....	5
256		ca.112	....	126,127
257	*H. dissiliens minor*	15	30	198
258	*Micrasterias angulosa*	60-64	....	289
259	*M. denticulata notata*	35-40	....	208
260	*M. rotata*	ca.172	....	126,127
261		ca.200	....	289
262	*M. thomasiana*	34-38	....	289
263	*Pleurotaenium trabecula*	104	....	125
264	*Sphaerozosma vertebratum*	ca.20	....	126,127
265	*Spondylosium pulchellum*	ca.18	....	126,127
266	*Staurastrum gracile*	ca.14	....	126,127
	Caulerpaceae			
267	*Bryopsis plumosa*	4	....	305
268	*Caulerpa prolifera*	5	10	226
	Dasycladaceae			
269	*Acetabularia mediterranea*	....	ca.20	218
270	*A. wettsteinii*	ca.10	....	220
271	*Cympolia barbata*	....	14	290
	Codiaceae			
272	*Codium decorticatum*	20	....	229
273	*C. elongatum*	ca.20	....	223
274	*C. tomentosum*	10	20	296
	Valoniaceae			
275	*Microdictyon tenuius*	16-18	32-36	113
276	*Valonia utricularis*	....	16	214
277		46-47	96	225
	Charophyta			
	Characeae			
278	*Chara* sp.	44	....	86
279	*C. aspera*	12	....	148
280		14	....	66
281	*C. aspera mota*	12	....	148
282	*C. ceratophylla*	14	....	261
283	*C. connivens*	14	....	66
284	*C. contraria*	ca.26	....	62
285		28	....	86,261
286		28,42	....	97
	Characeae			
287	*Chara contraria*	ca.30	....	148
288	*C. contraria hispidula*	40-50	....	62
289	*C. coronata*	14	....	117
290	*C. delicatula*	24	....	148
291		40+	....	119
292	*C. elegans*	24	....	148
293	*C. foetida*	18	....	148
294	*C. fragifera*	14	....	66
295		ca.30	....	22
296	*C. fragilis*	ca.20	....	62
297		24	....	148,261
298		32	....	66
299	*C. globularis*	28	....	97
300	*C. gracilis*	24	....	148
301	*C. hispida*	36	....	148
302	*C. jubata*	40+	....	261
303	*C. longibracteata*	ca.16	....	72
304	*C. sejuncta*	14	....	97
305	*C. vulgaris*	14	....	62
306		14,28	....	66
307		28	....	34,170
308	*C. vulgaris longibracteata*	14	....	162
309		ca.16	....	72
310	*C. vulgaris subinermis*	28	....	32
311	*C. zeylanica*	ca.28	....	249
312	*Lamprothamnus alopecuroides*	ca.50	....	148
313	*Nitella* sp.	15-16	30-32	270
314		18	....	89
315	*N. acuminata subglomerata*	18	....	97
316	*N. batrachosperma*	18	....	288
317	*N. cristata*	9	....	295
318	*N. flexilis*	12	....	66,118,119,148
319	*N. gracilis*	17	....	148
320		34	....	117
321	*N. hyalina*	12-14	....	242
322		16	....	66
323	*N. mucronata*	18	....	66
324	*N. opaca*	6	....	66
325	*N. syncarpa*	6	....	66
326	*N. translucens*	18	....	66,148
327	*Tolypella nidifica*	ca.42	....	148
328	*Tolypellopsis stelligera*	14	....	261
	Phaeophyta			
	Ectocarpaceae			
329	*Ectocarpus confervoides*	8	16	159
330	*E. fasiculatus*	....	16	129
331	*E. penicillatus*	8	16	129
332	*E. siliculosus*	8	16	232
333		8-9	....	190
334	*E. tomentosus*	....	16	129
335	*E. velutinus*	8	16	129
336	*E. virescens*	<10	....	253
337	*Pylaiella litoralis*	9-10	....	128
338		12	....	28
	Lithodermataceae			
339	*Hapterophycus canaliculatus*	12	....	96

/1/ Uncertain whether *n* or 2*n* when centered between columns B and C.

continued

3. CHROMOSOME NUMBERS: ALGAE

	Family and Species	Chromosome Number		Reference
		Haploid	Diploid	
	(A)	(B)	(C)	(D)
	Phaeophyta			
	Sphacelariaceae			
340	*Halopteris filicina*	16	....	129,158
341	*Sphacelaria bipinnata*	12-16	....	25
	Stypocaulaceae			
342	*Stypocaulon scoparium*	16	32	91,129
	Cutleriaceae			
343	*Cutleria multifida*	24	48	301
344	*Zanardinia prototypus*	22	44	302
	Tilopteridaceae			
345	*Haplospora globosa*	12, ca.13	....	28
	Dictyotaceae			
346	*Dictyopteris divaricata*	16	....	101
347	*D. membranacea*	16	....	67
348	*Dictyota dichotoma*	16	32	294
349	*Padina pavonia*	16	....	19
350	*Zonaria farlowii*	12	....	88
	Chordariaceae			
351	*Heterochordaria abietineae*	ca.20	ca.40	2
352	*Myriogloia sciurus*	8-9	16-18	191
	Sporochnaceae			
353	*Sporochnus pedunculatus*	20	....	152
	Striariaceae			
354	*Isthmoploea sphaerophora*	8	....	129
355	*Phloeospora brachiata*	10	....	158
356	*Stictyosiphon tortilis*	26	40+	177
	Myriotrichiaceae			
357	*Myriotrichia clavaeformis*	8	....	129
	Punctariaceae			
358	*Asperococcus fistulosus*	8	....	129
359	*Punctaria plantaginea*	8	....	129
	Dictyosiphonaceae			
360	*Dictyosiphon foeniculaceus*	18	....	4
	Chordaceae			
361	*Chorda filum*	20	....	141
	Laminariaceae			
362	*Costaria costata*	ca.30	....	183
363	*Laminaria angustata*	22	....	183
364	*L. cloustoni*	....	22	286
365	*L. digitata*	....	16	286
366		27-31	....	175
367	*L. flexicaulis*	13	....	151
368	*L. japonica*	22	....	3
369	*L. ochroleuca*	27-31	....	175
370	*L. saccharina*	13	....	151
371		27-31	....	175
	Lessoniaceae			
372	*Macrocystis integrifolia*	....	32	285
	Alariaceae			
373	*Egregia menziesii*	8	16	174
374	*Eisenia arborea*	15	....	95
375	*Pterygophora californica*	13	26	161
376	*Undaria pinnatifida*	22,30	....	108-110
	Notheiaceae			
377	*Hormosira banksii*	12	24	188
	Fucaceae			
378	*Ascophyllum nodosum*	14-15	ca.28	48
379	*Fucus evanescens*	32	....	100
380	*F. serratus*	16	32	244
381		....	26-28	48
382	*F. vesiculosus*	10	20	47
383		32	64	300
384	*Hesperophycus harveyanus*	....	17-18	287
385	*Pelvetia canaliculata*	ca.22	ca.40	246,247
386	*P. wrightii*	32	....	99,100
	Himanthaliaceae			
387	*Himanthalia* sp.	....	28	48
388	*H. elongata*	24, 26, 28,34	....	168
389		....	56-62	176
390	*H. lorea*	....	28	65
	Cystoseiraceae			
391	*Bifurcaria* sp.	....	64	67
392	*Cystophyllum crassipes*	....	64	102
393	*C. sisymbrioides*	32	....	236
394	*Cystoseira barbata*	18-20	....	181
395	*Halidrys siliquosa*	8	....	169
396		28-34	55+	178,180
	Sargassaceae			
397	*Coccophora langsdorfii*	32	....	266
398		ca.32	ca.60	258
399	*Hizikia fusiformis*	32	....	105
400	*Sargassum* spp.	32	....	259
401	*S. confusum*	32	....	1
402	*S. horneri*	16	32	138
403		32	64	93,186, 187
404	*S. patens*	....	64	103
405	*S. piluliferum*	32	64	104,106
406	*S. tortile*	32	....	107
	Rhodophyta			
	Bangiaceae			
407	*Porphyra linearis*	....	8	150
408	*P. umbilicalis laciniata*	5	....	137
	Lemaneaceae			
409	*Lemanea australis*	10	....	171,172
	Bonnemaisoniaceae			
410	*Asparagopsis armata*	10	....	254
411	*Bonnemaisonia asparagoides*	ca.18	....	254
	Helminthocladiaceae			
412	*Helminthocladia papenfussii*	ca.10	....	155
413	*Helminthora divaricata*	8-10	....	142
414	*Nemalion* sp.	ca.8	ca.16	297
415	*N. multifidum*	8	....	24
416		ca.10	....	140
	Chaetangiaceae			
417	*Chaetangium saccatum*	8-10	....	156
418	*Galaxaura corymbifera*	9-12	19-20	257
419	*G. diesingiana*	9-12	ca.17	257
420	*G. tenera*	9-12	18-22	257
	Gelidiaceae			
421	*Gelidium corneum*	4,5	9,10	35
	Rhizophyllidaceae			
422	*Polyides caprinus*	68-72	....	202

continued

3. CHROMOSOME NUMBERS: ALGAE

	Family and Species	Chromosome Number		Reference
		Haploid	Diploid	
	(A)	(B)	(C)	(D)
	Rhodophyta			
	Corallinaceae			
423	*Amphiroa aberrans*	24	....	235
424	*Corallina officinalis*	24	....	250
425	*C. rubens*	24	....	250
426	*Lithophyllum corallinae*	16	32	252
427	*L. littorale*	....	ca.30	252
428	*Mastophora lamourouxii*	24	....	251
429	*Melobesia farinosa*	ca.24	....	12
	Gracilariaceae			
430	*Gracilaria multipartita*	6-7	....	74
	Furcellariaceae			
431	*Furcellaria fastigiata*	ca.16	....	77
432		34	68	8-10
	Rhodophyllidaceae			
433	*Cystoclonium purpureum*	....	50	7
	Phyllophoraceae			
434	*Ahnfeltia plicata*	4	....	207
435		4,8	....	73
436	*Gymnogongrus griffithsia*	ca.4	....	73
437	*G. linearis*	ca.6	....	39
438	*G. platyphyllus*	8	....	39
439	*Phyllophora brodiaei*	4	8	23
	Rhodymeniaceae			
440	*Rhodymenia palmata*	ca.20	....	291
441		21	....	7
	Champiaceae			
442	*Lomentaria clavellosa*	10	....	255,256
443	*L. rosea*	....	18-20	255,256
	Ceramiaceae			
444	*Callithamnion brachiatum*	9-10	18-20	157
445	*C. corymbosum*	28,30,31	....	87
446	*Callithamnion tetricum*	ca.25	....	292
447	*Ceramium deslongchampii*	20	....	28
448	*C. rubrum*	6-8	....	77
449		34	....	7
450	*Plumaria elegans*[2]	31	62	41,43
451	*Spermothamnion roseolum*	20	....	233
452	*S. snyderi*	32	64	40,43
453	*S. turneri*[3]	30	60	40,42,43
	Delesseriaceae			
454	*Cryptopleura ramosa*	30	....	7
455	*Delesseria sanguinea*	31	....	7
456	*Membranoptera alata*	32	....	7
457	*Nitophyllum laceratum*	8	....	77
	Rhodomelaceae			
458	*Chondria crassicaulis*	20	40	298
459	*C. dasyphylla*	ca.20	....	142
460		ca.25	....	293
461	*C. tenuissima*	ca.25	....	293
462	*Laurencia hybrida*	ca.20	....	293
463		31	....	7
464	*L. obtusa majuscula*	20	40	298
465	*L. papillosa*	20	40	298
466	*L. pinnatifida*	ca.20	....	293
467		29	58	7
468	*Polysiphonia elongata*	37	....	7
469	*P. japonica*	20	40	298
470	*P. lanosa*	27	....	7
471	*P. nigrescens*	30	60	7
472	*P. platycarpa*	20	....	112
473	*Rhodomela confervoides*	32	....	7
474	*R. subfusca*	ca.20	....	293
	Dasyaceae			
475	*Dasya arbuscula*	....	ca.40	293
476	*D. elegans*	ca.20	....	206

/2/ $3n$ = 87-99. /3/ $3n$ = 90.

Contributor: Cave, Marion S.

References: [1] Abe, K. 1933. Science Repts. Tohoku Imp. Univ., Ser. 4, 8:259. [2] Abe, K. 1936. Ibid., Ser. 4, 11:239. [3] Abe, K. 1939. Ibid., Ser. 4, 14:327. [4] Abe, K. 1940. Ibid., Ser. 4, 15:317. [5] Acton, E. 1916. Ann. Botany (London) 30:379. [6] Akins, V. 1941. Bull. Torrey Botan. Club 69:429. [7] Austin, A. P. 1956. Nature 178:370. [8] Austin, A. P. 1957. Brit. Phycol. Bull. 5:16. [9] Austin, A. P. 1960. Ann. Botany (London), n.s. 24:257. [10] Austin, A. P. 1960. Ibid., n.s. 24:296. [11] Baker, W. B. 1926. Biol. Bull. 51:321. [12] Balakrishnan, M. S. 1946. In B. Sahni, ed. M. O. P. Iyengar commemoration volume. Indian Botanical Society, Bangalore, Mysore. p. 305. [13] Bischoff, H. W. 1959. Biol. Bull. 117:54. [14] Bold, H. C. 1933. Bull. Torrey Botan. Club 60:241. [15] Bristol, B. M. 1917. Ann. Botany (London) 31:107. [16] Brown, V. E. 1930. Quart. J. Microscop. Sci. 73:403. [17] Buffaloe, N. D. 1958. Bull. Torrey Botan. Club 85:157. [18] Carter, N. 1926. Ann. Botany (London) 40:665. [19] Carter, N. 1927. Ibid. 41:139. [20] Cave, M. S., ed. 1958-60. Index to plant chromosome numbers. Univ. North Carolina Press, Chapel Hill. Nos. 1-4 and suppl. [21] Cave, M. S., and M. A. Pocock. 1951. Am. J. Botany 38:800. [22] Cazalas, M. 1930. Botaniste 22:295. [23] Claussen, H. 1929. Ber. deut. botan. Ges. 47:544. [24] Cleland, R. E. 1919. Ann. Botany (London) 33:323. [25] Clint, H. B. 1927. Univ. Liverpool Hartley Botan. Lab. Publ. 3. [26] Coleman, A. W. 1959. J. Protozool. 6:249. [27] Czurda, V. 1937. In K. Linsbauer, ed. Handbuch der Pflanzenanatomie, II. Gebrüder Bornträger, Berlin. Bd. 6(2):Algen B, b.

continued

[28] Dammann, H. 1930. Wiss. Meeres- Untersuch. Abt. Helgoland, n.F. 18(4):1. [29] Dangeard, P. A. 1898. Botaniste 6:65, [30] Dangeard, P. A. 1900. Ibid. 7:193. [31] Dangeard, P. A. 1902. Ibid. 8:5. [32] Delay, C. 1949. Rev. cytol. et biol. végétales 11:315. [33] Delay, C. 1953. Ibid. 14:59. [34] Delay, C., and S. Carpentier. 1955. Ibid. 16:415. [35] Dixon, P. S. 1954. Brit. Phycol. Bull. 2:4. [36] Doflein, F. 1918. Zool. Anz. 49:289. [37] Doflein, F. 1919. Zool. Jahrb. 41:1. [38] Doraiswami, S. 1940. J. Indian Botan. Soc. 19:113. [39] Doubt, D. G. 1935. Am. J. Botany 22:294. [40] Drew, K. M. 1937. Ann. Botany (London), n.s. 1:464. [41] Drew, K. M. 1939. Ibid., n.s. 3:347. [42] Drew, K. M. 1943. Ibid., n.s. 7:23. [43] Drew, K. M. 1944. Biol. Revs. Cambridge Phil. Soc. 19:105. [44] Elliott, A. M. 1934. Arch. Protistenk. 82:250. [45] Entz, G. 1913. Verhandl. deut. zool. Ges. 23:249. [46] Entz, G. 1918. Arch. Protistenk. 38:324. [47] Farmer, J. B., and J. L. Williams. 1896. Ann. Botany (London) 10:479. [48] Farmer, J. B., and J. L. Williams. 1898. Trans. Roy. Soc. (London), B, 190:623. [49] Ferguson, J. M. 1932. Ann. Botany (London) 46:703. [50] Fott, B. 1935. Arch. Protistenk. 84:242. [51] Föyn, B. 1929. Ber. deut. botan. Ges. 47:495. [52] Föyn, B. 1934. Arch. Protistenk. 83:154. [53] Fujiyama, T. 1955. J. Fac. Fisheries Animal Husbandry Hiroshima Univ. 1:15. [54] Geitler, L. 1927. Arch. Protistenk. 58:465. [55] Geitler, L. 1927. Ibid. 59:506. [56] Geitler, L. 1928. Ibid. 61:419. [57] Geitler, L. 1930. Ibid. 71:79. [58] Geitler, L. 1932. Ibid. 78:1. [59] Geitler, L. 1935. Ibid. 85:10. [60] Geitler, L. 1935. Ber. deut. botan. Ges. 53:270. [61] Geitler, L. 1936. Planta 25:530. [62] Geitler, L. 1948. Oesterr. botan. Z. 95:147. [63] Geitler, L. 1951. Ibid. 98:206. [64] Geitler, L. 1952. Ibid. 99:506. [65] Gibb, D. C. 1937. J. Linnean Soc. London Botany 51:11. [66] Gillet, C. 1959. Rev. cytol. et biol. végétales 20:229. [67] Giraud, G. 1956. Rev. gén. botan. 63:202. [68] Godward, M. B. E. 1950. Ann. Botany (London), n.s. 14:39. [69] Godward, M. B. E. 1954. Brit. Phycol. Bull. 2:3. [70] Godward, M. B. E. 1956. J. Linnean Soc. London Botany 55:532. [71] Godward, M. B. E. 1959. Brit. Phycol. Bull. 7:43. [72] Gonçalves da Cunha, A. 1942. Trabajos inst. botan. Lisboa 6:1. [73] Gregory, B. D. 1930. Ann. Botany (London) 44:767. [74] Greig-Smith, E. 1954. Brit. Phycol. Bull. 2:4. [75] Gross, C. 1937. Bull. Torrey Botan. Club 64:1. [76] Gross, I. 1931. Arch. Protistenk. 73:206. [77] Grubb, V. M. 1925. J. Linnean Soc. London Botany 47:177. [78] Hall, R. P. 1925. Univ. Calif. (Berkeley) Publs. Zool. 26:281. [79] Hall, S. R. 1931. Biol. Bull. 60:327. [80] Hanatschek, H. 1932. Arch. Protistenk. 78:497. [81] Hartmann, M. 1918. Ibid. 39:1. [82] Hartmann, M. 1921. Ibid. 43:223. [83] Hartmann, M. 1929. Ber. deut. botan. Ges. 47:485. [84] Hartmann, M. 1934. Sitzber. preuss. Akad. Wiss. Physik.- math. Kl. 20:379. [85] Hasitschka-Jenschke, G. 1960. Oesterr. botan. Z. 107:194. [86] Hasitschka-Jenschke, G. 1960. Ibid. 107:228. [87] Hassinger-Huizinga, H. 1952. Arch. Protistenk. 98:91. [88] Haupt, A. W. 1932. Am. J. Botany 19:239. [89] Heitz, E. 1932. Planta 18:571. [90] Higgins, E. M. 1930. Ann. Botany (London) 44:587. [91] Higgins, E. M. 1931. Ibid. 45:350. [92] Higgins, E. M. 1931. Ibid. 45:533. [93] Hiroe, M., and S. Inoh. 1954. Botan. Mag. (Tokyo) 67:190. [94] Hofker, J. 1928. Ann. Protistol. (Paris) 1:167. [95] Hollenberg, G. J. 1939. Am. J. Botany 26:34. [96] Hollenberg, G. J. 1941. Ibid. 28:676. [97] Hotchkiss, A. T. 1958. Trans. Kentucky Acad. Sci. 19:14. [98] Hovasse, R. 1937. Bull. biol. France et Belg. 71:220. [99] Inoh, S. 1933. Rept. Muroran Inst. Phycol. 1:11. [100] Inoh, S. 1935. J. Fac. Sci. Hokkaido Imp. Univ., V, 5(1):9. [101] Inoh, S. 1936. Sci. Papers Inst. Algol. Research Hokkaido Imp. Univ. 1:213. [102] Inoh, S. 1944. J. Fac. Sci. Hokkaido Imp. Univ., V, 5(3):199. [103] Inoh, S., and M. Hiroe. 1954. Biol. J. Okayama Univ. 2:1. [104] Inoh, S., and M. Hiroe. 1954. Kromosomo (Tokyo) 21:760. [105] Inoh, S., and M. Hiroe. 1954. Ibid. 21:764. [106] Inoh, S., and M. Hiroe. 1954. Ibid. 21:767. [107] Inoh, S., and M. Hiroe. 1956. Ibid. 27-28:942. [108] Inoh, S., and T. Nishibayashi. 1954. Biol. J. Okayama Univ. 1:217. [109] Inoh, S., and T. Nishibayashi. 1955. Kromosomo (Tokyo) 22-24:788. [110] Inoh, S., and T. Nishibayashi. 1960. Ibid. 44-45:1498. [111] Ishikawa, C. 1894. J. Coll. Sci. Imp. Univ. Tokyo 6:295. [112] Iyengar, M. O. P., and M. S. Balakrishnan. 1950. Proc. Indian Acad. Sci. 29(B):105. [113] Iyengar, M. O. P., and K. R. Ramanathan. 1941. J. Indian Botan. Soc. 20:157. [114] Iyengar, M. O. P., and R. Subrahmanyan. 1944. Ibid. 23:125. [115] Jameson, A. P. 1914. Arch. Protistenk. 33:21. [116] Jorde, I. 1933. Nytt Mag. Naturvidensk. 73:1. [117] Karling, J. S. 1926. Bull. Torrey Botan. Club 53:319. [118] Karling, J. S. 1927. Ibid. 54:187. [119] Karling, J. S. 1928. Ibid. 55:11. [120] Karsten, G. 1912. Z. Botan. 4:417.

continued

[121] Karsten, G. 1918. Ibid. 10:1. [122] Kater, J. McA. 1927. Biol. Bull. 49:213. [123] Kater, J. McA. 1929. Univ. Calif. (Berkeley) Publs. Zool. 33:125. [124] Kaufmann, H. 1914. Z. Botan. 6:721. [125] King, G. C. 1954. Brit. Phycol. Bull. 2:3. [126] King, G. C. 1955. Ibid. 3:32. [127] King, G. C. 1960. New Phytologist 59:65. [128] Knight, M. 1923. Trans. Roy. Soc. Edinburgh 53:343. [129] Knight, M. 1929. Ibid. 56:307. [130] Köhler, K. 1956. Arch. Protistenk. 101:223. [131] Köhler-Wieder, R. 1937. Oesterr. botan. Z. 86:198. [132] Kolbe, R. W. 1927. Pflanzenforschung 7:1. [133] Kopetzky-Rechtperg, O. 1932. Beih. botan. Zentr. 49:686. [134] Kostrum, G. 1944. Oesterr. botan. Z. 93:172. [135] Kretschmer, H. 1930. Arch. Protistenk. 71:101. [136] Krieger, W. 1927. Ber. deut. botan. Ges. 45:281. [137] Krishnamurthy, V. 1959. Ann. Botany (London), n.s. 23:147. [138] Kunieda, H. 1928. J. Coll. Agr. Imp. Univ. Tokyo 9:383. [139] Kurssanov, L. J., and N. M. Schemakhanova. 1927. Arch. russ. protistol. 6:131. [140] Kylin, H. 1916. Ber. deut. botan. Ges. 34:257. [141] Kylin, H. 1918. Svensk Botan. Tidskr. 12:1. [142] Kylin, H. 1928. Lunds Univ. Årsskr., N. F. Avd. 2, 24(4). [143] Lackey, J. B. 1929. Arch. Protistenk. 66:175. [144] Lackey, J. B. 1934. Biol. Bull. 67:145. [145] Leedale, G. F. 1958. Nature 181:502. [146] Levan, A., and T. Levring. 1942. Hereditas 28:400. [147] Lind, E. M. 1932. Ann. Botany (London) 46:711. [148] Lindenbein, W. 1927. Planta 4:437. [149] List, H. 1930. Arch. Protistenk. 72:453. [150] Magne, F. 1952. Compt. rend. 234:986. [151] Magne, F. 1953. Ibid. 236:515. [152] Magne, F. 1953. Ibid. 236:1596. [153] Maguitt, M. 1925. J. soc. botan. Russie 10:177. [154] Mainx, F. 1927. Arch. Protistenk. 57:1. [155] Martin, M. T. 1939. J. Botany Brit. and For. 77:234. [156] Martin, M. T. 1939. J. Linnean Soc. London Botany 52:115. [157] Mathias, W. T. 1928. Univ. Liverpool Hartley Botan. Lab. Publ. 5. [158] Mathias, W. T. 1935. Ibid. 13. [159] May, V. 1930. Proc. Linnean Soc. N. S. Wales 64:537. [160] McAllister, F. 1913. Ann. Botany (London) 27:681. [161] McKay, H. H. 1933. Univ. Calif. (Berkeley) Publs. Botany 17:111. [162] Mendes, E. J. 1946. Portugaliae Acta Biol. 1:251. [163] Merton, H. 1908. Z. wiss. Zool. 90:445. [164] Metzner, J. 1945. Bull. Torrey Botan. Club 72:86. [165] Metzner, J. 1945. Ibid. 72:121. [166] Meyer, K. 1929. Arch. Protistenk. 66:421. [167] Moewus, F. 1935. Z. induktive Abstammungs.- u. Vererbungslehre 69:374. [168] Moss, B. L. 1958. Brit. Phycol. Bull. 6:31. [169] Moss, B. L., and E. Elliot. 1957. Ann. Botany (London), n.s. 21:143. [170] Moutschen, J., and M. Dahmen. 1956. Rev. cytol. et biol. végétales 17:433. [171] Mullahy, J. H. 1952. Bull. Torrey Botan. Club 79:393. [172] Mullahy, J. H. 1952. Ibid. 79:471. [173] Mundie, J. R. 1929. Botan. Gaz. 87:397. [174] Myers, M. F. 1928. Univ. Calif. (Berkeley) Publs. Botany 14:225. [175] Naylor, M. 1956. Ann. Botany (London), n.s. 20:431. [176] Naylor, M. 1957. Nature 180:46. [177] Naylor, M. 1958. Acta Adriat. 8:1. [178] Naylor, M. 1958. Ann. Botany (London), n.s. 22:205. [179] Naylor, M. 1958. Brit. Phycol. Bull. 6:34. [180] Naylor, M. 1958. Nature 181:853. [181] Nienburg, W. 1910. Flora (Ger.) 101:167. [182] Niizeki, S. 1957. Nat. Sci. Repts. Ochanomizu Univ. (Tokyo) 8:45. [183] Nishibayashi, T., and S. Inoh. 1957. Botan. Mag. (Tokyo) 70:228. [184] O'Donnell, E. H. J. 1957. Darwiniana 11:423. [185] Ohashi, H. 1930. Botan. Gaz. 90:177. [186] Okabe, S. 1929. Science Repts. Tohoku Imp. Univ., Ser. 4, 4:661. [187] Okabe, S. 1930. Ibid., Ser. 4, 5:757. [188] Osborn, J. E. M. 1948. Trans. Roy. Soc. New Zealand 77:47. [189] Palik, P. 1950. Acta Biol. Acad. Sci. Hung. 1:329. [190] Papenfuss, G. F. 1935. Botan. Gaz. 96:421. [191] Parke, M. B. 1933. Univ. Liverpool Hartley Botan. Lab. Publ. 9. [192] Pascher, A. 1916. Ber. deut. botan. Ges. 34:228. [193] Pätau, K. 1937. Cytologia (Tokyo), Fujii jubilaei vol. (2):667. [194] Persidsky, B. M. 1929. The development of the auxospores in the group of the Centricae (Bacillariaceae). Moscow. [195] Persidsky, B. M. 1935. Beih. botan. Zentr. 53(A):122. [196] Peterschilka, F. 1922. Arch. Protistenk. 45:153. [197] Peterschilka, F. 1924. Ibid. 47:325. [198] Potthoff, H. 1927. Planta 4:261. [199] Proskauer, J. 1952. Hydrobiologia 4:399. [200] Ramanathan, K. R. 1936. J. Indian Botan. Soc. 15:55. [201] Ramanathan, K. R. 1939. Ann. Botany (London), n.s. 3:375. [202] Rao, C. S. P. 1956. Ibid., n.s. 20:211. [203] Reichardt, A. 1927. Arch. Protistenk. 59:301. [204] Reichenow, E. 1910. Arb. kaiserl. Gesundh. 33:1. [205] Reichenow, E. 1928. Arch. Protistenk. 61:144. [206] Rosenberg, T. 1933. Dissertation. Lund Univ., Sweden. [207] Rosenvinge, L. K. 1931. Kgl. Danske Videnskab. Selskab Biol. Medd. 10(2):1. [208] Saraswathi, M. R. 1946. In B. Sahni, ed. M. O. P. Iyengar commemoration volume. Indian Botanical Society, Bangalore,

continued

Mysore. p. 279. [209] Sarma, Y. S. R. K. 1956. Nature 177:900 [210] Sarma, Y. S. R. K. 1957. Cytologia (Tokyo) 22:113. [211] Sarma, Y. S. R. K. 1957. Nature 180:46. [212] Sarma, Y. S. R. K. 1958. Brit. Phycol. Bull. 6:22. [213] Schaechter, M., and E. D. DeLamater. 1955. Am. J. Botany 42:417. [214] Schechner-Fries, M. 1934. Oesterr. botan. Z. 83:241. [215] Schmidt, P. 1931. Intern. Rev. ges. Hydrobiol. Hydrog. 25:68. [216] Schmidt, P. 1933. Flora (Ger.) 128:235. [217] Schulze, B. 1927. Arch. Protistenk. 58:508. [218] Schulze, K. L. 1939. Ibid. 92:179. [219] Schussnig, B. 1928. Oesterr. botan. Z. 77:62. [220] Schussnig, B. 1929. Ber. deut. botan. Ges. 47:266. [221] Schussnig, B. 1930. Z. Zellforsch. u. mikroskop. Anat. 10:642. [222] Schussnig, B. 1931. Planta 13:474. [223] Schussnig, B. 1932. Oesterr. botan. Z. 81:296. [224] Schussnig, B. 1938. Biol. Generalis 14:129. [225] Schussnig, B. 1938. Planta 28:43. [226] Schussnig, B. 1939. Botan. Notiser, p. 75. [227] Schussnig, B. 1939. Oesterr. botan. Z. 88:210. [228] Schussnig, B. 1944. Ber. deut. botan. Ges. 62:5. [229] Schussnig, B. 1950. Svensk Botan. Tidskr. 44:55. [230] Schussnig, B. 1951. Ibid. 45:597. [231] Schussnig, B. 1954. Arch. Protistenk. 100:287. [232] Schussnig, B., and E. Kothbauer. 1934. Oesterr. Botan. Z. 83:81. [233] Schussnig, B., and K. Odle. 1927. Arch. Protistenk. 58:220. [234] Schwarz, E. 1932. Ibid. 77:434. [235] Sewaga, S. 1941. J. Japan. Botany 17:164. [236] Shimotomai, N. 1928. Science Repts. Tohoku Imp. Univ., Ser. 4, 3:577. [237] Singh, R. N. 1945. New Phytologist 44:118. [238] Singh, R. N. 1954. Rev. Algol., n.s. 1:42. [239] Sinha, J. P. 1958. Brit. Phycol. Bull. 6:24. [240] Stein, J. R. 1958. Am. J. Botany 45:388. [241] Stein, J. R. 1958. Ibid. 45:664. [242] Stewart, L. M. 1937. J. Elisha Mitchell Sci. Soc. 53:173. [243] Stickney, M. E. 1908. Bull. Sci. Lab. Denison Univ. 14:233. [244] Strasburger, E. 1897. Jahrb. wiss. Botan. 30:351. [245] Subrahmanyan, R. 1945. Proc. Indian Acad. Sci. 22(B):331. [246] Subrahmanyan, R. 1956. J. Indian Botan. Soc. 35:374. [247] Subrahmanyan, R. 1957. Ibid. 36:12. [248] Suematsu, S. 1936. Science Repts. Tokyo Bunrika Daigaku, B, 3:35. [249] Sundaralingam, V. S. 1946. In B. Sahni, ed. M. O. P. Iyengar commemoration volume. Indian Botanical Society, Bangalore, Mysore. p. 289. [250] Suneson, S. 1937. Lunds. Univ. Årsskr., N. F. avd. 2, 33(2). [251] Suneson, S. 1945. Kgl. Fysiograf. Sällskap. Lund Förh. 15:251. [252] Suneson, S. 1950. Botan. Notiser, p. 429. [253] Svedelius, N. 1928. Svensk Botan. Tidskr. 22:289. [254] Svedelius, N. 1933. Nova Acta Regiae Soc. Sci. Upsaliensis, Ser. 4, 9(1). [255] Svedelius, N. 1935. Ber. deut. botan. Ges. 53:19. [256] Svedelius, N. 1937. Symbolae Botan. Upsaliensis 2:1. [257] Svedelius, N. 1942. Nova Acta Regiae Soc. Sci. Upsaliensis, Ser. 4, 13(4). [258] Tahara, M. 1929. Science Repts. Tohoku Imp. Univ., Ser. 4, 4:551. [259] Tahara, M., and N. Shimotomai. 1926. Ibid., Ser. 4, 1:189. [260] Täumer, L. 1959. Arch. Protistenk. 104:265. [261] Telezynski, H. 1929. Acta Soc. Botan. Polon. 6:230. [262] Tischler, G. 1927. Tabulae Biologicae 4:1. [263] Tischler, G. 1931. Ibid. 7:109. [264] Tischler, G. 1936. Ibid. 11:281. [265] Tischler, G. 1937. Ibid. 12:57. [266] Tomita, K. 1932. Science Repts. Tohoku Imp. Univ., Ser. 4, 7:43. [267] Tschermak, E. 1942. Planta 32:585. [268] Tschermak, E. 1944. Chromosoma 2:493. [269] T'Serclaes, J. 1922. Cellule 32:313. [270] Tuttle, A. H. 1924. Science 60:412. [271] Van Wisselingh, C. 1908. Beih. botan. Zentr. 23:137. [272] Van Wisselingh, C. 1912. Ibid. 29:409. [273] Von Cholnoky, B. 1927. Arch. Protistenk. 60:8. [274] Von Cholnoky, B. 1928. Ibid. 63:23. [275] Von Cholnoky, B. 1929. Ibid. 68:471. [276] Von Cholnoky, B. 1932. Ibid. 78:522. [277] Von Cholnoky, B. 1932. Beih. botan. Zentr. 49:221. [278] Von Cholnoky, B. 1932. Z. Zellforsch. u. mikroskop. Anat. 16:707. [279] Von Cholnoky, B. 1933. Arch. Protistenk. 80:321. [280] Von Cholnoky, B. 1933. Z. Zellforsch. u. mikroskop. Anat. 19:698. [281] Von Cholnoky, B. 1934. Oesterr. botan. Z. 83:187. [282] Von Neuenstein, H. 1914. Arch. Zellforsch. 13:1. [283] Von Stosch, H. A. 1951. Arch. Mikrobiol. 16:101. [284] Von Stosch, H. A. 1956. Ibid. 23:327. [285] Walker, F. T. 1952. Ann. Botany (London), n.s. 16:23. [286] Walker, F. T. 1954. Ibid., n.s. 18:113. [287] Walker, R. I. 1931. Cellule 40:173. [288] Walther, E. 1929. Arch. Julius Klaus-Stift. Vererbungsforsch. Sozialanthropol. u. Rassenhyg. 4:23. [289] Waris, H. 1950. Physiol. Plantarum 3:1. [290] Werz, G. 1953. Arch. Protistenk. 99:148. [291] Westbrook, M. A. 1928. Ann. Botany (London) 42:149. [292] Westbrook, M. A. 1930. Ibid. 44:1012. [293] Westbrook, M. A. 1935. Beih. botan. Zentr. 53:564. [294] Williams, J. L. 1904. Ann. Botany (London) 18:145. [295] Williams, M. B. 1959. Proc. Linnean Soc. N. S. Wales 84:346. [296] Williams, M. M. 1925. Ibid. 50:98. [297] Wolfe, J. J. 1904. Ann. Botany (London) 18:607. [298] Yabu, H., and K. Kawamura.

continued

1959. Mem. Fac. Fisheries Hokkaido Univ. 7:61. [299] Yabu, H., and J. Tokida. 1960. Botan. Mag. (Tokyo) 73:182. [300] Yamanouchi, S. 1909. Botan. Gaz. 47:173. [301] Yamanouchi, S. 1912. Ibid. 54:441. [302] Yamanouchi, S. 1913. Ibid. 56:1. [303] Zimmermann, W. 1921. Jahrb. wiss. Botan. 60:256. [304] Zimmermann, W. 1925. Wiss. Meeres-Untersuch. Abt. Helgoland, n.F. 16(1):1. [305] Zinnecker, E. 1935. Oesterr. botan. Z. 84:53. [306] Cave, M. S., and M. A. Pocock. 1956. Am. J. Botany 43:122. [307] Subrahmanyan, R. 1946. In B. Sahni, ed. M. O. P. Iyengar commemoration volume. Indian Botanical Society, Bangalore, Mysore. p. 239.

4. CHROMOSOME NUMBERS: FUNGI

The typically small size of the chromosomes in fungi makes it difficult to obtain accurate counts (generally determined at meiosis), and chromosome numbers must often be considered as estimates. Many counts of $n = 2$ have probably resulted from a confusion of the telophase spindles with chromosomes grouped in two masses at each pole. Classification adapted from Bessey, *Morphology and Taxonomy of Fungi*, 1950.

	Family and Species	Haploid Number	Reference
	(A)	(B)	(C)
	Mycetozoa		
	Ceratiomyxaceae		
1	*Ceratiomyxa fruticulosa*	8	98,151, 154, 343
	Physaraceae		
2	*Badhamia panicea*	8	152
3	*B. utricularis*	8	152,153, 202
4	*Fuligo septica*	6	122
5		ca. 87	266
6	*Physarella oblonga*	ca. 50	266
7	*Physarum didermoides*	8	152
8	*P. polycephalum*	ca. 90	266
	Didymiaceae		
9	*Didymium nigripes*	8	283
10		ca. 24-25	317
11	*D. nigripes xanthopus*	4	37
12		ca. 75	317
	Stemonitaceae		
13	*Comatricha nigra*	ca. 30	318
	Lamprodermaceae		
14	*Lamproderma arcyrionema*	ca. 53	267
	Cribrariaceae		
15	*Dictydium cancellatum*	ca. 25	266
	Tubiferaceae		
16	*Tubifera microsperma*	ca. 60	266
	Reticulariaceae		
17	*Reticularia lycoperdon*	4	347
18		ca. 6	202
	Trichiaceae		
19	*Hemitrichia vesparium*	90 ± 4	343
20	*Oligonema* sp.	8	181
21	*Trichia decipiens*	6	299
22		8	181
23	*T. persimilis*	8	181
	Arcyriaceae		
24	*Arcyria cinerea*	8	181
25	*A. nutans*	8	181
26	*A. pomiformis*	8	181
	Dictyosteliaceae		
27	*Dictyostelium discoideum*	7	342,344
28	*D. mucoroides*	4	288
29	*Polysphondylium violaceum*	8 or 9	344
	Plasmodiophoraceae		
30	*Ligniera junci*	8	50
	Plasmodiophoraceae		
31	*Plasmodiophora brassicae*	4	147
32		8	128,157, 210,316
33	*Sorodiscus callitrichis*	4	350
34	*S. heterantherae*	4-6	332
35	*S. radicicolus*	2?	51
36	*Sorosphaera veronicae*	4	147,330
37		8	210
38	*Spongospora subterranea*	4	146
39		8	249
40	*Tetramyxa parasitica*	ca. 8	210
	Phycomycetes		
	Olpidiaceae		
41	*Olpidium viciae*	4-5	188
	Synchytriaceae		
42	*Synchytrium australe*	5	166
43	*S. decipiens*	4	296
44	*S. endobioticum*	5	54
45		6	129
46	*S. fulgens*	5	189
47	*S. minutum*	5	187
48	*S. papillatum*	4	253
49	*S. ranunculi*	5	167
50	*S. taraxici*	4	18
	Rhizidiaceae		
51	*Asterophlyctis sarcoptoides*	ca. 5	6
52	*Rhizophydium coronum*	6-8	117
	Cladochytriaceae		
53	*Cladochytrium replicatum*	6-9?	164
54	*Polychytrium aggregatum*	5-6	1
	Physodermataceae		
55	*Physoderma pulposa*	4	201
56	*Urophlyctis alfalfae*	4	348
	Anisolpidiaceae		
57	*Anisolpidium ectocarpii*	5	165
	Blastocladiaceae		
58	*Allomyces arbuscula*	6	125
59		16[1]	341
60	*A. cystogenus*	14	341
61	*A. javanicus javanicus*	13-21	341
62	*A. javanicus macrogynus*	14-50+	81
63	*A. kniepii*	6	290
	Olpidiopsidaceae		
64	*Olpidiopsis achlyae*	6	219

/1/ n = 8-32 in various isolates of *A. arbuscula*.

continued

4. CHROMOSOME NUMBERS: FUNGI

	Family and Species	Haploid Number	Reference
	(A)	(B)	(C)
	Phycomycetes		
	Olpidiopsidaceae		
65	*Olpidiopsis vexans*	ca. 6	20
	Saprolegniaceae		
66	*Achlya bisexualis*	8 or more	257
67	*A. colorata*	3	355
68	*A. conspicua*	4	229
69	*A. debaryana*	8	231
70		11	206
71	*A. flagellata*	4	229,352
72	*A. megasperma*	5	355
73	*A. prolifera*	11	206
74	*A. racemosa*	4-6	38
75	*A. recurva*	4	355
76	*Aphanomyces levis*	12-18	168
77	*Brevilegnia diclina*	4-8	52
78	*Isoachlya anisospora*	78	26
79	*I. intermedia*	6	355
80	*Leptolegnia caudata*	ca. 8	53
81	*Saprolegnia ferax*	7 or more	142
82	*S. litoralis*	7	355
83	*S. mixta*	11	206
84	*S. monoica*	ca. 10-14	43
85		11	206
86	*S. thureti*	11	206
87	*Thraustotheca clavata*	5	281
88		11	285
89	*T. primoachlya*	5	355
	Pythiaceae		
90	*Phytophthora erythroseptica*	4-6	234,235
91	*P. himalayensis*	3	233
92	*Pythium debaryanum*	8	223
93	*P. deliense*	4 or 8?	269-271
94	*P. ultimum*	6-8	306
	Albuginaceae		
95	*Albugo bliti*	6	294
96		12	307
97	*A. candida*	8	130
98		12	307
99		12-16	61,182, 319
100	*A. evolvuli*	8?	305
101	*A. lepigoni*	4-5	268
102	*A. portulacae*	8	131,297
103		12	307
104		12-16	23
105	*A. tragopogonis*	8	130
106		12	307
	Peronosporaceae		
107	*Basidiophora entospora*	8	130
108	*Peronospora effusa*	6-8	307
109	*P. ficariae*	8	130
110		16	182
111	*P. fulva*	8	130
112	*P. leptosperma*	8	130
113	*P. media*	8	130
114	*P. tanaceti*	8	130
115	*P. viciae*	8	130
116	*Plasmopara pygmaea*	6	130
117	*P. viticola*	14-16	7,32
118	*Sclerospora graminicola*	ca. 4	295
119		10	130
120		14	216
	Mucoraceae		
121	*Absidia spinosa*	12	55
	Mucoraceae		
122	*Mucor hiemalis*	2	224
123	*M. silvaticus*	2	224
124	*Phycomyces nitens*	2	224
125		ca. 12	36
126	*Sporodinia grandis*	2	193
127	*Zygorhynchus moelleri*	2	224
	Entomophthoraceae		
128	*Ancylistes closterii*	2	58
129	*Basidiobolus ranarum*	ca. 60	241
130	*Entomophthora americana*	8	262
131	*E. sphaerosperma*	12?	280
	Ascomycetes		
	Laboulbeniaceae		
132	*Laboulbenia chaetophora*	4	85
133	*L. gyrinidarum*	4	85
	Dermatocarpaceae		
134	*Dermatocarpon aquaticum*	8	228,298
135	*D. cinereum*	8	228
136	*D. lachneum*	8	228
137	*Endocarpon miniatum*	4	57
	Collemaceae		
138	*Collema pulposum*	5-6(12?)	11
	Peltigeraceae		
139	*Peltigera canina*	2	226
140		4	208
141	*P. horizontalis*	2	226
142	*P. polydactyla*	2	226
143	*P. rufescens*	2	226
	Physciaceae		
144	*Physcia ciliaris*	8	57,103
	Pezizaceae		
145	*Aleuria* sp.	4(8?)	2
146	*A. aurantia*	2(4?)	92
147	*A. rutilans*	8(16?)	89
148		16	102,345
149	*Ascobolus equinus*	4-5	28
150	*A. immersus*	16(8?)	256
151	*A. magnificus*	4(8?)	112
152		8	353
153	*A. stercorarius*	4(8?)	91
154		8	118
155		16	27
156	*Ascodesmis microscopica*	4	57
157	*Ascophanus aurora*	2(4?)	114
158	*A. granulatus*	4(8?)	91,110
159	*Ciliaria hirta*	4	126
160	*Geopyxis catinus*	16	103
161	*Humarina leucoloma*	6	255
162		8	126
163	*Lamprospora constellatio*	6	126
164	*L. haemastigma*	6	126
165	*L. leiocarpa*	4	238
166	*Melastiza charteri*	4	126
167	*Otidea vitellina*	8	126
168	*Patella abundans*	8?	90
169	*P. albida*	8	126
170	*P. albocincta*	6-7	84
171	*P. melaloma*	2(4?)	108
172		4	246,248
173		6	126
174	*P. scutellata*	4	71
175		5	35
176		6	126
177		6(12?)	113

continued

4. CHROMOSOME NUMBERS: FUNGI

	Family and Species	Haploid Number	Reference
	(A)	(B)	(C)
	Ascomycetes		
	Pezizaceae		
178	*Patella stercorea*	2(4?)	91
179		4	259
180	*Paxina acetabulum*	6	126
181	*P. hispida*	8	126
182	*Peziza bolarioides*	16	15
183	*P. cerea*	8	102
184	*P. domiciliana*	8	282
185	*P. micropus*	8	126
186	*P. ochracea*	6	126
187	*P. praetervisa*	8	238
188	*P. repanda*	8	118
189	*P. saniosa*	8	126
190	*P. subumbrina*	4?	214
191	*P. succosa*	4	209,259
192		8	104,126
193	*P. venosa*	6	126
194	*P. vesiculosa*	4(8?)	92
195		8	102,126, 227
196	*Plectania coccinea*	8	238
197	*Pyronema domesticum*	7?	303
198	*P. omphalodes*	4	59,258
199		6	126
200		6(12?)	111
201		10	121
202		12	44,137, 218,227, 346
203	*Rhyparobius* sp.	ca. 8	19
204	*Scodellina leporina*	8	102,126
205	*Sepultaria arenicola*	8	126
	Helvellaceae		
206	*Helvella atra*	6	126
207	*H. crispa*	2(4?)	40
208		6	126
209		8	227
210	*H. lacunosa*	6	126
211	*Morchella deliciosa*	12?	323
212	*M. esculenta*	4	57,208
	Phacidiaceae		
213	*Coccomyces hiemalis*	4	13
214	*Cryptomyces pteridis*	5-6	176
215	*Rhytisma acerinum*	4	209
216		5	158
	Dermeaceae		
217	*Bulgaria inquinans*	6	126
218	*Pseudopeziza medicaginis*	4	259
219	*P. trifolii*	4	160
	Helotiaceae		
220	*Arachnopeziza aurelia*	4	259
221	*Helotium citrinum*	6	126
	Sclerotiniaceae		
222	*Botryotinia fuckeliana*	4?	172
223	*Monilinia fructicola*	4	134
224	*Sclerotinia trifoliorum*	6	29
225		8	88
226	*S. tuberosa*	8	238
	Geoglossaceae		
227	*Cudonia circinans*	6	126
228	*Geoglossum glabrum*	ca. 8	156
229	*G. hirsutum*	4	72
230	*Leotia lubrica*	8	126
231	*Mitrulla phalloides*	4	74
	Geoglossaceae		
232	*Spathularia clavata*	4	71,73
233		6	126
	Tuberaceae		
234	*Hydnobolites* sp.	4-5	84
	Taphrinaceae		
235	*Taphrina alni-incanae*	2	70
236	*T. auria*	2	70
237	*T. betulae*	2	70
238	*T. bullata*	2	70
239	*T. crataegi*	2	70
240	*T. deformans*	4	126,213
241	*T. institiae*	2	70
242	*T. pruni*	2	70
	Melanosporaceae		
243	*Gelasinospora autosteira*	6	301
244	*G. calospora*	6	220,301
245	*G. cerealis*	7	301
246	*Melanospora* spp.	4	313
247		8?	69
248	*Neurospora* sp. (8-spored)	7	86
249	*N. crassa*	7	215,286
250		9	199
251	*N. sitophila*	7	68,86
252	*N. tetrasperma*	6	47,56
253		7	68,86
	Sordariaceae		
254	*Pleurage anserina*	6	132
255	*P. curvula*	7	132
256	*P. curvula coronifera*	7	132
257	*P. decipiens*	7	132
258	*P. fimiseda*	6 or 7	132
259	*P. minuta* (4- and 8-spored)	6 or 7	132
260	*P. zygospora*	6	132
261	*Sordaria fimicola*	7	39,132
262		8	126
263	*S. macrospora*	7	132
264	*Sporormia obliquisepta*	8-10	331
	Chaetomiaceae		
265	*Chaetomium globosum*	2?	310
	Ophiostomataceae		
266	*Ceratocystis autographa*	2	17
267	*C. moniliformis*	4	230
268	*C. piceae*	2	17
269	*Ophiostoma fimbriata*	1?	4
270		3	109
271	*O. moniliformis*	1?	5
	Gnomoniaceae		
272	*Glomerella cingulata*	4	204,333
273	*Gnomonia erythrostoma*	4	34
274	*G. ulmea*	2?	251
	Phyllachoraceae		
275	*Phyllachora ambrosiae*	ca. 12	222
276	*P. graminis*	4	173
	Nectriaceae		
277	*Calonectria rigidiuscula*	7	138
278	*Gibberella cyanogena*	4	77
279	*G. lateritium*	6	138
280	*G. roseum*	6	138
281	*Nectria episphaeria coccophila*	7	138
282	*N. flava*	4	99
283	*N. ribis*	4	314
	Hypocreaceae		
284	*Hypomyces solani*	6	136
285	*H. solani cucurbitae*	2,3,4?	136

continued

4. CHROMOSOME NUMBERS: FUNGI

	Family and Species	Haploid Number	Reference
	(A)	(B)	(C)
	Ascomycetes		
	Hypocreaceae		
286	*Hypomyces solani cucurbitae*	4	78
287	*H. thyrianus*	4?	208
	Clavicipitaceae		
288	*Cordyceps agariciformis*	2	155
289	*C. mulitaris*	2	312
	Dothideaceae		
290	*Dothidea insculpta*	4	133
	Pseudosphaeriaceae		
291	*Cochliobolus sativus*	8	148
292	*Ophiobolus graminis*	4	159
293	*Teichospora* sp.	4	239
	Pleosporaceae		
294	*Physalospora obtusa*	10	10
295	*Pleospora gäumanii*	>5	232
296	*Venturia inaequalis*	4-6	12
297		7	63,163
	Stigmateaceae		
298	*Stigmatea geranii*	4	144
	Erysiphaceae		
299	*Erysiphe cichoracearum*	4	75,259
300	*E. communis*	8	119
301	*E. galeopsidis*	4	72
302	*E. polygoni*	4	75
303	*E. tortilis*	4	72
304	*Microsphaera alni*	4	72
305		8	273
306	*M. astragali*	4	25
307	*M. berberidis*	4	72
308	*M. glossulariae*	4	75
309	*M. quercina*	4-5	259
310	*Phyllactinia corylea*	4	75,259
311		8	91,124, 126
312		10	49
313	*Podosphaera oxyacanthae*	4	75
314	*Sphaerotheca castagnei*	4	57
315	*S. fuliginea*	8	145
316	*S. humuli*	4	75
317	*S. mors-uvae*	4	25
318	*Uncinula aceris*	4	75
319	*U. clandestina*	4	72
320	*U. salicis*	4	75
	Perisporiaceae		
321	*Perisporium funiculatum*	4	22
	Capnodiaceae		
322	*Apiosporium meridionale*	4?	8
	Aspergillaceae		
323	*Aspergillus albus*	2	324
324	*A. aureus*	2	324
325	*A. awamori*	2	324
326	*A. clavatus*	2	324
327	*A. fumigatus*	2	324
328	*A. giganteus*	2	324
329	*A. glaucus*	2	324
330	*A. gymnosardae*	2	324
331	*A. melleus*	2	324
332	*A. nidulans*	4	252
333		8	80
334	*A. niger*	2	324,339
335	*A. ochraceus*	2	324
336	*A. ostianus*	2	324
337	*A. varians*	2	324
	Aspergillaceae		
338	*Penicillium* sp.	2	79
339	*P. crustaceum*	2	284
340	*P. cyclopium*	6-7	260
341	*Thielavia basicola*	ca. 5	205
342	*T. sepedonium*	4	82
	Myriangiaceae		
343	*Myriangium curtisii*	4	221
344	*M. duriaei*	4	221
	Elaphomycetaceae		
345	*Ascoscleroderma cyanosporum*	4(8?)	45
346	*Elaphomyces cervinus*	4(8?)	45
347	*E. leveillei*	4(8?)	45
	Trichocomaceae		
348	*Trichocoma paradoxa*	4	31
	Ascosphaeriaceae		
349	*Ascosphaera apis*	4	291
	Endomycetaceae		
350	*Eremascus albus*	6	65,66
	Ascoideaceae		
351	*Ascoidea rubescens*	2	311
	Spermophthoraceae		
352	*Spermophthora gossypii*	ca. 8	105
	Schizosaccharomycetaceae		
353	*Schizosaccharomyces octosporus*	4	340
354	*S. pombe*	2	14
	Saccharomycetaceae		
355	*Ashbya gossypii*	4	106
356	*Eremothecium ashbyii*	ca. 4	107
357	*Nematospora phaseoli*	4-5	349
358	*Saccharomyces bayanus*	8-10	198
359	*S. cerevisiae*	1[a]	300
360		2	14
361		2[a]	64,287, 302
362		3[a]	237
363		4	95
364		4[a]	169
365		5[a]	194
366		6[a]	197,292
367	*S. ellipsoideus*	2[a]	94
368		4?	261
369	*Zygosaccharomyces priorianus*	3[a]	196
	Torulopsidaceae		
370	*Torula utilis*	4	236
	Basidiomycetes		
	Melampsoraceae		
371	*Coleosporium campanulae*	4	200
372	*C. helianthi*	8	243
373	*C. senecionis*	2	275
374	*C. sidae*	8	274
375	*C. sonchi-arvensis*	2	275
376		6-10	143
377	*C. tussilaginis*	8	186
378		8-10	9
379	*C. vernoniae*	8	247
380	*Cronartium flaccidum*	2	207
381	*C. ribicola*	8	46
382	*Melampsora betulina*	2	275
383	*M. biglowii*	4	279
384	*M. helioscopiae*	2	275
385	*Thekopsora areolata*	2	275

/a/ Computed from the diploid number.

continued

4. CHROMOSOME NUMBERS: FUNGI

	Family and Species	Haploid Number	Reference
	(A)	(B)	(C)
	Basidiomycetes		
	Melampsoraceae		
386	*Thekopsora hydrangeae*	4	244
	Pucciniaceae		
387	*Endophyllum euphorbiae-sylvaticae*	2	225,275
388	*E. sempervivi*	2	207
389		8	141
390	*Gymnosporangium clavariaeforme*	2	275
391		5	30
392	*G. clavipes*	8	24
393	*G. juniperi-virginianae*	2	293
394		8	24
395	*G. nidus-avis*	8	24
396	*G. sabinae*	2	275
397	*G. transformans*	8	24
398	*Ochrospora sorbi*	10 or more	289
399	*Phragmidium rubi*	2	275
400	*P. speciosum*	2	42
401	*P. subcorticium*	2	225
402	*Puccinia arenariae*	4	200,217
403	*P. asteris*	4	217
404	*P. bunii*	2	207
405	*P. buxi*	2	225
406	*P. carthami*	6	217
407	*P. coronata calamagrostis*	3	217
408	*P. coronata secalis*	3	217
409	*P. falcariae*	2	67
410	*P. graminis*	2	275
411		6	217
412	*P. helianthi*	6	217
413	*P. liliacearum*	2	207
414	*P. malvacearum*	4	217,279
415		5	3
416	*P. polygoni*	2	275
417	*P. rubigo-vera*	2	275
418	*P. sorghi*	4	279
419		6	217
420	*P. violae*	2	225
421	*P. xanthi*	4	217
422	*Triphragmium isopyri*	2	275
423	*T. ulmariae*	2	275
424		8	242
425	*Uromyces aloës*	6	304
426	*U. betae*	2	275
427	*U. erythronii*	2	275
428	*U. fabae*	4	279
429	*U. ficariae*	2	275
430	*U. hyperici*	4	279
	Ustilaginaceae		
431	*Sorosporium consanguineum*	2	140
432	*Sphacelotheca cruenta*	2	308,329
433	*S. reilianum*	2	308
434	*S. sorghi*	2	329
435	*Ustilago avenae*	2	150,171, 329
436	*U. crameri*	2	326
437	*U. halophila*	2	140
438	*U. hordei*	2	150,171, 327,329
439	*U. hypodytes*	2	171
440	*U. kolleri*	2	329
	Ustilaginaceae		
441	*U. longissima*	2	329
442	*U. nuda*	2	329
443	*U. scabiosae*	8-10[3]	120
444	*U. spegazinii agrostis*	2	140
445	*U. striiformis poae-pratensis*	2?	192
446	*U. violacea*	2	328,329
447	*U. williamsii*	2	140
448	*U. zeae*	2	174
	Tilletiaceae		
449	*Entyloma microsporum*	2?	60
450	*E. ranunculi*	2	171
451	*Tilletia rugispora*	2-3	139
452	*T. tritici*	2	174,329
453		4	354
454	*Urocystis anemones*	2?	60
	Auriculariaceae		
455	*Auricularia mesenterica*	2	207
456		4	127
457	*A. judae*	4	127
458	*Eocronartium muscicola*	4	87
459	*Helicogloea lagerheimi*	5	16
460	*Jola javensis*	2 or more	96
	Septobasidiaceae		
461	*Septobasidium alveolatum*	5?	245
462	*S. apiculatum*	5?	245
463	*S. grandisporum*	5?	245
464	*S. jamaicense*	5?	245
465	*S. septobasidioides*	5?	245
466	*S. sinuosum*	5?	245
	Dacrymycetaceae		
467	*Calocera cornea*	2	207
468	*C. viscosa*	6	127
469	*Dacrymyces* sp.	4	97,321
470	*D. deliquescens*	2	207
471	*Guepinia rufa*	6	127
	Tremellaceae		
472	*Exidia glandulosa*	4	335
473	*E. nucleata*	4	335
474	*E. recisa*	4	335
475	*E. saccharina*	4	335
476	*Phlogiotis helvelloides*	2	207
477	*Sebacina calcea*	8	351
478	*S. deminuta*	3	336
479	*S. effusa*	2	207
480	*S. epigaea*	3	336
481	*S. fugacissima*	3	336
482	*S. gloeocystidiata*	2?	183
483	*Tremella* sp.	4	321
484	*T. foliacea*	6	127
485	*T. frondosa*	4	334
486	*T. gemmata*	2?	183
487	*T. grilletii*	4	334
488	*T. mesenterica*	4	334
489		6	127
490	*T. tubercularia*	4	337
491	*Tremellodon gelatinosum*	4	115
492		6	127
	Tulasnellaceae		
493	*Tulasnella violea*	ca. 4	161
494		6-8	265
	Exobasidiaceae		
495	*Exobasidium andromedae*	ca. 2	207

/3/ Uncertain whether n or $2n$.

continued

4. CHROMOSOME NUMBERS: FUNGI

	Family and Species	Haploid Number	Reference
	(A)	(B)	(C)
	Basidiomycetes		
	Exobasidiaceae		
496	*Exobasidium discoideum*	2?	175
	Thelephoraceae		
497	*Coniophora arida*	4	170
498	*C. puteana*	4	170
499	*Corticium comedens*	2	207
500	*C. rolfsii*	4	100
501	*C. serum*	2	179
502	*C. varians*	2	179
503	*Cyphella ampla*	2	207
504	*C. villosa*	8	127
505	*Peniophora livida*	4 or 8?	338
506	*Sparassis crispa*	4	127
507	*S. laminosa*	4	127
508	*Stereum hirsutum*	6	127
509	*S. insignitum*	6	127
510	*S. sanguinolentum*	6	127
511	*Thelephora terrestris*	4	127
512	*Tomentella subtilis*	4-6?	123
513	*T. terrestris*	4	178
	Cantharellaceae		
514	*Cantharellus aurantiacus*	6	127
515	*C. cibarius*	ca. 2	162
516		6	127
517	*C. cinereus*	2	207
518	*C. minor*	6	325
519	*C. tubaeformis*	6	127
520	*Craterellus clavatus*	2	162
521	*C. cornucopioides*	ca. 2	162
522		4	325
523		6	127
524	*C. pistillaris*	ca. 3-4	162
525	*Leptotus bryophilus*	2	207
	Clavariaceae		
526	*Clavaria abietina*	6	127
527	*C. aurea*	3-4	162
528	*C. botrytis*	4	325
529	*C. corniculata*	6	127
530	*C. cristata*	4	325
531	*C. formosa*	6	127
532	*C. fusiformis*	6	127
533	*C. inaequalis*	4	325
534	*C. ligula*	3-4	162
535	*C. mucida*	4	325
536	*C. pallida*	6	127
537	*C. pistillaris*	ca. 4	162
538		6	127
539	*C. purpurea*	4	325
540	*C. rugosa*	2	207
541		6	127
542	*C. stricta*	6	127
543	*C. vermicularis*	4	325
544		6	127
	Hydnaceae		
545	*Hydnum coralloides*	6	127
546	*H. erinaceus*	6	127
547	*H. repandum*	6	127
548	*Mycoleptodon ochraceum*	4	127
549	*Pleurodon auriscalpium*	6	127
550	*Radulum quercinum*	4	127
551	*Sarcodon abietinum*	6	127
	Meruliaceae		
552	*Merulius tremellosus*	4	127
553	*Phlebia merismoides*	4	127
	Fistulinaceae		
554	*Fistulina hepatica*	2	207
555		4	127,325
	Polyporaceae		
556	*Coriolus versicolor*	6	127
557	*Ganoderma applanatum*	4	127
558	*Irpex pachyodon*	4	127
559	*Lenzites betulina*	6	127
560	*L. quercina*	6	127
561	*L. tricolor*	6	127
562	*Leptoporus adustus*	4	127
563	*L. albidus*	4	127
564	*L. tephroleucus*	4	127
565	*Leucoporus brumalis*	6	127
566	*Melanopus picipes*	6	127
567	*M. varius*	6	127
568	*Phaeolus fibrillosus*	6	127
569	*P. schweinitzi*	6	127
570	*Polyporus borealis*	8	127
571	*P. frondosus*	8	127
572	*P. giganteus*	8	127
573	*P. intybaceus*	8	127
574	*P. squamosus*	4	325
575		8	127
576	*P. sulfureus*	8	127
577	*Polystictus cinnabarinus*	4	325
578	*Poria mucida*	4	127
579	*P. vaporaria*	4	127
580	*Spongipellis spumens*	4	127
581	*Trametes cervina*	6	127
582	*T. gibbosa*	6	127
583	*T. odorata*	6	127
584	*T. trogi*	6	127
585	*Ungulina annosa*	4	127
586	*U. betulina*	4	127
587	*U. fraxinea*	4	127
588	*Xanthochrous perennis*	4	127
	Boletaceae		
589	*Boletus albellus*	3-4	195
590	*B. badius*	8	127
591	*B. bovinus*	8	127
592	*B. castaneus*	3-4	195
593	*B. chrysenteron*	3-4	195
594		8	127
595	*B. edulis*	6	325
596	*B. erythropus*	8	127
597	*B. flavus*	2	207
598	*B. granulatus*	3-4	195
599	*B. luridus*	4	325
600	*B. luteus*	4	325
601	*B. regius*	2	207
602	*B. vermiculosus*	3-4	195
603	*B. versipellis*	3-4	195
	Agaricaceae		
604	*Acanthocystis geogenius*	4	127
605	*Agaricus campestris*	4	276,277
606		9	48
607		12	149
608	*A. campestris bisporus*	12	83
609	*A. perrara*	2	135
610	*Amanita caesaria*	4	264
611	*A. citrina*	6	127
612	*A. junquillea*	6	127
613	*A. muscaria*	6-8	320
614	*A. pantherina*	2	207
615	*A. phalloides*	6	127

continued

4. CHROMOSOME NUMBERS: FUNGI

	Family and Species	Haploid Number	Reference
	(A)	(B)	(C)
	Basidiomycetes		
	Agaricaceae		
616	*Amanita spissa*	6	127
617	*Armillaria mellea*	4	177
618		6	127
619	*A. mucida*	4 or more	180
620	*Camarophyllus virgineus*	4	21
621	*Claudopus variabilis*	8	127
622	*Clitocybe aurantiaca*	2	207
623	*C. brumalis*	8	127
624	*C. cerussata*	8	127
625	*C. cyathyformis*	8	127
626	*C. laccata*	6	325
627	*C. nebularis*	8	127
628	*Clitopilus mundulus*	8	127
629	*C. prunulus*	8	127
630	*Collybia butyracea*	8	127
631	*C. conigena*	8	127
632	*C. fusipes*	8	127
633	*C. maculata*	8	127
634	*C. radicata*	4	325
635	*C. velutipes*	4	325
636	*Conocybe tenera*	6	127
637	*Coprinus atramentarius*	4	315,325
638		8	127
639	*C. ephemerus bisporus*	8-10	278
640	*C. fimetarius*	4	254
641	*C. hendersonii*	2(4?)	41
642	*C. lagopus*	2(4?)	41
643		8	62,127
644	*C. micaceus*	4	322
645		8	127
646	*C. plicatilis*	8	127
647	*C. radiatus*	2	207
648	*C. tomentosus*	2(4?)	41
649	*Cortinarius acutus*	8	127
650	*C. albo-violaceus*	8	127
651	*C. cinnamomeus*	4	322
652	*C. dibaphus*	8	127
653	*C. elatior*	8	127
654	*C. erythrinus*	8	127
655	*C. impennis*	8	127
656	*C. sanguineus*	8	127
657	*C. semisanguineus*	8	127
658	*C. torvus*	8	127
659	*C. violaceus*	8	127
660	*Cortinellus shiitake*	6	325
661	*Crepidotus mollis*	8	127
662	*C. nidulans*	8	127
663	*Cystoderma amiantinum*	8	127
664	*C. carcharias*	8	127
665	*C. granulosum*	8	127
666	*Deconica atrorufa*	6	127
667	*Entoloma bloxami*	8	127
668	*E. rhodopolium*	8	127
669	*Flammula carbonaria*	8	127
670	*F. hybrida*	8	127
671	*F. penetrans*	8	127
672	*F. sapinea*	8	127
673	*Galera hypnorum*	6	127
674	*G. pymaeoaffinis*	6	127
675	*G. spartea*	6	127
676	*G. spicula*	6	127
677	*Gomphidius glutinosus*	6	127
678	*G. roseus*	6	127
	Agaricaceae		
679	*Gomphidius viscidus*	6	127
680	*Hebeloma crustuliniforme*	8	127
681	*H. fastibile*	8	127
682	*H. hiemalis*	8	127
683	*H. longicaudum*	8	127
684	*H. sinapizans*	8	127
685	*H. sinuosum*	8	127
686	*Hygrocybe agathosmos*	2	207
687	*H. ceracea*	2	207
688	*H. conica*	2	93,207
689	*H. constans*	2?	183
690	*H. lucorum*	2	207
691	*Hygrophorus coccineus*	8	127
692	*H. cossus*	8	127
693	*H. hypothejus*	8	127
694	*H. niveus*	8	127
695	*H. olivaceo-albus*	8	127
696	*H. pustulatus*	8	127
697	*H. psittacinus*	8	127
698	*H. reai*	8	127
699	*Hypholoma appendiculatum*	2	207
700		6	325
701	*H. capnoides*	6	127
702	*H. cotonea*	6	127
703	*H. fasciculare*	2	322
704		6	127
705	*H. hydrophilum*	6	127
706	*H. perplexum*	8 or more	240
707	*H. scobinaceum*	6	127
708	*H. sublateritium*	6	127
709	*Inocybe asterospora*	8	127
710	*I. bresadolae*	8	127
711	*I. caesariata*	8	127
712	*I. corydalina*	8	127
713	*I. geophylla*	8	127
714	*I. piriodora*	8	127
715	*I. rimosa*	4	325
716	*I. sindonia*	8	127
717	*Laccaria amethystina*	8	127
718	*L. laccata*	8	127
719	*L. proxima*	8	127
720	*Lacrymaria velutina*	6	127
721	*Lactarius akahatsu*	6	325
722	*L. aurantiacus*	6	127
723	*L. blennius*	6	127
724	*L. chrysorrheus*	6	127
725	*L. deliciosus*	2	207
726	*L. hepaticus*	6	127
727	*L. mitissimus*	6	127
728	*L. quietus*	6	127
729	*L. rufus*	6	127
730	*L. salmonicolor*	6	127
731	*L. tabidus*	6	127
732	*L. torminosus*	6	127
733	*L. vellereus*	4	272
734		6	325
735	*L. zonarius*	6	127
736	*Lentinus cochleatus*	6	127
737	*L. tigrinus*	6	127
738	*L. variabilis*	2 or more	185
739	*Lepiota acutesquamosa*	6	101
740	*L. clypeolaria*	8	127
741	*L. fuliginosa*	8	127
742	*L. fulvella*	8	127
743	*L. lenticularis*	4	116

continued

4. CHROMOSOME NUMBERS: FUNGI

	Family and Species	Haploid Number	Reference
	(A)	(B)	(C)
	Basidiomycetes		
	Agaricaceae		
744	*Lepiota procera*	8	127
745	*L. semi-nuda*	8	127
746	*Lepista inversa*	6	127
747	*Leptonia euchroa*	8	127
748	*L. lampropoda*	8	127
749	*Macrocystidia cucumis*	6	127
750	*Marasmius androsaceus*	8	127
751	*M. peronatus*	8	127
752	*M. rotula*	8	127
753	*Melanoleuca humilis*	8	127
754	*M. vulgaris*	8	127
755	*Mycena epipterigia*	8	127
756	*M. fellea*	8	127
757	*M. flavescens*	8	127
758	*M. galericulata*	2	207
759		4	325
760		6-12	184
761		8	127
762	*M. haematopoda*	6	322
763		8	127
764	*M. inclinita*	8	127
765	*M. pura*	8	127
766	*M. rosella*	8	127
767	*M. viscosa*	8	127
768	*Naucoria sideroides*	8	127
769	*Nolanea hirtipes*	6	127
770	*Nyctalis asterophora*	4	127
771	*Octojuga variabilis*	6	127
772	*Omphalia fibula*	8	127
773	*O. schwartzii*	8	127
774	*Panaeolina foenisecii*	6	127
775	*Panellus stipticus*	4	127
776	*Panus torulosus*	6	127
777	*Paxillus atromentosus*	4	127
778	*P. involutus*	2	207
779		4	127
780	*Pholiota* sp.	2	322
781	*P. aurivella*	4	212
782	*P. destruens*	8	127
783	*P. lucifera*	2	207
784	*P. mutabilis*	8	127
785	*P. praecox*	6-8	320
786	*P. subsquarrosa*	8	127
787	*Pleurotus candidissimus*	6	127
788	*P. colombinus*	6	127
789	*P. conchatus*	6	127
790	*P. eryngii*	6	127
791	*P. lignatilis*	6	127
792	*P. ostreatus*	4	322
793		6	127
794	*P. pulmonarius*	6	127
795	*P. ulmarius*	6	127
796	*Pluteus cervinus*	8	127
797	*P. chrysophaeus*	8	127
798	*P. salicinus*	8	127
799	*Psalliota lepiotoides*	8	127
800	*P. radicata*	8	127
801	*P. silvicola*	8	127
802	*P. xanthoderma*	8	127
803	*Psathyrella disseminata*	2	207
804		4	325
805	*P. gracilis*	8	127
806	*P. hydrophila*	8	127

	Family and Species	Haploid Number	Reference
	(A)	(B)	(C)
	Agaricaceae		
807	*Pseudocoprinus disseminatus*	8	127
808	*Psilocybe semilanceata*	6	127
809	*P. uda*	6	127
810	*Rhodopaxillus nudus*	8	127
811	*R. sordidus*	8	127
812	*Rozites caperata*	8	127
813	*Russula atropurpurea*	6	127
814	*R. cyanoxantha*	6	127
815	*R. emetica*	4	263,325
816		6	127
817	*R. fallax*	6	127
818	*R. fellea*	6	127
819	*R. fragilis*	4	325
820		6	127
821	*R. fragilis nivea*	6	325
822	*R. lepida*	6	127
823	*R. mairei*	6	127
824	*R. ochraleuca*	6	127
825	*R. persicina*	6	127
826	*R. sardonia*	6	127
827	*R. subfoetans*	4	322
828	*R. virescens*	4	325
829	*Schizophyllum commune*	3	76
830		4	127
831	*Stropharia aeruginosa*	6	127
832	*S. coronilla*	6	127
833	*S. inuncta*	6	127
834	*S. semiglobata*	2	207
835	*Tricholoma album*	8	127
836	*T. argyraceum*	8	127
837	*T. columbetta*	8	127
838	*T. equestre*	8	127
839	*T. melaleucum*	4	325
840	*T. pessundatum*	8	127
841	*T. rutilans*	2	322
842		8	127
843	*T. saponaceum*	8	127
844	*T. sulfureum*	8	127
845	*Volvaria gloiocephala*	6	127
	Hydnangiaceae		
846	*Hydnangium carmeum*	2	309
847		5-6	250
	Clathraceae		
848	*Anthurus aseroeformis*	4	127
849	*Clathrus cancellatus*	4	127
	Phallaceae		
850	*Ithyphallus impudicus*	4	127
851	*Mutinus caninus*	4	127
	Sclerodermataceae		
852	*Pisolithus tinctorius*	4	191
853	*Scleroderma lycoperdoides*	2	190
854	*S. vulgare*	2	207
855		6	127
	Nidulariaceae		
856	*Cyathus olla*	2	211
857	*Nidularia globosa*	2	93,207
	Sphaerobolaceae		
858	*Sphaerobolus tubulosus*	3-4	203
	Lycoperdaceae		
859	*Bovista gigantea*	6	127
860	*B. plumbea*	6	127
861	*Calvatia candida*	2	33
862	*Lasiosphaera fenzlii*	4	325
863	*Lycoperdon caelatum*	2	207
864	*L. echinatum*	6	127

continued

4. CHROMOSOME NUMBERS: FUNGI

	Family and Species	Haploid Number	Reference
	(A)	(B)	(C)
	Basidiomycetes		
	Lycoperdaceae		
865	*Lycoperdon excipuliforme*	2	207
866	*L. gemmatum*	2	325
867	*L. piriforme*	2	207
	Lycoperdaceae		
868	*Lycoperdon piriforme*	6	127
	Geastraceae		
869	*Geaster hygrometricus*	2	325
870	*Geastrum fimbriatum*	2	33,207
	Tylostomataceae		
871	*Tylostoma mammosum*	4	101

Contributor: Olive, Lindsay S.

References: [1] Ajello, L. 1948. Am. J. Botany 35:1. [2] Aldinger, L. 1936. Ibid. 23:639. [3] Allen, R. 1933. Phytopathology 23:572. [4] Andrus, C. F., and L. L. Harter. 1933. J. Agr. Research 46:1059. [5] Andrus, C. F., and L. L. Harter. 1937. Ibid. 54:19. [6] Antikajian, G. 1949. Am. J. Botany 36:245. [7] Arens, K. 1929. Jahrb. wiss. Botan. 70:57. [8] Arnaud, G. 1912. Compt. rend. 155:726. [9] Ashworth, D. 1934. Cellule 43:187. [10] Aycock, R. 1951. Phytopathology 41:459. [11] Bachmann, F. M. 1913. Arch. Zellforsch. 10:369. [12] Backus, E. J., and G. W. Keitt. 1940. Bull. Torrey Botan. Club 67:765. [13] Backus, M. P. 1933. Ibid. 60:611. [14] Badian, J. 1937. Bull. intern. acad. polon. sci., B, 5:61. [15] Bagchee, K. 1925. Ann. Botany (London) 39:217. [16] Baker, G. 1936. Ann. Missouri Botan. Garden 23:69. [17] Bakshi, B. K. 1951. Ann. Botany (London), n.s. 15:53. [18] Bally, W. 1911. Jahrb. wiss. Botan. 50:95. [19] Barker, B. T. 1904. Rept. Brit. Assoc. Advances Sci. 74:825. [20] Barrett, J. T. 1912. Ann. Botany (London) 26:209. [21] Bauch, R. 1926. Z. Botan. 18:337. [22] Beatus, R. 1938. Jahrb. wiss. Botan. 87:301. [23] Berlese, A. N. 1898. Ibid. 31:159. [24] Berliner, M. D. 1954. Am. J. Botany 41:93. [25] Bezssonoff, N. 1914. Compt. rend. 158:1123. [26] Bhargava, K. S. 1946. Trans. Brit. Mycol. Soc. 29:101. [27] Björling, K. 1941. Kgl. Fysiograf. Sällskap. Lund Förh. 11:46. [28] Björling, K. 1944. Ibid. 14:147. [29] Björling, K. 1951. Phytopathol. Z. 18:129. [30] Blackman, V. H. 1904. Ann. Botany (London) 18:323. [31] Boedijn, K. 1935. Ann. Jard. Botan. Buitenzorg 44:243. [32] Bosc, M. 1946. Compt. rend. 223:584. [33] Brandza, M., and T. Solacolu. 1932. Publs. soc. nat. Romania 11:1. [34] Brooks, F. T. 1910. Ann. Botany (London) 24:585. [35] Brown, W. H. 1911. Botan. Gaz. 52:275. [36] Burgeff, H. 1915. Flora (Ger.) 108:353. [37] Cadman, E. 1931. Trans. Roy. Soc. Edinburgh 57:93. [38] Carlson, M. C. 1929. Ann. Botany (London) 43:111. [39] Carr, A. J. H., and L. S. Olive. 1958. Am. J. Botany 45:142. [40] Carruthers, C. 1911. Ann. Botany (London) 25:243. [41] Chow, C. H. 1934. Botaniste 26:89. [42] Christman, A. H. 1905. Botan. Gaz. 39:267. [43] Claussen, P. 1908. Ber. deut. botan. Ges. 26:144. [44] Claussen, P. 1912. Z. Botan. 4:1. [45] Clémencet, M. 1932. Botaniste 24:3. [46] Colley, R. H. 1918. J. Agr. Research 15:619. [47] Colson, B. 1934. Ann. Botany (London) 48:211. [48] Colson, B. 1935. Ibid. 49:1. [49] Colson, B. 1938. Ibid., n.s. 2:381. [50] Cook, W. R. I. 1928. Ibid. 42:347. [51] Cook, W. R. I. 1931. Ann. Mycol. Notitiam Sci. Mycol. Univ. 29:313. [52] Cooper, G. O. 1929. Trans. Wisconsin Acad. Sci. 24:309. [53] Couch, J. N. 1932. Am. J. Botany 19:584. [54] Curtis, K. M. 1921. Trans. Roy. Soc. (London), B, 210:409. [55] Cutter, V. M. 1942. Bull. Torrey Botan. Club 69:480. [56] Cutter, V. M. 1946. Mycologia 38:693. [57] Dangeard, P. A. 1903. Botaniste 9:35. [58] Dangeard, P. A. 1906. Ibid. 9:59. [59] Dangeard, P. A. 1907. Ibid. 10:1. [60] Das, M. C. 1949. J. Indian Phytopathol. Soc. 2:108. [61] Davis, B. M. 1900. Botan. Gaz. 29:297. [62] Day, P. R. 1958. Abstr. Commun. 7th Intern. Congr. Microbiol. 7:54. [63] Day, P. R., D. M. Boone, and G. W. Keitt. 1956. Am. J. Botany 43:835. [64] DeLamater, E. D. 1949. Ibid. 36:808. [65] DeLamater, E. D., and L. Schwartz. 1952. Science 115:481. [66] DeLamater, E. D., S. Yaverbaum, and L. Schwartz. 1953. Am. J. Botany 40:475. [67] Dittschlag, E. 1910. Centr. Bakteriol. Parasitenk. 28:473. [68] Dodge, B. O., J. R. Singleton, and A. Rolnick. 1950. Proc. Am. Phil. Soc. 94:38. [69] Doguet, G. 1955. Botaniste 39:1. [70] Eftimiu, P. 1927. Ibid. 18:1. [71] Eftimiu, P. 1929. Ibid. 20:228. [72] Eftimiu, P. 1929. Bull. soc. botan. France 76:10. [73] Eftimiu, P. 1929. Compt. rend. 188:267. [74] Eftimiu, P. 1933. Notationes Biol. (Bucharest) 1:1. [75] Eftimiu, P., and S. Kharbush. 1928. Botaniste 20:157. [76] Ehrlich, H. G., and E. S. McDonough. 1949.

continued

Am. J. Botany 36:360. [77] El-Ani, A. S. 1956. Science 123:850. [78] El-Ani, A. S. 1957. Am. J. Botany 43:769. [79] Elisei, F. G. 1939. Ist. botan. univ. Pavia Atti, Ser. 4, 11:13. [80] Elliott, C. G. 1960. Genet. Research 1:462. [81] Emerson, R., and C. M. Wilson. 1954. Mycologia 46:393. [82] Emmons, C. W. 1932. Bull. Torrey Botan. Club 59:415. [83] Evans, H. J. 1956. Nature 178:1005. [84] Faull, J. H. 1905. Proc. Boston Soc. Nat. Hist. 32:77. [85] Faull, J. H. 1912. Ann. Botany (London) 26:325. [86] Fincham, J. R. S. 1949. Ibid., n.s. 13:23. [87] Fitzpatrick, H. M. 1918. Am. J. Botany 5:397. [88] Frandsen, K. J. 1946. Studier over *Sclerotinia trifoliorum* Eriksson. Danske Forlag, Copenhagen. [89] Fraser, H. C. I. 1907. Ann. Botany (London) 21:307. [90] Fraser, H. C. I. 1913. Ibid. 27:553. [91] Fraser, H. C. I., and W. E. S. Brooks. 1909. Ibid. 23:537. [92] Fraser, H. C. I., and E. J. Welsford. 1908. Ibid. 22:465. [93] Fries, R. E. 1911. Svensk Botan. Tidskr. 5:241. [94] Fuhrmann, F. 1906. Centr. Bakteriol. Parasitenk. 15:769. [95] Ganeson, A. T. 1959. Compt. rend. trav. lab. Carlsberg 31:149. [96] Gäumann, E. 1922. Ann. Mycol. Notitiam Sci. Mycol. Univ. 20:272. [97] Gilbert, E. M. 1922. Trans. Wisconsin Acad. Sci. 20:387. [98] Gilbert, H. C. 1935. Am. J. Botany 22:52. [99] Gilles, A. 1947. Cellule 51:371. [100] Goto, K. 1936. Ann. Phytopathol. Soc. Japan 6:101. [101] Greis, H. 1937. Jahrb. wiss. Botan. 84:448. [102] Guilliermond, A. 1904. Rev. gén. botan. 16:129. [103] Guilliermond, A. 1905. Ann. Mycol. Notitiam Sci. Mycol. Univ. 3:343. [104] Guilliermond, A. 1909. Compt. rend. 149:350. [105] Guilliermond, A. 1928. Rev. gén. botan. 40:397. [106] Guilliermond, A. 1928. Ibid. 40:474. [107] Guilliermond, A. 1936. Rev. mycol. 1:115. [108] Gwynne-Vaughan, H. C. I. 1937. Ann. Botany (London), n.s. 1:99. [109] Gwynne-Vaughan, H. C. I., and Q. U. Broadhead. 1936. Ibid. 50:747. [110] Gwynne-Vaughan, H. C. I., and H. S. Williamson. 1930. Ibid. 44:127. [111] Gwynne-Vaughan, H. C. I., and H. S. Williamson. 1931. Ibid. 45:355. [112] Gwynne-Vaughan, H. C. I., and H. S. Williamson. 1932. Ibid. 46:653. [113] Gwynne-Vaughan, H. C. I., and H. S. Williamson. 1933. Ibid. 47:375. [114] Gwynne-Vaughan, H. C. I., and H. S. Williamson. 1934. Ibid. 48:261. [115] Hagerup, O. 1944-45. Friesia 3:46. [116] Hagerup, O. 1944-45. Ibid. 3:96. [117] Hanson, A. 1945. Am. J. Botany 32:479. [118] Harper, R. A. 1895. Ber. deut. botan. Ges. 13:67. [119] Harper, R. A. 1897. Jahrb. wiss. Botan. 30:249. [120] Harper, R. A. 1899. Trans. Wisconsin Acad. Sci. 12:475. [121] Harper, R. A. 1900. Ann. Botany (London) 14:321. [122] Harper, R. A. 1900. Botan. Gaz. 30:217. [123] Harper, R. A. 1902. Ibid. 33:1. [124] Harper, R. A. 1905. Carnegie Inst. Wash. Publ. 37. [125] Hatch, W. R. 1935. Ann. Botany (London) 49:623. [126] Heim, P. 1952. Rev. mycol. 17:3. [127] Heim, P. 1954. Ibid. 19:201. [128] Heim, P. 1955. Ibid. 20:131. [129] Heim, P. 1956. Ibid. 21:93. [130] Heim, P. 1958. Ibid. 23:373. [131] Heim, P. 1959. Compt. rend. 248:1012. [132] Heslot, H. 1958. Rev. cytol. et biol. végétales 19:1. [133] Hess, H., and E. Müller. 1951. Ber. schweiz. botan. Ges. 61:5. [134] Heuberger, J. W. 1934. Bull. Maryland Agr. Exptl. Sta. 371:167. [135] Hirmer, M. 1920. Z. Botan. 12:657. [136] Hirsch, H. 1949. Am. J. Botany 36:113. [137] Hirsch, H. 1950. Mycologia 42:301. [138] Hirsch, H., W. C. Snyder, and H. N. Hansen. 1949. Ibid. 41:411. [139] Hirschhorn, E. 1941. Lilloa 21:25. [140] Hirschhorn, E. 1945. Mycologia 37:217. [141] Hoffman, A. W. H. 1912. Centr. Bakteriol. Parasitenk. 32:137. [142] Höhnk, W. 1935. Naturw. Verein Bremen 29:308. [143] Holden, R. J., and R. A. Harper. 1903. Trans. Wisconsin Acad. Sci. 14:63. [144] Holm, L. 1952. Cellule 54:295. [145] Homma, Y. 1934. Trans. Sapporo Nat. Hist. Soc. 13:173. [146] Horne, A. S. 1911. Rept. Brit. Assoc. Advances Sci. 80:572. [147] Horne, A. S. 1930. Ann. Botany (London) 44:199. [148] Hrushovetz, S. B. 1956. Can. J. Botany 34:641. [149] Hughes, D. T. 1961. Nature 190:285. [150] Hüttig, W. 1931. Z. Botan. 24:529. [151] Jahn, E. 1908. Ber. deut. botan. Ges. 26:342. [152] Jahn, E. 1911. Ibid. 29:231. [153] Jahn, E. 1933. Ibid. 51:377. [154] Jahn, E. 1936. Ibid. 54:517. [155] Jenkins, W. A. 1934. Mycologia 26:220. [156] Jolivette, H. D. M. 1910. Trans. Wisconsin Acad. Sci. 16:1171. [157] Jones, P. M. 1928. Arch. Protistenk. 62:313. [158] Jones, S. G. 1925. Ann. Botany (London) 39:41. [159] Jones, S. G. 1926. Ibid. 40:607. [160] Jones, S. G. 1930. Trans. Roy. Soc. Edinburgh 56:507. [161] Juel, H. O. 1897. Bih. svensk. VetenskAkad. Handl. 23(12). [162] Juel, H. O. 1916. Nova Acta Regiae Soc. Sci. Upsaliensis, Ser. 4, 6. [163] Julian, J. B. 1958. Can. J. Botany 36:607. [164] Karling, J. S. 1937. Mem. Torrey Botan. Club 19:1. [165] Karling, J. S. 1943. Am. J. Botany 30:637. [166] Karling, J. S. 1955. Ibid. 42:37. [167] Karling, J. S. 1955. Mycologia 47:130. [168] Kasanowski, V. 1911. Ber. deut.

continued

botan. Ges. 29:210. [169] Kater, M. 1927. Biol. Bull. 52:436. [170] Kemper, W. 1937. Zentr. Bakteriol. Parasitenk. 97:100. [171] Kharbush, S. S. 1927. Ann. sci. nat. Botan. et biol. végétale 10:285. [172] Kharbush, S. S. 1927. Bull. soc. botan. France 74:257. [173] Kharbush, S. S. 1927. Rev. pathol. végétale et entomol. agr. France 14:267. [174] Kharbush, S. S. 1928. Ibid. 15:48. [175] Kharbush, S. S. 1929. Bull. soc. botan. France 76:560. [176] Killian, K. 1918. Z. Botan. 10:49. [177] Kniep, H. 1911. Ibid. 3:529. [178] Kniep, H. 1913. Ibid. 5:593. [179] Kniep, H. 1915. Ibid. 7:369. [180] Kniep, H. 1916. Ibid. 8:353. [181] Kränzlin, H. 1907. Arch. Protistenk. 89:170. [182] Krüger, F. 1910. Centr. Bakteriol. Parasitenk. 27:186. [183] Kühner, R. 1926. Botaniste 17:1. [184] Kühner, R. 1927. Ibid. 18:169. [185] Kühner, R. 1928. Bull. trimestr. soc. mycol. France 44:331. [186] Kursanov, L. I. 1915. Sci. Mem. Imp. Moscow Univ. Nat. Sci. Sect. Publ. 36. [187] Kusano, S. 1907. Tokyo Botan. Mag. 21:118. [188] Kusano, S. 1912. J. Coll. Agr. Imp. Univ. Tokyo 4:141. [189] Kusano, S. 1930. Ibid. 10:347. [190] Lander, C. 1933. Botan. Gaz. 95:330. [191] Lander, C. 1935. J. Elisha Mitchell Sci. Soc. 51:173. [192] Leach, J. G., and M. A. Ryan. 1946. Phytopathology 36:876. [193] Lendner, A. 1908. Bull. Herb. Boissier 8:77. [194] Levan, A. 1947. Hereditas 33:457. [195] Levine, M. 1913. Bull. Torrey Botan. Club 40:137. [196] Lietz, K. 1951. Arch. Mikrobiol. 16:275. [197] Lindegren, C. C. 1945. Mycologia 37:767. [198] Lindegren, C. C., and M. M. Rafalko. 1950. Exptl. Cell Research 1:169. [199] Lindegren, C. C., and S. Rumann. 1938. J. Genet. 36:395. [200] Lindfors, T. 1924. Svensk Botan. Tidskr. 18:1. [201] Lingappa, Y. 1959. Am. J. Botany 46:233. [202] Lister, A. 1893. J. Linnean Soc. London Botany 29:529. [203] Lorenz, F. 1933. Arch. Protistenk. 81:361. [204] Lucas, G. B. 1946. Am. J. Botany 33:802. [205] Lucas, G. B. 1949. Mycologia 41:553. [206] Mäckel, H. G. 1928. Jahrb. wiss. Botan. 69:517. [207] Maire, R. 1902. Thesis. Paris. [208] Maire, R. 1904. Compt. rend. soc. biol. 56:822. [209] Maire, R. 1905. Ann. Mycol. Notitiam Sci. Mycol. Univ. 3:123. [210] Maire, R., and A. Tison. 1909. Ibid. 7:226. [211] Malinowski, E. 1913. Compt. rend. soc. sci. et lettres Varsovie 6:582. [212] Martens, P., and R. Vandendries. 1933. Cellule 41:335. [213] Martin, E. 1940. Am. J. Botany 27:743. [214] Matsuura, H., and A. Gondo. 1935. J. Fac. Sci. Hokkaido Imp. Univ., V, 3:205. [215] McClintock, B. 1945. Am. J. Botany 32:671. [216] McDonough, E. S. 1937. Mycologia 29:151. [217] McGinnis, R. C. 1956. J. Heredity 47:255. [218] McIntosh, D. L. 1951. Ph. D. Thesis. Univ. Toronto. [219] McLarty, D. A. 1941. Bull. Torrey Botan. Club 68:75. [220] Meyer, J. 1957. Cellule 58:345. [221] Miller, J. H. 1938. Mycologia 30:158. [222] Miller, J. H. 1951. Am. J. Botany 38:830. [223] Miyake, K. 1901. Ann. Botany (London) 15:653. [224] Moreau, F. 1913. Thesis. Paris. [225] Moreau, F. 1914. Thesis. Paris. [226] Moreau, F., and F. Moreau. 1915. Compt. rend. 160:526. [227] Moreau, F., and F. Moreau. 1931. Rev. gén. botan. 43:465. [228] Moreau, F., and F. Moreau. 1932. Ibid. 44:305. [229] Moreau, F., and F. Moreau. 1935. Compt. rend. 201:1208. [230] Moreau, F., and F. Moreau. 1952. Rev. mycol., n.s. 17:141. [231] Mücke, M. 1908. Ber. deut. botan. Ges. 26:367. [232] Müller, E. 1951. Ber. schweiz. botan. Ges. 61:165. [233] Mundkur. B. D. 1949. Botan. Gaz. 110:475. [234] Murphy, P. A. 1914. Ann. Botany (London) 28:735. [235] Murphy, P. A. 1918. Ibid. 32:115. [236] Naidu, M. B., and V. M. Bakshi. 1946. Current Sci. (India) 15:164. [237] Naidu, M. B., and V. M. Bakshi. 1946. Ibid. 15:231. [238] Nardi, R. 1930. Bull. trimestr. soc. mycol. France 46.97. [239] Nichols, M. A. 1896. Botan. Gaz. 22:301. [240] Nichols, S. P. 1905. Trans. Wisconsin Acad. Sci. 15:30. [241] Olive, E. W. 1907. Ann. Mycol. Notitiam Sci. Mycol. Univ. 5:404. [242] Olive, E. W. 1908. Ann. Botany (London) 22:331. [243] Olive, L. S. 1942. J. Elisha Mitchell Sci. Soc. 58:43. [244] Olive, L. S. 1943. Ibid. 59:45. [245] Olive, L. S. 1943. Mycologia 35:557. [246] Olive, L. S. 1949. Science 110:185. [247] Olive, L. S. 1949. Am. J. Botany 36:41. [248] Olive, L. S. 1950. Ibid. 37:757. [249] Osborn, B. 1911. Ann. Botany (London) 25:327. [250] Petri, L. 1902. Nuovo giorn. botan. ital. 9:499. [251] Pomerleau, R. 1938. Contribs. inst. botan. univ. Montréal. 31. [252] Pontecorvo, G., E. Forbes, and O. B. Adam. 1949. Heredity 3:385. [253] Quintanilha, A. 1926. Bol. soc. broter., Ser. 2, 3:110. [254] Quintanilha, A. 1935. Ibid., Ser. 2, 10:289. [255] Racovitza, M., and A. Racovitza. 1945. Bull. sect. sci. acad. roumaine 28:247. [256] Ramlow, G. 1914. Mycolog. Centr. 5:177. [257] Raper, J. R. 1936. J. Elisha Mitchell Sci. Soc. 52:274. [258] Raymond, J. 1933. Compt. rend. 197:932. [259] Raymond, J. 1934. Botaniste 26:371. [260] Rees, H., and J. L. Jinks. 1952.

continued

Proc. Roy. Soc. (London), B, 140:100. [261] Renaud, J. 1938. Compt. rend. 206:1918. [262] Riddle, L. W. 1906. Rhodora 8:67. [263] Ritchie, D. D. 1941. Am. J. Botany 28:582. [264] Ritchie, D. D. 1948. Botan. Gaz. 109:521. [265] Rogers, D. P. 1932. Ibid. 94:86. [266] Ross, I. K. 1961. Am. J. Botany 48:244. [267] Ross, I. K. 1960. Mycologia 52:621. [268] Ruhland, W. 1903. Jahrb. wiss. Botan. 39:135. [269] Saksena, M. R. K. 1936. Rev. gén. botan. 48:156. [270] Saksena, M. R. K. 1936. Ibid. 48:215. [271] Saksena, M. R. K. 1936. Ibid. 48:273. [272] Salmon, J. 1937. Rev. cytol. et cytophisiol. végétales 2:376. [273] Sands, M. C. 1907. Trans. Wisconsin Acad. Sci. 15:733. [274] Sanwal, B. D. 1953. Bull. Torrey Botan. Club 80:205. [275] Sappin-Trouffy, P. 1896. Botaniste 5:59. [276] Sarazin, A. 1938. Compt. rend. 206:275. [277] Sass, J. E. 1928. Papers Mich. Acad. Sci. 9:287. [278] Sass, J. E. 1929. Am. J. Botany 16:663. [279] Savile, D. B. O. 1939. Ibid. 26:585. [280] Sawyer, W. H. 1931. Mycologia 23:411. [281] Schrader, E. 1938. Flora (Ger.) 32:125. [282] Schultz, E. S. 1927. Am. J. Botany 14:307. [283] Schünemann, E. 1930. Planta 9:645. [284] Schürhoff, P. N. 1907. Beih. botan. Zentr. 22:294. [285] Shanor, L. 1937. J. Elisha Mitchell Sci. Soc. 53:119. [286] Singleton, J. R. 1953. Am. J. Botany 40:124. [287] Sinoto, Y., and A. Yuasa. 1941. Cytologia (Tokyo) 11:464. [288] Skupienski, F. X. 1918. Compt. rend. 167:960. [289] Soong, T.-F. 1939. Flora (Ger.) 133:345. [290] Sörgel, G. 1936. Nachr. Ges. Wiss. Göttingen math.-physik. Kl., VI, 2:155. [291] Spiltoir, C. F. 1955. Am. J. Botany 42:501. [292] Srinath, K. V. 1946. Current Sci. (India) 15:50. [293] Stevens, E. 1930. Botan. Gaz. 89:394. [294] Stevens, F. L. 1899. Ibid. 28:225. [295] Stevens, F. L. 1902. Ibid. 38:300. [296] Stevens, F. L., and A. C. Stevens. 1903. Ibid. 35:405. [297] Stevens, R. B. 1940. Mycologia 32:46. [298] Stevens, R. B. 1941. Am. J. Botany 28:59. [299] Strasburger, E. 1894. Ann. Botany (London) 8:281. [300] Subramaniam, M. K., and B. Ranganathan. 1945. Current Sci. (India) 14:78. [301] Sun, S. H., J. Alexopoulos, and G. B. Wilson. 1954. Cytologia (Tokyo) 19:255. [302] Swellengrebel, M. 1905. Ann. inst. Pasteur 19:503. [303] Tandy, G. 1927. Ann. Botany (London) 41:321. [304] Thirumalachar, M. J. 1946-47. Botan. Gaz. 108:245. [305] Thirumalachar, M. J. 1948-49. Ibid. 110:487. [306] Trow, A. H. 1901. Ann. Botany (London) 15:269. [307] Tsang, K. C. 1929. Botaniste 21:1. [308] Vaheeduddin, S. 1942. Minn. Agr. Expt. Sta. Tech. Bull. 154. [309] Van Bambeke, C. 1903. Acad. roy. Belg. Cl. sci. Mém. 54:44. [310] Van der Weyen, A. 1954. Cellule 56:213. [311] Varitchak, B. 1928. Compt. rend. 186:96. [312] Varitchak, B. 1931. Botaniste 23:1. [313] Vincens, F. 1916. Compt. rend. 163:572. [314] Vincens, F. 1917. Thesis. Paris. [315] Vokes, M. 1931. Botan. Gaz. 91:194. [316] Von Prowazek, S. 1905. Arb. kaiserl. Gesundh. 22:396. [317] Von Stosch, H. A. 1935. Planta 23:623. [318] Von Stosch, H. A. 1937. Ber. deut. botan. Ges. 55:362. [319] Wager, H. 1896. Ann. Botany (London) 10:295. [320] Wager, H. 1911. Brit. Assoc. Advance. Sci. Rept. 81:775. [321] Wager, H. 1914. Naturalist (London), p. 364. [322] Wakayama, K. 1930. Cytologia (Tokyo) 1:369. [323] Wakayama, K. 1930. Ibid. 2:27. [324] Wakayama, K. 1931. Ibid. 2:291. [325] Wakayama, K. 1932. Ibid. 3:260. [326] Wang, C. S. 1943. Phytopathology 33:1122. [327] Wang, D. T. 1932. Compt. rend. 195:1041. [328] Wang, D. T. 1932. Ibid. 195:1417. [329] Wang, D. T. 1934. Botaniste 26:539. [330] Webb, C. R. 1935. Ann. Botany (London) 49:41. [331] Wells, D. E. 1957. Am. J. Botany 43:761. [332] Wernham, C. C. 1935. Mycologia 27:262. [333] Wheeler, H. E., et al. 1948. Am. J. Botany 35:722. [334] Whelden, R. M. 1934. Mycologia 26:415. [335] Whelden, R. M. 1935. Ibid. 27:41. [336] Whelden, R. M. 1935. Ibid. 27:503. [337] Whelden, R. M. 1935. Rhodora 37:121. [338] Whelden, R. M. 1936. Am. J. Botany 23:539. [339] Whelden, R. M. 1940. Mycologia 32:630. [340] Widra, A., and E. D. DeLamater. 1955. Am. J. Botany 42:423. [341] Wilson, C. M. 1952. Bull. Torrey Botan. Club 79:139. [342] Wilson, C. M. 1952. Proc. Natl. Acad. Sci. U. S. 38:659. [343] Wilson, C. M., and I. K. Ross. 1955. Am. J. Botany 42:743. [344] Wilson, C. M., and I. K. Ross. 1957. Ibid. 44:345. [345] Wilson, I. 1937. Ann. Botany (London), n.s. 1:655. [346] Wilson, I. 1952. Ibid., n.s. 16:321. [347] Wilson, M., and E. Cadman. 1928. Trans. Roy. Soc. Edinburgh 55:555. [348] Wilson, O. T. 1920. Botan. Gaz. 70:51. [349] Wingard, S. A. 1925. Bull. Torrey Botan. Club 52:249. [350] Winge, O. 1913. Arkiv Botan. 12(9):4. [351] Wittlake, E. B. 1938. Univ. Iowa Studies Nat. Hist. 17:351. [352] Wolf, F. T. 1938. Mycologia 30:456. [353] Wood, J. L. 1953. Bull. Torrey Botan. Club 80:1. [354] Yen, W.-Y. 1936. Compt. rend. soc. biol. 121:1304. [355] Ziegler, A. W. 1953. Am. J. Botany 40:60.

5. CHROMOSOME NUMBERS: BRYOPHYTES

Chromosome number is for the gametophyte. No attempt has been made to indicate whether counts were observed or calculated from mitotic figures of sporophyte or gametophyte, or from meiotic figures of spore mother cells. Parentheses following the total count in column B give the number of ordinary large chromosomes plus the number of small *m*-chromosomes. Previous chromosome lists of bryophytes have been consulted in the preparation of this table [8, 11, 12, 38, 39, 87, 164-166, 184, 193-195]. Authorities and synonymy for species were submitted by the contributor but have not been included in the table because of space limitations; such information can be obtained by consulting the appropriate reference. Sequence of families: Hepaticae according to Evans [41], and Musci according to Brotherus [20, 21].

	Family and Species	Haploid Number	Reference
	(A)	(B)	(C)
	Hepaticae		
	Haplomitriaceae		
1	*Calobryum blumei*	9	84
2	*C. rotundifolium*	9	150
3		10	151
4	*Haplomitrium hookeri*	9	15,84
	Ptilidiaceae		
5	*Herberta longifissa*	9	152
6	*H. remotiusculifolia*	9	153
7	*Isotachis japonica*	9	151
8	*Ptilidium pulcherrimum*	9	151
9	*Trichocolea tomentella*	9	52,151
10	*Trichocoleopsis bisseti*	9	151
11	*T. sacculata*	9	151
	Lepidoziaceae		
12	*Bazzania albicans*	9	150
13	*B. bidentula*	9	152,153
14	*B. madothecoides*	9	152,153
15	*B. magna*	9	152,153
16	*B. nodulosa*	9	152,153
17	*B. pompeana*	9	151
18	*B. pseudotriangularis*	9	152,153
19	*B. remotifolia*	9	152,153
20	*B. trilobata*	9-10	52
21	*B. yakushimensis*	9	151
22	*Lepidozia subtransversa*	9	152
	Calypogeiaceae		
23	*Calypogeia fissa*	18	84
24	*C. neesiana*	9	151
25	*C. suecica*	8+x/y	84
26		8-9	52
27	*C. tosana*	9	151
28	*C. trichomanis*	18	84
	Cephaloziaceae		
29	*Cephalozia bicuspidata*	18	109
30		36	52
31	*C. lammersiana*	27	109
32	*Nowellia curvifolia*	9	151
33	*Odontoschisma denudatum*	9	151
34	*Zoopsis liukiuensis*	9	151
	Lophocoleaceae		
35	*Chiloscyphus bescherelli*	9	151
36	*C. himalayensis*	9	103
37	*C. polyanthus*	9	151
38	*Leptoschyphus verrucosus*	9	151
39	*Lophocolea bidentata*	9	52
40		18	103
41	*L. ciliolata*	8	43
42	*L. formosana*	9	152,153
43	*L. heterophylla*	9	109
44	*L. minor*	9	109
	Harpanthaceae		
45	*Saccogyna bidentula*	9	152,153
46	*S. curiossisima*	9	151,152
	Jungermanniaceae		
47	*Anastrophyllum yakushimensis*	9	151
	Jungermanniaceae		
48	*Chandonanthus birmensis*	9	148
49	*C. hirtellus*	9	151
50	*Gymnocolea inflata*	9	84
51	*Jamesoniella verrucosa*	9	153
52	*Jungermannia fauriana*	9	151
53	*J. lanceolata*	9	151
54	*J. thermarum*	9	151
55	*Lophozia cornuta*	9	151
56	*L. formosana*	9	151
57	*L. hatcheri*	8-9	52
58	*L. ventricosa*	8-9	52
59	*Nardia geoscyphus*	18	52
60	*N. insecta*	36	109
61	*N. scalaris*	9	84
62	*Schiffneria viridis*	9	151
63	*Solenostoma ovicalyx*	9	151
64	*Sphenolobus yakushimensis*	9	148,151
65	*Tritomaria exsecta*	9	52
66	*T. exsectiformis*	18	52
	Plagiochilaceae		
67	*Plagiochila accedens*	9	103
68	*P. asplenioides*	8+x/y	52
69		9	84
70		10	66
	Scapaniaceae		
71	*Diplophyllum albicans*	8	83
72	*D. serrulatum*	9	151
73	*Microdiplophyllum plicatum*	9	151
74	*Scapania bolanderi*	9	152
75	*S. parvitexta*	9	151
76	*S. plagiochiloides*	9	152,153
77	*S. undulata*	8	43
78		9	151
	Schistochilaceae		
79	*Schistochila nuda*	9	151
	Porellaceae		
80	*Porella appendiculata*	8	103
81	*P. densifolia*	8	128,151
82	*P. denticulata*	8	103
83	*P. gollani*	8	103
84	*P. grandiloba*	8	152
85	*P. japonica*	8	128,151
86	*P. macroloba*	8	103
87	*P. perrottetiana*	8	128,151
88	*P. setigera*	8	128,151
89	*P. tosana*	8	128,151
90	*P. ulophylla*	8	151
91	*P. vernicosa*	8	151
	Radulaceae		
92	*Radula complanata*	6	142
93		12	103
94		16	57
95	*R. flaccida*	6	14
96	*R. kojana*	6	142
97	*R. lindbergiana*	8	84
98	*R. valida*	8	151

continued

5. CHROMOSOME NUMBERS: BRYOPHYTES

	Family and Species	Haploid Number	Reference
	(A)	(B)	(C)
	Hepaticae		
	Pleuroziaceae		
99	*Pleurozia giganteoides*	8	151
	Frullaniaceae		
100	*Frullania africana*	9	14
101	*F. amplicrania*	♂8, ♀9	161
102	*F. aoshimensis*	9	161
103	*F. boninensis*	9	146
104	*F. densiloba*	9	161
105	*F. dilitata*	♂8, ♀9	84,151
106	*F. diversitexta*	9	161
107	*F. fauriana*	♂8, ♀9	151
108	*F. fragilifolia*	9	84
109	*F. hamatiloba*	♂8, ♀9	161
110	*F. hampeana*	♂8, ♀9	161
111	*F. jackii*	17	84
112	*F. japonica*	♂8, ♀9	161
113	*F. kagoshimensis*	♂8, ♀9	161
114	*F. makinoana*	9	151
115	*F. mayebarae*	9	161
116	*F. meyeniana*	9	161
117	*F. moniliata*	♂8, ♀9	144
118		♂9	142
119		♂♀9	151
120	*F. moniliata obscura*	9	161
121	*F. moniliata rotundata*	9	151
122	*F. motoyana*	9	161
123	*F. muscicola*	♂8, ♀9	161
124	*F. nishiyamensis*	♂8, ♀9	151
125	*F. nodulosa*	9	161
126	*F. nodulosa nipponica*	♂♀9	156
127	*F. obscurifolia*	9	16
128	*F. ornithocephala*	♂8, ♀9	84
129	*F. osumiensis*	♂8, ♀9	161
130	*F. parvistipula*	♂♀9	161
131	*F. pedicellata*	♂8, ♀9	161
132	*F. retusa*	9	103
133	*F. sackawana*	♂8, ♀9	147
134		♂♀9	161
135	*F. serrata*	8	84
136	*F. spongiosa*	9	16
137	*F. squarrosa*	♂8, ♀9	13
138	*F. taiheizana*	♂8, ♀9	156
139	*F. tamarisci*	9	84
140	*F. tenuicaulis*	9	161
141	*F. truncatifolia*	♂8, ♀9	161
142	*F. usamiensis*	♂8, ♀9	161
143	*F. uvifera*	9	161
144	*F. valida*	♂8, ♀9	161
145	*F. viridis*	♂8, ♀9	151
146	*F. yakushimensis*	♂8, ♀9	151
147	*Jubula hutchinsiae javanica*	9	151
148	*J. japonica*	9	151
	Lejeuneaceae		
149	*Archilejeunea autoica*	9	13
150	*A. elobulata*	9	13
151	*Caudalejeunea hanningtonii*	9	13
152	*Ceratolejeunea zenkeri*	9	14
153	*Cololejeunea dissita*	9	13
154	*Leptocolea longilobula*	9	151
155	*Lopholejeunea aberrantia*	9	153
156	*Mastigolejeunea florea*	9	13
157	*Ptychanthus acuminatus*	9	151
158	*Ptychocoleus emergens*	9	14
	Treubiaceae		
159	*Treubia insignis*	8	47
160		9	84
	Fossombroniaceae		
161	*Fossombronia* sp. "British Cameroons"	ca. 9	14
162	*F. angulosa*	10	84
163	*F. australonipponica*	9	151
164	*F. caespitiformis*	9	52,84
165	*F. dumortieri*	8	43
166	*F. foveolata*	8	43
167	*F. himalayensis*	9	100
168	*F. husnoti*	8-9	52
169	*F. japonica*	9	151
170	*F. longiseta*	8	63
171	*F. pusilla*	8	30
172	*Petalophyllum indicum*	9	100
173	*P. ralfsii*	9	52,84
174	*Sewardiella tuberifera*	9	100,102
	Pelliaceae		
175	*Androcryphia confluens*	9,18	52
176	*Calycularia radiculosa*	8	28
177	*Pellia borealis*	18	84
178	*P. endiviifolia*	8+x/y	53,151
179		8+y	84
180		♂7, ♀9	83
181	*P. epiphylla*	8	43
182		9	53,182
183	*P. neesiana*	8+x/y	53,151
184		♂7, ♀9	83
185		♂♀9	115
	Blasiaceae		
186	*Blasia pusilla*	8	83
187		9	55
188	*Cavicularia densa*	9	151
	Pallaviciniaceae		
189	*Makinoa crispata*	8+x/y	136
190		♂♀9	151
191		♂9	84,198
192		♀9	55
193	*M. hibernica*	9	52
194	*Moerckia blyttii*	8+x/y	84
195	*M. flotowiana*	8+x/y	84
196	*M. hibernica*	9	55,84
197	*Pallavicinia decipiens*	4	42
198	*P. levieri*	8	29
199	*P. longispina*	7+x/y	151
200	*P. lyellii*	7+x/y	151
201		8	104
202		9	181
203	*P. radiculosa*	7+x/y	84
204		8	29
205	*P. zollingeri*	8	29,84
206	*Symphyogyna aspera*	8	90
	Metzgeriaceae		
207	*Metzgeria conjugata*	18-19	57
208	*M. furcata*	8-10	57
	Riccardiaceae		
209	*Cryptothallus mirabilis*	10	81,109
210	*Riccardia blasioides*	9+x/y	151
211	*R. holstii*	ca. 20	14
212	*R. incurvata*	9+x/y	84
213	*R. indica*	6	69
214	*R. latifrons*	10	84
215	*R. makinoana*	9+x/y	151

continued

5. CHROMOSOME NUMBERS: BRYOPHYTES

	Family and Species	Haploid Number	Reference
	(A)	(B)	(C)
	Hepaticae		
	Riccardiaceae		
216	*Riccardia multifida*	10	44
217		20	55,84
218	*R. palmata*	10	55,84
219	*R. pellioides*	9+x/y	151
220	*R. pinguis*	9+x/y	151
221		10	44,52
222	*R. sinuata*	19	55
223		30	84
224	*R. stephanii*	10,20	14
	Monocleaceae		
225	*Monoclea forsteri*	9	116
226	*M. gottschei*?	9	118
	Marchantiaceae		
227	*Bucegia romanica*	8	40
228	*Conocephalum conicum*	8	43
229		8-9	52
230		9	84,133, 158
231	*C. supradecompositum*	8+x/y	151
232		9	84,158
233	*Dumortiera hirsuta*	9	84,158
234		10	114
235		18,27	158
236	*D. hirsuta irrigua*	9	52
237	*D. nepalensis*	18	84
238	*Lunularia cruciata*	8	52
239		9	84
240	*Marchantia calcarea*	9	27,49,56
241		9-18	26
242	*M. cataractarum*	9	49,56
243	*M. cuneiloba*	9	158
244	*M. diptera*	8+x/y,♂♀9	158
245	*M. formosana*	9	151
246	*M. geminata*	9	49
247	*M. grisea*	9,10	50
248	*M. nitida*	9	49,56
249	*M. paleacea*	9	49,52,84
250	*M. palmata*	9	52,85
251	*M. palmata multiradia*	9,18	26
252	*M. palmatoides*	9	49
253	*M. parviloba*	8+x/y, 16+2x/2y	14
254	*M. planiloba*	9	49
255		18	26
256	*M. planiloba walteri*	18	27
257	*M. polymorpha*	9,10,11	49,50
258		8+x/y	84,158
259	*Marchantia radiata*	9	151
260	*M. stenolepida*	9	49,56
261	*M. tosana*	9	158
262	*M. treubii*	9	49,151
263	*Monoselenium tenerum*	8	164
264		9	52,158
265	*Preissia quadrata*	9	48,158
266	*Wiesnerella denudata*	9	151,158
	Rebouliaceae		
267	*Asterella blumeana*	23-27	52
268	*A. chichibuensis*	9	158
269	*A. crassa*	9	158
270	*A. koreana*	9	152
271	*A. lindenbergiana*	9	84,160
272	*A. liukiuensis*	9	151
	Rebouliaceae		
273	*Asterella ludwigii*	18	160
274	*A. monospiris*	9	153
275	*A. pusilla*	9	158
276	*A. sanoana*	9	158
277	*A. stahlii*	9	84
278	*A. umbelliformis*	9	158
279	*A. venosa*	26	52
280	*A. yoshinagana*	9	153
281	*Mannia barbifrons*	9	158
282	*M. brachypoda*	9	158
283	*M. fragrans*	9	84
284	*M. laevigata*	9	158
285	*M. rupestris*	9	84
286	*Plagiochasma* sp. "Hitoyosi"	9	149
287	*P. appendiculatum*	ca. 16	52
288	*P. articulatum*	8	93
289	*P. crenulatum*	ca. 16	52
290	*P. elongatum*	17-18	52
291	*P. intermedium*	9	158
292	*P. nipponica*	9	158
293	*P. reboulioides*	9	151
294	*P. rupestre*	18	109,153
295	*Reboulia hemisphaerica*	9	53,84, 158
296		16	18
	Sauteriaceae		
297	*Athalamia nana*	9	158
298	*Clevea hyalina*	9	84
299	*C. piloti*	9	84
300	*C. rousselliana*	9	52
301	*Peltolepis quadrata*	9	84
302	*P. quadrata japonica*	9	84
303		18,36	158
	Targioniaceae		
304	*Aitchinsoniella* sp.	9	92
305	*Cyathodium africanum*	9	14
306	*C. aureonitens*	9	84
307	*C. barodae*	3	31
308	*Targionia hypophylla*	9	158
309		ca. 24	52
310	*T. lorbeeriana*	27	109
	Corsiniaceae		
311	*Corsinia coriandrina*	16	52
312		18	160
	Ricciaceae		
313	*Oxymitra paleacea*	9	160
314		8+x/y	84
315	*Riccia* sp. "Algier"	8	52
316	*Riccia* sp. "Hiroshima"	8	149
317	*Riccia* sp. "Panape"	16	154
318	*R. arvensis*	8	134
319	*R. austinii*	9	134
320	*R. billardieri*	8	167
321	*R. californica*	9	134
322	*R. campbelliana*	8	134
323	*R. canaliculata*	8	108
324	*R. ciliifera*	8	83
325		7+x/y	84
326	*R. cruciata*	8	68
327		16	167
328	*R. crystallina*	4	79
329		8	68,84, 134
330	*R. curtisii*	8	60,99

continued

5. CHROMOSOME NUMBERS: BRYOPHYTES

	Family and Species	Haploid Number	Reference
	(A)	(B)	(C)
	Hepaticae		
	Ricciaceae		
331	*Riccia curtisii*	7+x/y	84
332	*R. discolor*	8	68,95
333	*R. donnellii*	8,16	134
334	*R. duplex*	16	108
335	*R. fluitans*	8	14,158
336		16	84
337	*R. frostii*	8	17
338	*R. gangetica*	24	167
339	*R. glauca*	8	67
340		9	52,151
341	*R. glauca subinermis*	9	134
342	*R. gougetiana*	8	84
343		10	134
344	*R. himalayensis*	8	94
345	*R. huebeneriana*	8	158
346	*R. intermedia*	8	16
347	*R. intumescens*	8	84
348		ca. 16	16
349	*R. japonica*	8	158
350	*R. lesquereuxii*	9	52
351	*R. melanospora*	16	68
352	*R. membranaceae*	8	14
353	*R. michelii*	10	84
354	*R. miyakeana*	16	158
355	*R. nigerica*	8	14
356	*R. nipponica*	8	158
357	*R. rhenana*	16	108
358	*R. sanguinea*	8	95
359	*R. sorocarpa*	8	84,134, 158
360		9?	52
361	*R. sullivantii*	8	134
362	*R. trichocarpa*	8	134
363	*R. zachariae*	16	108
364	*Ricciocarpus natans*	9	134,158
	Sphaerocarpaceae		
365	*Sphaerocarpos cristatus*	7+x/y	7
366	*S. donnellii*	8	110
367		7+x/y	5,83
368		♂7+y, ♀14+2x	85
369		14+x/y 14+2x/2y	6
370		21+2x/y	91
371	*S. michelii*	7+x/y	86
372	*S. stipitatus*	7+x/y	117
373	*S. texanus*	7+x/y	83,182
374		7?+x/y	125
	Riellaceae		
375	*Riella affinis*	9	118
376	*R. clausonis*	8	74
377	*R. helicophylla*	8+x/y	83,84
378	*R. purpureospora*	8+x/y	117
	Takakiaceae		
379	*Takakia lepidozioides*	4	159
	Anthoceratae		
	Anthocerataceae		
380	*Anthoceros* sp. "Okinawa 1"	5	118
381	*Anthoceros* sp. "Haightsplace"	6	120
382	*A. bulbiculosus*	4+x/y	119
383	*A. carolinianus*	4	78
	Anthocerataceae		
384	*Anthoceros carolinianus*	5-10	119
385	*A. crispus*	5-5+	118
386	*A. dichotomus*	5-6	52,85
387	*A. erectus*	5	101
388	*A. formosae*	6	153
389	*A. himalayensis*	5	101
390	*A. husnoti*	5,9	118
391	*A. japonicus*	6	151
392	*A. kahndalensis*	5	120,151
393	*A. laevis*	4	37,78
394		5	119
395		6	120,151
396		8	82
397	*A. mandoni*	5	118,119
398	*A. miyabeanus*	6	143
399	*A. nagasakiensis*	6	151
400	*A. pearsoni*	5	118
401	*A. punctatus*	4	178
402		5	118
403		6	151
404	*A. tjipanasanus*	6	120
405	*Aspiromitus* sp. "Singapore"	4+"g/m"	120
406	*A. miyabenus*	6	151
407	*A. sampalocensis*	4+"g/m"	120
408	*Megaceros* sp. "Chile 11"	5	118
409	*Megaceros* sp. "Peru 3"	6,8	118
410	*M. tosanus*	6	151
411	*Notothylas indica*	5	101
412	*N. japonica*	6	151
413	*N. levieri*	5	101
414	*N. orbicularis*	5?+ff	118
	Musci		
	Sphagnaceae		
415	*Sphagnum apiculatum*	12(10+2)	137
416		23(19+4)	61
417	*S. balticum*	12(10+2)	137
418	*S. compactum*	12-14 (10+2-4)	137
419		21(19+2)	22
420	*S. cuspidatum*	13-14 (10+3-4)	137
421		21(19+2)	22
422	*S. cuspidatum serrulatum*	21(19+2)	22
423	*S. erythrocalyx*	21(19+2)	22
424	*S. fimbriatum*	16-17 (10+6-7)	137
425		17-19	22
426		23(19+4)	61
427	*S. fuscum*	13-14 (10+3-4)	137
428		23(19+4)	61
429	*S. girgensohnii*	23(19+4)	61
430	*S. inundatum*	38+	61
431	*S. magellanicum*	17-19	22
432	*S. nemoreum*	14-19 (10+4-9)	137
433		23(19+4)	61
434	*S. palustre*	38+	61
435		42(38+4)	22
436	*S. plumulosum*	15-18 (10+5-8)	137
437		23(19+4)	61
438	*S. quinquefarium*	21(19+2)	22

continued

5. CHROMOSOME NUMBERS: BRYOPHYTES

	Family and Species	Haploid Number	Reference
	(A)	(B)	(C)
	Musci		
	Sphagnaceae		
439	*Sphagnum recurvum*	14-15 (10+4-5)	137
440		17-19	22
441	*S. robustum*	24-30 (19+5-11)	137
442		46(38+8)	61
443	*S. rubellum*	23(19+4)	61
444	*S. squarrosum*	20	103
445		21(19+2)	61
446		21-23 (19+2-4)	137
447		23(19+4)	171
448	*S. subsecundum*	21(19+2)	22
449	*S. tabulare*	19,21(19+2)	22
450	*S. tenerum*	25(19+6)	22
451	*S. teres*	23(19+4)	61
452	*S. warnstorfianum*	12-14 (10+2-4)	137
453		23(19+4)	61
	Andreaeaceae		
454	*Andreaea rothii*	10	9
	Fissidentaceae		
455	*Fissidens adiantoides*	19-20	54
456		24	8
457	*F. bryoides*	5	62
458		10	11
459	*F. cristatus*	12	8
460		15(13+2)	4
461		16	193
462	*F. cristatus minor*	16	193
463	*F. elimbatus*	6	121
464	*F. grandifrons*	16	33
465	*F. japonicus*	16	193
466	*F. limbatus*	5	140
467	*F. minutulus*	5	33
468	*F. obtusifolius*	6	33
469	*F. osmundioides*	11	9
470		16	33
471	*F. pauperculus*	12	140
472	*F. planicaulis*	14	196
473	*F. polypodioides*	16	33
474	*F. subbasilaris*	8	33
475	*F. taxifolius*	9	135
476		10	9
477		12	33,62, 105
	Ditrichaceae		
478	*Bruchia brevifolia*	15	24
479	*B. donnellii*	28	24
480	*B. drummondii*	28	24
481	*B. flexuosa*	14	24
482	*B. fusca*	15	24
483	*B. ravenelii*	14	24
484	*B. texana*	15	24
485	*Ceratodon heterophyllus*	13	138
486	*C. purpureus*	11-12	54,56
487		13(12+x/y)	65,130
488		13	11,140, 173
489	*C. purpureus xanthopus*	13	140
490	*C. stenocarpus*	13-15	73
491	*Distichium capillaceum*	14,28	11
492	*D. hageni*	42	138
493	*Ditrichum curritucki*	13	10,24
	Ditrichaceae		
494	*Ditrichum cylindricum*	12	138
495	*D. henryi*	13	10
496	*D. heteromallum*	13	73
497	*D. pallidum*	26	24
498	*D. schimperi*	26	140
499	*D. tortile*	14	73
500	*Pleuridium acuminatum*	26	24
501	*P. bolanderi*	26	140
502	*P. ravenelii*	13	24
503	*P. subulatum*	13	24
504	*Saelania glaucescens*	13	138
505	*Trematodon capillifolius*	15(14+1)	73
506	*T. longicollis*	28	24
507	*T. sabulosus*	15(14+1)	73
	Dicranaceae		
508	*Amphidium lapponicum*	16	11,169
509	*Campylopodium griffithii*	14(13+1)	72
510	*C. khasianum*	36(35+1)	72
511	*Campylopus goughii*	12?	73
512	*C. gracilis*	13	73
513	*C. laetus*	12	73
514	*C. pyriformis*	12	73
515	*Cynodontium alpestre*	14	138
516	*C. strumiferum*	14	11
517		15	169
518	*Dicranella cerviculata*	15	138
519	*D. crispa*	14	11
520		15	138
521	*D. emodivaria*	15(14+1)	73
522	*D. grevilleana*	15	138
523	*D. heteromalla*	13	73,193
524	*D. mollicula*	14	73
525		15	70
526	*D. rufescens*	10	9
527	*D. spiralis*	15	72
528	*D. subulata*	15	11
529	*D. varia*	14	140
530	*D. viridissima*	16	73
531	*Dicranoweisia cirrata*	11	139,140
532	*D. crispula*	11	11
533	*Dicranum caesium*	11	193
534	*D. condensatum*	12	24
535	*D. elongatum*	12	138
536	*D. flagellare*	23	9
537	*D. fuscescens*	12,24	11
538	*D. japonicum*	11	186,193
539	*D. majus*	11	186
540		12	138
541		17(12+5)	169,170
542	*D. nipponense*	11	193
543	*D. rugosum*	11	193
544		12	3,169
545		13(12+1)	62
546	*D. scoparium*	11	193
547		12	3,9,169
548	*D. spadiceum*	12	11
549	*D. spurium*	12	169
550	*D. strictum*	14(12+2)	11
551	*Microcampylopus* sp.	13	72
552	*Oncophorus virens*	14	11,138, 193
553	*O. wahlenbergii*	14	138,193
554	*Oreoweisia laxifolia*	14(13+1)	71-73
555	*Paraleucobryum longifolium*	12	169
556	*Rhabdoweisia fugax*	ca. 12	54
557	*Symblepharis helicophylla*	14(13+1)	73

continued

5. CHROMOSOME NUMBERS: BRYOPHYTES

	Family and Species	Haploid Number	Reference
	(A)	(B)	(C)
	Musci		
	Leucobryaceae		
558	*Leucobryum albidum*	6	9
559	*L. glaucum*	14	59
560	*L. textori*	11	193
561	*Octoblepharum albidum*	13,26	71-73
	Calymperaceae		
562	*Syrrhopodon gardneri*	13	71-73
	Encalyptaceae		
563	*Encalypta alpina*	14	138
564	*E. apophysata*	13	11
565	*E. procera*	27	138
566	*E. rhabdocarpa*	26	138
567	*E. vulgaris mutica*	13	140
	Pottiaceae		
568	*Acaulon rufescens*	26	23
569	*Aloina ambigua*	24(23+1)	140
570	*A. brevirostris*	28	138
571	*Anoectangium strachythecianum*	13	73
572	*A. thomsonii*	13	73
573	*Astomum crispum*	13	124
574	*A. ludovicianum*	13	23
575	*A. muhlenbergianum*	26	23
576	*Barbula agraria*	13	4
577	*B. brachyphylla*	10	140
578	*B. constricta*	13	73
579	*B. convoluta*	11	140
580	*B. cylindrica*	13	171
581	*B. ehrenbergii*	13	73
582	*B. fallax*	13	9
583	*B. flavescens*	13	73
584	*B. unguiculata*	13	65,123,169
585	*B. vinealis*	14	140
586	*Bryoerythrophyllum atrorubens*	14(13+1)	73
587	*B. recurvirostrum*	13	11,138
588	*B. wallichii*	13	73
589	*Desmatodon cernuus*	25	138
590	*D. hendersoni*	13(12+1)	140
591	*D. latifolius*	26	11
592	*Didymodon rufescens*	13	73
593	*Gymnostomum aurantiacum*	13	72
594	*G. calcareum*	13	73
595	*Hydrogonium consanguineum*	10	45
596	*H. gangeticum*	14	73
597	*Hymenostylium recurvirostrum*	13	11
598	*Hyophila involuta*	13	73
599	*H. tortula*	13	9
600	*Merceya gedeana*	13	73
601	*Molendoa roylei*	13	73
602	*Phascum cuspidatum*	52	171
603	*P. cuspidatum americanum*	26	23,140
604		28-29 (27+1-2)	140
605	*Pottia duvallianum*	30	140
606	*P. heimii*	26	11,138
607	*P. obtusifolia*	50	138
608	*P. truncata*	25	169
609	*Reimmersia inconspicua*	14(13+1)	73
610	*Semibarbula orientalis*	16	45
611	*Stegonia latifolia*	26	11
	Pottiaceae		
612	*Timmiella anomala*	15(14+1)	73
613	*T. vancouveriensis*	14	140
614	*Tortella humilis*	15	9
615		26	4
616	*T. tortuosa*	13	11
617	*Tortula bolanderi*	13	140
618	*T. intermedia*	12	59
619	*T. laevipila*	12	140
620		15	171
621	*T. mucronifolia*	12,24	11
622		30	138
623	*T. muralis*	48	140
624		50±1,50±2	173
625		60,66	171
626	*T. muralis rupestris*	40±2	173
627	*T. princeps*	12,24+,36+	140
628	*T. ruralis*	12	11
629	*T. subulata*	49(48+1)	140
630		ca. 60	62
631	*Trichostomum cylindricum*	13	72
632	*Weissia controversa*	13	23,72,140
633		14	168
634	*W. controversa australis*	13	9
635	*W. crispa*	13	70
636		26	73
637	*W. exserta*	13	72
638	*W. longidens*	13	122
	Grimmiaceae		
639	*Grimmia affinis*	13	11
640	*G. alpestris*	13	140
641	*G. alpicola*	13	11
642		14	9
643	*G. alpicola latifolia*	13	11
644	*G. apocarpa*	12	171
645		13	62,140
646		14	9,11
647	*G. commutata*	13	73
648	*G. montana*	13	11
649	*G. muhlenbeckii*	32(28+4)	168
650	*G. patens*	22	193
651	*G. platyphylla*	14	138
652	*G. pulvinata*	13	140
653	*G. trichophylla*	13	140
654		26	59
655	*Rhacomitrium canescens*	12	124,171,193
656	*R. canescens ericoides*	12	193
657	*R. depressum*	14	140
658	*R. fasciculare*	13	168
659	*R. heterostichum*	14	168
660	*R. hypnoides*	12	190
661		14	168
662	*R. javanicum*	14(13+1)	73
663	*R. lanuginosum*	12	193
664	*R. microcarpon*	14	168
	Ephemeraceae		
665	*Ephemerum cohaerens*	27	25
666	*E. crassinervium*	27	25
667	*E. crassinervium texanum*	27	25
668	*E. serratum*	27	25
669	*E. spinulosum*	27	25
670	*Nanomitrium austinii*	10,11	25
671	*N. megalosporum*	22	25

continued

5. CHROMOSOME NUMBERS: BRYOPHYTES

	Family and Species	Haploid Number	Reference
	(A)	(B)	(C)
	Musci		
	Funariaceae		
672	*Aphanorhegma serratum*	27	25
673	*Entosthodon drummondii*	27	25
674	*Funaria californica*	24	171
675	*F. calvescens*	14	113
676	*F. flavicans*	14	113
677	*F. hygrometrica*	14	11,171, 177
678		20	54
679		28	25,177
680		56	177
681	*F. hygrometrica* (bivalens)	28	176
682	*F. hygrometrica* (quadrivalens)	ca. 56	176
683	*F. mediterranea*	26	41
684	*F. microstoma obtusifolia*	28	138
685	*F. muhlenbergii patula*	28	140
686	*F. wallichii*	28	72
687	*Physcomitrella patens*	ca. 16	175
688		27	25
689	*Physcomitrellopsis indica*	31	112
690	*Physcomitrium* sp.	3,6	32
691	*P. cyathicarpum*	52-53 (51+1-2)	73
692	*P. eurystomum*	9	123
693	*P. immersum*	54	25
694	*P. japonicum*	18	32
695	*P. pyriforme*	9	111
696		18,36,72	177
697		27	25
698	*P. repandum*	52-53 (51+1-2)	73
	Splachnaceae		
699	*Haplodon wormskjoldii*	19	138
700	*Splachnum ampullaceum*	8	19
701	*S. ampullaceum* (bivalens)	16	19
702	*S. ampullaceum* (quadrivalens)	32	19
703	*S. ovatum*	9	11
704	*S. sphaericum*	8	127
705	*S. sphaericum* (bivalens)	16	127
706	*S. vasculosum*	9	138
707	*Tetraplodon mnioides*	19	138
	Tetraphidaceae		
708	*Tetraphis pellucida*	7	171
	Bryaceae		
709	*Anomobryum japonicum*	10	193
710	*Brachymenium exile*	11	193
711	*Bryum* sp.	50	138
712	*B. angustirete*	10	11
713	*B. arcticum*	20	138
714	*B. argenteum*	10	9,65, 193
715		11	140
716	*B. argenteum lanatum*	12	140
717	*B. bicolor*	10	173
718	*B. caespiticium*	10	173,176, 193
719		11(10+1)	173
720		20	122,123
721	*B. calophyllum*	40	140
722	*B. capillare*	9-10	54
723		10	97
724		15(10+5)	140
	Bryaceae		
725	*Bryum capillare*	20	1
726	*B. capillare* (bivalens)	20	97
727	*B. capillare rubrolimbatum*	10	123,193
728	*B. cellulare*	10	113
729	*B. coronatum*	20	124
730	*B. corrensii*	20,40	46
731	*B. cyclophyllum*	10	193
732	*B. gemmiparum*	20	1
733	*B. inclinatum*	30	138
734	*B. nitens*	10	33,111
735	*B. nitidulum*	20	138
736	*B. pallescens*	10	187
737	*B. pseudoalpinum*	10	193
738	*B. pseudopachytheca*	20	113
739	*B. pseudotriquetrum*	9-10	54
740		11(10+1)	140
741		20	11
742	*B. ramosum*	10	113
743	*B. turbinatum*?	11(10+1)	11
744	*B. uliginosum*	10	138
745	*Epipterygium tozeri*	11	140
746	*Leptobryum pyriforme*	20	11
747		24	1
748	*Orthodontium gracile*	12(10+2)	140
749	*O. lineare*	20	173
750	*Plagiobryum japonicum*	10	193
751	*Pohlia acuminata*	11	193
752	*P. carnea*	11	193
753	*P. columbica*	11	193
754	*P. cruda*	10	138
755		14(10+4)	11
756	*P. elongata*	11	113,188
757	*P. fauriei*	11	192
758	*P. flexuosa*	10	193
759		11	113
760	*P. japonica*	11	124
761	*P. longibracteata*	12	140
762	*P. longicolla*	22	188
763	*P. nutans*	14	54
764		21	138
765		22	173,188 193
766	*P. patentissima*	22	193
767	*P. revoluta*	11	193
768	*P. revolvens*	11	193
769	*P. suzukii*	20	193
770	*P. wahlenbergii*	11	193
771	*Rhodobryum giganteum*	11	132,193
772	*R. roseum*	10	33
773		11	196
	Mniaceae		
774	*Cinclidium stygium*	14	87
775	*C. subrotundum*	14	138
776	*Leucolepis menziesii*	5	87,140
777	*Mnium affine*	6	62,87
778	*M. affine ciliare*	6	87,183
779	*M. cinclidioides*	6	87
780	*M. cuspidatum*	6	57,87
781		12	62,87
782	*M. drummondii*	6	87
783	*M. flagellare*	7	155,163
784	*M. glabrescens*	6	87
785	*M. hornum*	6	54,87, 179
786		12	62

continued

5. CHROMOSOME NUMBERS: BRYOPHYTES

	Family and Species	Haploid Number	Reference
	(A)	(B)	(C)
	Musci		
	Mniaceae		
787	*Mnium hornum* (bivalens)	12	97
788	*M. hymenophylloides*	7	57
789	*M. insigne*	6	87
790	*M. longirostrum*	12	57,62
791	*M. maximoviczii*	7	57,132, 163
792	*M. medium*	12	62,87, 169
793	*M. microphyllum*	6	76
794		7	155,163
795	*M. orthorynchum*	6	57,87
796	*M. pseudopunctatum*	13	57,169
797		14	87
798	*M. punctatum*	7	54,87, 169
799	*M. rugicum*	6	62
800	*M. seligeri*	6	57,62
801	*M. serratum*	12	11,62, 87
802	*M. speciosum*	7	163
803	*M. spinosum*	6	57
804	*M. spinulosum*	8	11,87
805	*M. stellare*	7	57,87
806	*M. trichomanes*	6	76
807		7	155
808	*M. undulatum*	6	57,62
809		7	98
	Rhizogoniaceae		
810	*Rhizogonium dozyanum*	7	193
811	*R. spiniforme*	6	9
	Aulacomniaceae		
812	*Aulacomnium androgynum*	10-11	58
813		12	140
814	*A. heterostichum*	12	11
815	*A. palustre*	12	9,169
816	*A. turgidium*	12	138
	Meeseaceae		
817	*Meesea triquetra*	10	138
818	*M. uliginosa*	13	11
	Catascopiaceae		
819	*Catascopium nigritum*	16	11
	Bartramiaceae		
820	*Anacolia menziesii*	8	140
821	*A. menziesii bauri*	7	140
822	*Bartramia crispata*	8	193
823	*B. ithyphylla*	12	11,138, 169
824	*B. pomiformis*	8	9,193
825	*B. pomiformis crispa*	8	169
826	*B. subpellucida*	8	73,112
827	*Bartramidula carolinae*	24	2
828	*Breutelia arundinifolia*	6	77
829	*Conostomum boreale*	16	138
830	*Philonotis carinata*	6	193
831	*P. falcata*	6	193
832	*P. fontana*	6	11
833	*P. griffithiana*	6	73
834	*P. heterophylla*	6	73
835	*P. japonica*	6	193
836	*P. lancifolia*	6	193
837	*P. seriata*	6	193
838	*P. socia*	6,12	193
839	*P. taxissima*	6	45
	Bartramiaceae		
840	*Philonotis turneriana*	6	193
	Timmiaceae		
841	*Timmia austriaca*	17(16+1)	11
842	*T. megapolitana*	12	126
843		16	88
	Erpodiaceae		
844	*Aulacopilum japonicum*	13	124
	Ptychomitriaceae		
845	*Ptychomitrium drummondii*	13	9
	Orthotrichaceae		
846	*Macrocoma hymenostomum*	12	9
847	*Orthotrichum affine*	6	140
848	*O. alpestre*	11	11
849	*O. bolanderi*	6	140
850	*O. consobrinum*	11	195
851	*O. cupulatum*	11	138
852	*O. cupulatum nudum*	11	173
853	*O. jamesianum*	11	11
854	*O. laevigatum*	6	11
855	*O. lyellii*	6	140
856	*O. ohioense*	11	9
857	*O. pusillum*	11	9
858	*O. rivulare*	11	140
859	*O. roellii*	6	11
860	*O. rupestre*	6	140
861		12	1
862	*O. rupestre globosum*	6	140
863	*O. sordidum*	6	11
864	*O. speciosum*	6	11,138, 169
865	*O. stramineum*	13	171
866	*O. tenellum*	9,10	171
867		11	140
868	*O. texanum*	6	11,140
869	*Ulota cirrata*	22(20+2)	11
870	*U. crispa*	21	173
871	*U. curvifolia*	23(21+2)	169
872	*U. hutchinsiae*	10	59
873	*U. japonica*	8	186
874		10	195
	Fontinalaceae		
875	*Dichelyma falcatum*	10	169
876	*Fontinalis antipyretica*	8	51
	Climaciaceae		
877	*Climacium americanum*	11	196
878	*C. dendroides*	11	196
879	*C. japonicum*	11	132
880	*Pleuroziopsis ruthenica*	11	195
	Hedwigiaceae		
881	*Braunia californica*	11	140
882	*Hedwigia ciliata*	11	140
883		21-22	172
884		22	169
	Cryphaeaceae		
885	*Cryphaea glomerata*	11	9
	Leucodontaceae		
886	*Leucodon julaceus*	10	9
887	*L. sciuroides*	11	59
888	*L. secundus*	9	73
	Trachypodaceae		
889	*Duthiella speciosissima*	10	195
	Neckeraceae		
890	*Neckera humilis*	10	195
891	*Porothamnium bigelovii*	12	140
892	*Thamnium alopecurum*	11	195

continued

5. CHROMOSOME NUMBERS: BRYOPHYTES

	Family and Species	Haploid Number	Reference
	(A)	(B)	(C)
	Musci		
	Neckeraceae		
893	*Thamnium sandei*	11	122,195
894		22	195
	Lembophyllaceae		
895	*Dolichomitriopsis crenulata*	10	195
896	*D. diversiformis*	10	124,195
897	*Isothecium hakkodense*	10	195
	Hookeriaceae		
898	*Daltonia semitorta*	11	72
899	*Hookeria lucens*	ca. 12	54
900	*H. nipponensis*	7	155
	Hypopterygiaceae		
901	*Hypopterygium japonicum*	18	132
	Fabroniaceae		
902	*Clasmatodon parvulus*	11	9
	Leskeaceae		
903	*Leskea polycarpa*	13(11+2)	173
	Thuidiaceae		
904	*Anomodon giraldii*	11	196
905	*A. minor*	11	112
906	*A. rostratus*	11	194
907	*A. rugelii*	11	194
908	*Boulaya mittenii*	10	188
909	*Claopodium whippleanum*	11	140
910	*Haplocladium capillatum*	10	77
911	*H. microphyllum*	10	124
912		11(10+1)	4
913		11	1
914	*H. subulaceum*	10	196
915	*H. subulaceum subulatum*	10	124,196
916	*Helodium blandowii*	12	62
917	*Hylocomiopsis ovicarpa*	10	196
918	*Thuidium delicatulum*	11	9
919	*T. glaucinum*	10	123
920	*T. japonicum*	10	132
921	*T. micropteris*	10	194
922	*T. minutulum*	11(9+2)	4
923	*T. recognitum*	11	138
924	*T. scitum*	11	9
925	*T. uliginosum*	10	194
926	*T. viridiforme*	10	194
	Amblystegiaceae		
927	*Amblystegium juratzkanum*	13(12+1)	11,140
928	*A. serpens*	12,24,48	96
929		20	173
930		22	169,171
931	*A. serpens* (bivalens)	24	96,97, 176
932	*A. serpens* (quadrivalens)	48	97
933	*A. varium*	13(12+1)	11
934	*Calliergon cordifolium*	10	62
935	*C. richardsonii*	20	54
936	*C. stramineum*	11	196
937	*Calliergonella cuspidata*	9-10	54
938	*Campylium chrysophyllum*	9	185
939	*C. hispidulum*	14	1
940	*C. stellatum*	6-8	54
941		20(18+2)	11
942		22	138
943	*Cratoneuron commutatum*	7	11
944	*falcatum*	10	194
945	*C. filicinum japonicum*	9	185
946		10	194
947	*C. latifolium*	10	196
	Amblystegiaceae		
948	*Drepanocladus exannulatus*	12	171
949	*D. fluitans*	22	171
950		24	194
951	*D. revolvens*	23	138
952	*D. uncinatus*	12	11,138, 169
953		20	11
954	*Hygroamblystegium irriguum*	12	96
955		20	140
956	*H. orthocladon*	20	9
957	*Hygrohypnum luridum*	10	173
958		11(10+1)	11
959	*Leptodictyum riparium*	10	194
960		12,48,96	106
961		24	59,96
962	*Platyhypnidium rusciforme*	12	123,196
963	*P. shottmuelleri*	12	196
964	*Scorpidium scorpioides*	8	62
	Brachytheciaceae		
965	*Brachythecium albicans*	6(+1?)	62
966		9	59,169
967	*B. brotheri*	11,22	194
968	*B. buchanani*	10	122
969	*B. buchanani japonicum*	10	194
970	*B. coreanum*	11	194
971	*B. decurrentifolium*	10	194
972	*B. glareosum*	6	62
973		14	138
974	*B. piligerum*	18	194
975	*B. populeum*	9-10	185
976		10	194
977	*B. rhynchostegielloides*	10	194,196
978	*B. rivulare*	6	62
979		16	9
980	*B. rutabulum*	5,10	62,107
981		11	135
982	*B. salebrosum*	13	169
983	*B. starkei*	20	169
984	*B. subauriculatum*	11	194,196
985	*B. tsunodae*	18	194
986	*B. velutinum*	10	59,97
987		11	169
988	*Bryhnia noesica*	11	124,194, 196
989	*B. novae-angliae*	11	124,194, 196
990	*Camptothecium lutescens*	8	62
991		14	59
992	*Cirriphyllum boscii*	12	9
993	*C. piliferum*	12-14	62
994	*Eurhynchium confertum*	12	80
995	*E. eustegium*	11	194
996		12	185
997	*E. polystictum*	8	123,194, 196
998	*E. riparioides*	6-8	54
999	*E. schleicheri*	8-9	54
1000	*E. stokesii*	12	59
1001	*E. striatum*	6	62
1002		11	59
1003	*E. substrigosum*	10	138
1004	*E. zetterstedtii*	6	62
1005	*Homalothecium nevadense*	12	140
1006	*H. sericeum*	8	62
1007	*H. tokiodense*	11	196

continued

5. CHROMOSOME NUMBERS: BRYOPHYTES

	Family and Species	Haploid Number	Reference
	(A)	(B)	(C)
	Musci		
	Brachytheciaceae		
1008	*Myuroclada concinna*	10	77
1009		11	122,196
1010	*Oxyrhynchium praelongum*	11	59
1011		ca. 12	62
1012	*O. savatieri*	8	196
1013	*O. swartzii*	10	59
1014	*Rhynchostegium* sp.	20	196
1015	*R. serrulatum*	9	9
1016	*Tomenthypnum nitens*	12	62
	Entodontaceae		
1017	*Entodon challengeri*	11	122,194
1018	*E. chloroticus*	11	194
1019	*E. flaccidus*	11	194
1020	*E. ramulosus*	11	124,194
1021	*E. seductrix*	11	9
1022	*Pleurozium schreberi*	5	62,169
1023		7	194
1024	*Pseudoscleropodium purum*	7	194
1025		9-10	54
	Plagiotheciaceae		
1026	*Plagiothecium aomoriense*	10	194,196
1027	*P. denticulatum*	10	169,194, 196
1028		11	173
1029		20	3,9
1030		25	11
1031	*P. denticulatum laetum*	11	169
1032	*P. nemorale*	10	194,196
1033	*P. piliferum*	11	169
1034	*P. roseanum*	10	194,196
1035		20	3
1036	*P. sylvaticum*	8	194,196
	Hypnaceae		
1037	*Brotherella complanata*	10	197
1038	*B. fauriei*	8	197
1039	*B. henoni*	10	123,197
1040	*B. herbacea*	7	197
1041	*B. nakayamae*	10	197
1042	*B. recurvans*	7	197
1043	*B. yokohamae*	10	197
1044	*Ctenidium molluscum*	7	135
1045		10	80
1046	*Heterophyllium brachycarpum*	11	194
1047	*H. haldanianum*	22	9,194
1048	*Homomallium incurvatum*	12	171
1049	*Hypnum circinatulum*	6	191
1050	*H. cupressiforme*	10	169
1051		16	11
1052	*H. dieckii*	6	194
1053	*H. fertile*	11	9
1054	*H. fujiyamae*	10	194
1055	*H. homaliacea*	10	194,196
1056	*H. imponens*	6-7	54
1057	*H. lindbergii*	10	194
1058	*H. oldhami*	7	123,194, 196
1059	*H. plumaeforme*	10	124,194
1060	*H. pratensis*	10	194
1061	*H. reptile*	11	194
1062	*H. revolutum*	14	11
1063	*H. tristo-viride*	10	123
1064	*Isopterygium micans*	12(11+1)	4
	Hypnaceae		
1065	*Isopterygium pulchellum*	11,12	11
1066	*I. turfaceum*	11	169
1067	*Mittenothamnium diminutivum*	10	9
1068	*Ptilium crista-castrensis*	10	75,194
1069		11	169
1070		11(10+1)	11
1071	*Pylaisia polyantha*	11	138,171
1072	*P. selwynii*	11	9
1073	*Taxiphyllum taxirameum*	8	194
1074	*Taxithelium nepalense*	9	45
1075	*Vesicularia montagnei*	12	45
	Rhytidiaceae		
1076	*Gollania varians*	10	194
1077	*Lesquereuxia robusta*	11	194
1078	*Rhytidiadelphus calvescens*	10	194
1079	*R. squarrosus*	6-8	54
1080	*R. triquetrus*	6	62,194
1081	*Rhytidium rugosum*	10	194
	Hylocomiaceae		
1082	*Hylocomiastrum pyrenaicum*	12	194
1083	*H. umbratum*	7	194
1084	*Hylocomium cavifolium*	6	122,194
1085	*H. splendens*	10	169
1086		11	171
1087		12	194
	Buxbaumiaceae		
1088	*Buxbaumia aphylla*	8	141
1089	*B. indusiata*	8	141
	Diphysciaceae		
1090	*Diphysium foliosum*	8	141
1091		10	9
1092	*D. fulvifolium*	9	76
	Polytrichaceae		
1093	*Atrichum angustatum*	7	9,89
1094	*A. chlorochaeta*	21	77
1095	*A. crispum*	7	89
1096	*A. flavisetum*	7	32
1097	*A. obtusulum*	14	34
1098	*A. pallidum*	7	32,129
1099	*A. spinulosum*	7	162
1100	*A. subserratum*	14	32
1101	*A. tenellum*	14	171
1102	*A. undulatum*	7	89,157
1103		14	87,89, 162
1104		14-16	51
1105		16-17	180
1106		20-22	54
1107		21	75,77
1108	*A. undulatum haussnechtii*	14	77
1109		21	162
1110	*A. undulatum minus*	7	162,195
1111	*A. yakushimense*	7	162
1112	*Bartramiopsis lescurii*	7	145,195
1113	*Lyellia crispa*	ca. 7	129
1114	*Oligotrichum aligerum*	7	189
1115	*O. parallelum*	7	189,195
1116	*O. semilamellatum*	7	36,129
1117	*Pogonatum akitense*	7	195
1118	*P. aloides*	7	62,129
1119	*P. alpinum*	7	11,129, 195
1120	*P. alpinum septentrionale*	7	11,138
1121	*P. capillare*	7	76,138

continued

5. CHROMOSOME NUMBERS: BRYOPHYTES

	Family and Species	Haploid Number	Reference
	(A)	(B)	(C)
	Musci		
	Polytrichaceae		
1122	*Pogonatum contortum*	7	132,195
1123	*P. grandifolium*	7	75,189, 195
1124	*P. inflexum*	7	132,189, 195
1125	*P. microstomum*	7	111
1126		14	35
1127	*P. nanum*	7	65
1128	*P. pensilvanicum*	7	9
1129	*P. perichaetiale*	7	35
1130	*P. rhopalophorum*	8	64
1131	*P. spinulosum*	7	75,195
1132	*P. stevensii*	7	35,111
1133	*P. urnigerum*	6-7	54
1134		7	75,189, 195
1135	*Polytrichadelphus lyallii*	7	11
1136	*Polytrichum* sp.	14	75
1137	*P. alpestre*	7	62,138
1138	*P. commune*	7	54,75, 195
1139	*P. commune uliginosum*	7	75
	Polytrichaceae		
1140	*Polytrichum fastigiatum*	7	130
1141	*P. formosum*	6	174
1142		7	80,195
1143		7(6+x/y)	131
1144	*P. formosum attenuatum*	14	75
1145	*P. gracile*	14	62,171
1146	*P. himalayanum*	7	129
1147	*P. junghunianum*	7	129
1148	*P. juniperinum*	7	11,80, 195
1149	*P. leucopogon*	7	129
1150	*P. microstomum*	14	129
1151	*P. neesii*	7	129
1152	*P. nudiusculum*	7	129
1153	*P. ohioense*	14	3
1154	*P. perichaetiale*	7	129
1155	*P. piliferum*	7	11,54, 195
1156	*P. proliferum*	7	129
1157	*P. stevensii*	7	129
1158	*P. teysmanianum*	7	129
1159	*P. teysmanianum darjeelingensis*	7	129
1160	*P. yezoense*	14	195
1161	*Psilopilum cavifolium*	7	138

Contributor: Anderson, Lewis E.

References: [1] Al-Aish, M., and L. E. Anderson. 1960. Bryologist 63:17. [2] Al-Aish, M., and L. E. Anderson. 1960. Ibid. 63:26. [3] Al-Aish, M., and L. E. Anderson. 1960. Can. J. Botany 38:335. [4] Al-Aish, M., and L. E. Anderson. 1960. J. Elisha Mitchell Sci. Soc. 76:112. [5] Allen, C. E. 1919. Proc. Am. Phil. Soc. 58:289. [6] Allen, C. E. 1935. Am. J. Botany 22:664. [7] Allen, C. E. 1936. Botan. Gaz. 97:846. [8] Anderson, L. E., and V. S. Bryan. 1956. Rev. bryol. et. lichénol., n.s. 25:254. [9] Anderson, L. E., and V. S. Bryan. 1958. J. Elisha Mitchell Sci. Soc. 74:173. [10] Anderson, L. E., and V. S. Bryan. 1958. Brittonia 10:121. [11] Anderson, L. E., and H. Crum. 1958. Bull. Natl. Museum Can. Contribs. Botany 160:1. [12] Berrie, G. K. 1955. Trans. Brit. Bryol. Soc. 2:532. [13] Berrie, G. K. 1958. Ibid. 3:422. [14] Berrie, G. K. 1958. Ph. D. Thesis. London Univ., England. [15] Berrie, G. K. 1959. Bryologist 62:1. [16] Berrie, G. K. 1960. Trans. Brit. Bryol. Soc. 3:688. [17] Black, C. A. 1913. Ann. Botany (London) 27:511. [18] Blair, M. C. 1926. Botan. Gaz. 81:377. [19] Bornhagen, H. 1930. Beih. botan. Zentr. 46:407. [20] Brotherus, V. F. 1893-1909. In A. Engler and K. Prantl, ed. Die naturliche Pflanzenfamilien. W. Engelmann, Leipzig. v. 1-2. [21] Brotherus, V. F. 1924-25. Ibid. v. 10-11. [22] Bryan, V. S. 1955. Bryologist 58:16. [23] Bryan, V. S. 1956. Ibid. 59:118. [24] Bryan, V. S. 1956. Am. J. Botany 43:460. [25] Bryan, V. S. 1957. Bryologist 60:103. [26] Burgeff, H. 1937. Z. induktive Abstammungs.- u. Vererbungslehre 73:394. [27] Burgeff, H. 1943. Genetische Studien an Marchantia. G. Fischer, Jena. [28] Campbell, D. H. 1913. Stanford Univ. Publs., Dudley mem. vol. (1):43. [29] Campbell, D. H., and F. Williams. 1914. Ibid., Univ. Ser., p. 1. [30] Chalaud, G. 1930. Rev. gén. botan. 42:99. [31] Chavan, A. R. 1937. Am. J. Botany 24:484. [32] Chopra, N. 1959. Current Sci. (India) 28:114. [33] Chopra, N. 1960. Bull. Assoc. Southeast Biologists 7:25. [34] Chopra, R. S., and N. N. Bhandari. 1959. Cytologia (Tokyo) 24:358. [35] Chopra, R. S., and P. D. Sharma. 1958. Phytomorphology 8:41. [36] Chopra, R. S., and P. D. Sharma. 1959. J. Indian Botan. Soc. 38:400. [37] Davis, B. M. 1899. Botan. Gaz. 28:89. [38] Delay, C. 1953. Rev. cytol. et biol. végétales 14:59. [39] Döpp, W., and A. Döpp. 1936. Ann. Bryol. 9:142. [40] Eftimiu, P. 1933. Botaniste 25:117. [41] Evans, A. W. 1939. Botan. Rev. 5:49. [42] Farmer, J. B. 1894. Ann. Botany (London) 8:35. [43] Farmer, J. B. 1895. Ibid. 9:469. [44] Florin, R. 1922. Arkiv Botan. 18(5):1. [45] Gangulee, H. C.,

continued

and N. K. Chattergee. 1960. J. Indian Botan. Soc. 39(4):531. [46] Griesinger, R. 1937. Ber. deut. botan. Ges. 55:556. [47] Grün, C. 1913-14. Flora (Ger.) 106:331. [48] Haupt, A. W. 1926. Botan. Gaz. 82:30. [49] Haupt, G. 1932. Z. induktive Abstammungs.- u. Vererbungslehre 62:367. [50] Haupt, G. 1933. Ibid. 63:390. [51] Heitz, E. 1926. Z. Botan. 18:625. [52] Heitz, E. 1927. Abhandl. naturw. Verein Hamburg 21:48. [53] Heitz, E. 1927. Ber. deut. botan. Ges. 45:607. [54] Heitz, E. 1928. Jahrb. wiss. Botan. 69:762. [55] Heitz, E. 1928. Planta 5:725. [56] Heitz, E. 1932. Ber. deut. botan. Ges. 50:204. [57] Heitz, E. 1942. Arch. Julius Klaus-Stift. Vererbungsforsch. Sozialanthropol. u. Rassenhyg. 17:444. [58] Heitz, E. 1945. Ibid. 20(suppl.):119. [59] Ho, P. H. 1956. Rev. gén. botan. 63:1. [60] Höfer, K. 1928. Jahrb. wiss. Botan. 69:687. [61] Holmen, K. 1955. Botan. Tidsskr. 52:37. [62] Holmen, K. 1958. Ibid. 54:23. [63] Ikeno, S. 1903. Beih. botan. Zentr. 15:65. [64] Ikeno, S. 1904. Biol. Zentr. 24:211. [65] Jachimsky, H. 1935. Jahrb. wiss. Botan. 81:203. [66] Johansen, D. A. 1929. Bull. Torrey Botan. Club 56:285. [67] Johansen, D. A. 1934. Ibid. 61:381. [68] Kachroo, P. 1955. Bryologist 58:134. [69] Kashyap, S. R., and S. R. Panda. 1922. J. Indian Botany 3:79. [70] Khanna, K. R. 1959. Current Sci. (India) 28:163. [71] Khanna, K. R. 1959. Ibid. 28:497. [72] Khanna, K. R. 1960. Dissertation. Punjab Univ., Chandigarh. [73] Khanna, K. R. 1960. Caryologia 13:559. [74] Kruch, O. 1891. Malphigia 4:403. [75] Kurita, M. 1938. Z. induktive Abstammungs.- u. Vererbungslehre 74:24. [76] Kurita, M. 1939. Botany and Zool. (Tokyo) 7:385. [77] Kurita, M. 1950. Kromosomo (Tokyo) 7:300. [78] Lander, C. A. 1935. Am. J. Botany 22:42. [79] Lewis, C. E. 1906. Botan. Gaz. 41:109. [80] Lewis, K. R. 1957. Trans. Brit. Bryol. Soc. 3:279. [81] Lewis, K. R., and K. Benson-Evans. 1960. Phyton (Argentina) 14:21. [82] Lorbeer, G. 1924. Ber. deut. botan. Ges. 42:231. [83] Lorbeer, G. 1927. Z. induktive Abstammungs.- u. Vererbungslehre 44:1. [84] Lorbeer, G. 1934. Jahrb. wiss. Botan. 80:567. [85] Lorbeer, G. 1936. Ber. deut. botan. Ges. 54:98. [86] Lorbeer, G. 1941. Ibid. 59:369. [87] Lowry, R. J. 1948. Mem. Torrey Botan. Club 20:1. [88] Lowry, R. J. 1953. Bryologist 56:36. [89] Lowry, R. J. 1954. Am. J. Botany 41:410. [90] MacCormick, A. 1914. Botan. Gaz. 58:401. [91] MacKay, E., and C. E. Allen. 1936. Proc. Am. Phil. Soc. 76:781. [92] Mahabalé, T. S. 1942. Proc. Indian Acad. Sci. 16(B):141. [93] Mahabalé, T. S., and S. R. Deshpande. 1947. J. Univ. Bombay 15(5):23. [94] Mahabalé, T. S., and G. H. Gorgi. 1941. Current Sci. (India) 10:25. [95] Mahabalé, T. S., and G. H. Gorgi. 1947. J. Univ. Bombay 16(3):1. [96] Marchal, E. 1912. Bull. soc. botan. Belg. 51:189. [97] Marchal, E., and E. Marchal. 1911. Bull. classe sci. Acad. roy. Belg., p. 750. [98] Mazzeo, M. 1941. Nuovo giorn. botan. ital. 48:613. [99] McAllister, F. 1928. Bull. Torrey Botan. Club 55:1. [100] Mehra, P. N. 1938. Proc. Indian Acad. Sci. 8(B):1. [101] Mehra, P. N., and O. N. Handoo. 1953. Botan. Gaz. 114:371. [102] Mehra, P. N., and A. L. Khanna. 1950. Ibid. 112:31. [103] Mehra, P. N., and R. S. Panthania. 1959. Bryologist 62:242. [104] Moore, A. C. 1905. Botan. Gaz. 40:81. [105] Moutschen, J. 1952. Bull. soc. botan. Belg. 85:147. [106] Moutschen, J. 1952. Cellule 54:351. [107] Moutschen, J. 1956. Rev. bryol. et lichénol., n.s. 25:124 [108] Müller, K. 1941. Hedwigia 80:90. [109] Müller, K. 1951. In L. Rabenhorst, ed. Kryptogamen-Flora. Akademische Verlagsgesellschaft, Leipzig. v. 6. [110] Nevins, B. J. 1933. Cellule 41:291. [111] Pande, S. K., and N. Chopra. 1957. J. Indian Botan. Soc. 36:241. [112] Pande, S. K., and N. Chopra. 1957. Ibid. 36:539. [113] Pande, S. K., and N. Chopra. 1958. Proc. Natl. Inst. Sci. India 24(B2):94. [114] Patterson, P. M. 1933. J. Elisha Mitchell Sci. Soc. 49:122. [115] Proskauer, J. 1950. Bryologist 53:165. [116] Proskauer, J. 1951. Bull. Torrey Botan. Club 78:331. [117] Proskauer, J. 1955. J. S. African Botany 21:63. [118] Proskauer, J. 1957. Phytomorphology 7:113. [119] Proskauer, J. 1958. In L. Rabenhorst, ed. Kryptogamen-Flora. Akademische Verlagsgesellschaft, Leipzig. v. 6, pp. 1303-1319. [120] Rink, W. 1935. Flora (Ger.) 130:87. [121] Roy, R. P., and M. K. Jaipuriar. 1958. Current Sci. (India) 27:312. [122] Sannomiya, M. 1955. J. Hattori Botan. Lab. 15:114. [123] Sannomiya, M. 1957. Ibid. 18:98. [124] Sannomiya, M. 1958. Ibid. 19:67. [125] Schacke, M. A. 1919. Science 49:218. [126] Scheuber, L. M. 1932. Cellule 51:145. [127] Schweizer, J. 1923. Flora (Ger.) 116:1. [128] Segawa, M. 1955. Botan. Mag. (Tokyo) 68:283. [129] Sharma, P. S. 1960. Current Sci. (India) 29:231. [130] Shimotomai, N., and K. Kimura. 1934. Botan. Mag. (Tokyo) 48:629. [131] Shimotomai, N., and K. Kimura. 1936. Z. induktive Abstammungs.- u. Vererbungslehre

continued

5. CHROMOSOME NUMBERS: BRYOPHYTES

72:307. [132] Shimotomai, N., and Y. Koyama. 1932. Botan. Mag. (Tokyo) 46:385. [133] Showalter, A. M. 1921. Science 53:333. [134] Siler, M. B. 1934. Proc. Natl. Acad. Sci. U. S. 20:603. [135] Sinoir, Y. 1952. Rev. bryol. et lichénol., n.s. 21:32. [136] Sinoto, Y. 1930. Cytologia (Tokyo) 2:81. [137] Sorsa, V. 1955. Hereditas 41:250. [138] Steere, W. C. 1954. Botan. Gaz. 116:93. [139] Steere, W. C. 1954. Rapp. et commun. VIII. congr. intern. botan. (Paris) 14-16:72. [140] Steere, W. C., L. E. Anderson, and V. S. Bryan. 1954. Mem. Torrey Botan. Club 20:1. [141] Tarnavaschi, I. T. 1940-41. Bull. sect. sci. acad. roumaine 23:383. [142] Tatuno, S. 1935. Botan. Mag. (Tokyo) 49:628. [143] Tatuno, S. 1936. Ibid. 50:341. [144] Tatuno, S. 1936. Ibid. 50:526. [145] Tatuno, S. 1937. Ibid. 51:860. [146] Tatuno, S. 1937. Ibid. 51:931. [147] Tatuno, S. 1938. Ibid. 52:374. [148] Tatuno, S. 1938. Ibid. 52:480. [149] Tatuno, S. 1939. Ibid. 53:29. [150] Tatuno, S. 1941. Proc. Imp. Acad. (Tokyo) 17:396. [151] Tatuno, S. 1941. J. Sci. Hiroshima Univ., B(2), 4:73. [152] Tatuno, S. 1947. Japan. J. Genet. 19(suppl. 1):119. [153] Tatuno, S. 1948. Cytol. Genet., Oguma commem. vol. (1):102. [154] Tatuno, S. 1949. Japan. J. Genet. 24:101. [155] Tatuno, S. 1951. Kromosomo (Tokyo) 8:305. [156] Tatuno, S. 1952. J. Sci. Hiroshima Univ., B(2), 6:51. [157] Tatuno, S. 1953. Botan. Mag. (Tokyo) 66:150. [158] Tatuno, S. 1957. J. Sci. Hiroshima Univ., B(2), 8:81. [159] Tatuno, S. 1958. J. Hattori Botan. Lab. 20:119. [160] Tatuno, S. 1960. Cytologia (Tokyo) 25:214. [161] Tatuno, S. 1960. J. Hattori Botan. Lab. 23:99. [162] Tatuno, S. 1960. Ibid. 23:115. [163] Tatuno, S., and K. Yano. 1953. Cytologia (Tokyo) 18:36. [164] Tischler, G. 1927. Tabulae Biologicae 4:1. [165] Tischler, G. 1931. Ibid. 7:109. [166] Tischler, G. 1938. Ibid. 16:162. [167] Udar, R., and N. Chopra. 1957. J. Indian Botan. Soc. 36:191. [168] Vaarama, A. 1949. Portugaliae Acta Biol., A, R. B. Goldschmidt vol.(1):47. [169] Vaarama, A. 1950. Botan. Notiser, p. 239. [170] Vaarama, A. 1950. Nature 165:894. [171] Vaarama, A. 1953. Bryologist 56:169. [172] Vaarama, A. 1954. Arch. Soc. Zool. Botan. Fennicae "Vanamo" 8:195. [173] Vaarama, A. 1956. Irish Naturalists' J. 12:30. [174] Van Leeuwen-Reijnvaan, W., and J. Docters. 1908. Ber. deut. botan. Ges. 26:301. [175] Von Wettstein, F. 1924. Biol. Zentr. 44:145. [176] Von Wettstein, F. 1924. Z. induktive Abstammungs.- u. Vererbungslehre 33:253. [177] Von Wettstein, F. 1930. Nachr. Ges. Wiss. Göttingen math.-physik. Kl., VI, 2:109. [178] Wentzel, R. 1929. Dissertation. Univ. Marburg, Germany. [179] Wilson, M. 1908. Ann. Botany (London) 22:328. [180] Wilson, M. 1911. Ibid. 25:415. [181] Wolcott, G. B. 1941. J. Heredity 32:67. [182] Wolfson, A. M. 1927. Am. J. Botany 14:516. [183] Woodburn, W. L. 1915. Ibid. 29:441. [184] Wylie, A. P. 1957. Trans. Brit. Bryol. Soc. 3:260. [185] Yano, K. 1950. Botan. Mag. (Tokyo) 63:224. [186] Yano, K. 1951. Ibid. 64:234. [187] Yano, K. 1952. Ibid. 65:195. [188] Yano, K. 1953. Ibid. 66:43. [189] Yano, K. 1954. Ibid. 67:43. [190] Yano, K. 1954. Ibid. 67:243. [191] Yano, K. 1955. Ibid. 68:195. [192] Yano, K. 1956. Ibid. 69:156. [193] Yano, K. 1957. Mem. Fac. Education Niigata Univ. 6:1. [194] Yano, K. 1957. Mem. Takada Branch Niigata Univ. 1:85. [195] Yano, K. 1957. Ibid. 1:129. [196] Yano, K. 1957. Japan. J. Genet. 32:67. [197] Yano, K. 1960. J. Hattori Botan. Lab. 23:93. [198] Yazawa, H. 1931. Cytologia (Tokyo) 2:157.

6. CHROMOSOME NUMBERS: SPERMATOPHYTES

For additional information, consult reference 86. Classification adapted from Engler and Diels, *Syllabus der Pflanzenfamilien*, 1936.

	Family and Species	Diploid Number	Reference
	(A)	(B)	(C)
	Gymnospermae		
	Cycadaceae		
1	*Microcycas calocoma*	26	358
2	*Zamia floridana*	16	358
	Ginkgoaceae		
3	*Ginkgo biloba*	24	241
	Taxaceae		
4	*Taxus baccata*	24	72
	Podocarpaceae		
5	*Podocarpus nivalis*	38	384
	Araucariaceae		
6	*Araucaria brasiliana*	26	122

continued

6. CHROMOSOME NUMBERS: SPERMATOPHYTES

	Family and Species	Diploid Number	Reference
	(A)	(B)	(C)
	Gymnospermae		
	Cephalotaxaceae		
7	*Cephalotaxus* sp.	24	360,402
	Pinaceae		
8	*Abies concolor*	24	360
9	*A. nordmanniana*	24	360
10	*A. pindrow*	24	266
11	*A. veitchii*	24	360
12	*Cedrus deodara*	24	266
13	*C. libanensis*	24	360
14	*Larix decidua*	24,48	56
15	*L. occidentalis*	24	360
16	*Picea abies*	24,48	252
17	*P. glauca*	24	360
18	*P. mariana*	24	360
19	*Pinus caribaea*	24	266
20	*P. lambertiana*	24	266
21	*P. nigra*	24	360
22	*P. sylvestris*	24	360
23	*Pseudotsuga taxifolia*	26	360
24	*Tsuga canadensis*	24	360
25	*T. caroliniana*	24	360
	Taxodiaceae		
26	*Athrotaxis* sp.	22	145
27	*Sequoia sempervirens*	66	170,389
28	*Sequoiadendron giganteum*	22	200
29	*Taxodium distichum*	22	389
	Cupressaceae		
30	*Chamaecyparis lawsoniana*	22	360
31	*Cupressus sempervirens*	22	266
32	*Juniperus chinensis*	44	360
33	*J. communis*	22	360
34	*J. virginiana*	22,33	396
35	*Thuja occidentalis*	22	360
36	*T. plicata*	22	360
	Ephedraceae		
37	*Ephedra americana*	14	332
38	*E. distachya*	28	120
	Angiospermae (Monocotyledoneae)		
	Typhaceae		
39	*Typha angustifolia*	30	249
40	*T. latifolia*	30	154
	Sparganiaceae		
41	*Sparganium angustifolium*	30	249
42	*S. minimum*	30	463
	Potamogetonaceae		
43	*Potamogeton acutifolius*	26	249
44	*P. cristatus*	28	153
45	*P. pectinatus*	78	153
46	*Zostera marina*	12	155
	Scheuchzeriaceae		
47	*Triglochin maritima*	12	250
48		48	232
	Alismataceae		
49	*Alisma plantago-aquatica*	10,14,16, 28	465
50	*Sagittaria montevidensis*	20	418
	Butomaceae		
51	*Butomus umbellatus*	26	327
52	*Hydrocleis nymphoides*	16	327
	Hydrocharitaceae		
53	*Elodea canadensis*	48	342
54	*Enhalus acoroides*	14	192
55	*Hydrocharis morsus-ranae*	28	262
56	*Stratiotes aloides*	24	367
	Hydrocharitaceae		
57	*Vallisneria gigantea*	40	206
58	*V. spiralis*	20	206
	Gramineae		
59	*Agropyron cristatum*	14,28	158
60	*A. repens*	28,42	15
61	*Agrostis stolonifera*	28,35,42	27
62	*Alopecurus pratensis*	42	203
63	*Andropogon virginicus*	20	57
64	*Avena barbata*	28	180
65	*A. brevis*	14	388
66	*A. sativa*	42	112
67	*Bambusa bambos*	70	186
68		72	312
69	*Bouteloua curtipendula*	40,52,74, 80,82, 86,96	128
70	*Bromus inermis*	56	111,168
71	*Buchloe dactyloides*	56	300
72	*Calamagrostis rubescens*	28,42,56	305
73	*Coix aquatica*	10	192,255
74	*C. lacryma-jobi*	20	255
75	*Cynodon dactylon*	36	45
76		40	178
77	*Dactylis glomerata*	42	151
78	*Dendrocalamus giganteus*	72	192
79	*Eleusine coracana*	36	15
80	*Euchlaena mexicana*	20	255
81	*Festuca paniculata*	14,28,42	93
82	*Hordeum distichum*	14	208
83	*H. nodosum*	14,28	55
84		42	143
85	*H. vulgare*	14	217
86	*Lolium multiflorum*	14	319
87	*Oryza officinalis*	24	293
88	*O. sativa*	24	15
89	*Panicum miliaceum*	36	15
90	*P. obtusum*	20,40	46
91	*Paspalum dilatatum*	40	44
92	*Pennisetum spicatum*	14	15
93	*Phalaris arundinacea*	27-31,35	150
94	*Phleum nodosum*	14,21	303
95	*P. pratense*	42	284
96	*Poa compressa*	35,42,49	3
97		45,49,56	252
98	*P. pratensis*	36-123	301
99	*Saccharum officinarum*	80	187
100	*Secale cereale*	14	283
101	*Setaria viridis*	18	415
102	*Sorghum vulgare*	20	229
103	*Stipa occidentalis*	36	391
104	*Triticum aestivum*	42	337
105	*Zea mays*	20	333
106	*Zizania aquatica*	30	44
	Cyperaceae		
107	*Carex hirta*	112	159
108	*C. panicea*	32	159
109	*Cyperus papyrus*	ca. 102	414
	Palmae		
110	*Arenga pinnata*	32	348
111	*Borassus flabellifer*	36	34
112	*Caryota urens*	32	348
113	*Cocos nucifera*	32	343
114	*Elaeis guineensis*	32	348
115	*Phoenix dactylifera*	36	24
116	*Sabal palmetto*	36	38

continued

6. CHROMOSOME NUMBERS: SPERMATOPHYTES

	Family and Species	Diploid Number	Reference
	(A)	(B)	(C)
	Angiospermae (Monocotyledoneae)		
	Araceae		
117	*Acorus calamus*	24,36,48	466
118	*Arisaema dracontium*	56	35
119	*A. triphyllum*	28,56	181
120	*Symplocarpus foetidus*	30	183
	Lemnaceae		
121	*Lemna minor*	40	28
	Bromeliaceae		
122	*Ananas comosus*	50,75,100	60
123	*Bromelia pinguin*	96	59
	Commelinaceae		
124	*Rhoeo discolor*	12	445
125	*Tradescantia fluminensis*	60	5
126	*T. virginiana*	24	77
	Pontederiaceae		
127	*Eichhornia crassipes*	32	419
128	*Pontederia cordata*	16	38
	Juncaceae		
129	*Juncus effusus*	40	251
130	*Luzula campestris*	12,36	304
	Liliaceae		
131	*Allium ascalonicum*	16	242
132	*A. cepa*	16,32	70
133	*A. porrum*	32	242
134	*A. sativum*	16	243
135	*A. schoenoprasum*	16,24,32	244
136	*Aloe* sp.	14	347,383
137	*Asparagus officinalis*	20	289
138	*Brodiaea grandiflora*	42	48
139	*Colchicum autumnale*	38	412
140	*Convallaria majalis*	38	250
141	*Fritillaria imperialis*	24	81
142	*F. lanceolata*	24,36	81
143	*Hemerocallis flava*	22	73
144	*Hyacinthus orientalis*	16-31	82
145	*Lilium auratum*	24	395
146	*L. bulbiferum croceum*	24	341
147	*L. candidum*	24	341
148	*L. longiflorum*	24	139
149	*L. regale*	24	341
150	*Ornithogalum thyrsoides*	12	299
151	*Polygonatum multiflorum*	18,20,28	408
152	*Scilla nutans*	16	345
153	*Smilacina amplexicaulis*	36	328
154	*Smilax rotundifolia*	32	387
155	*Trillium sessile*	10	231
156	*Tulipa gesneriana*	24,36	435
157	*Veratrum album*	32	261
158	*V. nigrum*	64	273
159	*Yucca arkansana*	60	447
	Amaryllidaceae		
160	*Agave americana*	60,120, 180	140
161	*Bomarea edulis*	18	454
162	*Galanthus nivalis*	24,36	230
163	*Lycoris radiata alba*	39	346
164	*Narcissus jonquilla*	14	288
165	*N. poeticus*	14,21	287
166	*N. pseudonarcissus*	14	119
	Dioscoreaceae		
167	*Dioscorea sativa*	60	290
168	*Tamus communis*	48	268
	Iridaceae		
169	*Crocus sativus*	16,40	211
	Iridaceae		
170	*Crocus versicolor*	26	258
171	*Gladiolus nanus*	30,45,60	20
172	*Iris germanica*	44	373
173	*I. versicolor*	72,84,105	373
	Musaceae		
174	*Heliconia bihai*	24	54
175	*Musa paradisiaca*	22,33,44, 55,77,88	103
176	*M. textilis*	20	54
177	*Strelitzia reginae*	14	54
	Zingiberaceae		
178	*Curcuma longa*	32	349
179		62	325
180		64	403
181	*Zingiber officinale*	22	325
	Cannaceae		
182	*Canna edulis*	18	371
183		27	442
	Marantaceae		
184	*Maranta arundinacea variegata*	18	349
185		48	442
	Orchidaceae		
186	*Cattleya labiata*	40,41,42	209
187	*Cypripedium calceolus*	22	127
188	*Epipactis latifolia*	20,40	450
189	*Orchis maculata*	80	443
190	*O. mascula*	42	443
191	*Vanilla fragrans*	32	160
	Angiospermae (Dicotyledoneae)		
	Piperaceae		
192	*Peperomia sandersii*	24	405
193	*Piper betle*	32	192,202
194	*P. nigrum*	ca. 128	192
	Salicaceae		
195	*Populus alba*	38,57	440
196	*P. balsamifera*	38	381
197	*P. deltoides*	38	441
198	*P. tremuloides*	38	381
199	*Salix alba*	76	29
200	*S. babylonica*	76	89
201	*S. viminalis*	38	376
	Myricaceae		
202	*Comptonia peregrina*	32	398
203	*Myrica cerifera*	16	398
204	*M. gale*	48	148
	Juglandaceae		
205	*Carya cordiformis*	32	458
206	*C. glabra*	64	458
207	*C. laciniosa*	32	458
208	*C. tomentosa*	64	458
209	*Juglans cinerea*	32	458
210	*J. nigra*	32	458
211	*J. sieboldiana*	32	458
	Betulaceae		
212	*Alnus glutinosa*	28	452
213	*A. incana*	28	459
214	*A. rubra*	28	452
215	*A. rugosa*	28	459
216	*A. spaethii*	56	459
217	*Betula fontinalis*	28	459
218	*B. grossa*	84	459
219	*B. lenta*	28	459
220	*B. nigra*	28	124
221	*B. papyrifera*	56,70,84	459

continued

6. CHROMOSOME NUMBERS: SPERMATOPHYTES

	Family and Species	Diploid Number	Reference
	(A)	(B)	(C)
	Angiospermae (Dicotyledoneae)		
	Betulaceae		
222	*Betula populifolia*	28	124
223	*Carpinus betulus*	16,64	204
224	*C. caroliniana*	16	459
225	*C. orientalis*	16	459
226	*Corylus americana*	28	457
227	*C. avellana*	22	71
228	*C. rostrata*	28	457
229	*Ostrya virginiana*	16	459
	Fagaceae		
230	*Castanea dentata*	24	198
231	*Fagus sylvatica*	24	198
232	*Quercus alba*	24	403
233	*Q. macrocarpa*	24	350
234	*Q. muhlenbergii*	24	350
235	*Q. nigra*	24	198
236	*Q. robur*	24	105
	Ulmaceae		
237	*Celtis australis*	40	38
238	*C. occidentalis*	20	38
239	*Ulmus americana*	56	354
240	*U. fulva*	28	354
241	*U. hollandica*	28	354
242	*U. racemosa*	28	354
	Moraceae		
243	*Artocarpus incisus*	56	192
244	*Broussonetia papyrifera*	26	35
245	*Cannabis sativa*	20	265
246	*Castilloa elastica*	28	192
247	*Ficus carica*	26	61
248	*F. indica*	26	62
249	*Morus alba*	28	309
250	*M. nigra*	308	83
251	*M. rubra*	28	188
	Urticaceae		
252	*Boehmeria nivea*	28	223
253	*Urtica dioica*	48	249
254	*U. urens*	24,26,52	249
	Loranthaceae		
255	*Viscum album*	20	393
256	*V. articulatum*	24	393
	Polygonaceae		
257	*Coccoloba uvifera*	ca. 80	107
258	*Fagopyrum esculentum*	16	196
259	*Polygonum aviculare*	40,60	252
260	*P. bistorta*	44	197
261		46	385
262	*Rheum officinale*	22	197
263	*R. sanguineum*	44	107
264	*Rumex crispus*	60	248
265	*R. hydrolapathum*	ca. 200	248
	Chenopodiaceae		
266	*Atriplex littoralis*	18	462
267	*Beta vulgaris*	18	246,455
268	*Chenopodium album*	36	64
269	*Salicornia stricta*	18	90
270	*Spinacia oleracea*	12	130
	Amaranthaceae		
271	*Amaranthus graecizans*	32	162
272	*A. hybridus*	32	67
	Portulacaceae		
273	*Portulaca oleracea*	54	394
	Caryophyllaceae		
274	*Dianthus barbatus*	30	117
275	*D. caryophyllus*	30,90	137
	Caryophyllaceae		
276	*Dianthus deltoides*	30	117
277	*Saponaria officinalis*	28	117
278	*Stellaria media*	28	310
279		40	295
280		42,44	318
	Nymphaeaceae		
281	*Nelumbo lutea*	16	236
282	*Nuphar advena*	34	236
283	*Nymphaea capensis*	28	236
284	*N. gigantea*	224	235
285	*N. lotus*	56	236
286	*N. odorata*	84	236
	Ranunculaceae		
287	*Aconitum lycoctonum*	16	361
288	*A. napellus*	32	142
289	*Anemone caroliniana*	16	275
290	*A. pulsatilla*	32	142
291	*Aquilegia vulgaris*	14,28	316
292	*Caltha palustris*	28	252
293		32,48,56	385,386
294	*Cimicifuga americana*	16	234
295	*C. racemosa*	16	142
296	*Clematis vitalba*	16	262
297	*Delphinium* spp. (cultivated)	16,24,32, 48	323
298	*Helleborus foetidus*	32	234
299	*Nigella arvensis*	12	142
300	*N. sativa*	12	142
301	*Paeonia albiflora*	10	74
302	*P. tenuifolia hybrida*	20	74
303	*Ranunculus acris*	28,56	252
304	*R. lingua*	128	30
305	*R. repens*	32	298
306	*Thalictrum flavum*	28	142
307	*Trollius europaeus*	16	234
	Berberidaceae		
308	*Berberis canadensis*	28	96
309	*B. vulgaris*	28	233
310	*Mahonia aquifolium*	28	96
311	*Nandina domestica*	20	404
312	*Podophyllum peltatum*	12	233
	Magnoliaceae		
313	*Liriodendron tulipifera*	38	453
314	*Magnolia acuminata*	76	192
315	*M. grandiflora*	114	192
316	*M. tripetala*	38	192
317	*M. virginiana*	38	192
	Calycanthaceae		
318	*Calycanthus floridus*	22	355
319	*Chimonanthus fragrans*	22	403
	Annonaceae		
320	*Annona glabra*	28	37,192
321	*A. reticulata*	14	7,192
322	*Asimina triloba*	18,27	39
	Myristicaceae		
323	*Myristica fragrans*	42	371
	Lauraceae		
324	*Cinnamomum camphora*	24	404
325	*C. zeylanicum*	24	192
326	*Laurus nobilis*	42	23
327	*Persea americana*	24	36,192
328	*Sassafras albidum*	48	36
329	*Umbellularia californica*	24	19
	Papaveraceae		
330	*Argemone mexicana*	28	404
331	*Eschscholtzia californica*	12	239

continued

6. CHROMOSOME NUMBERS: SPERMATOPHYTES

	Family and Species	Diploid Number	Reference
	(A)	(B)	(C)
	Angiospermae (Dicotyledoneae)		
	Papaveraceae		
332	*Fumaria officinalis*	28	297
333	*Papaver orientale*	28	384
334		42	470
335	*P. rhoeas*	14	239
336	*P. somniferum*	22	130
	Capparidaceae		
337	*Capparis spinosa*	38	419
338	*Cleome spinosa*	20	432
	Cruciferae		
339	*Alyssum alyssoides*	32	256
340	*A. saxatile*	16	256
341	*Armoracia rusticana*	32	256
342	*Brassica campestris*	20	212
343	*B. napobrassica*	38	174
344	*B. nigra*	16	285
345	*B. oleracea*	18	175,212
346	*B. rapa*	20	278
347	*Cakile maritima*	18	461
348	*Capsella bursa-pastoris*	32	436
349	*Cheiranthus cheiri*	14	339
350	*Iberis amara*	14,16	199
351	*I. sempervirens*	22,44	372
352	*Lepidium sativum*	16	330
353		32	439
354	*Matthiola incana*	14	400
355	*Nasturtium officinale*	32	176
356	*Raphanus sativus*	18	212
357	*Sinapis alba*	24	212
	Resedaceae		
358	*Reseda odorata*	12	307
	Moringaceae		
359	*Moringa oleifera*	28	313
	Droseraceae		
360	*Dionaea muscipula*	30	379
361		32	26
362	*Drosera anglica*	40	335
363	*D. intermedia*	20	26
	Crassulaceae		
364	*Bryophyllum pinnatum*	40	433
365	*Kalanchoe blossfeldiana*	34	433
366	*Sedum acre*	16,48	461
367	*S. pusillum*	8	17
368	*S. telephium*	48	252
369	*Sempervivum tectorum*	72	336
	Saxifragaceae		
370	*Deutzia gracilis*	26	366
371	*D. scabra*	130	366
372	*Hydrangea arborescens*	36	353
373	*H. paniculata floribunda*	72	405
374	*Itea virginica*	22	366
375	*Philadelphus* spp. (cultivated)	26,28,39	189
376	*Ribes* spp.	16	76,269, 473
377	*Saxifraga pennsylvanica*	56,84,112	49
	Hamamelidaceae		
378	*Hamamelis vernalis*	24	4
379	*Liquidambar styraciflua*	30	4
	Platanaceae		
380	*Platanus acerifolia*	42	355
381	*P. occidentalis*	42	355
	Rosaceae		
382	*Amelanchier oblongifolia*	34	352
383	*A. spicata*	68	352
	Rosaceae		
384	*Chaenomeles lagenaria*	34	274
385	*Crataegus crus-galli*	68	274
386	*C. oxyacantha*	34	274
387	*Cydonia oblonga*	34	274
388	*Eriobotrya japonica*	34	274
389	*Fragaria chiloensis*	56	182
390	*F. vesca*	14	182
391	*F. virginiana*	56	182
392	*Malus coronaria*	51,68	100
393	*M. pumila*	34,51	85
394	*Mespilus germanica*	34	274
395	*Potentilla anserina*	28,42	113
396	*Prunus americana*	16	352
397	*P. amygdalus*	16	78
398	*P. armeniaca*	16	75
399	*P. avium*	16,24,32	75,80
400	*P. cerasus*	32	75
401	*P. domestica*	48	78
402	*P. insititia*	48	75
403	*P. laurocerasus*	ca. 176	270
404	*P. padus*	32	219
405	*P. persica*	16	78
406	*P. spinosa*	32	78
407	*P. triloba*	64	219
408	*P. virginiana*	32	352
409	*Pyrus communis*	34,51	85
410	*Rosa* spp. (cultivated)	14,21,28	467
411	*R. damascena*	28	410
412	*R. eglanteria*	35	410
413	*R. odorata*	14	179
414	*R. setigera*	14	410
415	*Rubus caesius*	28,35	166
416	*R. idaeus*	14,21,28	68
417	*R. loganbaccus*	42	420
418	*R. strigosus*	21	110
419	*Sorbus americana*	34	352
420	*Spiraea japonica*	18	356
421	*S. latifolia*	36	356
	Leguminosae		
422	*Acacia arabica*	52	10
423	*A. tenuifolia*	26	10
424	*Albizzia julibrissin*	26	338
425		52	470
426	*Anthyllis vulneraria*	12	65
427	*Arachis hypogaea*	40	126
428	*Astragalus boeticus*	16,30	430
429	*A. cicer*	64	430
430	*Cajanus indicus*	22,44,66	314
431	*Cercis canadensis*	12	369
432	*Cicer arietinum*	16	422
433	*Colutea arborescens*	16	428
434	*Dolichos lablab*	22	126
435	*Gleditsia triacanthos*	28	9
436	*Glycine soja*	40	338
437	*Glycyrrhiza glabra*	16	430
438	*Gymnocladus dioicus*	28	11
439	*Haematoxylon campechianum*	24	12
440	*Hymenaea courbaril*	24	12
441	*Indigofera anil*	12	369
442	*I. tinctoria*	16	326
443	*Lathyrus latifolius*	14	369
444	*L. odoratus*	14	372
445	*Lens esculenta*	14	165
446	*Lespedeza striata*	22	471
447	*Lupinus angustifolius*	40	254

continued

6. CHROMOSOME NUMBERS: SPERMATOPHYTES

	Family and Species	Diploid Number	Reference
	(A)	(B)	(C)
	Angiospermae (Dicotyledoneae)		
	Leguminosae		
448	*Lupinus luteus*	52	254
449	*Medicago sativa*	16	33
450		32,64	427
451	*Melilotus alba*	16,24	13
452	*M. indica*	16	429
453	*Phaseolus aureus*	22	213
454	*P. lunatus*	22	213
455	*P. vulgaris*	22	421
456	*Pisum sativum*	14	340
457	*Robinia pseudoacacia*	20	224
458	*Tamarindus indica*	24	12
459	*Tephrosia candida*	22	371
460	*Trifolium hybridum*	16	215
461	*T. incarnatum*	14	213
462	*T. pratense*	14	245
463	*T. repens*	32,48	280
464	*Vicia faba*	12	169
465	*V. sativa*	12,14	280
	Oxalidaceae		
466	*Oxalis acetosella*	22	290
467	*O. violacea*	28	469
	Geraniaceae		
468	*Erodium moschatum*	20	134
469	*Pelargonium zonale*	17,18,35, 36	134
	Tropaeolaceae		
470	*Tropaeolum majus*	28	446
	Linaceae		
471	*Linum usitatissimum*	30	329
472		32	220
	Erythroxylaceae		
473	*Erythroxylon coca*	24	164,192
	Zygophyllaceae		
474	*Guaiacum officinale*	ca. 26	192
475	*Larrea tridentata*	52,104	66
	Rutaceae		
476	*Citrus aurantifolia*	27	16
477	*C. aurantium*	18	403
478	*C. limon*	18,36	227
479	*C. nobilis*	18	291
480	*C. paradisi*	18,27,36	237
481	*C. sinensis*	45	227
482	*Fortunella hindsii*	18,36	247
	Meliaceae		
483	*Cedrela odorata*	50-52	371
484	*Swietenia mahagoni*	46-48	226
	Euphorbiaceae		
485	*Aleurites fordi*	22	238
486	*Euphorbia pulcherrima*	28	281
487	*E. splendens*	36	405
488	*Hevea brasiliensis*	36	317
489	*Ricinus communis*	20	147
	Callitrichaceae		
490	*Callitriche autumnalis*	6	205
	Buxaceae		
491	*Buxus sempervirens*	28	374
	Anacardiaceae		
492	*Anacardium occidentale*	42	192
493	*Mangifera indica*	40	282
494	*Pistacia atlantica latifolia*	28	474
495	*P. vera*	30	474
496	*Rhus toxicodendron*	30	144

	Family and Species	Diploid Number	Reference
	(A)	(B)	(C)
	Aquifoliaceae		
497	*Ilex aquifolium*	40	262
498	*I. opaca*	36	201
499	*I. verticillata*	36	201
500	*I. vomitoria*	40	201
	Aceraceae		
501	*Acer campestre*	26	125
502	*A. negundo*	26	125
503	*A. platanoides*	26,39	271
504	*A. pseudoplatanus*	52	125
505	*A. rubrum*	78,104	106
506	*A. saccharinum*	52	417
507	*A. saccharum*	26	417
	Hippocastanaceae		
508	*Aesculus hippocastanum*	40	434
509	*A. octandra*	40	434
510	*A. pavia*	40	434
	Balsaminaceae		
511	*Impatiens balsamina*	14	446
512	*I. biflora*	20	382
	Rhamnaceae		
513	*Rhamnus cathartica*	24	464
514	*R. frangula*	20	336
515		26	461
	Vitaceae		
516	*Ampelopsis cordata*	40	351
517	*Parthenocissus quinquefolia*	40	351
518	*Vitis labrusca*	38	294
519	*V. rotundifolia*	40	40
520	*V. vinifera*	38,57,76	308
	Tiliaceae		
521	*Tilia americana*	82	97
522	*T. amurensis*	164	97
523	*T. platyphyllos*	82	97
	Malvaceae		
524	*Abutilon avicennae*	42	378
525	*Althaea rosea*	42	378
526		56	404
527	*Gossypium barbadense*	52	448
528	*G. hirsutum*	52	472
529	*Hibiscus cannabinus*	36	378
530	*H. esculentus*	120	324
531		130	207
532	*H. rosa-sinensis*	168	378
533	*Malva sylvestris*	42	377
534	*M. verticillata*	ca. 84	377
	Bombacaceae		
535	*Bombax malabaricum*	ca. 72	192
536	*Ceiba pentandra*	72,80	167
	Sterculiaceae		
537	*Theobroma cacao*	20	371
	Theaceae		
538	*Camellia japonica*	30	191
539	*C. sasanqua*	90	191
540	*C. sinensis*	30	191
	Guttiferae		
541	*Garcinia mangostana*	ca. 76	226
542	*Hypericum gentianoides*	24	171
543	*H. perforatum*	32	302
	Violaceae		
544	*Viola arvensis*	34	58
545	*V. odorata*	20	58
546	*V. tricolor*	26	58
	Passifloraceae		
547	*Passiflora edulis*	18	192,399

continued

6. CHROMOSOME NUMBERS: SPERMATOPHYTES

	Family and Species	Diploid Number	Reference
	(A)	(B)	(C)
	Angiospermae (Dicotyledoneae)		
	Passifloraceae		
548	*Passiflora ligularis*	18	192,399
549	*P. quadrangularis*	18	192,399
	Caricaceae		
550	*Carica papaya*	18	109
551		36	172
552	*C. quercifolia*	18	192
	Begoniaceae		
553	*Begonia carminata*	42	259
554	*B. margaritae*	52	259
555	*B. semperflorens*	33,36,60, 66	260
	Cactaceae		
556	*Cereus tetragonus*	22	214
557	*Echinocereus engelmannii*	44	397
558	*E. procumbens*	22	214
559	*Echinopsis tubiflora*	22	214
560	*Opuntia dillenii*	66	51
561	*Pereskia aculeata*	22	214,331
562	*Zygocactus truncatus*	22	331
	Thymelaceae		
563	*Daphne mezereum*	18	262
	Lythraceae		
564	*Lythrum salicaria*	50	249
	Punicaceae		
565	*Punica granatum*	16	426
566		18,19	221
	Nyssaceae		
567	*Nyssa sylvatica*	44	98
	Myrtaceae		
568	*Eucalyptus globulus*	22	263
569	*E. resinifera*	22	8
570	*E. triantha*	22	8
571	*Myrtus communis*	22	141
572	*Pimenta acris*	22	192
573	*Psidium guajava*	22	8,192
574		33	228
	Oenotheraceae		
575	*Fuchsia* spp. (cultivated)	22,55,66, 77	152
576	*Oenothera biennis*	14	79
	Hippuridaceae		
577	*Hippuris vulgaris*	32	455
	Araliaceae		
578	*Hedera helix*	48	184
	Umbelliferae		
579	*Anethum graveolens*	22	413
580	*Angelica archangelica*	22	132
581	*Apium graveolens*	22	370
582	*Carum carvi*	20	132
583	*Conium maculatum*	22	132
584	*Daucus carota*	18	133
585	*Foeniculum vulgare*	22	132
586	*Pastinaca sativa*	22	306
587	*Petroselinum crispum*	22	336
588	*P. sativum*	23	413
589	*Pimpinella anisum*	20	413
	Cornaceae		
590	*Cornus alternifolia*	20	98
591	*C. florida*	22	98
592	*C. mas*	18,27	69
	Ericaceae		
593	*Arbutus unedo*	26	368
594	*Kalmia latifolia*	24	146

	Family and Species	Diploid Number	Reference
	(A)	(B)	(C)
	Ericaceae		
595	*Pyrola minor*	46	146
596	*Rhododendron calendulaceum*	52	193
597	*R. cinnabarinum*	78	193
598	*R. diaprepes*	26,39	193
599	*R. lapponicum*	26,52	193
600	*R. manipurense*	78,156	193
601	*R. pholidotum*	104	193
602	*R. saluenense*	26,52	193
603	*Vaccinium angustifolium*	24	87
604	*V. corymbosum*	48	87
605	*V. macrocarpus*	24	87
606	*V. oxycoccos*	48	87
	Primulaceae		
607	*Cyclamen persicum*	48	91
608	*Dodecatheon meadia*	88	423
609	*Hottonia palustris*	20	108
610	*Primula elatior*	22	47
611	*P. veris*	22	47
612	*P. vulgaris*	22	47
	Plumbaginaceae		
613	*Plumbago europaea*	14	320
	Ebenaceae		
614	*Diospyros kaki*	90	292
615	*D. lotus*	30	292
616	*D. virginiana*	60,90	18
	Oleaceae		
617	*Chionanthus virginicus*	46	357
618	*Forsythia europaea*	28	357
619	*F. suspensa*	28	357
620	*Fraxinus americana*	46,92,138	460
621	*F. excelsior*	46	357
622	*F. pennsylvanica*	46	357
623	*Jasminum nudiflorum*	52	35
624	*J. officinale*	26	225
625	*Ligustrum vulgare*	46	416
626	*Olea europaea*	46	42
627	*Osmanthus americanus*	138	416
628	*Syringa vulgaris*	46,47,48	416
	Loganiaceae		
629	*Buddleia davidii*	76	277
630	*B. globosa*	38	277
631	*Strychnos nux-vomica*	24	192
	Gentianaceae		
632	*Gentiana lutea*	40	118
	Apocynaceae		
633	*Apocynum cannabinum*	22	41
634	*Nerium oleander*	22	426
635	*Strophanthus sarmentosus*	18	384
636	*Vinca major*	92	336
637	*V. minor*	46	336
	Asclepiadaceae		
638	*Asclepias incarnata*	22	276
639	*Hoya carnosa*	22	311
	Convolvulaceae		
640	*Calonyction aculeatum*	30	210
641	*Convolvulus scammonia*	ca. 24	163
642	*Ipomoea batatas*	90	425
643	*Quamoclit pennata*	30	218
	Polemoniaceae		
644	*Cobaea scandens*	52	123,192
645	*Phlox divaricata*	14	272
646	*P. drummondii*	14	272
647	*P. maculata*	14	121
	Boraginaceae		
648	*Borago officinalis*	16	43

continued

6. CHROMOSOME NUMBERS: SPERMATOPHYTES

	Family and Species	Diploid Number	Reference
	(A)	(B)	(C)
	Angiospermae (Dicotyledoneae)		
	Boraginaceae		
649	*Heliotropium arborescens*	18	43
650	*Myosotis alpestris*	24,48,72	136
651	*M. arvensis*	54	136
652	*Pulmonaria saccharata*	14,16	401
	Verbenaceae		
653	*Clerodendron thomsonae*	ca. 48	38
654	*Verbena canadensis*	30	99
655	*V. hybrida*	10	25
656		20	130
657	*V. officinalis*	14	99
	Labiatae		
658	*Ajuga reptans*	32	364
659	*Coleus blumei*	24	130
660	*Lamium album*	18	431
661	*Lavandula officinalis*	54	131
662	*Mentha piperita officinalis*	72,84	286
663	*M. piperita vulgaris*	68,72	286
664	*M. spicata*	36,48	249
665	*Nepeta cataria*	36	406
666	*Origanum vulgare*	30	336
667		32	363
668	*Rosmarinus officinalis*	24	362
669	*Salvia officinalis*	14	177
670	*Stachys sylvatica*	48	249
671	*Thymus vulgaris*	30	437
	Solanaceae		
672	*Atropa belladonna*	50	173
673		72	102
674	*Capsicum annuum*	24	375
675	*Datura stramonium*	24	344
676	*Hyoscyamus niger*	34	438
677	*Lycopersicon esculentum*	24	21
678	*Nicotiana glauca*	24	138
679	*N. rustica*	48	138
680	*N. sylvestris*	24	138
681	*N. tabacum*	48	138
682	*Petunia violaceae*	14	95
683	*Solandra grandiflora*	24	192
684	*Solanum dulcamara*	24	102
685	*S. melongena*	24	185
686	*S. nigrum*	24,72	392
687	*S. tuberosum*	48	409
	Scrophulariaceae		
688	*Antirrhinum majus*	16	322
689	*Castilleja arctica*	46	386
690	*Digitalis ambigua*	56	50
691	*D. purpurea*	56	50
692	*Linaria vulgaris*	12	252
693	*Mimulus cardinalis*	16	406
694	*Paulownia tomentosa*	40	451
695	*Penstemon procerus*	16,32	216
696	*Scrophularia aquatica*	80	262
697	*S. nodosa*	36	363
698	*Verbascum blattaria*	30,32	149
699	*V. thapsus*	34,36	149
700	*Veronica chamaedrys*	32	250
701	*V. officinalis*	18,36	31
	Bignoniaceae		
702	*Campsis radicans*	40	355
703	*Catalpa bignonioides*	40	380
704	*C. speciosa*	40	380
705	*Tabebuia pallida*	40	371
	Gesneriaceae		
706	*Saintpaulia ionantha*	28	404
707	*Sinningia speciosa*	56	404
708	*Streptocarpus veitchii*	32	406
	Plantaginaceae		
709	*Plantago lanceolata*	12,13	32
710		24,96	253
711	*P. major*	12	431
712	*P. maritima*	12	148
	Rubiaceae		
713	*Cephalanthus occidentalis*	44	116
714	*Cinchona* spp.	34	88
715	*Coffea arabica*	44	267
716	*C. liberica*	22	116
717		44	167
718	*Gardenia jasminoides*	22	116
	Caprifoliaceae		
719	*Abelia uniflora*	36	94
720	*Lonicera periclymenum*	18,36	194,195
721	*L. sempervirens*	18	94
722		36	194,195
723	*Sambucus canadensis*	36	359
724	*Viburnum opulus*	18	190
725	*V. trilobum*	18	190
	Cucurbitaceae		
726	*Citrullus vulgaris*	22	222
727	*Cucumis melo*	24	468
728	*C. sativus*	14	161
729	*Cucurbita maxima*	40	315
730	*C. moschata*	40	315
731	*C. pepo*	40	52,114
732	*Lagenaria vulgaris*	22	264
	Campanulaceae		
733	*Campanula medium*	34	407
734	*C. persicifolia*	16,17,18, 32	84
735	*C. trachelium*	34	257
736	*Lobelia cardinalis*	14	101
737	*L. tupa*	42	101
	Compositae		
738	*Achillea millefolium*	18	156
739	*Ambrosia trifida*	24	63
740	*Anthemis cotula*	18	156
741	*Aster alpinus*	36	360
742	*A. frikartii*	52,54	6
743	*A. multiflorus*	10	92
744	*Calendula officinalis*	28	296
745		32	449
746	*Callistephus chinensis*	18	411
747	*Centaurea cyanus*	24	129
748	*Chrysanthemum frutescens*	18	157
749	*C. leucanthemum*	36,54	104
750	*C. maximum*	85,90,126, 148,154, 160,171	104
751	*Cichorium endivia*	18	334
752	*C. intybus*	18	390
753	*Cosmos bipinnatus*	24	404
754	*C. sulphureus*	24	404
755	*Dahlia variabilis*	64	240
756	*Gaillardia aristata*	36	63
757		72	14
758	*Helianthus annuus*	34	135
759	*H. tuberosus*	102	444
760	*Lactuca sativa*	18	424

continued

6. CHROMOSOME NUMBERS: SPERMATOPHYTES

	Family and Species	Diploid Number	Reference
	(A)	(B)	(C)
	Angiospermae (Dicotyledoneae)		
	Compositae		
761	*Parthenium argentatum*	36,54,72, 108-111	53
762	*Rudbeckia hirta*	38	22
763	*Senecio vulgaris*	40	1,2
764	*Solidago virgaurea*	18	249
765	*Sonchus oleraceus*	32	390
766	*Tagetes erecta*	24	115
767	*Taraxacum vulgare*	16,24,48	456
768	*Tragopogon porrifolius*	12	321
769	*Xanthium spinosum*	36	162
770	*Zinnia pauciflora*	24	365

Contributors: (a) Darlington, C. D., (b) Sax, Karl.

References: [1] Afzelius, K. 1924. Acta Horti Bergiani (Stockholm) 8:123. [2] Afzelius, K. 1949. Ibid. 15:65. [3] Åkerberg, E. 1942. Hereditas 28:1. [4] Anderson, E., and K. Sax. 1935. J. Arnold Arboretum Harvard Univ. 16:40. [5] Anderson, E., and K. Sax. 1936. Botan. Gaz. 97:433. [6] Annen, E. 1945. Ber. schweiz. botan. Ges. 55:81. [7] Asana, J. J., and R. D. Adatia. 1945. Current Sci. (India) 14:74. [8] Atchison, E. 1947. Am. J. Botany 34:159. [9] Atchison, E. 1947. J. Heredity 38:311. [10] Atchison, E. 1948. Am. J. Botany 35:651. [11] Atchison, E. 1949. J. Elisha Mitchell Sci. Soc. 65:118. [12] Atchison, E. 1951. Am. J. Botany 38:538. [13] Atwood, S. 1936. Ibid. 23:674. [14] Atwood, S. 1937. Cellule 46:389. [15] Avdulov, N. P. 1931. Bull. Appl. Botany Genet. Plant Breeding (U.S.S.R.), Ser. 2, Suppl. 43. [16] Bacchi, O. 1940. J. Agron. São Paulo 3:249. [17] Baldwin, J. T. 1940. Madroño 5:184. [18] Baldwin, J. T., and R. Culp. 1941. Am. J. Botany 28:942. [19] Bambacione, V. M. 1941. Ann. botan. (Rome) 22:99. [20] Bamford, R. 1935. J. Agr. Research 51:945. [21] Barton, D. W. 1950. Am. J. Botany 37:639. [22] Battaglia, E. 1947. Nuovo giorn. botan. ital. 54:560. [23] Battaglia, E. 1947. Rend. accad. nazl. Lincei, Ser. 8A, 2:463. [24] Beal, J. M. 1937. Botan. Gaz. 99:400. [25] Beale, G. H. 1940. J. Genet. 40:337. [26] Behre, K. 1929. Planta 7:208. [27] Björkman, S. O. 1954. Hereditas 40:254. [28] Blackburn, K. B. 1933. Proc. Univ. Durham Phil. Soc. 9:84. [29] Blackburn, K. B., and J. W. H. Harrison. 1924. Ann. Botany (London) 38:361. [30] Bøcher, T. W. 1938. Dansk Botan. Arkiv 9:1. [31] Bøcher, T. W. 1944. Ibid. 11:1. [32] Bøcher, T. W., K. Larsen, and K. Rahn. 1953. Hereditas 39:289. [33] Bolton, J. L., and J. E. R. Greenshields. 1950. Science 112:275. [34] Bosch, E. 1947. Ber. schweiz. botan. Ges. 57:37. [35] Bowden, W. M. 1940. Am. J. Botany 27:357. [36] Bowden, W. M. 1940. Chronica Botan. (Leiden) 6:123. [37] Bowden, W. M. 1945. Am. J. Botany 32:81. [38] Bowden, W. M. 1945. Ibid. 32:191. [39] Bowden, W. M. 1948. Ibid. 35:377. [40] Branas, M. 1932. Compt. rend. 194:121. [41] Breslawetz, L., G. B. Medwedewa, and M. Magilt. 1934. Z. Zücht., A, 19:229. [42] Breviglieri, N., and E. Battaglia. 1955. Caryologia 6:271. [43] Britton, D. M. 1951. Brittonia 7:233. [44] Brown, W. V. 1948. Am. J. Botany 35:382. [45] Brown, W. V. 1950. Bull. Torrey Botan. Club 77:63. [46] Brown, W. V. 1951. Ibid. 78:292. [47] Bruun, H. G. 1932. Symbolae Botan. Upsalienses 1:1. [48] Burbanck, M. P. 1941. Botan. Gaz. 103:247. [49] Burns, G. W. 1942. Am. Midland Naturalist 28:127. [50] Buxton, B. H., and W. C. F. Newton. 1928. J. Genet. 19:269. [51] Carpio, M. D. A. 1952. Genet. iberica 4:47. [52] Castetter, E. F. 1930. Am. J. Botany 17:41. [53] Catcheside, D. G. 1950. Genet. iberica 2:139. [54] Cheeseman, E. E., and L. N. H. Larter. 1935. J. Genet. 30:31. [55] Chin, T. C. 1941. Ann. Botany (London), n.s. 5:535. [56] Christiansen, H. 1950. Kgl. Danske Videnskab. Selskab Biol. Medd. 18:1. [57] Church, G. L. 1936. Am. J. Botany 23:12. [58] Clausen, J. 1931. Botan. Tidsskr. 41:317. [59] Collins, J. L., and K. R. Kerns. 1931. J. Heredity 22:139. [60] Collins, J. L., and K. R. Kerns. 1935. Proc. Hawaiian Acad. Sci. 10:10. [61] Condit, I. J. 1928. Univ. Calif. (Berkeley) Publs. Botany 11:233. [62] Condit, I. J. 1933. Ibid. 17:61. [63] Cooper, D. C., and K. L. Mahony. 1935. Am. J. Botany 22:843. [64] Cooper, G. O. 1935. Botan. Gaz. 97:169. [65] Corti, R. N. 1931. Nuovo giorn. botan. ital. 38:230. [66] Covas, G. 1949. Darwiniana 9:158. [67] Covas, G., and B. Schnack. 1944. Rev. argentina agron. 11:89. [68] Crane, M. B. 1936. Roy. Hort. Soc. Conf. Cherries and Soft Fruits, p. 121. [69] D'Amato, F. 1946. Nuovo giorn. botan. ital. 53:170. [70] D'Amato, F. 1948. Caryologia 1:48. [71] Danielsson, D. 1946.

continued

Sveriges Pomol. Fören. Årsskr., 1945, p. 7. [72] Dark, S. O. S. 1932. Ann. Botany (London) 46:965. [73] Dark, S. O. S. 1932. New Phytologist 31:310. [74] Dark, S. O. S. 1936. J. Genet. 32:353. [75] Darlington, C. D. 1928. Ibid. 19:213. [76] Darlington, C. D. 1929. Genetica (Haag) 11:267. [77] Darlington, C. D. 1929. J. Genet. 21:207. [78] Darlington, C. D. 1930. Ibid. 22:65. [79] Darlington, C. D. 1931. Ibid. 24:405. [80] Darlington, C. D. 1933. Ibid. 28:327. [81] Darlington, C. D. 1936. Proc. Roy. Soc. (London), B, 121:464. [82] Darlington, C.D., J. B. Hair, and R. Harcombe. 1951. Heredity 5:233. [83] Darlington, C. D., and L. F. La Cour. 1942. The handling of chromosomes. Allen and Unwin, London. [84] Darlington, C. D., and L. F. La Cour. 1950. Heredity 4:217. [85] Darlington, C. D., and A. A. Moffett. 1930. J. Genet. 22:129. [86] Darlington, C. D., and A. P. Wylie. 1955. Chromosome atlas of flowering plants. Allen and Unwin, London. [87] Darrow, G. M., et al. 1944. Bull. Torrey Botan. Club 71:498. [88] Dawson, R. F. 1948. Lloydia 11:81. [89] De Almeida, J. L. F. 1946. Bol. soc. broter. 20:201. [90] De Castro, D., and F. C. Fontes. 1946. Broter. cienc. nat. 15:38. [91] De Haan, I., and J. Doorenbos. 1951. Mededel. Landbouwhogeschool Wageningen 51:151. [92] Delisle, A. L. 1937. Am. J. Botany 24:741. [93] De Litardière, R. 1950. Bol. soc. broter. 24:79. [94] De Poucques, M. L. 1949. Rev. gén. botan. 56:5,74,172. [95] Dermen, H. 1931. Am. J. Botany 18:250. [96] Dermen, H. 1931. J. Arnold Arboretum Harvard Univ. 12:281. [97] Dermen, H. 1932. Ibid. 13:50. [98] Dermen, H. 1932. Ibid. 13:410. [99] Dermen, H. 1936. Cytologia (Tokyo) 7:160. [100] Dermen, H. 1949. J. Heredity 40:162. [101] De Vilmorin, R., and M. Simonet. 1927. Compt. rend. soc. biol. 96:166. [102] De Vilmorin, R., and M. Simonet. 1928. Z. induktive Abstammungs.- u. Vererbungslehre, Suppl. 2:1520. [103] Dodds, K. S., and N. W. Simmonds. 1948. J. Genet. 48:285. [104] Dowrick, G. J. 1952. Heredity 6:365. [105] Duffield, J. W. 1940. Am. J. Botany 27:787. [106] Duffield, J. W. 1943. Chronica Botan. (Leiden) 7:390. [107] Edman, G. 1929. Acta Horti Bergiani (Stockholm) 9:165. [108] Ehrenberg, L. 1945. Botan. Notiser, p. 430. [109] Eichhorn, A. 1937. Cytologia (Tokyo), Fujii jubilaei vol. (1):447. [110] Einset, J. 1947. Gentes Herbarum (Ithaca) 7:181. [111] Elliott, F. C. 1949. Iowa State Coll. J. Sci. 24:44. [112] Emme, H. 1930. Züchter 2:65. [113] Erlandsson, S. 1942. Hereditas 28:503. [114] Erwin, A. T., and E. S. Haber. 1930. Iowa Agr. Expt. Sta. Bull. 263:343. [115] Eyster, W. H. 1941. Proc. 7th Intern. Congr. Genet., Edinburgh, 1939, p. 117. [116] Fagerlind, F. 1937. Acta Horti Bergiani (Stockholm) 11:195. [117] Favarger, C. 1946. Ber. schweiz. botan. Ges. 56:365. [118] Favarger, C. 1949. Ibid. 59:62. [119] Fernandes, A., and R. Fernandes. 1946. Acta Univ. Conimbricensis 1. [120] Florin, R. 1932. Svensk Botan. Tidskr. 26:205. [121] Flory, W. S. 1934. Cytologia (Tokyo) 6:1. [122] Flory, W. S. 1936. J. Arnold Arboretum Harvard Univ. 17:83. [123] Flory, W. S. 1937. Cytologia (Tokyo), Fujii jubilaei vol. (1):171. [124] Flovik, K. 1940. Hereditas 26:430. [125] Foster, R. C. 1933. J. Arnold Arboretum Harvard Univ. 14:386. [126] Frahm-Liliveld, J. A. 1953. Euphytica (Netherlands) 2:46. [127] Francini, E. N. 1931. Nuovo giorn. botan. ital. 38:155. [128] Freter, L. E., and W. V. Brown. 1955. Bull. Torrey Botan. Club 82:121. [129] Fritsch, R. 1935. Dissertation. Univ. Berlin. [130] Furusato, K. 1940. Botany and Zool. (Tokyo) 8:1303. [131] Garcia, J. G. 1942. Bol. soc. broter. 16:183. [132] Gardé, A., and N. Gardé. 1949. Agronomia Lusitana 11:91. [133] Gardé, A., and N. Gardé. 1951. Genet. iberica 3:23. [134] Gauger, W. 1937. Planta 26:529. [135] Geisler, F. 1931. Butler Univ. Botan. Studies 2:53. [136] Geitler, L. 1936. Jahrb. wiss. Botan. 83:707. [137] Gentscheff, G. 1937. Dissertation. Univ. Sofia, Bulgaria. [138] Goodspeed, T. H. 1945. Univ. Calif. (Berkeley) Publs. Botany 18:335. [139] Goodspeed, T. H., F. M. Uber, and P. Avery. 1935. Ibid. 18:33. [140] Granick, E. B. 1944. Am. J. Botany 31:283. [141] Greco, R. N. 1929. Nuovo giorn. botan. ital. 36:57. [142] Gregory, W. C. 1941. Trans. Am. Phil. Soc., n.s. 31:443. [143] Griffee, F. 1927. Univ. Minn. Studies Biol. Sci. 6:319. [144] Grimm, J. 1912. Flora (Ger.) 104:309. [145] Gulline, H. F. 1952. Papers & Proc. Roy. Soc. Tasmania 86:131. [146] Hagerup, O. 1928. Dansk Botan. Arkiv 6:1. [147] Hagerup, O. 1932. Hereditas 16:19. [148] Hagerup, O. 1941. Botan. Tidsskr. 45:385. [149] Håkansson, A. 1926. Acta Univ. Lundensis, N. F. Avd. 2, 21:471. [150] Hansen, A. A., and H. D. Hill. 1953. Bull. Torrey Botan. Club 80:16. [151] Hansen, A. A., and H. D. Hill. 1953. Ibid. 80:113. [152] Haque, A. 1952. Rept. John Innes Hort. Inst. 42:47. [153] Harada, I. 1942. Japan. J. Genet. 18:92. [154] Harada, I. 1947. Cytologia (Tokyo) 14:214. [155] Harada, I. 1948. Japan. J. Genet. 23:13. [156] Harling, G. 1950. Acta Horti Bergiani (Stockholm)

continued

15:135. [157] Harling, G. 1951. Ibid. 16:73. [158] Hartung, M. E. 1946. Am. J. Botany 33:516. [159] Heilborn, O. 1939. Hereditas 25:224. [160] Heim, P. 1950. Encyclopedie mycologique. P. Lechevalier, Paris. [161] Heimlich, L. F. 1927. Proc. Natl. Acad. Sci. U. S. 13:113. [162] Heiser, C. B., and T. W. Whitaker. 1948. Am. J. Botany 35:179. [163] Heitz, E. 1927. In T. Heitz, ed. Abhandl. naturw. Hamburg 21:47. [164] Heitz, E. 1929. Ber. deut. botan. Ges. 47:274. [165] Heitz, T. 1927. Abhandl. naturw. Hamburg 21:47. [166] Heslop-Harrison, J. 1953. Ann. Botany (London), n.s. 17:539. [167] Heyn, A. N. J. 1936. Landbouw 12:11. [168] Hill, H. D., and W. M. Myers. 1948. J. Am. Soc. Agron. 40:466. [169] Hirayoshi, I., and M. Matsumura. 1952. Japan. J. Breeding 1:219. [170] Hirayoshi, I., and Y. Nakamura. 1943. Botany and Zool. (Tokyo) 11:73. [171] Hoar, C. S., and E. J. Haertl. 1932. Botan. Gaz. 93:197. [172] Hofmeyer, J. D. J. 1945. S. African J. Sci. 41:225. [173] Homedes, R. J. 1943. Anales escuela perit. agr. (Barcelona) 3. [174] Howard, H. W. 1938. J. Genet. 35:383. [175] Howard, H. W. 1939. Cytologia (Tokyo) 10:77. [176] Howard, H. W., and I. Manton. 1946. Ann. Botany (London), n.s. 10:1. [177] Hruby, K. 1935. Studies Plant Physiol. Lab. Charles Univ. 5:1. [178] Hurcombe, R. 1947. J. S. African Botany 13:107. [179] Hurst, C. C. 1928. Z. induktive Abstammungs.- u. Vererbungslehre, Suppl. 2:866. [180] Huskins, C. L. 1927. J. Genet. 18:315. [181] Huttleston, D. G. 1949. Bull. Torrey Botan. Club 76:307. [182] Ichijima, K. 1926. Genetics 11:590. [183] Ito, K. 1942. Cytologia (Tokyo) 12:313. [184] Jacobsen, P. 1954. Hereditas 40:252. [185] Janaki-Ammal, E. K. 1934. Cytologia (Tokyo) 5:453. [186] Janaki-Ammal, E. K. 1938. Nature 141:925. [187] Janaki-Ammal, E. K. 1941. J. Genet. 41:217. [188] Janaki-Ammal, E. K. 1948. J. Roy. Hort. Soc. 73:117. [189] Janaki-Ammal, E. K. 1951. Ibid. 76:269. [190] Janaki-Ammal, E. K. 1953. Current Sci. (India) 22:4. [191] Janaki-Ammal, E. K. 1953. Indian J. Genet. Plant Breeding 12:44. [192] Janaki-Ammal, E. K. Unpublished, 1955. [193] Janaki-Ammal, E. K., I. C. Enoch, and M. Bridgwater. 1950. Rhododendron Camellia Yearbook (London) 5:78. [194] Janaki-Ammal, E. K., and B. Saunders. 1952. Kew Bull. Roy. Botan. Gardens, p. 539. [195] Janaki-Ammal, E. K., and R. Seligman. 1952. J. Roy. Hort. Soc. 77:221. [196] Jaretzky, R. 1927. Ber. deut. botan. Ges. 45:48. [197] Jaretzky, R. 1928. Jahrb. wiss. Botan. 69:357. [198] Jaretzky, R. 1930. Planta 10:120. [199] Jaretzky, R. 1932. Jahrb. wiss. Botan. 76:485. [200] Jensen, H., and A. Levan. 1941. Hereditas 27:220. [201] Jensen, H. W. 1944. Am. Naturalist 78:375. [202] Johnson, D. S. 1910. J. Exptl. Zool. 9:715. [203] Johnsson, H. 1941. Acta Univ. Lundensis, N. F. Avd. 2, 37:3. [204] Johnsson, H. 1942. Hereditas 28:228. [205] Jørgensen, C. A. 1923. Dansk Botan. Tidsskr. 38:81. [206] Jørgensen, C. A. 1927. J. Genet. 18:63. [207] Joshi, A. B., and M. W. Hardas. 1953. Current Sci. (India) 22:384. [208] Kagawa, F. 1929. J. Coll. Agr. Tokyo Imp. Univ. 10:173. [209] Kamemoto, H. 1950. Bull. Am. Orchid Soc. 19:366. [210] Kano, T. 1929. Proc. Crop Sci. Soc. Japan 4:15. [211] Karasawa, K. 1940. Japan. J. Botany 11:129. [212] Karpechenko, G. D. 1924. Bull. Appl. Botany Plant Breeding (Leningrad) 13:4. [213] Karpechenko, G. D. 1925. Ibid. 14:143. [214] Katagiri, S. 1952. Japan. J. Breeding 1:233. [215] Kawakami, I. 1930. Botan. Mag. (Tokyo) 44:319. [216] Keck, D. D. 1945. Am. Midland Naturalist 33:128. [217] Kihara, H. 1924. Mem. Coll. Sci. Kyoto Imp. Univ. 1:1. [218] King, J. R., and R. Bamford. 1937. J. Heredity 28:279. [219] Kobel, F. 1928. Z. induktive Abstammungs.- u. Vererbungslehre, Suppl. 2:927. [220] Kostoff, D. 1940. Phytopathol. Z. 13:91. [221] Kostoff, D., H. Dogadkina, and A. Tichonowa. 1935. Doklady Akad. Nauk S.S.S.R., Ser. 8, 3:401. [222] Kozhuchow, Z. A. 1925. Bull. Appl. Botany Plant Breeding (Leningrad) 14:96. [223] Krause, O. 1930. Ber. deut. botan. Ges. 48:9. [224] Kreuter, E. 1930. Planta 11:1. [225] Krishnaswamy, N., and V. S. Raman. 1948. J. Indian Botan. Soc. 27:77. [226] Krishnaswamy, N., and V. S. Raman. 1949. Current Sci. (India) 18:376. [227] Krug, C. A. 1943. Botan. Gaz. 104:602. [228] Kumar, L. S. S., and S. G. Ranade. 1952. Current Sci. (India) 21:75. [229] Kuwada, Y. 1915. Botan. Mag. (Tokyo) 29:83. [230] La Cour, L. F. 1946. Rept. John Innes Hort. Inst. 36:19. [231] La Cour, L. F. 1951. Heredity 5:37. [232] La Cour, L. F. 1952. Rept. John Innes Hort. Inst. 42:47. [233] Langlet, O. F. J. 1928. Svensk Botan. Tidskr. 22:169. [234] Langlet, O. F. J. 1932. Ibid. 26:381. [235] Langlet, O. F. J. 1936. Ibid. 30:288. [236] Langlet, O. F. J., and E. Söderberg. 1927. Acta Horti Bergiani (Stockholm) 9:85. [237] Lapin, W. 1937. Trudy Vsesoyuz. Nauch.-Issledovatel. Inst. Vlazn. Subtrop. 1:1. [238] Lapin, W. 1937. Ibid. 1:69.

continued

6. CHROMOSOME NUMBERS: SPERMATOPHYTES

[239] Lawrence, W. J. C. 1930. Genetica (Haag) 12:269. [240] Lawrence, W. J. C. 1931. J. Genet. 24:257. [241] Lee, C. L. 1954. Am. J. Botany 41:545. [242] Levan, A. 1931. Hereditas 15:347. [243] Levan, A. 1935. Ibid. 20:289. [244] Levan, A. 1936. Ibid. 22:1. [245] Levan, A. 1942. Ibid. 28:245. [246] Levan, A. 1942. Ibid. 28:345. [247] Longley, A. E. 1925. J. Wash. Acad. Sci. 15:347. [248] Löve, A. 1942. Hereditas 28:289. [249] Löve, A., and D. Löve. 1942. Botan. Notiser, p. 19. [250] Löve, A., and D. Löve. 1944. Arkiv Botan. 31A(12):1. [251] Löve, A., and D. Löve. 1944. Ibid. 31B(1):1. [252] Löve, A., and D. Löve. 1948. Atvinnudeild Háskólans Rit Landbúnadardeildar (Reykjavik), B-flokkur, 3. [253] MacCullagh, D. 1934. Genetica (Haag) 16:1. [254] Malheiros, M. 1942. Agronomia Lusitana 4:231. [255] Mangelsdorf, P. C., and R. G. Reeves. 1939. Texas Agr. Expt. Sta. Bull. 574:75. [256] Manton, I. 1932. Ann. Botany (London) 46:509. [257] Marchal, E. 1920. Acad. roy. Belg. Classe sci. Mém., II, 4:3. [258] Mather, K. 1932. J. Genet. 26:129. [259] Matsuura, H., and S. Okuno. 1936. Japan. J. Genet. 12:42. [260] Matsuura, H., and S. Okuno. 1943. Cytologia (Tokyo) 13:1. [261] Matsuura, H., and T. Suto. 1935. J. Fac. Sci. Hokkaido Univ., V, 5:33. [262] Maude, P. F. 1940. New Phytologist 39:17. [263] McAulay, A. L., F. D. Cruickshank, and R. G. Brett. 1936. Nature 138:550. [264] McKay, J. W. 1931. Univ. Calif. (Berkeley) Publs. Botany 16:339. [265] Medwedewa, G. B. 1935. Z. induktive Abstammungs.- u. Verebungslehre 70:170. [266] Mehra, P. N., and T. N. Khoshoo. 1948. Proc. 34th Indian Sci. Congr., 1947, (3):167. [267] Mendes, A. J. T. 1945. Rev. agr. (Piracicaba) 20:412. [268] Meurman, O. 1925. Soc. Sci. Fennica, Commentationes Biol. 2:3. [269] Meurman, O. 1928. Hereditas 11:289. [270] Meurman, O. 1929. J. Genet. 21:85. [271] Meurman, O. 1933. Hereditas 18:145. [272] Meyer, J. R. 1944. Genetics 29:199. [273] Miller, E. W. 1930. Proc. Univ. Durham Phil. Soc. 8:267. [274] Moffett, A. A. 1931. J. Pomol. Hort. Sci. 9:100. [275] Moffett, A. A. 1932. J. Genet. 25:315. [276] Moore, R. J. 1946. Can. J. Research, C, 24:66. [277] Moore, R. J. 1947. Am. J. Botany 34:527. [278] Morinaga, T. 1929. Cytologia (Tokyo) 1:16. [279] Morinaga, T., et al. 1929. Botan. Mag. (Tokyo) 43:589. [280] Moriya, A., and A. Kondo. 1949. Japan. J. Genet. 25:131. [281] Moyer, L. S. 1934. Botan. Gaz. 95:678. [282] Mukherjee, S. K. 1950. Nature 166:196. [283] Müntzing, A. 1951. Hereditas 37:17. [284] Myers, W. M. 1944. J. Agr. Research 68:21. [285] Nagai, K., and T. Sasaoka. 1930. Japan. J. Genet. 5:151. [286] Nagao, M. 1941. Ibid. 17:109. [287] Nagao, S. 1929. Mem. Coll. Sci. Kyoto Imp. Univ., B, 4:177. [288] Nagao, S. 1933. Ibid., B, 8:81. [289] Nagao, S. 1938. Comment. Papers Agron. Akemine. [290] Nagajima, G. 1936. Japan. J. Genet. 12:211. [291] Nakamura, W. 1934. Bull. Kagoshima Imp. Coll. Agr. Forestry 1:11. [292] Namikawa, J., and M. Higashi. 1928. Botan. Mag. (Tokyo) 42:436. [293] Nandi, H. K. 1936. J. Genet. 33:327. [294] Nebel, B. R. 1929. Gartenbauwissenschaft 1:549. [295] Negodi, G. 1935. Atti soc. nat. e mat. Modena 67:3. [296] Negodi, G. 1936. Riv. biol. (Perugia) 20:15. [297] Negodi, G. 1951. Scientia Genet. (Turin) 4:94. [298] Neves, J. de B. 1944. Dissertation. Univ. Coimbra, Portugal. [299] Neves, J. de B. 1952. Bol. soc. broter. 26:1. [300] Nielsen, E. L. 1939. Am. J. Botany 26:366. [301] Nissen, Ø. 1950. Agron. J. 42:136. [302] Noack, K. L. 1939. Z. induktive Abstammungs.- u. Vererbungslehre 76:569. [303] Nordenskiöld, H. 1941. Botan. Notiser, p. 12. [304] Nordenskiöld, H. 1951. Hereditas 37:325. [305] Nygren, A. 1954. Ibid. 40:377. [306] Ogawa, K. 1929. Mem. Coll. Sci. Kyoto Imp. Univ. 4:309. [307] Oksijuk, P. 1935. J. botan. acad. sci. R. S. S. Ukraine 4:15. [308] Olmo, H. P. 1937. Cytologia (Tokyo), Fujii jubilaei vol. (1):606. [309] Osawa, J. 1920. Bull. Imp. Agr. Expt. Sta. Tokyo 1:318. [310] Pal, N. 1952. Proc. Natl. Inst. Sci. India 18:363. [311] Pardi, P. N. 1934. Nuovo giorn. botan. ital. 40:576. [312] Parthasarathy, N. 1946. Current Sci. (India) 15:233. [313] Patel, J. S., and G. V. Narayana. 1937. Ibid. 5:479. [314] Pathak, G. N., and R. S. Yadava. 1951. Ibid. 20:304. [315] Pearson, O. H., R. Hopp, and G. W. Bohn. 1951. Proc. Am. Soc. Hort. Sci. 57:310. [316] Pereira, A. de L. 1948. Portugaliae Acta Biol., A, 2:101. [317] Perry, B. A. 1943. Am. J. Botany 30:527. [318] Peterson, D. 1936. Botan. Notiser, p. 281. [319] Peto, F. H. 1933. J. Genet. 28:113. [320] Phillips, H. M. 1938. Chronica Botan. (Leiden) 4:385. [321] Poddubnaja-Arnoldi, W., N. Steschina, and A. Sosnovetz. 1935. Beih. botan. Zentr., A, 53:309. [322] Propach, H. 1935. Planta 23:349. [323] Propach, H. 1939. Gartenbauwissenschaft 14:642. [324] Purewal, S. S., and G. S. Randhawa. 1947. Indian J. Agr. Sci. 17:129. [325] Raghavan, T. S., and K. R. Venkatasubban. 1943. Proc. Indian Acad. Sci. 17(B):118.

continued

[326] Ramanathan, K. 1950. Current Sci. (India) 19:155. [327] Rao, Y. S. 1953. Proc. Natl. Inst. Sci. India 19:563. [328] Rattenbury, J. A. 1948. Madroño 9:258. [329] Ray, C. 1944. Am. J. Botany 31:241. [330] Reese, G. 1950. Planta 38:324. [331] Remski, M. F. 1954. Botan. Gaz. 116:163. [332] Resende, F. 1937. Planta 26:757. [333] Rhoades, M. M. 1950. J. Heredity 41:58. [334] Rick, C. M. 1953. Proc. Am. Soc. Hort. Sci. 61:459. [335] Rohweder, H. 1937. Planta 27:500. [336] Rutland, J. P. 1941. New Phytologist 40:210. [337] Sachs, L. 1953. J. Agr. Sci. 43:204. [338] Sakai, B. 1951. Kromosomo (Tokyo) 11:425. [339] Sakai, K. 1935. Japan. J. Genet. 11:68. [340] Sansome, E. R. 1933. Cytologia (Tokyo) 5:15. [341] Sansome, E. R., and L. La Cour. 1934. Lily Yearbook, p. 40. [342] Santos, J. K. 1924. Botan. Gaz. 77:353. [343] Santos, J. K. 1928. Philippine J. Sci. 37:417. [344] Satina, S., A. D. Bergner, and A. F. Blakeslee. 1941. Am. J. Botany 28:383. [345] Sato, D. 1935. Botan. Mag. (Tokyo) 49:298. [346] Sato, D. 1938. Cytologia (Tokyo) 9:203. [347] Sato, D. 1942. Japan. J. Botany 12:57. [348] Sato, D. 1946. Cytologia (Tokyo) 14:174. [349] Sato, D. 1948. Japan. J. Genet. 23:44. [350] Sax, H. J. 1930. J. Arnold Arboretum Harvard Univ. 11:220. [351] Sax, K. 1929. Proc. Am. Soc. Hort. Sci. 26:32. [352] Sax, K. 1931. J. Arnold Arboretum Harvard Univ. 12:3. [353] Sax, K. 1931. Ibid. 12:198. [354] Sax, K. 1933. Ibid. 14:82. [355] Sax, K. 1933. Ibid. 14:274. [356] Sax, K. 1936. Ibid. 17:352. [357] Sax, K., and E. C. Abbe. 1932. Ibid. 13:37. [358] Sax, K., and J. M. Beal. 1934. Ibid. 15:225. [359] Sax, K., and D. A. Kribs. 1930. Ibid. 11:147. [360] Sax, K., and H. J. Sax. 1933. Ibid. 14:356. [361] Schafer, B., and L. La Cour. 1934. Ann. Botany (London) 48:693. [362] Scheel, M. 1931. Botan. Arch. 32:148. [363] Scheerer, H. 1939. Planta 29:636. [364] Scheerer, H. 1940. Ibid. 30:716. [365] Schnack, B., and G. Covas. 1947. Haumania 1:32. [366] Schoennagel, E. 1931. Botan. Jahrb. 64:266. [367] Schürhoff, P. N. 1926. Die Zytologie der Blütenpflanzen. F. Enke, Stuttgart. [368] Sealy, J. R., and D. A. Webb. 1950. J. Ecol. 38:223. [369] Senn, H. A. 1938. Bibliographia genet. (Haag)12:175. [370] Shah, G. L. 1953. Current Sci. (India) 22:50. [371] Simmonds, N. W. 1954. Heredity 8:139. [372] Simonet, M. 1932. Compt. rend. 195:738. [373] Simonet, M. 1934. Ann. sci. nat. Botan. et biol. végétale, Ser. 10, 16:229. [374] Simonet, M., and C. Miedzyrzecki. 1932. Compt. rend. soc. biol. 111:969. [375] Sinha, N. P. 1950. Indian J. Genet. Plant Breeding 10:36. [376] Sinoto, Y. 1929. Cytologia (Tokyo) 1:109. [377] Skovsted, A. 1935. J. Genet. 31:263. [378] Skovsted, A. 1941. Compt. rend. trav. lab. Carlsberg, Ser. physiol., 23:195. [379] Smith, C. M. 1929. Botan. Gaz. 87:507. [380] Smith, E. C. 1941. J. Arnold Arboretum Harvard Univ. 22:219. [381] Smith, E. C. 1943. Ibid. 24:275. [382] Smith, F. H. 1934. Proc. Am. Phil. Soc. 74:193. [383] Snoad, B. 1951. Heredity 5:279. [384] Snoad, B. 1952. Rept. John Innes Hort. Inst. 42:47. [385] Sokolovskaja, A., and O. Strelkova. 1938. Compt. rend. acad. sci. U.R.S.S. 21:68. [386] Sokolovskaja, A., and O. Strelkova. 1941. Ibid. 32:144. [387] Speese, B. M. 1939. Am. J. Botany 26:853. [388] Spier, J. D. 1934. Can. J. Research 11:347. [389] Stebbins, G. L. 1948. Science 108:5. [390] Stebbins, G. L., J. A. Jenkins, and M. S. Walters. 1953. Univ. Calif. (Berkeley) Publs. Botany 26:401. [391] Stebbins, G. L., and R. M. Love. 1941. Am. J. Botany 28:371. [392] Stebbins, G. L., and E. P. Paddock. 1949. Madroño 10:70. [393] Steindl, F. 1935. Ber. schweiz. botan. Ges. 44:343. [394] Steiner, E. 1944. Botan. Gaz. 105:374. [395] Stewart, R. N. 1947. Am. J. Botany 34:19. [396] Stiff, M. L. 1951. Virginia J. Sci., n.s. 2:317. [397] Stockwell, P. 1935. Botan. Gaz. 96:565. [398] Stokes, J. 1937. Ibid. 99:387. [399] Storey, W. B. 1950. Pacific Sci. 4:37. [400] Straub, J. 1937. Ber. deut. botan. Ges. 55:160. [401] Strey, M. 1931. Planta 14:682. [402] Sugihara, Y. 1940. Science Repts. Tohoku Imp. Univ., Ser. 4, 15:13. [403] Sugiura, T. 1931. Botan. Mag. (Tokyo) 45:353. [404] Sugiura, T. 1936. Cytologia (Tokyo) 7:544. [405] Sugiura, T. 1936. Proc. Imp. Acad. Tokyo 12:144. [406] Sugiura, T. 1939-40. Cytologia (Tokyo) 10:73, 205, 324, 363, 558. [407] Sugiura, T. 1942. Ibid. 12:418. [408] Suomalainen, E. 1947. Ann. Acad. Sci. Fennicae, A(4), 13:1. [409] Swaminathan, M. S. 1954. Genetics 39:59. [410] Täckholm, G. 1922. Acta Horti Bergiani (Stockholm) 7(3). [411] Tahara, M., and N. Shimotomai. 1926. Botan. Mag. (Tokyo) 40:132. [412] Takenaka, Y. 1950. Cytologia (Tokyo) 16:95. [413] Tamamschjan, S. 1933. Bull. Appl. Botany Genet. Plant Breeding (U.S.S.R.), Ser. 2, 2:137. [414] Tanaka, N. 1937. Cytologia (Tokyo), Fujii jubilaei vol. (2):814. [415] Tateoka, T. 1954. Cytologia (Tokyo) 19:317. [416] Taylor, H. 1945. Brittonia 5:337. [417] Taylor, W. R.

continued

1920. Contribs. Botan. Lab. Univ. Penna. 5:111. [418] Taylor, W. R. 1925. Am. J. Botany 12:219. [419] Taylor, W. R. 1925. Ibid. 12:238. [420] Thomas, P. T. 1940. J. Genet. 40:141. [421] Thomas, P. T. Unpublished, 1955. [422] Thomas, P. T., and S. H. Revell. 1946. Ann. Botany (London), n.s. 10:159. [423] Thompson, H. J. 1953. Contribs. Stanford Univ. Dudley Herbarium 4:73. [424] Thompson, R. C., T. W. Whitaker, and W. F. Kosar. 1941. J. Agr. Research 63:91. [425] Ting, Y. C., and A. E. Kehr. 1953. J. Heredity 44:207. [426] Tjio, J. H. 1948. Hereditas 34:135. [427] Tomé, G. A. 1947. Rev. fac. agron. y vet. Univ. Buenos Aires 11:299. [428] Tschechow, W. 1930. Planta 9:673. [429] Tschechow, W. 1933. Bull. Appl. Botany Genet. Plant Breeding (U.S.S.R.), Ser. 2, 1:119. [430] Tschechow, W. 1935. Trudy Biol. Nauch.- Issledovatel. Inst. 1:143. [431] Turesson, G. 1938. Ann. Agr. Coll. Swed. 5:405. [432] Ufer, M. 1937. Z. induktive Abstammungs.- u. Vererbungslehre 73:390. [433] Uhl, C. H. 1948. Am. J. Botany 35:695. [434] Upcott, M. 1936. J. Genet. 33:135. [435] Upcott, M., and L. La Cour. 1936. Ibid. 33:237. [436] Vaarama, A. 1943. Hereditas 29:191. [437] Vaarama, A. 1947. Arch. Soc. Zool. Botan. Fennicae "Vanamo" 2:55. [438] Vaarama, A. 1950. Hereditas 36:342. [439] Vaarama, A. 1951. Ibid. 37:290. [440] Van Dillewijn, C. 1939. Ned. Boschbouw. Tijdschr. 12:470. [441] Van Dillewijn, C. 1942. Genetica (Haag) 22:131. [442] Venkatasubban, K. R. 1946. Proc. Indian Acad. Sci. 23(B):281. [443] Vermeulen, P. 1947. Studies on dactylorchids. National Univ., Utrecht, Netherlands. [444] Wagner, S. 1932. Z. induktive Abstammungs.- u. Vererbungslehre 61:76. [445] Walters, M. S., and D. U. Gerstel. 1948. Am. J. Botany 35:141. [446] Warburg, E. F. 1938. New Phytologist 37:189. [447] Watkins, G. M. 1936. Am. J. Botany 23:328. [448] Webber, J. M. 1934. J. Agr. Research 49:223. [449] Weddle, C. 1941. Proc. Am. Soc. Hort. Sci. 39:393. [450] Weijer, J. 1952. Genetica (Haag) 26:1. [451] Westfall, J. J. 1949. Am. J. Botany 36:805. [452] Wetzel, R. 1929. Dissertation. Marburg Univ., Germany. [453] Whitaker, T. W. 1933. J. Arnold Arboretum Harvard Univ. 14:376. [454] Whyte, R. O. 1929. New Phytologist 28:319. [455] Winge, Ø. 1917. Compt. rend. trav. lab. Carlsberg 13:131. [456] Woess, E. T. 1949. Oesterr. botan. Z. 96:56. [457] Woodworth, R. H. 1929. Botan. Gaz. 88:383. [458] Woodworth, R. H. 1930. Am. J. Botany 17:863. [459] Woodworth, R. H. 1931. J. Arnold Arboretum Harvard Univ. 12:206. [460] Wright, J. W. 1944. J. Forestry 42:489. [461] Wulff, H. D. 1937. Ber. deut. botan. Ges. 55:262. [462] Wulff, H. D. 1937. Jahrb. wiss. Botan. 84:812. [463] Wulff, H. D. 1938. Ber. deut. botan. Ges. 56:247. [464] Wulff, H. D. 1939. Ibid. 57:84. [465] Wulff, H. D. 1950. Ibid. 63:64. [466] Wulff, H. D. 1954. Arch. Pharm. 287:529. [467] Wylie, A. P. 1954. Am. Rose Ann. 39:36. [468] Yamaha, G., and S. Suematsu. 1936. Science Repts. Tokyo Bunrika Daigaku, B, 3:21. [469] Yamashita, K. 1935. Japan. J. Genet. 11:360. [470] Yamazaki, R. 1936. Ibid. 12:101. [471] Young, J. O. 1940. Botan. Gaz. 101:839. [472] Zaitzew, G. S. 1927. Bull. Appl. Botany Genet. Plant Breeding (U.S.S.R.), Ser. 2, 18:1. [473] Zielinski, Q. B. 1953. Botan. Gaz. 114:265. [474] Zohary, M. 1953. Palestine J. Botany, Jerusalem Ser., 5:4.

II. LINKAGE GROUPS, HERITABILITY, AND HYBRIDIZATION

7. SEX LINKAGE: MAN

	Mutation	Phenotypic Expression			Reference
		Hemizygote $\overline{X}Y$	Heterozygote $\overline{X}X$	Homozygote $\overline{X}\overline{X}$	
	(A)	(B)	(C)	(D)	(E)
1	Ocular albinism	Lack of pigment in globe	Fundal changes	Unknown	9
2	Opic atrophy	Blindness	Occasional blindness	Unknown	30
3	Choroidemia	Night blindness, constricted visual fields, blindness	Depigmented retina	Unknown	17
4	Color blindness, red-green[1]	Inability to distinguish red and green	Mild manifestation	Inability to distinguish red and green	13,18, 21,31
5	Macular dystrophy	Loss of central vision	Absent	Unknown	27
6	Hemeralopia	Night blindness with myopia	Absent	Unknown	27
7	Megalocornea	Large cornea	Occasional manifestation	Unknown	11
8	Microphthalmia	Abnormally small eyes and blindness	Absent	Absent	22
9	Nystagmus	Severe involuntary movement of eyeball	Slight involuntary movement of eyeball	Unknown	23,27
10	Ophthalmoplegia	Paralysis of eye muscles, myopia, knee jerks absent	Knee jerks absent	Unknown	24
11	Retinal detachment, congenital	Retinal detachment and blindness	Absent	Blindness[2]	7,28,33
12	Retinitis pigmentosa	Choroidoretinal degeneration	Tapetal reflex	Unknown	10
13	Deaf-mutism	Profound deafness at birth	Absent	Profound deafness at birth	19,25
	Hemophilia				
14	Classical[3]	Severe bleeder	Absent	Severe bleeder	4,14, 18,26
15	Mild[4]	Mild bleeder	Slight occasional manifestation	Unknown	12
16	Plasma thromboplastin component deficiency	Severe bleeder	Slight manifestation	Unknown	3,15
17	Blood group Xg^a	Erythrocytes agglutinate with antiserum	Erythrocytes agglutinate with antiserum	Erythrocytes agglutinate with antiserum	16
18	Hypophosphatemia	Low serum inorganic phosphorus	Low serum inorganic phosphorus	Unknown	34
19	Glucose-6-PO_4 dehydrogenase deficiency	Hemolytic anemia with drugs	Absent	Hemolytic anemia with drugs	5
20	Hypoparathyroidism	Low serum Ca^{++}, tetany	Absent	Unknown	20
21	Nephrogenic diabetes insipidus	High urinary output unaffected by pitressin	Slight increase in urinary output	Unknown	32
22	Peroneal atrophy	Peroneal atrophy	Occasional manifestation	Unknown	1
23	Duchenne muscular dystrophy	Progressive atrophy of muscles	Mild serum enzymatic changes	Unknown	6,29
24	Anhidrotic ectodermal dysplasia	Widespread ectodermal defects	Absent	Unknown	8
25	Ichthyosis simplex	Scaly skin	Absent	Scaly skin	8
26	Keratosis follicularis (Lameris)	Multiple horny skin growths	Absent	Unknown	8
27	Alopecia congenita	Hairlessness	Absent	Unknown	8
28	White occipital lock of hair	White lock of hair at occiput	Absent	Unknown	8
29	Idiocy	Idiocy with microcephaly	Absent	Unknown	2

/1/ Gene symbol = b. /2/ Questionable. /3/ Gene symbol = h. /4/ Gene symbol = h^m.

Contributor: Graham, John B.

References: [1] Allan, W. 1939. Arch. Internal Med. 63:1123. [2] Allan, W., et al. 1944. Am. J. Mental Deficiency 48:325. [3] Barrow, E. M., et al. 1960. J. Lab. Clin. Med. 55:936. [4] Bell, J., and J. B. S. Haldane. 1937. Proc. Roy. Soc. (London), B, 123:119. [5] Childs, B., et al. 1958. Bull. Johns Hopkins Hosp. 102:21. [6] Chung, C. S., et al. 1960. Am. J. Human Genet. 12:52. [7] Clark, E. 1898. Trans. Ophthalmol. Soc. United

continued

7. SEX LINKAGE: MAN

Kingdom 18:136. [8] Cockayne, E. A. 1933. Inherited abnormalities of the skin and its appendages. Oxford Univ. Press, London. [9] Falls, H. F. 1951. Am. J. Ophthalmol. 34:41. [10] Falls, H. F., and C. W. Cotterman. 1948. Arch. Ophthalmol. (Chicago) 40:685. [11] Gates, R. R. 1946. Human genetics. Macmillan, New York. [12] Graham, J. B., W. W. McLendon, and K. M. Brinkhous. 1953. Am. J. Med. Sci. 225:46. [13] Horton, H. W. 1949. Am. J. Human Genet. 1:55. [14] Israels, M. C. G., et al. 1951. Lancet 1:1375. [15] Lewis, J. H., and J. H. Ferguson. 1953. Proc. Soc. Exptl. Biol. Med. 82:445. [16] Mann, J. D., et al. 1962. Lancet 1:8. [17] McCulloch, C., and R. J. P. McCulloch. 1948. Trans. Am. Acad. Ophthalmol. Otolaryngol. 52:160. [18] Murakami, U., et al. 1951. Nagoya J. Med. Sci. 14:58. [19] Parker, N. 1958. Am. J. Human Genet. 10:196. [20] Peden, V. H. 1960. Ibid. 12:323. [21] Pickford, R. W. 1948. Nature 162:684. [22] Roberts, J. A. F. 1937. Brit. Med. J. 2:1213. [23] Rucker, C. W. 1949. Am. J. Human Genet. 1:52. [24] Salleras, A., and J. C. Ortiz de Zárate. 1950. Brit. J. Ophthalmol. 34:662. [25] Satalff, J., et al. 1955. Am. J. Human Genet. 7:201. [26] Snyder, L. H. 1946. Principles of heredity. D. C. Heath, Boston. [27] Sorsby, A. 1951. Genetics in ophthalmology. Butterworth, London. [28] Sorsby, A., et al. 1951. Brit. J. Ophthalmol. 35:1. [29] Stephens, F. E., and F. H. Tyler. 1951. Am. J. Human Genet. 3:111. [30] Waardenburg, P. J. 1932. Bibliographia genet. (Haag) 7:1. [31] White, T. 1940. J. Genet. 40:403. [32] Williams, R. H., and C. Henry. 1947. Ann. Internal Med. 27:84. [33] Wilson, W. M. G. 1949. Can. Med. Assoc. J. 60:580. [34] Winters, R. W., et al. 1958. Medicine 37:97.

8. LINKAGE GROUPS: VERTEBRATES

The size or length of a linkage map reflects the extent of genetics investigation rather than the number of genes possessed by the animal. Capital letters (in columns giving Gene Symbol, Linkage, and Mutation) indicate dominant genes.

Part I: GUINEA PIG

Cavia porcellus has 32 pair of chromosomes (±1 pair), including an XY pair in males. Linkage groups have been found for 2 pair.

	Gene Symbol (A)	Linkage (B)	Recombination Percentage (C)	Mutation (D)	Phenotypic Expression (E)	Reference (F)
				Linkage Group I		
1	*R*	*R--Px*	43.8±1.6	Rough fur	Rough fur, at least on hind toes	1-4
2	*Px*	*Px--R*	43.8±1.6	Pollex	Tendency to atavistic return of thumb, little toe, and, on rare occasions, big toe	
				Linkage Group II		
3	*si*	*si--m*	21.7±5.2	silvered (stationary from birth)	Silver-coated fur; incomplete recessive	5
4	*m*	*m--si*	21.7±5.2	modifier	Modifies rough fur effect; homozygote high-grade roughness	

Contributor: Wright, Sewall

References: [1] Castle, W. E., and A. Forbes. 1906. Carnegie Inst. Wash. Publ. 49:3. [2] Wright, S. 1928. Genetics 13:508. [3] Wright, S. 1941. Ibid. 26:650. [4] Wright, S. 1949. J. Exptl. Zool. 112:303. [5] Wright, S. 1959. Genetics 44:387.

continued

8. LINKAGE GROUPS: VERTEBRATES

Part II: MOUSE

Mus musculus has 20 pair of chromosomes; linkage groups have been found for 19 pair.

	Gene Symbol	Linkage	Recombination Percentage	Mutation	Phenotypic Expression	Reference
	(A)	(B)	(C)	(D)	(E)	(F)
				Linkage Group I		
1	*fr*	*fr--sh-1*	16	frizzy	Fine thin hair, curled vibrissae	31
2	*ol*[1]	*ol--c*	17	oligodactyly	Reduced number of digits	48
3	*H-1*	*H-1--c*	7	Histocompatibility-1	Susceptibility to tissue transplants	91,93
4	*Hb*[1]	*Hb--c*	5[2], 2[3]	Hemoglobin pattern	Electrophoretic pattern of hemoglobin	76
5	*sh-1*	*sh-1--c*	4[2], 3[3]	shaker-1	Circling, head shaking, deafness	31,45,46
6	*c*	*c--p*	16[2], 12[3]	albino	Absence of pigment in hair and eyes	31,45,46, 76
7	*hf*	*c--hf*	3	hepatic fusion	Fusion of left median and left lateral lobes of liver	4
8	*tp*	*tp--p*	5	taupe	Reduced pigment in coat	79
9	*H-4*[1]	*H-4--p*	0	Histocompatibility-4	Susceptibility to tissue transplants	93
10	*p*	*hf--p*	13	pink-eyed dilution	Pink eyes, reduced black or brown pigment	4
11	*qv*	*p--qv*	12	quivering	Locomotor instability, pronounced trembling in adults, priapism in old males	103
12	*da*	*p--da*	17	dark	Darkens back of agouti or yellow mice	28
13	*pu*	*p--pu*	22	Pudgy	Tail short or absent, torso shortened	81
				Linkage Group II		
14	*lu*	*lu--dse*	17	luxoid	Tibial hemimelia and preaxial polydactyly	44
15	*d*	*d--se*	0.1	dilute	Clumped pigment granules in hair	39
16	*se*[1]	*dse--du*	20	short ear	Reduced cartilaginous skeleton	44,90
17	*sv*[1]	*se--sv*	1	Snell's waltzer (recessive)	Circling, head shaking	43
18	*tk*[1]	*dse--tk*	11	tail kinks	Kinky tail, abnormal cervical and upper thoracic vertebrae	29
19	*du*	*du--dse*	20	ducky	Waddling gait	44,90
				Linkage Group III		
20	*pn*	*pn--s*	30	pugnose	Frontal and nasal bones short and wide	53
21	*s*[4]	*s--hr*	8	piebald	Unpigmented areas of fur	87
22	*ag*	*ag--hr*	0	agitans	Impaired locomotion, tremor, death at 3-4 wk	49
23	*hr*	*hr--W*	42	hairless	Hair shed beginning at 10-14 da	38
24	*wl*[1,5]	*hr--wl*	4	wabbler-lethal	Impaired locomotion, death at 3-4 wk	59
25	*pi*	*hr--pi*	36	pirouette	Circling, head shaking, deafness	18
26	*W*	*pi--W*	7	Dominant spotting	White spotting and dilution of coat color, macrocytic anemia, sterility	17
27	*Ph*[1]	*W--Ph*	0.1	Patch	White spotting	47
28	*le*[1]	*W--le*	12	light ears	Dilution of coat color	58
29	*lx*	*W--lx*	18	luxate	Tibial hemimelia, preaxial polydactyly	7
30	*rl*	*lx--rl*	16	reeler	Impaired locomotion, death at 3-4 wk	24
				Linkage Group IV		
31	*r*	*r--si*	15	rodless retina	Absence of rods	52
32	*si*	*si--pg*	close	silvered	Absence or reduction of pigment in coat	30
33	*pg*[1]	*pg--si*	close	pigmy	Small size	30
34	*av*[1]	*si--av*	33	Ames' waltzer (recessive)	Circling, head shaking	83
				Linkage Group V		
35	*Ra*	*Ra--a*	22	Ragged	Thin coat	11,60,72
36	*Op*	*Op--a*	27	Opossum	Very thin coat; probably an allele of *Ra*	40
37	*H-3*[1]	*H-3--a*	10	Histocompatibility-3	Susceptibility to tissue transplants	91
38	*kr*	*kr--a*	1	Kreisler (recessive)	Circling, head shaking, deafness	48,58
39	*bp*	*bp--a*	0.3	brachypodism	Short feet	77
40	*a*	*a--un*	5	non-agouti	Removes yellow band from hairs	5,35
41	*un*	*un--we*	7[2], 5[3]	undulated	Wavy tail and abnormal vertebral column	26,35
42	*we*	*we--pa*	4[2], 2[3]	wellhaarig	Wavy coat and vibrissae	26,35,58

/1/ Listed order not established. /2/ For heterozygous females. /3/ For heterozygous males. /4/ *s--W* recombination, 47% [33]. /5/ *wl--W* recombination, 43% [59].

continued

8. LINKAGE GROUPS: VERTEBRATES

Part II: MOUSE

	Gene Symbol	Linkage	Recombination Percentage	Mutation	Phenotypic Expression	Reference
	(A)	(B)	(C)	(D)	(E)	(F)
				Linkage Group V		
43	*mg*[1]	*a--mg*	13[2], 10[3]	mahogany	Dark coat, especially ears and tail	60
44	*pa*	*pa--ro*	1	pallid	Pink eyes, reduction of pigment in coat, frequent absence of otoliths	26
45	*ro*	*a--fi*	36[2], 27[3]	rough	Air spaces in hair abnormal, waved vibrissae	9,97
46	*dm*[1]	*a--dm*	13	diminutive	Small size, malformed vertebrae and ribs	95
47	*fi*	*pa--fi*	19	fidget	Circling, head shaking, occasional polydactyly	6
48	*Sd*	*fi--Sd*	22	Danforth's short tail	Short tail, urogenital abnormalities	97
				Linkage Group VI		
49	*N*	*N--Ca*	1[2], 3[3]	Naked	Hair breaks off near skin level	12,66,69
50	*Ca*	*Ca--bt*	4[2], 11[3]	Caracul	Wavy coat and vibrissae	66,69
51	*hl*	*Ca--hl*	2[2], 6[3]	hair-loss	Loses hair, usually naked by 2-3 mo	50
52	*Ht*[1]	*Ca--Ht*	2[2], 3[3]	Hightail	Tail emerges high, short and thick at base, not kinked	80,81
53	*bt*	*hl--bt*	9	belted	White belt	50
				Linkage Group VII		
54	*Re*	*Re--Al*	7	Rex	Wavy coat and vibrissae	14,58
55	*Al*	*Al--sh-2*	21	Alopecia	Hair thin and patchy beginning at 1 or 2 mo	58
56	*ti*[1,6]	*Re--ti*	20[2], 21[3]	tipsy	Muscular incoordination, wabbling gait	84
57	*Tr*[7]	*Re--Tr*	23	Trembler	Convulsions in young, head trembling in adults	32
58	*sh-2*[8]	*Re--sh-2*	28[2], 19[3]	shaker-2	Circling, head shaking, deafness	10,23,70
59	*vt*[1,9]	*Re--vt*	27[2], 18[3]	vestigial	Tail short or absent	67
60	*wa-2*	*vt--wa-2*	23	waved-2	Wavy coat and vibrissae	68
61	*Tm*[1]			Pulmonary tumors	Susceptibility to spontaneous and induced pulmonary tumors	96
				Linkage Group VIII		
62	*m*	*m--Pt*	3	misty	Dilute coat color, tail and belly spots	55
63	*Pt*	*Pt--b*	5	Pintail	Short tail	51,55
64	*b*	*m--b*	5	brown	Brown instead of black pigment	86,100
65	*an*[1]	*b--an*	5	anemia	Macrocytic anemia throughout life	48
66	*vc*	*b--vc*	7	vacillans	Muscular incoordination	85,86
67	*wi*[1]	*b--wi*	6	whirler	Circling, head shaking	55
68	*wd*	*b--wd*	31	waddler	Swaying of hindquarters during locomotion	102
				Linkage Group IX		
69	*T*	*T--Fu*	4	Brachyury	Short tail	2,20-22
70	*Fu*	*Fu--tf*	1	Fused	Tail and vertebral abnormalities	19
71	*tf*[1]	*T--tf*	8	tufted	Successive waves of hair loss and regrowth from anterior to posterior	65
72	*H-2*	*Fu--H-2*	4	Histocompatibility-2	Susceptibility to tissue transplantation	1,2,89
				Linkage Group X		
73	*v*	*v--ji*	18	waltzer	Circling, head shaking, deafness	88
74	*ji*	*ji--v*	18	jittery	Muscular incoordination, death at 3-4 wk	88
				Linkage Group XI		
75	*tc*[1]	*tc--mi*	8	truncate	Short tail, often with intermediate vertebrae of tail or sacrum missing	57
76	*mi*	*mi--px*	3	microphthalmia	Reduced pigment, failure of bone resorption	8
77	*px*	*px--wa-1*	1	postaxial hemimelia	Postaxial side of limbs defective	8
78	*wa-1*	*wa-1--Lc*	8	waved-1	Waved hair and vibrissae	75

/1/ Listed order not established. /2/ For heterozygous females. /3/ For heterozygous males. /6/ *ti--vt* recombination, 9% [84]. /7/ *Tr--sh-2* recombination, 3% [32]. /8/ *sh-2--wa-2* recombination, 24% for heterozygous females and 30% for heterozygous males [10, 14, 36, 92, 101]. /9/ *sh-2--vt* recombination, 2% [68].

continued

8. LINKAGE GROUPS: VERTEBRATES

Part II: MOUSE

	Gene Symbol	Linkage	Recombination Percentage	Mutation	Phenotypic Expression	Reference
	(A)	(B)	(C)	(D)	(E)	(F)
				Linkage Group XI		
79	*Lc*	*mi--wa-1*	11	Lurcher	Swaying of hindquarters and falling to one side	3
80	*ob*[1]	*mi--ob*	29	obese	Obesity with hyperglycemia	16
				Linkage Group XII		
81	*ru*	*ru--je*	49	ruby eye	Reduced pigmentation of eyes and hair	15,27,37, 98
82	*je*	*je--ru*	49	jerker	Circling, head shaking, deafness	15,27,39, 98
				Linkage Group XIII		
83	*Lp*	*Lp--ln*	38[2], 35[3]	Loop tail	Looped tail, abnormal behavior	94
84	*py*	*py--ln*	38[2], 24[3]	polydactyly	Preaxial polydactyly	34,71
85	*dr*[1]	*dr--Dh*	22	dreher	Circling, head shaking	63
86	*Dh*	*Dh--ln*	2	Dominant hemimelia	Preaxial hemimelia, absence of spleen	63
87	*ln*	*ln--Sp*	5	leaden	Clumped pigment granules in hair	71,94
88	*th*[1]	*th--ln*	5	tilted head	Head tilted to right or left side	61
89	*Sp*	*Sp--fz*	40[2], 33[3]	Splotch	White spotting on belly, feet, and tail	71,94
90	*fz*	*ln--fz*	43[2], 36[3]	fuzzy	Thin wavy hair and vibrissae	71,94
				Linkage Group XIV		
91	*cr*	*cr--ch*	15	crinkled	Absence of guard hairs and zigzags	54,74
92	*ch*	*ch--f*	18	congenital hydrocephalus	Severe reduction in cartilaginous skeleton	54,74
93	*f*	*f--ch*	18	flexed tail	Anemia at birth, flexed tail, belly spot	54,74
				Linkage Group XV		
94	*Tw*	*Tw--ax*	0	Twirler	Circling, head shaking	62
95	*ax*	*ax--Tw*	0	ataxia	Muscular incoordination, death at 3-4 wk	62
				Linkage Group XVI		
96	*Va*	*Va--de*	28	Varitint-waddler	Dilute and spotted coat, circling, head shaking, deafness	13
97	*de*	*de--Va*	28	droopy ear	Ears set low on head, pinnae project laterally	13
				Linkage Group XVII		
98	*sa*	*sa--bg*	9	satin	Silky hair texture with high sheen	82
99	*bg*	*bg--sa*	9	beige	Diluted coat color	82
				Linkage Group XVIII		
100	*Hk*	*Hk--Os*	17	Hook	Short tail, anus displaced toward tail	42
101	*Os*	*Os--tg*	0	Oligosyndactylism	Digits reduced in number and fused	41
102	*tg*[1]	*tg--Os*	0	tottering	Wobbly gait, occasional convulsions	41
				Linkage Group XX (Sex Chromosome)		
103	*Bn*	*Bn--Ta*	12	Bent	Short crooked tail	73
104	*Gy*[1]	*Gy--Ta*	close	Gyro	Circling, abnormal long bones and ribs in males	64
105	*Ta*	*Ta--Mo*	4	Tabby	Dark transverse stripes	25,26
106	*Blo*	*Ta--Blo*	3	Blotchy	Irregular patches of light fur, males viable	78
107	*Mo*	*Mo--Ta*	4	Mottled	Patches of light hair, males die in utero	25,26
108	*To*[1]	*Bn--To*	22	Tortoise	Like *Mo*; possibly an allele	56
109	*jp*	*Ta--jp*	20	jimpy	Muscular incoordination, death at 3-4 wk	73
110	*sf*[1]	*Ta--sf*	44	scurfy	Scaliness, tight skin, death at 3-4 wk	99

/1/ Listed order not established. /2/ For heterozygous females. /3/ For heterozygous males.

Contributors: (a) Green, Margaret C., (b) Snell, George D., (c) St. Amand, W., (d) Novitski, E.

References: [1] Allen, S. L. 1955. Cancer Research 15:315. [2] Allen, S. L. 1955. Genetics 40:627.

continued

[3] Bunker, H., and G. D. Snell. 1948. J. Heredity 39:28. [4] Bunker, L. E., Jr. 1959. Ibid. 50:40. [5] Carter, T. C. 1947. Heredity 1:367. [6] Carter, T. C. 1951. J. Genet. 50:264. [7] Carter, T. C. 1951. Ibid. 50:300. [8] Carter, T. C. Unpublished, 1958. [9] Carter, T. C., and H. Grüneberg. 1950. Heredity 4:373. [10] Carter, T. C., and R. J. S. Phillips. 1953. Z. induktive Abstammungs.- u. Vererbungslehre 85:564. [11] Carter, T. C., and R. J. S. Phillips. 1954. J. Heredity 45:151. [12] Cooper, C. B. 1939. Ibid. 30:212. [13] Curry, G. A. 1959. J. Embryol. Exptl. Morphol. 7:39. [14] Dickie, M. M. 1955. J. Heredity 46:31. [15] Dickie, M. M. Unpublished, 1958. [16] Dickie, M. M., and P. W. Lane. 1957. Mouse News Letter 17:52. [17] Dickie, M. M., and G. W. Woolley. 1946. J. Heredity 37:335. [18] Dickie, M. M., and G. W. Woolley. 1948. Ibid. 39:288. [19] Dunn, L. C. 1958. Mouse News Letter 18:24. [20] Dunn, L. C., and E. Caspari. 1945. Genetics 30:543. [21] Dunn, L. C., and S. Gluecksohn-Waelsh. 1953. Ibid. 38:512. [22] Dunn, L. C., and S. Gluecksohn-Waelsch. 1954. J. Genet. 52:383. [23] Falconer, D. S. 1947. Heredity 1:133. [24] Falconer, D. S. 1952. Ibid. 6:255. [25] Falconer, D. S. 1953. Z. induktive Abstammungs.-u. Vererbungslehre 85:210. [26] Falconer, D. S. 1954. Ibid. 86:263. [27] Falconer, D. S. 1956. Mouse News Letter 15:24. [28] Falconer, D. S. 1957. Ibid. 17:40. [29] Falconer, D. S. 1961. Ibid. 25:30. [30] Falconer, D. S., and J. W. B. King. 1953. Ibid. 9(suppl.):7. [31] Falconer, D. S., and G. D. Snell. 1952. J. Heredity 43:53. [32] Falconer, D. S., and W. R. Sobey. 1953. Ibid. 49:159. [33] Fisher, R. A. 1946. Am. Naturalist 80:568. [34] Fisher, R. A. 1953. Heredity 7:91. [35] Fisher, R. A., and W. Landauer. 1953. Am. Naturalist 87:116. [36] Fisher, R. A., M. F. Lyon, and A. R. G. Owen. 1947. Heredity 1:355. [37] Fisher, R. A., and G. D. Snell. 1948. Ibid. 2:271. [38] Gates, W. H., and T. Pullig. 1945. Genetics 30:4. [39] Goodwins, I. R., and M. A. C. Vincent. 1955. Heredity 9:413. [40] Green, E. L., and S. J. Mann. 1961. J. Heredity 52:223. [41] Green, M. C. 1960. Mouse News Letter 22:34. [42] Green, M. C. 1960. Ibid. 23:34. [43] Green, M. C. 1961. Ibid. 25:38. [44] Green, M. C. 1961. J. Heredity 52:73. [45] Grüneberg, H. 1935. J. Genet. 31:157. [46] Grüneberg, H. 1936. Ibid. 33:255. [47] Grüneberg, H., and G. M. Truslove. 1960. Genet. Research 1:69. [48] Hertwig, P. 1942. Z. induktive Abstammungs.- u. Vererbungslehre 80:220. [49] Hoecker, G., et al. 1954. J. Heredity 45:10. [50] Hollander, W. F. 1959. Mouse News Letter 20:34. [51] Hollander, W. F., and L. C. Strong. 1951. J. Heredity 42:179. [52] Keeler, C. E. 1930. Howe Lab. Ophthalmol. Bull. 3. [53] Kidwell, J. F. 1961. Mouse News Letter 24:39. [54] King, J. W. B. 1956. Nature 178:1126. [55] Lane, P. W. 1960. Mouse News Letter 23:35. [56] Lane, P. W. 1960. Ibid. 23:36. [57] Lane, P. W. 1961. Ibid. 25:38. [58] Lane, P. W. Unpublished, 1960. [59] Lane, P. W., and M. M. Dickie. 1961. J. Heredity 52:159. [60] Lane, P. W., and M. C. Green. 1960. Ibid. 51:228. [61] Larsen, M. M. 1961. Mouse News Letter 24:60. [62] Lyon, M. F. 1958. J. Embryol. Exptl. Morphol. 6:105. [63] Lyon, M. F. 1961. Genet. Research 2:92. [64] Lyon, M. F. 1961. Mouse News Letter 24:34. [65] Lyon, M. F., and R. J. S. Phillips. 1959. Heredity 13:23. [66] Mallyon, S. A. 1951. Nature 168:118. [67] Michie, D. 1955. J. Genet. 53:270. [68] Mitchie, D. 1955. Ibid. 53:280. [69] Murray, J. M., and G. D. Snell. 1945. J. Heredity 36:266. [70] Nasrat, G. E. 1956. Proc. Zool. Soc. (Bengal) 9:85. [71] Parsons, P. A. 1958. Heredity 12:77. [72] Parsons, P. A. 1958. Ibid. 12:357. [73] Phillips, R. J. S. 1954. Z. induktive Abstammungs.- u. Vererbungslehre 86:322. [74] Phillips, R. J. S. 1956. J. Heredity 47:302. [75] Phillips, R. J. S. 1960. J. Genet. 57:35. [76] Popp, R. A., and W. St. Amand. 1960. J. Heredity 51:141. [77] Runner, M. N. 1959. Ibid. 50:81. [78] Russell, L. B. 1960. Mouse News Letter 23:58. [79] Russell, L. B. 1961. Ibid. 25:64. [80] St. Amand, W., and M. B. Cupp. 1957. Ibid. 16:37. [81] St. Amand, W., and M. B. Cupp. 1957. Ibid. 17:88. [82] St. Amand, W., and M. B. Cupp. 1958. Ibid. 19:38. [83] Schaible, R. H. 1961. Ibid. 24:38. [84] Searle, A. G. 1961. Genet. Research 2:122. [85] Sirlin, J. L. 1956. J. Genet. 54:42. [86] Sirlin, J. L. 1957. Heredity 11:259. [87] Snell, G. D. 1931. Genetics 16:42. [88] Snell, G. D. 1945. J. Heredity 36:279. [89] Snell, G. D. 1952. Heredity 6:247. [90] Snell, G. D. 1955. J. Heredity 46:27. [91] Snell, G. D. 1958. J. Natl. Cancer Inst. 21:843. [92] Snell, G. D., and L. W. Law. 1939. J. Heredity 30:447. [93] Snell, G. D., and L. C. Stevens. 1961. Immunology 4:366. [94] Snell, G. D., et al. 1954. Heredity 8:271. [95] Stevens, L. C., and J. A. Mackensen. 1961. Mouse News

continued

Letter 24:41. [96] Tatchell, J. A. H. 1961. Nature 190:837. [97] Wallace, M. E. 1957. Heredity 11:223. [98] Wallace, M. E. 1958. Ibid. 12:453. [99] Welshons, W. J., and L. B. Russell. 1959. Proc. Natl. Acad. Sci. U. S. 45:560. [100] Woolley, G. W. 1945. J. Heredity 36:269. [101] Wright, M. E. 1947. Heredity 1:349. [102] Yoon, C. H. 1961. J. Heredity 52:279. [103] Yoon, C. H., and E. P. Les. 1957. Ibid. 48:176.

Part III: RAT

Rattus norvegicus has 21 pair of chromosomes; linkage groups have been found for 5 pair. Seven genes--jaundice (*j*), curly coat (Cu_2), cataract (*Ca*), blue dilution of coat (*d*), hooded coat pattern (*h*), cowlick (*cw*), and shaker (*sr*) --have been found to be independent of linkage groups I-V, and of each other, and are provisionally regarded as markers of 7 additional chromosome pair. [3, 5, 6, 9, 10]

	Gene Symbol	Locus	Mutation	Phenotypic Expression	Reference
	(A)	(B)	(C)	(D)	(E)
				Linkage Group I	
1	*p*	0	pink eye	Coat yellow, eyes pink	1, 2, 7, 14
2	*r*	20.5	red-eyed yellow	Coat yellow, eyes red	
3	*c*	21	albinism	Absence of pigment from coat and eyes	
4	*l*	24.3	lethal	Skeletal abnormalities	
5	*w*	66.3	waltzing	Runs in circles	
				Linkage Group II	
6	*Sh*	0	Shaggy	Hair and vibrissae curved	2, 7-9, 13
7	*Cu*	4	Curly	Hairs of coat and vibrissae curved	
8	*an*	14.3	anemia	Lack of erythrocytes; young anemic	
9	*in*	28	incisorless	Incisors lacking	
10	*s*	47	silvered	Coat silvered	
11	*b*	52	brown	Black pigment of coat and eyes replaced by brown	
				Linkage Group III	
12	*n*	0	naked	Naked except for short fuzzy coat	2, 4, 12
13	*hr*	34.7	hairless	Hair lost at approximately 4 wk	
14	*wo*	75	wobbly	Ataxic locomotion	
				Linkage Group IV	
15	*k*	0	kinky	Hairs of coat and vibrissae kinky	2, 8
16	*st*	34.1	stub	Short stubby tail	
				Linkage Group V	
17	*A*	0	Agouti	Fur color agouti, wild type	2, 11
18	*f*	44.6	fawn	Coat tawny blue to fawn	

Contributors: (a) Castle, W. E., (b) Novitski, E.

References: [1] Castle, W. E. 1916. Carnegie Inst. Wash. Publ. 241:175. [2] Castle, W. E. 1947. Proc. Natl. Acad. Sci. U. S. 33:109. [3] Castle, W. E. 1951. Genetics 36:254. [4] Castle, W. E. 1955. J. Heredity 46:84. [5] Castle, W. E., E. R. Dempster, and H. C. Shurrager. 1955. Ibid. 46:9. [6] Castle, W. E., and H. D. King. 1940. Proc. Natl. Acad. Sci. U. S. 26:578. [7] Castle, W. E., and H. D. King. 1941. Ibid. 27:394. [8] Castle, W. E., and H. D. King. 1944. Ibid. 30:79. [9] Castle, W. E., and H. D. King. 1947. J. Heredity 38:341. [10] Castle, W. E., and H. D. King. 1948. Proc. Natl. Acad. Sci. U. S. 34:135. [11] Castle, W. E., and H. D. King. 1949. Ibid. 35:545. [12] Castle, W. E., H. D. King, and A. L. Daniels. 1941. Ibid. 27:250. [13] King, H. D., and W. E. Castle. 1935. Ibid. 21:390. [14] King, H. D., and W. E. Castle. 1937. Ibid. 23:56.

continued

8. LINKAGE GROUPS: VERTEBRATES

Part IV: RABBIT

Oryctolagus cuniculus has 22 pair of chromosomes; linkage groups have been found for 6 pair. For additional information, consult references 7-9, 12.

	Gene Symbol	Locus	Mutation	Phenotypic Expression	Reference
	(A)	(B)	(C)	(D)	(E)
				Linkage Group I	
1	*c*	0	albinism	Coat color alleles vary from chinchilla to complete albinism	1,2,5
2	*y*	14.4	yellow fat	Yellow fat	3,11
3	*b*	42.8	brown	Brown coat	3,11
				Linkage Group II	
4	*du*	0	dutch pattern	White belt on colored background	3,11
5	*En*	1.2	English	Colored spots on white background	1,4,6
6	*l*	14.3	angora hair	Increase in hair fiber length	1,4
				Linkage Group III	
7	r_1	0	rex-1	Short, plushlike coat	3,11
8	r_2	17.2	rex-2	Short, plushlike coat	2,4
				Linkage Group IV	
9	*a*	0	non-agouti	Black coat	3,11
10	*dw*	14.7	dwarf	Small size, lethal shortly after birth	3,11
11	*w*	29.9	wide-banded agouti	Wide banding of agouti hairs	5,10
				Linkage Group V	
12	*br*	0	brachydactyly	Abnormality of toes	11
13	*f*	28.3	furless	Fur restricted to extremities	5
14	*an*	36.8	erythrocyte agglutination	Erythrocytes agglutinate	14
				Linkage Group VI	
15	*E*	0	Extension	Extension of dark pigment	11
16	*At*	26.2	Production of atropinesterase	Production of atropinesterase	13

Contributors: (a) Sawin, Paul B., (b) Novitski, E.

References: [1] Castle, W. E. 1926. Carnegie Inst. Wash. Publ. 337:3. [2] Castle, W. E. 1936. Proc. Natl. Acad. Sci. U. S. 22:222. [3] Castle, W. E. 1940. Mammalian genetics. Harvard Univ. Press, Cambridge. [4] Castle, W. E., and N. Nachtsheim. 1933. Proc. Natl. Acad. Sci. U. S. 19:1006. [5] Castle, W. E., and P. B. Sawin. 1941. Ibid. 27:519. [6] Pease, M. S. 1928. Verhandl. Ver. intern. Kongr. Vererbungswiss. 2:1153. [7] Rifaat, O. M. 1954. Heredity 8:107. [8] Robinson, R. 1956. J. Genet. 54:358. [9] Robinson, R. 1958. Bibliographia genet. (Haag) 17:229. [10] Sawin, P. B. 1934. J. Heredity 25:477. [11] Sawin, P. B. 1944. Proc. Natl. Acad. Sci. U. S. 30:220. [12] Sawin, P. B. 1955. Advances in Genet. 7:183. [13] Sawin, P. B., and D. Glick. 1943. Proc. Natl. Acad. Sci. U. S. 29:55. [14] Sawin, P. B., M. A. Griffin, and C. A. Stuart. 1944. Ibid. 30:217

continued

8. LINKAGE GROUPS: VERTEBRATES

Part V: CHICKEN

Gallus domesticus has 39 pair of chromosomes; linkage groups have been found for 6 pair (groups IV and V may eventually be joined).

	Gene Symbol	Linkage	Recombination Percentage	Mutation	Phenotypic Expression	Reference
	(A)	(B)	(C)	(D)	(E)	(F)
	Linkage Group I (Sex Chromosome)					
1	*ko*	*ko--B*	13	head streak in down	Head streak in down	1,2
2	*B*	*B--Id*	10	Barring	Barring of feathers	
3	*Sd*	*B--Sd*	<1	Dilution	Dilution to blue	
4	*Id*	*Id--br*	27	Inhibitor	Inhibits melanin in dermis	
5	*br*	*br--Li*	10	brown eyes	Brown eyes	
6	*Li*	*Li--S*	16	Light down	Light down in chicks not black	
7	*S*	*S--al*	1.2	Silver	Silver plumage color	
8	*al*	*al--K*	1.6	albinism	Incomplete albinism	
9	*K*	*K--dw*	6.6	Slow feathering	Slow feathering	
10	*dw*	*dw--S*	7	dwarf	Small size	
11	*px*	*al--px*	11	paroxysm	Lethal	
12	*n*	*px--n*	6	naked	Without feathers	
13	*sh*	*n--sh*	14	shaker	Lethal nervous disorder	
14	*xl*[1]			lethal	Death at 3 wk	
15	*j*[1]			jittery	Lethal nervous disorder	
	Linkage Group II					
16	*Cp*	*Cp--R*	0.4	Creeper	Achondroplasia	1
17	*R*	*R--U*	30	Rose comb	Rose comb	
18	*U*	*U--R*	30	Uropygial	Bifurcation of uropygial papilla	
	Linkage Group III					
19	*fr*	*fr--Cr*	46	fray	Defective wing and tail feathers	1,3
20	*Cr*	*Cr--I*	12.5	Crest	Topknot and cerebral hernia	
21	*I*	*I--F*	17	Dominant white	White plumage	
22	*F*	*F--I*	17	Frizzling	Recurved feathers	
	Linkage Group IV					
23	*O*	*O--P*	5	Blue egg	Eggshell blue	1
24	*P*	*P--ma*	33	Pea comb	Pea comb	
25	*ma*	*ma--Na*	46	marbling	Pattern in down of chick	
26	*Na*	*Na--ma*	46	Naked neck	Pterylae reduced	
	Linkage Group V					
27	*Na*	*Na--h*	43	Naked neck	Pterylae reduced	3
28	*h*	*h--Fl*	11	silkie	Barbules lack hooklets	
29	*Fl*	*Fl--h*	11	Flightless	Remiges break off	
	Linkage Group VI					
30	*D*	*D--M*	26	Duplex comb	Bifurcation of comb	1,3
31	*M*	*M--Po*	33	Multiple spurs	Multiple spurs	
32	*Po*	*Po--M*	33	Polydactyly	Supernumerary digits	

/1/ Listed order not established.

Contributor: Hutt, F. B.

References: [1] Hutt, F. B. 1949. Genetics of the fowl. McGraw-Hill, New York. [2] Hutt, F. B. 1960. Heredity 15:97. [3] Warren, D. C. 1949. Genetics 34:333.

9. LINKAGE GROUPS: INVERTEBRATES

The size or length of a linkage map reflects the extent of genetics investigation rather than the number of genes possessed by the insect. Capital letters (in columns giving Gene Symbol, Linkage, and Mutation) indicate dominant genes.

Part I: FRUIT FLY

Drosophila melanogaster has 4 pair of chromosomes; linkage groups have been found for all 4 pair. For information on other species of *Drosophila*, consult the following references: *D. affinis* [30, 39], *D. ananassae* [17, 25-27, 30], *D. hydei* [32-34], *D. montium* [28, 29], *D. persimilis* [10, 18, 35], *D. prosaltans* [31], *D. pseudoobscura* [24, 30, 39, 42], *D. similans* [30, 38, 41], *D. subobscura* [2, 6-9, 13-16, 21-23, 36, 37], *D. virilis* [3-5, 19, 30], *D. willistoni* [12, 20]. Gene Symbol (column A): *l̲* = lethal, *1* = the number one, *l* = the letter l. Locus (column B): (Dp) = duplication, (Df) = deficiency. A number of loci have recently proved to be pseudoallelic (show crossing over with low frequency within subdivisions of an individual locus); such loci are indicated in column C as (pseudo).

	Gene Symbol	Locus	Mutation	Phenotypic Expression
	(A)	(B)	(C)	(D)
	X Chromosome [11, 43]			
1	*l̲(1)Jl*	0	lethal (1) Jacobs-Muller	Almost completely lethal; survivors scute, sterile
2	*l̲(1)55a*	0-	lethal (1) 55a	Lethal, heterozygote hyperviable
3	*su-wa*	0-	suppressor of apricot	w^a eye color made to resemble w^{co}
4	*y*	0	yellow	Body yellow; bristles and hairs yellow or brown in different alleles
5	*brc*	0	brachymacrochaete	Macrochaetae reduced
6	*ac*	0+	achaete	Postdorsocentrals missing; intraocular and eye hairs fewer
7	*Hw*	0+ (Dp)	Hairy-wing	Extra bristles along wing veins, on head and thorax
8	*sc*	0+	scute	Scutellar bristles missing, others missing or reduced
9	*svr*	0+	silver	Body silvery, bristles dark
10	*su-s*	0+	suppressor of sable	Suppresses *s* and *v*
11	*dor*	0+	deep orange	Eyes orange; females sterile
12	*l̲(1)7e*	0+	lethal (1) 7e	Dies in larval stage
13	*saw*	0+	sawtooth	Wing hairs serrated
14	*su-b*	0.1	suppressor of black	Suppresses *b*
15	*om*	0.1±	ommatidia	Eyes slightly rough
16	*M(1)Bld*	0.1+ (Df)	Minute (1) Blond	Extreme minute (small bristles, low viability, homozygous lethal)
17	*l̲(1)7*	0.3	lethal (1) 7	Dies as late larva; tumors present
18	*fla*	0.3±	flat eye	Eyes small, flat
19	*sta*	0.3±	stubarista	Antennae and aristae short, bristles reduced, eye rotated
20	*tw*	0.4±	twisted	Abdomen twisted counterclockwise
21	*mwi*	0.4±	misheld wings	Wings divergent, upheld; eyes oval
22	*uq*	0.5±	unequal wings	Wings short, often unequal
23	*kz*	0.7	kurz	Bristles short, fine; postscutellars often absent
24	*rey*	0.7±	rough eye	Eyes small, rough
25	*pn*	0.8	prune	Eyes brownish, darkening with age, often mottled
26	*mk*	0.8±	murky	Body and eyes dark; females sterile
27	*gt*	0.9	giant	Giant larvae, pupae, adults; variable
28	*rsc*	0.9±	reduplicated sex combs	Sex combs on all six legs of male
29	*fc*	0.9±	faulty chaete	Bristles short, thin; some absent
30	*ovi*	0.9±	ovioculus	Eyes small, egg-shaped; males sterile
31	*z*	1.0	zeste	Eyes yellow in female at 25°C; temperature-sensitive; interacts with *w* alleles
32	*fb*	1.0±	fine bristle	Bristles short, fine
33	*l̲(1)ml*	1.0	lethal (1) melanoma-like	Dies as late larva, melanotic inclusions
34	*bsc*	1.1	bent scutellars	Scutellars and other bristles often bent
35	*mis*	1.3±	misproportioned	Abdomen abnormal in shape and size
36	*w*	1.5	white (pseudo)	White eyes, ocelli, testes, malpighian tubes
37	rst^2	1.7	roughest^2	Eyes rough, body dwarfed, some bristles reduced
38	*To*	2.3-	Tousled	Thoracic bristles disarranged, duplicated
39	*Co*	3.0± (Dp)	Confluens	Wing veins thick, with deltas
40	*nd*	3.0±	notchoid (pseudo with *spl-fa-N*)	Eyes small, wings notched
41	*spl*	3.0±	split (pseudo with *spl-fa-N*)	Eyes rough, small; bristles often split or missing
42	*fa*	3.0±	facet (pseudo with *spl-fa-N*)	Eyes rough, wings nicked

continued

9. LINKAGE GROUPS: INVERTEBRATES

Part I: FRUIT FLY

	Gene Symbol	Locus	Mutation	Phenotypic Expression
	(A)	(B)	(C)	(D)
	X Chromosome [11,43]			
43	*N*	3.0± (often Df)	Notch (pseudo with *spl-fa-N*)	Wings notched; male lethal
44	*Ax*	3.0±	Abruptex	Wings short, veins incomplete; thorax with mid-furrow
45	*rud*	3.3±	ruddle	Eyes reddish brown
46	*slc*	3.6±	slim chaete	Bristles fine, short
47	*Sc*	4.0±	Scotched eye	Ommatidia disarranged; male lethal
48	*dm*	4.6	diminutive	Body and bristles small; females sterile
49	*M(1)3E*	5.0±	Minute (1) 3E	Slight minute (body small, bristles fine, homozygous lethal)
50	su^{x}-*dx*	5.0±	suppressor of deltex	*dx* made nearly +; male fertile
51	*ec*	5.5	echinus	Eyes rough, large; facets large
52	*mf*	5.5±	macrofine	Body small, macrochaetes fine
53	*te*	5.6±	tenuchaete	Bristles fine, short; eyes dark
54	*Oc*	5.7±	Ocellarless	One or both ocellar bristles missing
55	*mo*	6.7±	microoculus	Eyes small, wings narrow
56	*amb*	6.8±	amber	Body pale yellow, bristles reduced; male sterile
57	*bi*	6.9	bifid	Wing veins fused into bifid stalk
58	*M(1)4BC*	7.0±	Minute (1) at 4BC	Strong minute (body small, bristles fine, homozygous lethal)
59	*peb*	7.3±	pebbled	Eyes slightly roughened
60	*lac*	7.3±	lacquered	Body color light, glistening; eyes small
61	*rb*	7.5	ruby	Eyes clear ruby, darkening to garnet
62	*dow*	8.0	downy	Bristles fuzzy; males sterile
63	*rg*	11.0	rugose	Eyes rough; wings thin, frayed
64	*bo*	12.5	bordeaux	Eyes dark wine
65	*omm*	12.8	ommatoreductum	Peripheral ommatidia absent, giving rough eye; head, thorax abnormal
66	*cx*	13.6	curlex	Wings bent upward
67	*cv*	13.7	crossveinless	Crossveins absent or nearly so
68	*mur*	14.3	murrey	Eyes reddish purple; body size, bristles reduced
69	*rmp*	14.4±	rumpled	Wings unexpanded, bristles disarranged
70	*rux*	15.0	roughex	Eyes small, rough
71	*Ext*	15.2±	Extras	Wing veins thickened, extra veins present
72	*vs*	16.3	vesiculated	Wings warped, divergent, blistered
73	*dx*	17.0	deltex	Wings thickened and with deltas
74	*ov*	17.5	oval	Eyes oval and rough
75	*tmc*	17.5±	tonomacrochaetes	Macrochaetae thin; abdomen pale
76	shf^{2}	17.9	shifted^{2}	Wing veins shifted closer together
77	*cm*	18.9	carmine	Eyes dark ruby
78	*scp*	19.3	scooped	Wings upturned, warped
79	*bis*	19.8± (Df)	bistre	Eyes and ocelli dark brown; males sterile
80	*ct*	20.0	cut	Wings cut to points, scalloped
81	*sn*	21.0	singed (pseudo)	Bristles and hairs curled; female sterile
82	*l(1)mys*	21.7	lethal (1) myospheroid	Dies as embryo with spheroid muscles
83	*ha*	22.7±	hair bristles	Bristles fine, short; fly small
84	*oc*	23.1	ocelliless	Ocelli absent; females sterile
85	*pam*	23.1	platinum	Male body and bristles almost colorless, bristle bases dark; sterile
86	gg^{2}	23.1±	goggle^{2}	Eyes bulging, head bristles fewer
87	*ptg*	23.2	pentagon	Thoracic trident and scutellar spot dark
88	*ccw*	23.4±	concave wing	Wings reduced, concave
89	*ch-b*	23.8	chilblained-b	Tarsi conglutinated
90	*tbd*	25.0±	tiny-bristloid	Bristles medium-fine; fly small; viability good
91	*Lg*	27.0±	Large	Body large; late hatching
92	dd^{2}	27.2	displaced^{2}	Antennae sunken; eyes and head deformed
93	*t*	27.5	tan	Body yellowish, antennae light yellow
94	*amx*	27.7-	almondex	Eyes narrow, rough; females sterile
95	*lz*	27.7	lozenge (pseudo)	Eyes narrow, facets abnormal; females usually sterile
96	*tar*	27.7±	tarry	Femur and tibia blackened
97	*dvr*	28.1	divers	Wings short, dark; with *y*, wings curled
98	*sma*	29.9±	smaller	Body size reduced
99	*su-Cbx*	30.0±	suppressor of Contra-bithorax	Almost completely suppresses *Cbx* effect in males
100	*tpw*	30.8±	tapered wing	Wings short, pointed at L3 vein tip

continued

9. LINKAGE GROUPS: INVERTEBRATES

Part I: FRUIT FLY

	Gene Symbol	Locus	Mutation	Phenotypic Expression
	(A)	(B)	(C)	(D)
			X Chromosome [11,43]	
101	*flp*	31.0±	flap wings	Wings concave; eyes bulging, rough
102	*ny*	32.0±	notchy	Wing tips nicked
103	*en-*w^e	32.0±	enhancer of white-eosin	With w^e alleles, gives nearly white eyes; suppresses *f*
104	*sto*	32.5	stocky	Fly short; eyes large, pear-shaped
105	*clm*	32.6±	clumpy marginals	Marginal wing hairs clumped
106	*ras*	32.8	raspberry	Eyes dark ruby
107	*ww*	32.9±	wider-wing	Wings short, broad
108	*v*	33.0	vermilion (pseudo)	Eyes bright vermilion, ocelli colorless
109	*osh*	33.0±	outshifted	Wings short, divergent; body light tan
110	*dwx*	33.2	dwarfex	Body small, wings coarse
111	*sbr*	33.4	small bristle	Bristles small, some missing
112	*csk*	33.4±	costakink	Wings reduced, costal vein kinked
113	*bla*	33.6±	bladder-wing	Wings deformed, with bladders; males sterile
114	*m*	36.1+	miniature	Wings small, dark
115	*dy*	36.2-	dusky	Wings small, dark
116	*ty-l*	36.4	tiny-like	Bristles short, fine
117	*trb*	37.0±	thread bristle	Bristles short, fine
118	*fw*	38.3	furrowed	Eyes furrowed, scutellum short, bristles gnarled
119	*alo*	38.3±	alopecia	Microchaetae nearly absent
120	*ups*	40.8	upright scutellars	Posterior scutellars vertical
121	*som*	40.8	sombre	Body dark, eyes dull
122	*up*	41.0±	upheld	Wings held upright
123	*pun*	41.1±	puny	Flies small, late-hatching
124	*taw*	41.1±	tawny	Head and thorax dark, abdomen light
125	*wy*	41.9	wavy	Wings waved, curled upward
126	*kk*	42.0±	kinky	Bristles bent or forked
127	*s*	43.0	sable	Body dark
128	*cop*	43.3±	copper	Eyes brownish red
129	*ten*	43.9	tenuischaete	Bristles short, thin; body small
130	*g*	44.4	garnet (pseudo)	Eyes garnet pink
131	*ty*	44.5	tiny	Bristles, body small; females sterile
132	*na*	45.2	narrow abdomen	Abdomen cylindrical; females sterile
133	*shp*	47.5±	shrimp	Overall size reduction
134	*thb*	47.6±	thin bristle	Bristles thin
135	*pl*	47.9	pleated	Wings pleated longitudinally
136	*rim*	48.1±	rimy	Eyes brownish with white hairs; wings pleated
137	*sge*	48.4±	shifted genitals	Genitalia rotated
138	*thm*	48.9	thin-macros	Macrochaetae thin
139	*vb*	49.3	vibrissae	Vibrissae in tuft
140	*mgt*	49.6±	midget	Body small; late-hatching
141	*thv*	49.7±	thick vein	Wing veins thick; eyes small, dark
142	*sla*	50.0±	slimma	Body narrow
143	*sd*	51.5	scalloped	Wing margins excised
144	*exi*	51.5±	exiguous	Body small, dark
145	*tc*	51.6±	tinychaete	Bristles fine
146	*Bg*	51.6	Bag	Wings short, blunt, inflated
147	*smt*	51.9±	small thorax	Head and thorax small
148	*drw*	52.3±	droopy wing	Fly small, wings drooped; males sterile
149	*ber*	52.2±	berrytail	Abdomen narrow, with berrylike posterior protrusion bearing abnormal genitalia
150	*msc*	52.6±	melanoscutellum	Scutellum dark; eyes and wings abnormal in shape
151	*Shw*	53.3	Shaker-downheld	Legs, abdomen shake under ether; wings droop
152	*sl*	53.5	small-wing	Wings short, oblong; eyes large
153	*mc*	54.0	microchaete	Hairs irregular, bristles small
154	*un*	54.4	uneven	Eyes rough, small
155	r^9	54.5	rudimentary^9	Wings truncated; females sterile
156	*acc*	54.5+	acclinal wing	Wings upheld, sloping
157	if^3	55.0±	inflated^3	Wings inflated, veins thickened
158	*M(1)o*	56.6	Minute (1) o	Minute (bristles fine, viability low, homozygous lethal)
159	*f*	56.7	forked (pseudo)	Bristles short, gnarled
160	*B*	57.0 (Dp)	Bar	Eyes narrow bar in homozygote, kidney-shaped in heterozygote

continued

9. LINKAGE GROUPS: INVERTEBRATES

Part I: FRUIT FLY

	Gene Symbol	Locus	Mutation	Phenotypic Expression
	(A)	(B)	(C)	(D)
			X Chromosome [11,43]	
161	*der*	57.2±	deranged	Thoracic bristles disarranged; wings upheld
162	*Sh*	58.0	Shaker	Legs, abdomen shake under light ether
163	*siw*	58.5±	side wing	Wings held parallel to sides of abdomen
164	*od*	59.2	outstretched	Wings divergent
165	*sy*	59.2	small-eye	Eyes small, rounded
166	*Bx*	59.4	Beadex	Wings excised
167	*rwg*	59.5±	reduced wings	Wings short, upheld; wing hairs disarranged
168	*fu*	59.5	fused	Wing veins fused; ocelli, ocellar bristles reduced or absent
169	*hdp*	59.6±	heldup	Wings upheld
170	*bk*	59.8±	buckled	Wings misshapen, divergent
171	*crk*	60.1±	crooked setae	Bristles disarranged, abnormal
172	*smd*	60.1±	smalloid	Body size reduced
173	*ton*	60.1±	tonochaete	Bristles short, fine
174	*meg*	61.9±	megaoculus	Eyes rough; eyes, wings abnormally shaped
175	*M(1)36f*	62.0±	Minute (1) 36f	Slight minute (bristles fine, homozygous lethal)
176	*car*	62.5	carnation	Eyes dark ruby
177	*M(1)n*	62.7	Minute (1) n	Minute type (fine bristles, low viability, homozygous lethal)
178	*fo*	63.0±	folded	Wings unexpanded
179	*kno*	63.9±	knobbyhead	Head small, abnormal; males infertile
180	*sw*	64.0	short-wing	Wings trimmed, warped; eyes reduced, rough
181	*su-f*	64.0±	suppressor of forked	Certain *f* alleles made nearly +
182	*mel*	64.1±	melanized	Body slightly dark, eyes dull red
183	*wa-l*	64.4±	warty-like	Ommatidia disarranged
184	*ot*	65.1±	outheld	Wings held out; males inviable, sterile
185	bb^5 (called *bb*)	66.0	bobbed	Bristles small, sclerites irregular
			Chromosome II [1]	
186	*net*	0	net	Extreme plexus venation
187	*al*	0	aristaless	Aristae reduced, scutellars divergent
188	*l(2)gl*	0+	lethal (2) giant larva	Larval lethal
189	*ocr*	0	ochracea	Eye color light, darkening with age
190	*ex*	0.1	expanded	Wings broad, spread; eyes rough
191	*ds*	0.3	dachsous	Wings shorter, crossveins closer
192	*S*	1.3	Star (pseudo)	Eyes small, rough; homozygous lethal
193	*Su-S*	1.3±	Suppressor of Star	Suppresses *S*; *Su-S/S* is +
194	*ast*	1.3±	asteroid	Eyes small, rough
195	*shr*	2.3±	shrunken	Body small, wizened
196	*shv*	3.8±	short vein	Constant terminal gaps in veins L2 and L4
197	*ho*	4.0	heldout	Wings extended
198	*fes*	5.0±	female-sterile	Eggs do not develop
199	*E-S*	6.0±	Enhancer of Star	Increases expression of star *(S)*
200	*Cy*	7.0	Curly	Wings curled upward; homozygous lethal
201	*l(2)ay*	8.3	lethal (2) ay	Lethal
202	*Dt*	10.0±	Detached	Vein L2 does not reach margin
203	*ang*	10.5	angle wing	Wings held up from dorsal surface
204	*ed*	11.0	echinoid	Eyes large, rough
205	*M(2)C*	11.0-12.0 (Df)	Minute (2) Curry	Fairly strong minute
206	*ft*	12.0	fat	Body short, fat; scutellar bristles far apart
207	*G*	12.0	Gull	Wings large, spread; homozygous lethal
208	*M(2)z*	12.9±	Minute (2) z	Medium minute
209	*M(2)B*	13.0 (Df)	Minute (2) Bridges	Medium minute
210	*dp*	13.0	dumpy	Wings truncated; vortices on thorax
211	*dw-24F*	13.0±	dwarf in 24F	Eyes dull, body dwarfed
212	*M(2)S1*	15.0	Minute (2) Schultz' 1	Strong minute
213	*l(2)cg*	15.0±	lethal (2) comb-gap	Lethal from *cg* stock
214	*Sk*	16.0	Streak	Central streak on thorax; homozygous lethal
215	*tkv*	16.0±	thick-veins	Veins thick, irregular
216	*cl*	16.5	clot	Eye color maroon, close to sepia *(se)*
217	*pi*	17.0±	pied	Facets jumbled
218	*Sp*	22.0	Sternopleural	Extra sternopleural bristles; homozygous lethal
219	*spd*	22.3±	spade	Wings shortened; broad

continued

9. LINKAGE GROUPS: INVERTEBRATES

Part I: FRUIT FLY

	Gene Symbol	Locus	Mutation	Phenotypic Expression
	(A)	(B)	(C)	(D)
	Chromosome II [1]			
220	*gt-4*	24.0	giant-4	Giant flies
221	*d*	31.0	dachs	Tarsi 4-jointed, venation shifted
222	*fy*	33.0±	fuzzy	Thoracic hairs fuzzy
223	*fol*	39.0±	folded wings	Wings folded; overlap
224	*da*	39.3±	daughterless	Homozygous females produce no daughters
225	*J*	41.0	Jammed	Wing narrow strip
226	*M(2)S11*	43.0±	Minute (2) Schultz' 11	Slight minute
227	*ab*	44.0	abrupt	Shortened L5 vein, scutellars few
228	*oph*	45.0±	ophthalmopedia	Eyes kidney-shaped or with appendage
229	*rk*	46.0±	rickets	Segments of legs flattened and bent
230	*l(2)*bs^3*-d*	46.0±	lethal (2) with bs^3-d	Lethal
231	*M(2)e*	46.0±	Minute (2) e	Medium minute
232	*b*	48.5	black	Body, legs, veins black
233	*j*	48.7	jaunty	Wings upturned
234	*el*	50.0	elbow	Wings bent, alulae and balancers small
235	*lm*	50.0±	limited	Sternites small; female sterile
236	*M(2)S13*	50.0±	Minute (2) Schultz' 13	Strong minute
237	*l(2)H*	50.0±	lethal (2) Humphrey	Pupal semilethal
238	*Su-H*	50.5	Suppressor of hairless	Homozygous lethal
239	*rd*	51.0	reduced	Bristles small, irregular; female sterile
240	*pu*	51.0±	pupal	Wings unexpanded
241	*pys*	52.0±	polychaetous	Extra and double bristles
242	*cr-u*	52.5±	cream-underscored	Specific dilutor of w^e and Pale; male sterile
243	*nub*	53.0	nubbin	Wings very small and thin with tendency to curve up or down
244	*ck*	53.0±	crinkled	Wings flimsy
245	*rdo*	53.0±	reduced ocelli	Ocelli reduced in size, color moved to region between ocelli
246	*l(2)Bld*	53.1	lethal (2) opposite T (1,2) Bld	Lethal
247	*M(2)S5*	53.5	Minute (2) Schultz' 5	Medium minute
248	*hk*	53.9	hook	Bristles bent or barbed
249	*bri*	54.3±	bright	Eye color bright red
250	*pr*	54.5	purple	Eye color purplish ruby
251	*rn*	54.5±	rotund	Wings round, tarsi 3-jointed; sterile
252	*rh*	54.7±	roughish	Eyes moderately rough
253	*Bl*	54.8	Bristle	Bristles short, beaded; homozygous semilethal
254	*Alu*	54.9	Alula	Alula fused to wing; wing warped
255	*Jag*	54.9	Jagged	Wings nicked, eyes rough
256	*lt*	55.0	light	Eye color yellowish pink
257	*tri*	55.0±	trident	Thorax darkened
258	*M(2)D*	55.0± (Df)	Minute (2) D	Body color and bristles pale
259	*rl*	55.1-	rolled	Wing edges rolled, frayed
260	*M(2)S2*	55.1 (Df)	Minute (2) Schultz' 2	Minute type
261	*M(2)S4*	55.1 (Df)	Minute (2) Schultz' 4	Medium minute
262	*M(2)S8*	55.1 (Df)	Minute (2) Schultz' 8	Slight minute
263	*M(2)S10*	55.1 (Df)	Minute (2) Schultz' 10	Slight minute
264	*stw*	55.1	straw	Body, wings, bristles yellow
265	*blt*	55.2±	blot	Wings inflated, blackened
266	*Cu*	55.2±	Curl	Lateral compression and indentation-fold of unfolded imaginal wing
267	*tk*	55.3	thick	Legs, tarsi thickened; wings short
268	*pk*	55.3	prickle	Bristles, hairs irregular
269	*ap*	55.4	apterous	Wings, balancers missing
270	*msf*	55.6-	misformed	Eyes misformed, wings crumpled
271	*bur*	55.7±	burgundy	Dull, darkish-brown eye color
272	*ti*	55.9	tarsi irregular	Tarsal segments fused, eyes rough
273	*ltd*	56.0±	lightoid	Eye color translucent yellowish pink, ocelli colorless
274	*M(2)S12*	56.0±	Minute (2) Schultz' 12	Slight minute
275	*std*	56.5±	staroid	Eyes small, very rough; male sterile
276	*ta*	56.6±	tapered	Wings narrow and pointed, veins close
277	*dil*	57.0±	specific dilutor	Dilutor of *bw* and *w* alleles
278	*buo*	57.1	burnt orange	Eye color orange brown
279	*M(2)38b*	57.0±	Minute (2) 38b	Extreme minute

continued

9. LINKAGE GROUPS: INVERTEBRATES

Part I: FRUIT FLY

	Gene Symbol	Locus	Mutation	Phenotypic Expression
	(A)	(B)	(C)	(D)
	Chromosome II [1]			
280	*cn*	57.5	cinnabar	Eye color bright scarlet, ocelli colorless
281	*puf*	58.0±	puff	Wings blistered
282	*blo*	58.5	bloated	Wings ballooned, extra veins
283	*smk*	58.6±	smoky	Body color dark
284	*Np*	58.7-60.2 (Df)	Notopleural	Bristles short, wings broad; homozygous lethal
285	*at*	60.1±	arctus oculus	Number of facets reduced
286	*arch*	60.5±	arch	Wings downcurved in both axes
287	*ad*	60.7	arcoid	Wings arched, broad, short; crossveins close
288	*chl*	60.8	chaetelle	Bristles very small; slight plexus
289	*whd*	61.0±	withered	Wings warped or shrunken
290	*tom*	61.5±	tomboy	Homozygous females with male-like pigmentation of posterior tergites
291	*en*	62.0	engrailed	Scuttellar notch, broken veins, extra sex comb
292	*upw*	62.0±	upward	Wings upturned
293	*l(2)rn*	63.0±	lethal (2) with rotund	Lethal
294	*Bkd*	65.0±	Blackoid	Dark body color
295	*M(2)40c*	65.0±	Minute (2) 40c	Minute type
296	*po*	65.2	pale-ocelli	Ocelli nearly colorless
297	*sca*	66.7	scabrous	Eyes rough, some bristles missing
298	*vg*	67.0	vestigial	Wings, balancers vestigial
299	*l(2)C*	67.0	lethal (2) Curry	Lethal before pupal stage
300	*wx*	69.7	waxy	Wings heavy, waxy; male sterile
301	U^{H20}	70.0±	Upturned U^{H20}	Wings curled
302	$l(2)mr^{2}$	70.0±	lethal (2) with morula^{2}	Lethal
303	*Pfd*	70.8	Pufdi	Wings puffed, divergent; homozygous lethal
304	*bat*	71.0	bat	Wings extended, bent back
305	*cg*	71.1	comb-gap	Sex combs large; gap in wing vein L4; female sterile
306	*dr*	71.2±	droopy	Wings spread wide apart and drooping
307	*sf*	71.5±	safranin	Eye color dark chocolate
308	*L*	72.0	Lobe	Eyes small, nicked at anterior edge
309	*kn*	72.3	knot	Veins L3 and L4 close; eyes oblique
310	*Ch*	72.5	Chubby	Larva, pupa, adult short
311	*dke*	73.0±	dark eye	Eye color soft, dark, dull, with tiny fleck
312	*gp*	74.0±	gap	Vein L4 broken
313	*c*	75.5	curved	Wings thin, spread, lifted, curved
314	*Wr*	76.0±	Wrinkled	Wings wrinkled; suppresses lobe *(L)*
315	*M(2)S7*	77.5	Minute (2) Schultz' 7	Strong minute
316	*pw-c*	79.0±	pink-wing-c	Eye color dilute, wings short, blunt
317	*fr*	80.0±	fringed	Wing margins ragged
318	*fj*	81.0±	four-jointed	Tarsi 4-jointed; wings short
319	*rf*	81.0±	roof wings	Wings drooped at sides
320	*wt*	82.0±	welt	Eyes seamed, reduced
321	*abr*	83.0±	abero	Abdominal bands irregular; wings frayed, eyes rough; female sterile
322	*nw*	83.0±	narrow	Wings narrow
323	*I-f*	86.5	Intensifier of forked	Enhances *f*
324	*sm*	91.5	smooth	Abdomen hairless
325	*M(2)173*	92.3	Minute (2) 173	Moderate minute
326	*hy*	93.3	humpy	Thorax ridged, wings truncated
327	*l(2)Su-H*	99.0±	lethal (2) from suppressor of hairless	Lethal
328	*a*	99.2	arc	Wings broad, bent down, crossveins closer
329	*M(2)l*	99.0-102.2 (Df)	Minute (2) l	Extreme minute
330	*px*	100.5	plexus	Network of extra veins
331	*pa*	101.0±	patulous	Wings spread wide apart
332	$M(2)l^{2}$	101.2	Minute (2)l^{2}	Slight minute
333	*hv*	104.0	heavy vein	Veins thick, posterior crossveins oblique
334	*l(2)bw*	104.0±	lethal (2) brown	Probable deficiency; lethal
335	*bw*	104.5	brown	Eye color brownish to garnet
336	*mi*	104.7	minus	Bristles hairlike; body small
337	*abb*	105.5	abbreviated	Bristles slightly reduced; female sterile
338	*slt*	106.3	slight	Body small, bristles reduced

continued

Part I: FRUIT FLY

	Gene Symbol	Locus	Mutation	Phenotypic Expression
	(A)	(B)	(C)	(D)
			Chromosome II [1]	
339	*pd*	106.4	purpleoid	Eye color dark pink, like purple
340	*ll*	106.7±	lanceolate	Wings narrow, pointed
341	*mr*	106.7	morula	Eyes rough, bristles small
342	*l(2)ax*	106.9	lethal (2) ax	Very early larval lethal
343	*sp*	107.0	speck	Black speck in wing axil; body color olive
344	*or*	107.2	orange	Bright orange eye color
345	*Px*	107.0-107.4 (Df)	Plexate	Venation as in blistered mutation *(bs)*; veins thickened, broken; homozygous lethal
346	*bs*	107.3	blistered	Wings blistered, small; extra veins
347	*Pin*	107.3±	Pin	Thoracic bristles pinlike
348	*ba*	107.4	balloon	Wings inflated, extra veins
349	*M(2)33a*	108.0± (Df)	Minute (2) 33a	Strong minute
			Chromosome III [1]	
350	*ru*	0	roughoid	Eyes small, rough; erupted facets
351	*mp*	0	microptera	Wings small, ballooned; tarsi 4-jointed
352	*aa*	0±	anarista	Aristae small, without branches
353	*ve*	0.2	veinlet	Longitudinal wing veins interrupted
354	*R*	1.4	Roughened	Eyes rough; homozygous semilethal
355	*rai*	17.0±	raisin	Deep brown eye color
356	*jv*	19.2	javelin	Bristles and hairs cylindrical
357	*dv*	20.0	divergent	Wings spread
358	*Me*	20.0±	Moire	Eye color brownish, 7 flecks; homozygous lethal
359	*Hn*	23.0	Henna	Eye color dull, dark; homozygous lethal
360	*be-3*	25.0±	benign tumor in 3	Nonlethal melanotic tumors
361	*se*	26.0	sepia	Eye color brownish red, darkening to black
362	*su-t*	26.0±	suppressor of tan	Converts *t* to +
363	*h*	26.5	hairy	Extra hairs on scutellars, veins, pleurae, and head
364	*abd*	27.0±	abdominal	Abdominal bands broken, etched
365	*rs*	35.0	rose	Eye color translucent pink
366	*eyg*	35.5	eye-gone	Eyes and head reduced
367	*gv*	36.2	grooved	Longitudinal medial groove in thorax
368	*cr-3*	36.5±	cream in 3	Specific dilutor of w^e eye color
369	*rt*	37.0±	rotated	Abdomen twisted counterclockwise
370	*app*	37.5	approximated	Crossveins close; tarsi 4-jointed
371	*pyd*	39.0±	polychaetoid	Extra bristles
372	*M(3)S37*	39.7±	Minute (3) Schultz' 37	Extreme minute
373	*tt*	40.0	tilt	Wings spread, warped, with gap in vein L3
374	*M(3)33j*	40.2 (Df)	Minute (3) 33j	Medium minute
375	*M(3)h*	40.2	Minute (3) h	Medium minute; allele of *M(3)33j*
376	*M(3)y*	40.2	Minute (3) y	Medium minute; allele of *M(3)33j*
377	*vo-3*	40.4±	vortex in 3	Intensifier of dp^v
378	*D*	40.4±	Dichaete	Wings spread; homozygous lethal
379	*Ly*	40.5 (Df)	Lyra	Wings cut, narrow; homozygous lethal
380	*Gl*	41.4	Glued	Eyes small, facets rounded; homozygous lethal
381	*fz*	41.7±	frizzled	Thoracic hairs, bristles turn toward mid-line
382	*rp*	41.7±	rotated-penis	Male genitalia rotated; male sterile
383	*wk*	42.0±	weak	Bristles weak, irregular; body small
384	*Wi*	43.0	Washed eye	Modified *w;* homozygous lethal
385	*th*	43.2	thread	Aristae threadlike, without branches
386	*mb*	43.4±	minusbar	Modified *B* to larger eye
387	*Cm*	43.5±	Crimp	Posterior wing edge crimped; homozygous lethal
388	*bul*	43.6	bulge	Eyes bulging, wings squared off
389	*M(3)S38*	44.0±	Minute (3) Schultz' 38	Strong minute
390	*st*	44.0	scarlet	Eye color scarlet, ocelli white
391	*tra*	45.0±	transformed	Transforms females to normal-appearing males
392	*cp*	45.3	clipped	Wing margins clipped
393	*mot-28*	46.0	mottled-28	Eyes mottled with brown
394	*W*	46.0	Wrinkled	Wings incompletely unfolded, pebbled
395	*as*	46.0±	ascute	Wings held downward
396	*je*	46.0±	jelly	Eye color dark pinkish
397	*Pdr*	46.0±	Purpleoider	Intensifier of *pd*

continued

9. LINKAGE GROUPS: INVERTEBRATES

Part I: FRUIT FLY

	Gene Symbol	Locus	Mutation	Phenotypic Expression
	(A)	(B)	(C)	(D)
			Chromosome III [1]	
398	*in*	47.0	inturned	Thoracic bristles directed toward midline
399	*M(3)S39*	47.0±	Minute (3) Schultz' 39	Strong minute
400	*dn*	47.0±	doughnut	Eye of *se dn* with light central spot; male sterile
401	*ri*	47.1	radius incompletus	Vein L2 shows gap
402	*eg*	47.3	eagle	Wings spread, raised
403	*Dfd*	47.5	Deformed	Eyes small; homozygous lethal
404	*wp*	47.5	warped	Wings spread, doubly warped
405	*pb*	47.7	proboscipedia	Mouth parts footlike; adult lethal
406	*p*	48.0	pink	Eye color dull ruby
407	*Bb*	48.0±	Bubble	Wings small, inflated; male sterile; homozygous female lethal
408	*bod*	48.3	bowed	Wings arched
409	*tet*	48.5	tetraltera	Wings haltere-like
410	*by*	48.7	blistery	Wings blistered distally
411	*M(3)S34*	49.0±	Minute (3) Schultz' 34	Slight minute
412	*ma*	49.7	maroon	Eye color dull ruby
413	*cu*	50.0	curled	Wings upcurved, body dark, postscutellars crossed
414	*M(3)S31*	50.0 (Df)	Minute (3) Schultz' 31	Medium minute
415	*mu*	50.0±	mussed	Wings thin, crumpled
416	*ry*	51.0±	rosy	Eye color deep ruby
417	*kar*	52.0	karmoisin	Eye color like scarlet mutation *(st)* but duller, ocelli colorless
418	*C3G*	55.0±	Crossover suppressor in 3 of Gowen	Eliminates crossing over
419	*red*	55.5±	red	Red malpighian tubules
420	*jvl*	56.7	javelin-like	Bristles cylindrical, crooked
421	*cv-c*	57.9	crossveinless-c	Posterior crossvein absent or reduced
422	*Sb*	58.2	Stubble	Bristles short, thick; homozygous lethal
423	*ss*	58.5	spineless	Bristles very small
424	*bx*	58.8	bithorax (pseudo)	Balancers winglike; metathorax resembles mesothorax
425	*cal*	59.5±	coal	Black body color, similar to e^4
426	*Rf*	59.0±	Roof	Wings drooping at sides
427	*fl*	59.9	fluted	Wings creased, darkish
428	*sr*	62.0	stripe	Dark dorsal stripe
429	*M(3)f*	62.4	Minute (3) f	Minute type
430	*gl*	63.1	glass	Eye color dilute, facets fused
431	*gl-l*	64.0±	glass-like	Eyes orange, rough, and small
432	*k*	64.0±	kidney	Eyes kidney-shaped
433	*M(3)S35*	64.0±	Minute (3) Schultz' 35	Extreme minute
434	*sed*	64.5±	sepiaoid	Eye color chocolate
435	*cv-d*	65.0±	crossveinless-d	Posterior crossvein absent or reduced
436	*Cur*	66.0±	Curl	Curly wings; homozygous lethal
437	*Dl*	66.2	Delta	Veins thick at margin; homozygous lethal
438	*H*	69.5	Hairless	Some bristles and hair; homozygous lethal
439	*e*	70.7	ebony	Body color black
440	*det*	72.5	detached	Crossveins broken, wings folded under
441	*cd*	75.7	cardinal	Eye color dull scarlet, ocelli white
442	*wo*	76.2	white ocelli	Ocelli colorless
443	*obt*	77.5±	obtuse	Wings short, blunt
444	*bar-3*	79.1	bar-3	Phenotype like *B/B*
445	*M(3)124*	79.7	Minute (3) 124	Strong minute; allele of *M(3)w*
446	*M(3)B*	79.7	Minute (3) Burkart	Moderate minute; allele of *M(3)w*
447	$M(3)B^2$	79.7	Minute (3) Bridges	Strong minute; allele of *M(3)w*
448	*M(3)w*	79.7	Minute (3) w	Strong minute
449	*l(3)a*	79.7	lethal (3) first found	Lethal; allele of *M(3)w*
450	*M(3)Fla*	80.0±	Minute (3) Florida	Strong minute; allele of *M(3)w*
451	*M(3)36e*	84.5	Minute (3) 36e	Medium minute
452	*M(3)be*	87.0±	Minute (3) beta	Medium minute
453	*mah*	88.0±	mahogany	Eye color brownish, darkening
454	*Pr*	90.0	Prickly	Bristles vestigial; homozygous semilethal
455	*m(3)j*	90.2	minute (3) j	Extreme minute
456	*l(3)PR*	90.2	lethal with In(3R)P	Lethal; allele of *M(3)j*

continued

9. LINKAGE GROUPS: INVERTEBRATES

Part I: FRUIT FLY

	Gene Symbol	Locus	Mutation	Phenotypic Expression
	(A)	(B)	(C)	(D)
	Chromosome III [1]			
457	*tx*	91.0±	taxi	Wings divergent
458	*ro*	91.1	rough	Eyes rough, small
459	*l(3)XaR*	91.8	lethal (3) XaR	Balancer of *T(2, 3)Xa*
460	*cmp*	93.0±	crumpled	Wings smaller, crumpled
461	*Bd*	93.8	Beaded	Wing margins excised; homozygous lethal
462	*Pw*	94.1	Pointed-wing	Wings pointed at tip; homozygous lethal
463	*bf*	95.0±	brief	Body small, bristles minute-like; male sterile
464	*rsd*	95.4	raised	Wings rise straight up
465	Su^{B}*-pr*	95.5	Suppressor of purple	Male sterile
466	*ra*	97.3	rase	Bristles, hairs smaller, fewer
467	*Dp*	99.3±	Duplication	Similar to ultra bar
468	*ld*	100.0±	loboid	Eyes lobe-like
469	*ca*	100.7	claret	Eye color clear ruby
470	*M(3)l*	101.0	Minute (3)l	Medium minute
471	*bv*	104.3	brevis	Bristles short, stubby
472	*M(3)g*	106.2	Minute (3)g	Slight minute, requires *E-M(3)g*
	Chromosome IV [40]			
473	*ci*	0	cubitus-interruptus	Vein L4 interrupted
474	*M-4*	0-0.2±	Minute-4	Medium minute; deficiency for *ci, ar, gvl,* and *Scn*
475	*ar*	0-0.2	abdomen rotatum	Abdomen twisted clockwise
476	*gvl*	0.2	grooveless	Scutellar groove diminished
477	*bt*	1.4	bent	Wings bent, legs knobby
478	*ey*	2.0	eyeless	Eyes small or absent
479	*sv*	3.0	shaven	Abdominal bristles fewer

Contributors: (a) Warren, Katherine Brehme, (b) Novitski, E.

References: [1] Bridges, C. B., and K. S. Brehme. 1944. Carnegie Inst. Wash. Publ. 552. [2] Buzzati-Traverso, A. 1948. Drosophila Inform. Service 22:66. [3] Chino, M. 1936. Japan. J. Genet. 12:205. [4] Chino, M. 1937. Ibid. 13:105. [5] Chino, M. 1939. Drosophila Inform. Service 11:32. [6] Christie, A. L. M. 1939. J. Genet. 39:58. [7] Clarke, J. M. 1951. Drosophila Inform. Service 25:94. [8] Clarke, J. M. 1952. Ibid. 26:87. [9] Demerec, M. 1954. Ibid. 28:93. [10] Donald, H. P. 1936. J. Genet. 33:105. [11] Fahny, M. B., and O. Fahny. 1957-60. Drosophila Inform. Service 31-34. [12] Ferry, R. M., R. C. Lancefield, and C. W. Metz. 1923. J. Heredity 14:373. [13] Gordon, C., H. Spurway, and P. A. R. Street. 1939. J. Genet. 38:45. [14] Haldane, J. B. S. 1945. Drosophila Inform. Service 19:56. [15] Jermyn, J. E., et al. 1943. Ibid. 17:52. [16] Kiil, V. 1946. Ibid. 20:82. [17] Kikkawa, H. 1938. Genetica (Haag) 20:458. [18] Lamy, R. 1944. Drosophila Inform. Service 18:52. [19] Lancefield, D. E. 1922. Genetics 7:375. [20] Lancefield, R. C., and C. W. Metz. 1922. Am. Naturalist 56:211. [21] Mainx, F. 1949. Drosophila Inform. Service 23:78. [22] Mainx, F. 1950. Ibid. 24:77. [23] Milani, R. 1949. Ibid. 23:78. [24] Miller, D. D. 1954. Ibid. 28:100. [25] Moriwaki, D. 1935. Genetica (Haag) 17:41. [26] Moriwaki, D. 1938. J. Genet. 14:1. [27] Moriwaki, D. 1949. Drosophila Inform. Service 23:77. [28] Osima, T. 1940. Cytologia (Tokyo) 10:450. [29] Osima, T. 1940. Drosophila Inform. Service 13:55. [30] Patterson, J. T., and W. S. Stone. 1952. Evolution in the genus *Drosophila.* Macmillan, New York. [31] Spassky, B., S. Zimmering, and T. Dobzhansky. 1950. Heredity 4:189. [32] Spencer, W. P. 1935. Drosophila Inform. Service 4:48. [33] Spencer, W. P. 1944. Ibid. 18:51. [34] Spencer, W. P. 1949. Genetics, paleontology, and evolution. Princeton Univ. Press, Princeton, N. J. [35] Spiess, E. B. 1952. Drosophila Inform. Service 26:87. [36] Spurway, H. 1939. Ibid. 12:54. [37] Spurway, H. 1951. Ibid. 25:95. [38] Sturtevant, A. H. 1929. Carnegie Inst. Wash. Publ. 399. [39] Sturtevant, A. H. 1940. Genetics 25:343. [40] Sturtevant, A. H. 1951. Proc. Natl. Acad. Sci. U. S. 37:405. [41] Sturtevant, A. H., and E. Novitski. 1941. Genetics 26:517. [42] Sturtevant, A. H., and C. C. Tan. 1937. J. Genet. 34:415. [43] Warren, K. B. Unpublished. Natl. Institutes of Health, Bethesda, Md., 1962.

continued

9. LINKAGE GROUPS: INVERTEBRATES

Part II: PARASITIC WASP

Habrobracon juglandis has 10 pair of chromosomes; linkage groups have been found for 8 pair. Linkage (column B): slanting line (/) indicates complete linkage.

	Gene Symbol	Linkage	Recombination Percentage	Mutation	Phenotypic Expression
	(A)	(B)	(C)	(D)	(E)
					Linkage Group I
1	*Sk*	*Sk--r*	12	Speckled	Bright red flecks of pigment in white eye
2	*r*	*r--gl*	13	reduced	Small wings; reduced, irregular venation
3	*gl*	*gl--x*	30	glass	Small eyes; lacking facet outlines
4	*X*	*X--fu*	10	Sex	9 alleles known (each consisting of many factors determining sex differences) that produce similar phenotypes in males and in females
5	*fu*	*fu--sb*	22	fused	Antennal segments fused; tarsal segments lacking or fused
6	*sb*	*sb--bl*	42	stubby	Males with antennae 7-9 segments long; females with antennae 5-7 segments long
7	*bl*	*bl--le*	30	black	Body color black
8	*le*	*le--c*	12	lemon	Body color pale lemon yellow
9	*c*	*c--l*	14	canteloupe	Eyes light pink, darken to deep red
10	*l*	*l--n*	3	long	Antennal segments elongated; leg segments longer and thinner than in wild type
11	*n*	*n--ho*	7	narrow	Narrow wings; cuts off irregular slices of costal and inner wing margins
12	*ho*	*ho--vl*	8	honey	Body lacks black pigment entirely
13	*vl*	*vl--ro*	15	veinless	Wing veins missing, except along costal margin
14	*ro*	*ro--bu*	12	rough	4th radius vein absent, adjacent veins roughened
15	*bu*	*bu--cr*	37	bulged	Eyes abnormally bulged transversely
16	*cr*	*cr--sl/co*	41	crescent	Eyes small; pigment in ocelli reduced, crescent-shaped
17	*sl*	*sl/co--ct*	33	semilong	Antennal and leg segments lengthened
18	*co*			coalescent	Antennal segments coalescent
19	*ct*	*ct--rd*	32	cut	Outer wing margin indented or straightened, giving cut appearance
20	*rd*	*rd--gy*	37	red	Eye color varies from light red to dark red, almost black with temperature increase
21	*gy*	*gy--ac/el*	7	gynoid	Short antennae in male, resembling those in female; abdominal sclerites resemble those in female
22	*ac*	*ac/el--gy*	7	aciform	Terminal half of antennae very slender, needlelike
23	*el*			eyeless	Head malformed; eye rudiments present
					Linkage Group II
24	*k*	*k--dw*	28	kidney	Eyes kidney-shaped
25	*dw*	*dw--m*	5	dwindling	Irregularity and fusion of antennal segments
26	*m*	*m--o*	11	miniature	Reduced body size; semilethal; may die as pupa
27	*o*	*o--m*	11	orange	Eyes orange, varying to pink and red
					Linkage Group III
28	*bk*	*bk--wh/pl*	25	broken	Outer margin of primary wing broken and wings fragile
29	*wh*	*wh/pl--st*	9	white	White eye; ocelli colorless
30	*pl*			pellucid	Compound eyes semitransparent
31	*st*	*st--wh/pl*	9	stumpy	Extreme reduction of tarsal segments
					Linkage Group IV
32	*sv*	*sv--td*	23	shot-veins	Wing veins broken and distorted
33	*td*	*td--ma*	27	truncated	Wings extremely reduced, irregular in shape
34	*ma*	*ma--td*	27	maroon	Light ocelli; compound eyes deep reddish brown
					Linkage Group V
35	*wa*	*wa--br*	22	wavy	Wings shortened, costal margin wavy
36	*br*	*br--wa*	22	broad	Thorax abnormally broadened
					Linkage Group VI
37	*ta*	*ta--un2*	40	tapering	Antennae deficient, with much fusion and irregularity of segments distally
38	*un2*	*un2--ta*	40	undulating-2	Surface of wings in undulating waves

continued

9. LINKAGE GROUPS: INVERTEBRATES

Part II: PARASITIC WASP

	Gene Symbol	Linkage	Recombination Percentage	Mutation	Phenotypic Expression
	(A)	(B)	(C)	(D)	(E)
					Linkage Group VII
39	*pk*	pk/ew^3		pink	Compound eyes pink
40	ew^3			extended wings	Wings extended in active wasps
					Linkage Group VIII
41	*wt*	*wt--bf*	17	wet	Wing microchaetae very long and irregular, giving wet appearance
42	*bf*	*bf--wt*	17	black feet	Tarsi abnormally black

Contributors: (a) Whiting, P. W., (b) Novitski, E.

References: [1] Carson, H. L. 1941. Am. Naturalist 75:608. [2] Clark, A. M. 1942. J. Heredity 33:78. [3] Clark, A. M. 1943. Proc. Penna. Acad. Sci. 17:47. [4] Helsel, E. D. 1944. Am. Naturalist 78:188. [5] Martin, A., Jr. 1947. An introduction to the genetics of *Habrobracon juglandis* (Ashmead). Hobson Book Press, New York. [6] Martin, A., Jr. 1947. Proc. Penna. Acad. Sci. 21:32. [7] Martin, A., Jr. 1947. Ibid. 21:36. [8] Martin, A., Jr. 1948. Univ. Pittsburgh Bull. 44:1. [9] Torvik-Greb, M. 1935. Biol. Bull. 68:25. [10] Whiting, P. W. 1943. Genetics 28:365. [11] Whiting, P. W. 1946. Ibid. 32:112. [12] Whiting, P. W. 1950. J. Heredity 41:71. [13] Whiting, P. W., and L. H. Benkert. 1934. Genetics 19:268. [14] Whiting, P. W., and A. R. Whiting. 1934. J. Genet. 29:311.

Part III: SILKWORM

Bombyx mori has 28 pair of chromosomes; linkage groups have been found for 15 pair.

	Gene Symbol	Locus	Mutation	Phenotypic Expression
	(A)	(B)	(C)	(D)
				Linkage Group I (Z Chromosome)
1	*os*	0	sex-linked	Low translucency of larva
2	*Ge*	14.0	Giant egg	Length and width 1.26 and 1.11, respectively, times the normal egg
3	*e*	36.4	elongate	First and second abdominal segments of larva unusually elongated
4	*Vg*	38.7	Vestigial	Wings poorly developed
5	*od*	49.6	translucent	Skin of larva shows high translucency
				Linkage Group II
6	*P*	0	Plain	Full grown larva white; $+p$, p^B, p^M, p^S, p^{Sa}, multiple or pseudo-alleles of *p*
7	*S*	6.1	New striped	Dark stripe on larva; heterozygote almost as dark as homozygote
8	*Gr*	6.9	Gray egg	Milky white shell, dark serosa pigment
9	*Y*	25.6	Yellow blood	Deep yellow hemolymph in larva
10	*oa*	26.7	mottled translucent	Mottled translucency on larval skin
11	*Rc*	31.8	Rusty	Yellowish-brown cocoon, lighter inner layer
				Linkage Group III
12	*Ze*	0	Zebra	Black band on anterior end of each segment; pair of black spots on ventral side of each larval segment
13	*ap*	0	apodal	All thoracic legs rudimentary
14	*lem*	22.8	lemon	Greenish-yellow coloring over skin visible from 2nd instar
				Linkage Group IV
15	*L*	0	Multilunar	Pairs of large brownish or yellowish round spots on thoracic and abdominal segments
16	*sk*	25.8	stick	Larva body slender and hard
17	*Spc*	33.1	Speckle	Many dark spots on larval skin; female sterile

continued

Part III: SILKWORM

	Gene Symbol	Locus	Mutation	Phenotypic Expression
	(A)	(B)	(C)	(D)
				Linkage Group V
18	*pe*	0	pink-eyed	White egg; pigment absent from serosa
19	*ok*	4.7	kinshiryu	High translucency of larva
20	*re*	31.7	red egg	Reddish-brown serosa
21	*oc*	40.8	chinese	High translucency of larva
				Linkage Group VI
22	*E*	0	Plain supernumerary legs	Supernumerary legs in 1st and 2nd abdominal segments of larva; E^{Ca}, E^{D}, E^{H}, E^{Kp}, E^{N}, multiple or pseudoalleles of *E*
23	*Nc*	1.4	No crescent supernumerary legs	Crescents absent; supernumerary leg in the 2nd abdominal segment
24	^{+}M	3.0	Tetra molting	Standard type, larva pupates after 4th molt; M^{3}, M^{5}, multiple or pseudoalleles of ^{+}M
25	b_2	8.0	brown egg 2	Grayish-brown pigment in serosa
26	*F*	13.6	Flesh	Cocoon color reddish yellow or salmon color
27	*l-k*	17.7	lethal-k	Embryo killed few days before hatching
				Linkage Group VII
28	*q*	0	quail	Larval body tinted reddish purple and covered with shred-like lines
29	*Gb*	7.0	Green b	Greenish cocoon color
30	*obt*	21.0	b_8-mottled	Moderate translucency of larva; not lethal
				Linkage Group VIII
31	*ae*	0	amylase negative	Amylase in digestive fluid weak
32	*be*	1.1	amylase negative	Amylase in body fluid (hemolymph) weak
				Linkage Group IX
33	*I*	0	Yellow inhibitor	Suppression of yellow blood and yellow cocoon
34	*I-a*	5.9	Dominant chocolate	Similar to chocolate mutation *(ch)*; head black
35	*bd*	6.7	dilute black	Whole larval body dilute black
36	*og*	7.4	giallo ascoli	High translucency; female almost sterile
				Linkage Group X
37	w_1*(w-1)*	0	white egg 1	No pigment in serosa; white eyes in moth
38	*fl*	0+	wingless	Fore and hind wings absent in pupa and moth
39	w_2*(w-2)*	3.4	white egg 2	Egg gradually changes from white to light reddish color; white eyes in moth
40	w_3*(w-3)*	6.9	white egg 3	Light purplish-brown egg; black eyes in moth
				Linkage Group XI
41	*K*	0	Knobbed	Dermal protuberances appear on dorsal sides of several segments of larva, pupa and moth
42	*Bu*	5.5	Burnt	Larva skin from 2nd to 5th segments shows burnlike scar
43	*bp*	17.1	black pupa	Black pupae (2 strains)
44	*mp*	24.0	micropterous	Small wings
				Linkage Group XII
45	*Ng*	0	No glue	Eggs easily separated from papers because of poor development of mucous glands in females
46	*C*	14.0	Golden egg	Cocoon golden yellow outside, nearly white inside
47	*rd*	52.1	clumpy	Irregular egg shape and highly variable
				Linkage Group XIII
48	*ch*	0	chocolate	Newly hatched larva reddish brown
49	*cf*	11.3	crayfish	Fore and hind wings swollen and protrude laterally from body in pupa
				Linkage Group XIV
50	*Di*	0	Dirty	Irregular black lines and dots cover dorsal surface of larva
51	*U*	2.7	Ursa	Dark brown pigments cover dorsal and lateral sides of larva
52	*odk*	10.7	mottled	Low translucency
				Linkage Group XV
53	*Se*	0	White side egg	Egg surface irregular and with many furrows
54	*Gc*	7.8	Green c	Green cocoon

continued

9. LINKAGE GROUPS: INVERTEBRATES

Part III: SILKWORM

Contributors: (a) Novitski, E., (b) Kikkawa, H.

References: [1] Tanaka, Y. 1953. Advances in Genet. 5:239. [2] Tazima, Y. 1957. Proc. Intern. Genet. Symposium, Japan, 1956, p. 280.

10. LINKAGE GROUPS: PLANTS

Part I: NEUROSPORA CRASSA

Genes for *Neurospora crassa* are listed in order of locus on the chromosome; they proceed from left arm to right arm, with the CENTROMERE the dividing marker. A line under the symbol indicates that the exact position has not been determined. Bracket (}) signifies no recombination between loci.

	Gene Symbol	Mutation	Phenotypic Expression	Reference
	(A)	(B)	(C)	(D)
	Linkage Group I[1]			
1	*fr*	Frost	Delicate branching and non-conidial aerial growth	31
2	*nit-2*	Nitrate-2	Does not reduce nitrate	33
3	*leu-3*	Leucine-3	Requires leucine	3,31
4	*leu-4*	Leucine-4	Requires leucine	13
5	*un(b39)*	Unknown (b39)	Grows at 25°C, not at 34°C; distal to *A/a*; not tested for allelism with *un(55701)*	21
6	*un(55701)*	Unknown (55701)	Unknown requirement; *55701t* grows at 25°C, but not on minimal medium at 35°C	3,16,18
7	*A/a* }	Sex	Mating type	3,31
8	*dot*	Dot	Restricted colonial growth (data scanty)	33
9	*pat*	Patch	Circadian rhythm of dense and sparse mycelial growth; location proximal to *A/a*	39
10	*phen*	Phenylalanine	Requires phenylalanine or leucine, or other aromatic amino acids; location uncertain with respect to *ad-5*	2
11	*ad-5*	Adenine-5	Requires adenine	3,31,33
12	*amyc*	Amycelial	Growth budding; forms dot-like colonies; location proximal to *ad-5*	18,31
13	*arg-1*	Arginine-1	Requires arginine; does not utilize ornithine or citrulline	31
14	*arg-3*	Arginine-3	Requires arginine or citrulline; does not utilize ornithine	3,31
15	*ti*	Tiny	Very restricted colonial growth	30,31
16	*suc*	Succinic	Requires succinic acid or metabolically related compounds; closely linked to centromere	3
17	*cyt-1*	Cytochrome-1	Slow growth; altered cytochrome system; shows 5% recombination with *suc*	25
18	*sn*	Snowflake	Conidiating colonial; location between *arg-3* and *hist-2*	23
	CENTROMERE			
19	*hist-2*	Histidine-2	Requires histidine	44
20	*rg*	Ragged	Poor conidiation; colonial growth	31
21	*lys-4*	Lysine-4	Requires lysine	3,31,44
22	*hist-3*	Histidine-3	Requires histidine	3,44
23	*ad-3*	Adenine-3	Requires adenine; accumulates purple pigment on limiting adenine	3,5,6,31,36
24	*cut*	Cut	Tube culture appears as if mycelia were cut off part way up slant; location between *hist-2* and *arg-6*	21
25	*nic-2*	Nicotinic-2	Requires nicotinamide; accumulates red-brown pigment in the medium	3,31
26	*cr*	Crisp	Early uniform conidiation	3,31
27	*m-1*	Modifier of *vis(3717)*	Location proximal to *vis(3717)*	17
28	*vis(3717)*	Visible (3717)	Semi-colonial growth (located on right arm)	3,17
29	*m-2*	Modifier of *vis(3717)*	Location distal to *vis(3717)*	17

/1/ Other markers known to be in Linkage Group I but presumably lost: *pa*--pale--conidia clumped and pale in color; *nd*--natural death--growth ceases progressively when fungus is homocaryotic; *dir*--dirty--conidia misshapen and few, yellow exudate; *gap*--gap--conidia produced in upper part of culture tube. [3]

continued

10. LINKAGE GROUPS: PLANTS

Part I: NEUROSPORA CRASSA

	Gene Symbol	Mutation	Phenotypic Expression	Reference
	(A)	(B)	(C)	(D)
			Linkage Group I	
30	*st*	Sticky	Can only be scored by direct comparison with wild type; location between *hist-2* and *thi-1*	31
31	*un(44409)*	Unknown (44409)	Unknown requirement; strain *44409t* grows at 25°C on complete medium; but not at 34°C	3,31
32	*slo*	Slow	Slow growth; location proximal to *thi-1*	31
33	*thi-1*	Thiamine-1	Requires thiamine	3,31
34	*mac*	Methionine-adenine-cysteine	Requires methionine; grows best on all 3 substances or complete medium; location between *thi-1* and *al-2*	31
35	*me-6* (called *me(35809)* in ref. 3)	Methionine-6	Requires methionine	3,27,31
36	*csh*	Cushion	Restricted colonial growth; location between *thi-1* and *nit-1*	36
37	*nit-1* (called *n-nit* in ref. 3,40)	Nitrate-1	Does not reduce nitrate	3,31,40
38	*un(STL6)*	Unknown (STL6)	Sub-optimal response to methionine; best scored at 35°C; fluffy morphology with late conidiation	31
39	*arg-6*	Arginine-6	Requires ornithine, citrulline, or arginine	3,31
40	*T*	Tyrosinase thermostability	T^S and T^L govern tyrosinase thermostability; location between *hist-2* and *al-2*	15
41	*su-1-me*	Suppressor-1-methionine	Suppresses *me-2* and *me-7*; shows 1% recombination with *al-2*	3
42	*al-2*	Albino-2	Albino	3,31
43	*aur*	Aurescent	White at first; later forms pigmented terminal conidia	3,31
44	*hs*	Homoserine	Requires homoserine	3,31
45	*can* (called *r-can* in ref. 3)	Canavanine	Resistance to canavanine	3,31-33
46	*lys-3*	Lysine-3	Requires lysine	3,31,35
47	*nic-1* (also called *Q* locus)	Nicotinic-1	Requires nicotinamide	35
48	*os*	Osmotic	Inhibited by high osmotic pressure; can be scored by appearance; conidia rare	31
49	*so*	Soft	Dense pigmented growth in lower part of slant	31
			Linkage Group II	
50	*cfl*	Cauliflower	Dense conidiation in bunches at top of slant	33
51	*thr-2*	Threonine-2	Requires threonine; leaky	8,27,33
52	*thr-3*	Threonine-3	Requires threonine; extremely close to *thr-2*; leaky	33
53	*bal*	Balloon	Restricted growth; hemispherical colony	14,31
	CENTROMERE			
54	*da*	Dapple	Flecks of conidia on agar surface; location uncertain with respect to *bal* and centromere	33
55	*arg-5*	Arginine-5	Requires ornithine, citrulline, or arginine	3,31
56	*arom-3*	Aromatic-3	Requires phenylalanine, tyrosine, tryptophan, and para-aminobenzoic acid; does not use shikimic acid	14
57	*cpt*	Carpet	Flat growth on agar slants; location uncertain with respect to *arom-3*	33
58	*pe*	Peach	Peach-colored conidia (see line 64)	3
59	*su-pe*	Suppressor of microconidial	Suppresses microconidial action of pe^m in *col-1*, pe^m genotype; location 14-22 map units from *pe*	12
60	*arom-1*	Aromatic-1	Requires phenylalanine, tyrosine, tryptophan, and para-aminobenzoic acid; grows on shikimic acid	3
61	*arom-4*	Aromatic-4	Requires phenylalanine, tyrosine, tryptophan, and para-aminobenzoic acid; does not use shikimic acid	14
62	*ac-1*	Acetate-1	Requires acetate plus ethanol	3
63	*tu*	Tuft	Conidia in large clusters at top of culture; location between *pe* and *fl*	3
64	*fl*	Fluffy	No macroconidia; few or no microconidia; *pe fl* genotype forms abundant microconidia	3

continued

10. LINKAGE GROUPS: PLANTS

Part I: NEUROSPORA CRASSA

	Gene Symbol	Mutation	Phenotypic Expression	Reference
	(A)	(B)	(C)	(D)
			Linkage Group II	
65	*tryp-3* (also called *td*)	Tryptophan-3	Requires tryptophan; does not use indole	3
66	*het-2*	Heterocaryon formation	Determines heterocaryon compatibility; alleles *d*, *D*	11
			Linkage Group III	
	CENTROMERE			
67	*thi-4*	Thiamine-4	Requires thiamine; location uncertain with respect to *sc*	3
68	*thi-lo*	Modifier of *thi-1*	In presence of *thi-lo*, *thi-1* requires intact thiamine; may be allelic with *thi-4*	7
69	*sc*	Scumbo	Flat, irregular, concentric growth	3
70	*mel-3*	Melon-3	Colonial, forming hemispherical colony; location uncertain with respect to centromere and markers *thi-4* to *leu-1*	26
71	*ser-1*	Serine-1	Requires serine; can use glycine; very leaky	3
72	*prol-1*	Proline-1	Requires proline; will not use ornithine, citrulline, or arginine	3
73	*com*	Compact	Small colonies	31,34
74	*me-8*	Methionine-8	Requires methionine	28
75	*ad-4*	Adenine-4	Requires adenine; will not use hypoxanthine	3,34
76	*leu-1*	Leucine-1	Requires leucine	3,34
77	*su-mel-3*	Suppressor-melon-3	A loose colonial results from interaction of *mel-3* and *su-mel-3*; location distal to *leu-1*	26
78	*hist-7*	Histidine-7	Requires histidine; located between *ad-4* and *tryp-1*	44
79	*ad-2*	Adenine-2	Requires adenine or hypoxanthine	3,33,34
80	*tryp-1*	Tryptophan-1	Requires indole or tryptophan; accumulates yellow pigment	3
81	*thi-2*	Thiamine-2	Requires intact thiamine	3,34
82	*ro-2*	Ropy-2	Cable-like aggregations of hyphae; location between *tryp-1* and *vel*	31,34
83	*vel*	Velvet	Soft, conidiating colonial	31,34
84	*tyr-1*	Tyrosine-1	Requires tyrosine; very leaky	3,34
			Linkage Group IV	
	CENTROMERE			
85	*pyr-1*	Pyrimidine-1	Requires pyrimidine; uridine and cytidine 10-60 times as active as uracil	3,22,24
86	*pdx-1*	Pyridoxine-1	Requires pyridoxine	3,22,24
87	*pdx-2*	Pyridoxine-2	Requires pyridoxine	3
88	*rib-2*	Riboflavin-2	Requires riboflavin; location between *pdx-1* and *pyr-3*	3,22
89	*arg-2*	Arginine-2	Requires arginine; also uses citrulline	3,24
90	*col-4* (called *co* in ref. 24)	Colonial-4	Colonial, macroconidial	3,22,24
91	*me-1*	Methionine-1	Requires methionine; location between *pdx-1* and *pyr-3*	3,28
92	*pyr-3*	Pyrimidine-3	Requires pyrimidine (see line 85)	3,24
93	*pt*	Phenylalanine-tyrosine	Requires phenylalanine plus tyrosine; location uncertain with respect to *pyr-3*; accumulates brown pigment in medium on aging; fluoresces under ultraviolet light	22
94	*tryp-4*	Tryptophan-4	Requires indole or tryptophan; location between *pdx-1* and *pan-1*	3,22
95	*leu(37501)*	Leucine-37501	Requires leucine; location between *pdx-1* and *pan-1*	22
96	*ad-6*	Adenine-6	Requires adenine; location between *pdx-1* and *pan-1*	3,22
97	*me-2*	Methionine-2	Requires methionine; location between *tryp-4* and *pan-1*	3,22,28
98	*fld*	Fluffyoid	Aconidial; location proximal to *pan-1*	33
99	*thi-5*	Thiamine-5	Requires thiamine; shows 1% recombination with *pan-1*	33
100	*pan-1*	Pantothenic-1	Requires pantothenic acid	3,22
101	*ro-1*	Ropy-1	Cable-like aggregations of hyphae	22,31
102	*nit-3* (called *nitr* in ref. 16)	Nitrate-3	Does not reduce nitrate; shows 13% recombination with *pan-1*	16,33
103	*chol-1*	Choline-1	Requires choline; location between *ad-6* and *me-5*	3,22
104	*col-1*	Colonial-1	Colonial growth; distal to *chol-1*	3
105	*cot*	Colonial-temperature sensitive	Colonial growth at 34°C; may be allelic with *col-1*	22,24

continued

10. LINKAGE GROUPS: PLANTS

Part I: NEUROSPORA CRASSA

	Gene Symbol	Mutation	Phenotypic Expression	Reference
	(A)	(B)	(C)	(D)
			Linkage Group IV	
106	*ol*	Oleic acid	Requires higher fatty acid: lauric or larger, or Tween 80	33
107	*le-1*	Ascospore lethal	Colonial growth; location distal to *cot*	26
108	*hist-4*	Histidine-4	Requires histidine	22
109	*me-5*	Methionine-5	Requires methionine	3,22,24,34
110	*pyr-2*	Pyrimidine-2	Requires pyrimidine (see line 85)	3,22
111	*dn*	Dingy	Gray lumps, presumably microconidia, on agar slants	24
112	*mat*	Mat	Colonial; grows better on sucrose than on glycerol; location distal to *pyr-2*	22,31
			Linkage Group V	
	CENTROMERE			
113	*lys-1*	Lysine-1	Requires lysine; location uncertain with respect to centromere	3
114	*sh*	Shallow	Spreading morphological; hyphae on surface of agar slant; location uncertain with respect to *lys-1*	33
115	*iv-1*	Isoleucine-valine-1	Requires isoleucine and valine	3
116	*val*	Valine	Requires valine	43
117	*iv-2*	Isoleucine-valine-2	Requires isoleucine and valine; location uncertain with respect to *iv-1* and *val*	3
118	*lys-2*	Lysine-2	Requires lysine; location between *lys-1* and *hist-1*	42,43
119	*sp*	Spray	Aerial mycelium fans outwards	31,43
120	*arg-4*	Arginine-4	Requires arginine; also uses ornithine or citrulline; may be allelic with *arg-7*; location between *sp* and *inos*	3,33,37
121	*arg-7*	Arginine-7	Requires arginine; also uses ornithine or citrulline; may be allelic with *arg-4*	3,33,37
122	*am*	Amination-deficient	Requires α-amino nitrogen; leaky	9,31
123	*i*	Enhancer of *am*	Inhibits growth of *am* on medium containing inorganic nitrogen plus glutamic acid; shows 8% recombination with *am*	10
124	*wa*	Washed	Thin, spreading surface growth and conidiation; location between *lys-2* and *inos*	33
125	*hist-1*	Histidine-1	Requires histidine	3,43
126	*inos*	Inositol	Requires inositol	3,43
127	*arg-8*	Arginine-8	Requires arginine; data scanty	33
128	*pab-1*	para-Aminobenzoic acid-1	Requires para-aminobenzoic acid	3,43
129	*me-3*	Methionine-3	Requires methionine	3,43
130	*bis*	Biscuit	Conidiating colonial	31,43
131	*ser-2*	Serine-2	Requires serine; very leaky	33
132	*ad-7*	Adenine-7	Requires adenine	42,43
133	*pab-2*	para-Aminobenzoic acid-2	Requires para-aminobenzoic acid	43
134	*asp*	Asparagine	Requires asparagine	3,43
135	*pl*	Plug	Dense hyphae filling tube	31,43
			Linkage Group VI[a]	
136	*ad-8*	Adenine-8	Requires adenine; far out on left arm	19
137	*cyt-2*	Cytochrome-2	Slow growth; altered cytochrome system	38
138	*asco*	Ascospores colorless	Low germination; requires lysine; *lys-5(DS6-85)* is an allele of *asco*	38,41
139	*un(66204)*	Unknown (66204)	*66204t* does not grow on minimal medium at $35^{\circ}C$	3,38
140	*cys-2*	Cysteine-2	Requires cysteine or methionine (alleles designated *cys-c*, *cys-t* in ref. 39)	38,39
141	*cys-1*	Cysteine-1	Requires cysteine or methionine	3,38
142	*ylo*	Yellow	Yellow conidia	3,38
143	*ad-1*	Adenine-1	Requires adenine	3,4,38
	CENTROMERE			
144	*pan-2*	Pantothenic-2	Requires pantothenic acid	4
145	*rib-1*	Riboflavin-1	Requires riboflavin at $35^{\circ}C$; location uncertain with respect to *pan-2* and *del*	3,38

/a/ Also known to be in Linkage Group VI but presumably lost: *phen(38602)*--phenylalanine (38602)--requires phenylalanine. [2, 16]

continued

10. LINKAGE GROUPS: PLANTS

Part I: NEUROSPORA CRASSA

	Gene Symbol	Mutation	Phenotypic Expression	Reference
	(A)	(B)	(C)	(D)
			Linkage Group VI	
146	*del*	Delicate	Growth less than that of wild type	20,31
147	*tryp-2*	Tryptophan-2	Requires anthranilic acid, indole, or tryptophan; leaky	3,38
			Linkage Group VII	
148	*nic-3*	Nicotinic-3	Requires nicotinamide	31,33
	CENTROMERE			
149	*sfo*	Sulfonamide	Requires sulfonamide; location uncertain with respect to centromere	3
150	*thi-3*	Thiamine-3	Requires thiamine; leaky; best scored on agar slants after several days	3,31
151	*bn*	Button	Non-conidiating colonial	31
152	*me-9*	Methionine-9	Requires methionine; leaky	29
153	*me-7*	Methionine-7	Requires methionine; proximal to *arg-11*	33
154	*col-2*	Colonial-2	Colonial; non-conidiating	1,3,33
155	*col-3*	Colonial-3	Colonial; non-conidiating	1,3,33
156	*thr-1*	Threonine-1	Requires threonine; proximal to *arg-11*	33
157	*wc*	White collar	No carotenoids except at low temperature; proximal to *arg-11*	33
158	*for*	Formate	Requires formate or adenine plus methionine; proximal to *arg-11*	33
159	*arg-11*	Arginine-11	Requires arginine, adenine, and uridine	31
160	*arg-10*	Arginine-10	Requires arginine; does not use ornithine or citrulline	31
161	*nt*	Nicotinic-tryptophan	Requires nicotinamide or tryptophan	3,31
162	*sk*	Skin	Flat growth; non-conidiating	31

Contributors: Barratt, R. W., and Strickland, W. N.

References: [1] Barratt, R. W., and L. Garnjobst. 1949. Genetics 34:351. [2] Barratt, R. W., and W. Ogata. 1954. Am. J. Botany 41:763. [3] Barratt, R. W., et al. 1954. Advances in Genet. 6:1. [4] Case, M. E., and N. H. Giles. 1958. Proc. Natl. Acad. Sci. U.S. 44:378. [5] de Serres, F. J. 1956. Genetics 41:668. [6] de Serres, F.J. Unpublished, 1961. [7] Eberhart, B. M., and E. L. Tatum. 1959. J. Gen Microbiol. 20:43. [8] Emerson, S. 1950. Cold Spring Harbor Symposia Quant. Biol. 14:40. [9] Fincham, J. R. S. 1954. J. Gen. Microbiol. 11:236. [10] Fincham, J. R. S., and J. A. Pateman. 1957. J. Genet. 55:456. [11] Garnjobst, L. 1953. Am. J. Botany 40:607. [12] Grigg, G. W. 1958. J. Gen. Microbiol. 19:15. [13] Gross, S. R. Unpublished, 1961. [14] Gross, S. R., and A. Fein. 1960. Genetics 45:885. [15] Horowitz, N. H., and M. Fling. 1956. Proc. Natl. Acad. Sci. U.S. 42:498. [16] Houlahan, M. B., G. W. Beadle, and H. G. Calhoun. 1949. Genetics 34:493. [17] Howe, H. B. 1956. Ibid. 41:610. [18] Howe, H. B. Unpublished, 1961. [19] Ishikawa, T. 1960. Genetics 45:993. [20] Ishikawa, T. Unpublished, 1961. [21] Kuwana, H. 1960. Japan. J. Genet. 35:49. [22] Maling, B. D. 1959. Genetics 44:1215. [23] Mitchell, M. B. 1958. Ibid. 43:799. [24] Mitchell, M. B., and H. K. Mitchell. 1954. Proc. Natl. Acad. Sci. U.S. 40:436. [25] Mitchell, M. B., H. K. Mitchell, and A. Tissieres. 1953. Ibid. 39:606. [26] Murray, J. C. 1959-60. Dissertation Abstr. 20:3480. [27] Murray, N. E. 1960. Heredity 15:199. [28] Murray, N. E. 1960. Ibid. 15:207. [29] Murray, N. E. Unpublished, 1961. [30] Newmeyer, D. Unpublished, 1961. [31] Perkins, D. D. 1959. Genetics 44:1185. [32] Perkins, D. D. 1960. Microbiol. Genet. Bull. 17:17. [33] Perkins, D. D. Unpublished, 1961. [34] Perkins, D. D., and C. Ishitani. 1959. Genetics 44:1209. [35] St. Lawrence, P. 1956. Proc. Natl. Acad. Sci. U.S. 42:189. [36] St. Lawrence, P. Unpublished, 1961. [37] Srb, A. M. 1946. Ph. D. Thesis. Stanford Univ., Palo Alto. [38] Stadler, D. R. 1956. Genetics 41:528. [39] Stadler, D. R. 1959. Ibid. 44:647. [40] Stadler, D. R. 1959. Nature 184:170. [41] Stadler, D. R. 1959. Proc. Natl. Acad. Sci. U.S. 45:1625. [42] Strickland, W. N. Unpublished, 1961. [43] Strickland, W. N., D. D. Perkins, and C. C. Veatch. 1959. Genetics 44:1221. [44] Webber, B. B., and M. E. Case. 1960. Ibid. 45:1605.

continued

10. LINKAGE GROUPS: PLANTS

Part II: CORN

The genes in each linkage group for *Zea mays* are carried by the corresponding chromosome, e.g., linkage group I, chromosome 1; linkage group II, chromosome 2, etc. Capital letters (columns A and C) indicate dominant genes.

	Gene Symbol	Locus	Mutation	Phenotypic Expression
	(A)	(B)	(C)	(D)
				Linkage Group I
1	*sr*	0	striate	Leaves striated
2	ga_6	15	gametophyte factor	Gametophyte viability
3	zb_4	21	zebra striping	Leaves with alternating transverse bands of green and whitish sectors
4	ms_{17}	25	male sterile	Male sterile
5	ts_2	27	tassel seed	Terminal inflorescence with pistillate flowers
6	*P*	28	Pericarp	Pericarp color
7	*zl*	30	zygotic lethal	Lethal zygote
8	*as*	53	asynaptic	Chromosomes unpaired at meiosis
9	*hm*	66	*Helminthosporium* susceptibility (recessive)	Susceptible to *Helminthosporium* infection
10	*br*	80	brachytic	Stalk has short internodes
11	*Vg*	84	Vestigial glumes	Glumes underdeveloped
12	f_1	85	fine striped	Fine striped, green and white leaves
13	an_1	107	anther ear	Stamens develop in pistillate inflorescence
14	*Kn*	128	Knotted leaves	Wart-like growths on leaves and stalk
15	gs_1	134	green striped	Leaves with light green stripes between vascular bundles
16	Ts_6	157	Tassel seed	Terminal inflorescence with pistillate flowers
17	bm_2	161	brown midrib	Brown pigment in leaf midrib
				Linkage Group II
18	ws_3	0	white sheath	Leaf sheaths and stalk deficient in chlorophyll
19	*al*	4	albescent	Seedlings become whitish
20	lg_1	11	liguleless	Absence of ligule on leaves
21	gl_2	30	glossy seedling	Seedlings smooth and shining
22	*B*	49	Anthocyanin booster	Increases anthocyanin pigments
23	*sk*	56	silkless	Ears without silks
24	fl_1	68	floury endosperm	Endosperm powdery
25	ts_1	74	tassel seed	Terminal inflorescence with pistillate flowers
26	v_4	83	virescent	Young seedlings deficient in chlorophyll
27	*Ch*	128	Chocolate	Chocolate pericarp
				Linkage Group III
28	cr_1	0	crinkly leaves	Leaves crinkled
29	d_1	18	dwarf	Abnormally undersized
30	*rt*	32	rootless	Lacking roots
31	Lg_3	38	Liguleless	Absence of ligule on leaves
32	*Rg*	40	Ragged leaves	Leaves appear split and torn due to development of necrotic areas
33	ts_4	47	tassel seed	Terminal inflorescence with pistillate flowers
34	ba_1	64	barren stalk	No ear produced
35	na_1	75	nana (dwarf)	Abnormally undersized
36	a_1	103	anthocyanin	Anthocyanin pigments present
37	sh_2	103.0+	shrunken endosperm	Endosperm shrunken
38	*et*	115	etched endosperm	Endosperm etched
39	ga_7	121	gametophyte factor	Gametophyte viability
				Linkage Group IV
40	de_1	0	defective endosperm	Endosperm defective
41	Ga_1	35	Gametophyte factor	Gametophyte viability
42	Ts_5	56	Tassel seed	Terminal inflorescence with pistillate flowers
43	sp_1	66	small pollen	Pollen of small size
44	su_1	71	sugary endosperm	Endosperm sugary
45	de_{16}	74	defective endosperm	Endosperm defective
46	zb_6	84	zebra striping	Leaves with alternating transverse bands of green and whitish sectors
47	*Tu*	100	Tunicate (pod corn)	Enlarged glumes in male and female inflorescences
48	j_2	105	japonica striping	Leaves green and white striped
49	gl_3	111	glossy seedling	Seedlings smooth and shining

continued

10. LINKAGE GROUPS: PLANTS

Part II: CORN

	Gene Symbol	Locus	Mutation	Phenotypic Expression
	(A)	(B)	(C)	(D)
				Linkage Group V
50	gl_{17}	0	glossy seedling	Seedlings smooth and shining
51	a_2	1	anthocyanin	Anthocyanin pigment present
52	bm_1	7	brown midrib	Brown pigment in leaf midrib
53	bt_1	8	brittle endosperm	Endosperm brittle
54	v_3	11	virescent	Young seedlings deficient in chlorophyll
55	*bv*	13	brevis (dwarf) plant	Undersized
56	*pr*	32	red aleurone color	Aleurone red
57	*ys*	41	yellow stripe	Leaves green and yellow striped
58	v_2	73	virescent	Young seedlings deficient in chlorophyll
				Linkage Group VI
59	*po*	0	polymitotic	Spores undergo extra meiotic-like divisions; male sterile
60	*Y*	13	Yellow endosperm	Endosperm yellow
61	pg_{11}	33	pale green	Light green seedlings and plants
62	*Pl*	44	Purple plant	Plant purple
63	*Bh*	45	Blotched aleurone	Aleurone blotched
64	*sm*	54	salmon silk	
65	*py*	64	pigmy	Dwarf plant
				Linkage Group VII
66	o_2	0	opaque endosperm	Endosperm opaque
67	*in*	4	intensifier of aleurone color	Color of aleurone intensified
68	v_5	8	virescent	Young seedlings deficient in chlorophyll
69	ra_1	22	ramosa	Branching of ear and tassel
70	gl_1	26	glossy seedling	Seedlings smooth and shining
71	*Tp*	36	Teopod	Plant with many tillers and narrow leaves; ears and tassels have enlarged bracts
72	*sl*	40	slashed leaves	
73	*ij*	42	iojap	Leaves green and white striped
74	*Bn*	60	Brown endosperm	Endosperm brown
75	*bd*	96	branched silkless	Ears branched without silks
				Linkage Group VIII
76	v_{16}	0	virescent	Young seedlings deficient in chlorophyll
77	ms_8	14	male sterile	Male sterile
78	j_1	28	japonica striping	Leaves green and white striped
				Linkage Group IX
79	*Dt*	0	Dotted	Controller of a_2 mutability
80	yg_2	7	yellow-green	Seedlings and plants yellow green
81	*C*	26	Aleurone color	Determines color of aleurone
82	sh_1	29	shrunken endosperm	Endosperm shrunken
83	*bz*	31	bronze	Aleurone and plant bronze
84	*bp*	44	brown pericarp	Brown pericarp
85	*wx*	59	waxy endosperm	Waxy endosperm
86	pg_{12}	66	pale green	Seedlings and plants light green
87	v_1	71	virescent	Young seedlings deficient in chlorophyll
88	bk_2	74	brittle stalk	Stalk brittle
89	*Wc*	106	White cap of endosperm	Cap of endosperm white
				Linkage Group X
90	*Rp*	0	Resistance to *Puccinia*	Resistance to *Puccinia* infection
91	*Og*	16	Old gold striping	Leaves green and yellow striped
92	*li*	28	lineate	Leaves with fine longitudinal striations
93	l_8	38	luteus seedling	Yellow seedlings
94	g_1	43	golden	Plant golden
95	*R*	57	Aleurone and plant color	Determines color of aleurone and plant

Contributor: Rhoades, M. M.

continued

10. LINKAGE GROUPS: PLANTS

Part II: CORN

References: [1] Burnham, C. R. 1947. Maize Genet. Coop. News Letter 21:36. [2] Burnham, C. R. 1955. Ibid. 29:51. [3] Rhoades, M. M. 1950. J. Heredity 41:59. [4] Rhoades, M. M. 1955. In G. F. Sprague, ed. Corn and corn improvement. Academic Press, New York. pp. 123-219.

Part III: TOMATO

Linkage groups for *Lycopersicon esculentum* do not correspond to similarly numbered chromosomes. Some linkage groups have not been assigned to a particular chromosome, while some chromosomes have not been given a linkage group number. Capital letters (columns A and C) indicate dominant genes.

	Gene Symbol	Locus	Mutation	Phenotypic Expression
	(A)	(B)	(C)	(D)
			Linkage Group I (Chromosome 2)	
1	*dv*	0	dwarf virescent	Stunted plants
2	*m*	3	mottled leaves	Leaves and cotyledons mottled
3	*d*	5	dwarf plant	Plant dwarfed; leaves dark and rugose
4	*p*	9	peach	Peach or pubescent fruit
5	*op*	13	opaca	Yellow-green patches on leaves
6	*dil*	17	dilute	Leaves light green
7	*ps*	20	positional sterile	Positional-sterile flowers; prevents normal opening of corolla
8	*ro*	22	rosette	Rosette; very short internodes, no flowers
9	*O*	29	Oval fruit	Spherical, oblate and elongate fruit
10	*aw*	30	without anthocyanin	No anthocyanin; stem green, not purple
11	*suf*	33	sufflava	Uniform light green leaves
12	ms_{10}	35	male sterile-10	Pale anthers; exserted pistils; sterile
13	*bk*	36	beaked fruit	Sharp-pointed protuberance on blossom-end of fruit
14	*Cu*	38	Curl	Veins and petiole greatly foreshortened, leaves curled
15	*Me*	39	Mouse ears	Leaves pinnately compound, segments clavate
16	*wv*	42	white virescent	Plant virescent
17	*Wo*	48	Woolly plant	Woolly leaves and stems
18	*s*	53	compound inflorescence	Inflorescence much-branched, greatly increased number of flowers
19	*ne*	60	necrotic leaves	Necrotic leaf spots; leaves slowly killed
20	*Lc*	67	Few fruit locules	Fruits with only 2 or 3 locules
			Linkage Group II (Chromosome 3)	
21	*r*	0	yellow fruit flesh	Yellow flesh color
22	*wf*	15	white flower	White or tan corolla
			Linkage Group III (Chromosome 1)	
23	*br*	0	brachytic	Brachytic plants with short internodes
24	*y*	30	colorless fruit skin	Clear colorless skin on fruit
25	Cf_1	65	*Cladosporium* resistance	Resistance to races 1 and 3 of *Cladosporium fulvum*
			Linkage Group IV (Chromosome 6)	
26	*c*	0	potato leaf	Potato leaf; reduced number of leaf segments
27	*sp*	2	self-pruning (determinate habit)	Self-pruning or determinate stems
28	*md*	25	mottled-2	Small chlorotic spots on leaves
29	*Mi*	59	Nematode resistance	Resistance to *Meloidogyne incognita*
30	*yv*	60	yellow virescent	Leaves yellowish
31	Cf_3	61	*Cladosporium* resistance	Resistance to races 1-4 of *Cladosporium*
			Linkage Group V	
32	*bi*	0	bifurcata inflorescence	Branched inflorescence
33	*f*	2	fasciated fruit	Fasciated or many-loculed fruits
34	*a*	29	anthocyanin absent	Anthocyaninless; stems and leaves green, never purple
35	*hl*	49	hairless	Hairless plants; no hairs on hypocotyl
36	*gh*	54	ghost plants	Chlorophyll-deficient plants
37	j_1	69	jointless pedicel	Jointless pedicels
38	Cf_3	86	*Cladosporium* resistance	Resistance to races 1-4 of *Cladosporium*

continued

10. LINKAGE GROUPS: PLANTS

Part III: TOMATO

	Gene Symbol	Locus	Mutation	Phenotypic Expression
	(A)	(B)	(C)	(D)
			Linkage Groups VI and VIII (Chromosome 8)	
39	*al*	0	anthocyanin loser	Anthocyanin loser, purple stems become green in 10-21 days
40	*gf*	23	green flesh	Persistent chlorophyll in fruit
41	*dl*	40	dialytic stamens	Dialytic; stamens are not united in a tube
42	*bu*	49	bushy	Bushy stems; short internodes, long petioles
43	*ch*	65	chartreuse petals	Small, yellow-green corolla
44	l_1	76	lutescent foliage	Premature yellowing of leaves; yellowish unripe fruits
			(Chromosome 9)	
45	*wd*	0	wilty dwarf	Wilty dwarf plants; grayish-green, droopy leaves
46	*ah*	1.5	Hoffman's anthocyaninless (recessive)	Green stems
			Linkage Group VII (Chromosome 10)	
47	*pe*	0	sticky peel	Sticky fruit epidermis
48	*lg*	8	light green foliage	Light green foliage
49	*u*	43	uniform-ripening fruit	Uniform light-green color of unripe fruits; no dark shoulders
50	*H*	61	Hairs absent	Non-hairy or smooth stems; hypocotyl and growing point hairy
51	*nd*	72	netted	Leaves chlorotic with chlorophyll concentrated around veins
52	l_2	79	lutescent-2	Leaves turn yellow
53	*t*	92	tangerine fruit color	Flesh and stamens orange color
54	*Xa*	124	Xantha seedlings	Xanthophyllic or yellow leaves
55	*ag*	139	Andrus' green stem (recessive)	Green stem but purple cotyledons
			Linkage Groups X and XII (Chromosome 7)	
56	*wt*	0	wilty foliage	Wilty leaflets; leaf margins curl adaxially
57	*tf*	15	trifoliate	Terminal leaflet tripartite
58	*n*	30	nipple-tipped fruit	Nipple tips on fruit
59	*mc*	46	macrocalyx	Sepals much enlarged
			Linkage Group XI (Chromosome 4)	
60	*e*	0	entire leaves	Entire or broad leaflets, as in Vilmorin's potato leaf
61	*di*	20	divergens	Leaf and stem color gray green
62	w_1	28	wiry foliage	Wiry; slender, strap-like leaflets; dwarfed plants
			Unnumbered Linkage Group A	
63	*rv*	0	reticulate virescent	Leaves virescent, veins prominent
64	*sf*	34	solanifolium	Potato-like leaves
			Unnumbered Linkage Group B	
65	*La*	0	Lanceolate	Entire, small leaves
66	*na*	28	nana	Tiny plants with short leaves

Contributors: (a) Butler, L., (b) Rick, Charles M.

References: [1] Butler, L. 1960. Can. J. Botany 38:365. [2] Butler, L. 1960. Tomato Genet. Coop. Rept. 10:5. [3] Rick, C. M., and L. Butler. 1956. Advances in Genet. 8:267.

11. GENOTYPES AND PHENOTYPES: PARAMECIUM AURELIA

Only representative examples of genetically-controlled characters in *Paramecium aurelia* are given below, although many others are now known. Arabic numerals associated with genotypes, cytoplasmic particles, and phenotypes are Sonneborn stock numbers. It is important to remember that each stock has the genetic capacity to form a whole battery of different antigens, that the environment can cause the replacement of one antigen by another, and that the expression of the antigens is influenced by the interaction of genes, cytoplasm, and environment.

	Syngen	Gene[1]	Cytoplasmic Particle or Condition	Environmental Condition and Growth Rate	Phenotypic Expression[2] Homozygous	Phenotypic Expression[2] Heterozygous	Reference
	(A)	(B)	(C)	(D)	(E)	(F)	(G)
1	1	*Mt*		High temperature favors development of mating type II	Either or both mating types I and II can develop in exconjugants (two-type); only one mating type expressed at a time	Two-type	17,18
2		*mt*			Only mating type I develops (one-type)	Two-type	
3		g^{41}	Expression of 1 gene (and its alleles) occurs in only 1 of these 3 sets at a time and is favored by the optimum temp. shown in column D	25°C	Antigen 41 G } Serotype G	Both antigens expressed simultaneously	2
4		g^{60}			Antigen 60 G } Serotype G		
5		g^{61}			Antigen 61 G } Serotype G		
6		g^{90}			Antigen 90 G } Serotype G		
7		d^{60}		29-33°C	Antigen 60 D } Serotype D	Both antigens expressed simultaneously	
8		d^{41}			Antigen 41 D } Serotype D		
9		*d*			Antigen 90-61 D } Serotype D		
10		*s*		18°C	Antigen 90-60-41 S } Serotype S	Both antigens expressed simultaneously	
11		s^{61}			Antigen 61 S } Serotype S		
12		*Cl*			Dark crystals in cytoplasm	Dark crystals in cytoplasm	10
13		*cl*			Lacks crystals in cytoplasm (clear)		
14		*Dp*		Starved population	Normal	Nearly normal	
15		*dp*			Most animals short, wide, with blunt posterior, concave aboral side (dumpy)		
16		*M1; M2*	mu 540	Starvation increases concentration of mu	In conjugation kills mate 513, 523, 544, etc., in about 10 hours, *M1-M2* both present; or in about 30 hours when only 1 gene present	Kills mate in about 24 hours, *M1-M2* both present; or in about 40 hours when only 1 gene present	4,5,7
17		*M1; M2*	No mu	mu vanishes from cytoplasm in 8-15 fissions after loss of *M1* or *M2*	In conjugation is killed by mate 540		
18	2	?	kappa G	Moderate growth rate	Paramecin (Pn) G released, kills sensitives by spinning; is killed by Pn50; refractile regions present on kappa particles (= brights)		12,13
19		?	kappa Gml	Moderate growth rate	PnGml released, kills sensitives by paralysis; brights present		
20		?	kappa H	Moderate growth rate	PnH released, kills sensitives by vacuolation; is killed by PnG; brights present		
21		?	kappa 50	Moderate growth rate	Pn50 released, kills sensitives by spinning and vacuolation; is killed by PnG; brights present		
22		?	kappa G	Rapid growth rate	Weak killer of resistant nonkiller		
23		?	kappa G	Prolonged rapid growth rate	Loss of kappa, becomes sensitive to killing by Pn		
24		?	No kappa		Resistant nonkillers; some strains sensitive to killing by Pn		
25		*t*			No growth above 29°C	Normal growth at 29-31°C	14
26		?[3]			Abnormal form of undischarged trichocyst (stock 197)	Trichocysts normal	15

/1/ Line 1: Macronuclear anlagen alike or different. Line 2: Macronuclear anlagen different. /2/ Lines 3-11: Phenotype is recognized by assay of rabbit antiserums to ciliary antigens. /3/ Single gene, unnamed to date [15].

continued

11. GENOTYPES AND PHENOTYPES: PARAMECIUM AURELIA

	Syngen	Gene	Cytoplasmic Particle or Condition	Environmental Condition and Growth Rate	Phenotypic Expression[4] Homozygous	Phenotypic Expression[4] Heterozygous	Reference
	(A)	(B)	(C)	(D)	(E)	(F)	(G)
27	4	*a29*	Gene that is expressed (and/or its alleles) excludes expression of other serotype-determining genes	Exposure to antiserum or appropriate thermal ranges can transform serotypes otherwise stable at low fission rates	Antigen 29 A } Serotype A	Both antigens expressed simultaneously	20,22
28		*a51*			Antigen 51 A } Serotype A		
29		*h29*			Antigen 29 H } Serotype H	Both 29 H and 51 H present at 19°C; only 29 H at 27°C	
30		*h51*			Antigen 51 H } Serotype H		
31		*K*	kappa 51 hump	Killer animals remain killers indefinitely even when grown at maximum rate at 27°C[5]	Hump Pn51 released, kills sensitives by humping; brights present; sensitive to Pn51 spinner	Fewer kappa particles, weaker killer	6,8,19
32		*k*	kappa 51 hump		Loss of kappa, becomes sensitive in absence of *K*		
33		*K*	kappa 51r		Resistant to hump Pn51, nonkiller or very weak killer; brights absent; sensitive to Pn51 spinner	?	
34		*K*	kappa 51 spinner	Low growth rate	Resistant to Pn51 spinner; sensitive to Pn51 hump		6,9
35		*K*	kappa 51 hump slow	Low growth rate	Resistant to Pn51 hump; sensitive to Pn51 spinner		
36		*K*	No kappa	Killer animals remain killers indefinitely even when grown at maximum rate at 27°C[5]	Sensitive	Sensitive	6,8,19
37		*k*	No kappa		Sensitive	Sensitive	
38		*K*	pi		Sensitive to all Pn, contains kappa-like particles; pi brights absent	Contains pi; sensitive	
39		*k*	pi		Loss of pi in absence of *K*	Contains pi; sensitive	
40		*S1;S2*	kappa 51	Increased probability of loss under extremes of temperature or low food supply	Loss of kappa within 60 fissions	Sporadic loss of of kappa	1,21
41	8	*M*	mu 138	Moderate growth rate	In conjugation kills mate 51, 150, 131, 130; brights absent from mu particles; sensitive to Pn51	Mu is retained, animal is mate killer	11,16
42		*M*	mu 130	Moderate growth rate	In conjugation kills 150, 131; is killed by 138; brights absent; sensitive to Pn51	Mu is retained, animal is mate killer	
43		*M*	mu 131	Moderate growth rate	In conjugation kills 150; is killed by 138, 130; brights absent; sensitive to Pn51	Mu is retained, animal is mate killer	
44		*M*	mu 138, 130, or 131	High growth rate at 32°C	Loss of mu, sensitive to 138, 130, 131; sensitive to Pn51		
45		*m*	No mu		In conjugation is killed by 138, 130, 131; sensitive to Pn51		

/4/ Lines 27-30: At least 14 other ciliary serotypes are known in syngen 4. /5/ Sometimes the kappa particles multiply even more rapidly than the host paramecium [3].

Contributors: (a) Ehret, Charles F., and Powers, E. Lawrence, (b) Hanson, Earl D., (c) Butzel, Henry M., Jr., (d) Austin, Mary L.

References: [1] Balbinder, E. 1956. Genetics 41:634. [2] Beale, G. H. 1952. Ibid. 37:62. [3] Beale, G. H. 1954. The genetics of *Paramecium aurelia*. Cambridge Univ. Press, England. [4] Beale, G. H. 1957. Proc. Roy. Phys. Soc. Edinburgh 26:11. [5] Beale, G. H., and A. Jurand. 1960. J. Gen Microbiol. 23:243. [6] Dippell, R. V. 1950. Heredity 4:165. [7] Gibson, I., and G. H. Beale. 1961. Genet. Research 2:82. [8] Hanson, E. D. 1954. Genetics 39:229. [9] Hanson, E. D. 1956. Ibid. 41(1):21. [10] Kimball, R. F. 1953. Microbial Genet. Bull. 8:10. [11] Levine, M. 1953. Genetics 38:561. [12] Preer, J. R., Jr. 1948. Ibid. 33:349. [13] Preer, J. R., Jr. 1953. Proc. Natl. Acad. Sci. U.S. 39:1228. [14] Preer, J. R., Jr. 1957. J. Genet. 55:375. [15] Preer, J. R., Jr. 1959. In D. Rudnick, ed. Developmental cytology. Ronald Press, New York. p. 3. [16] Siegel, R. W. 1953.

continued

11. GENOTYPES AND PHENOTYPES: PARAMECIUM AURELIA

Genetics 38:550. [17] Sonneborn, T. M. 1939. Am. Naturalist 73:390. [18] Sonneborn, T. M. 1943. Proc. Natl. Acad. Sci. U.S. 29:329. [19] Sonneborn, T. M. 1947. Cold Spring Harbor Symposia Quant. Biol. 11:236. [20] Sonneborn, T. M. 1950. Heredity 4:11. [21] Sonneborn, T. M. 1959. Advances in virus research. Academic Press, New York. [22] Sonneborn, T. M., and E. Balbinder. 1953. Microbial Genet. Bull. 7:24.

12. SPONTANEOUS MUTATION RATES

Part I: MAN

Knowledge of mutation rates in man, as in other organisms, is still considered provisional, and the traits for which estimates are available are a highly select fraction of all genes. Estimates for chondrodystrophy, aniridia, and neurofibromatosis may be more reliable than those for epiloia and Waardenburg's syndrome. Values in parentheses are ranges, estimate "c" (cf. Introduction).

	Character	Method of Estimation[1]	Mutations per Gene per Generation	Remarks	Reference
	(A)	(B)	(C)	(D)	(E)
	Dominant Genes				
1	Epiloia	Direct	(0.4-0.8) x 10^{-5}		5,12
2	Chondrodystrophy	Direct[2]	4.2 x 10^{-5}	Estimates may be spuriously high because of some evidence for occurrence of phenocopies [15]	9
3			4.9 x 10^{-5}		7,9
4		Direct	7 x 10^{-5}		3
5		Indirect	4.3 x 10^{-5}		7,9
6	Pelger's nuclear anomaly	Direct	2.7 x 10^{-5}		10
7	Aniridia	Direct	0.5 x 10^{-5}		8
8	Retinoblastoma	Direct	1.4 x 10^{-5}	Estimates based on assumption that all sporadic cases are due to mutation	7,13
9			2.3 x 10^{-5}		11
10			4.3 x 10^{-6}	Estimate based on proposition that approximately 75% of all sporadic cases are phenocopies	18
11	Waardenburg's syndrome	Direct	3.7 x 10^{-6}		19
12	Neurofibromatosis	Direct	(1.3-2.5) x 10^{-4}		4
13		Indirect	(0.8-1.0) x 10^{-4}		
14	Facio-scapulo-humeral progressive muscular dystrophy	Direct	4.7 x 10^{-6}		2
15		Indirect	4.7 x 10^{-6}		
16	Multiple polyposis of the colon	Indirect	(1-3) x 10^{-5}		14
	Sex-linked Recessive Genes				
17	Hemophilia	Indirect	3.2 x 10^{-5}	Estimate may include 3 distinct types of hemophilia: classical sex-linked hemophilia resulting from deficiency of antihemophilic globulin, a sex-linked clotting defect from lack of "plasma thromboplastin component," and an autosomally-inherited clotting defect from lack of "plasma thromboplastin antecedent"	1,6
18	Childhood progressive muscular dystrophy	Direct	3.2 x 10^{-5}		2
19			1 x 10^{-4}	Not a true direct estimate but an approximation which overestimates the mutation rate	15
20		Indirect	3.8 x 10^{-5}		2
21			(4.5-6.5) x 10^{-5}		16,17
22			1 x 10^{-4}		15

/1/ Estimates are considered to be direct when based on observed mutations, indirect when not so based; all indirect estimates make use of determinations of the relative fitness and frequency at birth of the trait, and assume that the population is in equilibrium. /2/ Independent estimates from different data contained in reference 9.

Contributors: Neel, James V., and Reed, T. Edward

References: [1] Andreassen, M. 1943. Opera ex Domo Biol. Hered. Humanae Univ. Hafniensis (Copenhagen), v. 6. [2] Becker, P. E., and F. Lenz. 1955. Z. menschl. Vererbungs.- u. Konstitutionslehre 33:42. [3] Böök, J. A. 1952. J. Génét. Humaine 1:24. [4] Crowe, F. W., W. J. Schull, and J. V. Neel. 1956. American lectures

continued

12. SPONTANEOUS MUTATION RATES

Part I: MAN

in dermatology. C. C. Thomas, Springfield, Ill. [5] Gunther, M., and L. S. Penrose. 1935. J. Genet. 31:413. [6] Haldane, J. B. S. 1947. Ann. Eugenics 13:262. [7] Haldane, J. B. S. 1949. Hereditas, Suppl.:267. [8] Møllenbach, C. J. 1947. Opera ex Domo Biol. Hered. Humanae Univ. Hafniensis (Copenhagen), v. 15. [9] Mørch, E. T. 1941. Ibid., v. 3. [10] Nachtsheim, H. 1954. Naturwissenschaften 41:385. [11] Neel, J. V., and H. F. Falls. 1951. Science 114:419. [12] Penrose, L. S. 1936. Ann. Eugenics 7:1. [13] Philip, U., and A. Sorsby. Unpublished, 1949. [14] Reed, T. E., and J. V. Neel. 1955. Am. J. Human Genet. 7:236. [15] Stephens, F. E., and F. H. Tyler. 1951. Ibid. 3:111. [16] Stevenson, A. C. 1953. Ann. Eugenics 18:50. [17] Stevenson, A. C. 1955. Ann. Human Genet. 19:159. [18] Vogel, F. 1954. Z. menschl. Vererbungs.- u. Konstitutionslehre 32:308. [19] Waardenburg, P. J. 1951. Am. J. Human Genet. 3:195.

Part II: BACTERIA

Mutation rates were measured by screening bacteria populations for a given mutant phenotype (usually by a selective technique). Since the scored mutants were not tested for allelism, it is not clear whether these data represent mutation rates for a single genetic locus or overall rates for several loci affecting the same character.

	Family and Species	Character Changed	Mutation Rate per Bacterium per Generation	Remarks	Reference
	(A)	(B)	(C)	(D)	(E)
	Pseudomonadaceae				
1	*Phytomonas stewartii*	From non-colonial to colonial type	1×10^{-6}	Estimates not based on fluctuation test	19
2	*Pseudomonas aeruginosa*	To streptomycin resistance	4×10^{-10}	Mutation from susceptibility (1 µg streptomycin/ml) to complete resistance (1000 µg/ml)	2
3	*P. fluorescens*	To itaconate utilization	2×10^{-8}		11
	Enterobacteriaceae				
4	*Escherichia coli*	To phage T_1 resistance	3×10^{-8}		20
5		To phage T_3 resistance	1×10^{-7}		10
6		To phage T_5 resistance	4×10^{-8}	Determined in steady-state populations maintained in chemostat	12
7		To phage T_6 resistance	2×10^{-8}		
8		To lactose fermentation	1×10^{-6}		17,24
9	*E. coli* ML	To lactose fermentation	2×10^{-7}		24
10	*E. coli* B	To furadroxyl resistance	3×10^{-7}	First-step furadroxyl resistant mutants of *E. coli* B appear to be identical with B/r (radiation resistant mutant)	31
11		To radiation resistance	1×10^{-5}		33
12	*E. coli* B/r/1t	To phage T_5 resistance	2×10^{-8}	Determined in steady-state populations maintained in chemostat	21
13	*E. coli* B/1t*f*	To phage T_5 resistance	3.2×10^{-8}	Determined in steady-state populations maintained in chemostat	21
14	*E. coli* K-12	From normal to small colony	1×10^{-5}		6
15		To streptomycin resistance	4×10^{-10}	Mutation from susceptibility (1 µg streptomycin/ml) to complete resistance (1000 µg/ml)	32
16			4×10^{-8}	Strain 58-278 M containing a "mutator gene"	32
17		To streptomycin dependence	1×10^{-10}		32
18	*E. coli* K-12 (Sd)	To streptomycin independence	1×10^{-8}		5
19	*E. coli* (Harvard)	To auxotrophy	1×10^{-3}		14
20	*E. coli* 12-22	To tryptophan independence	6×10^{-11}		9
21	*E. coli* M-4	To tryptophan independence	3×10^{-10}		9
22	*E. coli* Sd-4-55	To tryptophan independence	1×10^{-9}		9
23	*E. coli* 12-32	To tryptophan independence	3×10^{-9}		9
24	*E. coli* WP-2	To tryptophan independence	6×10^{-9}		9
25	*E. coli* 12-61	To tryptophan independence	7×10^{-9}		9
26	*E. coli* Sd-4-73	To methionine independence	3×10^{-10}		9
27	*E. coli* WP-7	To methionine independence	4×10^{-10}		9

continued

12. SPONTANEOUS MUTATION RATES

Part II: BACTERIA

	Family and Species	Character Changed	Mutation Rate per Bacterium per Generation	Remarks	Reference
	(A)	(B)	(C)	(D)	(E)
	Enterobacteriaceae				
28	*Escherichia coli* 12-66	To methionine independence	2×10^{-9}		9
29	*E. coli* 12-11	To methionine independence	1×10^{-8}		9
30	*E. coli* 12-29	To leucine independence	6×10^{-11}		9
31	*E. coli* 12-57	To leucine independence	1×10^{-9}		9
32	*E. coli* 12-91	To histidine independence	3×10^{-10}		9
33	*E. coli* WP-6	To histidine independence	3×10^{-9}		9
34	*E. coli* W-74	To histidine independence	4.3×10^{-8}	Determined in steady-state populations maintained in chemostat	21
35			14.9×10^{-8}		
36		To phage T_5 resistance	3.8×10^{-8}	Determined in steady-state populations maintained in chemostat	
37			4.3×10^{-8}		
38			3.5×10^{-8}		
39			11×10^{-8}		
40	*E. coli* h^-	To histidine independence	3×10^{-8}	Mutation from h^- to h^+	25
41	*E. coli* h^+	To histidine dependence	1×10^{-6}	Mutation from h^+ to h^-	18
42	*Salmonella aertrycke*	From rough to smooth colonial type	5×10^{-2}	Estimates not based on fluctuation test	26
43	*S. typhimurium*	From group to specific flagellar antigen	3×10^{-4}	Estimates not based on fluctuation test	28
44		From specific to group flagellar antigen	1×10^{-5}	Estimates not based on fluctuation test	28
45		To threonine resistance	4×10^{-6}		23
46		To tryptophan independence	5×10^{-8}		7
47	*S. typhosa*	To streptomycin resistance	5×10^{-6}	Mutation from susceptibility (1 µg streptomycin/ml) to partial resistance (25 µg/ml)	3
48			1×10^{-10}	Mutation from susceptibility (1 µg streptomycin/ml) to complete resistance (1000 µg/ml)	2
49	*Serratia marcescens*	From red to white colony	1×10^{-4}	Estimates not based on fluctuation test	26
	Brucellaceae				
50	*Hemophilus influenzae*	To streptomycin resistance	4×10^{-9}	Mutation from susceptibility (1 µg streptomycin/ml) to complete resistance (1000 µg/ml)	1
51	*H. pertussis*	To streptomycin resistance	1×10^{-9}	Mutation from susceptibility (1 µg streptomycin/ml) to complete resistance (1000 µg/ml)	4
52			6×10^{-10}	Mutation from susceptibility (1 µg streptomycin/ml) to partial resistance (25 µg/ml)	3
53	*Pasteurella pestis* (avirulent)	To streptomycin resistance	1×10^{-11}	Mutation from susceptibility (1 µg streptomycin/ml) to complete resistance (1000 µg/ml)	13
54	*P. pestis* (virulent)	To streptomycin resistance	1×10^{-12}	Mutation from susceptibility (1 µg streptomycin/ml) to complete resistance (1000 µg/ml)	13
	Micrococcaceae				
55	*Staphylococcus aureus*	To penicillin resistance	1×10^{-8}	Estimated mutation rate for each step; resistance not due to penicillinase production	8
56		To sulphathiazole resistance	1×10^{-9}		22
	Lactobacillaceae				
57	*Diplococcus pneumoniae*	To penicillin resistance	1×10^{-7}	Estimated mutation rate for each step; resistance not due to penicillinase production	15
	Bacillaceae				
58	*Bacillus cereus*	To penicillinase production	3×10^{-8}		27
59	*B. megaterium*	To isoniazid resistance	6×10^{-5}		30
60		To *p*-aminosalicylic acid resistance	1×10^{-6}		

continued

12. SPONTANEOUS MUTATION RATES

Part II: BACTERIA

	Family and Species	Character Changed	Mutation Rate per Bacterium per Generation	Remarks	Reference
	(A)	(B)	(C)	(D)	(E)
	Bacillaceae				
61	*Bacillus megaterium*	To isoniazid + *p*-aminosalicylic acid resistance	8×10^{-10}	Mutation rate for double resistance (involving two separate genetic changes)	30
	Mycobacteriaceae				
62	*Mycobacterium ranae*	To isoniazid resistance	3×10^{-6}		29
63		To streptomycin resistance	1×10^{-9}	Mutation from susceptibility (1 μg streptomycin/ml) to complete resistance (1000 μg/ml)	16
64			1×10^{-7}	Mutation from partial resistance (25 μg streptomycin/ml) to complete resistance (1000 μg/ml)	16

Contributors: (a) Szybalski, Waclaw, (b) Moser, Hermann A.

References: [1] Alexander, H. E., and G. Leidy. 1947. J. Exptl. Med. 85:607. [2] Alexander, H. E., and G. Leidy. 1949. Pediatrics 4:214. [3] Alexander, H. E., G. Leidy, W. Redman, and E. Simakow. 1950. Ibid. 5:78. [4] Alexander, H. E., and W. Redman. 1949. Ibid. 4:461. [5] Bertani, G. 1951. Genetics 36:598. [6] Clowes, R. C., and D. Rowley. 1955. J. Gen. Microbiol. 13:461. [7] De la Garza Curcho, M. 1948. J. Bacteriol. 56:374. [8] Demerec, M. 1948. Ibid. 56:63. [9] Demerec, M. 1953. Symposia Soc. Exptl. Biol. 7:43. [10] Demerec, M., and U. Fano. 1945. Genetics 30:119. [11] Englesberg, E., and R. Y. Stanier. 1949. J. Bacteriol. 58:171. [12] Fox, M. S. 1955. J. Gen. Physiol. 39:267. [13] Garber, E. D., K. Noble, and N. Carouso. 1953. J. Bacteriol. 65:485. [14] Goldstein, A., and J. S. Smoot. 1955. Ibid. 70:588. [15] Hotchkiss, R. D., 1951. Cold Spring Harbor Symposia Quant. Biol. 16:457. [16] Hsie, J. Y., and V. Bryson. 1950. Am. Rev. Tuberc. 62:286. [17] Lewis, I. M. 1934. J. Bacteriol. 28:619. [18] Lieb, M. 1951. Genetics 36:460. [19] Lincoln, R. E. 1940. J. Agr. Research 60:217. [20] Luria, S. E., and M. Delbrück. 1943. Genetics 28:491. [21] Moser, H. A. 1958. Carnegie Inst. Wash. Publ. 614. [22] Oakberg, E. F., and S. E. Luria. 1947. Genetics 32:249. [23] Page, L. A., R. J. Goodlow, and W. Braun. 1951. J. Bacteriol. 62:639. [24] Ryan, F. J. 1952. J. Gen Microbiol. 7:69. [25] Ryan, F. J., and L. K. Schneider. 1949. Genetics 34:72. [26] Shapiro, A. 1946. Cold Spring Harbor Symposia Quant. Biol. 11:228. [27] Sneath, P. H. A. 1955. J. Gen. Microbiol. 13:561. [28] Stocker, B. A. D. 1949. J. Hyg. 47:398. [29] Szybalski, W., and V. Bryson. 1952. Am. Rev. Tuberc. 65:768. [30] Szybalski, W., and V. Bryson. 1953. J. Bacteriol. 66:468. [31] Szybalski, W., and T. C. Nelson. 1954. Bacteriol. Proc., p. 51. [32] Traffers, H. P., V. Spinelli, and N. O. Belser. 1954. Proc. Natl. Acad. Sci. U.S. 40:1064. [33] Witkin, E. M. 1947. Genetics 32:221.

13. INBRED STRAINS: MOUSE

The mouse is the animal of choice in experimental studies in oncology, but wide use has also been made of inbred strains in studies in bacteriology, nutrition, morphology, and endocrinology [54]. A strain is considered inbred when brother and sister matings have continued for 20 or more generations. Strain symbol is given in capital letters, numbers, or a combination of letters and numbers. Substrain symbol is separated from the strain symbol by a slant line. Substrains developed by foster nursing are indicated by appending an f to the strain symbol, and the strain used as foster parent may be indicated by the addition of its symbol. Most of the genes listed are mutations affecting coat color: cc = albino, + = gray or "wild type." Where known, the histocompatibility-2 *(H-2)* allele [57], the transferrin *(Trf)* allele [7], and the hemoglobin *(Hb)* type [51] for each strain are given. For additional information on these and other strains, consult reference 58.

	Strain or Substrain Symbols: Recommended[1]	Strain or Substrain Symbols: Synonyms[2]	Generations of Inbreeding[3]	Genetic Formula	Remarks	Reference
	(A)	(B)	(C)	(D)	(E)	(F)
1	A		131	$aabbccH\text{-}2^aH\text{-}2^a$, Trf^b	Mammary tumor incidence high in breeding females, low in virgins; lung tumor incidence high in breeders and virgins; 5-10% of young with cleft palate; high incidence of renal disease in old	3,10,12,18-22,40,47,50,55,57,62,65
2	A/He	A/Heston	118	$aabbccH\text{-}2^aH\text{-}2^a$	Lung tumor in 90%	23,50,52
3	A/Jax		113	$aabbccH\text{-}2^aH\text{-}2^a$, Trf^b, Hb^2	Lower incidence of mammary tumor and granulocytes than in most substrains	52
4	AK/n	AK, AK-n	20+, +15	*aacc*	High leukemia incidence	16
5	AKR	AK, AKm, Afb, RIL, Rockefeller Institute Leukemia	71	$aaccH\text{-}2^{k'}H\text{-}2^{k'}$, Trf^b, Hb^2	High leukemia incidence	5,8,13,20,27,42,50,52,57
6	BALB	Balb, Bagg albino, CSH Bagg albino	82	$bbccH\text{-}2^dH\text{-}2^d$		13,22,35,36,38,50
7	BALB/c	BalbC, C, Bagg albino	105	$bbccH\text{-}2^dH\text{-}2^d$, Trf^b, Hb^2	Low mammary tumor incidence (high when milk agent introduced); susceptible to induction of lung tumors; some leukemia reported	1,19-21,27,32,47,52,55,57
8	BALB/Gw	BALB/Gowen	62+	*bbcc*	Low resistance to *Salmonella typhimurium*	15,67,69
9	BL	Bagg L, BALB/R	46	*aabbcc*	Mammary tumor incidence 27% in breeding females, 4% in virgins; lung tumors in 37% of old	29,33
10	BRS	BrS, Br-S, Br-s	55	*aabb*	From a branch of strain NH treated for 8 or more generations with methylcholanthrene; high gastric tumor incidence	58,63,66
11	BRSUNT	BrSunt, Br-S untreated	69	*aabb*	A branch of BRS continued without methylcholanthrene; high gastricc tumor incidence	66
12	BUB		46	*aacc*	Used in study of macrophage	11
13	C	cinnamon	86	*bb*	Tendency to bifurcation of seminal vesicles	25,58
14	CBA	XXXIX	113	$+H\text{-}2^kH\text{-}2^k$, Trf^a	Mammary tumor incidence 1.1-22.2%; some hepatomas reported; moderate leukemia incidence	19,21,27,52,55,57,62,65
15	CE	Cd, c^e, ce, extreme dilution	65	$A^wA^wc^ec^e$, Trf^b	Wide range of tumor types, but low incidence; high incidence of adrenal cortical carcinoma when ovariectomized at birth	58,68
16	C3H	Z	114	$+H\text{-}2^kH\text{-}2^k$, Trf^b, Hb^2	Low red and white cell counts; high mammary tumor incidence in breeding and virgin females; many hepatomas reported	1,9,12,13,16,19-22,32,47,50,52,56,57,59,62,65,68
17	C3Hf	$C3H_b$, $C3H_f$, C3HfB	40 since fostering	+	From C3H born by caesarean section and foster nursed on strain C57BL; low mammary tumor incidence	16,22,49

/1/ Recommended by the Committee on Standardized Genetic Nomenclature for Mice [58]. /2/ Appearing in the literature. /3/ Recorded in 1960 or 1961.

continued

13. INBRED STRAINS: MOUSE

	Strain or Substrain Symbols: Recommended[1]	Synonyms[2]	Generations of Inbreeding[3]	Genetic Formula	Remarks	Reference
	(A)	(B)	(C)	(D)	(E)	(F)
18	C57BL	C57 black, B	60	$aaTrf^{b}$	Mammary tumor incidence 1% in breeding females, 0 in virgins; various types of internal tumors reported, mostly lymphosarcoma; eye abnormalities in 10% of mice, varying widely in substrains	1,7,12,13, 17,19-22, 27,31,32, 47,53,57, 65,68
19	C57BL/6	C57 black subline 6, B/6	70	$aaH{-}2^{b}H{-}2^{b}$, Trf^{b}, Hb^{1}	Extensively used substrain	9,52
20	C57BR/a	C57 brown subline a, BR/a	100	$aabbH{-}2^{k}H{-}2^{k}$	Used in transplantation studies; low mammary tumor incidence	19,21,57,58
21	C57BR/cd	C57 brown subline cd, BR/cd	107	$aabbH{-}2^{k}H{-}2^{k}$, Trf^{b}, Hb^{1}	Low mammary tumor incidence	19,21,52,57, 58
22	C57L	C57 leaden, leaden, M, L, LN	85	$aabblnlnH{-}2^{b}H{-}2^{b}$, Trf^{b}, Hb^{1}	Low mammary tumor incidence; Hodgkin's-like lesions reported	18-22,41, 50,52,57
23	C58		119	$aaH{-}2^{k}$, Hb^{1}	High leukemia incidence	13,20,21,27, 36-38
24	DBA	Dilute brown, dba, dbr, D	58	$aabbdd$	High mammary tumor incidence in breeding females, medium to high in virgins	19-22,27, 28,55,68
25	DBAf	dba_{b}	31	$aabbdd$	Fostered on C57BL or other low mammary cancer strains; low mammary tumor incidence, lacking milk agent	2,58
26	DBA/1	dba subline 1, dba-1, D/1	41+	$aabbddH{-}2^{q}H{-}2^{q}$, Trf^{b}, Hb^{2}	Resistant to DBA/2 transplantable tumors; susceptible to tuberculosis infection	9,32,40,47, 50,52,57
27	DBA/2	dba subline 2, dba subline 212, dba-2, D/2	73	$aabbddH{-}2^{d}H{-}2^{d}$, Trf^{b}, Hb^{2}	Resistant to DBA/1 transplantable tumors; leukemia in 30-40% of mice (but only 2.4% in recent tests at Jackson Laboratory)	20,52,57
28	E		58	cc	Medium resistance to *Salmonella typhimurium*	15
29	F		85	$aabbc^{ch}c^{ch}ddss$	Leukemia in 50%	26,62
30	FA		36	$aabbc^{ch}c^{ch}ddss$	Resistant to induction of lung tumors; high incidence of leukemia, including granulocytic forms	55
31	FB		26		Resistant to induction of lung tumors; moderate leukemia incidence	55
32	I		68	$aabbddppssH{-}2^{i}$	Used in nutrition studies; low mammary tumor incidence; spontaneous rectal prolapse; high stomach lesion incidence	1,12,19,20, 47,52,62, 65
33	IF		67	$a^{t}a^{t}$	Mammary tissue very sensitive to carcinogenic agents; low incidence of spontaneous mammary tumors in virgins	46
34	JK	short ear	68	$aabbppseseH{-}2^{j}$	Low incidence of all types of cancer	60,62,65,66
35	L		75	$A^{w}A^{w}c^{ch}c^{ch}$	Low mammary tumor incidence; some lymphoblastoma reported	30,62
36	LGW	L	59	$aasisi$	Susceptible to *Salmonella typhimurium*	15,67,69
37	MA	Marsh, Marsh albino	55	$ccH{-}2^{k}$	High mammary tumor incidence	17,19,39,43
38	MA/MY	ND, MA/Murray	53	$ccH{-}2^{k}$, Hb^{2}	Low mammary tumor incidence	44,50
39	N		67	$aabbddss$	Low tumor incidence	19,22,61,62, 65
40	NB		64	$aabbc^{ch}p/c^{ch}pdse/dse$	Used in X-ray studies; leukemia easily induced by carcinogenic hydrocarbons	53
41	NH		33	$ddppss$	Low tumor incidence; lung tumors in 30-42% of the very old; old females become obese	55,61,63,68

/1/ Recommended by the Committee on Standardized Genetic Nomenclature for Mice [58]. /2/ Appearing in the literature. /3/ Recorded in 1960 or 1961.

continued

13. INBRED STRAINS: MOUSE

	Strain or Substrain Symbols		Generations of Inbreeding[3]	Genetic Formula	Remarks	Reference
	Recommended[1]	Synonyms[2]				
	(A)	(B)	(C)	(D)	(E)	(F)
42	P		76	$aabbdse/dsepprdr$-$dH\text{-}2^pH\text{-}2^p$	Useful in genetic studies	57
43	PBR	pBr	56	$aabbpp$	Mammary tumors in breeders	58,64
44	PL	PL(B), Princeton leukemia, LII	46	cc	Low mammary tumor incidence; leukemia in 80-90%	45,58
45	RF	RFM, Rf, Rfa	25+	$ccTrf^b$, Hb^2	Low leukemia incidence	8,13,20
46	RI		48	$aabbcc$	Resistant to infections	15,67,69
47	RIII	Paris, R3	47+	$ccTrf^b$	High mammary tumor incidence	17,19,40,50
48	RIII/Jax	Radium Institute (Paris) line III	38+	cc	Resistant to RIII/Wy transplantable tumors	58
49	RIII/Wy	R3	53	$ccH\text{-}2^r$	Resistant to RIII/Jax transplantable tumors	58
50	S		65	cc	Resistant to *Salmonella typhimurium* and to radiation	14,15,24,67, 69
51	ST	Street	62	$aabbccH\text{-}2^kH\text{-}2^k$	Incidence of plasma cell and stem cell leukemias, 1-2%; incidence of tumors, principally pulmonary adenomas and mammary carcinomas, 3%	48,50,52,57
52	STOLI	Sto-Li, Storrs-Little	98	$aabbddpp$	Low leukemia incidence	13,21,27, 36-38
53	SWR	Swiss, Swiss-R, Swiss-8	69	$ccHb^1$	Lung tumors in 44%; mammary tumors in 19% of breeding females	20,22,34
54	WLL	White Label, White Label-Leeds, Kreyberg albino	53	cc	Carries mammary tumor inciter or "milk agent"; mammary tumor in 30%	4,28,40
55	WLO	White Label Oslo			Low mammary tumor incidence	3
56	YBL	Y, yellows	41+	A^Ya	Yellow mice produced by outcross are obese, but there is no obesity in inbred line; low mammary tumor incidence; some sarcomas reported; lung tumors in 10-20%	1,19,22
57	Z		56	cc	Medium susceptibility to typhoid	15,67
58	ZR	Zr/Chase	22	$aabbppss$	Used in studies of insulin tolerance; anophthalmic	6
59	XVII	17	28	cc	Low tumor incidence; good breeders	29
60	50	L			Mammary tumor in 60-65%	29
61	129		34	$A^wA^wc^{ch}p/cpH\text{-}2^bH\text{-}2^b$, Hb^2	Useful for ovarian transplant and ova transfer studies	57

/1/ Recommended by the Committee on Standardized Genetic Nomenclature for Mice [58]. /2/ Appearing in the literature. /3/ Recorded in 1960 or 1961.

Contributors: (a) Snell, George D., and Staats, Joan, (b) Law, Lloyd W., (c) Heston, W. E.

References: [1] Andervont, H. B. 1940. J. Natl. Cancer Inst. 1:147. [2] Andervont, H. B., and T. B. Dunn. 1950. Ibid. 10:895. [3] Bittner, J. J. 1941. Cancer Research 1:113, 115. [4] Bouser, G. M., and K. I. Connal. 1939. J. Pathol. Bacteriol. 48:263. [5] Burchenal, J. H., et al. 1948. Cancer 1:399. [6] Chase, H. B., et al. 1947. Anat. Record 99:678. [7] Cohen, B. L., and D. C. Shreffler. 1961. Genet. Research 2:306. [8] Cole, R. K., and J. Furth. 1941. Cancer Research 1:957. [9] Donovick, R., et al. 1949. Am. Rev. Tuberc. 60:109. [10] Dunn, T. B. 1944. J. Natl. Cancer Inst. 5:17. [11] Eastman, T. W. 1952. Am. J. Anat. 90:1. [12] Fenton, P. E., and C. J. Carr. 1951. J. Nutrition 43:441. [13] Furth, J. 1946. Physiol. Revs. 26:47. [14] Gowen, J. W. 1948. Ann. Rev. Microbiol. 2:215. [15] Gowen, J. W., and M. R. Zelle. 1945. J. Infectious Diseases 77:85. [16] Gross, L. 1951. Proc. Soc. Exptl. Biol. Med. 78:342. [17] Haagensen, C. D., and H. T. Randall. 1942. Arch. Pathol. 33:411. [18] Heston, W. E. 1942. J. Natl. Cancer Inst. 3:79. [19] Heston, W. E. 1945. Publ. Am. Assoc. Advance. Sci. 22:55. [20] Heston, W. E. 1948. Advances in Genet. 2:99. [21] Heston, W. E. 1949. R. B. Jackson Mem. Lab. 20th Commem. Lectures. [22] Heston, W. E. 1951. Growth, 15(suppl.):23. [23] Heston, W. E., et al. 1952. J. Natl. Cancer Inst. 12:1141. [24] Hetzer, H. O. 1937. Genetics 22:264. [25] Hooker, C. W., and L. C. Strong.

continued

1941. Anat. Record 81:333. [26] Kirschbaum, A. 1944. Proc. Soc. Exptl. Biol. Med. 55:147. [27] Kirschbaum, A. 1951. Cancer Research 11:741. [28] Kreyberg, L. 1952. Brit. J. Cancer 6:140. [29] Law, L. W. 1948. J. Heredity 39:300. [30] Lewis, M. R., and L. C. Strong. 1934. Am. J. Cancer 20:72. [31] Little, C. C., W. S. Murray, and A. M. Cloudman. 1939. Ibid. 36:431. [32] Liu, C., and F. B. Bang. 1952. Am. J. Hyg. 55:182. [33] Lynch, C. J. 1926. J. Exptl. Med. 43:339. [34] Lynch, C. J. 1940. Proc. Soc. Exptl. Biol. Med. 43:186. [35] MacDowell, E. C., E. Allen, and C. G. MacDowell. 1927-28. J. Gen. Physiol. 11:57. [36] MacDowell, E. C., J. S. Potter, and M. J. Taylor. 1945. Cancer Research 5:65. [37] MacDowell, E. C., and M. N. Richter. 1935. Arch. Pathol. 20:709. [38] MacDowell, E. C., and M. J. Taylor. 1948. Proc. Soc. Exptl. Biol. Med. 68:571. [39] Marsh, M. C. 1929. J. Cancer Research 13:313. [40] Muhlbock, O. 1951. Koninkl. Ned. Akad. Wetenschap. Proc., C, 54:386. [41] Murphy, E. Unpublished, 1953. [42] Murphy, J. B. 1944. Cancer Research 4:622. [43] Murray, W. S. 1938. Am. J. Cancer 34:434. [44] Murray, W. S., and S. G. Warner. 1946-47. J. Natl. Cancer Inst. 7:183. [45] Nelson, J. B. 1948. J. Infectious Diseases 82:169. [46] Orr, J. W. 1951. Acta Unio Intern. contra Cancrum 7:294. [47] Pierce, C., R. J. Dubos, and G. Middlebrook. 1947. J. Exptl. Med. 86:159. [48] Rask-Nielsen, R., and H. Gormsen. 1951. Acta Unio Intern. contra Cancrum 7:701. [49] Rash-Nielsen, R., and H. Gormsen. 1956. J. Natl. Cancer Inst. 16:1137. [50] Richardson, F. L. 1951. Anat. Record 111:669. [51] Russell, E. S., and P. S. Gerald. 1958. Science 128:1569. [52] Russell, E. S., E. F. Neufeld, and C. T. Higgins. 1951. Proc. Soc. Exptl. Biol. Med. 78:761. [53] Russell, L. B. 1950. J. Exptl. Zool. 114:545. [54] Russell, W. L. 1941. In G. D. Snell, ed. Biology of the laboratory mouse. Blakiston, Philadelphia. [55] Shapiro, J. R., and A. Kirschbaum. 1951. Cancer Research 11:644. [56] Silverstone, H., and A. Tannenbaum. 1951. Acta Unio Intern. contra Cancrum 7:616. [57] Snell, G. D. 1952. Cancer Research 12:543. [58] Snell, G. D., et al. 1960. Ibid. 20:145. [59] Strong, L. C. 1935. Genetics 20:586. [60] Strong, L. C. 1937. J. Heredity 28:40. [61] Strong, L. C. 1940. Am. J. Cancer 39:347. [62] Strong, L. C. 1942. Cancer Research 2:531. [63] Strong, L. C. 1945. J. Natl. Cancer Inst. 5:339. [64] Strong, L. C. 1951. J. Gerontol. 6:340. [65] Strong, L. C. 1952. Yale J. Biol. Med. 25:34. [66] Strong, L. C., and W. F. Hollander. 1951. Cancer Research 11:94. [67] Weir, J. A. 1949. J. Infectious Diseases 84:252. [68] Woolley, G. W., and C. C. Little. 1945. Cancer Research 5:193. [69] Zelle, M. R. 1942. J. Infectious Diseases 71:131.

14. HERITABILITY ESTIMATES OF ANATOMICAL MEASUREMENTS: MAN

Heritability indexes: Hv (for variance) = $\frac{\sigma_W^2 DZ - \sigma_W^2 MZ}{\sigma_W^2 DZ}$, and Hc (for concordance) = $\frac{C_{MZ} - C_{DZ}}{100 - C_{DZ}}$. DZ = dizygotic; MZ = monozygotic; σ_W^2 = within pair variance, $\frac{1}{n}\Sigma(X_A - X_B)^2$, for n pairs of twins A and B; C = the percentage of concordant MZ or DZ pairs.

Part I: BODY AND HEAD

According to heritability index Hv. Number of monozygotic and dizygotic twin pairs given under name of investigator.

	Characteristic	Martin Number	Percent Heritability Estimates by: Clark	Dahlberg	Osborne and DeGeorge	Strandskov and Vandenberg	Vogel	Von Verschuer	Wendt
			44 MZ 37 DZ	96 MZ 95 DZ	59 MZ 37 DZ	52 MZ 61 DZ	31 MZ 31 DZ	71 MZ 38 DZ	56 MZ 52 DZ
	(A)	(B)	(C)	(D)	(E)	(F)	(G)	(H)	(I)
	Body								
1	Stature	1	88	89	90	92	82	62	93
2	Suprasternal height	4	...	88	72	...	87	...	90
3	Suprasymphysis height	6	...	84	...	...	69	...	80
4	Shoulder height	8	...	83	...	...	81	...	90

continued

14. HERITABILITY ESTIMATES OF ANATOMICAL MEASUREMENTS: MAN

Part I: BODY AND HEAD

	Characteristic	Martin Number	Percent Heritability Estimates by						
			Clark	Dahlberg	Osborne and DeGeorge	Strandskov and Vandenberg	Vogel	Von Verschuer	Wendt
			44 MZ 37 DZ	96 MZ 95 DZ	59 MZ 37 DZ	52 MZ 61 DZ	31 MZ 31 DZ	71 MZ 38 DZ	56 MZ 52 DZ
	(A)	(B)	(C)	(D)	(E)	(F)	(G)	(H)	(I)
	Body								
5	Stylion height	10	...	...	...	...	59	...	60
6	Middle-fingertip height	11	...	67	...	...	66	...	47
7	Sitting height	23	72	...	85	...	...	...	...
8	Trunk length	27	...	56	...	...	...	52	...
9	Bicristal or bi-iliac	40	59	63	53	...	61	41	76
10	Hip breadth maximum[1]	42	...	...	49	...	84	...	85
11	Total arm length	45	90	80	86	...	...	84	...
12	Forearm length	48	81	...	67	...	...	...	...
13	Hand length	49	82	...	51	...	...	23	...
14	Middle-finger length	51	88	...	80	...	...	...	...
15	Hand breadth	52	80	...	7	78	...	57	...
16	Leg length	53	...	...	90	...	...	68	...
17	Biacromial width	55	31	74	40	...	54	64	73
18	Foot length	58	81	...	82	...	89	...	81
19	Chest girth	61	61	...	50	...	82	33	82
20	Waist girth	62	25	...	44	...	...	...	...
21	Neck girth	63	67	...	60	...	...	...	...
22	Hip girth	64	63	...	55	...	...	...	...
23	Upper-arm girth	65	62	...	32	...	...	...	...
24	Forearm girth	66	53	...	30	...	85	...	85
25	Minimal waist girth	67	65	...	69	...	...	...	...
26	Maximal calf girth	69	75	...	45	...	80	...	88
27	Minimal ankle girth	70	54	...	61	...	...	...	...
28	Weight	73	69	...	27	77	88	33	86
	Head								
29	Head length	1	54	...	0	69	80	71	...
30	Head breadth	3	72	53	84	73	85	49	...
31	Minimal frontal breadth	4	61	80	52	50	79	...	...
32	Bizygomatic breadth	6	60	46	47	83	71	...	...
33	Bigonial breadth	8	71	49	72	...	73	80	...
34	Interocular breadth	9	60	...	37	...	...	...	...
35	Biocular breadth	10	41	...	65	76	...	...	...
36	Nose breadth	13	66	...	64	...	62	37	...
37	Head height	16	69	76	0	...	...	...	...
38	Total face height	18	74	64	58	66	8	80	...
39	Nasion to prosthion	20	72	...	70	...	...	...	...
40	Nose height	21	76	...	73	44	86	93	...
41	Ear breadth	30	52	...	65	...	...	...	...
42	Head girth	45	74	...	64	...	75	71	...
	Reference	3	1	2	4	5	6	7	6

/1/ Bitrochanteric.

Contributor: Vandenberg, Steven G.

References: [1] Clark, P. J. 1956. Am. J. Human Genet. 8:49. [2] Dahlberg, G. 1926. Twin births and twins from a hereditary point of view. Tiden, Stockholm. [3] Martin, R. 1928. Lehrbuch der Anthropologie. G. Fischer, Jena. [4] Osborne, R. H., and F. W. DeGeorge. 1959. Genetic basis of morphological variation. Harvard Univ. Press, Cambridge. [5] Strandskov, H. H., and S. G. Vandenberg. In press, 1962. [6] Vogel, F., and G. G. Wendt. 1956. Z. menschl. Vererbungs.- u. Konstitutionslehre 33:425. [7] Von Verschuer, O. 1954. Wirksame Faktoren im Leben des Menschen. F. Steiner, Wiesbaden.

continued

14. HERITABILITY ESTIMATES OF ANATOMICAL MEASUREMENTS: MAN

Part II: FACIAL ANGLES

According to heritability index Hv. Number of twin pairs = 50 monozygotic and 50 dizygotic.

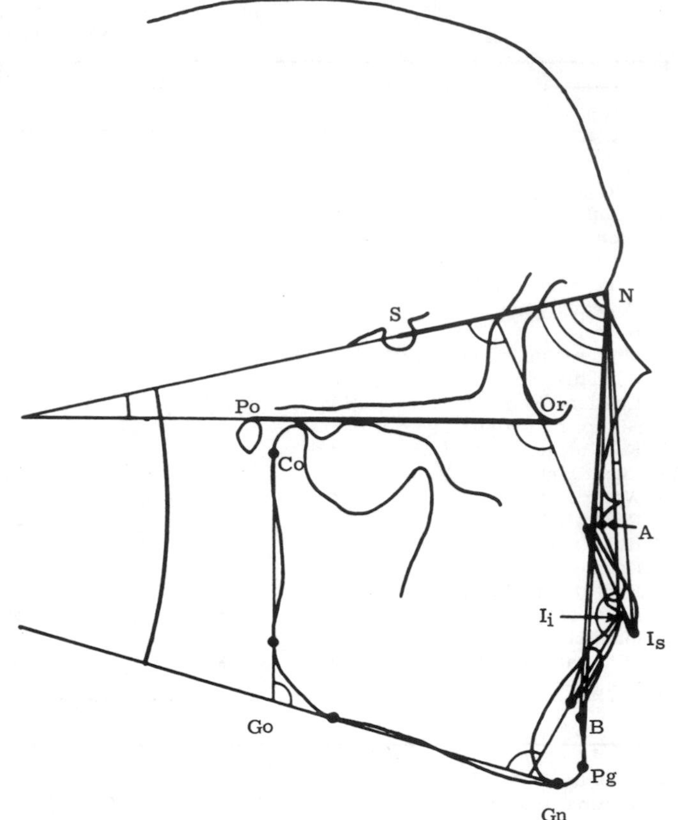

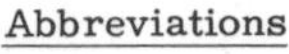

Abbreviations

S = sella turcica
N = nasion
Po = porion
Or = orbitale
FH = Frankfort horizontal (Po-Or in diagram)
I_s = incision superior
I_i = incision inferior
A = subspinal point
B = supramental point
Pg = pogonion
Gn = gnathion
Go = gonion
Co = condylion
UA = long axis of upper medial incisors
LA = long axis of lower medial incisors

	Angle	Percent Heritability Estimate		Angle	Percent Heritability Estimate		Angle	Percent Heritability Estimate		Angle	Percent Heritability Estimate
	(A)	(B)		(A)	(B)		(A)	(B)		(A)	(B)
1	SN-FH	57	5	SNI_i	70	9	FH-NPg	64	13	LA-GnGo	47
2	SNA	55	6	ANB	79	10	UA-SN	53	14	BNPg	59
3	SNI_s	53	7	I_sNI_i	56	11	UA-FH	44	15	GnGo-NS	68
4	SNB	75	8	SNPg	75	12	UA-LA	48	16	Co-Go-Gn	55

Contributor: Vandenberg, Steven G.

Reference: Lundström, A. 1955. Am. J. Orthodontics 41:910.

continued

14. HERITABILITY ESTIMATES OF ANATOMICAL MEASUREMENTS: MAN

Part III: DENTAL DIMENSIONS

According to heritability index Hv.

	Characteristic	Upper Jaw			Lower Jaw			Reference
		No. of Twin Pairs		Percent Heritability Estimate	No. of Twin Pairs		Percent Heritability Estimate	
		Monozygotic	Dizygotic		Monozygotic	Dizygotic		
	(A)	(B)	(C)	(D)	(E)	(F)	(G)	(H)
	Mesiodistal Teeth							
	Width, right side							
1	1st incisor (I_1)	30	18	71	26	15	80	1
2		36	32	81	31	32	78	2
3	2nd incisor (I_2)	29	18	85	29	17	79	1
4		35	32	73	34	28	79	2
5	Canine (C)	29	18	51	29	17	72	1
6		35	31	68	36	31	74	2
7	1st premolar (P_1)	35	28	61	26	21	56	2
8	2nd premolar (P_2)	27	21	63	19	13	53	2
9	1st molar (M_1)	12	15	84	14	15	68	2
10	2nd molar (M_2)	13	16	54	10	13	55	2
	Width, left side							
11	1st incisor (I_1)	31	16	79	27	18	92	1
12		34	32	75	35	32	82	2
13	2nd incisor (I_2)	31	16	67	28	15	78	1
14		35	33	67	36	28	74	2
15	Canine (C)	26	14	0	26	21	54	1
16		35	32	71	33	29	64	2
17	1st premolar (P_1)	35	30	55	28	25	63	2
18	2nd premolar (P_2)	25	18	59	21	15	69	2
19	1st molar (M_1)	12	10	65	20	17	84	2
20	2nd molar (M_2)	13	16	51	18	13	65	2
	Average width of right and left sides							
21	1st incisor (I_1)	91	93	87	93	91	81	3
22	2nd incisor (I_2)	90	98	73	95	94	86	3
23	Canine (C)	87	87	81	93	95	78	3
24	1st premolar (P_1)	62	73	84	80	95	80	3
25	2nd premolar (P_2)	53	60	74	62	67	67	3
26	1st molar (M_1)	45	45	68	43	47	55	3
	Dental Arches, Inclination, and Overbite							
27	Arch space M_1 - M_1	60	44	77	52	46	79	3
28	Space difference M_1 - M_1	59	44	73	51	45	61	3
29	Arch space I_2 - I_2	60	44	71	53	46	67	3
30	Space difference I_2 - I_2	60	44	43	53	46	57	3
31	Space difference C - M_1 (left)	59	44	67	50	45	3	3
32	Width of dental arch at P_1	58	40	81	47	42	71	3
33	Width of dental arch at M_1	60	44	55	52	45	75	3
34	Length of dental arch	60	44	82	52	45	75	3
35	Sagittal occlusion at M_1 (left)	38	32	40	35	30	62	3
36	Inclination of medial upper incisors	60	44	67	...	...	...	3
37	Height of palate vault	60	44	72	...	...	...	3
38	Sagittal overbite	44	34	78	...	...	...	3
39	Vertical overbite	42	31	68	...	...	...	3

Contributor: Vandenberg, Steven G.

References: [1] Horowitz, S. L., R. H. Osborne, and F. V. DeGeorge. 1958. Angle Orthodontist 28:87. [2] Hunter, W. S. 1959. Ph.D. Thesis. Univ. Michigan, Ann Arbor. [3] Lundström, A. 1948. Tooth size and occlusion in twins. S. Karger, New York.

continued

14. HERITABILITY ESTIMATES OF ANATOMICAL MEASUREMENTS: MAN

Part IV: PALATE AND IRIS

Palate estimates according to heritability index Hv; iris estimates according to heritability index Hc.

	Characteristic	No. of Twin Pairs Monozygotic	No. of Twin Pairs Dizygotic	Percent Heritability Estimate	Reference
	(A)	(B)	(C)	(D)	(E)
	Ridges and Papillae on Palate				
	Papilla				
1	Length	113	121	70	1
2	Width	113	121	66	1
3	Width:length index	113	121	69	1
	Direction in degrees[1]				
4	Rugae I	113	121	33	1
5	Rugae II	113	121	16	1
	Iris Pattern				
6	Location of pattern	20	12	100	2
7	Height of pattern	20	12	100	2
8	Degree of jaggedness	20	12	37	2
9	Diffuse atrophy	20	12	40	2
10	Hypoplasy	20	12	90	2
11	Marginal atrophy	20	12	100	2

/1/ Mean for right and left sides.

Contributor: Vandenberg, Steven G.

References: [1] Lysell, L. 1955. Acta Odontol. Scand., Suppl. 18. [2] Ritter, H. 1958. Z. Morphol. Anthropol. 49:148.

15. HERITABILITY ESTIMATES OF BIOCHEMICAL AND ELECTROENCEPHALOGRAPHIC MEASUREMENTS: MAN

For heritability indexes, see Table 14.

Part I: BIOCHEMICAL

According to heritability index Hv.

	Characteristic	No. of Twin Pairs Monozygotic	No. of Twin Pairs Dizygotic	Percent Heritability Estimate	Reference
	(A)	(B)	(C)	(D)	(E)
	Urine Amino Acids				
1	β-Aminoisobutyric	15	11	93	1
2	Leucine	15	11	24	1
3	Lysine	15	11	79	1
4	Taurine	15	11	64	1
5	Tyrosine	15	11	69	1
6	Valine	15	11	86	1
7	Spot number 22	15	11	73	1
8	Rf 84	15	11	71	1
9	Rf 92	15	11	92	1
	Serum Lipids				
	Cholesterol and phospholipid levels[1]				
10	Male adult twins[2]	14	6	60	2
11	Female adult twins[2]	14	9	41	2
12	Female adult twins[3]	10	13	31	2

/1/ Genetic factors are not equally important in all environments. /2/ Pairs residing together. /3/ Separate residences.

Contributor: Vandenberg, Steven G.

References: [1] Gartler, S. M., T. Dobzhansky, and H. K. Berry. 1955. Am. J. Human Genet. 7:108. [2] Osborne, R. H., and D. Aldersberg. 1958. Science 127:1294.

continued

15. HERITABILITY ESTIMATES OF BIOCHEMICAL AND ELECTROENCEPHALOGRAPHIC MEASUREMENTS: MAN

Part II: ELECTROENCEPHALOGRAPHIC

Estimates for rest and stress according to heritability index Hv; estimates for sleep according to heritability index Hc.

	Characteristic	No. of Twin Pairs: Monozygotic	No. of Twin Pairs: Dizygotic	Percent Heritability Estimate
	(A)	(B)	(C)	(D)
	During Rest			
1	Basic frequency	102	77	100
	Percent theta and delta waves			
2	Precentral	82	69	66
3	Occipital	81	69	67
4	Rohracher alpha index	88	69	86
5	Amplitude	86	68	66
6	Percent occipital waves[1]	84	66	89
7	Continuity (Motokawa)[2]	87	68	22
	During Stress			
	Hyperventilation			
8	Alpha activation	95	90	75
	Hyperventilation			
9	Slow wave trains	95	90	52
	Oxygen lack			
10	Alpha activation	61	63	65
11	Slow wave trains	61	63	49
	During Sleep			
12	Drowsiness (Stadium 1)	64	53	100
13	Very light sleep (Stadium 2)	62	50	93
14	Light sleep (Stadium 3)	56	49	100
15	Moderately deep sleep (Stadium 4)	41	37	100

/1/ In which phases of right and left sides coincide. /2/ Number of wave trains above the mean amplitude.

Contributor: Vandenberg, Steven G.

Reference: Vogel, F. 1958. Über die Erblichkeit des normalen Elektroenzephalogramms. G. Thieme, Stuttgart.

16. HERITABILITY ESTIMATES: FARM ANIMALS

In applying heritability estimates to practical breeding situations, those characteristics showing the highest heritability are presumed to be the most responsive to selection, while those showing the lowest heritability are presumed to be the least responsive to selection.

Part I: CATTLE

Method (column C): P = paternal half-sib correlation, M = maternal half-sib correlation, F = full-sib correlation, DO = dam-offspring regression, SO = sire-offspring regression, R = repeatability coefficient, X = miscellaneous methods.

	Characteristic	Breed	Heritability Estimate: Method	Heritability Estimate: %	Reference
	(A)	(B)	(C)	(D)	(E)
	Beef Cattle				
	Body weight				
1	Birth	Angus, Hereford, Shorthorn	P	49	10,17,24, 29,31,34, 58,62
2			DO	44	35
3			SO	34	31,35
4			X	42	36
5		Japanese Black	P	51	40
6	Weaning	Angus, Hereford, Shorthorn	P	35	11,19,24, 29,31,34, 47,50,56, 58,62,66
	Body weight				
7	Weaning	Angus, Hereford, Shorthorn	DO	43	13,35,56
8			SO	34	12,31,35
9			X	19	35
10		Brahman x Angus	P	0	18
11			DO	10	18
12			SO	0	18
13	Yearling	Hereford	P	29	34,50
14			DO	43	35
15	Final pasture	Hereford	P	51	31,34,66
16			DO	43	35
17	Final feedlot	Angus, Hereford	SO	80	12,29,31
18		Hereford	P	56	29,31,50, 58,59,62

continued

16. HERITABILITY ESTIMATES: FARM ANIMALS

Part I: CATTLE

	Characteristic	Breed	Heritability Estimate		Reference
			Method	%	
	(A)	(B)	(C)	(D)	(E)
	Beef Cattle				
	Body weight gain				
19	Birth-weaning	Hereford	P	22	24,34
20			DO	7	35
21			SO	17	35
22			X	12	36
23	Weaning-yearling	Hereford	P	34	34,50,64,66
24			DO	40	36
25	Pasture	Angus, Hereford, Shorthorn	P	33	11,34,64,66
26			DO	38	11,35
27			X	40	36
28	Feedlot	Angus, Hereford, Shorthorn	P	52	17,29-31, 50,52,58, 59,64,67
29			SO	66	11,12,31
30			X	39	28
31		Brahman	P	46	67
32		Brahman x Hereford	SO	54	67
33	Efficiency of gain	Angus, Hereford, Shorthorn	P	46	11,17,31, 58,59
34			SO	35	11,31
	Score				
35	Weaning	Angus, Hereford, Shorthorn	P	35	11,29,34, 38,46,57
36			DO	37	35,36,38
37			SO	34	32,35
38			X	29	36,57
39	Yearling	Angus, Hereford, Shorthorn	P	18	11,34,50
40			DO	20	35,36
41	Conformation	Angus	P	54	8
42			DO	77	8
43			SO	33	8
	Grade				
44	Slaughter	Angus, Hereford, Shorthorn	P	35	11,17,29, 47,58
45			SO	63	32
46	Carcass	Angus, Hereford, Shorthorn	P	34	11,17,29,58
47			SO	84	32
48	Shrinkage	Hereford	P	91	58
49	Dressing percent	Hereford, Shorthorn	P	71	17,58
50	Thickness of fat	Hereford	P	38	58
51	Tenderness of meat	Angus,	P	65	15
52		Brahman x Hereford	X	50	16
53		Hereford	P	88	16
54	Shear force	Brahman x Hereford	X	95	16
55	Area of eye muscle	Hereford	P	70	29,32,58
56	Eyelid pigmentation	Hereford	P	46	3
57			DO	44	3
58	Cancer eye susceptibility	Hereford	P	17	6
59			DO	29	6
60			X	46	2
61	Gestation length	Angus, Brahman x Hereford, Hereford, Shorthorn	P	35	41,68,69
62			M	36	68,69
63			DO	24	48
64			X	34	41
65		Shorthorn	F	36	68
66			R	20	68
67	Calving interval	Angus, Hereford	P	4	9,48
68			DO	7	9,48
69			R	3	9,48
	Maternal effects				
70	Birth weight	Hereford	R	18	7,34,50
71	Weaning weight	Brahman x Angus	P	19	18
72			R	33	18
73		Hereford	R	42	7,14,18,24, 33,34,37, 50,56
	Dairy Cattle				
74	Milk yield	Ayrshire	P	43	51
75		Black Pied Lowland	X	27	39
76		Brown Swiss	DO	42	27
77		Friesian	DO	40	21
78		Holstein	DO	39	1
79		Montbeliarde	P	34	4
80		White Fulani	P	20	22
81			DO	62	22
82	Butterfat yield	Black Pied Lowland	X	31	39
83		Brown Swiss	DO	37	27
84		Guernsey, Holstein, Jersey	DO	21-25	43
85		Holstein	DO	36	1
86		Jersey	DO	20	45
87	Butterfat percentage	Ayrshire	P	52	51
88		Brown Swiss	DO	80	27
89		Friesian	DO	84	21
90		Holstein	DO	66	1
91	Solids-not-fat percentage	Ayrshire	P	65	51,65
92			DO	53	55
93		Ayrshire, Brown Swiss, Guernsey, Holstein, Jersey	DO	52	51,65
94		Guernsey, Holstein	P	93-97	70
95			DO	57	70
96		Holstein, Jersey	DO	35	25
97	Protein percentage	Ayrshire	DO	48	55

continued

16. HERITABILITY ESTIMATES: FARM ANIMALS

Part I: CATTLE

	Characteristic	Breed	Heritability Estimate Method	Heritability Estimate %	Reference
	(A)	(B)	(C)	(D)	(E)
	Dairy Cattle				
98	Protein percentage	Ayrshire, Brown Swiss, Guernsey, Holstein, Jersey	DO	53	65
99	Mastitis	Ayrshire, Guernsey, Holstein, Jersey	P, DO	27	44
100		Jersey (New Zealand)	DO	38	49
101	Conformation components	Several breeds	DO	16-32	5
102		Swiss	DO	28-35	26
103	Type ratings	Ayrshire	DO	8	23
104		Holstein	DO	18-21	61
105		Jersey	DO	12	63
106	Service per conception	Holstein	DO	3	42
107		Holstein, Jersey	DO	7	53
108	Calving interval	Holstein	P	0	20
109			DO	0-3	42,54
110		Tharparkar	DO	-18	60

Contributors: (a) Koch, Robert M., (b) Gifford, Warren, (c) Stonaker, H. H., (d) Legates, J. E., (e) Lush, Jay L.

References: [1] Abe, T. 1959. Japan. J. Zootech. Sci. 30:21. [2] Anderson, D. E. 1960. J. Heredity 51:51. [3] Anderson, D. E., D. Chambers, and J. L. Lush. 1957. J. Animal Sci. 16:1007. [4] Auriol, P., and B. Mougin. 1961. Ann. inst. natl. recherche agron., D, 10:5. [5] Berousek, E. R. 1957. J. Dairy Sci. 40:1389. [6] Blackwell, R. L., D. E. Anderson, and J. H. Knox. 1956. J. Animal Sci. 15:943. [7] Botkin, M. P., and J. A. Whatley, Jr. 1953. Ibid. 12:552. [8] Brown, C. J., et al. 1960. Arkansas Agr. Expt. Sta. Bull. 628. [9] Brown, L. O., et al. 1954. J. Animal Sci. 13:511. [10] Burris, M. J., and C. T. Blunn. 1952. Ibid. 11:34. [11] Carter, R. C., and C. M. Kincaid. 1959. Ibid. 18:323. [12] Chambers, D., J. B. Armstrong, and D. F. Stephens. 1961. Oklahoma Agr. Expt. Sta. Misc. Publ. 64:95. [13] Chambers, D., N. M. Kieffer, and L. S. Pope. 1958. Oklahoma Agr. Expt. Sta. 32nd Feeders Day Rept., p. 67. [14] Chambers, D., et al. 1956. Oklahoma Agr. Expt. Sta. Misc. Publ. 45:30. [15] Christians, C. J., et al. 1961. J. Animal Sci. 20:904. [16] Cover, S., T. C. Cartwright, and O. D. Butler. 1957. Ibid. 16:946. [17] Dawson, W. M., T. S. Yao, and A. C. Cook. 1955. Ibid. 14:208. [18] Dawson, W. M., et al. 1954. Ibid. 13:556. [19] Dinkel, C. A., and A. L. Musson. 1956. S. Dakota Agr. Expt. Sta. Circ. 130. [20] Dunbar, R. S., Jr., and C. R. Henderson. 1953. J. Dairy Sci. 36:1063. [21] El Shimy, S. A. F. 1957. Z. Tierzücht. Züchtungsbiol. 69:321. [22] Foster, W. H. 1960. Samaru Research Bull. Minist. Agr. Northern Nigeria 2. [23] Freeman, A. E., and R. S. Dunbar, Jr. 1955. J. Dairy Sci. 38:428. [24] Gregory, K. E., C. T. Blunn, and M. L. Baker. 1950. J. Animal Sci. 9:338. [25] Johnson, K. R. 1957. J. Dairy Sci. 40:723. [26] Johnson, K. R., and D. L. Fourt. 1960. Ibid. 43:975. [27] Johnson, L. A., and E. L. Corley. 1961. Ibid. 44:535. [28] Kincaid, C. M., and R. C. Carter. 1958. J. Animal Sci. 17:675. [29] Knapp, B., Jr., and R. T. Clark. 1950. Ibid. 9:582. [30] Knapp, B., Jr., and R. T. Clark. 1951. Ibid. 10:365. [31] Knapp, B., Jr., and A. W. Nordskog. 1946. Ibid. 5:62. [32] Knapp, B., Jr., and A. W. Nordskog. 1946. Ibid. 5:194. [33] Koch, R. M. 1951. Ibid. 10:768. [34] Koch, R. M., and R. T. Clark. 1955. Ibid. 14:775. [35] Koch, R. M., and R. T. Clark. 1955. Ibid. 14:786. [36] Koch, R. M., and R. T. Clark. 1955. Ibid. 14:979. [37] Koger, M., and J. H. Knox. 1947. Ibid. 6:461. [38] Koger, M., and J. H. Knox. 1952. Ibid. 11:361. [39] Koriath, G. 1960. Arch. Tierzucht 3:178. [40] Kumazaki, K., H. Tanaka, and Y. Kihara. 1956. Chugoku Agr. Expt. Sta. (Himeji) Bull., B, 5:184. [41] Lasley, J. F., B. N. Day, and J. E. Comfort. 1961. J. Animal Sci. 20:737. [42] Legates, J. E. 1954. Ibid. 13:81. [43] Legates, J. E. 1957. J. Dairy Sci. 40:630. [44] Legates, J. E., and C. D. Grinnells. 1952. Ibid. 35:829. [45] Legates, J. E., and J. L. Lush. 1954. Ibid. 37:744. [46] Lehmann, R. P., et al. 1961. J. Animal Sci. 20:53. [47] Lindholm, H. B., and H. H. Stonaker. 1957. Ibid. 16:998. [48] Lindley, C. E., et al. 1958. Ibid. 17:336. [49] Lush, J. L. 1950. J. Dairy Sci. 33:121. [50] McCormick, W. C., B. L. Southwell, and E. J. Warwick.

continued

16. HERITABILITY ESTIMATES: FARM ANIMALS

Part I: CATTLE

1956. Georgia Agr. Expt. Sta. Tech. Bull., n.s. 5. [51] O'Connor, L. K. 1959. Proc. 15th Intern. Dairy Congr., London, 1:158. [52] Patterson, R. E., et al. 1955. J. Animal Sci. 14:1034. [53] Pou, J. W., et al. 1953. J. Dairy Sci. 36:909. [54] Rennie, J. C. 1954. Iowa State Coll. J. Sci. 28:392. [55] Robertson, A., R. Waite, and J. C. D. White. 1956. J. Dairy Research 23:82. [56] Rollins, W. C., and K. A. Wagnon. 1956. J. Animal Sci. 15:125. [57] Rollins, W. C., and K. A. Wagnon. 1956. Ibid. 15:529. [58] Shelby, C. E., R. T. Clark, and R. R. Woodward. 1955. Ibid. 14:372. [59] Shelby, C. E., et al. 1960. Ibid. 19:450. [60] Singh, O. N. 1958. Indian J. Vet. Sci. 28:21. [61] Stone, J. B., J. C. Rennie, and G. E. Rathby. 1955. J. Dairy Sci. 38:616. [62] Swiger, L. A. 1961. J. Animal Sci. 20:183. [63] Tabler, K. A., and R. W. Touchberry. 1955. J. Dairy Sci. 38:1147. [64] Urick, J., et al. 1957. J. Animal Sci. 16:217. [65] Von Krosigk, C. M., J. O. Young, and G. A. Richardson. 1960. J. Dairy Sci. 43:877. [66] Wagnon, K. A., and W. C. Rollins. 1959. J. Animal Sci. 18:918. [67] Warwick, B. L., and T. C. Cartwright. 1955. Ibid. 14:363. [68] Wheat, J. D., and J. K. Riggs. 1958. Ibid. 17:249. [69] Wheat, J. D., J. K. Riggs, and R. R. Shrode. 1959. Ibid. 18:820. [70] Wilcox, C. J., et al. 1959. J. Dairy Sci. 42:1132.

Part II: SHEEP

Method (column C): P = paternal half-sib correlation, DO = dam-offspring regression, DOC = dam-offspring correlation; SO = sire-offspring regression.

	Characteristic	Breed	Heritability Estimate		Reference
			Method	%	
	(A)	(B)	(C)	(D)	(E)
	Body weight				
1	Birth	Corriedale, Dorset, Hampshire, Shropshire	DO	33	3
2		Corriedale (Can.)	DO	36	27
3		Hampshire, Oxford, Rambouillet, Shropshire, Southdown	P, DO	61	30
4		Karakul and crosses	P	18	50
5			DO	34	50
6		Merino (Austral.)	P	34	42
7		Ossimi	DO	34	34
8		Rahmani	P	16	21
9		Rambouillet	DO	27	27
10		Suffolk	DO	9	5
11		Shropshire	DO	10	11
12		Southdown	DO	40	11
13		Welsh Mountain	DOC	39	10
14	Weaning	Columbia x Columbia-Rambouillet	DO	35	47
15		Corriedale, Dorset, Hampshire, Shropshire	DO	18	3
16		Corriedale (Can.)	DO	45	27
17		Hampshire, Oxford, Rambouillet, Shropshire, Southdown	P, DO	33	30
18		Merino (Austral.)	P	9	42
19		Rahmani	P	18	21
	Body weight				
20	Weaning	Rambouillet	P	33[1]	39
21			DO	20[1]	39
22		Rambouillet and crosses	P	56	49
23			DO	77	49
24		Romnelet	DO	28	48
25		Welsh Mountain	DOC	48	10
26	4 mo	Ossimi	DO	10	34
27	120 da	Columbia	P	16	17
28			DO	21	17
29		Corriedale	P	32	17
30			DO	45	17
31		Hampshire and crosses	P	7	14
32		Suffolk	DO	41	5
33		Targhee	P	8	17
34			DO	-1	17
35	124 da	Rambouillet	P, DO	30	15
36	140 da	Shropshire	DO	12	11
37		Southdown	DO	6	11
38	149 da	Columbia	DO	33	12
39		Rambouillet	DO	31	12
40		Targhee	DO	39	12
41	155 da	Shropshire	P	34	22
42	Shearling	Corriedale (Can.)	DO	46	27
43		Rambouillet	DO	52	27
44	5-11 mo	Merino (Austral.)	P	4-27	43
45	6 mo	Ossimi	DO	29	34
46	10-12 mo	Merino (Austral.)	DO	36	28
47	11-17 mo	Merino (Austral.)	P	22-31	43
48	1 yr	Rahmani	P	19	21
49		Romnelet	DO	37	48

/1/ Adjusted.

continued

16. HERITABILITY ESTIMATES: FARM ANIMALS

Part II: SHEEP

	Characteristic	Breed	Heritability Estimate		Reference
			Method	%	
	(A)	(B)	(C)	(D)	(E)
	Body weight				
50	13+ mo	Targhee	P	37	46
51	14 mo	Rambouillet	DO	40	44
52	18 mo	Merino (S. Afr.)	P	42-54	4
53		Welsh Mountain	DOC	59	10
	Rate of gain				
54	Birth-50 lbs	Dorset x Rambouillet[2]	P	11	18
55	Birth-90 lbs	Dorset x Rambouillet[2]	P	35	18
56	50-90 lbs	Dorset x Rambouillet[2]	P	38	18
57	To weaning	Merino (Austral.)	P	9	42
58	120 da	Hampshire and crosses	P	18	14
59	1 yr	Rambouillet	P	58	40
60	To market weight	Hampshire sires	P	37	19
61		Southdown sires	P	4	19
	Body type score				
62	4 mo	Columbia	P	5-10	26
63		Rambouillet	P	4-8	26
64		Targhee	P	15-22	26
65	120 da	Columbia	P	4	17
66			DO	17	17
67		Corriedale	P	28	17
68			DO	11	17
69		Targhee	P	1	17
70			DO	-7	17
71	124 da	Rambouillet	P, DO	13	16
72	140 da	Shropshire	DO	14	11
73		Southdown	DO	40	11
74	149 da	Columbia	DO	25	12
75		Rambouillet	DO	19	12
76		Targhee	DO	13	12
77	1 yr	Rambouillet	P	20	40
78	1 yr & mature	Romney	DO	14	31
79	13+ mo	Targhee	P	32	46
80	14 mo	Rambouillet	DO	12	44
	Condition score				
81	4 mo	Columbia	P	2-4	26
82		Rambouillet	P	5-23	26
83		Targhee	P	11-29	26
84	120 da	Columbia	P	13	17
85			DO	11	17
86		Corriedale	P	34	17
87			DO	41	17
88		Targhee	P	31	17
89			DO	16	17
90	124 da	Rambouillet	P, DO	4	16
91	149 da	Columbia	DO	16	12
92		Rambouillet	DO	27	12
93		Targhee	DO	29	12
94	13+ mo	Targhee	P	23	46
95	Market grade, 140 da	Shropshire	DO	8	11
96		Southdown	DO	-58	11
	Face covering				
97	4 mo	Columbia	P	13-14	26
98		Rambouillet	P	40-66	26
99		Targhee	P	19-38	26
100	120 da	Columbia	P	44	17
101	120 da	Columbia	DO	48	17
102		Corriedale	P, DO	42	17
103		Targhee	P	38	17
104			DO	56	17
105	124 da	Rambouillet	P, DO	56	16
106	149 da	Columbia	DO	41	12
107		Rambouillet	DO	78	12
108		Targhee	DO	44	12
109	247 da	Shropshire	P	61	22
110	10-12 mo	Merino (Austral.)	DOC	29	51
111	1 yr	Rambouillet	P	48	40
112	13+ mo	Targhee	P	42	46
113	14 mo	Rambouillet	DO	32	44
114	15-16 mo	Merino (Austral.)	DOC	36-52	51
	Neck folds				
115	4 mo	Columbia	P	0-6	26
116		Rambouillet	P	4-59	26
117		Targhee	P	2-15	26
118	120 da	Columbia	P	5	17
119			DO	6	17
120		Corriedale	P	1	17
121			DO	-6	17
122		Targhee	P	17	17
123			DO	15	17
124	124 da	Rambouillet	P, DO	39	16
125	13+ mo	Rambouillet	P	21	46
126	14 mo	Targhee	DO	26	44
	Skin folds				
127	149 da	Columbia	DO	66	12
128		Rambouillet	DO	58	12
129		Targhee	DO	25	12
130	10-12 mo	Merino (Austral.)	DOC	46	51
131	1 yr	Rambouillet	P	20	40
132			SO	33	38
133	15-16 mo	Merino (Austral.)	DOC	35-48	51
134	22 mo	Merino (Austral.)	DO	50	29
	Grease fleece weight				
135	10-12 mo	Merino (Austral.)	DOC	33	51
136	12 mo	Romney (N. Zeal.)	DO	17	31
137	1 yr	Rambouillet	P	66	40
138	13 mo	Corriedale	DO	24	35
139		Rambouillet	DO	40	35
140	13+ mo	Targhee	P	29	46
141	14 mo	Rambouillet	DO	28	44
142	15-16 mo	Merino (Austral.)	DOC	43-45	51
143	22 mo	Merino (Austral.)	DO	40	29
144	2 yr	Welsh Mountain	DOC	61	10
	Clean fleece weight				
145	10-12 mo	Merino (Austral.)	DOC	29	51
146	1 yr	Rambouillet	P	61	40
147	Yearling	Rambouillet	SO	22	38
148	13+ mo	Targhee	P	53	46
149	14 mo	Rambouillet	DO	38	44
150	22 mo	Merino (Austral.)	DO	47	29
	Clean yield				
151	10-12 mo	Merino (Austral.)	DOC	50	51
152	12 mo	Rambouillet	P	43	40

/2/ Or Rambouillet-Panama.

continued

16. HERITABILITY ESTIMATES: FARM ANIMALS

Part II: SHEEP

	Characteristic	Breed	Heritability Estimate		Reference
			Method	%	
	(A)	(B)	(C)	(D)	(E)
	Clean yield				
153	13+ mo	Targhee	P	43	46
154	15-16 mo	Merino (Austral.)	DOC	44-49	51
155	22 mo	Merino (Austral.)	DO	39	29
	Staple length				
156	Weaning	Columbia x Columbia-Rambouillet	DO	72	47
157	4 mo	Columbia	P	27-42	26
158		Rambouillet	P	20-38	26
159		Targhee	P	19-24	26
160	120 da	Columbia	P	38	17
161			DO	46	17
162		Corriedale	P	5	17
163			DO	40	17
164		Targhee	P	60	17
165			DO	49	17
166		Farm sheep	DO	17	1
167	124 da	Rambouillet	P, DO	40	15
168	149 da	Columbia	DO	48	12
169		Rambouillet	DO	48	12
170		Targhee	DO	36	12
171	239 da	Shropshire	P	49	22
172	10-12 mo	Merino (Austral.)	DOC	31	51
173	1 yr	Rambouillet	P	67	40
174	Yearling	Rambouillet	SO	48	38
175	Yearling & mature	Romney (N. Zeal.)	DO	35	31
176	13+ mo	Targhee	P	40	46
177	14 mo	Rambouillet	DO	36	44
178	15-16 mo	Merino (Austral.)	DOC	35-37	51
179	20 mo	Welsh Mountain	P	73	10
180	22 mo	Merino (Austral.)	DO	56	29
	Fiber diameter				
181	60 da	Corriedale (Jap.)	P	4	24
182	10-12 mo	Merino (Austral.)	DOC	37	51
183	1 yr	Rambouillet	P	57	40
184	13+ mo	Targhee	P	36	46
	Fiber diameter				
185	15-16 mo	Merino (Austral.)	DOC	12-45	51
	Fleece grade				
186	4 mo	Columbia	P	12-29	26
187		Rambouillet	P	41-43	26
188		Targhee	P	33	26
189	13+ mo	Targhee	P	24-39	46
190	Gestation length	Rambouillet	P	40-50	45
191	Date of lambing	Southdown and Hampshire	P	46	25
192			DO	30	25
193	Multiple birth	Mixed breeds	DO	3-7	9
194		Cheviot	P	22	36
195		Columbia, Rambouillet, Targhee	DO	17	12
196		Hampshire[3]	DO	10	6
197		Landrace (Swed.)	P	9	36
198		Navajo	DOC	40[4]	41
199			DOC	12[5]	41
200		Navajo crossbreds	DOC	8[4]	41
201			DOC	22[5]	41
202		Ossimi	DO	4	33
203		Oxford Down	P	8	36
204		Rahmani	DO	8	20
205		Romney (N. Zeal.)	P, DO	0-15	32
206		Shropshire	P	4	36
207		Texel (Egypt)	P	30	23
208		Texel (Neth.)	DO	8	37
	Milk production				
209	1st lactation	Sardinian	DO	0	2
210		Upper Visso	DO	25	7
211	1st or 2nd lactation	Upper Visso	DO	29	8
212	2nd lactation	Sardinian	DO	17	2
213	3rd lactation	Sardinian	DO	34	2
214	Number of lambs reared	Farm sheep	DO	7	13

/3/ Principally. /4/ 2 years old. /5/ Mature.

Contributor: Terrill, Clair E.

References: [1] Bailey, C. M., et al. 1961. J. Animal Sci. 20:680. [2] Bettini, T. M. 1952. Riv. zootec. 25:116. [3] Blackwell, R. L., and C. R. Henderson. 1955. J. Animal Sci. 14:831. [4] Bosman, S. W. 1958. Proc. 1st Congr. S. African Genet. Soc., p. 38. [5] Cassard, D. W., and W. C. Weir. 1956. J. Animal Sci. 15:1221. [6] Cockerham, C. C. 1949. M.S. Thesis. Univ. North Carolina, Chapel Hill. [7] Dassat, P. 1950-51. Ann. accad. agr. Torino 93:241. [8] Dassat, P., and I. L. Mason. 1954. Caryologia 6(suppl.). [9] Desai, R. N., and L. M. Winters. 1951. Indian J. Vet. Sci. 21:191. [10] Doney, J. M. 1958. Australian J. Agr. Research 9:819. [11] Ensminger, M. E., et al. 1943. J. Animal Sci. 2:157. [12] Ercanbrack, S. K. 1952. Ph.D. Thesis. Iowa State Univ., Iowa City. [13] Felts, L. L. 1958. Ph.D. Thesis. Univ. Wisconsin, Madison. [14] Givens, C. S., Jr., R. C. Carter, and J. A. Gaines. 1960. J. Animal Sci. 19:134. [15] Hazel, L. N., and C. E. Terrill. 1945. Ibid. 4:347. [16] Hazel, L. N., and C. E. Terrill. 1946. Ibid. 5:55. [17] Hazel, L. N., and C. E. Terrill. 1946. Ibid. 5:371. [18] Harrington, R. B., D. G. Brothers, and J. V. Whiteman. 1962. Ibid. 21:78. [19] Hundley, W. S., Jr., and R. C. Carter. 1956. Ibid. 15:1226. [20] Karam, H. A. 1957. Ibid. 16:990. [21] Karam, H. A. 1959.

continued

16. HERITABILITY ESTIMATES: FARM ANIMALS

Part II: SHEEP

Empire J. Exptl. Agr. 27:313. [22] Karam, H. A., A. B. Chapman, and A. L. Pope. 1953. J. Animal Sci. 12:148. [23] Karam, H. A., and M. T. Ragab. 1958. Ibid. 17:235. [24] Katada, A. 1957. J. Fac. Sci. Hokkaido Univ., VI, 13:239. [25] Kentucky Agr. Expt. Sta. 1953. 66th Ann. Rept., p. 38. [26] Kyle, W. H. 1951. J. Animal Sci. 10:1027. [27] MacNaughton, W. M. 1956. Ph.D. Thesis. Iowa State Univ., Iowa City. [28] Morley, F. H. W. 1951. N. S. Wales Dept. Agr. Bull. 73. [29] Morley, F. H. W. 1955. Australian J. Agr. Research 6:77. [30] Nelson, R. H., and G. Venkatachalam. 1949. J. Animal Sci. 8:607. [31] Rae, A. L. 1950. Ph.D. Thesis. Iowa State Univ., Iowa City. [32] Rae, A. L., and T. S. Chiang. 1955. Proc. New Zealand Soc. Animal Prod. 15:103. [33] Ragab, M. T., and A. A. Asker. 1954. Empire J. Exptl. Agr. 22:224. [34] Ragab, M. T., A. A. Asker, and M. R. Kadi. 1953. Ibid. 21:304. [35] Rasmussen, K. 1942. Sci. Agr. 23:104. [36] Rendel, J. 1956. J. Animal Sci. 15:193. [37] Sharafeldin, M. A. 1960. Mededel. Landbouwhogeschool Wageningen 60:1. [38] Shelton, M. J. 1959. J. Animal Sci. 18:925. [39] Shelton, M. J., and F. Campbell. 1962. Ibid. 21:91. [40] Shelton, M. J., et al. 1954. Ibid. 13:215. [41] Sidwell, G. M. 1956. Ibid. 15:202. [42] Tallis, G. M. 1960. Ibid. 19:1208. [43] Taneja, G. C. 1955. Australian J. Agr. Research 6:343. [44] Terrill, C. E., and L. N. Hazel. 1943. J. Animal Sci. 2:358. [45] Terrill, C. E., and L. N. Hazel. 1947. Am. J. Vet. Research 8:66. [46] Terrill, C. E., et al. 1956. J. Animal Sci. 15:1215. [47] Twombly, L. T., et al. 1961. Ibid. 20:678. [48] Vesely, J. A., and S. B. Slen. 1961. Can. J. Animal Sci. 41:109. [49] Warwick, B. L., and T. C. Cartwright. 1957. J. Animal Sci. 16:1025. [50] Yao, T. S., V. L. Simmons, and R. G. Schott. 1953. Ibid. 12:431. [51] Young, S. S. Y., H. N. Turner, and C. H. S. Dolling. 1960. Australian J. Agr. Research 11:604.

Part III: SWINE

Breed (column B): PC = Poland China; LR = Landrace; Minn. No. 1 = Minnesota No. 1; Minn. No. 3 = Minnesota No. 3; Md. No. 1 = Maryland No. 1. Method (column C): P = paternal half-sib correlation, I = intra-sire regression of offspring on dam, MP = regression of offspring and mean of parents, DD = daughter-dam correlation, D = strain differences, R = repeatability of performance by sow, RV = regression of variance on genetic relationship between pigs, S = selection response, X = average of two or more methods.

	Characteristic	Breed	Heritability Estimate		Reference
			Method	%	
	(A)	(B)	(C)	(D)	(E)
	Body weight				
1	Birth	Composite	X	8	35,40
2		Duroc	X	-12	3,17
3		Hampshire	X	6	14,31
4		Md. No. 1	P	30	20
5	21 da	Duroc	P	4	3
6		Hampshire	X	11	14,31
7		Md. No. 1	P	5	20
8		Not stated	I	-6	40
9	56 da	Composite	I	-8	11,12
10		Duroc	P	15	3
11		Hampshire	X	8	14,31
12		Md. No. 1	P	13	20
13	60 da	PC	P	7	10
14	63 da	Duroc	I	14	38
15	72 da	Duroc	MP	9	17
16	84 da	Duroc	P	26	3
17	112 da	Duroc	P	28	3
18		Not stated	P	0	40
19	140 da	Duroc	P	19	3
20		Not stated	P	21	40
	Body weight				
21	150 da	Hampshire	X	15	31
22	154 da	Composite	X	12	2,5,11
23		Hampshire	X	16	14
24	168 da	Duroc	P	25	3
25		Not stated	P	27	40
26	180 da	Composite	X	24	12,16
27		Duroc	X	22	38,50
28		Hampshire	X	25	14,31
29		PC	X	36	21,48
30	200 da	Yorkshire	MP	27	47
	Body weight gain				
31	Birth-21 da	Duroc	P	7	3
32	Birth-56 da	Crosses	P	2	6
33		Duroc	P	18	6,22
34	21-56 da	Duroc	P	15	3
35		Not stated	I	-2	40
36	56-84 da	Duroc	P	20	3
37		Not stated	I	12	40
38	56-112 da	Crosses	P	35	6
39		Duroc	P	40	6,22

continued

16. HERITABILITY ESTIMATES: FARM ANIMALS

Part III: SWINE

	Characteristic	Breed	Heritability Estimate		Reference
			Method	%	
	(A)	(B)	(C)	(D)	(E)
	Body weight gain				
40	56-112 da	Not stated	P	28	40
41	56-168 da	Not stated	P	45	40
42	84-112 da	Duroc	P	31	3
43		Not stated	I	10	40
44	112-140 da	Duroc	P	4	3
45		Not stated	I	10	40
46	112-154 da	Crosses	P	34	6
47		Duroc	P	25	6
48	112-168 da	Duroc	P	17	22
49	140-168 da	Duroc	P	13	3
50		Not stated	I	10	40
	Daily weight gain				
51	Birth-200 lb	Not stated	X	12	40
52	44-200 lb	Danish LR	P	45	18,41
53	44-215 lb	German LR	P	54	41
54		Swedish LR & York	P	21	41
55	50-200 lb	PC & Minn. No. 1	I	26	12
56	56 da-200 lb	Composite	X	28	9,12,16,40,42
57		Danish LR	X	23	34
58		Minn. No. 3	I	28	43
59	56 da-225 lb	Duroc	P	18	7
60	56-112 da	Duroc	P	18	7
61	60 da-200 lb	Composite	RV	33	13
62	72 da-225 lb	Duroc	MP	43	17
63	112 da-225 lb	Duroc	P	14	7
	Litter size				
64	Birth	Composite	X	10	5,11,15,30,32,36,45
65		Berkshire	DD	44	36
66		Chester White	R	13	35
67		Duroc	X	23	8,38,44
68		German grazing hog	P	12	33
69		German LR	P	14	33
70		Md. No. 1	P	22	20
71		PC	DD	15	36
72		Tamworth	DD	34	36
73	21 da	Duroc	X	27	8
74		Md. No. 1	P	32	20
75		Swedish LR & York	R	7	30
76	28 da	Chester White	R	16	25
77	56 da	Composite	I	10	5,11,15
78		Duroc	X	19	8,44
79		Md. No. 1	P	27	20
80	56-70 da	Composite	R	17	36
81		Chester White	R	20	25
82		Duroc	I	-3	38
83	154 da	PC & LR	I	-15	11
84		Not stated	I	9	5
85	168 da	Duroc	X	37	8
86	180 da	Duroc	I	-12	38
	Litter weight				
87	Birth	Composite	I	36	15
88	21 da	Swedish LR & York	R	12	30
	Litter weight				
89	56 da	Composite	I	4	5,15
90		Duroc	X	27	8,44
91	60 da	Composite	R	18	36
92	154 da	Not stated	I	11	5
93	168 da	Duroc	X	18	8
94	Productivity index	PC	I	16	21
95	Feed economy	Composite	P	26	2
96		Duroc	X	25	17
97		Danish LR	P	58	18
98		Swedish LR	P	18	27
99		Yorkshire	X	44	19
100	Market score	Duroc	X	33	50
101		PC	I	10	12
102	Age at slaughter	Danish LR	P	28	41
103		German LR	P	23	41
104		Swedish LR & York	P	52	27,41
105	Age at 200 lb	Yorkshire	X	70	19
106	Carcass weight	Large White	D	30	29
107	Dressing percent	PC & LR	P	38	16
	Thickness of back fat				
108	Live hog	Composite	P	108	9
109		Duroc	S	49	26
110	Carcass	Composite	X	68	2,9,13,15,49
111		Duroc	P	12	8
112		Danish LR	X	57	18,28,34,41
113		German LR	P	46	41
114	Thickness of shoulder fat	Yorkshire	X	46	19
115	Thickness of loin fat	Yorkshire	X	54	19
116	Thickness of belly	Danish LR	X	55	34,41
117		German LR	P	16	41
118		Swedish LR & York	X	53	27,29,41
119	Length of carcass	Composite	X	53	2,9,16,19,27,29,41,47,49
120		Danish LR	X	58	18,34,41
121		German LR	P	52	41
122	Length of hind leg	Composite	P	66	2,16
123		Duroc	P	23	7
124		Large White	D	61	29
125	Percent lean cuts	Composite	P	43	2,9,16
126	Percent fat cuts	Composite	P	60	2,16
127	Percent ham	Yorkshire	X	58	19
128	Percent shoulder	Yorkshire	X	47	19
129		Composite	P	18	9
130	Percent Wiltshire side	Danish LR	X	23	34
131	Percent bacon	Danish LR	P	44	28
132	Size of ham	Swedish LR	P	61	27
133	Ham circumference	Duroc	P	17	7
134	Loin area	Composite	X	72	9,50

continued

16. HERITABILITY ESTIMATES: FARM ANIMALS

Part III: SWINE

	Characteristic	Breed	Heritability Estimate		Reference
			Method	%	
	(A)	(B)	(C)	(D)	(E)
135	Loin area	Yorkshire	X	54	19,47
136	Loin eye depth	Large White	D	29	29
137	Pounds of loin	Composite	P	85	9
138	Depth of carcass	Large White	D	0	29
139	Width of carcass	Large White	D	47	29
140	Carcass score	Yorkshire	X	40	19
141	Belly score	Yorkshire	X	25	19
142	Lean meat score	Danish LR	P	69	28
143	Firmness of fat score	Swedish LR	P	35	27
144	Conformation score	PC	I	20	46
145	Type score within strains	PC	P	38	24
146	Type score between strains	PC	D	92	24
147	Length of gestation	PC & LR	...	21	39
148	No. of teats	Composite	I	39	1
149	No. of vertebrae	Composite	MP	74	4
150	No. of corpora lutea	Composite	P	10	32
151	Scrotal hernia	PC & LR	X	15	37
152	Amount of spotting	Beltsville No. 1	X	76	23

Contributor: Hetzer, Herbert O.

References: [1] Allen, A. D., L. F. Tribble, and J. F. Lasley. 1959. Missouri Agr. Expt. Sta. Research Bull. 694. [2] Anderson, D. E. 1955. Iowa State Coll. J. Sci. 29:362. [3] Baker, M. L., L. N. Hazel, and C. F. Reinmiller. 1943. J. Animal Sci. 2(1):3. [4] Berge, S. 1948. Ibid. 7(2):233. [5] Bernard, C. S., A. B. Chapman, and R. H. Grummer. 1954. Ibid. 13(2):389. [6] Blunn, C. T., G. N. Baker, and L. E. Hanson. 1953. Ibid. 12(1):39. [7] Blunn, C. T., and M. L. Baker. 1947. Ibid. 6(4):424. [8] Blunn, C. T., and M. L. Baker. 1949. Ibid. 8(1):89. [9] Brinks, J. S. 1960. Dissertation Abstr. 20:4492. [10] Bywaters, J. H. 1937. Genetics 22:457. [11] Cockerham, C. C. 1952. J. Animal Sci. 11(4):738. [12] Comstock, R. E., et al. 1942. J. Agr. Research 65(8):379. [13] Cox, D. F. 1959. J. Animal Sci. 18:1464. [14] Craig, J. V., H. W. Norton, and S. W. Terrill. 1956. Ibid. 15(1):242. [15] Cummings, J. N., L. M. Winters, and H. A. Stewart. 1947. Ibid. 6(3):297. [16] Dickerson, G. E. 1947. Iowa Agr. Expt. Sta. Research Bull. 354. [17] Dickerson, G. E., and J. G. Grimes. 1947. J. Animal Sci. 6(3):265. [18] Fredeen, H. T., and P. Jonsson. 1957. Z. Tierzücht. Züchtungsbiol. 70:348. [19] Fredeen, H. T. 1953. Iowa State Coll. J. Sci. 27(2):173. [20] Green, W. W. 1958. Maryland Agr. Expt. Sta. Bull., A, 90. [21] Hazel, L. N. 1943. Genetics 28(6):476. [22] Hazel, L. N., M. L. Baker, and C. F. Reinmiller. 1943. J. Animal Sci. 2(2):118. [23] Hetzer, H. O. 1954. J. Heredity 45(5):214. [24] Hetzer, H. O., G. E. Dickerson, and J. H. Zeller. 1944. J. Animal Sci. 3(4):390. [25] Hetzer, H. O., W. V. Lambert, and J. H. Zeller. 1940. U. S. Dept. Agr. Circ. 570. [26] Hetzer, H. O., J. H. Zeller, and R. L. Hiner. 1959. Proc. 10th Intern. Congr. Genet., Montreal, 1958, 2:119. [27] Johannsson, I., and N. Korkman. 1950. Acta Agr. Scand. 1:62. [28] Jonsson, P. 1958. Ibid. 8:88. [29] King, J. W. B. 1957. Proc. Brit. Soc. Animal Prod., p. 49. [30] Korkman, N. 1947. Acta Agr. Suecana 2:253. [31] Krider, J. L., et al. 1946. J. Animal Sci. 5(1):3. [32] Lasley, E. L. 1957. Ibid. 16:335. [33] Lauprecht, E., and H. Doring. 1953. Z. Tierzücht. Züchtungsbiol. 62(2):131. [34] Lush, J. L. 1936. Iowa Agr. Expt. Sta. Research Bull. 204. [35] Lush, J. L., H. O. Hetzer, and C. C. Culbertson. 1934. Genetics 19(4):329. [36] Lush, J. L., and A. E. Molln. 1942. U. S. Dept. Agr. Tech. Bull. 836. [37] Magee, W. T. 1951. J. Animal Sci. 10(2):516. [38] McClung, M. R. 1955. Iowa State Coll. J. Sci. 29(3):455. [39] Musson, A. L. 1951. J. Animal Sci. 10(4):1028. [40] Nordskog, A. W., R. E. Comstock, and L. M. Winters. 1944. Ibid. 3(3):257. [41] Osterhoff, D. 1956. Z. Tierzücht. Züchtungsbiol. 68:689. [42] Reddy, V. B., J. F. Lasley, and L. F. Tribble. 1959. Missouri Agr. Expt. Sta. Research Bull. 689. [43] Rempel, W. E., and H. F. El-Issawi. 1959. J. Animal Sci. 18:1468. [44] Shelby, C. E. 1954. Iowa State Coll. J. Sci. 28(3):399. [45] Stewart, H. A. 1945. J. Animal Sci. 4(4):359. [46] Stonaker, H. H., and J. L. Lush. 1942. Ibid. 1(2):99. [47] Stothart, J. G. 1947. Sci. Agr. 27(8):354. [48] Whatley, J. A., Jr. 1942. J. Agr. Research 65(5):249. [49] Whatley, J. A., Jr., and F. D. Enfield. 1957. J. Animal Sci. 16:1006. [50] Whatley, J. A., Jr., and R. H. Nelson. 1942. Ibid. 1(1):70.

continued

16. HERITABILITY ESTIMATES: FARM ANIMALS

Part IV: CHICKEN

Method (column C): P = paternal half-sib correlation, M = maternal half-sib correlation, F = full-sib correlation, OD = offspring-dam regression.

	Characteristic	Breed or Variety	Heritability Estimate		Reference
			Method	%	
	(A)	(B)	(C)	(D)	(E)
	Body weight				
1	8 wk	Composite	F	46	24
2			OD	40	24
3		Barred Plymouth Rock	P	31	4
4			F	33	8
5			OD	39	4
6		New Hampshire	P	16	3
7			F	33	8
8			OD	45	4
9	10 wk	Composite	F	46	9
10			OD	33	9
11		White Wyandotte	M	20-63	10
12	12 wk	New Hampshire	P	42	11
13			M	60	11
14			F	38	1
15		White Leghorn[1]	P	20	6
16	22 wk	White Leghorn	P	27	7
17	Body depth	New Hampshire	P	11	3
18			F	43	3
19	Keel length	New Hampshire	P	27	3
20			F	55	1
21	Breast width	New Hampshire	P	13	11
22			M	29	11
23			F	20	1
24	Shank length	New Hampshire	P	50	11
25			M	48	11
26			F	38	1
27		White Leghorn	F	33-54	13
28	Thyroid weight	New Hampshire	F	48	3
29	Testes weight	New Hampshire	F	29	3
30	Feathering at 8 wk	Barred Plymouth Rock	F	42	8
31		New Hampshire	F	33	8
32	Sexual maturity	Composite	F	20	9
33			OD	7	9
34		White Leghorn	P	24	12
35			F	31	12
36			OD	35	12
	Total mortality				
37	1st laying hr	White Leghorn	P	8	15,19
38			M	11	19
39			F	8	15
40	319 da after housing	Composite	F	12	9
41	Leukosis mortality	White Leghorn	P	5	19
42			M	3	19
43			F	8	15
44	Reproductive disorders	White Leghorn	P	2	19
45			M	6	19
46	Fertility[2]	White Leghorn	OD	6	23
47	Hatchability	Composite	OD	16	21
	Egg production				
48	Annual, survivors	Barred Plymouth Rock	M	41	17
49			F	25	16
50			OD	30	17
	Egg production				
51	Annual, survivors	White Leghorn	P	21	2
52			M	22	2
53			F	22	2
54			OD	9	2
55	Rate, Dec-Mar	Composite	F	41	24
56			OD	11	24
57	Rate, Mar-June	Composite	F	38	24
58			OD	0	24
59	Rate, Dec-June	Composite	F	51	24
60			OD	0	24
61	Pause	Composite	F	16-20	9
62			OD	21-23	9
63	Persistency	Composite	F	10	9
64	Index	White Leghorn	P	23	2
65			M	10	2
66			F	16	2
67			OD	57	2
	Egg weight				
68	Sexual maturity (10 eggs)	White Leghorn	P	60	12
69			F	50	12
70			OD	61	12
71	Mar (all eggs)	Brown Leghorn	P	128	18
72			F	81	18
73	Mar (1 egg)	Composite	F	52	24
74			OD	52	24
75	Apr (10 eggs)	Composite	OD	61	21
76		White Leghorn	F	47	12
77			OD	39	12
78	Nov (10 eggs)	White Leghorn	P	48	12
79			F	36	12
80			OD	61	12
81	Dec-May (representative egg sample)	Composite	F	50	5
82		Barred Plymouth Rock	F	40	20
83		New Hampshire	F	67	20
84		White Leghorn	F	93	20
85	Jan-May (all eggs)	White Leghorn	OD	55	22
	Egg quality factors				
86	Albumin weight	Composite	F	22	5
87		Barred Plymouth Rock	F	14	20
88		New Hampshire	F	83	20
89		White Leghorn	F	110	20
90	Yolk weight	Barred Plymouth Rock	F	2	20
91		New Hampshire	F	0	20
92		White Leghorn	F	20	20
93	Blood spots	White Leghorn	F	67	14
94			OD	46	14
95	Shell texture	Composite	F	27	5
96	Shell thickness	Composite	F	27	5

/1/ Single comb. /2/ Winter and spring.

Contributors: (a) Stonaker, H. H., (b) Nordskog, A. W., (c) Asmundson, V. S.

continued

16. HERITABILITY ESTIMATES: FARM ANIMALS

Part IV: CHICKEN

References: [1] Abplanalp, H., V. S. Asmundson, and I. M. Lerner. 1960. Poultry Sci. 39:151. [2] Dempster, E. R., I. M. Lerner, and D. C. Lowry. 1952. Genetics 37:693. [3] El-Ibiary, H. M., and C. S. Shaffner. 1951. Poultry Sci. 30:435. [4] Fagan, H. B. 1949. Thesis. Iowa State College, Ames. [5] Farnsworth, G. M. 1953. Thesis. Iowa State College, Ames. [6] Garber, M. J., and C. B. Godbey. 1952. Poultry Sci. 31:945. [7] Hazel, L. N., and W. F. Lamoreux. 1947. Ibid. 26:508. [8] Hurry, H. F., and A. W. Nordskog. 1953. Ibid. 32:18. [9] Krueger, W. F., et al. 1952. Ibid. 31:922. [10] Lankford, L., and M. R. McClung. 1952. Ibid. 31:923. [11] Lerner, I. M., V. S. Asmundson, and D. M. Cruden. 1947. Ibid. 26:515. [12] Lerner, I. M., and D. M. Cruden. 1951. Ibid. 30:34. [13] Lerner, I. M., and E. R. Dempster. 1951. Heredity 5:75. [14] Lerner, I. M., L. W. Taylor, and D. C. Lowry. 1951. Poultry Sci. 30:748. [15] Lush, J. L., W. F. Lamoreux, and L. N. Hazel. 1948. Ibid. 27:375. [16] Munro, S. S. 1935-36. Sci. Agr. 16:591. [17] Munro, S. S., S. Bird, and J. W. Hopkins. 1936-37. Ibid. 17:386. [18] Osborne, R. 1953. Poultry Sci. 32:60. [19] Robertson, A., and I. M. Lerner. 1949. Genetics 34:395. [20] Scheinberg, S. L., H. Ward, and A. W. Nordskog. 1953. Poultry Sci. 32:504. [21] Shoffner, R. N., and H. J. Sloan. 1948. Rept. 8th World's Poultry Congr. 1:269. [22] Waters, N. F. 1941. Poultry Sci. 20:14. [23] Wilson, W. O. 1948. Ibid. 27:719. [24] Wyatt, A. J. 1953. Thesis. Iowa State College, Ames.

Part V: TURKEY

Breed or Variety (column B): BSW = Beltsville Small White, BBB = Broad-Breasted Bronze. Method (column C): P = paternal half-sib correlation, M = maternal half-sib correlation, F = full-sib correlation, OD = offspring-dam regression.

	Characteristic	Breed or Variety	Heritability Estimate: Method	Heritability Estimate: % ♂	Heritability Estimate: % ♀	Reference
	(A)	(B)	(C)	(D)	(E)	(F)
	Body weight					
1	2 wk	Medium White	P	28	13	6
2			F	69	73	6
3	4 wk	BSW	F	26	19	1
4		BBB	P	49	38	1
5			F	40	44	1
6		Medium White	P	4	...	6
7			M	37	76	6
8			F	20	38	6
9	8 wk	BSW	P	11	8	1
10			F	33	16	1
11		BBB	P	56	28	1
12			F	60	56	8
13		Medium White	P	19	32	6
14			M	21	72	6
15			F	20	38	6
16	14 wk	BSW	P	6	18	1
17			F	19	16	1
18		BBB	P	72	39	1
19			F	62	29	1
20	16 wk	BBB	F	52	83	8
21		Medium White	P	46	21	6
22			M	27	67	6
23			F	36	44	6
24		White Holland	P	23	59	10
25			M	62	42	10
26			F	42	50	10
27			OD	62	41	10
28	24 wk	BSW	OD	69	24	9
	Body weight					
29	24 wk	BBB	F	57	58	8
30			OD	112	46	9
31		Bronze	OD	48	55	9
32		Medium White	P	38	29	1
33			M	12	2	1
34			F	25	16	1
35		White Holland	P	33	61	10
36			M	68	60	10
37			F	51	60	10
38			OD	68	59	10
39	25 wk	BBB	P	2	71	7
40			M	34	29	7
41			F	18	50	7
42		White Holland	P	71	71	7
43			M	29	24	7
44			F	50	47	7
45	26 wk	BSW	P	13	19	6
46			F	20	24	6
47		BBB	P	52	29	6
48			F	52	25	6
	Body depth					
49	8 wk	BBB	F	82	49	8
50	16 wk	BBB	F	51	57	8
51	24 wk	BSW	OD	24	44	9
52		BBB	F	16	76	8
53			OD	37	51	9
54		Bronze	OD	21	70	9

continued

16. HERITABILITY ESTIMATES: FARM ANIMALS

Part V: TURKEY

	Characteristic	Breed or Variety	Heritability Estimate Method	Heritability Estimate % ♂	Heritability Estimate % ♀	Reference
	(A)	(B)	(C)	(D)	(E)	(F)
	Breast width					
55	8 wk	BBB	F[1]	41	10	8
56			F[2]	55	57	8
57	16 wk	BBB	F[1]	15	77	8
58			F[2]	9	27	8
59	24 wk	BSW	OD	-13	23	9
60		BBB	F[1]	28	47	8
61			F[2]	25	40	8
62			OD	50	69	9
63		Bronze	OD	9	18	9
64	26 wk	BSW	F	37	40	6
65		BBB	P	4	4	6
66			F	23	13	6
67	Breast depth, 26 wk	BSW	F	41	21	6
68		BBB	P	22	21	6
69			F	30	40	6
	Keel length					
70	8 wk	BBB	F	70	38	8
71	16 wk	BBB	F	27	74	8
72	24 wk	BSW	OD	26	-12	9
73		BBB	F	63	94	8
74			OD	39	6	9
75		Bronze	OD	36	32	9
76	26 wk	BSW	F	-5	14	6
77		BBB	P	32	15	6
78			F	22	18	6
	Shank length					
79	8 wk	BBB	F	80	42	8
80	16 wk	BBB	F	58	73	8
81	24 wk	BSW	OD	49	43	9
82		BBB	F	48	48	8
83			OD	-62	20	9
84		Bronze	OD	25	46	9
85	26 wk	BSW	F	52	...	6
86		BBB	P	25	...	6
87			F	34	...	6
	Tibial circumference					
88	16 wk	BBB	F	42	44	8
89	24 wk	BBB	F	29	62	8
	Fertility					
90	1-7 da	BBB	M	...	53	2
91			F	...	26	2
92	8-14 da	BBB	M	...	26	2
93			F	...	12	2
94	....	BBB	F	...	30	5
	Hatchability					
95	1-7 da	BBB	P	...	3	2
96			F	...	13	2
97			OD	...	40	2
98	8-14 da	BBB	P	...	14	2
99			F	...	21	2
100			OD	...	26	2
101	Feb-June	BSW	OD	...	1	13
102		Bronze	OD	...	33	13
	Egg production					
103	Feb-June	BSW	OD	...	11	13
104		BBB	P	...	9	3
105			F	...	14	3
106			OD	...	16	3
107		Bronze	OD	...	2	13
108		White Holland	P	...	29	11
109			M	...	27	11
110			F	...	28	11
111			OD	...	3	11
112	Partial (1st 30 da)	Bronze	P	...	6	4
113			M	...	21	4
114			F	...	14	4
115	Complete (100 da)	Bronze	P	...	14	4
116			M	...	26	4
117			F	...	20	4
	Egg weight					
118	Feb (10 eggs)	BBB	P	...	53	11
119			F	...	50	11
120			OD	...	64	11
121	May (10 eggs)	White	P	...	22	12
122			M	...	62	12
123			F	...	42	12

/1/ Width at 1 cm above keel and about 1 cm from its anterior end. /2/ One-half of width at one-fifth of body depth, at anterior point of keel.

Contributors: (a) McCartney, Morley G., (b) Asmundson, V. S., (c) Bumgardner, Harvey L.

References: [1] Abplanalp, H., and I. L. Kosin. 1952. Poultry Sci. 31:781. [2] Abplanalp, H., and I. L. Kosin. 1953. Ibid. 32:321. [3] Blow, W. L., and E. W. Glazener. 1954. Ibid. 33:417. [4] Blow, W. L., H. A. Stewart, and E. W. Glazener. 1958. Ibid. 37:193. [5] Blow, W. L., et al. 1951. Ibid. 30:313. [6] Bumgardner, H. L., and C. S. Shaffner. 1954. Ibid. 33:602. [7] Goodman, B. L., C. C. Brunson, and G. F. Godfrey. 1954. Ibid. 33:305. [8] Johnson, A. S., and V. S. Asmundson. 1957. Ibid. 36:296. [9] Kondra, D. A., and R. N. Shoffner. 1955. Ibid. 34:1262. [10] McCartney, M. G. 1955. Ibid. 34:617. [11] McCartney, M. G. 1955. Ibid. 34:1280. [12] McCartney, M. G. 1956. Ibid. 35:230. [13] Wilson, W. O., and L. E. Johnson. 1946. Ibid. 25:278.

17. HYBRID FERTILITY: ANIMALS

Number of hybrids reported in the animal kingdom: Mammalia, 300; Aves, 1599; Reptilia, 40; Amphibia, 271; Pisces, 212; Protochordata, 1; Echinodermata, 36; Arthropoda, 289; Mollusca, 12.

Contributor: Knobloch, Irving W.

Reference: Knobloch, I. W. Unpublished. Michigan State Univ., East Lansing, 1961.

Part I: MAMMALS AND BIRDS

For additional information on other species, consult references 1 and 2. Asterisk (*) indicates that reciprocal cross is possible; the more usual mating, however, is the one shown. Hybrid Progeny (columns B and C): F = fertile, I = infertile, RF = rarely fertile, UF = usually fertile, LF = low fertility, PF = partial fertility.

	Order and Parental Species: Male	x Female	Hybrid Progeny: Male	Hybrid Progeny: Female
	(A)		(B)	(C)
	Mammalia [1]			
	Primates			
1	**Macaca irus*	x *M. mulatta*	F	F
	Artiodactyla			
2	**Bison bison*	x *B. bonasus*	F	F
3	**B. bison*	x *Bos grunniens*	I	RF
4	**Bison bison*	x *Bos taurus*	I	F
5	**Bison bonasus*	x *Bos taurus*	I	RF
6	**Bos banteng*	x *B. taurus*	I	F
7	**B. frontalis*	x *B. indicus*	I	F
8	**B. gaurus*	x *B. taurus*	RF	RF
9	**B. grunniens*	x *B. taurus*	RF	F
10	**Camelus bactrianus*	x *C. dromedarius*	I	F
11	*Capra caucasica*	x *C. hircus*	F	F
12	*C. falconeri*	x *C. hircus*	F	F
13	**C. hircus*	x *C. ibex*	F	F
14	*Cervus canadensis*	x *C. elaphus*	F	F
15	*Lama glama*	x *L. pacos*	F	F
16	*L. vicugna*	x *L. pacos*	F	F
17	*Ovis ammon*	x *O. aries*	F	F
18	**O. aries*	x *O. musimon*	F	F
19	*O. canadensis*	x *O. aries*	LF	LF
20	**O. canadensis*	x *O. musimon*	F	F
21	**O. orientalis*	x *O. aries*	F	F
22	*O. orientalis*	x *O. musimon*	F	F
23	*Sus barbatus*	x *S. scrofa*	F	F
	Perissodactyla			
24	**Equus asinus*	x *E. burchelli*	I	RF
25	**E. asinus*	x *E. caballus*	I	RF
26	**E. asinus*	x *E. grevyi*	I	I
27	**E. asinus*	x *E. hemionus*	I	I
28	**E. asinus*	x *E. zebra*	I	I
29	**E. burchelli*	x *E. caballus*	I	I
30	**E. caballus*	x *E. hemionus*	I	RF
31	**E. caballus*	x *E. przewalskii*	F	F
32	**E. caballus*	x *E. zebra*	I	I
33	*E. grevyi*	x *E. caballus*	I	I
	Carnivora			
34	**Canis aureus*	x *C. familiaris*	F	F
35	*C. familiaris*	x *C. latrans*	I	...
36	**C. familiaris*	x *C. lupus*	F	F
37	**Panthera leo*	x *P. tigris*	RF	F
38	*Thalarctos maritimus*	x *Ursus arctos*	F?	F
	Rodentia			
39	*Cavia aperea*	x *C. porcellus*	F	F
40	*Cavia cutleri*	x *C. porcellus*	F	F
41	**C. porcellus*	x *C. fulgida*	I	F
42	**Mus bactrianus*	x *M. musculus*	F	F
43	*Peromyscus comanche*	x *P. nasutus*	F?	...
44	*P. leucocephalus*	x *P. polionotus*	F?	F
45	*P. leucopus*	x *P. gossypinus*	F	F
46	*P. nasutus*	x *P. truei*	I	F
47	*P. polionotus*	x *P. maniculatus*	F	F
	Aves [2]			
	Passeriformes			
48	**Carduelis carduelis*	x *C. cannabina*	RF	I
49	**C. carduelis*	x *Serinus canarius*	RF	I
50	*C. cucullata*	x *S. canarius*	RF	I
51	*C. spinus*	x *S. canarius*	RF	I
52	**Chloris chloris*	x *S. canarius*	RF	I
53	*Lonchura molabarica*	x *L. domestica*	RF	...
54	**Passer hispaniolensis*	x *P. domesticus*	F	F
55	*Serinus serinus*	x *S. canarius*	F	RF
56	*Vermivora chrysoptera*	x *V. pinus*	F	F
	Piciformes			
57	*Colaptes auratus*	x *C. cafer*	F	F
	Psittaciformes			
58	*Agapornis fischeri*	x *A. lilianae*	F	F
59	**A. fischeri*	x *A. nigrigenis*	F	F
60	**A. fischeri*	x *A. personata*	F	F
61	*A. fischeri*	x *A. pullaria*	F	F
62	**A. fischeri*	x *A. roseicollis*	F	F
63	**A. lilianae*	x *A. nigrigenis*	F	F
64	**A. lilianae*	x *A. personata*	F	F
65	*A. lilianae*	x *A. roseicollis*	F	F
66	**A. nigrigenis*	x *A. personata*	F	F
67	**Platycercus elegans*	x *P. eximius*	F	F
68	**P. eximius*	x *P. icterotis*	F	RF
	Columbiformes			
69	**Columba guinea*	x *C. livia*	LF	I?
70	**C. livia*	x *C. leuconota*	F	I
71	*C. livia*	x *Streptopelia orientalis*	RF	...
72	**C. livia*	x *S. risoria*	RF	I
73	*C. livia*	x *S. turtur*	RF	I

continued

17. HYBRID FERTILITY: ANIMALS

Part I: MAMMALS AND BIRDS

	Order and Parental Species: Male (A)	x	Female (A)	Hybrid Progeny: Male (B)	Hybrid Progeny: Female (C)
	Aves [2]				
	Columbiformes				
74	*Columba migratoria*	x	*Streptopelia risoria*	I	...
75	**C. oenas*	x	*C. livia*	F	I
76	*C. oenas*	x	*C. palumbus*	RF	...
77	**C. palumbus*	x	*C. livia*	RF	I
78	*C. picazuro*	x	*C. livia*	RF?	I
79	*C. rufina*	x	*C. livia*	F	I
80	*C. speciosa*	x	*C. maculosa*	I	I
81	*Geopelia cuneata*	x	*G. striata*	I	I
82	**Oenopopelia humilis*	x	*Streptopelia risoria*	F	F
83	*Spilopelia chinensis*	x	*Stigmatopelia senegalensis*	F	F
84	*Spilopelia chinensis*	x	*Streptopelia risoria*	F	RF
85	*Spilopelia chinensis*	x	*Streptopelia turtur*	F	RF
86	**Streptopelia orientalis*	x	*S. risoria*	PF	PF
87	*S. risoria*	x	*Stigmatopelia senegalensis*	PF	PF
88	**Streptopelia turtur*	x	*Stigmatopelia senegalensis*	F	RF
89	**Streptopelia turtur*	x	*S. risoria*	UF	PF
90	*Zenaida zenaida*	x	*Zenaidura macroura*	F?	F?
91	*Zenaidura macroura*	x	*Streptopelia risoria*	I	I
	Gruiformes				
92	*Grus rubicunda*	x	*G. antigone*	F	...
	Galliformes				
93	*Acryllium vulturinum*	x	*Numida meleagris*	I	...
94	**Calophasis mikado*	x	*C. elliotti*	F	F
95	**Chrysolophus amherstiae*	x	*C. pictus*	F	F
96	**C. amherstiae*	x	*Phasianus colchicus*	F	I
97	**C. amherstiae*	x	*P. versicolor*	F	I
98	**C. pictus*	x	*Gallus domesticus*	I	...
99	**C. pictus*	x	*Gennaeus nycthemerus*	F	I
100	**C. pictus*	x	*Phasianus colchicus*	RF	I
101	**C. pictus*	x	*Syrmaticus reevesii*	RF	I
102	*Crax fasciolata*	x	*C. alberti*	....	RF
103	*Crossoptilon auritum*	x	*C. mantchuricum*	F	F
104	*C. mantchuricum*	x	*Gennaeus nycthemerus*	F	I
105	**Gallus domesticus*	x	*Numida meleagris*	I	...
106	**G. domesticus*	x	*Phasianus colchicus*	I	I
107	*Gennaeus edwardsi*	x	*G. imperialis*	F	F
108	*G. imperialis*	x	*G. horsfieldii*	F	F
109	*G. leucomelanos*	x	*Lophura ignita*	F	I
110	*G. lineatus*	x	*G. leucomelanos*	F	F
	Galliformes				
111	**Gennaeus lineatus*	x	*G. nycthemerus*	F	F
112	*G. nycthemerus*	x	*G. horsfieldii*	F♀	RF
113	**G. nycthemerus*	x	*G. leucomelanos*	F	F
114	**G. nycthemerus*	x	*G. swinhoii*	F	RF
115	**G. nycthemerus*	x	*Phasianus colchicus*	F	I
116	**G. nycthemerus*	x	*Syrmaticus reevesii*	RF	I?
117	**Lagopus lagopus*	x	*Lyrurus tetrix*	I	I
118	**Lyrurus tetrix*	x	*Tetrao urogallus*	F	I?
119	*Meleagris ocellata*	x	*M. gallopavo*	F	I
120	*Numida meleagris*	x	*N. mitrata*	F	F
121	**Pavo cristatus*	x	*Gallus domesticus*	I	...
122	**P. cristatus*	x	*Numida meleagris*	I	...
123	**P. cristatus*	x	*P. muticus*	F	F
124	**Phasianus colchicus*	x	*P. versicolor*	UF	UF
125	**P. versicolor*	x	*Syrmaticus reevesii*	RF	I
126	**Syrmaticus reevesii*	x	*P. colchicus*	RF	I
127	*S. soemmerringii*	x	*Chrysolophus pictus*	I	I
128	**S. soemmerringii*	x	*S. reevesii*	F	I
	Anseriformes				
129	**Aix sponsa*	x	*Anas bahamensis*	I	I
130	**Aix sponsa*	x	*Anas penelope*	I	I
131	**Aix sponsa*	x	*Anas platyrhynchos*	I	I
132	**Aix sponsa*	x	*Netta peposaca*	I	I
133	**Anas acuta*	x	*A. platyrhynchos*	F	F
134	**A. bahamensis*	x	*Amazonetta brasiliensis*	I	I
135	**Anas bahamensis*	x	*A. georgica*	F	F
136	*A. crecca*	x	*A. acuta*	...	RF
137	**A. fulvigula*	x	*A. platyrhynchos*	F	F
138	*A. georgica*	x	*A. sibilatrix*	I?	RF
139	**A. melleri*	x	*A. platyrhynchos*	F	F
140	**A. penelope*	x	*A. platyrhynchos*	I	I?
141	**A. platyrhynchos*	x	*A. penelope*	I	I
142	**A. platyrhynchos*	x	*A. poecilorhyncha*	F	F
143	**A. platyrhynchos*	x	*A. strepera*	RF	RF
144	**A. platyrhynchos*	x	*A. undulata*	F	RF
145	**A. platyrhynchos*	x	*Anser anser*	I	...
146	**Anas platyrhynchos*	x	*Cairina moschata*	I	I
147	*A. poecilorhyncha*	x	*A. superciliosa*	F	F
148	**A. sibilatrix*	x	*Aix sponsa*	I	I
149	**Anas sibilatrix*	x	*A. platyrhynchos*	I?	I?
150	**A. strepera*	x	*A. penelope*	I?	RF
151	**A. superciliosa*	x	*A. platyrhynchos*	F	F
152	**A. superciliosa*	x	*A. undulata*	F	F
153	**A. undulata*	x	*A. poecilorhyncha*	F	F
154	**Anser anser*	x	*A. caerulescens*	F	F
155	**A. anser*	x	*A. cygnoides*	F	F
156	*A. anser*	x	*A. indicus*	F	F
157	**A. anser*	x	*Branta canadensis*	I	I

continued

17. HYBRID FERTILITY: ANIMALS

Part I: MAMMALS AND BIRDS

	Order and Parental Species		Hybrid Progeny	
	Male	x Female	Male	Female
	(A)		(B)	(C)
	Aves [2]			
	Anseriformes			
158	*Anser caerulescens*	x *A. albifrons*	UF	UF
159	*A. caerulescens*	x *A. brachyrhynchos*	F	...
160	**A. caerulescens*	x *A. canagicus*	F	F
161	**A. caerulescens*	x *Branta canadensis*	I	I
162	**A. cygnoides*	x *A. caerulescens*	F	F
163	**A. cygnoides*	x *B. canadensis*	I	I
164	*A. cygnoides*	x *Cairina moschata*	I	I
165	**A. erythropus*	x *A. albifrons*	F	F
166	**Aythya ferina*	x *Aix sponsa*	I	I
167	**Aythya ferina*	x *Anas platyrhynchos*	I	I
168	**Aythya ferina*	x *A. fuligula*	F	...
169	*A. fuligula*	x *A. nyroca*	F	F
170	**A. fuligula*	x *Anas penelope*	I	I
171	*Branta canadensis*	x *Anser albifrons*	I	I
172	**B. canadensis*	x *B. leucopsis*	I	...
	Anseriformes			
173	**Branta leucopsis*	x *Anser anser*	RF	I
174	*Chloëphaga picta*	x *Alopochen aegyptiaca*	I	I
175	*Cyanochen cyanopterus*	x *A. aegyptiaca*	RF	RF
176	*Cygnus atratus*	x *Anser anser*	I	I
177	*C. columbianus*	x *C. olor*	F	I
178	*C. olor*	x *A. anser*	I	I
179	**Netta peposaca*	x *Aix sponsa*	I	I
180	*N. peposaca*	x *N. rufina*	F	...
181	*N. rufina*	x *Anas poecilorhyncha*	RF	I
182	**Plectropterus gambensis*	x *Cairina moschata*	I	...
183	**Tadorna ferruginea*	x *T. cana*	F	...
184	*T. tadorna*	x *Alopochen aegyptiaca*	I	I
185	*T. tadorna*	x *Anas platyrhynchos*	RF	I

Contributor: Irwin, M. R.

References: [1] Gray, A. P. 1954. Mammalian hybrids. Commonwealth Bureau of Animal Breeding and Genetics, Edinburgh. [2] Gray, A. P. 1958. Bird hybrids. Commonwealth Bureau of Animal Breeding and Genetics, Edinburgh.

Part II: INSECTS

Hybrid Progeny (columns B and C): I = infertile, F = fertile, RF = rarely fertile, PF = partially fertile.

	Parental Species		Hybrid Progeny		Reference
	Male	x Female	Male	Female	
	(A)		(B)	(C)	(D)
	Diptera				
1	*Drosophila aldrichi*	x *D. mulleri*	I	I	3
2	*D. americana*	x *D. virilis*	F	F	3
3	*D. arizonensis*	x *D. aldrichi*	...	I	3
4	*D. arizonensis*	x *D. mulleri*	I	...	3
5	*D. arizonensis*	x *D. mojavensis*	F	F	3
6	*D. athabasca*	x *D. algonquin*	I	F	3
7	*D. athabasca*	x *D. azteca*	I	I	3
8	*D. melanogaster*	x *D. simulans*	I	I	3
9	*D. miranda*	x *D. pseudoobscura*	I	RF	3
10	*D. mojavensis*	x *D. arizonensis*	I	F	3
11	*D. mojavensis*	x *D. mulleri*	I	F	3
12	*D. montana*	x *D. texana*	F	F	4
13	*D. montana*	x *D. virilis*	F	F	4
14	*D. neorepleta*	x *D. melanopalpa*	F	F	3
15	*D. occidentalis*	x *D. munda*	F	F	5
16	*D. persimilis*	x *D. miranda*	I	RF	3
17	*Drosophila persimilis*	x *D. pseudoobscura*	I	PF	2
18	*D. pseudoobscura*	x *D. miranda*	I	RF	3
19	*D. similans*	x *D. melanogaster*	...	I	3
20	*D. subquinaria*	x *D. munda*	I	I	5
21	*D. texana*	x *D. montana*	F	F	4
	Lepidoptera				
22	*Clostera anachoreta*	x *C. curtula*	F	I	1
23	*Lycia hirtaria*	x *Nyssia graecaria*	I	...	1
24	*L. hirtaria*	x *N. zonaria*	I	...	1
25	*L. hirtaria*	x *Poecilopsis isabellae*	F	I	1
26	*L. hirtaria*	x *P. pomonaria*	F	F	1
27	*Nyssia zonaria*	x *L. hirtaria*	F	I	1
28	*Oporabia dilutata*	x *O. autumnata*	F	I	1

continued

17. HYBRID FERTILITY: ANIMALS

Part II: INSECTS

	Parental Species		Hybrid Progeny		Reference
	Male	x Female	Male	Female	
	(A)		(B)	(C)	(D)
	Lepidoptera				
29	*Poecilopsis pomonaria*	x *Lycia hirtaria*	F	I	1
30	*P. pomonaria*	x *P. lapponaria*	F	I	1
31	*Saturnia pavonia*	x *S. pyri*	F	I	1
32	*S. pavonia*	x *S. spini*	F	I	1
33	*Tephrosia bistortata*	x *T. crepuscularia*	F	F	1
34	*T. crepuscularia*	x *T. bistortata*	F	F	1

Contributor: Irwin, M. R.

References: [1] Craft, W. A. 1938. Quart. Rev. Biol. 13:19. [2] Dobzhansky, T. 1941. Genetics and the origin of species. Ed. 2. Columbia Univ. Press, New York. [3] Patterson, J. T. 1942. Univ. Texas Publ. 4228:7 [4] Patterson, J. T., and A. B. Griffin. 1944. Ibid. 4445:212. [5] Sears, J. W. 1947. Ibid. 4720:137.

18. HYBRIDIZATION: PLANTS

Number of hybrids reported in the plant kingdom: Schizomycophyta, 2; Eumycophyta, 67; Chlorophyta, 19; Bryophyta, 43; Pteridophyta, 158; Spermatophyta, 15,000 (exclusive of orchids). [7]

	Parental Species			F_1 Hybrid Fertility	Reference
	Parent I	Parent II	Compatibility		
	(A)	(B)	(C)	(D)	(E)
	Citrus				
1	*Citrus aurantifolia*	*C. limon*	Cross-fertile	....	31,32
2		*Fortunella japonica*	Cross-fertile	Partially cross-fertile	27,32
3	*C. aurantium*	*Poncirus trifoliata*	Cross-fertile	....	32
4	*C. grandis*	*C. aurantium*	Cross-fertile	....	29
5		*C. medica*	Cross-fertile[1]	....	30,32
6		*C. paradisi*	Cross-fertile	....	3,23,29
7		*C. reticulata*	Cross-fertile	....	3,23,29
8		*C. sinensis*	Cross-fertile	....	3,23,29
9	*C. ichangensis*	*P. trifoliata*	Cross-fertile	....	23
10	*C. limon*	*C. paradisi*	Cross-fertile	....	2,3
11		*C. reticulata*	Cross-fertile	....	2,3,32
12		*C. sinensis*	Cross-fertile	....	2,3,29,32
13		*P. trifoliata*	Cross-fertile	....	23,25
14	*C. paradisi*	*C. reticulata*	Cross-fertile	Self-sterile; cross-fertile	2,3,28,29,32,33
15		*C. sinensis*	Cross-fertile	....	2,3
16	*C. reticulata*	*C. ichangensis*	Cross-fertile	....	32
17		*C. sinensis*	Cross-fertile	Cross-fertile	2,3,28,29,32
18		*F. japonica*	Cross-fertile	....	24
19		*P. trifoliata*	Cross-fertile	Cross-fertile	32,33
20	*C. sinensis*	*P. trifoliata*	Cross-fertile	Partially self- and cross-fertile	16,24,26-28
21	*F. japonica*	*P. trifoliata*	Cross-fertile	....	27
	Pepper				
22	*Capsicum annuum*	*C. cardenasii*[2]	Cross-sterile	....	4
23		*C. chacoense*	Cross-fertile	Self-sterile	4
24		*C. eximium*[2]	Cross-fertile	....	19
25		*C. frutescens*	Slightly cross-fertile	Partially self-sterile	5,20,21
26		*C. galapogense*	Cross-sterile	....	4
27		*C. microcarpum*[3]	Cross-sterile	....	19

/1/ Some crosses may produce dwarf plants. /2/ This species is self-incompatible. /3/ Hybrids probably obtainable by means of embryo culture.

continued

	Parental Species			F_1 Hybrid Fertility	Reference
	Parent I	Parent II	Compatibility		
	(A)	(B)	(C)	(D)	(E)
			Pepper		
28	*Capsicum annuum*	*C. pendulum*[4]	Cross-sterile	Self- and cross-sterile	5,21
29		*C. praetermissum*	Cross-sterile	...	19
30		*C. pubescens*	Cross-sterile	...	5,21
31		*C. schottianum*	Cross-sterile	...	19
32		*C. sinense*	Cross-fertile	Partially self- and cross-sterile	5,21
33	*C. cardenasii*[2]	*C. chacoense*	Cross-sterile	...	4
34		*C. eximium*[2]	Slightly cross-fertile	Self-incompatible, F_1 sibs partially cross-fertile	4
35		*C. frutescens*	Cross-sterile	...	4
36		*C. pendulum*	Cross-sterile	...	4
37		*C. praetermissum*	Cross-sterile	...	4
38		*C. pubescens*	Cross-fertile	Self-fertile	4
39		*C. sinense*	Cross-sterile	...	4
40	*C. chacoense*	*C. frutescens*	Cross-fertile	Self-fertile	19
41		*C. galapogense*	Cross-sterile	...	19
42		*C. pendulum*	Cross-sterile	...	19
43		*C. pubescens*	Cross-sterile	...	19
44		*C. sinense*	Slightly cross-fertile	Self-sterile; partially cross-fertile	19
45	*C. eximium*[2]	*C. pendulum*	Cross-sterile	...	19
46		*C. praetermissum*	Cross-sterile	...	4
47		*C. schottianum*	Cross-sterile	...	19
48	*C. frutescens*	*C. galapogense*	Cross-sterile	...	4
49		*C. pendulum*	Cross-fertile	Self-sterile	5,21
50		*C. praetermissum*	Slightly cross-fertile	Slightly cross-fertile	4
51		*C. pubescens*	Cross-sterile	...	5,21
52		*C. sinense*	Cross-fertile	Partially self- and cross-fertile	5,21
53	*C. galapogense*	*C. pendulum*	Cross-sterile	...	19
54		*C. praetermissum*	Cross-sterile	...	4
55		*C. pubescens*	Cross-sterile	...	19
56		*C. sinense*	Cross-sterile	...	19
57	*C. microcarpum*	*C. praetermissum*	Cross-fertile	Partially self-sterile	19
58	*C. pendulum*	*C. pubescens*	Cross-sterile	...	5,21
59		*C. schottianum*	Cross-sterile	...	19
60		*C. sinense*	Cross-fertile	Self- and cross-sterile	5,21
61	*C. sinense*	*C. pubescens*	Cross-sterile[5]	Self- and cross-sterile	5,21
			Tomato		
62	*Lycopersicon esculentum*[6]	*L. chilense*	Slightly cross-fertile	Self-sterile; partially cross-fertile	9,15
63		*L. hirsutum*	Partially cross-fertile	Partially self- and cross-sterile	1,10-12,17
64		*L. peruvianum*[7]	Cross-sterile[4]	Self-sterile; partially cross-fertile	1,6,13,18,22
65		*L. pimpinellifolium*	Cross-fertile	Self- and cross-fertile	8,11,22
66	*L. hirsutum*	*L. pimpinellifolium*	Partially cross-fertile	Partially self-fertile; cross-fertile	11
67	*L. peruvianum*[7]	*L. chilense*	Cross-sterile	Self-sterile; partially cross-fertile	15
68		*L. pimpinellifolium*	Cross-sterile[4]	Self-sterile; partially cross-fertile	11
69	*L. peruvianum humifusum*	*L. chilense*	Cross-fertile	Self-sterile; cross-fertile	15
70		*L. peruvianum*[7]	Slightly cross-fertile	Self-sterile; partially cross-fertile	15

/2/ This species is self-incompatible. /4/ Hybrids obtainable by means of embryo culture, occasionally without culture. /5/ Hybrids obtainable by means of embryo culture. /6/ Including *L. cheesmani minor* [14]. /7/ Including *L. glandulosum* [15].

Contributors: (a) Soost, Robert K., (b) Smith, Paul G., (c) Knobloch, Irving W.

References: [1] Alexander, L. H., R. E. Lincoln, and V. Wright. 1942. Plant Disease Reptr., Suppl. 136:49. [2] Frost, H. B. 1926. Hilgardia 1:365. [3] Frost, H. B. Unpublished. Records California Citrus Expt. Sta., Div. of Plant Breeding, 1953. [4] Heiser, C. B., Jr., and P. G. Smith. 1950. Brittonia 10:194. [5] Hirose, T., et al. 1960. Science Repts. Kyoto Prefect. Univ. Agr. 12:40. [6] Holmes, R. O. 1939. Phytopathology 29:215. [7] Knobloch, I. W. Unpublished. Michigan State Univ., East Lansing, 1961. [8] Lesley, J. W. Unpublished. Univ. California Div. of Plant Breeding, Riverside, 1953. [9] Lesley, M. M., and J. W. Lesley. 1943. J. Heredity

continued

18. HYBRIDIZATION: PLANTS

34:199. [10] Lesley, M. M., and J. W. Lesley. 1946. Genetics 31:233. [11] MacArthur, J. W., and L. P. Chaisson. 1947. Ibid. 32:165. [12] Porte, W. S., S. P. Doolittle, and F. L. Wellman. 1939. Phytopathology 29:725. [13] Porte, W. S., and H. B. Walker. 1945. Ibid. 35:931. [14] Rick, C. M. 1956. Am. J. Botany 43:687. [15] Rick, C. M., and R. Lamm. 1955. Ibid. 42:663. [16] Robinson, T. R. 1932. Proc. 6th Intern. Congr. Genet., Ithaca, N. Y., 1932, 2:171. [17] Sawant, A. 1958. Genetics 43:502. [18] Smith, P. G. 1944. Proc. Am. Soc. Hort. Sci. 44:413. [19] Smith, P. G. Unpublished. Univ. California Dept. of Vegetable Crops, Davis, 1961. [20] Smith, P. G., and C. B. Heiser, Jr. 1951. Am. J. Botany 38:362. [21] Smith, P. G., and C. B. Heiser, Jr. 1957. Proc. Am. Soc. Hort. Sci. 70:286. [22] Soost, R. K. Unpublished. Univ. California Dept. of Horticulture, Riverside, 1961. [23] Soost, R. K., and J. W. Cameron. Unpublished. Univ. California Dept. of Horticulture, Riverside, 1953. [24] Swingle, W. T. 1910. Proc. Florida State Hort. Soc. 23:36. [25] Swingle, W. T. 1913. Proc. 4th Intern. Congr. Genet., Paris, 1911, p. 381. [26] Swingle, W. T. 1927. Mem. N. Y. Hort. Soc. 3:19. [27] Swingle, W. T., and T. R. Robinson. 1923. J. Agr. Research 23:229. [28] Swingle, W. T., T. R. Robinson, and E. M. Savage. 1931. U. S. Dept. Agr. Circ. 181. [29] Torres, J. P. 1938. Philippine J. Agr. 9:161. [30] Toxopeus, H. J. 1931. Ver. Landbouw Ned.-Indië Landbouw Tijdschr. 6:807. [31] Webber, H. J. 1906. In U. S. Dept. Agr. Yearbook, 1905, p. 275. [32] Webber, H. J., and L. D. Batchelor. 1948. The citrus industry. Univ. California Press, Berkeley. v. 1, ch. 4, 8, 9. [33] Webber, H. J., and W. T. Swingle. 1905. In U. S. Dept. Agr. Yearbook, 1904, p. 221.

19. HYBRID VIGOR: CORN

	Combination			Grain Yield			
	Number	Type	Cross	Actual	Relative in % of F_1	Relative Calculated[1]	Reference
	(A)	(B)	(C)	(D)	(E)	(F)	(G)
	Bushels per Acre						
1	2 inbred lines, F_1 and F_2, 6 yr, 1 plot each year	Inbred lines	(AxA), (BxB), --(IxI)--	20.0	19.8		1
2		Single crosses, F_1	(AxB), (BxI)	101.0	100.0		
3		Single crosses, F_2	(AxB)x(AxB)	69.0	68.3	59.9	
4	10 *6*-state regional elite inbred lines, all 45 F_1s and their F_2s; 4 replications (with 1 replication of each group assigned at random to each replication), 1 year	Inbred lines	(AxA), (BxB), --(IxI)--	28.2	35.3		2
5		Single crosses, F_1	(AxB), (BxI)	79.9	100.0		
6		Single crosses, F_2	(AxB)x(AxB)	50.8	63.6	67.6	
7	7 inbred lines, 10F_1s and their F_2s; 6 replications, random breeding lines, 1 year	Inbred lines	(AxA), (BxB), --(IxI)--	23.7	37.8		4
8		Single crosses, F_1	(AxB), (BxI)	62.8	100.0		
9		Single crosses, F_2	(AxB)x(AxB)	44.2	70.4	68.9	
10	4 inbred lines, 4 *3*-way F_1s and their F_2s; 6 replications, random breeding lines, 1 year	Inbred lines	(AxA), (BxB), --(IxI)--	23.8	37.1		4
11		*3*-way crosses, F_1	(AxB)xI	64.2	100.0		
12		*3*-way crosses, F_2	[(AxB)xI]x[(AxB)xI]	49.3	76.8	76.4	
13	7 inbred lines, 10 *4*-way F_1s and their F_2s; 6 replications, random breeding lines, 1 year	Inbred lines	(AxA), (BxB), --(IxI)--	25.0	39.0		4
14		*4*-way crosses, F_1	(AxB)x(DxI)	64.1	100.0		
15		*4*-way crosses, F_2	[(AxB)x(DxI)]x [(AxB)x(DxI)]	54.0	84.2	84.8	
16	10 self-fertilized lines, 6 F_1s, 11 F_2s, 11 crossbreds; 1 plot each	Inbred lines	(AxA), (BxB), --(IxI)--	25.0	35.0		6
17		Single crosses, F_1	(AxB), (BxI)	71.4	100.0		
18		Single crosses, F_2	(AxB)x(AxB)	42.6	59.7	67.5	
19		Bulk hand-crossed each generation		63.5			
20	13 lines, 4 F_1s, 5 F_2s, 5 backcrosses, 2 *3*-way, 3 *4*-way, 5 imperfect iteratives, 10 crossbreds; 1 plot each	Inbred lines	(AxA), (BxB), --(IxI)--	16.7	21.0		6
21		Single crosses, F_1	(AxB), (BxI)	79.4	100.0		
22		Single crosses, F_2	(AxB)x(AxB)	51.4	64.7	60.5	
23		Back crosses	(AxB)xA, (BxI)xI	47.6	59.9	60.5	

/1/ From inbred parents and F_1, on the assumption that loss of hybrid vigor from F_1 to F_2 and F_1 to backcross is proportional to increment of inbreeding (no epistasy).

continued

19. HYBRID VIGOR: CORN

	Combination			Grain Yield			
	Number	Type	Cross	Actual	Relative in % of F_1	Relative Calculated[1]	Reference
	(A)	(B)	(C)	(D)	(E)	(F)	(G)
	Bushels per Acre						
24	13 lines, 4 F_1s, 5 F_2s, 5 backcrosses, 2 *3*-way, 3 *4*-way, 5 imperfect iteratives, 10 crossbreds; 1 plot each	*3*-way crosses, F_1	(A x B) x I	96.0	120.9	100.0	6
25		*4*-way crosses, F_1	(A x B) x (D x I)	78.5	98.9	100.0	
26		"Imperfect iterative"	(A x B) x (A x C), (C x D) x (I x D)	54.1	68.1	80.3	
27		Bulk hand-crossed each generation		57.0			
28	6 elite inbred lines, 5 replications; all 15 F_1s, 4 replications; and their F_2s, 5 replications; 1 year (the 3 groups in separate contiguous plantings)	Inbred lines	(A x A), (B x B), --(I x I)--	37.4	38.6		8
29		Single crosses, F_1	(A x B), (B x I)	96.8	100.0		
30		Single crosses, F_2	(A x B) x (A x B)	69.9	72.2	69.3	
31	4 inbred lines, 6 replications; all 6 F_1s and their F_2s, 4 replications; all 12 backcrosses, 2 replications; all 12 *3*-way, 2 replications; all 3 *4*-way, 8 replications; all 12 imperfect iteratives, 2 replications; 1 year; groups random	Inbred lines	(A x A), (B x B), --(I x I)--	41.5	48.9		7
32		Single crosses, F_1	(A x B), (B x I)	84.9	100.0		
33		Single crosses, F_2	(A x B) x (A x B)	62.2	73.3	74.4	
34		Backcrosses	(A x B) x A, (B x I) x I	67.9	80.0	74.4	
35		*3*-way crosses, F_1	(A x B) x I	84.9	100.0	100.0	
36		*4*-way crosses, F_1	(A x B) x (D x I)	81.9	96.5	100.0	
37		"Imperfect iterative"	(A x B) x (A x C), (C x D) x (I x D)	75.2	88.6	87.2	
	Pounds per Plot						
38	6 inbred lines, 6 F_1s, 6 backcrosses, 4 or more replications, 1 year	Inbred lines	(A x A), (B x B), --(I x I)--	3.6	18.3		5
39		Single crosses, F_1	(A x B), (B x I)	19.7	100.0		
40		Backcrosses	(A x B) x A, (B x I) x I	11.7	59.4	59.1	
	Relative						
41	3 "highly selected" inbred lines, all 3 F_1s and their F_2s, all 6 backcrosses, and all 3 *3*-way; 3 years	Inbred lines	(A x A), (B x B), --(I x I)--		36.2		3
42		Single crosses, F_1	(A x B), (B x I)		100.0		
43		Single crosses, F_2	(A x B) x (A x B)		65.8	68.1	
44		Backcrosses	(A x B) x A, (B x I) x I		71.7	68.1	
45		*3*-way crosses, F_1	(A x B) x I		102.3	100.0	
46	677 inbred lines selected from 27,641 lines by corn breeders from 22 states; average yield of inbreds in % of hybrids estimated by 22 breeders	Inbred lines	(A x A), (B x B), --(I x I)--		30.0		3
47		Single crosses, F_1	(A x B), (B x I)		100.0		

/1/ From inbred parents and F_1, on the assumption that loss of hybrid vigor from F_1 to F_2 and F_1 to backcross is proportional to increment of inbreeding (no epistasy).

Contributors: (a) Hull, Fred H., (b) Sprague, G. F., (c) Kinman, Murray L., (d) Stringfield, G. H.

References: [1] Jones, D. F., and P. G. Mangelsdorf. 1925. Connecticut Agr. Expt. Sta. Bull. 266. [2] Kinman, M. L., and G. F. Sprague. 1945. J. Am. Soc. Agron. 37:341. [3] Lindstrom, E. W. 1941. Proc. 7th Intern. Congr. Genet., Edinburgh, 1939, p. 191. [4] Neal, N. P. 1935. J. Am. Soc. Agron. 27:666. [5] Richey, F. D., and G. F. Sprague. 1931. U. S. Dept. Agr. Tech. Bull. 267. [6] Shull, G. H. 1952. Heterosis. Iowa State College Press, Ames. ch. 2. [7] Stringfield, G. H. 1950. Agron. J. 42:145. [8] Stringfield, G. H. Unpublished. U. S. Dept. Agr., Wooster, Ohio. 1939.

III. CELLS AND TISSUES

20. MITOTIC INDEXES: MAMMALS AND AMPHIBIANS

Values in parentheses are ranges, estimate "b" (cf. Introduction).

	Species	Tissue	Time of Day	Mitoses per 1000 cells	Remarks	Reference
	(A)	(B)	(C)	(D)	(E)	(F)
1	*Homo sapiens*	Bone marrow	10 a.m.-1 p.m.	9.0(7-11)	Young men; tissue obtained by sternal puncture	8
2		Erythroblasts		12-20	Tissue obtained by sternal puncture	7
3		Myeloblasts		21.8	Tissue obtained by sternal puncture	21
4		Myelocytes		4.6	Tissue obtained by sternal puncture	21
5		Duodenum		29.2(21.2-37.0)	Adult males and females	2
		Epidermis				
6		Shoulder	4 a.m.	2.05(1.55-2.55)	Young adults	18
7			8 a.m.	1.1(0.7-1.6)	Young adults	
8			Noon	0.9(0.6-1.2)	Young adults	
9			4 p.m.	2.9(2.65-3.10)	Young adults	
10			8 p.m.	1.1(1.0-1.3)	Young adults	
11			12 p.m.	6.05(5.4-6.7)	Young adults	
12		Abdomen	a.m.	0.24	Newborn-20 years old	24
13				0.37	21-40 years old	
14				0.50	41-60 years old	
15				0.49	61-80 years old	
16	*Felis catus*	Lymph nodes	2:30 a.m.	16	Kittens, 3 days old	9
17			10:30 a.m.	5	Kittens, 3 days old	
18			2:30 p.m.	6	Kittens, 3 days old	
19			10:30 p.m.	28	Kittens, 3 days old	
20		Spleen	2:30 a.m.	4	Kittens, 3 days old	9
21			10:30 a.m.	1	Kittens, 3 days old	
22			2:30 p.m.	10	Kittens, 3 days old	
23			10:30 p.m.	4	Kittens, 3 days old	
24		Thymus	2:30 a.m.	26	Kittens, 3 days old	9
25			10:30 a.m.	7	Kittens, 3 days old	
26			2:30 p.m.	22	Kittens, 3 days old	
27			10:30 p.m.	17	Kittens, 3 days old	
28	*Mus musculus*	Bone marrow	4 a.m.	22.6		16
29			8 a.m.	12.4		
30			Noon	11.5		
31			4 p.m.	14.0		
32			8 p.m.	11.9		
33			12 p.m.	12.8		
34		Erythrocytic series		5.0(3.6-6.4)	CF_1 mice, 8- to 16-week-old females	12
35		Myelocytic series		3.8(3.0-4.6)	CF_1 mice, 8- to 16-week-old females	12
36		Adrenal		2.2(1.6-2.8)	CF_1 mice, 8- to 16-week-old females	12
37		Lymph nodes		6.7(5.1-8.5)	CF_1 mice, 8- to 16-week-old females	12
38		Intestine		9.3(8.5-10.1)	CF_1 mice, 8- to 16-week-old females	12
39		Epidermis, abdominal	4 a.m.	9.5	Young mice	5
40			8 a.m.	7.0	Young mice	
41			Noon	6.0	Young mice	
42			4 p.m.	7.5	Young mice	
43			8 p.m.	15	Young mice	
44			12 p.m.	14	Young mice	
45		Sebaceous glands, germinal layer	5 p.m.	8.3	C57 black mice	13
	Rattus rattus	Bone marrow				
46		Erythrocytic series		6.5(5.7-7.3)	Sprague-Dawley strain	25
47		Myelocytic series		13.2(11.8-12.6)	Sprague-Dawley strain	25
48		Lymph nodes		2.0(1.0-3.0)		11
49		Spleen (lymphoid areas)		40		11
50		Thymus		13		11
51		Cortex		15	Reticular cells	17
52				65	Large lymphocytes	
53				131	Medium lymphocytes	
54				15	Small lymphocytes	

continued

20. MITOTIC INDEXES: MAMMALS AND AMPHIBIANS

	Species	Tissue	Time of Day	Mitoses per 1000 cells	Remarks	Reference
	(A)	(B)	(C)	(D)	(E)	(F)
55	*Rattus rattus*	Liver	4 a.m.	2.1(1.1-3.0)	Rats, 24 days old	10
56			8 a.m.	13.1(6.9-19.3)	Rats, 24 days old	
57			12 a.m.	10.3(7.4-13.2)	Rats, 24 days old	
58			4 p.m.	4.95(3.5-6.4)	Rats, 24 days old	
59			8 p.m.	2.7(1.5-3.8)	Rats, 24 days old	
60			12 p.m.	2.3(1.8-2.9)	Rats, 24 days old	
61		Submaxillary gland		0.2-1.2	Diurnal variation	3
62		Fore stomach		6.7(4.1-9.3)		23
		Pyloric mucosa				
63		Surface epithelium		86	Counted 4 hours	14
64		Glandular epithelium		94	After colchicine administration	14
		Intestine				
65		Crypts and villi	11 a.m.?	33	Pooled results	15
66		Crypts of jejunum		13.7(11.6-15.8)	Sprague-Dawley strain	25
67		Ileum	10 a.m.	88	Sherman rats weighing 260 grams	22
68			11 p.m.	92	Sherman rats weighing 260 grams	
69		Epidermis	4 a.m.	8.1(7.85-8.45)		19
70			8 a.m.	5.75(4.5-7.0)		
71			12 a.m.	6.7(5.30-7.45)		
72			4 p.m.	4.9(3.4-6.5)		
73			8 p.m.	11.8(9.6-13.0)		
74			12 p.m.	14.0(11.70-16.35)		
75		Sebaceous glands		123.9	Rats weighing 175 grams	1
76				133.0	Rats weighing 176 grams	
77				130.3	Rats weighing 256 grams	
78		Cornea		6.2		20
79	*Rana temporaria*	Intestine		6	Tadpoles at metamorphosis	6
80		Skin		13	Tadpoles, 3 days old; no diurnal variation	4
81				10	Adult frogs	

Contributors: (a) Firket, Henri, (b) Leblond, C. P., and MacConnachie, H. F.

References: [1] Bertalanffy, F. 1957. Anat. Record 129:231. [2] Bertalanffy, F., and K. Nagy. 1958. Ibid. 130:271. [3] Blumenfeld, C. M. 1942. Arch. Pathol. 33:770. [4] Cameron, J. A. 1936. J. Morphol. 59:327. [5] Carleton, A. 1934. J. Anat. 68:251. [6] Champy, C. 1922. Arch. morphol. (Paris) 4:1. [7] Fieschi, A. 1938. In A. Ferrata, ed. Bibliotheca haematologica. Pavia Tipografia Cooperativa, Italy. v. 6. [8] Fledner, T. M., et al. 1959. Acta Haematol. 22:65. [9] Fortuyn van Leyden, C. E. D. 1924. Verslag Akad. Wetenschap. (Amsterdam) 33:133. [10] Jackson, B. 1959. Anat. Record 134:365. [11] Kindred, J. E. 1942. Am. J. Anat. 71:207. [12] Knowlton, N. P., and W. R. Widner. 1950. Cancer Research 10:59. [13] Lapiere, C. 1953. Compt. rend. soc. biol. 147:1302. [14] Leblond, C. P. 1953. Anat. Record 115:341. [15] Leblond, C. P., and C. E. Stevens. 1948. Ibid. 100:357. [16] Miletti, A. 1950. Arch. ital. anat. embriol. 54:339. [17] Sainte-Marie, G., and C. P. Leblond. 1958. Proc. Soc. Exptl. Biol. Med. 98:909. [18] Scheving, L. E. 1959. Anat. Record 135:7. [19] Scheving, L. E., and J. E. Pauly. 1960. Acta Anat. 43:337. [20] Schultze, B., G. Apponi, and A. Nover. 1961. Albrecht von Graefe's Arch. Ophthalmol. 163:130. [21] Segerdahl, E. 1935. Acta Med. Scand., Suppl. 64. [22] Stevens Hooper, C. E. 1961. Am. J. Anat. 108:231. [23] Teir, H., and I. Carpen. 1959. Acta Pathol. Microbiol. Scand. 47:291. [24] Thuringer, J. M., and A. A. Katzberg. 1959. J. Invest. Dermatol. 33:35. [25] Widner, W. R., J. B. Storer, and C. C. Lushbaugh. 1951. Cancer Research 11:877.

21. DURATION OF MITOSIS: VERTEBRATES

Part I: DIRECT MEASUREMENTS: MAMMALS, BIRDS, AND AMPHIBIANS

Duration of Mitosis (columns D-I): Prophase--from appearance of chromosomes to fading of nuclear membrane and nucleoli; Prometaphase--so long as chromosomes are dispersed in cytoplasm; Metaphase--when chromosomes are arranged in equatorial plate; Anaphase--separation of chromosomes; Telophase--from beginning of cytoplasmic cleavage to complete separation; Reconstruction phase--until nuclei have returned to interkinetic aspect.

	Class and Species	Tissue	Temp. °C	Duration of Mitosis, min							Reference
				Prophase	Prometaphase	Metaphase	Anaphase	Telophase	Reconstruction phase	Total[1]	
	(A)	(B)	(C)	(D)	(E)	(F)	(G)	(H)	(I)	(J)	(K)
	Mammalia										
1	*Homo sapiens*	Heart fibroblasts in culture	37				3.3	3.5			8
2	*Mus musculus*	Spleen mesenchyme in culture	38	15	6	13	5	4	16[2]	59	2
3	*Rattus rattus*	Connective tissue in culture	38							25-45	6
4	*Oryctolagus cuniculus*	Connective tissue in culture		19		12	3.9	9.75	21.2	35-65	11
	Aves										
5	*Gallus* sp.	Mesenchyme in culture	39	30-60		2-10	3-7	2-10	30-120	40-90	7
6		Choroid fibroblasts in culture	39	2-10	8	5-10	28		60-120	35-65	10
7		Fibroblasts in culture		19-25		4-7	3.5-6.0	7.5-14.0		34-52	3
8		Fibroblasts and myoblasts in culture	37.5	±10	25-35		3.8	20-35	25-30	55-100	1
	Amphibia										
9	*Salamandra maculosa*	Kidney in embryos	20	59	55		6	29	46	195	9
10	*Triton* sp.	Erythrocytes in regenerating blood	±20	25	39	3.7	14	10	50	90	5
11		Liver fibroblasts in culture	26	>18		17-38	14-26		28[3]	±120	4
12	*Rana* sp.	Fibroblasts in culture	20-24	>32		20-29	6-11		16[4]	90	4

/1/ Not including reconstruction phase. /2/ Incomplete reconstruction phase. /3/ Ending at appearance of nucleoli. /4/ Ending at completion of cytoplasmic cleavage.

Contributor: Firket, Henri

References: [1] Chèvremont, M. 1956. Notions de cytologie et histologie. Desoer, Liège. [2] Fell, H. B., and A. F. W. Hughes. 1949. Quart. J. Microscop. Sci. 90:355. [3] Hughes, A. F. W., and H. B. Fell. 1952. In A. F. W. Hughes, ed. The mitotic cycle. Butterworth, London. [4] Hughes, A. F. W., and M. M. E. Preston. 1949. J. Roy. Microscop. Soc. 69:121. [5] Jolly, J. 1904. Arch. anat. microscop. (Paris) 6:455. [6] Lambert, R. A., and F. M. Hanes. 1913. Virchow's Arch. pathol. Anat. u. Physiol. 211:89. [7] Lewis, W. H., and M. R. Lewis. 1917. Anat. Record 13:359. [8] Olivo, O. M. 1929. Compt. rend. assoc. anat. 29:441. [9] Peter, K. Z. 1924. Z. Morphol. u. Anthropol. 24:23. [10] Strangeways, T. S. P. 1922. Proc. Roy. Soc. (London), B, 94:137. [11] Van Mollendorf, N. 1938. Arch. exptl. Zellforsch. Gewebezücht. 21:1.

Part II: INDIRECT MEASUREMENTS: MAMMALS

Indirect measurement of mitotic duration is less exact than direct measurement; however, it is only by the indirect method that in vivo estimates can be made. Such estimates are derived from mitotic index counts and from calculations based on fairly reliable assumptions.

	Species	Tissue	Method	Duration of Mitosis, min	Reference
	(A)	(B)	(C)	(D)	(E)
1	*Homo sapiens*	Myeloblasts	Calculated[1]	37	7
2	*Mus musculus*	Ear epidermis, ♂	Colchicine	120-180	2
3	*Mus musculus*	Ear epidermis, ♀ (diestrus)	Colchicine	120-180	2
4		Ear epidermis, ♀ (estrus)	Colchicine	45	2

/1/ From rate of renewal of glandular leukocytes and mitotic index.

continued

21. DURATION OF MITOSIS: VERTEBRATES

Part II: INDIRECT MEASUREMENTS: MAMMALS

	Species	Tissue	Method	Duration of Mitosis, min	Reference
	(A)	(B)	(C)	(D)	(E)
5	*Mus musculus*	Adrenal gland	X ray	14.4	5
6		Lymph nodes	X ray	23.2	5
7		Ovary	X ray	21.1	5
8		Epidermis	X ray	30.2	5
9		Jejunum	X ray	23.9	5
10		Erythroblasts	X ray	29.5	5
11		Myeloblasts	X ray	35.3	5
12	*Rattus rattus*	Cornea	Ether and colchicine	70	3
13		Regenerating liver tissue	Calculated[2]	49	1
14	*Rattus rattus*	Intestinal epithelium	Colchicine	68	6
15		Jejunum	X ray	27.5	8
16		Erythroblasts	X ray	24.6	8
17		Myeloblasts	X ray	25.7	8
18	*Oryctolagus cuniculus*	Oral epithelium	Colchicine	64	4

/2/ From mitotic index and average doubling time of cells.

Contributor: Firket, Henri

References: [1] Brues, A. M., and B. B. Marble. 1937. J. Exptl. Med. 65:15. [2] Bullough, W. S. 1950. J. Endocrinol. 6:351. [3] Buschke, W., J. S. Friedenwald, and W. Fleischmann. 1943. Bull. Johns Hopkins Hosp. 73:143. [4] Henry, J. L., et al. 1952. Arch. Pathol. 54:281. [5] Knowlton, N. P., and W. R. Widner. 1950. Cancer Research 10:59. [6] Leblond, C. P., and C. E. Stevens. 1948. Anat. Record 100:357. [7] Moeschlin, S. 1946. Schweiz. med. Wochschr. 76:1051. [8] Widner, W. R., J. B. Storer, and C. C. Lushbaugh. 1951. Cancer Research 11:877.

22. DURATION OF MITOSIS: PLANTS

	Species	Tissue	Temp. °C	Duration of Mitosis, min					Reference
				Prophase	Metaphase	Anaphase	Telophase	Total	
	(A)	(B)	(C)	(D)	(E)	(F)	(G)	(H)	(I)
	Direct Measurements								
1	*Sphacelaria fusca*	Brown alga	17	10	7	4	9	30	7
2	*Arrhenatherum* sp.	Grass	19	36-45	7-10	15-20	20-35	78-110	6
3	*Tradescantia* sp.	Staminal hairs	20	181	14	15	130	340	1,2
	Indirect Measurements								
4	*Allium cepa*	Root tip	20	71	6.5	2.4	3.8	83	5
5	*Pisum* sp.	Root tip	20	78	14.4	4.2	13.2	110	3
6	*Vicia faba*	Root tip	19	90	31	34	34	155	4

Contributor: Hughes, Arthur

References: [1] Barber, H. N. 1939. Chromosoma 1:33. [2] Bělăr, K. 1929. Z. Zellforsch. u. mikroskop. Anat. 10:73. [3] Brown, R. 1951. J. Exptl. Botany 2:96. [4] Gray, L. H., and M. E. Scholes. 1951. Brit. J. Radiol. 24:82. [5] Laughlin, H. H. 1919. Carnegie Inst. Wash. Publ. 265:488. [6] Martens, P. 1927. Cellule 38:67. [7] Zimmermann, W. 1923. Z. Botan. 15:113.

23. CELL DIAMETERS: VERTEBRATES

Values in parentheses are ranges, estimate "c" (cf. Introduction).

	Species	Cell Site	Cell Structure	Cell Diameter µ	Reference
	(A)	(B)	(C)	(D)	(E)
	Homo sapiens	Lateral geniculate body[1]			2
1		Layer 1	Whole cell	23	
2		Layer 2	Whole cell	24	
3		Layer 3	Whole cell	19	
4		Layer 4	Whole cell	17	
5		Layer 5	Whole cell	16	
6		Layer 6	Whole cell	14	
7		Epithelium, uterus	Flat ovoid cell[2]	30 x 5	6
8		Epidermis	Flat polygon cell	35 x 3	6
	Macaca mulatta	Lateral geniculate body[1]			2
9		Layer 1	Whole cell	23.5	
10		Layer 2	Whole cell	24.5	
11		Layer 3	Whole cell	17.6	
12		Layer 4	Whole cell	15.3	
13		Layer 5	Whole cell	14.9	
14		Layer 6	Whole cell	14.5	
15	*Bos* sp[3]	Thymus	Nucleus	(7.5-9.4)	7
16	*Phocaena phocaena*	Cerebellum	Large, ovoid cerebellar cell	48.6 x 23.8	1
17			Ovoid Purkinje cell	30.4 x 24.6	
18	*Balaenoptera sulfurea*	Cerebellum	Large, ovoid cerebellar cell	42.6 x 11.6	1
19			Ovoid Purkinje cell	32.0 x 19.5	
20	*Mus* sp.	Liver	Nucleus	10.8	7
21		Testes	Spermatogonium	5.6 (5.4-5.9)	5
22			Spermatid	5.5 (5.2-5.8)	
		Tissue culture			9
23		Fibroblast[4]	Whole cell	4.4	
24			Cytoplasm	2.0	
25			Nucleus	1.4	
26		Sarcoma	Whole cell	6.4	
27			Cytoplasm	2.7	
28			Nucleus	1.6	
29	*Rattus* sp.	Liver	Nucleus	(5-11)	8,10
	Rana sp.	Sciatic nerve	Axoneuron		4
30			Outer diameter	(10-15)	
31			Inner diameter	(5-9)	
32		Liver	Whole cell	26.3	3
33			Nucleus	14.6	

/1/ Central vision area of cerebral cortex. /2/ From cervical region. /3/ Calf. /4/ Embryonic.

Contributor: Kurnick, N. B.

References: [1] Addison, W. H. F. 1934. Psychiat. neurol. bladen (Amsterdam) 38:587. [2] Chacko, L. W. 1949. J. Anat. 83:254. [3] Chalkley, D. T. 1953. Science 118:599. [4] Engstrom, A., and H. Luthy. 1950. Exptl. Cell Research 1:81. [5] Eschenbrennen, A. B., E. Miller, and E. Lorenz. 1949. J. Natl. Cancer Inst. 9:133. [6] Hoffman, J. G. 1953. The size and growth of tissue cells. C. C. Thomas, Springfield, Ill. [7] Kurnick, N. B. 1950. Exptl. Cell Research 1:151. [8] Kurnick, N. B. Unpublished. Univ. California at Los Angeles Medical Center, 1955. [9] Mellors, R. C., A. Kupfer, and A. Hollender. 1953. Cancer 6:372. [10] Rather, L. J. 1951. Bull. Johns Hopkins Hosp. 88:40.

24. CELL VOLUMES: ANIMALS

Part I: VERTEBRATES

Values in parentheses are ranges, estimate "b" unless otherwise indicated (cf. Introduction).

	Species	Cell Site	Cell Volume μ^3	Remarks	Reference
	(A)	(B)	(C)	(D)	(E)
1	*Homo sapiens*	Amnion	860	17-mm-long embryo; whole cell	8
2			1930	Extraplacental at 3 months; whole cell	
3			2080	Placental at 3 months; whole cell	
4			4320	Placental at term; whole cell	
5		Epithelium, oral	6000	Embryo; early spinous layer of inner cheek; whole cell	7

continued

24. CELL VOLUMES: ANIMALS

Part I: VERTEBRATES

	Species	Cell Site	Cell Volume μ^3	Remarks	Reference
	(A)	(B)	(C)	(D)	(E)
6	*Homo sapiens*	Epithelium, oral	18,000	Embryo; early cornified layer of inner cheek; whole cell	7
		Cerebral cortex, nerve cell			
7		Betz	2328(2204-2452)	Nucleus; calculated from formula $V = 4/3\pi ab^2$	15
8		Other than Betz	371(347-395)		
9		Area FA_{γ}	371(349-393)	Nucleus; calculated from formula $V = 4/3\pi ab^2$; cerebral area designations according to Von Economo	14
10		Area FB	290(268-312)		
11		Area FCB_m	343(329-357)		
12		Area FD_m	392(372-412)		
13		Area FF	253(229-277)		
14		Area PA	190(178-202)		
15		Ganglion	300(22-5000)[c]	Cytoplasm; calculated	1
16			150(40-575)[c]	Nucleus; calculated	
17		Fat layer, abdominal wall	480,000	Subcutaneous fat; whole cell	7
	Cebus sp.	Cerebral cortex, nerve cell			
18		Betz	1131(1067-1195)	Nucleus; calculated from formula $V = 4/3\pi ab^2$	15
19		Other than Betz	306(288-324)		
20	*Macaca mulatta*	Spinal cord, cervical region	(12,000-120,000)[c]	Anterior horn cell	4
	Felis catus	Cerebral cortex, nerve cell			
21		Betz	1515(1441-1589)	Nucleus; calculated from formula $V = 4/3\pi ab^2$	15
22		Other than Betz	441(425-457)		
23		Spinal cord, cervical region	(5,400-40,000)[c]	Anterior horn cell	3
24			(650-4300)[c]	Nucleus of anterior horn cell	
	Mus sp.	Tumor			
25		6C3HED	719(555-883)	Lymphoma; whole cell	12
26		DBA	585(411-759)		
27		EL4	393(367-419)		
28		DbrB	600(150-1700)[c]	Transplantable adenocarcinoma; whole cell	13
29			200(25-650)[c]	Transplantable adenocarcinoma; nucleus	
30		Ehrlich	2050(1864-2236)	Anaplastic carcinoma	12
31		Krebs-2	2029(1885-2173)		
		Tissue culture			
32		Fibroblast	1390	Embryo; whole cell	10
33			1242	Embryo; cytoplasm	
34			148	Embryo; nucleus	
35		Sarcoma	1980	Whole cell	10
36			1783	Cytoplasm	
37			197	Nucleus	
38	*Rattus* sp.	Liver	2000	Whole cell	6,11
39			235(125-500)[c]	Nucleus	
40		Parenchyma	1900	Male; diploid cell	5
41			1500	Female; diploid cell	
42		Tissue culture sarcoma	(600-5600)[c]	Anaplastic sarcoma; whole cell	9
43	*Rana* sp.	Liver	8730	Whole cell	2
44			7200	Cytoplasm	
45			1500	Nucleus	
46	*Triturus viridescens*	Blastema	8500	In regenerating foreleg after 31 days; whole cell	3
47		Epidermis	3200	On regenerating foreleg after 31 days; whole cell	

Contributors: (a) Kurnick, N. B., (b) Hoffman, Joseph Gilbert

References: [1] Bok, S. T. 1934. Psychiat. neurol. bladen (Amsterdam) 38:318. [2] Chalkley, D. T. 1953. Science 118:599. [3] Chalkley, D. T. 1954. J. Morphol. 94:21. [4] Conklin, E. G. 1912. J. Exptl. Zool. 12:4. [5] Harrison, M. F. 1953. Proc. Roy. Soc. (London), B, 141:203. [6] Kurnick, N. B. Unpublished. Univ. California at Los Angeles Medical Center, 1955. [7] Lewis, F. T. 1925. Proc. Am. Acad. Arts. Sci. 61:1. [8] Lewis, F. T. 1931. Anat. Record 50:235. [9] Lewis, W. H. 1948. Ibid. 100:247. [10] Mellors, R. C.,

continued

24. CELL VOLUMES: ANIMALS

Part I: VERTEBRATES

A. Kupfer, and A. Hollender. 1953. Cancer 6:372. [11] Rather, L. J. 1951. Bull. Johns Hopkins Hosp. 88:40. [12] Révész, L., and G. Klein. 1954. J. Natl. Cancer Inst. 15:253. [13] Trombetta, V. V. 1939. Am. J. Botany 26:519. [14] Von Bonin, G. 1937. J. Comp. Neurol. 66:103. [15] Von Bonin, G. 1938. Ibid. 69:381.

Part II: INVERTEBRATES

Values are for whole cells, unless otherwise specified. Values in parentheses are ranges, estimate "c" (cf. Introduction).

	Species	Cell	Cell Volume μ^3	Reference
	(A)	(B)	(C)	(D)
1	*Amphioxus lanceolatus*	Egg	658,000	1
2	*Cynthia partita*	Egg	595,000	1
3	*Crepidula adunca*	Egg	3.5×10^7	1
4	*C. convexa*	Egg	1.13×10^7	1
5	*C. fornicata*	Egg	3.12×10^6	1
6	*C. plana*	Egg	1.44×10^6	1
		Epithelium		1
7		Ectoderm[1]	375	
8		Foot	539	
9		Gastric	3338	
	Crepidula plana	Epithelium		1
10		Gill chamber	438	
11		Gill filament	408	
12		Intestine	1452	
13		Liver duct	1742	
14	*Cumingia tellinoides*	Egg	47,700	1
15	*Fulgur carica*	Egg	2.13×10^9	1
16	*Drosophila* sp.	Salivary gland	(602-12,740)[2]	2
17			(134-439)[3]	
18		Anlage	(17-30)[2]	2

/1/ Near anus. /2/ Nucleus. /3/ Nucleolus.

Contributors: (a) Hoffman, Joseph Gilbert, (b) Kurnick, N. B.

References: [1] Conklin, E. G. 1912. J. Exptl. Zool. 12:4. [2] Kurnick, N. B., and I. H. Herskowitz. 1952. J. Cellular Comp. Physiol. 39:281.

25. CELL VOLUMES: PLANTS

Values are for whole cells. Values in parentheses are ranges, estimate "c" unless otherwise indicated (cf. Introduction).

	Species	Tissue	Cell Volume μ^3	Remarks	Reference
	(A)	(B)	(C)	(D)	(E)
1	*Bacillus megaterium*	Entire organism	29.38(27.94-30.82)[b]	Early phase of declining growth rate	10
2			35.04(33.72-36.36)[b]	Late phase of declining growth rate	
3	*Fucus platycarpus*	Hypha	(7,000-95,000)		2
4		Paraphysis	(20,000-82,000)		2
5		Oogonium	(1,000-42,000)	Mononucleate stage	2
6			(16,000-72,000)	4-nuclei stage	
7			(7,700-42,000)	8-nuclei stage	
8	*Acer* sp.	Epithelium	7300	Leaf stem	6
9	*Allium cepa*	Root tip	(1,200-10,000)	Meristem cell	9
10			(40,000 to 1.1×10^6)	Mature cell	
11	*Avena* sp.	Coleoptile	19,900	Cell in 3rd segment of 1.5-mm coleoptile	1
12			34,970	Cell in 3rd segment of 14-mm coleoptile	
13	*Bryophyllum calycinum*	Stem tip	(220-9000)	Meristem cell	9
14			(9,000-950,000)	Mature cell	
15	*Cucumis* sp.	Epidermis	520	Prism cell, 60-mm cucumber	5
16			1055	Prism cell, 100-mm cucumber	
17			7280	Prism cell, 200-mm cucumber	

continued

25. CELL VOLUMES: PLANTS

	Species	Tissue	Cell Volume μ^3	Remarks	Reference
	(A)	(B)	(C)	(D)	(E)
18	*Cucumis sativus*	Root tip	(300-400)	Meristem cell	9
19	*Cucurbita pepo*	Root tip	(420-10,000)	Meristem cell	9
20			(10,000-174,800)	Mature cell	
21		Stem tip	(450-10,000)	Meristem cell	9
22			(10,000-20,000)	Mature cell	
23	*Elodea canadensis*	Leaf	(2,000-180,000)	Cell from growing leaf	9
24			(35,000-250,000)	Cell from mature leaf	
25	*Eupatorium dubium*	Pith	1,256,000	Parenchymal cell	7
26	*E. perfoliatum*	Pith	562,570	Small cell from 9th and 10th internode below flower axis	8
27			1,603,000	Large cell from 9th and 10th internode below flower axis	
28	*Helianthus annus*	Root tip	(1200-5000)	Meristem cell	9
29	*Juncus effusus*	Pith	33,000	Stellate cell	4
30	*Lilium regale*	Root tip	(5,500-12,000)	Meristem cell	9
31	*Lycopersicon* sp.	Stem hair	(7,000-100,000)	At 7th day	9
32			(30,000 to 10^6)	At 28th day	
33			(6,500-30,000)	Mature plant	
34	*L. racemerigum*	Apical meristem	1394(1234-1554)[b]	At first appearance	11
35			678(580-776)[b]	At 6th day	
36			302(284-320)[b]	At 70th day	
37	*Pisum sativum*	Stem tip	(800-9000)	Meristem cell	9
38			(9,000-30,000)	Maturing cell	
39	*Sambucus canadensis*	Pith	(80,000-1,000,000)		4
40	*Tradescantia* sp.	Epithelium	(2,850-25,500)	Lateral accessory guard cell	6
41			240,000	Stem, mature internode	
42	*Vicia faba*	Root cap	30,810	Marginal cell	3
43			42,250	Central cell	
44			20,200	General meristem cell	
45			23,700	Provascular cell	
46			37,600	Protophloem I	
47			31,220	Protophloem II	
48			54,100	Protoxylem	

Contributor: Hoffman, Joseph Gilbert

References: [1] Avery, G. S., Jr., and F. Engel. 1954. Am. J. Botany 41:310. [2] Höppner, H. 1939. Z. Botan. 34:497. [3] Jensen, W. A. 1955. Exptl. Cell Research 8:506. [4] Lewis, F. T. 1925. Proc. Am. Acad. Arts Sci. 61:1. [5] Lewis, F. T. 1928. Anat. Record 38:341. [6] Lewis, F. T. 1930. Ibid. 47:59. [7] Lewis, F. T. 1944. Am. J. Botany 31:619. [8] Marvin, J. W. 1944. Ibid. 31:208. [9] Trombetta, V. V. 1939. Ibid. 26:519. [10] Weibull, C. 1955. Exptl. Cell Research 9:139. [11] Whaley, W. G. 1944. Am. J. Botany 31:682.

26. CELL TYPES: SEED PLANTS

Because only approximate boundaries can be drawn between certain cell types in seed plants, the data have been restricted to the more salient and histologically-apparent characteristics of the more common cell types. Spores, gametes, and many of the specialized cells have been omitted.

	Cell Type	Specification	Description
	(A)	(B)	(C)
1	Apical meristem	Origin	Lineal descendents of cells of embryo, except in adventitious shoots and roots
2		Site	Apices of vegetative shoots, developing inflorescences and flowers; in root, beneath inner edge of root cap
3		Morphology	Cells polyhedral; primary wall thin or irregularly thickened; primary pit fields may be present; nucleus large, ovoid; cytoplasm vacuolated; mitochondria, plastid primordia, and storage products may be present
4		Function	Point of origin of primary meristematic tissues (protoderm, ground meristem, procambium) from which primary body of shoot and root develops; in shoot apex, gives rise to tissue of leaf primordia

continued

26. CELL TYPES: SEED PLANTS

	Cell Type	Specification	Description
	(A)	(B)	(C)
5	Vascular cambium	Origin	Procambium, and parenchyma in interfascicular areas, cortex, and phloem
6		Site	Lateral in stem and root, between secondary xylem and secondary phloem
7		Morphology	Two types of cambial cells: elongated fusiform initials (from which tracheary elements, sieve elements, fibers, and vertical parenchyma are derived), and ray initials (from which vascular rays originate); cytoplasm in both cell types highly vacuolated; primary walls have conspicuous pit fields
8		Function	Produces secondary phloem and secondary xylem cells; growth in diameter of woody stems and roots results from tissue formation by cambial cells
9	Phellogen (cork cambium)	Origin	In stems, first phellogen cells arise from cortex (most commonly from outermost layer), or from epidermis or phloem parenchyma cells; in roots, from pericycle
10		Site	Lateral in stem and root, between phellem and subjacent phelloderm, cortical or phloem tissue; also beneath surface exposed by abscission of organs (leaf scars) or beneath wounds
11		Morphology	Cells rectangular and radially flattened in transectional view, polygonal or nearly isodiametric in longisection; walls thin, cytoplasm vacuolated; may contain tannins and chloroplasts
12		Function	Produces phellem cells outwardly and in many cases phelloderm cells inwardly; forms complementary tissue of lenticels
13	Epidermis	Origin	Protoderm
14		Site	Surface layer of foliar and floral organs, young stems and roots
15		Morphology	Cells polygonal, elongated, or with undulated contour in surface view; variable in radial dimensions; walls thin or thick, the outer wall often thicker; primary pit fields present; walls typically cutinized (may be lignified or silicified), the outer wall covered by cuticle, except in roots; plastids, anthocyanin pigments, and ergastic substances may occur
16		Function	Mechanical protection; restriction of transpiration; storage of water and metabolic products; photosynthesis; water absorption in roots; by division and dedifferentiation may contribute to origin of adventitious shoots and roots
17	Guard cell	Origin	Typically originate in pairs by division of specific "mother cells" of the protoderm; (in many plants paired guard cells are flanked or surrounded by distinctive subsidiary cells)
18		Site	Epidermis of foliage leaves and young stems; occurs in the epidermis of various types of floral organs; absent from epidermis of roots
19		Morphology	Cells usually crescentic or kidney-shaped in surface view; walls unevenly thickened, cutinized and overlaid by cuticle; often with ridgelike extensions above and below pore; conspicuous starch-forming chloroplasts present; protoplast physiologically active in mature cells but rarely divides in response to wound or other stimuli
20		Function	A pair of guard cells and the intercellular space or pore between them form a stoma. Reversible changes in turgor of guard cells result in the opening or closure of the pore, permitting diffusion of gases through the epidermis.
21	Phellem (cork)	Origin	Phellogen; in stems of some monocotyledons, tangentially dividing cortical parenchyma cells produce irregular bands of suberized cells termed storied cork
22		Site	Peripheral regions of stem, root, and some fruits; occurs in bud scales and petioles; often produced as a result of wounding
23		Morphology	Cells rectangular in transection and radially flattened; irregular or rectangular in longisection; wall typically suberized and devoid of pits; nonliving at maturity; may contain resin and tannins
24		Function	Mechanical protection; restriction of transpiration
25	Parenchyma	Origin	Ground meristem, procambium, vascular cambium, and phellogen
26		Site	Dominant cell type in cortex, pith, mesophyll, fleshy fruits, and endosperm of seeds; occurs in phloem and xylem as component of vertical strands and vascular rays
27		Morphology	Cells approximately tetrakaidecahedral to elongated, or stellately branched; primary walls thin or thick, often with conspicuous pit fields; thick, lignified secondary walls with pits common in secondary xylem; plastids and a large number of ergastic substances present
28		Function	Photosynthesis; food and water storage; secretion and excretion; commonly the protoplast retains marked capacity for growth, division and differentiation, and therefore is prominently concerned in wound healing, formation of callus tissue, and the origin of adventitious shoots and roots
29	Collenchyma	Origin	Ground meristem
30		Site	Sole component of cylinders or strands of tissue in the subepidermal portions of stems, petioles, and larger veins of leaves; may occur in root cortex
31		Morphology	Cells relatively short and prismatic, or elongated with tapering ends; primary walls unevenly thickened and composed of cellulose, pectin, and a high percentage of water; primary pit fields present; chloroplasts common; collenchyma and cortical parenchyma cells frequently intergrade in form and structure
32		Function	Mechanical support for growing stems and leaves; protoplast retains capacity for growth, division, and differentiation

continued

26. CELL TYPES: SEED PLANTS

	Cell Type	Specification	Description
	(A)	(B)	(C)
33	Sclereid	Origin	Protoderm, ground meristem, phellogen, vascular cambium, and procambium; frequently arise by sclerosis of a fully developed parenchyma cell
34		Site	Common in seed coats and fruits; diffusely arranged (as idioblasts or as a component of cell clusters) in cortex, functioning phloem, outer bark, pith, and mesophyll; in leaves of some dicotyledons, sclereids are restricted to vein endings (terminal sclereids)
35		Morphology	Cells may be polyhedral, columnar, fusiform, filiform, irregularly lobed or branched; in some cases they intergrade in form with fibers; secondary wall thick and lignified (sometimes with imbedded crystals); pits usually simple, often ramiform; protoplast may be retained at maturity
36		Function	Produces hard, incompressible texture of many tissues
37	Fiber	Origin	Protoderm, ground meristem, procambium, and vascular cambium
38		Site	Cortex, primary and secondary vascular tissues of stem and root; epidermis of some leaves; component of hypodermal strands or layers and of the sclerenchymatous sheaths of vascular bundles in many kinds of leaves; cells may occur as idioblasts
39		Morphology	Typical prosenchymatous cell, frequently elongated; secondary wall usually thick, often highly lignified; pits abundant or scarce, simple or with greatly reduced borders; protoplast usually absent at maturity; a living protoplast and various ergastic materials occur in septate fibers; in secondary xylem of dicotyledons, fibers and tracheids frequently intergrade in form and structure
40		Function	Mechanical support
41	Tracheid	Origin	Procambium and vascular cambium
42		Site	Primary and secondary xylem; in a modified form, the distinctive cell type in transfusion tissue of gymnosperm leaves; in leaves of some angiosperms, tracheidlike cells, termed "storage tracheids," occur as idioblasts, as cells associated with veinlets, or as components of cell groups or layers; commonly formed in masses in cultures of callus tissue
43		Morphology	Cells imperforate and typically elongated with blunt, tapering, or inclined ends; patterns of lignified secondary wall thickenings diversified and often intergrading (annular, helical, scalariform, reticulate, pitted); devoid of protoplast at maturity
44		Function	Conduction of water and mineral solutes; mechanical support
45	Vessel member	Origin	Procambium and vascular cambium
46		Site	Primary and secondary xylem of most dicotyledons; absent from xylem of all gymnosperms except members of the Gnetales; in some monocotyledons, restricted to primary xylem of root
47		Morphology	Cell-form ranges from elongate to drum-shaped, with inclined or transversely oriented end walls; a series of superposed vessel members constitutes a vessel; perforation plates usually restricted to end walls and are either simple (one perforation) or multiperforate (scalariform, reticulate, or foraminate); secondary walls lignified (with same range of patterns as in tracheids); devoid of protoplast at maturity
48		Function	Conduction of water and mineral solutes; possibly furnishes mechanical support
49	Sieve cell	Origin	Procambium and vascular cambium
50		Site	Primary and secondary phloem of gymnosperms
51		Morphology	Cells elongated, with overlapping inclined or tapering ends; sieve areas numerous, uniform and relatively undifferentiated; a sieve area is a portion of the primary wall, traversed by strands of cytoplasm, each strand enclosed in a cylinder of callose; protoplast enucleate at maturity; usually associated with certain ray and phloem-parenchyma cells termed albuminous cells
52		Function	Conduction of organic solutes
53	Sieve-tube member	Origin	Procambium and vascular cambium
54		Site	Primary and secondary phloem of angiosperms
55		Morphology	Cells elongated, with inclined or transverse end walls; a series of superposed sieve-tube members constitutes a sieve tube; end walls with highly specialized sieve areas termed sieve plates; sieve plates are either simple (one sieve area) or compound (several sieve areas in scalariform or reticulate arrangement); lateral walls usually bear less differentiated sieve areas; protoplast enucleate at maturity; each sieve-tube member associated with one or more nucleate cells (companion cells) which are ontogenetically developed as daughter cells of the sieve-tube member
56		Function	Conduction of organic solutes
57	Laticifer	Origin	Nonarticulated laticifers originate from single cells in the embryo and grow intrusively throughout plant; articulated laticifers arise from interconnected series of cells in which partial or complete removal of certain walls occurs
58		Site	Cortex, secondary phloem and xylem, pith, mesophyll
59		Morphology	Nonarticulated type is either an unbranched tube or a profusely ramified system of nonseptate tubes; articulated laticifers may become joined by lateral anastomoses to form a complex network; primary walls nonlignified and often thick; both types contain latex and are multinucleate

continued

26. CELL TYPES: SEED PLANTS

	Cell Type	Specification	Description
	(A)	(B)	(C)
60	Laticifer	Function	Probably largely excretory because of storage of such apparently nonfunctional metabolic products as resins and rubber; the role of laticifers as food-conducting or food-storing structures is doubtful

Contributors: (a) Foster, Adriance S., (b) Burns, George W., (c) Armer, Sister Joseph Marie

References: [1] Bailey, I. W. 1954. Contributions to plant anatomy. Chronica Botanica, Waltham, Mass. [2] Carlquist, S. 1961. Comparative plant anatomy. Holt, Rinehart, and Winston; New York. [3] Esau, K. 1953. Plant anatomy. J. Wiley and Sons, New York. [4] Foster, A. S. 1949. Practical plant anatomy. Ed. 2. Van Nostrand, Princeton. [5] Foster, A. S. 1956. Protoplasma 46:184. [6] Huber, B. 1961. Grundzüge der Pflanzenanatomie. J. Springer, Berlin. [7] Metcalfe, C. R., and L. Chalk. 1950. Anatomy of the dicotyledons. Clarendon Press, Oxford.

27. POSTNATAL TISSUE GROWTH: MAMMALS

	Tissue	Growth Feature	Growth Characteristics	Reference
	(A)	(B)	(C)	(D)
1	Adrenal	Division	Mitosis, adult rat: zona capsula and zona fasciculata, 0.13% each; zona glomerulosa, 0.17%; zona reticularis, 0.06%; total gland, 0.12%. For young rat, percentages higher than for adult.	12,78
2		Mode of growth	Principally by cell division. Capsule may contribute.	12
3		Life span	In cortex, uncertain; phagocytosis occurs in zona reticularis	12
4		Replacement	In cortex, cell division and migration of cells from superficial to deeper layers	12,78
5		Regenerative capacity	In cortex after damage, repair by cell division (limited in adult). Active regeneration follows postnatal degeneration. Mitosis scant in medulla; postnatal growth due to cell enlargement.	49,64,78, 92
6	Alimentary canal	Division	Dividing cells in crypts of duodenum and ileum. In rat, make up 3% of all cells; cycle, 1.13 hours. In stomach, dividing cells at base of foveolae.	50,68,73
7		Mode of growth	Cell division and differentiation in mucous membrane. Muscle, by combination of cell division and increase in cell size.	80
8		Life span	Oral mucosa, rabbit: 5.1(4.5-5.7)/1000 cells; diurnal variation, 3.8(3.6-4.0) and 7.2(6.6-7.8). Mitotic duration calculated as 64 minutes. Intermitotic period calculated as 208 hours.	56
9			Small intestine, rat: 60-70% of superficial epithelium shed per day; cell lives 1.57 days in duodenum, 1.35 days in ileum	68
10		Replacement	Cells multiply in crypts in base of foveolae, move toward lumen and differentiate	50,68
11		Regenerative capacity	Brunner's glands can undergo limited regeneration	43
12			Stomach, cat: movement at 0.2-0.4 mm/hr; sudden loss of epithelium made good in a few hours	50,68
13			Stomach, dog: After removal of mucous membrane, denuded area covered by growth of undifferentiated epithelium at rate of 2 mm/wk. Healing occurs in 10 days if muscularis mucosae intact, in 130 days if muscle destroyed.	42,59,82
14	Blood erythrocytes	Division	Confined largely to erythroblasts in bone marrow. Dividing cells, man: 1.17-1.83%.	81,88
15		Mode of growth	In precursors, growth phase sharply separated from hemoglobin formation	93
16		Life span	120 days most generally accepted	25
17		Replacement	In man, 0.83% red cells replaced each day	25
18		Regenerative capacity	In man, recovery in 50 days from 600-ml blood loss. In rabbit, recovery in 3 weeks from 30% blood loss. In rat, recovery in 7 days from 30% blood loss.	18,45
19	Blood granulocytes	Division	Confined largely to myeloblasts (2.7%) and myelocytes (0.46%) in bone marrow	88
20		Mode of growth	Growth stages sharply demarcated from stages of granule formation	93

continued

27. POSTNATAL TISSUE GROWTH: MAMMALS

	Tissue	Growth Feature	Growth Characteristics	Reference
	(A)	(B)	(C)	(D)
21	Blood granulocytes	Life span	Neutrophils estimated at 7-80 hours; eosinophils, 10-14 days. In cat, neutrophils disappear from blood at rate of 881/cu mm/hr.	60,66
22		Replacement	In cat, replaced 1.5 times per day	66
23	Blood lymphocytes	Division	In tissues of origin. Dividing cells, 3-month-old rat: thymus, 0.22%; lymph nodes, 0.058%; lymph follicles in spleen, 0.058%.	5
24		Mode of growth	Derived from reticulum cells and may be converted to other forms (?). In cat, 35 x 10^6 kg/hr enter circulation. In dog, 25 x 10^6 kg/hr enter circulation.	2,16,75, 101
25		Life span	Approximately 24 hours. Removed from blood by lungs, spleen, lymph glands, skin, intestine.	6,41,52, 96,101
26		Replacement	Replacement in blood stream about twice a day	2,101,102
27		Regenerative capacity	In young rabbit, limited regeneration of lymph nodes after removal; mesenchyme cells form complete gland in 3-4 weeks	46
28	Blood platelets	Mode of growth	Evidence favors formation in marrow from cytoplasmic fragmentation of megakaryocytes	100
29		Life span	In cat, 2-4 days; utilization at rate of 2500 cu mm blood/hr	67
30		Replacement	After loss, new formation begins in a few hours. Normal level regained in 3-4 days.	94
31	Brain and spinal cord	Division	Very rare but has been reported	4
32		Mode of growth	Growth of axones, myelination of fiber tracts. May not be completed until 18th year in man.	61
33		Life span	Coextensive with normal function	80
34		Replacement	Confined to neuroglia	80
35		Regenerative capacity	Very largely confined to neuroglia; some axone formation. Regeneration of motor axones occurs at 4 mm/da after latent period of ±7 days. A large number of factors affect rate. In cat, preganglionic fibers in peripheral nerves regenerate in 36-61 days; function restored in 44 days.	26,48,57, 97,103
36	Hair	Growth rate	In man, varies with site: head, 2.7 mm/wk; arm, 1.5 mm/wk; face, 2.1-3.5 mm/wk	24,26,31, 39,95
37		Life cycle	Depends on thickness. In man: head, 3 years; eyebrow, 120 days. In rat: body, 35 days.	
38		Replacement	By multiplication and differentiation of cells at bottom of hair follicles	
39	Heart	Division	Negligible in the cardiac muscle	73
40		Mode of growth	In man from birth to maturity, diameter of muscle fibers increases 2.6 times (to 14μ). In rabbit, diameter of muscle fibers increases 2.6 times (to 19μ).	89
41		Life span	Coextensive with normal function	80
42		Replacement	None	80
43		Regenerative capacity	Negligible; hypertrophy caused by increase in size of fibers. In man, normal diameter, 14μ; hypertrophied, 25μ. In rabbit, normal diameter, 19.2μ; hypertrophied, 22.2μ.	89
44	Kidney	Division	Rare after early postnatal life, except for regeneration in rodents	80
45		Mode of growth	Increase in size of cells and structures. In man from birth to maturity, diameter of glomerulus increases from 118μ to 240μ; diameter of proximal collecting tubules from 18-34μ to 40-64μ. In rat, early postnatal growth partially caused by peripheral, undifferentiated nephrogenic zone; number of nephrons doubled in first two weeks of life.	13,33,62
46		Life span	Very largely coextensive with normal function	80
47		Replacement	By cell division in tubules	80
48		Regenerative capacity	In rat, true regeneration observed. Hypertrophy caused by enlargement of existing elements, but increased cell division demonstrated after unilateral nephrectomy in rat.	26,27
49	Liver	Division	In rat, dividing cells rise from low values to 3.3% on 23rd day, then return to low	19,74
50			Mitosis, albino rat: 0.005%	19
51		Mode of growth	In early life, considerable contribution from cell division; later from increase in cell size	74
52		Life span	No figure available	74
53		Replacement	Dividing cells persist in small numbers in adult, presumably to replace cell loss	74
54		Regenerative capacity	In rat, extirpation of two-thirds regenerated in 21 days, caused by cell division in parenchymal cells and, to a smaller extent, in duct cells; division also occurs in Kupffer cells and connective tissue cells	1

continued

27. POSTNATAL TISSUE GROWTH: MAMMALS

	Tissue	Growth Feature	Growth Characteristics	Reference
	(A)	(B)	(C)	(D)
55	Muscle, smooth	Division	Fibers retain some power of division	73
56		Mode of growth	New formation possible from undifferentiated connective tissue cells	
57		Regenerative capacity	Regeneration after injury limited; fibrous scar usual	
58	Muscle, striped	Division	Scant; confined to nuclei. Some amitotic division.	73
59		Mode of growth	Enlargement, and possible splitting, of fibers. In newborn, some continued formation from mesenchyme cells. Hypertrophy caused by increase of sarcoplasm in pre-existing cells.	73
60		Life span	Coextensive with normal function	80
61		Replacement	Normally none	80
62		Regenerative capacity	Protoplasmic outgrowth from pre-existing fibers in which nuclei may divide by amitosis. Outgrowth begins 3rd day after injury, progresses at 1-1.5 mm/da. New fibers 30% of normal diameter in 21 days; normal diameter in 4 months. No new formation from indifferent cells.	30,32
63	Nails	Mode of growth	Thumbnail, man: daily increase of 95μ (fingernails grow 4 times as fast as toenails)	24,26,31, 39,95
64	Ovary	Division	Mitosis demonstrated in germinal epithelium, and during pregnancy in granulosa and theca interna cells	11,38
65		Mode of growth	In rabbit, follicles increase in size exponentially with time; completed in 18 days. Total number of oocytes in gland related to age: log (number) = 4.561-0.476 log(age in days).	36,37,51, 69
66		Life span	Fertility loss of shed ova: ferret, 30 hours; guinea pig, 26 hours; rabbit, 12 hours	54
67		Regenerative capacity	No regeneration of ova, but there is marked regenerative activity of germinal epithelium after hormonal stimulation	47
68	Pancreas	Mode of growth	In man, decrease in relative amount of connective tissue after birth; adult proportions reached at 11th-16th year	40
69		Regenerative capacity	Limited amount after resection or duct ligation. Mitosis in acinar cells and duct epithelium, the latter giving rise to acinar and islet cells.	26
70	Parathyroid	Division	Dividing cells, mouse: 8 days, 0.07%; 18 days, 0.71%; 28 days, 0.1%	44
71		Mode of growth	Multiplication of clear or stem cells which differentiate into "dark" cells	34,44
72		Regenerative capacity	Negligible. Hypertrophy and hyperplasia in chronic nephritis.	3
73	Pituitary	Division	Observed in normal animals. Increased by hormonal stimulation.	26
74	Prostate	Division	Mitosis, rat: numerous up to 20th day, scant at 100 days	83
75		Mode of growth	In man, some squamous metaplasia in newborn	26
76			In rat, by cell proliferation up to 20 days, then by increase in cell size and diameter of acini. From 11 to 55 days, height of cell increases from 18μ to 34μ, and diameter of acini from 43μ to 170μ. Growth affected by hormonal activity.	7,83,84
77		Regenerative capacity	In man, regeneration very rare after surgical removal	26
78	Salivary gland	Division	Mitosis per 1000 acinar cells, rat: parotid, 1.02±0.23; sublingual, 0.70±0.23; submandibular, 0.64±0.17. Mitosis per 1000 tubular cells, rat: submandibular, 0.44±0.12.	28
79		Life span	Acinar cells, rat: parotid, 41 days; sublingual, 60 days; submandibular, 65 days. Tubular cells, rat: submandibular, 95 days.	28
80		Replacement	In rat, by division of acinar or tubular cells	28,77
81		Regenerative capacity	In rat, slight regeneration by proliferation of acinar cells and of intercalated ducts	28,77
82	Skin	Division	Occurs in varying proportions in stratum spinosum. Number of divisions varies with time of day, carbohydrate metabolism, hormonal stimulation, etc. In newborn mouse, 2-4% nucleated cells in mitosis; in adult mouse, 2-8 dividing cells/cm length of 7μ ear section.	20,21,35, 55
83			In 8- to 16-week-old mouse, mitotic cycle = 30.2±12 minutes	63
84			In 250-gram rat, mitosis in the planta averages 5.24% for 24 hours at 27°C	91
85		Mode of growth	Division of cells in deeper layers, followed by differentiation	80
86		Life span	Variable; dependent on rate of shedding of keratinized cells	56,91
87			Plantar epidermis cells, rat: 19.1 days, of which 16.9 days are spent in basal layer and 2.2 days in stratum granulosum	91
88			In 80- to 150-gram rat, mitotic index for corneal epithelium = 0.4%	23

continued

27. POSTNATAL TISSUE GROWTH: MAMMALS

	Tissue	Growth Feature	Growth Characteristics	Reference
	(A)	(B)	(C)	(D)
89	Skin	Replacement	Adjustment between cell loss and cell formation	22
90		Regenerative capacity	Re-epithelization of wounds by proliferation and migration of adjacent cells. Regeneration possible from hair follicles. Rate of healing greater in larger wounds. Growth of granulation tissue checked by epithelium overgrowth.	14,15,29, 76
91	Submaxillary gland	Regenerative capacity	In rat, regeneration by division of acinar cells in 1st week, followed by proliferation of ducts with acini formed from terminal portions	26
92	Testis	Division	In albino rat, cycle of spermatogonal division, 48 minutes; spermatogenic wave lasts 4 days; spermatogenic cycle takes 16 days	86
93		Life span	Sperm survival time: man, 48-72 hours; horse, 12 hours; mouse, 13.5 hours; rabbit, 96 hours; bat, possibly through winter	8,9,53,90
94		Regenerative capacity	Possible after slight injury. In rabbit, 1 day in abdominal cavity causes loss of spermatogenic elements; restoration in 2 weeks.	10
95	Thymus	Division	Mitosis: adult rabbit, 0.52%; 3-month-old rat, 0.22%	5
96		Mode of growth	In man, increases from birth to puberty, decreases in later life (weight at birth, 12 g; at puberty, 40 g; at 60 years, 15 g)	29
97	Thyroid	Division	In guinea pig, 100-125 dividing cells recorded in whole gland	17
98		Mode of growth	Following possibilities reported: new follicles by budding, proliferation of interfollicular cells, proliferation of cells derived from follicles	34,71,98, 99,104
99		Regenerative capacity	After partial removal, hypertrophy of remainder preventable by iodine administration	70,72,85
100	Uterus	Mode of growth	During menstruation: in proliferative stage, mitosis in endometrium rises to 0.56%, and nuclei of muscle fibers increase in size; regression in secretory phase; denuded surface covered in 7 days by cells from remaining glands. During pregnancy: enlargement of preexisting epithelial cells, glands, and muscle fibers; cell division of epithelial and muscle elements; new muscle fibers may form from indifferent cells.	26,65,79, 87
101		Regenerative capacity	In mouse, experimental incision healed in 48 hours without scar	58

Contributors: (a) O'Connor, R. J., (b) Glucksmann, A., (c) Hewitt, Harold B.

References: [1] Abercrombie, M., and R. D. Harkness. 1951. Proc. Roy. Soc. (London), B, 138:544. [2] Adams, W. S., R. H. Saunders, and J. S. Lawrence. 1945. Am. J. Physiol. 144:297. [3] Albright, F. 1933. New Engl. J. Med. 209:476. [4] Allen, E. 1912. J. Comp. Neurol. 22:547. [5] Andreasen, E., and S. Christensen. 1949. Anat. Record 103:401. [6] Andrew, W., and N. V. Andrew. 1949. Ibid. 104:217. [7] Andrews, G. S. 1951. J. Anat. 85:44. [8] Arey, L. B. 1946. Developmental anatomy. W. B. Saunders, Philadelphia. [9] Asdell, S. A. 1946. Patterns of mammalian reproduction. Comstock, Ithaca. [10] Asdell, S. A., and G. W. Salisbury. 1941. Anat. Record 80:145. [11] Bassett, D. L. 1949. Ibid. 103:597. [12] Baxter, J. S. 1946. J. Anat. 80:139. [13] Baxter, J. S., and J. M. Yoffey. 1948. Ibid. 82:189. [14] Bentley, F. H. 1936. Ibid. 70:498. [15] Bishop, G. H. 1945. Am. J. Anat. 76:153. [16] Bloom, W. 1928. Arch. exptl. Zellforsch. Gewebezücht. 5:269. [17] Blumenthal, H. T. 1950. Growth 14:231. [18] Boycott, A. E. 1933. Trans. Roy. Soc. Trop. Med. Hyg. 27:529. [19] Brues, A. M., and B. B. Marble. 1937. J. Exptl. Med. 65:15. [20] Bullough, W. S. 1948. Proc. Roy. Soc. (London), B, 135:212. [21] Bullough, W. S. 1952. Biol. Revs. Cambridge Phil. Soc. 27:133. [22] Bullough, W. S., and F. J. Ebling. 1952. J. Anat. 86:29. [23] Buschke, W., J. S. Friedenwald, and W. Fleischmann. 1943. Bull. Johns Hopkins Hosp. 73:143. [24] Butcher, E. O. 1935. Anat. Record 61:5. [25] Callender, S. T., E. O. Powell, and L. J. Witts. 1945. J. Pathol. Bacteriol. 57:129. [26] Cameron, G. R. 1952. Pathology of the cell. Oliver and Boyd, Edinburgh. [27] Carnot, P., and R. May. 1938. Compt. rend. soc. biol. 128:641. [28] Cherry, C. P., and A. Glucksmann. 1959. Brit. J. Radiol. 32:596. [29] Clark, W. E. leG. 1939. The tissues of the body. Clarendon Press, Oxford. [30] Clark, W. E. leG. 1946. J. Anat. 80:24. [31] Clark, W. E. leG., and L. H. D. Buxton. 1938. Brit. J. Dermatol. Syphilis 50:221. [32] Clark, W. E. leG., and H. S. Wajda. 1947. J. Anat. 81:56. [33] Corning, H. K. 1925. Lehrbuch der entwicklungsgeschichte des Menschen. Bergmann, Munich. [34] Cowdry, E. V. 1944. A textbook of histology. Ed. 3. H. Kimpton, London. [35] Cowdry, E. V., and H. C. Thompson. 1944. Anat. Record

continued

88:403. [36] Desaive, P. 1947. Arch. biol. (Paris) 58:331. [37] Desaive, P. 1948. Ibid. 59:34. [38] Dornfeld, E. J., and J. H. Berrian. 1951. Anat. Record 109:129. [39] Eaton, P., and M. W. Eaton. 1937. Science 86:354. [40] Emery, J. L. 1951. J. Anat. 85:159. [41] Farr, R. S. 1951. Anat. Record 109:515. [42] Ferguson, A. N. 1928. Am. J. Anat. 42:403. [43] Florey, H. W., and H. E. Harding. 1935. J. Pathol. Bacteriol. 40:211. [44] Foster, C. L. 1946. J. Anat. 80:171. [45] Fowler, W. M., and A. P. Barer. 1942. J. Am. Med. Assoc. 118:421. [46] Furuta, W. J. 1947. Am. J. Anat. 80:437. [47] Gardner, W. U. 1947. Cancer Research 7:549. [48] Gibson, W. C. 1940. J. Neurophysiol. 3:237. [49] Graham, G. S. 1916. J. Med. Research 34:241. [50] Grant, R. 1945. Anat. Record 91:175. [51] Green, S. H., A. M. Mandl, and S. Zuckerman. 1951. J. Anat. 85:325. [52] Haden, R. L. 1940. Principles of hematology. Ed. 2. Lea and Febiger, London. [53] Hamilton, W. J., J. D. Boyd, and H. W. Mossman. 1945. Human embryology. W. Heffer, Cambridge. [54] Hammond, J. 1941. Biol. Revs. Cambridge Phil. Soc. 16:165. [55] Hanson, J. 1947. J. Anat. 81:174. [56] Henry, J. L., et al. 1952. Arch. Pathol. 54:281. [57] Hinsey, J. C., R. A. Phillips, and K. Hare. 1939. Am. J. Physiol. 126:534. [58] Hooker, C. W. 1941. Anat. Record 79:211. [59] Hurst, A. F., and M. J. Stewart. 1929. Gastric and duodenal ulcer. Oxford Univ. Press, London. [60] Jeanneret, H., and R. Fischer. 1941. Schweiz. med. Wochschr. 22:204. [61] Johnston, T. B., and J. Whillis, ed. 1942. Gray's anatomy. Ed. 28. Longmans, Green; London. [62] Kittleson, J. A. 1917. Anat. Record 13:385. [63] Knowlton, N. P., and W. R. Widner. 1950. Cancer Research 10:59. [64] Kolmer, W. 1918. Arch. mikroskop. Anat. u. Entwicklungsmech. 91:1. [65] Krichesky, E. 1942. Anat. Record 82:551. [66] Lawrence, J. S., D. M. Ervin, and R. M. Wetrich. 1945. Am. J. Physiol. 144:284. [67] Lawrence, J. S., and W. N. Valentine. 1947. Blood 2:40. [68] Leblond, C. P., and C. E. Stevens. 1948. Anat. Record 100:357. [69] Mandl, A. M., and S. Zuckerman. 1951. J. Endocrinol. 7:190. [70] Marine, D. 1926. Arch. Pathol. Lab. Med. 2:829. [71] Marine, D. 1932. In E. V. Cowdry, ed. Special cytology. Ed. 2. P. B. Hoeber, New York. v. 2, p. 797. [72] Marine, D., and C. H. Lenhart. 1909. Arch. Internal Med. 4:253. [73] Maximow, A. A., and W. Bloom. 1944. A textbook of histology. W. B. Saunders, Philadelphia. [74] McKellar, M. 1949. Am. J. Anat. 85:263. [75] Medawar, J. 1940. Brit. J. Exptl. Pathol. 21:205. [76] Medawar, P. B. 1945. Brit. Med. Bull. 3:70. [77] Millstein, B. B. 1950. Brit. J. Exptl. Pathol. 31:664. [78] Mitchell, R. M. 1948. Anat. Record 101:161. [79] Novak, E. 1947. Gynecological and obstetrical pathology. Ed. 2. W. B. Saunders, Philadelphia. [80] O'Connor, R. J. Unpublished, 1952. [81] Picena, J. P. 1937. Rev. méd. Rosario 27:1167. [82] Popoff, N. W. 1939. Arch. Pathol. 27:841. [83] Price, D. 1936. Am. J. Anat. 60:79. [84] Price, D. 1947. Physiol. Zool. 20:213. [85] Rienhoff, W. F. 1931. Medicine 10:257. [86] Roosen-Runge, E. C. 1951. Am. J. Anat. 88:163. [87] Salvatore, C. A. 1950. Anat. Record 108:93. [88] Segerdahl, E. 1935. Acta Med. Scand., Suppl. 64. [89] Shipley, R. A., L. J. Shipley, and J. T. Wearn. 1937. J. Exptl. Med. 65:29. [90] Snell, G. D. 1941. Biology of the laboratory mouse. Blakiston, Philadelphia. [91] Storey, W. F., and C. P. Leblond. 1951. Ann. N. Y. Acad. Sci. 53:537. [92] Swinyard, C. A. 1943. Anat. Record 87:141. [93] Thorell, B. 1947. Acta Med. Scand., Suppl. 200. [94] Tocantins, L. M. 1936. Arch. Pathol. 21:69. [95] Trotter, M. 1922. Arch. Dermatol. and Syphilol. 7:93. [96] Weisberger, A. S., et al. 1951. Blood 6:916. [97] Weiss, P., and H. B. Biscoe. 1948. J. Exptl. Zool. 107:315. [98] Williams, R. G. 1939. Anat. Record 73:307. [99] Wilson, G. E. 1927. Ibid. 37:31. [100] Wintrobe, M. M. 1951. Clinical hematology. H. Kimpton, London. p. 235. [101] Yoffey, J. M. 1933. J. Anat. 67:250. [102] Yoffey, J. M. 1936. Ibid. 70:507. [103] Young, J. Z. 1942. Physiol. Revs. 22:318. [104] Zechel, G. 1931. Surg. Gynecol. Obstet. 52:228.

28. COMPENSATORY HYPERTROPHY: MAMMALS

Part I: ADRENAL COMPENSATORY HYPERTROPHY: CAT, DOG, RABBIT, AND RAT

Values in parentheses are ranges, estimate "b" (cf. Introduction).

	Animal	Age and Sex	No. of Subjects	Time after Unilateral Adrenalectomy	Compensatory Hypertrophy[1]	Reference
	(A)	(B)	(C)	(D)	(E)	(F)
1	Cat		5	20-39 da	149(129-169)	6
2	Dog	♂	4	1 wk	124(102-146)	1
3		Adult, ♂♀	6	2 wk	119	2
4	Rabbit	♀	10	2-40 wk	158(134-182)	3
5		♂	20	19-88 wk	248(206-290)	3
6	Rat	♂	12	2 wk	151(135-167)	5
7		90 da, ♀	27	40 da	163(145-181)	4

/1/ Lines 1, 2, 4-7 determined from $\frac{\text{weight of hypertrophied adrenal}}{\text{weight of removed adrenal}} \times 100$; line 3 determined from $\frac{\text{weight of hypertrophied adrenal/kg body weight}}{\text{weight of removed adrenal/kg body weight}} \times 100$.

Contributor: Barrows, Charles H.

References: [1] Bransome, E. D., Jr., and W. J. Reddy. 1961. Endocrinology 69:997. [2] Ganong, W. F., and D. M. Hume. 1954. Ibid. 55:474. [3] Kojima, T. 1929. Tohoku J. Exptl. Med. 13:357. [4] MacKay, E. M., and L. L. MacKay. 1926. J. Exptl. Med. 43:395. [5] McCann, S. M., A. Fruit, and B. D. Fulford. 1958. Endocrinology 63:29. [6] Moore, B., and C. O. Purinton. 1901. Am. J. Physiol. 5:182.

Part II: EFFECT OF TIME ON ADRENAL AND RENAL COMPENSATORY HYPERTROPHY: RAT

Values in parentheses are ranges, estimate "b" (cf. Introduction).

	Days after Unilateral Removal	No. of Subjects and Sex[1]	Compensatory Hypertrophy[2]	Reference
	(A)	(B)	(C)	(D)
	Adrenal			
1	2	10♀	117.7(114.5-120.9)	4
2	4	19♀	119.8(114.6-125.0)	
3	5	9♀	124.2(117.2-131.2)	
4	7	51♀	123.6(119.2-128.0)	
5	5	239♂	63	1
6	10	171♂	65	
7	20	205♂	68	
8	40	182♂	67	
9	5	218♀	61	1
10	10	163♀	62	
11	20	150♀	63	
12	40	131♀	71	
	Kidney			
13	5	239♂	65	2
14	10	171♂	68	
15	20	205♂	71	
16	40	182♂	72	
17	5	218♀	65	2
18	10	163♀	68	
19	20	150♀	70	
20	40	131♀	72	
21	5	♂♀	21	3
22	10	♂♀	26	
23	20	♂♀	35	
24	40	♂♀	36	

/1/ Age of rats, lines 5-20: 30-220 days (no significant effect of age). /2/ Lines 1-4 determined from $\frac{\text{weight of hypertrophied right adrenal}}{\text{weight of removed left adrenal}} \times 100$; lines 5-12 determined from $\frac{\text{weight of hypertrophied adrenal}}{\text{weight of both adrenals of control}}$; lines 13-20 determined from $\frac{\text{weight of hypertrophied kidney}}{\text{weight of both kidneys of control}}$; lines 21-24 given as percent increase in weight of hypertrophied kidney.

Contributor: Barrows, Charles H.

continued

28. COMPENSATORY HYPERTROPHY: MAMMALS

Part II: EFFECT OF TIME ON ADRENAL AND RENAL COMPENSATORY HYPERTROPHY: RAT

References: [1] Addis, T., and W. Lew. 1940. J. Exptl. Med. 71:325. [2] Addis, T., B. A. Myers, and J. Oliver 1924. Arch. Internal Med. 34:243. [3] MacKay, E. M., L. L. MacKay, and T. Addis. 1932. J. Exptl. Med. 56:255. [4] Smelik, P. G., P. R. Bouman, and D. DeWeid. 1959. Acta Endocrinol. 31:451.

Part III: EFFECT OF AGE ON ADRENAL AND RENAL COMPENSATORY HYPERTROPHY: RAT

Values in lines 1-37 are given at 30 days after unilateral removal of organ, in lines 37-45 at 40 days, and in lines 46 and 47 at 8 weeks.

	Age	No. of Subjects and Sex	Compensatory Hypertrophy[1]	Reference
	(A)	(B)	(C)	(D)
	Adrenal			
1	1 mo	24♂	135	3
2	6.5 mo	9♂	148	
3	11 & 17 mo	7♂	128	
4	17.5 mo	11♂	109	
5	20 mo	10♂	114	
6	22 mo	7♂	129	
7	23 & 23.5 mo	7♂	159	
8	25 & 27.5 mo	3♂	142	
9	4 mo	12♀	133	3
10	6.5 mo	13♀	130	
11	9.5 mo	10♀	145	
12	12 mo	13♀	160	
13	15.5 mo	12♀	125	
14	17.5 mo	9♀	122	
15	20-22 mo	12♀	120	
16	22.5 mo	8♀	132	
17	24 mo	15♀	141	
18	26 & 29 mo	12♀	140	
	Kidney			
19	1 mo	15♂	140	3
20	4 mo	14♂	142	
21	5 & 6 mo	15♂	140	
22	7.5 mo	11♂	131	
23	10.5 mo	9♂	133	3
24	15.5 mo	10♂	122	
25	11 & 17 mo	8♂	124	
26	12.5 mo	10♂	125	
27	24 & 24.5 mo	17♂	125	
28	26.5 mo	10♂	122	
29	29 & 31 mo	5♂	138	
30	13.5 mo	10♀	131	3
31	17 mo	11♀	123	
32	19.5 mo	10♀	127	
33	20-22 mo	12♀	125	
34	23 mo	19♀	121	
35	26 mo	12♀	120	
36	29-31 mo	9♀	131	
37	5 da	22♂	165.2	2
38	15 da	20♂	157.5	
39	30 da	25♂	143.7	
40	60 da	24♂	134.6	
41	90 da	25♂	132.0	
42	180 da	24♂	130.9	
43	270 da	27♂	132.9	
44	360 da	22♂	123.1	
45	540 da	23♂	122.8	
46	12 mo	13♀	144	1
47	21 mo	11♀	133	

/1/ Lines 1-18 determined from $\frac{\text{weight of hypertrophied adrenal}}{\text{weight of normal adrenal from control}} \times 100$; lines 19-45 determined from $\frac{\text{weight of hypertrophied kidney}}{\text{weight of removed kidney}} \times 100$; lines 46 and 47 determined from $\frac{\text{weight of hypertrophied kidney}}{\text{mean weight of both kidneys of control}} \times 100$.

Contributor: Barrows, Charles H.

References: [1] Barrows, C. H., Jr., L. M. Roeder, and D. A. Olewine. 1962. J. Gerontol. 17:148. [2] MacKay, E. M., L. L. MacKay, and T. Addis. 1932. J. Exptl. Med. 56:255. [3] Verzár, F., and F. Hügin. 1957. Acta Anat. 30:918.

continued

29. REGENERATION: RAT, SALAMANDER, AND FROG

Part I: COURSE OF EVENTS IN LIVER REGENERATION: RAT

	Process	Regeneration after Partial Hepatectomy			Reference
		Initiation	Maximum Rate	Completion	
	(A)	(B)	(C)	(D)	(E)
1	Restoration of liver mass[1]	Immediately	10-24 hr	10-20 da	3,5,9
2	Restoration of hepatic cells[2]	24 hr	24-48 hr	10-20 da	1,3,5
3	Mitosis in hepatic cells	24 hr	24-48 hr	10-20 da	1,4,6,13
4	Protein synthesis	Immediately[3]	12-36 hr[4]	....	7,8,11
5	RNA synthesis, cytoplasmic	Immediately[3]	6-28 hr[4]	....	2,8,10-12
6	RNA synthesis, nuclear	6 hr[3]	24-48 hr[4]	....	2,8,10-12
7	DNA synthesis	18 hr[3]	24-48 hr[4]	....	2,8,10-12

/1/ Restoration of original wet weight and volume of liver corrected for changes in body weight. /2/ Restoration of original number of liver cell nuclei. /3/ Earliest significant increase of labelled precursors above levels characteristic of normal intact liver (expressed as specific activity). /4/ Increase expressed as mg/liver/unit time.

Contributor: Glinos, André D.

References: [1] Abercrombie, M., and R. D. Harkness. 1951. Proc. Roy. Soc. (London), B, 138:544. [2] Aquist, S., and E. P. Anderson. 1956. Acta Chem. Scand. 10:1583. [3] Brues, A. M., D. R. Drury, and M. C. Brues. 1936. Arch. Pathol. 22:658. [4] Brues, A. M., and B. B. Marble. 1937. J. Exptl. Med. 65:15. [5] Bucher, M. L. R., and A. D. Glinos. 1950. Cancer Research 10:324. [6] Cater, D. B., B. E. Holmes, and L. K. Mee. 1956. Acta Radiol. 46:655. [7] Ferran, V., and R. D. Harkness. 1954. J. Physiol. 124:443. [8] Glinos, A. D. 1958. In W. D. McElroy and D. Glass, ed. The chemical basis of development. Johns Hopkins Press, Baltimore. p. 813. [9] Harkness, R. D. 1951. J. Physiol. 117:267. [10] Nygaard, O., and H. P. Rush. 1955. Cancer Research 15:240. [11] Schneider, J. H., and V. R. Potter. 1957. Ibid. 17:701. [12] Takagi, Y., L. I. Hect, and V. R. Potter. 1956. Ibid. 16:994. [13] Weinbren, K., and W. Fitschen. 1959. Brit. J. Exptl. Pathol. 40:107.

Part II: COURSE OF EVENTS IN LEG REGENERATION: SALAMANDER

Subjects were *Ambystoma* and *Triturus* species.

	Regenerative Process	Duration, da			Regenerative Process	Duration, da	
		Larva	Adult			Larva	Adult
	(A)	(B)	(C)		(A)	(B)	(C)
1	Epidermal closure	0.25-0.50	0.50-0.75	5	Blastema formation	5-10	12-28
2	Demolition phase	1-3	1-8	6	Palette stage	12-14	30-32
3	Dedifferentiation	2.5-8.0	8-25	7	Tissue differentiation	10.5-18.0	31-60
4	Peak of mitosis	9.0-12.5	19-37	8	Completion	20-38	70+

Contributor: Thornton, C. S.

References: [1] Butler, E. G. 1933. J. Exptl. Zool. 65:271. [2] Chalkley, D. T. 1954. J. Morphol. 94:21. [3] Thornton, C. S. 1938. Ibid. 62:17.

continued

29. REGENERATION: RAT, SALAMANDER, AND FROG

Part III: LENGTH AND VOLUME INCREASES DURING LEG REGENERATION: SALAMANDER

Subjects were adult salamanders, *Triturus viridescens*. Values in parentheses are ranges, estimate "c" (cf. Introduction).

	Days after Wounding	No. of Subjects	Length Increase mm	Volume Increase cu mm
	(A)	(B)	(C)	(D)
1	8	3	0.48(0.43-0.58)	0.52(0.30-0.71)
2	10	15	0.50(0.33-0.65)	0.49(0.20-0.74)
3	13	15	0.58(0.43-0.75)	0.57(0.39-1.25)
4	14	5	0.73(0.66-0.84)	0.86(0.61-1.00)
5	15	18	0.68(0.38-1.08)	0.88(0.25-1.63)
6	16	5	0.98(0.80-1.32)	1.14(0.80-1.83)
7	17	12	1.01(0.55-1.03)	1.06(0.62-1.45)
8	18	9	1.20(0.91-1.55)	1.09(0.67-1.58)
9	21	7	1.55(1.25-1.85)	1.09(0.86-1.25)
10	24	10	1.92(1.25-2.37)	1.48(1.20-1.64)
11	27	5	2.26(2.16-2.33)	1.66(1.23-2.11)
12	33	6	3.12(2.39-3.59)	2.75(1.93-3.34)
13	42	7	3.95(2.93-4.87)	3.06(1.80-4.86)
14	54	6	4.20(3.83-4.63)	3.61(2.99-4.53)

Contributor: Thornton, C. S.

Reference: Singer, M., and L. Craven. 1948. J. Exptl. Zool. 108:279.

Part IV: EFFECT OF SEVERITY OF WOUNDING: FROG AND SALAMANDER

	Larva	Amputation	No. of Subjects	Regeneration: No. of Days	Regeneration: Growth mm	Reference
	(A)	(B)	(C)	(D)	(E)	(F)
1	*Rana clamitans*	Tail	8	24	0.436	3
2			3	100	0.616	
3			4	150	0.505	
4		Tail + 1 leg	7	24	0.487	
5			4	100	0.572	
6		Tail + 2 legs	8	24	0.464	
7			6	100	0.623	
8			3	150	0.608	
9		Tail 3.2 mm	20	3	0.4	1
10				6	1	
11				9	1.4	
12				32	1.4 (44%)	
13		5.2 mm	20	3	0.5	
14				6	1.5	
15				9	2	
16				12	2.3	
17				32	2.3 (44%)	
18		10.4 mm	20	3	0.6	
19				6	2	
20				9	3.2	
21				12	4	
22	*Rana clamitans*	Tail 10.4 mm	20	15	5	1
23				32	5 (48%)	
24		14.8 mm	20	3	0	
25				6	2.4	
26				9	4.9	
27				12	5.8	
28				15	6.7	
29				18	7.2	
30				32	7.2 (48%)	
31	*Ambystoma jeffersonianum*	Tail 15.01 mm[1]	34	11.2	2.83 (18.7%)	2
32		15.36 mm[2]	45	11.2	3.30 (21.4%)	2
33	28 da old	Tail, 8.94 mm	10	24	9.36 (105%)	4
34	34 da old	Tail, 10.52 mm	8	15	6.22 (59.6%)	4
35	48 da old	Tail, 10.63 mm	21	15	5.87 (55.2%)	4
36	134 da old	Tail, 21.43 mm	10	11	2.96 (13.9%)	4

/1/ 1st amputation. /2/ 4th amputation.

Contributor: Thornton, C. S.

References: [1] Ellis, M. P. 1909. J. Exptl. Zool. 7:421. [2] Zeleny, C. 1909. Ibid. 7:477. [3] Zeleny, C. 1909. Ibid. 7:513. [4] Zeleny, C. 1909. Ibid. 7:563.

continued

29. REGENERATION: RAT, SALAMANDER, AND FROG

Part V: MITOTIC INDEX FOR REGENERATION OF LEG STUMP TISSUE: SALAMANDER

Index was constructed from observations on 3 legs from adult salamanders, *Triturus viridescens.*

	Days after Amputation	Mitotic Index				
		Epidermis	Blastema[1]	Muscle	Cartilage	Nerve Sheaths
	(A)	(B)	(C)	(D)	(E)	(F)
1	1	0.72	0	0	0	0
2	7	0.64	0.53	5	0	0.21
3	13	0.89	0.67	5	0	0.47
4	19	0.87	0.65	3	0	0.17
5	25	0.84	0.53	0	0.93	0.22
6	31	0.66	0.29	3	1.78	0.51
7	37	0.13	0.17	29	0.04	0.24

/1/ And connective tissues.

Contributor: Thornton, C. S.

Reference: Chalkley, D. T. 1954. J. Morphol. 94:21.

30. REGENERATION: EARTHWORM

Values are for the barnyard earthworm, *Eisenia foetida.* Values in parentheses are ranges, estimate "c" (cf. Introduction).

Part I: EFFECT OF TIME ON REGENERATION

Earthworms were cut at intersegment 50/51 and kept in soil at 25°C.

	Days after Cutting	No. of Subjects	No. of New Segments	Length mm
	(A)	(B)	(C)	(D)
1	8	30	14.7(0-22)	....
2	12	28	25.5(8-33)	....
3	14	45	....	2.6(1-5)
4	16	46	33.9(10-50)	4.7(2-7)
5	18	19	32.8(21-43)	....
6	20	16	37.2(26-47)	....
7	21	49	....	7.2(1-11)
8	24	36	40.4(4-62)	7.5(3-14)
9	32	30	40.4(5-58)	8.9(1-14)
10	37	57	....	9.4(2-25)
11	40	23	41.3(5-63)	9.6(2-15)
12	60	10	....	12.1(11-16)
13	60	180	39.5(22-57)	....

Contributor: Moment, Gairdner B.

Reference: Moment, G. B. 1949. J. Exptl. Zool. 112:1.

Part II: EFFECT OF AMPUTATION LEVEL ON REGENERATION

	Intersegment Amputation Level	No. of Subjects	No. of New Segments
	(A)	(B)	(C)
1	40/41	7	52.0(47-56)
2	50/51	180	39.5(22-57)
3	60/61	19	29.6(19-38)
4	70/71	31	21.3(6-31)
5	80/81	118	9.8(2-22)

Contributor: Moment, Gairdner B.

References: [1] Moment, G. B. 1946. J. Exptl. Zool. 103:3. [2] Moment, G. B. 1953. Physiol. Zool. 26:2.

31. REGENERATION: HYDRA

Hypostomal cut = amputation, in a stretched position, as close to the tentacles as possible without leaving any tentacles on the hydra; mid-stomach cut = severance of hydra, in a stretched position, in the mid-stomach region. Regeneration is expressed as length-to-width ratio of the longest tentacle.

Part I: EFFECT OF TIME AND SEVERANCE SITE ON REGENERATION

Each value represents the average of 36 replicates. Temperature during regeneration period was 27°C.

	Organism	Cut	Regeneration at					No. of Tentacles at 48 hr
			18 hr	20 hr	22 hr	24 hr	26 hr	
	(A)	(B)	(C)	(D)	(E)	(F)	(G)	(H)
	Chlorohydra viridissima							
1	Green	Hypostomal	3.4	...	...	...	...	6.1
2		Mid-stomach	2.6	3.3	...	...	...	7.1
3	Brown	Hypostomal	3.0	...	...	...	...	6.0
4		Mid-stomach	2.1	2.8	...	...	...	7.0
	Hydra littoralis							
5	Strain I	Hypostomal	1.8	2.6	3.2	...	...	6.3
6		Mid-stomach	0.6	1.2	1.9	2.3	...	6.6
7	Strain II	Hypostomal	0.81	1.6	2.5	...	...	4.5
8		Mid-stomach	0.09	0.14	0.26	0.57	0.89	3.0
9	Strain III	Hypostomal	1.6	2.1	2.4	...	...	1.2
10		Mid-stomach	0.22	0.24	0.28	...	0.41	0.33
11	Strain IV	Hypostomal	1.4	2.5	3.0	...	...	6.2
12		Mid-stomach	0	0	0.09	0.22	0.40	5.4
13	*H. oligactis*	Hypostomal	0.7	1.6	2.7	...	...	5.5
14		Mid-stomach	0	0	0	0	0.11	1.4

Contributor: Eakin, Robert E.

Reference: Spangenberg, D. B., and R. E. Eakin. 1961. J. Exptl. Zool. 147:259.

Part II: EFFECT OF TEMPERATURE ON REGENERATION

Each value represents the average of 15 replicates for *Hydra littoralis*, Strain I. Severance site was hypostomal.

	Temp. °C	Regeneration at											
		12 hr	14 hr	16 hr	18 hr	20 hr	22 hr	24 hr	26 hr	28 hr	32 hr	36 hr	48 hr
	(A)	(B)	(C)	(D)	(E)	(F)	(G)	(H)	(I)	(J)	(K)	(L)	(M)
1	15	...	...	...	...	...	...	...	...	...	0.3	0.4	1.2
2	20	...	...	...	...	...	...	0.4	0.9	1.5	2.4	...	...
3	25	0.3	0.4	0.6	0.9	1.3	1.8	2.4	2.8	...	...	...	...
4	27	0.3	0.4	0.8	1.4	2.2	2.9	...	...	...	...	...	...
5	30	0.3	0.5	0.9	1.5	2.0	2.5	...	...	...	...	...	...

Contributor: Eakin, Robert E.

Reference: Ham, R. G., D. C. Fitzgerald, and R. E. Eakin. 1956. J. Exptl. Zool. 133:559.

32. TISSUE CULTURE: ANIMALS

With tissue culture, cells removed from an organism can be maintained in a condition of survival or growth for a few hours up to an indefinite number of years. In general, embryonic cells are easier to grow than the adult highly-specialized or differentiated cells.

Part I: EMBRYONIC CARTILAGINOUS TIBIA

Embryonic bone rudiments were cultivated in the cartilaginous phase of growth on chemically defined media, in an atmosphere of 5% carbon dioxide in air, using the floating lens technique devised by Chen [3]. Media were renewed every two days by transferring the lens paper plus adherent tissue to a new culture chamber.

	Embryo	Age da	Explants no.	Initial Size[1]	Cultivation da	Response Type	Response Growth[1]	Reference
	(A)	(B)	(C)	(D)	(E)	(F)	(G)	(H)
1	Mouse	15	6	1.0 mm	6	Length	2.1 mm	2
2		15, post coitum	6	1.0 mm	6	Length	2.1 mm	1
3	Rat	17	8	1.4 mm	10	Length	3.8 mm	2
4		17, post coitum	8	1.4 mm	10	Length	3.2 mm	1
5		17	20	0.32 mg	8	Wet weight	1.61 mg	1
6		17	20	62 µg	8	Dry weight	159 µg	1
7	Chick	7	9	2.0 mm	10	Length	6.5 mm	1
8		7	9	2.0 mm	10	Length	5.8 mm	2
9		7	24	0.52 mg	8	Wet weight	2.77 mg	1
10		7	24	70 µg	8	Dry weight	201 µg	1
11		8	15	3.91 µg	8	DNA content	6.42 µg	1
12	Turkey	9	24	3.85 mm	10	Length	9.33 mm	1
13		9	24	1.62 mg	10	Wet weight	9.62 mg	1
14		9	24	2.85 µg	10	DNA content	6.43 µg	1

/1/ Mean value.

Contributor: Heyner, Susan

References: [1] Biggers, J. D., R. B. L. Gwatkin, and S. Heyner. 1961. Exptl. Cell Research 25:41. [2] Biggers, J. D., and J. A. Lucy. 1960. J. Exptl. Zool. 144:233. [3] Chen, J. M. 1954. Exptl. Cell Research 7:518.

Part II: CELL LINES FROM NON-NEOPLASTIC TISSUE

The cultivation of cell lines is particularly useful in the study of cell susceptibility to viruses. For a comprehensive review of the subject, consult *Some Animal Cell Lines from Normal and Neoplastic Tissue,* compiled and edited by Leonard Hayflick, 1960, and on deposit as document number 7071 with the American Documentation Institute Auxiliary Publications Project, Photoduplication Service, Library of Congress, Washington 25, D. C.[1] Cell type (column D): E = epithelial-like; F = fibroblast-like; M = monocytic. Remarks (column F): SV = spectrum of viruses; NDV = Newcastle disease virus; ECHO = enteric cytopathogenic human orphan; LCM = lymphocytic choriomeningitis; VSV = vesicular stomatitis virus; EEE = eastern equine encephalitis.

	Animal	Tissue Origin	Cell Line	Cell Type	Chromosome Number	Remarks	Reference
	(A)	(B)	(C)	(D)	(E)	(F)	(G)
1	Man	Amnion	FL amnion	E			17
2			A1[2]	E	Polyploid	SV: poliovirus	12
3			Amnion strain-Fernandes	E	67 (subtriploid)	SV: bluetongue; adenovirus 1,2,3,4,6, 7; NDV (Victoria strain); mumps (ABC strain); poliovirus 1,2,3; herpes simplex; measles	16
4			Unspecified	E		SV: poliovirus 1,2,3; ECHO 1,2,9; negative for adenovirus 2,4, and ECHO 3,11	2
5			WISH	E	75± (heteroploid)	SV: poliovirus 1,2,3; adenovirus 3	27,36
6		Appendix	Chang appendix	E			6

/1/ A copy may be secured by citing the document number and by remitting $2.50 for photoprints, or $1.75 for 35-mm microfilm. Advance payment is required. Make checks or money orders payable to: Chief, Photoduplication Service, Library of Congress. /2/ Information applies also to cell lines A2, A3, A4, and A5.

continued

32. TISSUE CULTURE: ANIMALS

Part II: CELL LINES FROM NON-NEOPLASTIC TISSUE

	Animal	Tissue Origin	Cell Line	Cell Type	Chromosome Number	Remarks	Reference
	(A)	(B)	(C)	(D)	(E)	(F)	(G)
7	Man	Blood, peripheral	Detroit-B16[3]		(65-75)		4
8			HERT 1[4]	E			40
9		Bone marrow	Detroit-143		(65-75)		4
10		Sternal	Detroit-98	E	(65-75)		3
11		Sternal (diabetes mellitus)	Detroit-52	E	(65-75)		3
12		Conjunctiva	Chang conjunctiva	E	82(65-85)	SV: poliovirus 1,2,3	6,29
13		Cervix, adult	Li Wi	E			21
14		Esophagus	5-12-1A[5]	E	70(65-79)	SV: poliovirus 1,2,3; herpes simplex; vaccinia	45
15		♂ (fetus, tracheoesophageal fistula)	Minn. EE	E			46
16		Foreskin	D-189	F	72± (heteroploid)		33,36
17			FS4-705	F			44
18		Heart, right atrial appendage	Girardi heart	E		SV: measles	23
19		Jejunum and ileum, fetus	Intestine 407	E		SV: herpes simplex; vaccinia; VSV; poliovirus 1,2,3; Coxsackie B_1, B_2, B_3, B_4; adenovirus 3; NDV; mumps Po; negative for mumps Ba, partial for influenza WSE	28
20		Kidney	Chang kidney	E			6
21		Cortex	T-1	E		SV: adenovirus 3,4,7,14; poliovirus 1, 2,3; herpes simplex; vaccinia; cowpox; variola; foamy virus; measles; mumps; Coxsackie B_1, B_2, B_3, B_4, B_5; negative for influenza, NDV, ECHO 9	49
22		Liver	Chang liver	E	77(65-90)		6,29
23			HLil	E	75		52
24			6-6-2[5]	E	75(58-78)		45
25		♂	Liver cells	E			46
26		Embryo	Liver 407	E		SV: herpes simplex; vaccinia; VSV; poliovirus 1,2,3; Coxsackie B_1; adenovirus 3; NDV; mumps Po; negative for mumps Ba, partial for influenza WSE	28
27		♂ fetus	HLM	E			34
28		Lung	HL-C (Nakanishi)	E	77(65-96)		37
29			HL-S (Nakanishi)	E	76(69-80)		
30		Fetus	Lung-To	F?		SV: herpes simplex; pseudorabies; vaccinia; VSV; partial for mumps Ba, influenza PR8, WSE	28
31		Lymph node (reticuloendotheliosis)	LN	E		Striking acid phosphatase activity; heavy PAS staining; slow with poliovirus 1	1
		Mucosa, nasal				SV: poliovirus 1; adenovirus 2,4,7; Coxsackie B_3; ECHO 7; herpes simplex; chimp "rhinitis"	32
32		♂	DHov	E			
33		♀	DMB	E			
34		Palate, ♂ (cleft)	Palate fibrocyte	E			46
35		Parotid gland, ♂ fetus	Unspecified	E		SV: poliovirus 1,2,3; adenovirus 2; ECHO 1,2,3,9; negative for adenovirus 4, ECHO 11	2
36		Pituitary gland	S-4374-VAM-I	E	79(76-81)	Produces gonadotropin	48
37			4371-A-23+A-17	E		Produces somatotropic hormone	
38			4373-X	E		Produces ACTH, gonadotropin, and somatotropic hormone	

/3/ Information applies also to cell lines Detroit-B17 and Detroit-B173. /4/ Information applies also to cell lines HERT 2, HERT 3, HERT 4. /5/ Reference does not clarify whether tissue origin was normal or cancerous.

continued

32. TISSUE CULTURE: ANIMALS

Part II: CELL LINES FROM NON-NEOPLASTIC TISSUE

	Animal	Tissue Origin	Cell Line	Cell Type	Chromosome Number	Remarks	Reference
	(A)	(B)	(C)	(D)	(E)	(F)	(G)
39	Man	Pituitary gland Fetus	Wistar 6[6]	E			9
40		Skin	AU	E		SV: herpes simplex; vaccinia	54
41		♂	1769	E		SV: adenovirus 1,4; Hicks; poliovirus 1,2,3; Coxsackie B_3; herpes simplex; B virus; vaccinia; encephalomyocarditis; LCM; St. Louis encephalitis; yellow fever	41
42		Skin and muscle, fetus	MAF-E	E		SV: herpes simplex; vaccinia; poliovirus 1,2,3; Coxsackie B_3, B_4; adenovirus 3; NDV; mumps Po, mumps 6; negative for mumps Ba, partial for influenza PR8	28
43		Synovial tissue	Unspecified	F	(54-62)	SV: poliovirus I (Mahoney)	7
44				F	(58-78)	Poliovirus I resistant	
45				E	(49-74)	Poliovirus I sensitive	
46		Knee joint	Mayes	E	133		30
47		Tendon, quadriceps	U.As II	F			22
48		Tonsil, adult	T-16	E		SV: adenovirus 1,2,3,4,5,6,7; Bertha; Coxsackie B, B_2; herpes simplex; mumps (Enders); NDV (Victoria, G.B.); poliovirus 1,2,3; vaccinia; negative for Coxsackie A_2, A_3, E_4, Highpoint, Wiederhold "C," Sendai, measles, influenza PR8, A, B	14
49		Uterus	U12-705	F			44
50	Cattle	Kidney	MDBK	F?		SV: VSV (Indiana, New Jersey); infectious bovine rhinotracheitis	35
51		Lens	T-5a[7]	E		SV: adenovirus 1,2,3,4,5,7a,8; negative for poliovirus 1,2,3	50
52		Muscle, gluteus; fetus	Bovine muscle	F			8
53	Goat	Kidney	MDOK	E		SV: VSV (Indiana, New Jersey); infectious bovine rhinotracheitis; bluetongue	35
54	Hamster, Chinese	Lung	C	F	Triploid		19
55			P	F	Majority diploid		19
56			V	F	Predominantly diploid		19
57			C-M/C		Triploid		18
58	Monkey	Corpus callosum and brain stem	EM	E		SV: poliovirus 1,2,3	43
59		Heart	Unspecified	E			42
60		Kidney	MK1	E	>50	Untransformed?	52
61			MK2	E	67	Transformed line from line MK1	52,53
62			MK3	E	>50		52
63			Unspecified	E			39
64		Lung	MLu1	E	75		52,53
65	Mouse	Bone marrow	H-1a[8]	E		Mouse strain: C3H; pooled tissue	5
66			H-4c	M		Mouse strain: C3H; pooled tissue	
67		Connective tissue, subcutaneous	L	F		Mouse strain: C3H	13
68			Unspecified	E		Mouse strain: Swiss	38
69			Unspecified	E		Mouse strain: A	38
70		Liver	Unspecified	E		Mouse strain: C3H, Andervont line	15
71		Parenchymal epithelium	721	E		Mouse strain: C3H/HeN	51
72		Skin, embryo	Unspecified	F			31
73		Unspecified	X-1	F	88(76-90)		45
74			X-2	F	76(72-81)		

/6/ Information also applies to cell line Wistar 12. /7/ Information applies also to cell lines T-5b and T-5c. /8/ Information applies also to cell lines H-1b, H-1e, H-4a, H-4b, H-4d.

continued

32. TISSUE CULTURE: ANIMALS

Part II: CELL LINES FROM NON-NEOPLASTIC TISSUE

	Animal	Tissue Origin	Cell Line	Cell Type	Chromosome Number	Remarks	Reference
	(A)	(B)	(C)	(D)	(E)	(F)	(G)
75	Rabbit	Bone marrow	RBM-1-G	F	95		25
76		Kidney	Wistar 7	E			9
77			Wistar 8	F	(63-71)		9,10
78		♀	RbK	E		SV: poliovirus	11
79		Embryo	ERK1	E	70		52,53
80			ERK2	E	80	Untransformed?	53
81			Wistar 9	F	(63-70)		9,10
82			Wistar 10	F			9
83		Leg, embryo	RS1-F17	F		SV: vaccinia	26
84		Lung	ZP-1/58	F		SV: herpes simplex; vaccinia; negative for influenza, polio	47
85		Muscle, skeletal	RM3/F17	F		SV: vaccinia	26
86		Testicle	RT6-F17	F		SV: vaccinia	26
87	Rat	Areolae, subcutaneous	14p	F			21
88			ANSAT-21 (or AN-21)			EEE	20
89		Heart (5 da old)	N111	E		Slonaker-Addis strain	24
90			N120	E		Slonaker-Addis strain	
91		Lung	KrP-2/58	E		SV: herpes simplex; negative for influenza, polio	47

Contributors: (a) Hayflick, Leonard, (b) Moorhead, P. S.

References: [1] Bell, S., and R. E. Johnson. 1956. Proc. Soc. Exptl. Biol. Med. 96:515. [2] Bergman, S., S. B. Nilsson, and S. G. Olsson. 1959. Acta Pathol. Microbiol. Scand. 47:387. [3] Berman, L., and C. S. Stulberg. 1956. Proc. Soc. Exptl. Biol. Med. 92:730. [4] Berman, L., C. S. Stulberg, and F. H. Ruddle. 1957. Cancer Research 17:668. [5] Billen, D., and G. A. Debrunner. 1960. J. Natl. Cancer Inst. 25:1127. [6] Chang, R. S. 1954. Proc. Soc. Exptl. Biol. Med. 87:440. [7] Chessin, L. N., and K. Hirschhorn. 1961. Exptl. Cell Research 23:138. [8] Colter, J. S., et al. 1958. J. Natl. Cancer Inst. 20:1141. [9] Defendi, V., and J. S. Colter. 1959. Ibid. 23:411. [10] Defendi, V., et al. 1960. Ibid. 25:359. [11] Drew, R. M. 1957. Science 126:747. [12] Dunnebacke, T. H., and E. M. Zitcer. 1957. Cancer Research 17:1043. [13] Earle, W. R. 1943. J. Natl. Cancer Inst. 4:165. [14] Evans, A. S. 1957. Proc. Soc. Exptl. Biol. Med. 96:752. [15] Evans, V. J., et al. 1952. J. Natl. Cancer Inst. 12:1245. [16] Fernandes, M. V. 1958. Texas Repts. Biol. and Med. 16:48. [17] Fogh, J., and R. O. Lund. 1957. Proc. Soc. Exptl. Biol. Med. 94:532. [18] Ford, D. K., R. Wakonig, and G. Yerganian. 1959. J. Natl. Cancer Inst. 22:765. [19] Ford, D. K., and G. Yerganian. 1958. Ibid. 21:393. [20] Gey, G. O. 1954-55. Harvey Lectures 50:154. [21] Gey, G. O., F. B. Bang, and M. K. Gey. 1954. Texas Repts. Biol. and Med. 12:805. [22] Gey, G. O., and M. K. Gey. 1936. Am. J. Cancer 27:45. [23] Girardi, A. J., et al. 1958. Proc. Soc. Exptl. Biol. Med. 98:18. [24] Goldblatt, H., and G. Cameron. 1953. J. Exptl. Med. 97:525. [25] Goldstein, M. N., and E. Havas. 1960. Proc. Soc. Exptl. Biol. Med. 104:75. [26] Haff, R. F., and H. E. Swim. 1956. Ibid. 93:200. [27] Hayflick, L. 1961. Exptl. Cell Research 23:14. [28] Henle, G., and F. Deinhardt. 1957. J. Immunol. 79:54. [29] Hsu, T. C., and P. S. Moorhead. 1957. J. Natl. Cancer Inst. 18:463. [30] Hsu, T. C., C. M. Pomerat, and P. S. Moorhead. 1957. Ibid. 19:867. [31] Hull, R. N. 1953. Science 117:223. [32] Jordan, W. S. 1956. Proc. Soc. Exptl. Biol. Med. 92:867. [33] Leighton, J., I. Kline, and H. C. Orr. 1956. Science 123:502. [34] Leslie, I., and R. Sinclair. 1959. Exptl. Cell Research 17:272. [35] Madin, S. H., and N. B. Darby, Jr. 1958. Proc. Soc. Exptl. Biol. Med. 98:574. [36] Moorhead, P. S. Unpublished, 1961. [37] Nakanishi, Y. H., M. Mizutani, and C. M. Pomerat. 1959. Texas Repts. Biol. and Med. 17:542. [38] Parker, R. C. 1955. Can. Cancer Conf. 1:42. [39] Parker, R. C., L. N. Castor, and E. A. McCulloch. 1957. Spec. Publ. N. Y. Acad. Sci. 5:303. [40] Paul, J. 1958. Nature 182:808. [41] Perry, V. P., et al. 1956. Am. J. Hyg. 63:52. [42] Salk, J. E., and E. N. Ward. 1957. Science 126:1338. [43] Seiden, G. E., and S. R. Korey. 1959. Exptl. Cell Research 17:345. [44] Swim, H. E., and R. F. Parker. 1957. Am. J. Hyg. 66:235. [45] Syverton,

continued

J. T. 1957. Spec. Publ. N. Y. Acad. Sci. 5:331. [46] Syverton, J. T., and L. C. McLaren. 1957. Cancer Research 17:923. [47] Szanto, J. 1960. Acta Virol. 4:380. [48] Thompson, K. W., et al. 1959. Proc. Soc. Exptl. Biol. Med. 102:403. [49] Van der Veen, J., L. Bots, and A. Mes. 1958. Arch. ges. Virusforsch. 8(2):230. [50] Van der Veen, J., and C. F. A. Heyen. 1959. Nature 183:1137. [51] Westfall, B. B., E. V. Peppers, and W. R. Earle. 1960. J. Natl. Cancer Inst. 24:417. [52] Westwood, J. C. N., I. A. Macpherson, and D. H. J. Titmus. 1957. Brit. J. Exptl. Pathol. 38:138. [53] Westwood, J. C. N., and D. H. J. Titmus. 1957. Ibid. 38:587. [54] Wheeler, C. E., C. M. Canby, and E. P. Cawley. 1957. J. Invest. Dermatol. 29:383.

33. TISSUE CULTURE: PLANTS

Nutrient fluids used in plant tissue cultures are chiefly composed of chemicals. Culture Medium (column C): GA = Gautheret's agar; CM = coconut milk (liquid endosperm of *Cocos rucifera*); IAA = indoleacetic acid; HA = Hildebrandt's agar; WL = White's liquid; WA = White's agar; WAS = modified White's agar for sunflower tissues; HAS = modified Hildebrandt's agar for sunflower tissues; WAT = modified White's agar for tobacco tissues; BNA = Burkholder-Nickell agar; BL = Bonner's liquid. Relative Increase (column F): W_1/W_0 = final weight divided by initial weight. Relative Growth Rate (column G): r = instantaneous growth rate expressed as percent increase/day.

	Family and Species	Tissue	Culture Medium	Growth Period da	Initial Weight mg	Relative Increase W_1/W_0	Relative Growth Rate 100 r	Reference
	(A)	(B)	(C)	(D)	(E)	(F)	(G)	(H)
	Taxaceae							
1	*Taxus brevifolia*	Pollen	WA + 15% CM and 0.6 ppm 2,4-D	28		3	3.92	24
	Gramineae							
2	*Zea mays*	Endosperm	WA + 1.5 x 10^{-2} M asparagine	25	120	3.6	5.12	22
	Araceae							
3	*Amorphophallus rivieri*	Tuber	GA + 15% CM	30	250	8	6.92	13
	Polygonaceae							
4	*Rumex acetosa*	Root tumor[1]	BNA + 0.4 mg/L thiamine	21		12	11.8	16
5			BNA	25-34		6.0	19.9	17
6				40		16	6.92	
7			BNA + 30% CM	21		11.1	11.5	15
	Cruciferae							
8	*Brassica campestris*	Root	GA	60	100	4.1	2.35[2]	6
9			GA + 0.3 mg/L IAA	60	100	5.6	2.87	
	Rosaceae							
10	*Rosa* sp.	Stem	WL + 6 mg/L 2,4-D, 0.1% yeast extract + 0.1% malt extract	14		19.9	19.3	18
	Leguminosae							
11	*Pisum sativum*	Root callus	BL + 1 g/L yeast extract + 1 x 10^{-6}M 2,4-D	56	90	10.9	4.26	23
	Vitaceae							
12	*Vitis vinifera*	Stem	HA[3]	42	30	40	8.78	19
13		Gall[4]		42	30	30	8.10	
	Umbelliferae							
14	*Daucus carota*	Root	WL	21	15	11.1	11.4	12
15		Root cambium	GA + 0.1 mg/L IAA	18	125	3.56	7.04	4
16				304	0.5	300,000	4.14	5
17				0-7	170	2	9.9	7
18				7-15	340	1.61	6	7
19				15-21	548	1.72	9	7
20				21-41	941	1.97	3.3	7
21				41-67	1852	2.13	2.7	7
22				67	170	20.32	4.5	7

/1/ Wound tumor disease of sorrel and other plants, resulting from infection by *Aureogenus magnivena*. /2/ Growth ceased by 4th subculture, but tissue survived for another year. /3/ Plus 3.0 g/L casein hydrolysate, 0.1 mg/L each NAA and kinetin, 40 mg/L adenine. /4/ Induced by *Phylloxera vestatrix*.

continued

	Family and Species	Tissue	Culture Medium	Growth Period da	Initial Weight mg	Relative Increase W_1/W_0	Relative Growth Rate 100 r	Reference
	(A)	(B)	(C)	(D)	(E)	(F)	(G)	(H)
	Umbelliferae							
23	*Daucus carota*	Vascular cambium	GA	60	100	5	2.68	6
24			GA + 0.3 mg/L IAA	60	100	7.1	3.26	
25		Root phloem	WL + 15% CM	0-2	3.98	1.15	7	2
26				2-4	4.6	1.2	9.1	
27				4-6	5.55	1.58	22.9	
28				6-8	8.75	1.72	27.1	
29				8-10	15.05	1.98	34.2	
30				10-12	29.8	1.9	32.1	
31				12-14	56.6	1.63	22.4	
32				14-16	92.15	1.56	22.2	
33				16-20	139	1.41	8.6	
34				20-24	196.9	1.19	4.3	
35				24	3.98	59	16.98	
	Apocynaceae							
36	*Vinca rosea*	Crown gall	HA	42	35	12.7	6.05	9
	Solanaceae							
37	*Nicotiana glauca* x *N. langsdorffii*[5]	Stem	WA	35	19.1	6.1	5.17	1
38				42	6.8	14.2	6.32	
39			WAT	42	25	4.84	3.75	11
40				42	25	7.80	4.89	
41	*Solanum tuberosum*	Tuber	WA + 6% CM and 18 mg/L 2,4-D	35	3	54.7	11.4	21
	Compositae							
42	*Chrysanthemum frutescens*	Crown gall	HA	42	35	3.71	3.12	9
43	*Cichorium intybus*	Tuber	GA	60	100	3.7	2.18	6
44			GA + 0.3 mg/L IAA	60	100	5.9	2.96	
45	*Helianthus annuus*	Crown gall[6]	WA[7]	42	25	15.6	6.54	10
46			WA	42	25	5.2	3.92	10
47			WAS	42	25	13.6	6.21	10
48			HAS[8]	42	25	80	10.41	20
49	*H. tuberosus*	Tuber	GA	60	100	1.95[9]	1.11	6
50			GA + 0.3 mg/L IAA	60	100	5.4	2.81	6
51			GA	35	283	1.08	0.22	3
52			GA + 0.3 mg/L IAA	35	247	1.86	1.77	3
53			GA + 100% CM	35	237	4.36	4.21	3
54			GA + 25% CM	35	245	3.03	3.17	3
55		Crown gall[6]	GA	60	100	5.1	2.72	6
56			GA + 0.3 mg/L IAA	60	100	4.5	2.51	
57	*Scorzonera hispanica*	Root	GA	60	100	2.53	1.57	8
58			GA + 1.0 mg/L IAA	60	100	10.86	3.98	
59		Crown gall[6]	GA	60	100	8.85	3.63	8
60			GA + 1.0 mg/L IAA	60	100	9.20	3.70	
61	*Tagetes erecta*	Stem	HAS	35	20	55	11.44	14
62		Crown gall	HAS	42	35	25	7.65	9
63			HAS + 0.5% dulcitol	42	35	28.7	7.98	
64			HAS + 0.5% methanol	42	35	30.6	8.14	

/5/ One of a number of tobacco hybrids forming spontaneous tumors at certain stages of development. /6/ Free from inducing microorganism *(Agrobacterium tumefaciens)*. /7/ Optimal growth at sucrose concentration of 1% at pH 5, 26°C. /8/ Nitrate present as optimum of 0.016 M instead of 0.0038 M. /9/ Growth during first subculture; dead after 3rd subculture.

Contributor: Caplin, Samuel M.

References: [1] Caplin, S. M. 1947. Botan. Gaz. 108:379. [2] Caplin, S. M., and F. C. Steward. 1949. Nature 163:920. [3] Duhamet, L., and J. Magrou. 1949. Compt. rend. 229:1353. [4] Gautheret, R. J. 1939. Ibid. 208:1340. [5] Gautheret, R. J. 1942. Titres et travaux scientifiques. Jouve, Paris. [6] Gautheret, R. J. 1947. Compt. rend. soc. biol. 142:774. [7] Gautheret, R. J. 1947. Rev. gén. botan. 54:5. [8] Gautheret, R. J. 1948. Compt. rend. soc. biol. 142:774. [9] Hildebrandt, A. C., and A. J. Riker. 1949. Am. J. Botany 36:74. [10] Hildebrandt, A. C., A. J. Riker, and B. M. Duggar. 1945. Ibid. 32:357. [11] Hildebrandt, A. C., A. J. Riker,

continued

and B. M. Duggar. 1946. Ibid. 33:591. [12] Melchers, G., and U. Engelmann. 1955. Max Planck Inst. Publ. Biol. (Tübingen) 20:564. [13] Morel, G. 1950. Compt. rend. 230:1099. [14] Muir, W. H., A. C. Hildebrandt, and A. J. Riker. 1958. Am. J. Botany 45:589. [15] Nickell, L. G. 1950. Botan. Gaz. 112:225. [16] Nickell, L. G. 1952. Bull. Torrey Botan. Club 79:427. [17] Nickell, L. G., and P. R. Burkholder. 1949. Am. J. Botany 37:538. [18] Nickell, L. G., and W. Tulecke. 1959. Science 130:863. [19] Pelet, F., et al. 1960. Am. J. Botany 47:186. [20] Riker, A. J., and A. E. Gutsche. 1948. Ibid. 35:227. [21] Steward, F. C., and S. M. Caplin. 1951. Science 113:518. [22] Straus, J. 1960. Am. J. Botany 47:641. [23] Torrey, J. G., and Y. Shigemura. 1957. Ibid. 44:325. [24] Tulecke, W. 1959. Bull. Torrey Botan. Club 86:283.

IV. VERTEBRATE REPRODUCTION

34. SPERM: VERTEBRATES

Part I: DIMENSIONS

Dimensions determined from cinemicrographs of living sperm. Values are microns (μ).

	Order	Species	Head			Middle-Piece Length		Tail Length	Total Length
			Length	Width	Thickness	Neck	Body		
	(A)	(B)	(C)	(D)	(E)	(F)	(G)	(H)	(I)
					Mammalia				
1	Primates	*Homo sapiens*	5.0	3.5	2.5	0.5	4.0	45.0	54.5
2		*Macaca mulatta*	5.7	3.6	2.0	<0.5	10.0	59.3	75
3	Artiodactyla	*Bos taurus*	8.5	4.0	0.3-0.4	>0.5	9.5-10.0	43.5	65
4		*Odocoileus virginianus*	10	6	1	<1	7	35	52
5		*Sus scrofa*	8	4	1	<1	10	38	57
6	Perissodactyla	*Equus caballus*	6.5	3.7	<2	<0.5	9.3	41.7	58
7	Carnivora	*Canis familiaris*	6.5	3.5	>1.0	>0.5	9.0	44.0	60
8		*Felis catus*	5.0	2.6	1.0	0.5	7.0	42.5	55
9		*Mustela vison*	7.0	6.1	1.0	<0.5	6	30	43
10	Rodentia	*Mesocricetus auratus*	13.0	2.3	>1.0	<0.5	49.0	92.5	155
11		*Rattus rattus*	18.0	1.5	1.0	....	....	164.0	182
12	Lagomorpha	*Oryctolagus cuniculus*	8.5	0.5	>1.0	>0.5	8.5	38.5	56
13	Edentata	*Dasypus novemcinctus*	9	6	2	<0.5	14	45	68
					Aves				
14	Galliformes	*Gallus domesticus*	11.0	0.7	0.7	....	4.0	70.0	85
15		*Meleagris gallopavo*	13.0	0.7	0.7	....	4.0	68.0	85
					Reptilia				
16	Serpentes	*Heterodon* sp.	13.0	1.2	1.2	....	80.0	37.0	130
					Amphibia				
17	Salientia	*Rana pipiens*	18.0	1.2	1.2	....	2.5	79.5	100
					Pisces				
18	Percomorphi	*Haplochromis multicolor*	2.0	2.0	2.0	....	7.6	19.2	22
19	Microcyprini	*Xiphophorus helleri*	3.5	1.2	1.2	....	0.8	49.9	61
20	Isospondyli	*Clupea pallasi*	2.0	1.5	>1.5	....	1.0	40	43

Contributors: (a) Chang, M. C., (b) Farris, Edmond J., (c) Almquist, J. O.

References: [1] Farris, E. J. 1950. Human fertility and problems of the male. Author's Press, White Plains, N. Y. [2] Saacke, R. G. Unpublished, 1962. [3] Yanagimachi, R. 1957. Zool. Mag. (Tokyo) 66:222.

Part II: VOLUME, VIABILITY, AND TRANSPORT

Values in parentheses are ranges, estimate "c" (cf. Introduction).

	Order	Species	Semen		Spermatozoa					Reference
			Volume of Ejaculate ml	pH	Concentration million/ml	Survival in Female Genital Tract, hr		Transit Time		
						Fertility[1]	Motility[2]	Vagina to Tube[3]	Cervix to Tube[3]	
	(A)	(B)	(C)	(D)	(E)	(F)	(G)	(H)	(I)	(J)
					Mammalia					
1	Primates	*Homo sapiens*	3.5 (2.0-6.0)	7.4 (7.1-7.5)	100 (50-150)	(1.5-72.0)	(48-72)	3 hr	30 min	16,24,27,31
2	Artiodactyla	*Bos taurus*	4.0 (0.5-12.0)	(6.4-7.8)	1000 (300-2000)	(28-51)	24	6 hr	(2.5-140.0) min	1-3,13,22, 28,29,33

/1/ Duration of fertilizing capacity. /2/ Life of sperm. /3/ Ovarian end of fallopian tube.

continued

34. SPERM: VERTEBRATES

Part II: VOLUME, VIABILITY, AND TRANSPORT

	Order	Species	Semen: Volume of Ejaculate ml	Semen: pH	Spermatozoa: Concentration million/ml	Survival in Female Genital Tract, hr: Fertility[1]	Survival in Female Genital Tract, hr: Motility[2]	Transit Time: Vagina to Tube[3]	Transit Time: Cervix to Tube[3]	Reference
	(A)	(B)	(C)	(D)	(E)	(F)	(G)	(H)	(I)	(J)
					Mammalia					
3	Artiodactyla	*Capra hircus*	0.7 (0.5-0.9)	(6.0-6.8)	2600 (650-7500)		(36-48)			23,25
4		*Ovis aries*	0.9 (0.1-2.5)	(6.2-6.8)	3000 (500-6000)	30	(24-48)	(5-6) hr	6 min	1,5,9,16, 26,33
5		*Sus scrofa*	250 (125-500)	(7.3-7.9)	100 (25-1000)		(36-48)	(4-6) hr		1,2,16,19, 23
6	Perissodactyla	*Equus asinus*	50 (10-115)		400 (95-600)					2,16,21
7		*E. caballus*	70 (30-320)	(6.9-7.8)	120 (30-800)	138	12	30 min	15 min	1,2,4,9,16, 21,23
8	Carnivora	*Canis familiaris*	10 (1-25)	(5.8-7.0)	125 (10-540)		(36-60)	20 min[4]	15 sec	2,6,12,14
9		*Felis catus*	<1		500				100 min	7,15
10		*Vulpes fulva*	6 (0.1-33.0)	(6.2-6.4)	55 (30-250)			8 min[5]		2,16
11	Rodentia	*Cavia porcellus*	(1-5)			22		15 min	Immediate	2,8
12	Lagomorpha	*Oryctolagus cuniculus*	1 (0.4-6.0)	(6.6-7.5)	700 (100-2000)	30	<96	(3-4) hr		2,11,16
13	Chiroptera	*Myotis* sp.	0.05		6000 (5000-8000)					16
					Aves					
14	Galliformes	*Gallus domesticus*	0.6 (0.4-1.0)	(6.8-8.4)	3800 (800-6800)	15 (4-29)				20,30,32
15		*Meleagris gallopavo*	0.21 (0.08-0.37)	(7.0-8.1)	6800 (4800-8200)	43 (7-62)				10,17,18

/1/ Duration of fertilizing capacity. /2/ Life of sperm. /3/ Ovarian end of fallopian tube. /4/ From beginning of copulation. /5/ After mating.

Contributors: (a) Almquist, J. O., (b) Chang, M. C., (c) Winters, L. M., (d) Van Demark, N. L.

References: [1] Anderson, J. 1945. The semen of animals and its use for artificial insemination. Imp. Bur. Animal Breeding and Genetics, Edinburgh. [2] Asdell, S. A. 1946. Patterns of mammalian reproduction. Comstock, Ithaca. [3] Bishop, M. W. H., et al. 1954. J. Agr. Sci. 44:227. [4] Burkhardt, J. 1949. Ibid. 39:201. [5] Dauzier, L., and S. Wintenberger. 1952. Compt. rend. soc. biol. 146:660. [6] Evans, E. J. 1933. Am. J. Physiol. 105:287. [7] Farris, E. J. 1950. The care and breeding of laboratory animals. J. Wiley and Sons, New York. [8] Florey, H., and A. Walton. 1932. J. Physiol. 74:5. [9] Frank, A. H. 1950. U. S. Dept. Agr. Circ. 567. [10] Hale, E. B. 1955. Poultry Sci. 34:228. [11] Hammond, J., and S. A. Asdell. 1926. Brit. J. Exptl. Biol. 4:155. [12] Harrop, A. E. 1956. Proc. 3rd Intern. Congr. Animal Reproduction, p. 95. [13] Laing, J. A. 1945. J. Agr. Sci. 35:72. [14] Lambert, W. V., and F. F. McKenzie. 1940. U. S. Dept. Agr. Circ. 567. [15] Lesbouyries, G. 1949. Reproduction des mammiferes domestiques, sexualité. Vigot Frères, Paris. [16] Mann, T. 1954. The biochemistry of semen. Methuen, London. [17] McCartney, M. G. 1956. Poultry Sci. 35:137. [18] McCartney, M. G., and K. I. Brown. 1959. Ibid. 38:390. [19] McKenzie, F. F., J. C. Miller, and L. C. Bauguess. 1938. Missouri Agr. Expt. Sta. Research Bull. 279. [20] Nicolaides, C. 1934. Poultry Sci. 13:178. [21] Nishikawa, Y. 1959. Studies on reproduction in horses. Japan Racing Association, Tokyo. [22] Parkes, A. S., ed. 1952. Marshall's Physiology of reproduction. Ed. 3. Longmans, Green; London. v. 2. [23] Rice, V. A., and F. N. Andrews. 1951. Breeding and improvement of farm animals. McGraw-Hill, New York. [24] Rubenstein, B. B., et al. 1951. Fertility and Sterility 2:15. [25] Shukla, D. D., and P. Bhattacharya. 1949. Indian J. Vet. Sci. 19:161. [26] Starke, N. C. 1949. Onderstepoort J. Vet. Sci. Animal Ind. 22:415. [27] Stein, I. F., and M. R. Cohen. 1950.

continued

34. SPERM: VERTEBRATES

Part II: VOLUME, VIABILITY, AND TRANSPORT

Fertility and Sterility 1:169. [28] Van Demark, N. L., and A. N. Moeller. 1951. Am. J. Physiol. 165:674. [29] Vandeplassche, M., and F. Paredis. 1949. Tijdschr. Diergeneesk. 74:831. [30] Wales, R. G., and I. G. White. 1958. Australian J. Biol. Sci. 11:177. [31] White, I. G. 1958. Animal Breeding Abstr. 26(2):109. [32] Wilcox, F. H., and C. S. Shaffner. 1957. J. Appl. Physiol. 11:429. [33] Winters, L. M. 1948. Animal breeding. J. Wiley and Sons, New York.

Part III: ARTIFICIAL INSEMINATION

Sperm Collection (column C): M = masturbation, AV = artificial vagina, EE = electroejaculation, MM = manual manipulation, VD = stripping from vas deferens. Storage Temperature (column F): NS = not stored. Insemination Site (column H): C = cervix, U = uterus, IP = intraperitoneal, H = uterine horn, V = anterior vagina, O = oviduct.

	Order	Species	Sperm Collection	Diluent	Semen: Extender Ratio[1]	Storage[1] Temp. °C	Storage[1] Time	Insemination Site	Insemination Time	Insemination Vol	Reference
	(A)	(B)	(C)	(D)	(E)	(F)	(G)	(H)	(I)	(J)	(K)
					Mammalia						
1	Primates	*Homo sapiens*	M	Buffered glucose, glycerine	1:1[2]	5[3]	15 hr	C	10-14 da after end of menstruation	0.5 ml	34,43
2	Artiodactyla	*Bos taurus*	AV or EE	Yolk-citrate glycerol, milk glycerol, yolk-citrate glycine, yolk-citrate carbonate plus CO_2	<1:200	5[3]	3-4 da[4]	C or U	End of estrus	1.0 ml	1-3,6,7, 13,15,16, 33,36,37, 41,47,48, 54,55
3		*Bubalus* sp.	AV	Yolk-citrate glucose or yolk glycine	1:5	5	48 hr	C or U	End of estrus	1.0 ml	30,35,40, 45
4		*Capra hircus*	AV	Milk or yolk-citrate	1:15	2-5	24 hr	C	Last half of estrus	0.1-0.2 ml	11,12,14, 28,35,42, 46
5		*Ovis aries*	AV or EE	Milk or yolk-citrate	1:15	2-5	24 hr	C	Last half of estrus	0.1-0.2 ml	11,12,14, 28,35,42, 46
6		*Sus scrofa*	AV	Yolk-citrate glucose, milk glucose	1:2 or 1:3	5-20	Not >12 hr	C or U	10-25 hr after onset of estrus	20-50 ml	17,20,25, 31,35,51
7	Perissodactyla	*Equus caballus*	AV	Yolk-glucose	1:1	5	<40 hr	U	12-20 hr after onset of estrus	10-50 ml	17,29,35
8	Carnivora	*Canis familiaris*	AV or MM	Yolk-citrate, milk	1:7	5	<24 hr	U	11-13 da after initial bleeding	1.0 ml	17,21,35
9	Rodentia	*Cavia porcellus*	EE	Locke's fluid		NS		IP	1-16 hr after estrus	$3\text{-}5 \times 10^7$ sperm	18,39
10		*Mus musculus*	VD	Locke's fluid		NS		U	1.2-4.5 hr after mating with vasectomized male	0.02-0.10 ml	23,44
11		*Rattus rattus*	VD	Liver extract-glucose		NS		H	During estrus	0.1-0.2 ml	5,32
12	Lagomorpha	*Oryctolagus cuniculus*	AV	Modified Krebs' solution		NS		V	4-6 hr after mating with vasectomized buck	0.25-1.0 ml[5]	4,10,19,26

/1/ Unfrozen, unless otherwise indicated. /2/ Frozen, 10:1. /3/ Frozen, -79 or -196°C. /4/ Frozen, >6 yr. /5/ 1×10^6 sperm per insemination.

continued

34. SPERM: VERTEBRATES

Part III: ARTIFICIAL INSEMINATION

	Order	Species	Sperm Col-lection	Diluent	Semen: Extender Ratio[1]	Storage[1] Temp. °C	Storage[1] Time	Insemination Site	Insemination Time	Insemination Vol	Reference
	(A)	(B)	(C)	(D)	(E)	(F)	(G)	(H)	(I)	(J)	(K)
					Aves						
13	Galliformes	*Gallus domesticus*	MM	Phosphate buffer	1:10	10-25	8 hr	O	1-2 wk intervals	0.01 ml	8,9,34,35, 38,52
14		*Meleagris gallopavo*	MM	Milk or phosphate buffer	None	NS		O	2 wk intervals	0.01 ml	8,27,34, 35,49,53, 56
15	Anseriformes	*Anas* sp.	MM	Physiological saline	1:5 to 1:20	NS		O	5 da intervals	0.3 ml	34,35,50
16		*Anser* sp.	MM			NS		O	1 wk intervals	0.05 ml	22,24,34, 35

/1/ Unfrozen, unless otherwise indicated.

Contributor: Elliott, F. I.

References: [1] Almquist, J. O. 1959. Artificial Insemination Digest 7:11. [2] Almquist, J. O., and P. W. Prince. 1950. J. Dairy Sci. 33:393. [3] Amann, R. P., and J. O. Almquist. 1957. Ibid. 40:1542. [4] Black, W. G., G. Otto, and L. E. Casida. 1951. Endocrinology 49:237. [5] Blandau, R. J., and E. S. Jordan. 1941. J. Lab. Clin. Med. 26:1361. [6] Bratton, R. W., R. H. Foote, and C. R. Henderson. 1954. J. Dairy Sci. 37:1353. [7] Bratton, R. W., et al. 1949. Ibid. 32:604. [8] Burrows, W. H., and J. P. Quinn. 1937. Poultry Sci. 16:19. [9] Cooper, D. M., and J. G. Rowell. 1960. Animal Breeding Abstr. 28:395. [10] Cupps, P. T. 1959. Ibid. 26:429. [11] Dauzier, L., and F. du Mesnil du Buisson. 1959. Ibid. 27:200. [12] Duran del Campo, A. 1960. Ibid. 28:424. [13] Dziuk, P. J., E. F. Graham, and W. E. Petersen. 1954. J. Dairy Sci. 37:1035. [14] Easley, G. T. 1951. J. Am. Vet. Med. Assoc. 119:278. [15] Foote, R. H., and R. W. Bratton. 1949. J. Dairy Sci. 32:723. [16] Foote, R. H., et al. 1960. Ibid. 43:1330. [17] Frank, A. H. 1950. U. S. Dept. Agr. Circ. 567. [18] Freund, M. 1960. Animal Breeding Abstr. 28:1561. [19] Hadek, R. 1959. Ibid. 27:2010. [20] Hancock, J. L., and G. J. R. Hovell. 1961. Animal Production 3(2):153. [21] Harrop, A. E. 1954. Brit. Vet. J. 110:194. [22] Johnson, A. S. 1954. Poultry Sci. 33:638. [23] Kile, J. C., Jr. 1951. Anat. Record 109:109. [24] Kinney, T., and R. E. Burger. 1960. Animal Breeding Abstr. 28:2271. [25] Lardy, H. A., and P. H. Phillips. 1942. Am. J. Physiol. 138:741. [26] Macirone, C., and A. Walton. 1938. J. Agr. Sci. 28:122. [27] McCartney, M. G., et al. 1961. Animal Breeding Abstr. 29:522. [28] Morrant, A. J., and R. B. Dun. 1960. Australian Vet. J. 36:1. [29] Murphree, R. L., et al. 1949. J. Animal Sci. 8:642. [30] Nishikawa, Y., Y. Cheng, and Y. Cheng. 1957. Animal Breeding Abstr. 25:1266. [31] Niwa, T., A. Mizuho, and A. Soejima. 1960. Bull. Natl. Inst. Agr. Sci., G, 19:25. [32] Ogawa, S., and Y. Suzuki. 1958. Animal Breeding Abstr. 26:374. [33] Olds, D., et al. 1953. J. Dairy Sci. 36:1031. [34] Parkes, A. S., ed. 1952. Marshall's Physiology of reproduction. Ed. 3. Longmans, Green; London. v. 2, p. 681. [35] Perry, E. J. 1960. The artificial insemination of farm animals. Rutgers Univ. Press, New Brunswick. [36] Pickett, B. W., et al. 1960. Artificial Insemination Digest 8:6. [37] Polge, C., and K. F. Jakobsen. 1960. Animal Breeding Abstr. 28:143. [38] Rowell, J. G., and D. M. Cooper. 1960. Poultry Sci. 39:1381. [39] Rowlands, I. W. 1957. Endocrinology 16:98. [40] Roy, A., R. K. Srivastava, and M. D. Pandey. 1957. Animal Breeding Abstr. 25:161. [41] Salisbury, G. W. 1957. Ibid. 25:111. [42] Setinski, Z., J. Pelicaric, and M. Kaciga. 1958. Ibid. 26:281. [43] Sherman, J. K., and R. G. Bunge. 1953. Proc. Soc. Exptl. Biol. Med. 82:686. [44] Snell, G. D., K. P. Hummel, and W. H. Abelmann. 1944. Anat. Record 90:243. [45] Srivastava, P. N., and S. S. Prabhu. 1957. Animal Breeding Abstr. 25:165. [46] Szumowski, P., B. Markovic, and A. Cano. 1956. Ibid. 24:376. [47] Trimberger, G. W., and H. P. Davis. 1943. Nebraska Agr. Expt. Sta. Research Bull. 129. [48] Van Demark, N. L., and U. D. Sharma. 1957. J. Dairy Sci. 40:438. [49] Van Tienhoven, A., and R. G. D. Steel. 1957. Poultry Sci. 36:473. [50] Watanabe, M., and Y. Sugimori. 1957. Zootec. e Vet. 12:119.

continued

34. SPERM: VERTEBRATES

Part III: ARTIFICIAL INSEMINATION

[51] Wiggins, E. L., R. H. Grummer, and L. E. Casida. 1951. J. Animal Sci. 10:138. [52] Wilcox, F. H. 1960. Poultry Sci. 39:459. [53] Wilcox, F. H., and C. S. Shoffner. 1960. Ibid. 39:1580. [54] Willett, E. L., and G. L. Larson. 1952. J. Dairy Sci. 35:899. [55] Willett, E. L., and G. W. Salisbury. 1942. Cornell Univ. Agr. Expt. Sta. Mem. 249. [56] Wyne, J. W., et al. 1959. Poultry Sci. 38:828.

35. OVUM: VERTEBRATES

Part I: DIAMETER AND VOLUME EXTREMES WITHIN TAXONOMIC CLASSES

	Class	Species	Extreme	Diameter mm	Volume cu mm	Reference
	(A)	(B)	(C)	(D)	(E)	(F)
1	Mammalia	*Ovis aries*	Largest	0.15	0.0018	1
2		*Mus musculus*	Smallest	0.087	0.000363	2
3	Aves	*Struthio* sp.	Largest	80 (shell 155 x 130)	268,000	3
4		*Archilochus* sp.	Smallest	6 (shell 14.0 x 9.5)	113	3
5	Reptilia	*Python molurus*	Largest	120 x 60	226,195	4
6		*Draco volans*	Smallest	5	65	4
7	Amphibia	*Ceratohyla bubalis* and *Nototrema* sp.	Largest	10	524	4
8		*Bufo calamita* and *Rana arvalis*	Smallest	0.7	0.18	4
9	Pisces	*Chlamydoselachus anguineus*	Largest	150	1,766,000	7
10		*Heterandria formosa*	Smallest	0.4	0.0335	5,6

Contributor: Mayer, Dennis T.

References: [1] Amoroso, E. C., W. F. B. Griffiths, and W. J. Hamilton. 1942. J. Anat. 76:377. [2] Lewis, W. H., and E. S. Wright. 1935. Contribs. Embryol. Carnegie Inst. Wash. 25:113. [3] Needham, J. 1931. Clinical embryology. Cambridge Univ. Press, London. [4] Parkes, A. S., ed. 1952. Marshall's Physiology of reproduction. Ed. 3. Longmans, Green; New York. v. 2, p. 10. [5] Schrimshaw, N. S. 1944. Biol. Bull. 87:37. [6] Schrimshaw, N. S. 1945. Ibid. 88:233. [7] Wilson, E. B. 1925. The cell in development and heredity. Macmillan, New York.

Part II: DIMENSIONS, VIABILITY, AND TRANSPORT

	Order and Species	Ovum Diameter mm	Thickness of Zona Pellucida mm	Follicle Size at Ovulation mm	Ovum Viability hr	Ovum Transport Time[1] da	Time of Ovulation	Reference
	(A)	(B)	(C)	(D)	(E)	(F)	(G)	(H)
	Primates							
1	*Homo sapiens*	0.089-0.091[2]	0.019-0.035[3]		24[4]	3[5]	14±2 da prior to next menstrual period	6,33,34,47
2	*Macaca mulatta*	0.109-0.173	0.0115-0.0340[6]		<24	3	9th-20th da of menstrual cycle	1,7,15,37,52
	Artiodactyla							
3	*Bos taurus*	0.135-0.157	0.012-0.015	10-20[7]	12-24	3-4	13.5-15.5 hr after end of estrus	7,16,27,30,53, 55
4	*Capra hircus*	0.140-0.145	0.0125			2.5-4.0	Near end of estrus	2,3,16,29,44

/1/ From tube to uterus. /2/ Calculated for unfertilized tubal ovum with vitelline membrane only; with zona pellucida, calculated diameter is 0.133 mm, and with corona radiata, 0.178-0.202 mm. [47] /3/ Zona pellucida of unfertilized tubal ovum. /4/ Probably fertilizable for not more than 12 hours [32]. /5/ Probably maximum time necessary for segmenting ovum to reach uterine cavity [34]; time between fertilization and implantation, 6-7 days [31]. /6/ Clear, highly refractile membrane, sharply defined; inner third is pale iridescent blue. [1] /7/ Diameter.

continued

35. OVUM: VERTEBRATES

Part II: DIMENSIONS, VIABILITY, AND TRANSPORT

	Order and Species	Ovum Diameter mm	Thickness of Zona Pellucida mm	Follicle Size at Ovulation mm	Ovum Viability hr	Ovum Transport Time[1] da	Time of Ovulation	Reference
	(A)	(B)	(C)	(D)	(E)	(F)	(G)	(H)
	Artiodactyla							
5	*Ovis aries*	0.120-0.180	0.011-0.016	15-19	12-24	2-4	18-24 hr after onset of estrus	3,7,8,12,16,19, 29,45,46,50,53, 56
6	*Sus scrofa*	0.120-0.140	0.015	7-10	12-48	3-4	36 hr after onset of estrus	4,7,16,29,35,44, 53
	Perissodactyla							
7	*Equus caballus*	0.099-0.141	0.0135[8]	35-55	24	4	24-48 hr before end of estrus	2,5,7,26,29,42, 43,46,56
	Carnivora							
8	*Canis familiaris*	0.135-0.145	0.135	10[7]	96-192	6-8	24-48 hr after onset of estrus	7,16,29,43,44
9	*Felis catus*	0.120-0.130	0.012-0.115			4-8	24-30 hr after coitus	6,7,23,29,40,44
10	*Mustela furo*	0.116-0.132	0.004-0.006[8]			5-6	30 hr after coitus	25,28,29,41,44
	Rodentia							
11	*Cavia porcellus*	0.075-0.107	0.012	0.8	<26	3.5	10 hr after onset of estrus	7,10,29,44,49,54
12	*Mus musculus*	0.070-0.087		0.5	12	1.45	2 hr after onset of estrus	7,11,21,22,29, 38,39,43,44,48
13	*Rattus rattus*	0.070-0.076		0.9	<12-33	3	7.5-12.5 hr after onset of estrus	4,7,9,29,43,44
	Lagomorpha							
14	*Oryctolagus cuniculus*	0.110-0.146	0.011-0.023	1.8[7]	6	2.5-4.0	10-12 hr after coitus	7,20,29,44
	Edentata							
15	*Dasypus novemcinctus*	0.080						29,43
	Chiroptera							
16	*Rhinolophus ferrum-equinum*	0.095-0.140	0.090-0.110			>21		14,24,29,51
	Marsupialia							
17	*Didelphis virginiana*	0.130-0.160[9]	0.004-0.008[8]			2	Probably early in estrus	1,7,13,15,29,36, 37,52
18	*Dasyurus viverrinus*	0.240	Present				5 da after coitus or estrus	7,29,43
	Monotremata							
19	*Ornithorhynchus paradoxus*	2.5-4.5[10]	Present					14,17,18,29

/1/ From tube to uterus. /7/ Diameter. /8/ Homogeneous and gelatinous. /9/ With shell membrane, dimensions increase to 0.40-0.50 mm. /10/ Shell up to 6.5 mm [14].

Contributors: (a) Shettles, Landrum B., and Engle, Earl T., (b) Hertig, Arthur T., (c) Winters, L. M., (d) Reynolds, Albert E.

References: [1] Allen, E. 1928. Anat. Record 37:351. [2] Amoroso, E. C., W. F. B. Griffiths, and W. J. Hamilton. 1939. Vet. Record 51:168. [3] Amoroso, E. C., W. F. B. Griffiths, and W. J. Hamilton. 1942. J. Anat. 76:377. [4] Andersen, D. H. 1927. Am. J. Physiol. 82:557. [5] Andrews, F. N., and F. F. McKenzie. 1941. Missouri Agr. Expt. Sta. Research Bull. 329. [6] Arey, L. B. 1946. Developmental anatomy. W. B. Saunders, Philadelphia. [7] Asdell, S. A. 1946. Patterns of mammalian reproduction. Comstock, Ithaca. [8] Assheton, R. 1898. Quart. J. Microscop. Sci. 41:205. [9] Blandau, R. J., and E. S. Jordan. 1941. Am. J. Anat. 68:275. [10] Blandau, R. J., and W. C. Young. 1939. Ibid. 64:308. [11] Burdick, H. O., R. Whitney, and B. Emerson. 1942. Endocrinology 31:101. [12] Clark, R. T. 1934. Anat. Record 60:135. [13] Corner, G. W. 1923. Contribs. Embryol. Carnegie Inst. Wash. 15:73. [14] Corner, G. W. 1938. In E. V. Cowdry, ed. Special cytology. P. B. Hoeber, New York. [15] Corner, G. W. 1952. Brit. Med. J. 2:403. [16] Dukes, H. H. 1947. The physiology of

continued

domestic animals. Comstock, Ithaca. [17] Garde, M. L. 1930. J. Anat. 64:422. [18] Gatenby, J. B., and J. P. Hill. 1924. Quart. J. Microscop. Sci. 68:229. [19] Green, W. W., and L. M. Winters. 1946. J. Morphol. 78:305. [20] Gregory, P. W. 1930. Contribs. Embryol. Carnegie Inst. Wash. 21:141. [21] Gresson, R. A. R. 1933. Quart. J. Microscop. Sci. 75:697. [22] Gresson, R. A. R. 1940. Ibid. 81:569. [23] Gros, G. 1935. Compt. rend. soc. biol. 131:172. [24] Guthrie, M. J., and K. R. Jeffers. 1938. J. Morphol. 62:523. [25] Hamilton, W. J. 1934. Trans. Roy. Soc. Edinburgh 58:251. [26] Hamilton, W. J., and F. T. Day. 1945. J. Anat. 79:127. [27] Hamilton, W. J., and J. A. Laing. 1946. Ibid. 80:194. [28] Hammond, J., and A. Walton. 1934. J. Exptl. Biol. 11:307. [29] Hartman, C. G. 1929. Quart. Rev. Biol. 4:373. [30] Hartman, C. G., et al. 1931. Anat. Record 48:267. [31] Hertig, A. T., and J. Rock. 1945. Contribs. Embryol. Carnegie Inst. Wash. 31:65. [32] Hertig, A. T., and J. Rock. 1951. Am. J. Obstet. Gynecol. 61A:8. [33] Hertig, A. T., J. Rock, and E. C. Adams. 1956. Am. J. Anat. 98:435. [34] Hertig, A. T., et al. 1954. Contribs. Embryol. Carnegie Inst. Wash. 35:199. [35] Heuser, C. H., and G. L. Streeter. 1929. Ibid. 20:1. [36] Lewis, W. H., and C. G. Hartman. 1933. Ibid. 24:187. [37] Lewis, W. H., and C. G. Hartman. 1941. Ibid. 29:7. [38] Lewis, W. H., and E. S. Wright. 1935. Ibid. 25:113. [39] Long, J. A. 1912. Univ. Calif. (Berkeley) Publs. Zool. 9:105. [40] Longley, W. H. 1912. Am. J. Anat. 12:139. [41] Mainland, D. 1932. J. Anat. 66:586. [42] Mirskaya, L. M., and A. A. Salzman. 1935. Adv. Zootech. Sci. Moscow 1:157. [43] Parkes, A. S., ed. 1952. Marshall's Physiology of reproduction. Ed. 3. Longmans, Green; London. [44] Pincus, G. 1936. The eggs of mammals. Macmillan, New York. [45] Quinlan, J., G. S. Maré, and L. L. Roux. 1932. 18th Rept. Div. Vet. Serv. and Animal Ind. Union S. Africa (2):813. [46] Rice, V. A., and F. N. Andrews. 1951. Breeding and improvement of farm animals. McGraw-Hill, New York. [47] Rock, J., and A. T. Hertig. 1944. Am. J. Obstet. Gynecol. 47:343. [48] Snell, G. D. 1941. Biology of the laboratory mouse. Blakiston, Philadelphia. [49] Squier, R. R. 1932. Contribs. Embryol. Carnegie Inst. Wash. 23:223. [50] Van Beneden, E. 1911. Arch. biol. (Paris) 26:1. [51] Van Beneden, E., and C. Julian. 1880. Ibid. 1:551. [52] Van der Stricht, O. 1923. Ibid. 33:229. [53] Winters, L. M. 1948. Animal Breeding. J. Wiley and Sons, New York. [54] Winters, L. M. Unpublished. Univ. Minnesota, St. Paul, 1952. [55] Winters, L. M., W. W. Green, and R. E. Comstock. 1942. Univ. Minn. Agr. Expt. Sta. Tech. Bull. 151. [56] Zietzschmann, O. 1943. Handbuch der vergleichenden Anatomie der Haustiere. J. Springer, Berlin.

Part III: STRUCTURE

Symbols: (+) = present, (-) = absent, (0) = not recognizable.

	Order and Species	Polarity[1]	Corona Radiata	Tertiary Membrane	Vitelline Membrane	Cytoplasm	Nucleus	Reference
	(A)	(B)	(C)	(D)	(E)	(F)	(G)	(H)
	Primates							
1	*Homo sapiens*	0	+	-	+[2]	Transparent, yellowish, finely granular; vitellus does not completely fill space within zona; polyovular follicles occur	Central or eccentric; 1st polar body extruded and maturation spindle formed before ovulation; nucleolus with chromatin	2,3,10, 22,28, 46,49, 51,52
2	*Macaca mulatta*	+	+	-	±[3]	Yellowish, fine yolk granules; vitellus fills zona; polyovular follicles	1st polar body extruded before ovulation; polynuclear ova	1,9,10, 28,38, 39,46
	Artiodactyla							
3	*Bos taurus*	0	-	-	±[3]	Scattered fat granules (0.001-0.004 mm)	1st polar body formed before ovulation; polynuclear ova may occur	13,24, 28,29, 46

/1/ Of uncleaved egg. /2/ Very slight membrane (merely cytoplasmic membrane of vitellus). /3/ Perivitelline space present.

continued

35. OVUM: VERTEBRATES

Part III: STRUCTURE

	Order and Species	Polarity[1]	Corona Radiata	Tertiary Membrane	Vitelline Membrane	Cytoplasm	Nucleus	Reference
	(A)	(B)	(C)	(D)	(E)	(F)	(G)	(H)
	Artiodactyla							
4	*Capra hircus*	0	-	-		Fine fat granules, evenly distributed	1st polar body formed before ovulation	5,46
5	*Ovis aries*	0	-	-	±[4]	Yellowish granular material; dense, numerous, nonfat yolk globules; mitochondria first appear concentrated in periphery; polyovular follicles may occur	1st polar body extruded before ovulation; polynuclear ova may occur	6,8,20, 28,43, 46
6	*Sus scrofa*	0	-	-	±[3]	Yolk heavy with fat; polyovular follicles may occur	1st polar body formed before ovulation; polynuclear ova may occur	1,6,10, 11,28, 31,46, 47
	Perissodactyla							
7	*Equus caballus*	0	-	+[5]	+[4]	Highly refractile fat globules so dense that vitellus is dark	1st polar body extruded before ovulation	4,10,23
	Carnivora							
8	*Canis familiaris*	+	+	-	+	Highly refractile fat globules so dense that vitellus is dark; mitochondria concentrated in cortex; polyovular follicles	Membrane, nucleolus, and/or chromatin visible; ovum discharged from ovary while nuclear material in germinative vesicle form; polynuclear ova	3,14,21, 28,46, 56,57
9	*Felis catus*	+	+	-	+	Deutoplasm with fat globules; mitochondria concentrated in cortex; polyovular follicles	1st polar body extruded before, and 2nd maturation spindle established at, ovulation; polynuclear ova	28,35, 46,57, 58
10	*Mustela furo*	+	+	-	±[3]	Highly refractile fat granules so dense that vitellus is dark	1st polar body formed before ovulation (ovulation only after coitus)	21,41,46
	Rodentia							
11	*Cavia porcellus*	+	+	-	±[3]	Small fat globules at vegetal pole; mitochondria scattered; golgi apparatus as fenestrated membrane at periphery	1st polar body formed before ovulation; polynuclear ova	7,28,30, 36,45, 46,54
12	*Mus musculus*	+	+	-	+	Yellowish granular material; scattered nonfat yolk globules; vitellus fills zona; mitochondria first appear concentrated in periphery; golgi bodies more numerous toward one pole	Clear nongranular nucleus in center; 1st polar body formed in ovary; polynuclear ova	17,19, 20,24, 28,40, 45,46
13	*Rattus rattus*	0	+	-	±[3]	Optically heterogeneous, not transparent; 2 or 3 vacuoles detectable near center	1st polar body formed before ovulation	12,17, 46,53
	Lagomorpha							
14	*Oryctolagus cuniculus*	0	+	-	±[3]	Transparent; mitochondria first appear concentrated in periphery; golgi material is loose network of thick threads at periphery	1st polar body extruded before ovulation; polynuclear ova	3,18,28, 45,46, 48,50
	Edentata							
15	*Dasypus novemcinctus*				+	Deutoplasmic granules	One or two may be formed with maturation spindle; 1st spindle formed in ovary; 4 young develop from 1 egg	44,46

/1/ Of uncleaved egg. /3/ Perivitelline space present. /4/ Perivitelline space filled with finely granular material. /5/ Thin albuminous coat in tubal ovum.

continued

35. OVUM: VERTEBRATES

Part III: STRUCTURE

	Order and Species	Polarity[1]	Corona Radiata	Tertiary Membrane	Vitelline Membrane	Cytoplasm	Nucleus	Reference
	(A)	(B)	(C)	(D)	(E)	(F)	(G)	(H)
	Chiroptera							
16	*Rhinolophus ferrum-equinum*	+	+	-	+	Fat droplets, yolk vesicles; mitochondria concentrated in cortex	1st polar body formed before ovulation; polynuclear ova	10,25, 28,37, 46,55, 57
	Marsupialia							
17	*Didelphis virginiana*	+[6]	-	+[7]	+	Usually elliptical; yolk differentiated in 3 zones; fat chiefly in middle or submarginal zone; in some ova, large fat vacuole occurs at one pole, usually opposite polar body; polyovular follicles	1st polar body given off in ovary; chromosomes, as with all mammals, are short rods in the form of open ring; polynuclear ova	10,26, 27,46
18	*Dasyurus viverrinus*	+	-	+[8]		Yolk accumulated at animal pole	Pronuclei in granular formative cytoplasm; 1st polar body extruded in ovary	10,32, 46
	Monotremata							
19	*Ornithorhynchus paradoxus*	+	-	+[9]	+	Bulk is formed of yellowish yolk spheres, up to 0.036 mm, dispersed in peripheral and central zone; latebra in center of yolk	0.014-0.20 mm in diameter; diffusely staining, vesicular in character, has faint reticulum, dark-staining vacuolated nucleolus; 1st polar body given off in ovary; egg normally monospermic	10,16, 34,46

/1/ Of uncleaved egg. /6/ Determined by position of polar body. /7/ Produced by secretory activity of oviduct (albuminous coat is 0.05 mm thick, shell membrane is 0.0012 mm thick) [26,32,33,42]. /8/ Laminated albuminous layer and very thin shell membrane formed in the tube [10,32]. /9/ Well-developed membrane, consisting of an albuminous coat (more than 2 mm thick), a shell membrane, and a parchmentlike shell [10,15,34].

Contributors: Shettles, Landrum B., and Engle, Earl T.

References: [1] Allen, E. 1928. Anat. Record 37:351. [2] Allen, E., et al. 1930. Am. J. Anat. 46:1. [3] Allen, E., et al. 1930. Contribs. Embryol. Carnegie Inst. Wash. 22:45. [4] Amoroso, E. C., W. F. B. Griffiths, and W. J. Hamilton. 1939. Vet. Record 51:168. [5] Amoroso, E. C., W. F. B. Griffiths, and W. J. Hamilton. 1942. J. Anat. 76:377. [6] Assheton, R. 1898. Quart J. Microscop. Sci. 41:329. [7] Cattaneo, D. 1913-14. Arch. ital. anat. embriol. 12:1. [8] Clark, R. T. 1934. Anat. Record 60:135. [9] Corner, G. W. 1923. Contribs. Embryol. Carnegie Inst. Wash. 15:73. [10] Corner, G. W. 1938. In E. V. Cowdry, ed. Special cytology. P. B. Hoeber, New York. [11] Corner, G. W., and A. E. Amsbaugh. 1917. Anat. Record 12:287. [12] Defrise, A. 1933. Ibid. 57:239. [13] Evans, E. I., and F. W. Miller. 1935. Ibid. 62:25. [14] Evans, H. M., and H. H. Cole. 1931. Mem. Univ. Calif. 9:65. [15] Flynn, T. T., and J. P. Hill. 1939. Trans. Zool. Soc. London 24:445. [16] Gatenby, J. B., and J. P. Hill. 1924. Quart. J. Microscop. Sci. 68:229. [17] Gilchrist, F., and G. Pincus. 1932. Anat. Record 54:275. [18] Gregory, P. W. 1930. Contribs. Embryol. Carnegie Inst. Wash. 21:141. [19] Gresson, R. A. R. 1933. Quart. J. Microscop. Sci. 75:697. [20] Gresson, R. A. R. 1941. Ibid. 82:35. [21] Hamilton, W. J. 1934. Trans. Roy. Soc. Edinburgh 58:251. [22] Hamilton, W. J. 1944. J. Anat. 78:1. [23] Hamilton, W. J., and F. T. Day. 1945. Ibid. 79:127. [24] Hamilton, W. J., and J. A. Laing. 1946. Ibid. 80:194. [25] Hamlett, G. W. D. 1935. Am. J. Anat. 56:327. [26] Hartman, C. G. 1916. J. Morphol. 27:1. [27] Hartman, C. G. 1919. Ibid. 32:1. [28] Hartman, C. G. 1926. Am. J. Anat. 37:1. [29] Hartman, C. G., et al. 1931. Anat. Record 48:267. [30] Henneguy, L. F. 1926. Compt. rend. soc. biol. 94:764. [31] Heuser, C. H., and G. L. Streeter. 1929. Contribs. Embryol. Carnegie Inst. Wash. 20:1. [32] Hill, J. P. 1910. Quart. J. Microscop. Sci. 56:1. [33] Hill, J. P.

continued

35. OVUM: VERTEBRATES

Part III: STRUCTURE

1918. Ibid. 63:91. [34] Hill, J. P. 1933. Trans. Zool. Soc. London 21:413. [35] Hill, J. P., and M. Tribe. 1924. Quart. J. Microscop. Sci. 68:514. [36] Lams, H. 1913. Arch. biol. (Paris) 28:229. [37] Levi, G. 1915. Arch. Zellforsch. 13:47. [38] Lewis, W. H., and C. G. Hartman. 1933. Contribs. Embryol. Carnegie Inst. Wash. 24:187. [39] Lewis, W. H., and C. G. Hartman. 1941. Ibid. 29:7. [40] Lewis, W. H., and E. S. Wright. 1935. Ibid. 25:113. [41] Mainland, D. 1932. J. Anat. 66:586. [42] McCrady, E., Jr. 1938. Am. Anat. Mem. 16. [43] McKenzie, F. F., and C. E. Terrill. 1937. Research Bull. Univ. Missouri Agr. Expt. Sta. 264. [44] Newman, H. M. 1913. Biol. Bull. 25:52. [45] Nihoul, J. 1926. Cellule 37:23. [46] Parkes, A. S., ed. 1952. Marshall's Physiology of reproduction. Ed. 3. Longmans, Green; New York. [47] Patten, B. M. 1948. Embryology of the pig. Ed. 3. Blakiston, Philadelphia. [48] Pincus, G., and E. V. Enzmann. 1932. J. Exptl. Biol. 9:403. [49] Pincus, G., and B. Saunders. 1937. Anat. Record 69:163. [50] Rio Hortega, P. 1913. Trabajos lab. invest. biol. 11:163. [51] Rock, J., and A. T. Hertig. 1944. Am. J. Obstet. Gynecol. 47:343. [52] Shettles, L. B. 1960. Ovum humanum. Hafner, New York. [53] Sobotta, J., and G. Burckhard. 1911. Anat. Hefte 42:436. [54] Squier, R. R. 1932. Contribs. Embryol. Carnegie Inst. Wash. 23:223. [55] Van Beneden, E. 1911. Arch. biol. (Paris) 26:1. [56] Van der Stricht, O. 1908. Compt. rend. soc. anat. 10e reunion (Marseilles) 1. [57] Van der Stricht, O. 1923. Arch. biol. (Paris) 33:229. [58] Van der Stricht, R. 1911. Ibid. 26:365.

36. OVULATION: EUTHERIAN MAMMALS

Type of Ovulation (column B): S = spontaneous, I = induced by coitus, U = unknown. Ovaries Involved (column D): 1, LR = one involved, left and right ovaries alternate; 1, R = one involved, right predominates; 1, L = one involved, left predominates; RO = right only; U = unknown. Classification adapted from Simpson, *The Principles of Classification and a Classification of Mammals*, 1945.

	Family and Species	Type of Ovulation	No. of Ova Released	Ovaries Involved	Reference
	(A)	(B)	(C)	(D)	(E)
	Primates				
	Hominidae				
1	*Homo sapiens*	S	1	1, LR	2
	Cercopithecidae				
2	*Macaca mulatta*	S	1	1, LR	2
3	*Papio hamadryas*	S	1	1, LR	54
	Callithricidae				
4	*Leontocebus geoffroyi*	U	2	Both	53
	Cebidae				
5	*Alouatta palliata*	U	1	1, LR	13
6	*Ateles geoffroyi*	U	1	1, LR	13
7	*Cebus azarae*	S	1	1, LR	24
	Tarsiidae				
8	*Tarsius* sp.	S	1	1, LR	7,16
	Artiodactyla				
	Bovidae				
9	*Bos taurus*	S	1	1, R	2
10	*Capra hircus*	S	2-4	1, LR	2
11	*Ovis aries*	S	1-2	1, R	2
	Camelidae				
12	*Camelus* sp.	U	1-2	1, L	46
	Tayassuidae				
13	*Tayassu angulatus*	U	2	Both	52
	Suidae				
14	*Sus scrofa*	S	6-12	Both	2
	Perissodactyla				
	Equidae				
15	*Equus caballus*	S	1	1, LR	9
	Tubulidentata				
	Orycteropodidae				
16	*Orycteropus* sp.	U	5	Both	47
	Carnivora				
	Otariidae				
17	*Callorhinus ursinus*	I	1	1, LR	17
	Felidae				
18	*Felis catus*	I	4-6	Both	2
19	*F. sylvestris*	U	5	Both	31
20	*Lynx rufus*	U	3-4	Both	16
	Hyaenidae				
21	*Crocuta crocuta*	U	2-4	1, LR	30
	Mustelidae				
22	*Mustela erminea*	S	10-11	Both	11
23	*M. furo*	I	8-9	Both	25
24	*M. vison*	I	7	Both	26
	Canidae				
25	*Canis familiaris*	S	8-10	Both	2
26	*C. latrans*	S	.....	Both	23
27	*Vulpes fulva*	S	3-4	Both	2
28	*V. vulpes*	S	5-6	Both	41

continued

36. OVULATION: EUTHERIAN MAMMALS

	Family and Species	Type of Ovulation	No. of Ova Released	Ovaries Involved	Reference
	(A)	(B)	(C)	(D)	(E)
	Cetacea				
	Balaenopteridae				
29	*Megaptera nodosa*	U	1-2	Both	2
	Delphinidae				
30	*Globicephala melaena*	S	1	1, LR	27
	Rodentia				
	Chinchillidae				
31	*Lagidium peruanum*	U	1	RO	37
	Caviidae				
32	*Cavia porcellus*	S	2-4	Both	2
	Erethizontidae				
33	*Erethizon dorsatum*	U	1	1, LR	34,45
	Muridae				
34	*Mus musculus*	S	6	Both	2
35	*Rattus erythroleucus*	S	12	Both	4
36	*R. rattus*	S	10	Both	2
	Cricetidae				
37	*Arvicola amphibius*	S	6	Both	39
38	*Clethrionomys glareolus*	S	5	Both	6
39	*Cricetulus griseus*	S	.....	Both	35
40	*Cricetus auratus*	S	.....	Both	2,49
41	*Microtus agrestis*	S	6	Both	5
42	*Neotoma floridana*	S	4	Both	2,8
43	*Ondatra zibethica*	U	4-6	Both	16,18
44	*Peromyscus gossypinus*	S	5-6	Both	40
	Heteromyidae				
45	*Dipodomys ordii*	U	3-4	Both	16
46	*Perognathus parvus*	U	6	Both	16
	Geomyidae				
47	*Geomys bursarius*	U	4-6	Both	2
48	*Thomomys bottae*	S	6	Both	33
	Sciuridae				
49	*Citellus tridecemlineatus*	I	8	Both	14,19
50	*Cynomys leucurus*	U	5-6	Both	43
51	*Marmota flaviventris*	U	2-4	Both	16
52	*Sciurus carolinensis*	U	4	Both	12
	Lagomorpha				
	Leporidae				
53	*Lepus americanus*	U	3	Both	1
54	*L. californicus*	I	4	Both	16
55	*Oryctolagus cuniculus*	I	10	Both	2
56	*Sylvilagus floridanus*	I	4-6	Both	42
	Ochotonidae				
57	*Ochotona princeps*	U	2-4	Both	15
	Edentata				
	Dasypodidae				
58	*Dasypus novemcinctus*	U	1	1, LR	22
	Chiroptera				
	Vespertilionidae				
59	*Corynorhinus rafinesquei*	I[1]	1	1, LR	38
60	*Myotis lucifugus*	S[2]	1	1, LR	2,21, 50
61	*Scotophilus wroughtoni*	U	2	Both	20
	Desmodontidae				
62	*Desmodus rotundus*	S	1	1, LR	51
	Rhinolophidae				
63	*Rhinolophus* sp.	S	1	RO	29
	Nycteridae				
64	*Nycteris luteola*	S	1	U	32
	Insectivora				
	Talpidae				
65	*Talpa europaea*	U	4	Both	28
	Soricidae				
66	*Blarina brevicauda*	I	6	Both	36
67	*Sorex araneus*	I	7	Both	3
	Macroscelididae				
68	*Elephantulus myurus*	U	120	Both	48
	Erinaceida				
69	*Erinaceus europaeus*	S	5	Both	10
	Tenrecidae				
70	*Setifer setosus*	I	4-6	Both	44

/1/ But delayed. /2/ The evidence for *Corynorhinus* makes questionable the existence of spontaneous ovulation in other vespertilionid bats (at least until ovulatory status is ascertained for females denied copulation).

Contributor: Duke, Kenneth L.

References: [1] Aldous, C. M. 1937. J. Mammal. 18:46. [2] Asdell, S. A. 1946. Patterns of mammalian reproduction. Comstock, Ithaca. [3] Brambell, F. W. R. 1935. Trans. Roy. Soc. (London), B, 225:1. [4] Brambell, F. W. R., and D. H. S. Davis. 1941. Proc. Zool. Soc. (London), B, 111:1. [5] Brambell, F. W. R., and K. Hall. 1939. Ibid., A, 109:133. [6] Brambell, F. W. R., and I. W. Rowlands. 1936. Trans. Roy. Soc. (London), B, 226:71. [7] Catchpole, H. R., and J. F. Fulton. 1943. J. Mammal. 24:90. [8] Chapman, A. O. 1951. Univ. Kansas Sci. Bull. 34:267. [9] Cole, C. H., et al. 1931. Anat. Record 49:199. [10] Deanesly, R. 1934. Trans. Roy. Soc. (London), B, 223:239. [11] Deanesly, R. 1935. Ibid., B, 225:459. [12] Deanesly, R., and A. S. Parkes. 1933. Ibid., B, 222:47. [13] Dempsey, E. W. 1939. Am. J. Anat. 64:381. [14] Drips, D. 1919. Ibid. 25:117. [15] Duke, L. L. 1952. Anat. Record 112:737. [16] Duke, K. L. Unpublished, 1953. [17] Enders, R. K., et al. 1946. Anat. Record 94:213. [18] Forbes, T. R. 1942. Science 95:382. [19] Foster, M. L. 1934. Am. J. Anat. 54:487. [20] Gopalakrishna, A. 1949. Proc. Indian Acad. Sci. 30(B):17. [21] Guthrie, M., and K. Jeffers. 1938.

continued

Anat. Record 71:477. [22] Hamlett, G. W. D. 1932. Z. wiss. Zool. 141:143. [23] Hamlett, G. W. D. 1938. U. S. Dept. Agr. Tech. Bull. 616. [24] Hamlett, G. W. D. 1939. Anat. Record 73:171. [25] Hammond, J., and F. H. A. Marshall. 1930. Proc. Roy. Soc. (London), B, 105:607. [26] Hansson, A. 1947. Acta Zool. (Stockholm) 28:1. [27] Harrison, R. J. 1949. J. Anat. 83:238. [28] Matthews, L. H. 1935. Proc. Zool. Soc. (London) (2):347. [29] Matthews, L. H. 1937. Trans. Zool. Soc. (London) 23:224. [30] Matthews, L. H. 1939. Trans. Roy. Soc. (London), B, 230:1. [31] Matthews, L. H. 1941. Proc. Zool. Soc. (London), B, 111:59. [32] Matthews, L. H. 1941. Ibid., B, 111:289. [33] Miller, M. A. 1946. J. Mammal. 27:335. [34] Mossman, H. W., and I. Judas. 1949. Am. J. Anat. 85:1. [35] Parkes, A. S. 1931. Proc. Roy. Soc. (London), B, 108:138. [36] Pearson, O. P. 1944. Am. J. Anat. 75:39. [37] Pearson, O. P. 1949. Ibid. 84:143. [38] Pearson, O. P., et al. 1952. J. Mammal. 33:273. [39] Perry, J. S. 1942. Proc. Zool. Soc. (London), A, 112:118. [40] Pournelle, G. H. 1952. J. Mammal. 33:1. [41] Rowlands, I. W., and A. S. Parkes. 1935. Proc. Zool. Soc. (London), p. 823. [42] Schwartz, C. W. 1942. J. Mammal. 23:1. [43] Stockard, A. H. 1929. Ibid. 10:209. [44] Strauss, F. 1938. Bio-morphosis 1:281. [45] Struthers, P. H. 1928. J. Mammal. 9:300. [46] Tayeb, M. A. F. 1948. Vet. J. 104:179. [47] Van der Horst, C. J. 1949. Proc. Zool. Soc. (S. Africa) 119:1. [48] Van der Horst, C. J., and J. Gillman. 1940. Nature 145:974. [49] Ward, M. C. 1946. Anat. Record 94:139. [50] Wimsatt, W. A. 1944. Am. J. Anat. 74:129. [51] Wimsatt, W. A., and H. Trapido. 1952. Ibid. 91:415. [52] Wislocki, G. B. 1931. J. Mammal. 12:1. [53] Wislocki, G. B. 1939. Am. J. Anat. 64:445. [54] Zuckerman, S., and A. S. Parkes. 1932. Proc. Zool. Soc. (London), p. 139.

37. FERTILIZATION AND ZYGOTE DEVELOPMENT: MAMMALS

Data frequently have been retimed, reassessed, and/or approximated.

Part I: OVUM FERTILIZATION

	Order	Species	Starting Point[1]	Sperm Penetration	Second Polar Body Formation	Male Pronucleus Formation	Reference
	(A)	(B)	(C)	(D)	(E)	(F)	(G)
1	Primates	*Homo sapiens*	Ovulation	<1 da	36 hr	....	12, 24
2	Artiodactyla	*Bos taurus*	Ovulation	....	....	11-39 hr	10
3		*Ovis aries*	Coitus	....	....	<36 hr	6
4	Carnivora	*Felis catus*	Coitus	2-3 da	>22 hr	....	4, 13
5		*Mustela frenata*	Coitus	<53-80 hr	>74 hr	53-80 hr	28
6		*M. furo*	Coitus	6-30 hr	<41 hr	41-52 hr	9, 11, 19, 23
7		*Vulpes fulva*	Coitus	2-3 da	>3-4 da	....	21
8	Rodentia	*Cavia porcellus*	Coitus	10 hr	13.5 hr	12-31 hr	15
9		*Cricetus auratus*	Coitus	6-8 hr	>6 hr	12-24 hr	5, 26
10		*Mus musculus*	Coitus	0.25-2.0 hr	5-7 hr	6-24 hr	8, 16, 17, 25
11		*Rattus rattus*	Coitus	10 hr	10-14+ hr	14-35 hr	1, 2, 14, 18, 20
12	Lagomorpha	*Oryctolagus cuniculus*	Coitus	10-13 hr	13-14.5 hr	14-18 hr	3, 7, 22, 27

/1/ For times given in columns D-F.

Contributors: (a) Beatty, R. A., (b) Asdell, S. A., (c) Hertig, Arthur T.

References: [1] Austin, C. R. 1952. Australian J. Sci. Research, B, 5:354. [2] Austin, C. R., and A. W. H. Braden. 1954. Australian J. Biol. Sci. 7:179. [3] Chang, M. C. 1951. Fertility and Sterility 2:205. [4] Dawson, A. B., and H. B. Friedgood. 1940. Anat. Record 76:411. [5] Graves, A. P. 1945. Am. J. Anat. 77:219. [6] Green, W. W., and L. M. Winters. 1945. Univ. Minn. Tech. Bull. 169. [7] Gregory, P. W. 1930. Carnegie Inst. Wash. Publ. 21:141. [8] Gresson, R. A. R. 1941. Quart. J. Microscop. Sci. 83:35. [9] Hamilton, W. J. 1934. Trans. Roy. Soc. Edinburgh 58:251. [10] Hamilton, W. J., and J. A. Laing. 1946. J. Anat. 80:194. [11] Hammond, J., and A. Walton. 1934. J. Exptl. Biol. 11:307. [12] Hertig, A. T., et al. 1954. Contribs. Embryol. Carnegie Inst. Wash. 35:199. [13] Hill, J. P., and M. Tribe. 1924. Quart. J. Microscop. Sci. 68:513.

continued

37. FERTILIZATION AND ZYGOTE DEVELOPMENT: MAMMALS

Part I: OVUM FERTILIZATION

[14] Huber, G. C. 1915. J. Morphol. 26:247. [15] Lams, H. 1913. Arch. biol. (Liège) 28:229. [16] Lewis, W. H., and E. S. Wright. 1935. Contribs. Embryol. Carnegie Inst. Wash. 25:113. [17] Long, J. A., and E. L. Mark. 1911. Carnegie Inst. Wash. Publ. 142:1. [18] Macdonald, E., and J. A. Long. 1934. Am. J. Anat. 55:343. [19] Mainland, D. 1930. J. Anat. 64:262. [20] Odor, D. L., and R. J. Blandau. 1951. Am. J. Anat. 89:29. [21] Pearson, O. P., and R. K. Enders. 1943. Anat. Record 85:69. [22] Pincus, G., and E. V. Enzmann. 1932. J. Exptl. Biol. 9:403. [23] Robinson, A. 1918. Trans. Roy. Soc. Edinburgh 52:303. [24] Rock, J., and A. T. Hertig. 1942. Am. J. Obstet. Gynecol. 44:973. [25] Snell, G. D. 1941. Biology of the laboratory mouse. Blakiston, Philadelphia. [26] Venable, J. H. 1946. Anat. Record 94:105. [27] Waterman, A. J. 1943. Am. J. Anat. 72:473. [28] Wright, P. L. 1948. Anat. Record 100:593.

Part II: ZYGOTE CLEAVAGE RATES

	Order	Species	Starting Point[1]	First Cleavage Spindle	2-Cell	4-Cell	8-Cell	16-Cell	32-Cell	Blastocoele Formation	Reference
	(A)	(B)	(C)	(D)	(E)	(F)	(G)	(H)	(I)	(J)	(K)
1	Primates	*Homo sapiens*	Ovulation	....	36 hr	....	....	....	....	5 da.	23
2		*Macaca* sp.	Ovulation	....	26-49 hr	24-52 hr	....	4-6 da	....	....	28,29
3	Artiodactyla	*Bos taurus*	Ovulation	27-32 hr	27-42 hr	31-54 hr	50-83 hr	4 da	59-131	8-9 da	10,20,22, 26,40
4		*Capra hircus*	Coitus	30 hr	30-48 hr	48-60 hr	85 hr	120 hr	....	5 da	2
5		*Ovis aries*	Coitus	....	38-39 hr	42 hr	42-44 hr	3 da	4-5 da	6-7 da	3,11,14
6		*Sus scrofa*	Coitus	51 hr	25-51 hr	25-74 hr	90 hr	....	....	5-6 da	15,24
7	Perissodactyla	*Equus caballus*	Ovulation	....	24 hr	30-36 hr	53 hr	98-100 hr	....	....	19
8	Carnivora	*Mustela frenata*	Coitus	....	70-85 hr	70-99 hr	4-8 da	8 da	11 da	11-15 da	41
9		*M. furo*	Coitus	53-70 hr	51-71 hr	64-74 hr	64-116 hr	95-120 hr	....	4.5-6 da	18,36
10		*M. vison*	Coitus	....	3 da	3-4 da	4-7 da	5-6 da	7 da	....	21
11	Rodentia	*Cavia porcellus*	Coitus	27-38 hr	23-48 hr	30-75 hr	80-82 hr	>107 hr	....	115 hr	27,38
12		*Cricetus auratus*	Coitus	....	24-36 hr	48-60 hr	72 hr	66-72 hr	....	78 hr	13,39
13		*Mus musculus*	Coitus	21-28 hr	21-43 hr	38-50 hr	50-64 hr	60-70 hr	68-80 hr	66-82 hr	17,30,37
14		*Rattus rattus*	Coitus	24-35 hr	1-2 da	2-3 da	3-4 da	4 da	....	4.5 da	1,4,5,12, 25,31-33
15	Lagomorpha	*Oryctolagus cuniculus*	Coitus	24 hr	21-25 hr	25-32 hr	32-40 hr	40-47 hr	48 hr	75-96 hr	6-9,16, 35,42
16	Insectivora	*Blarina brevicauda*	Coitus	....	60-64 hr	81 hr	....	....	....	....	34

/1/ For times given in columns D-J.

Contributors: (a) Beatty, R. A., (b) Hertig, Arthur T.

References: [1] Alden, R. H. 1948. Am. J. Anat. 83:143. [2] Amoroso, E. C., W. F. B. Griffiths, and W. J. Hamilton. 1942. J. Anat. 76:377. [3] Assheton, R. 1898. Quart. J. Microscop. Sci. 41:205. [4] Austin, C. R. 1951. Nature 168:558. [5] Austin, C. R. 1952. Australian J. Sci. Research, B, 5:354. [6] Chang, M. C. 1948. Nature 161:978. [7] Chang, M. C. 1948. Proc. Soc. Exptl. Biol. Med. 68:680. [8] Chang, M. C. 1950. J. Exptl. Zool. 14:197. [9] Chang, M. C. 1951. Fertility and Sterility 2:205. [10] Chang, M. C. 1952. Anat. Record 113:143. [11] Clarke, R. T. 1934. Ibid. 60:135. [12] Gilchrist, F., and G. Pincus. 1932. Ibid. 54:275. [13] Graves, A. P. 1945. Am. J. Anat. 77:219. [14] Green, W. W., and L. M. Winters. 1945. Univ. Minn. Tech. Bull. 169. [15] Green, W. W., and L. M. Winters. 1946. J. Morphol. 78:305. [16] Gregory, P. W.

continued

37. FERTILIZATION AND ZYGOTE DEVELOPMENT: MAMMALS

Part II: ZYGOTE CLEAVAGE RATES

1930. Contribs. Embryol. Carnegie Inst. Wash. 21:141. [17] Gresson, R. A. R. 1941. Quart. J. Microscop. Sci. 83:35. [18] Hamilton, W. J. 1934. Trans. Roy. Soc. Edinburgh 58:251. [19] Hamilton, W. J., and F. T. Day. 1945. J. Anat. 79:127. [20] Hamilton, W. J., and J. A. Laing. 1946. Ibid. 80:194. [21] Hansson, A. 1947. Acta Zool. (Stockholm) 28:1. [22] Hartman, C. G., et al. 1931. Anat. Record 48:267. [23] Hertig, A. T., et al. 1954. Contribs. Embryol. Carnegie Inst. Wash. 35:199. [24] Heuser, C. H., and G. L. Streeter. 1929. Ibid. 20:1. [25] Huber, G. C. 1915. J. Morphol. 26:247. [26] Laing, J. A. 1945. Vet. Record 57:275. [27] Lams, H. 1913. Arch. biol. (Liège) 28:229. [28] Lewis, W. H., and C. G. Hartman. 1933. Contribs. Embryol. Carnegie Inst. Wash. 24:187. [29] Lewis, W. H., and C. G. Hartman. 1941. Ibid. 29:7. [30] Lewis, W. H., and E. S. Wright. 1935. Ibid. 25:113. [31] Macdonald, E., and J. A. Long. 1934. Am. J. Anat. 55:343. [32] Nicholas, J. S. 1942. In J. Q. Griffith and E. J. Farris, ed. The rat in laboratory investigation. J. B. Lippincott, Philadelphia. [33] Odor, D. L., and R. J. Blandau. 1951. Am. J. Anat. 89:29. [34] Pearson, O. P. 1944. Ibid. 75:39. [35] Pincus, G. 1936. The eggs of mammals. Macmillan, New York. [36] Robinson, A. 1918. Trans. Roy. Soc. Edinburgh 52:303. [37] Snell, G. D. 1941. Biology of the laboratory mouse. Blakiston, Philadelphia. [38] Squier, R. R. 1932. Contribs. Embryol. Carnegie Inst. Wash. 23:223. [39] Venable, J. H. 1946. Anat. Record 94:105. [40] Winters, L. M., W. W. Green, and R. E. Comstock. 1942. Univ. Minn. Tech. Bull. 151. [41] Wright, P. L. 1948. Anat. Record 100:593. [42] Venge, O. 1950. Acta Zool. (Stockholm) 31:1.

Part III: ZYGOTE TRANSPORT TO UTERUS AND IMPLANTATION TIME

Stage at Entry into Uterus (column D): M-B = early morula to late blastocyst.

	Order	Species	Starting Point[1]	Stage (or Age) at Entry into Uterus	Implantation Time	Reference
	(A)	(B)	(C)	(D)	(E)	(F)
1	Primates	*Homo sapiens*	Ovulation	12-cell (3 da)	7 da	28,29
2		*Macaca* sp.	Ovulation	16-cell (4 da)	9-11 da	32,37
3	Artiodactyla	*Bos taurus*	Ovulation	8- to 16-cell (3-4 da)	25-35 da	12,20,36,49
4		*Capra hircus*	Coitus	32 hr	....	2
5		*Capreolus capreolus*	....	....	4 mo	23
6		*Ovis aries*	Coitus	72-96 hr	9-11 da	3,8,15
7		*Sus scrofa*	Coitus	3- to 4-cell (4-5 da)	<11 da	16,30,31,38
8	Carnivora	*Callorhinus ursinus*	....	Blastocyst	>2 mo	9
9		*Felis catus*	....	Blastocyst	....	34
10		*Meles meles*	....	....	6 mo	23
11		*Mustela frenata*	Coitus	M-B (11-15 da)	8 mo	50
12		*M. furo*	Coitus	M-B (117-144 hr)	9-12 da	18,19,42
13		*M. vison*	Coitus	Blastocyst (8 da)	25 da	24
14		*Taxidea taxus*	....	....	2 mo	21
15	Rodentia	*Cavia porcellus*	Coitus	4- to 8-cell (3.5-4.5 da)	6 da	38,43,44,46
16		*Citellus* sp.	Coitus	4-cell (4 da)	4-5 da	13
17		*Cricetus auratus*	Coitus	4- to 8-cell (2.5 da)	5+ da	14,47
18		*Mus musculus*	Coitus	M-B (66-72 hr)	4-5 da	38,45
19		*Rattus rattus*	Coitus	M-B (3.5-5 da)	5-6 da	1,38-40
20	Lagomorpha	*Oryctolagus cuniculus*	Coitus	M-B (72-96 hr)	7-8 da	4-7,17,48
21	Edentata	*Dasypus novemcinctus*	....	Blastocyst	4 mo	22
22	Insectivora	*Blarina brevicauda*	Coitus	....	4.5-10 da	41
23		*Erinaceus europaeus*	....	8-cell	....	35
24	Marsupialia	*Dasyurus viverrinus*	....	1-cell	....	33
25		*Didelphis virginiana*	Coitus	Pronuclear stage (24 hr)	....	25-27
26	Monotremata	*Ornithorhynchus paradoxus*	....	1-cell	None	11
27		*Tachyglossus aculeatus*	....	1-cell	None	10,11

/1/ For stages or times given in columns D and E.

continued

37. FERTILIZATION AND ZYGOTE DEVELOPMENT: MAMMALS

Part III: ZYGOTE TRANSPORT TO UTERUS AND IMPLANTATION TIME

Contributors: (a) Beatty, R. A., (b) Hertig, Arthur T.

References: [1] Alden, R. H. 1948. Am. J. Anat. 83:143. [2] Amoroso, E. C., W. F. B. Griffiths, and W. J. Hamilton. 1942. J. Anat. 76:377. [3] Assheton, R. 1898. Quart. J. Microscop. Sci. 41:205. [4] Chang, M. C. 1948. Nature 161:978. [5] Chang, M. C. 1948. Proc. Soc. Exptl. Biol. Med. 68:680. [6] Chang, M. C. 1950. J. Exptl. Zool. 114:197. [7] Chang, M. C. 1951. Fertility and Sterility 2:205. [8] Clarke, R. T. 1934. Anat. Record 60:135. [9] Enders, R. K., O. P. Pearson, and A. K. Pearson. 1946. Ibid. 94:213. [10] Flynn, T. T. 1930. Quart. J. Microscop. Sci. 74:119. [11] Flynn, T. T., and J. P. Hill. 1939. Trans. Zool. Soc. (London) 24:445. [12] Foley, R. C., and R. P. Reece. 1953. Mass. Agr. Expt. Sta. Bull. 468. [13] Foster, M. A. 1934. Am. J. Anat. 54:487. [14] Graves, A. P. 1945. Ibid. 77:219. [15] Green, W. W., and L. M. Winters. 1945. Univ. Minn. Tech. Bull. 169. [16] Green, W. W., and L. M. Winters. 1946. J. Morphol. 78:305. [17] Gregory, P. W. 1930. Contribs. Embryol. Carnegie Inst. Wash. 21:141. [18] Hamilton, W. J. 1934. Trans. Roy. Soc. Edinburgh 58:251. [19] Hamilton, W. J. 1937. Ibid. 59:165. [20] Hamilton, W. J., and J. A. Laing. 1946. J. Anat. 80:194. [21] Hamlett, G. W. D. 1932. Anat. Record 53:283. [22] Hamlett, G. W. D. 1932. Z. wiss. Zool. 141:143. [23] Hamlett, G. W. D. 1935. Quart. Rev. Biol. 10:432. [24] Hansson, A. 1947. Acta Zool. (Stockholm) 28:1. [25] Hartman, C. G. 1916. J. Morphol. 27:1. [26] Hartman, C. G. 1919. Ibid. 32:1. [27] Hartman, C. G. 1928. Ibid. 46:143. [28] Hertig, A. T., and J. Rock. 1945. Contribs. Embryol. Carnegie Inst. Wash. 31:65. [29] Hertig, A. T., et al. 1954. Ibid. 35:199. [30] Heuser, C. H. 1927. Ibid. 19:229. [31] Heuser, C. H., and G. L. Streeter. 1929. Ibid. 20:1. [32] Heuser, C. H., and G. L. Streeter. 1941. Ibid. 29:1. [33] Hill, J. P. 1910. Quart. J. Microscop. Sci. 56:1. [34] Hill, J. P., and M. Tribe. 1924. Ibid. 68:513. [35] Hubrecht, A. A. W. 1912. Zool. Jahrb., Suppl. 2:739. [36] Laing, J. A. 1945. Vet. Record 57:275. [37] Lewis, W. H., and C. G. Hartman. 1933. Contribs. Embryol. Carnegie Inst. Wash. 24:187. [38] Lewis, W. H., and E. S. Wright. 1935. Ibid. 25:113. [39] Macdonald, E., and J. A. Long. 1934. Am. J. Anat. 55:343. [40] Nicholas, J. S. 1942. In J. Q. Griffith and E. J. Farris, ed. The rat in laboratory investigation. J. B. Lippincott, Philadelphia. [41] Pearson, O. P. 1944. Am. J. Anat. 75:39. [42] Robinson, A. 1918. Trans. Roy. Soc. Edinburgh 52:303. [43] Sansom, G. S., and J. P. Hill. 1931. Trans. Zool. Soc. (London) 21:295. [44] Scott, J. P. 1937. Am. J. Anat. 60:397. [45] Snell, G. D. 1941. Biology of the laboratory mouse. Blakiston, Philadelphia. [46] Squier, R. R. 1932. Contribs. Embryol. Carnegie Inst. Wash. 23:223. [47] Venable, J. H. 1946. Anat. Record 94:105. [48] Waterman, A. J. 1943. Am. J. Anat. 72:473. [49] Winters, L. M., W. W. Green, and R. E. Comstock. 1942. Univ. Minn. Tech. Bull. 151. [50] Wright, P. L. 1948. Anat. Record 100:593.

Part IV: INTRA- AND INTER-SPECIFIC ZYGOTE TRANSFER

Zygote was in pre-implantation stage when transferred to host genital tract.

	Donor	Host	Degree of Development	Reference
	(A)	(B)	(C)	(D)
1	*Bos taurus*	*Bos taurus*	To term	59,60
2		*Oryctolagus cuniculus*	One cleavage	55
3	*Capra hircus*	*Capra hircus*	To term	57,58
4		*Ovis aries*	Dead embryo at 45 days	57,58
5	*Ovis aries*	*Ovis aries*	To term	3,4,23,26-28,34-36,38,57, 58
6		*Capra hircus*	Stillborn	36
7	*Sus scrofa*	*Sus scrofa*	To term	31
8	*Cavia porcellus*	*Mus musculus*	None	7
9	*Mus musculus*	*Mus musculus*	To term	6,19-21,37,49-53
10		*Cavia porcellus*	Development in blastocyst shape	7

continued

37. FERTILIZATION AND ZYGOTE DEVELOPMENT: MAMMALS

Part IV: INTRA- AND INTER-SPECIFIC ZYGOTE TRANSFER

	Donor	Host	Degree of Development	Reference
	(A)	(B)	(C)	(D)
11	*Mus musculus*	*Rattus rattus*	One cleavage	7
12		*Oryctolagus cuniculus*	One cleavage	7
13	*Rattus rattus*	*Rattus rattus*	To term	39-43
14		*Mus musculus*	None	7
15		*Oryctolagus cuniculus*	None	7
16	*Oryctolagus cuniculus*	*Oryctolagus cuniculus*	To term	1,2,5,8-18,22,24,25,29, 30,32,33,44-48,54,56
17		*Cavia porcellus*	One cleavage	7
18		*Mus musculus*	One cleavage	7
19		*Rattus rattus*	One cleavage, blastocoele formation	7

Contributor: Beatty, R. A.

References: [1] Adams, C. E. 1954. Proc. Brit. Soc. Animal Prod., p. 97. [2] Adams, C. E. 1956. Proc. 3rd. Intern. Congr. Animal Reprod., Cambridge, (3):5. [3] Averill, R. L. W. 1958. J. Agr. Sci. 50:17. [4] Averill, R. L. W., and L. E. A. Rowson. 1958. J. Endocrinol. 16:326. [5] Avis, F. R., and P. B. Sawin. 1951. J. Heredity 42:259. [6] Beatty, R. A. 1951. Nature 168:995. [7] Briones, H., and R. A. Beatty. 1954. J. Exptl. Zool. 125:99. [8] Chang, M. C. 1947. Nature 159:602. [9] Chang, M. C. 1948. Ibid. 161:978. [10] Chang, M. C. 1948. Proc. Soc. Exptl. Biol. Med. 68:680. [11] Chang, M. C. 1949. J. Gen. Physiol. 32:291. [12] Chang, M. C. 1950. J. Exptl. Zool. 114:197. [13] Chang, M. C. 1950. Science 111:544. [14] Chang, M. C. 1951. Endocrinology 48:17. [15] Chang, M. C. 1951. Fertility and Sterility 2:205. [16] Chang, M. C. 1952. J. Exptl. Zool. 121:351. [17] Chang, M. C., and G. Pincus. 1949. Federation Proc. 8:23. [18] Dowling, D. F. 1949. J. Agr. Sci. 39:374. [19] Fekete, E. 1947. Anat. Record 98:409. [20] Fekete, E., and C. C. Little. 1942. Cancer Research 2:525. [21] Green, E. L., and M. C. Green. 1959. J. Heredity 50:109. [22] Hammond, J. 1933. In J. S. Nicholas. Proc. Soc. Exptl. Biol. Med. 30:1111. [23] Hancock, J. L., and G. J. R. Hovell. 1961. J. Reprod. and Fertility 2:295. [24] Heape, W. 1890. Proc. Roy. Soc. (London), B, 48:457. [25] Heape, W. 1897. Ibid., B, 62:178. [26] Hunter, G. L. 1956. J. Agr. Sci. 48:36. [27] Hunter, G. L., C. E. Adams, and L. E. Rowson. 1954. Nature 174:890. [28] Hunter, G. L., C. E. Adams, and L. E. Rowson. 1955. J. Agr. Sci. 46:143. [29] Kurbatov, A. D. 1951. Uspekhi Sovremennoi Biol. 31:300. [30] Kurbatov, A. D., and M. M. Tihomirova. 1952. Agrobiologiya (4):83. [31] Kvasnickii, A. V. 1951. Animal Breeding Abstr. 19:758. [32] Kvasnickii, A. V., and M. N. Manjkovskaya. 1950. Ibid. 18:1081. [33] Kvasnickii, A. V., and N. A. Martynanko. 1952. Ibid. 20:340. [34] Lopyrin, A. I., N. V. Loginova, and P. L. Karpov. 1950. Ibid. 18:1449. [35] Lopyrin, A. I., N. V. Loginova, and P. L. Karpov. 1951. Ibid. 19:1262. [36] Lopyrin, A. I., N. V. Loginova, and P. L. Karpov. 1952. Ibid. 20:729. [37] McLaren, A., and J. D. Biggers. 1958. Nature 182:877. [38] Moore, N. W., L. E. A. Rowson, and R. V. Short. 1960. J. Reprod. and Fertility 1:332. [39] Nicholas, J. S. 1933. Proc. Soc. Exptl. Biol. Med. 30:1111. [40] Nicholas, J. S. 1947. Quart. Rev. Biol. 22:179. [41] Nicholas, J. S., and B. V. Hall. 1942. J. Exptl. Zool. 90:441. [42] Noyes, R. W. 1952. Fertility and Sterility 3:1. [43] Noyes, R. W., L. L. Doyle, and D. L. Bentley. 1961. J. Reprod. and Fertility 2:238. [44] Pincus, G. 1936. The eggs of mammals. Macmillan, New York. [45] Pincus, G. 1939. J. Exptl. Zool. 82:85. [46] Pincus, G. 1939. Proc. Natl. Acad. Sci. U. S. 25:557. [47] Pincus, G., and E. V. Enzmann. 1934. Ibid. 20:121. [48] Pincus, G., and E. V. Enzmann. 1935. J. Exptl. Med. 62:665. [49] Runner, M. N. 1947. Anat. Record 99:564. [50] Runner, M. N. 1949. Ibid. 103:585. [51] Runner, M. N. 1951. J. Exptl. Zool. 116:1. [52] Runner, M. N., and A. Gates. 1954. J. Heredity 45:51. [53] Runner, M. N., and J. Palm. 1952. Anat. Record 112:383. [54] Serebrjakov, P. N., and A. I. Kraseninnikova. 1951. Sovet. Zootekh. (1):43. [55] Umbaugh, R. E. 1949. Am. J. Vet. Research 10:295. [56] Venge, O. 1950. Acta Zool. (Stockholm) 31(1):1. [57] Warwick, B. L., and R. O. Berry. 1949. J. Heredity 40:297. [58] Warwick, B. L., and R. O. Berry. 1951. Proc. 1st Natl. Egg Transfer

continued

Conf., San Antonio, Texas. [59] Willett, E. L., et al. 1951. Science 113:247. [60] Willett, E. L., et al. 1953. J. Dairy Sci. 36:520.

38. CORPUS LUTEUM OF PREGNANCY: VERTEBRATES

Part I: MAMMALS

Corpus Luteum (columns B and C): MD = maximum development, RC = retrogressive changes.

	Order and Species	Corpus Luteum		Theca Interna Cells	Reference
		Estrus Cycle	Pregnancy		
	(A)	(B)	(C)	(D)	(E)
	Primates				
1	*Homo sapiens*	MD, 6th da; RC, 10th da	MD, 7th-10th wk; RC, gradually from 7th-12th wk	Form paralutein cells; "K" cells may invade gland; form 8% of pregnancy corpus	6,24, 29,46, 54,57, 66,67, 81
2	*Macaca mulatta*	MD, 8th da; RC, 13th da (corpora aberrantia persist 23 wk; accessory corpora in 17% of cycles)	MD, 12th da and constant to 19th da; "transition" stage, 19th-24th da; RC, 25th da	Retained until 4th da, not distinguishable 4th-6th da; form paralutein cells in pregnancy corpus	12-14, 16,48
3	*Papio porcarius*	MD, 7th-8th da; RC, 13th da	MD, 3rd wk; RC, after 4th-5th wk, then corpus stable for 26 wk; disappears rapidly after parturition	Form vascular reticular system	84
	Artiodactyla				
4	*Bos taurus*	MD, 9th-10th da; RC, 14th-16th da	MD, 90th da; RC, 150th da; central cavity present in gland; marked color changes	Invade luteal tissue from 6th da; may become connective tissue	7,38, 53
5	*Capra hircus*	MD, 9th da; RC, 12th da; no trace by 6th wk	MD, 30th da; RC, slowly from 60th da	Invade luteal tissue but distinguishable for several weeks	33,44
6	*Dama dama*		MD, 30th da; corpus still active at 150th da	Invade luteal tissue	46
7	*Ovis aries*	MD, 6th-8th da; RC, 14th da; trace at 24th da	Remains large to 14th da; RC, 120th-140th da	Invade luteal tissue but atrophy rapidly	9,30, 52,69, 79
8	*Sus scrofa*	MD, 6th-9th da; RC, 13th-16th da	MD, 75th da; RC, 110th da	Some cells invade luteal tissue, some remain at gland periphery	3,10, 11,15
	Perissodactyla				
9	*Equus caballus*	MD, 12th-14th da; RC, 14th da	MD, 14th da; RC, 35th-40th da, followed by large crop of accessory corpora lutea which degenerate from 150th da	Incorporated in luteal tissue; may hypertrophy markedly in pregnancy	2,8,43
	Proboscidea				
10	*Loxodonta africana*		Accessory corpora formed early or at ovulation, retrogress at mid-term; replacements persist until term, then decline rapidly	Form investing layer which retains its character after parturition	64
	Carnivora				
11	*Callorhinus ursinus*		Luteal cells heavily vacuolated during delayed implantation; corpus larger at end of gestation than at 2-3 mo; heavily vacuolated at parturition, but persist 2 mo longer	Remain as paralutein cells in early pregnancy, but do not appear active during period of delayed implantation or from a few weeks thereafter	26,47

continued

38. CORPUS LUTEUM OF PREGNANCY: VERTEBRATES

Part I: MAMMALS

	Order and Species	Corpus Luteum: Estrus Cycle	Corpus Luteum: Pregnancy	Theca Interna Cells	Reference
	(A)	(B)	(C)	(D)	(E)
	Carnivora				
12	*Canis familiaris*		MD, 18th da; RC, after 30th da		27,31, 55
13	*Felis catus*		MD, 10th-16th da; RC, 20th da; corpus rejuvenated during lactation and may persist 6-8 mo after mating	Migrate into gland on 2nd da; resume fibroblastic appearance after 3rd da; some cells remain at gland periphery	17-20
14	*Meles meles*	Ovulation may occur more than once during 10-mo period of delay	Inactive during delayed implantation; persists through pregnancy; retrogresses rapidly after parturition	Do not participate in gland formation	56
15	*Mustela furo*		MD, 3rd-5th wk; RC, 3rd-4th da before parturition		40,41, 70
16	*M. vison*		MD, 10th-12th da; inactive phase during delayed implantation; persists through pregnancy and 4th-5th wk postpartum	Migrate into gland 10-18 hr after ovulation	25,42
17	*Phoca vitulina*		Heavily vacuolated at parturition, but persists for several weeks	Remain as paralutein cells in early pregnancy	34,46, 47
	Cetacea				
18	*Balaenoptera musculus*		Active during pregnancy; degenerates after parturition, but corpus albicans persists for many years	Invade gland in radial strands; may become connective tissue after parturition	65,78
19	*Globicephala melaena*		Young corpus has heavily vacuolated cells; persists in degenerate form after parturition	Some cells remain at gland periphery	45
	Rodentia				
20	*Cavia porcellus*	MD, 9th-10th da; RC, 11th da	MD, 20th da; RC, after parturition	Hypertrophy and rapidly become indistinguishable from luteal cells	63,71
21	*Cricetus auratus*	MD, 2nd da; RC, rapidly after 3rd da	MD, 2nd-3rd da; RC, rapidly after parturition		23
22	*Mus musculus*	MD, 2nd-3rd da; RC, 3rd da	MD, 9th-11th da; RC present, but corpus active at parturition	Proliferate actively during 1st da; invade luteal tissue but may become connective tissue; no trace after 36-60 hr	5,21, 73
23	*Rattus rattus*	MD, 2nd-3rd da; RC, after 3rd da	MD, 9th-11th da; RC, slowly after parturition	Early proliferation; may form luteal cells	4,50, 62,80
	Lagomorpha				
24	*Oryctolagus cuniculus*		MD, 8th da; maximum diameter at mid-pregnancy; corpus resorbed slowly after parturition	Invade corpus and presumably form vascular and connective tissue	1,21, 39,74
	Edentata				
25	*Dasypus novemcinctus*		Corpus large during period of delayed implantation (animal breeds in July, implantation occurs in Nov.); MD, at implantation; RC, mid-term		35-37, 59
	Chiroptera				
26	*Corynorhinus rafinesquei*		MD, soon after attachment of blastocyst; RC, early in pregnancy		61
27	*Desmodus rotundus murinus*		MD, when blastocyst is present in oviduct; RC, after mid-pregnancy	Do not participate in gland formation	83
28	*Myotis lucifugus*		Pre-ovulatory luteinization of granulosa cells; MD, 4th-5th da	No true differentiation of theca interna cells	32,82

continued

38. CORPUS LUTEUM OF PREGNANCY: VERTEBRATES

Part I: MAMMALS

	Order and Species	Corpus Luteum		Theca Interna Cells	Reference
		Estrus Cycle	Pregnancy		
	(A)	(B)	(C)	(D)	(E)
	Insectivora				
29	*Blarina brevicauda*		MD, at 3-mm embryo stage, RC, rapidly after 7-mm embryo stage; vanished at parturition		60
30	*Elephantulus myurus*	MD, at mid-dense stroma stage of uterus; RC, at same time as pre-estrus change in uterus	MD, at 10-mm embryo stage, but corpus continues to increase in size; RC, at 30-mm embryo stage	Form a core to everted corpus; may give rise to connective tissue	75-77
31	*Erinaceus europaeus*	Granulosa cells not luteinized; gland shrinks steadily until time of next ovulation	RC, during lactation		22
32	*Neomys fodiens bicolor*		Corpora merge with interstitial tissue at 4- to 8-cell ovum stage	Enlarge in early pregnancy	68
	Marsupialia				
33	*Dasyurus viverrinus*		MD, 3rd da; corpus persists 7-8 wk, then declines after lactation; no trace after 4th mo	May contribute connective tissue	49,58, 72
34	*Didelphis virginiana*	MD, 3rd da; RC, 7th-8th da; almost completely gone by 20th da	MD, 3rd da; RC, 12th-13th da; disappears by 3rd mo	Do not contribute to gland	51
	Monotremata				
35	*Ornithorhynchus paradoxus*		MD, at time of blastocyst formation; RC, shortly before egg is laid	Invade luteal tissue; also remain in groups at gland periphery	28

Contributors: (a) Harrison, R. J., (b) Rowlands, I. W.

References: [1] Allen, P., F. W. R. Brambell, and I. H. Mills. 1947. J. Exptl. Biol. 23:312. [2] Amoroso, E. C., J. L. Hancock, and I. W. Rowlands. 1948. Nature 161:355. [3] Barker, W. L. 1951. Endocrinology 48:772. [4] Boling, J. L. 1942. Anat. Record 82:131. [5] Brambell, F. W. R. 1928. Proc. Roy. Soc. (London), B, 103:258. [6] Brewer, J. I. 1942. Am. J. Obstet. Gynecol. 44:1048. [7] Cole, H. H. 1930. Am. J. Anat. 46:261. [8] Cole, H. H., C. E. Howell, and G. H. Hart. 1931. Anat. Record 49:199. [9] Cole, H. H., and R. F. Miller. 1935. Am. J. Anat. 57:39. [10] Corner, G. W. 1915. Contribs. Embryol. Carnegie Inst. Wash. 2:69. [11] Corner, G. W. 1919. Am. J. Anat. 26:117. [12] Corner, G. W. 1940. Anales fac. med. Montevideo 25:553. [13] Corner, G. W. 1942. Contribs. Embryol. Carnegie Inst. Wash. 30:85. [14] Corner, G. W. 1945. Ibid. 31:117. [15] Corner, G. W. 1948. Ibid. 32:1. [16] Corner, G. W., G. W. Bartelmez, and C. G. Hartman. 1936. Am. J. Anat. 59:433. [17] Dawson, A. B. 1941. Ibid. 79:155. [18] Dawson, A. B. 1946. Ibid. 95:29. [19] Dawson, A. B., and H. B. Friedgood. 1940. Ibid. 76:411. [20] Dawson, A. B., and B. A. Kosters. 1944. Am. J. Anat. 75:1. [21] Deanesly, R. 1930. Proc. Roy. Soc. (London), B, 107:60. [22] Deanesly, R. 1934. Trans. Roy. Soc. (London), B, 223:239. [23] Deanesly, R. 1938. Proc. Zool. Soc. (London), A, 108:31. [24] Dubreuil, G. 1944. Compt. rend. soc. biol. 138:699. [25] Enders, R. K. 1952. Proc. Am. Phil. Soc. 96:691. [26] Enders, R. K., O. P. Pearson, and A. K. Pearson. 1946. Anat. Record 94:213. [27] Evans, H. M., and H. H. Cole. 1931. Mem. Univ. Calif. 9:66. [28] Flynn, T. T., and J. P. Hill. 1938-40. Trans. Zool. Soc. London 24:445. [29] Gillman, J., and H. B. Stein. 1941. Surg. Gynecol. Obstet. 72:129. [30] Grant, R. 1936. Trans. Roy. Soc. Edinburgh 58:1. [31] Griffiths, W. F. B., and E. C. Amoroso. 1939. Vet. Record 51:1279. [32] Guthrie, M. J., and K. R. Jeffers. 1938. Anat. Record 71:477. [33] Hamilton, W. J., and R. J. Harrison. 1951. J. Anat. 85:316. [34] Hamilton, W. J., R. J. Harrison, and B. A. Young. 1960. Ibid. 94:1. [35] Hamlett, G. W. D. 1932. Z. wiss. Zool. 141:143.

continued

Part I: MAMMALS

[36] Hamlett, G. W. D. 1935. Quart. Rev. Biol. 10:432. [37] Hamlett, G. W. D. 1937. Am. J. Physiol. 118:664. [38] Hammond, J. 1927. The physiology of reproduction in the cow. Cambridge Univ. Press, London. [39] Hammond, J., and F. H. A. Marshall. 1925. Reproduction in the rabbit. Oliver and Boyd, London. [40] Hammond, J., and F. H. A. Marshall. 1930. Proc. Roy. Soc. (London), B, 105:607. [41] Hammond, J., and A. Walton. 1934. J. Exptl. Biol. 11:307. [42] Hansson, A. 1947. Acta Zool. (Stockholm) 28:1. [43] Harrison, R. J. 1946. J. Anat. 80:160. [44] Harrison, R. J. 1948. Ibid. 82:21. [45] Harrison, R. J. 1949. Ibid. 83:238. [46] Harrison, R. J. 1960. Mammalia 24:372. [47] Harrison, R. J., L. H. Matthews, and J. M. Roberts. 1952. Trans. Zool. Soc. (London) 27:437. [48] Hartman, C. G., and G. W. Corner. 1947. Anat. Record 98:539. [49] Hill, J. P., and C. H. O'Donoghue. 1913. Quart. J. Microscop. Sci. 59:133. [50] Long, J. A., and H. M. Evans. 1922. Mem. Univ. Calif. 6:1. [51] Martínez-Esteve, P. 1942. Contribs. Embryol. Carnegie Inst. Wash. 30:17. [52] McKenzie, F. F., and C. E. Terrill. 1937. Missouri Agr. Expt. Sta. Research Bull. 264. [53] McNutt, G. W. 1924. J. Am. Vet. Med. Assoc. 65:556. [54] Meyer, R. 1911. Arch. Gynäkol. 93:354. [55] Mulligan, R. M. 1942. J. Morphol. 71:431. [56] Neal, E. G., and R. J. Harrison. 1958. Trans. Zool. Soc. (London) 29:67. [57] Nelson, W. W., and R. R. Greene. 1953. Surg. Gynecol. Obstet. 97:1. [58] O'Donoghue, C. H. 1912. Anat. Anz. 41:353. [59] Patterson, J. T. 1913. J. Morphol. 24:559. [60] Pearson, O. P. 1944. Am. J. Anat. 75:39. [61] Pearson, O. P., M. R. Koford, and A. K. Pearson. 1952. J. Mammal. 33:273. [62] Pederson, E. S. 1951. Am. J. Anat. 88:397. [63] Pencharz, R. I., and W. R. Lyons. 1934. Proc. Soc. Exptl. Biol. Med. 31:1131. [64] Perry, J. S. 1953. Trans. Roy. Soc. (London), B, 237:93. [65] Peters, N. 1939. Zool. Anz. 127:193. [66] Pratt, J. P. 1935. Arch. Pathol. Lab. Med. 19:380. [67] Pratt, J. P. 1935. Ibid. 19:545. [68] Price, M. 1953. Proc. Zool. Soc. (London) 123:599. [69] Quinlan, J., and G. S. Maré. 1931. 17th Rept. Vet. Research S. Africa, p. 663. [70] Robinson, A. 1918. Trans. Roy. Soc. Edinburgh 52:303. [71] Rowlands, I. W. 1955. In G. E. Wolstenholme and E. C. P. Miller, ed. Ciba foundation colloquia on ageing. Little and Brown, Boston. v. 2, p. 69. [72] Sandes, F. P. 1903. Proc. Linnean Soc. N. S. Wales 28:364. [73] Togari, C. 1924. Arch. Japan. Exptl. Med. (Nagoya) 1(4):23. [74] Togari, C. 1926. Folia Anat. Japon. 4:337. [75] Van der Horst, C. J., and N. Gillman. 1940. S. African J. Med. Sci. 5:73. [76] Van der Horst, C. J., and N. Gillman. 1942. Ibid. 7:21. [77] Van der Horst, C. J., and N. Gillman. 1946. Ibid., 11(biol. suppl.):87. [78] Van Lennep, E. W. 1950. Koninkl. Ned. Akad. Wetenschap. Proc., C, 53:593. [79] Warbritton, V. 1934. J. Morphol. 56:181. [80] Weichert, C. K., and A. W. Schurgast. 1942. Anat. Record 83:321. [81] White, R. F., et al. 1951. Contribs. Embryol. Carnegie Inst. Wash. 34:55. [82] Wimsatt, W. A. 1944. Am. J. Anat. 74:129. [83] Wimsatt, W. A., and H. Trapido. 1952. Ibid. 91:415. [84] Zuckerman, S., and A. S. Parkes. 1932. Proc. Zool. Soc. (London), p. 138.

Part II: REPTILES AND CARTILAGINOUS FISHES

Corpus Luteum (column B): RC = retrogressive changes, MD = maximum development.

	Order and Species	Corpus Luteum of Pregnancy	Theca Interna Cells	Reference
	(A)	(B)	(C)	(D)
	Reptilia			
	Serpentes			
1	*Enhydrina schistosa*	RC, slowly from 44-mm embryo stage	Hypertrophy after ovulation; contribute connective tissue ingrowths to gland	13
2	*Hydrophis cyanocinctus*	MD, 195-mm embryo stage; degenerates after parturition	Little distinction between theca interna and theca externa	13
3	*Natrix cyclopion*	Corpus maintained throughout gestation; degenerates slowly after parturition		11

continued

38. CORPUS LUTEUM OF PREGNANCY: VERTEBRATES

Part II: REPTILES AND CARTILAGINOUS FISHES

	Order and Species	Corpus Luteum of Pregnancy	Theca Interna Cells	Reference
	(A)	(B)	(C)	(D)
	Reptilia			
	Serpentes			
4	*Storeria dekayi*	Corpus maintained throughout gestation; degenerates slowly after parturition		11
5	*Thamnophis radix*	Corpus maintained throughout gestation; degenerates slowly after parturition	Contribute to supporting tissue of corpus; luteinization of thecal cells	3-5, 8,11
6	*T. sirtalis*	Corpus maintained throughout gestation; degenerates slowly after parturition	Contribute to supporting tissue of corpus; luteinization of thecal cells	3-5, 8,11
	Sauria			
7	*Amphibolurus muricatus*	MD, 1st-2nd wk; RC, 3rd wk; disappears 2nd wk after egg laying	May grow into gland to provide blood vessels and connective tissue	15
8	*Anguis fragilis*	Persists during embryo development	Remain at gland periphery	6
9	*Hoplodactylus maculatus*	MD, 30-somite stage; RC, 33-mm embryo stage	No part in gland formation	2
10	*Lacerta viridis*	Present during gestation	May give rise to connective tissue	2
11	*L. vivipara*	MD, 1st mo after ovulation; RC, end of 2nd mo	Form peripheral cellular layer; later may give rise to supporting connective tissue	10,14, 15
12	*Lygosoma quoyii*	MD, approximately 2nd wk; RC, end of 2nd mo	No ingrowth among luteal cells	15
13	*Xantusia vigilis*	MD, 4th wk; RC, 8th-9th wk; disappears 4th wk postpartum	Surround corpus; may contribute to vascular and connective tissue	9
	Chelonia			
14	*Terrapene carolina*	Corpus persists until egg laying; degenerated by 6th-9th wk thereafter	Hypertrophy; form part of gland	1
	Chondrichthyes			
	Batoidei			
15	*Rhinobatos granulatus*	Each ovary can contain over 20 corpora in varying stages of development	Hypertrophy, contribute to luteal tissue	12
	Selachii			
16	*Squalus acanthias*	Corpus reduced to half-size when embryo 3.5-7.5 cm; much reduced at birth	Form mechanical support to gland cells	7

Contributors: (a) Harrison, R. J., (b) Rowlands, I. W.

References: [1] Altland, P. D. 1951. J. Morphol. 89:599. [2] Boyd, M. 1940. Quart. J. Microscop. Sci. 82:337. [3] Bragdon, D. E. 1951. J. Exptl. Zool. 118:419. [4] Cieslak, E. S. 1945. Physiol. Zool. 18:299. [5] Clausen, H. J. 1940. Endocrinology 27:700. [6] Cunningham, J. T., and W. A. M. Smart. 1934. Proc. Roy. Soc. (London), B, 116:258. [7] Hisaw, F. L., and A. Albert. 1947. Biol. Bull. 92:187. [8] Medewar, P. B. 1953. Evolution 7:320. [9] Miller, M. R. 1948. Univ. Calif. (Berkeley) Publs. Zool. 47:197. [10] Panigel, M. 1951. Ann. endocrinol. (Paris) 12:206. [11] Rahn, H. 1939. Proc. Soc. Exptl. Biol. Med. 40:381. [12] Samuel, M. 1944. Proc. Indian Acad. Sci. 18(B):133. [13] Samuel, M. 1944. Ibid. 20(B):143. [14] Smith, M. 1951. The British amphibians and reptiles. Collins, London. [15] Weekes, C. 1934. Proc. Linnean Soc. N. S. Wales 59:380.

39. CHORIO-ALLANTOIC PLACENTATION: MAMMALS

There may be many exceptions to the data presented, as placental studies have been made on only a small percentage of the genera in most of the major taxonomic groups. Transitional types have been placed with the closest major category, and developmental stages and accessory placental areas have been omitted. Tissues (columns B-E): (+) present, (-) absent.

	Placental Type[1]	Placental Tissues[2]: Maternal: Endothelium	Placental Tissues[2]: Maternal: Epithelium	Placental Tissues[2]: Fetal: Trophoblast	Placental Tissues[2]: Fetal: Endothelium	Occurrence of Placental Types Among Main Taxonomic Groups: Scientific Grouping	Occurrence of Placental Types Among Main Taxonomic Groups: Representative Animals	Reference
	(A)	(B)	(C)	(D)	(E)	(F)	(G)	(H)
1	Epitheliochorial[3]	+	+	+	+	Prosimii (except Tupaiidae and Tarsiidae)	Bush-baby, lemur, loris	1,4,5,6,18, 31
2						Artiodactyla	Antelope, bison, camel, cattle, deer, goat, pronghorn, sheep, swine	1,6,18,25, 26
3						Perissodactyla	Horse, tapir	1,6,18
4						Cetacea	Dolphin, whale	21,30
5						Pholidota	Pangolin	2
6						Insectivora *(Scalopus, Scapanus, Parascalops)* [4]	American mole	7,16
7	Endotheliochorial[5]	+	-	+	+	Elephantidae	Elephant	15
8						Tubulidentata	Aardvark	8
9						Carnivora	Bear, cat, dog, raccoon, sea lion, seal, weasel	1,6,18
10						Rodentia *(Castor, Pedetes)*	Beaver, jumping hare	9
11						Bradypodidae	Sloth	1,6,18
12						Chiroptera (most)	Most bats	1,6,18,27
13						Insectivora (Tupaiidae[6])	Tree shrew	6,23
14	Hemochorial[7]	-	-	+	+	Anthropoidea	Man, ape, monkey	1,5,6,18,31
15						Tarsiidae	Tarsier	5,18
16						Sirenia	Manatee	28
17						Hyracoidea	Hyrax	22,32
18						Rodentia (most)	Most rodents	1,6,11,18
19						Dasypodidae	New World armadillo	1,3,6
20						Myrmecophagidae	South American anteater	24
21						Dermoptera	Flying "lemur"	18
22						Chiroptera (Molossidae)	Free-tailed and mastiff bats	6,27
23						Insectivora (most)	Alamiqui, Cape golden mole, elephant shrew, European mole, hedgehog, jes, tenrec	1,6,7, 17-20
24	Hemoendothelial[8]	-	-	-	+	Rodentia (Hystricomorpha, Muroidea, Geomyoidea)[9]	Guinea pig, kangaroo rat, mouse, North American porcupine, pocket gopher, rat	1,6,12,14, 18,29
25						Lagomorpha	Pika, rabbit	1,6,18,29
26	Endothelio-endothelial[10]	+	-	-	+	Insectivora (Soricidae)	Shrew, musk shrew	10,13

/1/ Placental functions also reside in other fetal membranes (e.g., the choriovitelline and inverted yolk-sac placentas, and even the nonvascular chorion), and the manner of development of these membranes and the general characteristics of the chorion, allantois, and yolk sac have greater phylogenetic significance than does the composition of the placental barrier which may vary widely within closely related groups. /2/ References 1, 3, 5, 6, 18. /3/ Most of the functional portion of the "syndesmochorial" placenta of ruminants is actually epitheliochorial. Only at the atrophic (presumably nonfunctional) fetal portion of the maternal cotyledon does the maternal epithelium disappear. No definitive chorio-allantoic placenta is known which is truly syndesmochorial, although the condition does occur in certain limited accessory placental areas and temporarily during development in some species. /4/ Information for *Neurotrichus* and *Condylura*, though incomplete, indicates an epitheliochorial condition. /5/ Basement membranes of the endothelium of fetal capillaries, and of maternal capillaries when present, are probably demonstrable by special techniques in most placentas. However, the thick "PAS positive" membranes containing reticulum fibers are only easily seen in the position of maternal endothelial basement membranes in certain carnivores (dog, raccoon, badger) and a few bats *(Noctilio)*. /6/ The nature of the placental barrier in *Tupaia* is still uncertain. The membranes in general are very similar to those of the Soricidae. There is no resemblance to the membranes of the Lemuriformes, in which group some modern taxonomists place the Tupaiidae. /7/ Hemochorial may be either villous or labyrinthine, or transitional between the two types (trabecular). /8/ Preliminary electronmicroscopy of the rabbit placenta [29] indicates than an ultra thin layer of trophoblastic cytoplasm may always intervene between the maternal blood and the fetal capillaries, thereby making the hemoendothelial condition nonexistent. However, until a more thorough survey has been made of the rabbit placenta, and of other placentas that appear to reach a similar condition, it seems advisable to retain the category. /9/ The contributor believes these rodents to be partly hemoendothelial as well as hemochorial. /10/ In this group most of the trophoblast disappears from the allantochorion before development of the villi.

continued

39. CHORIO-ALLANTOIC PLACENTATION: MAMMALS

Contributor: Mossman, Harland W.

References: [1] Amoroso, E. C. 1952. In A. S. Parkes, ed. Marshall's Physiology of reproduction. Ed. 3. Longmans, Green; New York. v. 2. [2] De Lange, Jr. 1930. Compt. rend. assoc. anat. 25e réunion (Amsterdam), p. 1. [3] Enders, R. C. 1960. J. Anat. 94:205. [4] Gerard, P. 1932. Arch. biol. (Liège) 43:93. [5] Hill, J. P. 1932. Trans. Roy. Soc. (London), B, 221:45. [6] Mossman, H. W. 1937. Contribs. Embryol. Carnegie Inst. Wash. 26:129. [7] Mossman, H. W. 1939. Proc. Zool. Soc. (London), B, 109:59. [8] Mossman, H. W. 1957. Mitt. naturforsch. Ges. Bern, n.F. 14:119. [9] Mossman, H. W. 1957. Proc. Zool. Soc. (Calcutta), Mookerjee mem. vol., p. 183. [10] Mossman, H. W., and N. O. Owers. 1960. Anat. Record 136:247. [11] Mossman, H. W., and L. A. Weisfeldt. 1939. Am. J. Anat. 64:59. [12] Nielson, P. E. 1940. Anat. Record 77:103. [13] Owers, N. O. 1960. Am. J. Anat. 106:1. [14] Perrotta, C. A. 1959. Ibid. 104:35. [15] Perry, J. S. Unpublished, 1962. [16] Prasad, M. R. N. 1958. Thesis. Univ. Wisconsin, Madison. [17] Starck, D. 1949. Z. Anat. Entwicklungsgeschichte 114:319. [18] Starck, D. 1959. In Handbuch der Zoologie. W. de Gruyter, Berlin. Bd. 8, Lieferung 22. [19] Strauss, F. 1942. Rev. suisse zool. 49:269. [20] Strauss, F. 1943. Schweiz. med. Wochschr. 73:5. [21] Stump, C. W., J. P. Robins, and M. L. Garde. 1960. Australian J. Marine and Freshwater Research 11:365. [22] Sturgess, I. 1948. Thesis, Univ. Witwatersrand, Johannesburg. A. Bonniers, Stockholm. [23] Van der Horst, C. J. 1949. Koninkl. Ned. Akad. Wetenschap. Proc., C, 52:3. [24] Walls, E. W. 1939. J. Anat. 73:311. [25] Wimsatt, W. A. 1950. Am. J. Anat. 87:391. [26] Wimsatt, W. A. 1951. Ibid. 89:233. [27] Wimsatt, W. A. 1958. Acta Anat. 32:141. [28] Wislocki, G. B. 1935. Mem. Museum Comp. Zool. Harvard Coll. 54:159. [29] Wislocki, G. B., and E. W. Dempsey. 1955. Anat. Record 123:33. [30] Wislocki, G. B., and R. K. Enders. 1941. Am. J. Anat. 68:97. [31] Wislocki, G. B., and G. L. Streeter. 1938. Contribs. Embryol. Carnegie Inst. Wash. 27:1. [32] Wislocki, G. B., and O. P. van der Westhuysen. 1940. Ibid. 28:65.

40. BREEDING CYCLES: MAMMALS

	Order and Species	Age at First Breeding mo	Optimum Breeding Period	Duration of Estrus	Copulation Time	Sperm Deposit Site	Fertilization Time[1]	Postpartum Return to Estrus	Conception Interval	Reference
	(A)	(B)	(C)	(D)	(E)	(F)	(G)	(H)	(I)	(J)
	Artiodactyla									
1	*Bos taurus*	15-24	Mid to late estrus	14-18 hr	Seconds	Anterior vagina	Few hours after ovulation	7-105 da	11-15 mo	3,10,17, 18,21, 23,30
2	*Capra hircus*	5-18	Mid to late estrus	24-72 hr	Seconds	Anterior vagina		Next season	1 yr	3,11,13, 31
3	*Ovis aries*	6-18	Mid to late estrus	20-48 hr	Seconds	Anterior vagina	Few hours after ovulation	Next season	1 yr	3,13,19, 21,32
4	*Sus scrofa*	5-10	Late midestrus	2-3 da	Several minutes	Cervix		3-4 da after weaning	5-12 mo	1,3,10, 16,21, 22
	Perissodactyla									
5	*Equus caballus*	24-36	Late estrus	1-15 da	10-30 min	Uterus		6-13 da	12-24 mo	1-3,13, 20,27, 31
	Carnivora									
6	*Canis familiaris*	6-8, or 1st estrus	Every 2nd da after estrus[2]	9 da	15-30 min	Anterior vagina or cervix	Several days	30-90 da	5-12 mo	1,3,10, 15,29, 31

/1/ Oviduct is fertilization site, uterine horn is implanation site. /2/ Also any time after 4th day of estrus.

continued

40. BREEDING CYCLES: MAMMALS

	Order and Species	Age at First Breeding mo	Optimum Breeding Period	Duration of Estrus	Copulation Time	Sperm Deposit Site	Fertilization Time[1]	Postpartum Return to Estrus	Conception Interval	Reference
	(A)	(B)	(C)	(D)	(E)	(F)	(G)	(H)	(I)	(J)
	Carnivora									
7	*Felis catus*	10	Varies geographically	4 da in presence of ♂, 9-10 da in absence of ♂	30 min		2 da after mating	2-3 wk after weaning	Varies[3]	10,12
	Rodentia									
8	*Cavia porcellus*	1.5-2.0		6-11 hr		Uterus	Few hours after ovulation	6-8 hr	Varies[4]	3,12,31, 33
9	*Mesocricetus auratus*	♂1.5, ♀2.0-2.5	Early and mid-estrus	12-23 hr (18 hr usually)	30-60 min	Uterus	2 hr after ovulation	5-10 min		4,7,9, 25,26, 28
10	*Mus musculus*	2.5-3.5	Varies with strain	9-20 hr		Uterus	5 hr after ovulation	2-4 da after removal of litter	Varies[4]	8,24
11	*Rattus rattus*	1.5-2.5	Varies with strain	9-21 hr		Uterus	4 hr after ovulation	2-4 da after removal of litter	Varies[4]	3,5,6,12
	Lagomorpha									
12	*Oryctolagus cuniculus*	3.4-4.5,[5] 6.5-7.5[6]	May-July in United States	1 mo or longer	Seconds	Anterior vagina or cervix	Immediately after ovulation	Immediate	Varies[3]	3,5,10, 14,31

/1/ Oviduct is fertilization site, uterine horn is implantation site. /3/ May reproduce continually. /4/ With different strain or management. /5/ If born in autumn. /6/ If born in spring.

Contributors: (a) Chang, M. C., (b) Winters, L. M., (c) McKenzie, Fred F.

References: [1] Anderson, J. 1945. The semen of animals and its use for artificial insemination. Imp. Bureau Animal Breeding and Genetics, Edinburgh. [2] Andrews, F. N., and F. F. McKenzie. 1941. Missouri Agr. Expt. Sta. Research Bull. 329. [3] Asdell, S. A. 1946. Patterns of mammalian reproduction. Comstock, Ithaca. [4] Austin, C. R. 1956. J. Roy. Microscop. Soc. 75:141. [5] Austin, C. R., and A. W. Braden. 1954. Australian J. Biol. Sci. 7:179. [6] Blandau, R. J. 1945. Am. J. Anat. 77:253. [7] Bond, C. R. 1945. Physiol. Zool. 18:52. [8] Braden, A. W., and C. R. Austin. 1954. Australian J. Biol. Sci. 7:552. [9] Chang, M. C., and L. Fernandez-Cano. 1958. Anat. Record 132:307. [10] Dukes, H. H. 1947. The physiology of domestic animals. Ed. 6. Comstock, Ithaca. [11] Espe, D. L., C. Y. Cannon, and E. N. Hansen. 1936. Iowa Agr. Expt. Sta. Circ. 111. [12] Farris, E. J. 1950. The care and breeding of laboratory animals. J. Wiley and Sons, New York. [13] Frank, A. H. 1950. U. S. Dept. Agr. Circ. 567. [14] Hammond, J. 1925. Reproduction in the rabbit. Oliver and Boyd, Edinburgh. [15] Hancock, J. L., and I. W. Rowlands. 1949. Vet. Record 61:771. [16] Ito, S., A. Kudo, and T. Niwa. 1959. Ann. Inst. Natl. Agron., D, 8(suppl.):105. [17] Knight, C. W., et al. 1951. J. Dairy Sci. 34:199. [18] Lewis, R. C., and R. E. Horwood. 1950. Quart. Bull. Mich. Agr. Expt. Sta. 32:546. [19] McKenzie, F. F., and C. E. Terrill. 1937. Missouri Agr. Expt. Sta. Bull. 234. [20] Nishikawa, Y. 1959. Studies on reproduction in horses. Japan Racing Association, Tokyo. [21] Rice, V. A., et al. 1957. Breeding and improvement of farm animals. Ed. 5. McGraw-Hill, New York. [22] Russell, E. Z., and J. H. Zeller. 1940. U. S. Dept. Agr. Farmers Bull. 1437. [23] Salisbury, G. W., and N. L. van Demark. 1951. J. Dairy Sci. 31:68. [24] Snell, G. D. 1941. Biology of the laboratory mouse. Blakiston, Philadelphia. [25] Soderwall, A. L., and G. K. Armen. 1951. Proc. Oregon Acad. Sci. 2:83. [26] Soderwall, A. L., et al. 1960. J. Gerontol. 15:246. [27] Speelman, S. R. 1941. U. S. Dept. Agr. Farmers Bull. 803. [28] Strauss, F. 1956. J. Embryol. Exptl. Morphol. 4:42. [29] Whitney, L. F. 1940. Vet. Med. 35:182. [30] Winters, L. M. 1948. Animal breeding. Ed. 4. J. Wiley and Sons, New York. [31] Winters, L. M. Unpublished. Univ. Minnesota, St. Paul, 1952. [32] Winters, L. M., and G. Feuffel. 1936. Univ. Minn. Agr. Expt. Sta. Tech. Bull. 118. [33] Young, W. C. 1933. Am. J. Physiol. 105:393.

41. PROPAGATION: MAMMALS

For additional information, consult reference 12. Location (column B): (s) = southern, or south; (e) = eastern, or east; (w) = western, or west; (n) = northern, or north; (cen) = central. Type of Estrus Cycle (column E): P = polyestrous (the cycles occur in series, continuously, or seasonally); M = monoestrous (the cycle occurs typically as an isolated event during the breeding season). Values in parentheses are ranges, estimate "c" or "d" unless otherwise indicated (cf. Introduction). Classification adapted from Simpson, *The Principles of Classification and a Classification of Mammals.* 1945.

	Family and Species	Location	Age or Size at Puberty	Breeding Season	Estrus Cycle: Type	Estrus Cycle: Duration da	Gestation Period da	Young per Litter	Reference
	(A)	(B)	(C)	(D)	(E)	(F)	(G)	(H)	(I)
	Primates								
	Hominidae								
1	*Homo sapiens*	....	♀, 13.5 (11-16)^b yr	All year	P	28.4 (24-33)^b	278[1] (253-303)^b	1[2]	9,51,152, 199,216, 229,303, 418
	Pongidae								
2	*Gorilla gorilla*	Africa	♀, ca. 5 yr	....	P	45	(257-259)	1	286,390
3	*Hylobates hoolock*	India	7 yr	....	.....	28	270	1	105,257
4	*H. lar*	Asia (se)	8-10 yr	All year	P	(29-30)	210	1	57,58
5	*Pan troglodytes*	Africa (equatorial)	8-9 yr	All year	P	(34-35)	237(216-261)	1[3]	351,432, 433
6	*Pongo pygmaeus*	Malaysia	....	....	P	±29	(210-270)	....	124
	Cercopithecidae								
7	*Cercopithecus aethiops*	Africa	....	All year	P	31	210	1	360
8	*Comopithecus hamadryas*	Africa (sw)	....	All year	P	(31-36)	183(154-189)	1	178,360,437, 441
9	*Macaca irus*	Malaya	....	All year	P	(25-39)	(160-170)	....	203,372
10	*M. mulatta*	....	♂, 3-4 yr; ♀, 1.5-2.5 yr	All year	P	28	168(144-194)	1	4,75,179, 403-406
11	*M. nemestrina*	....	♀,50 mo	All year	P	32	(171-210)	1	48,149,439
12	*M. radiata*	India (s)	....	....	P	30	162(153-169)	....	179
13	*M. sinica*	Ceylon	♀, 2.5-3.0 yr	All year	P	29	....	....	191
14	*M. sylvana*	Barbary Coast	....	....	P	(27-33)	210	....	48
15	*Papio comatus*	S. Africa	....	All year	P	(29-42)	(173-193)	1	131,132
16	*P. cynocephalus*	Guinea	....	All year	P	(25-41)	....	1	439,440
17	*P. porcarius*	S. Africa	4 yr	All year	P	(29-42)	210	1	98,360,437, 439
18	*Presbytis entellus*	India	6-7	Apr-Aug	P	30	196	(1-2)	34,182,260
19	*Theropithecus gelada*	Abyssinia	♀,5 yr	All year	P	(32-36)	....	1	258
	Callithricidae								
20	*Hapale jacchus*	S. America	♀,14 mo	....	.....	....	146(140-150)	2(1-3)	237
	Cebidae								
21	*Ateles geoffroyi*	S. America	....	All year	P	(24-27)	....	1	137,374
22	*Cebus azarae*	S. America	....	All year	P	(16-20)	180	1	165,192
23	*C. fatuellus*	S. America	....	Probably no fixed season	.....	....	180	(1-2)	440,377
	Tarsidae								
24	*Tarsius tarsier*	Malaysia	....	All year	P	(23-24)	....	1	438
	Lorisidae								
25	*Galago senegalensis*	Africa (cen)	♂, 20 mo	Dec-July	P	42	120	(1-2)[4]	438
26	*Nycticebus coucang*	Asia (se)	....	All year	P	....	(144-180)	1	12
	Lemuridae								
27	*Lemur macaco*	Madagascar	....	Sept-Jan	.....	....	146	(1-2)	12
	Artiodactyla								
	Bovidae								
28	*Aepyceros melampus*	Africa (cen & s)	....	Apr-May	.....	....	(195-210)	1[3]	12
29	*Anoa depressicornis*	Asia	....	All year	.....	....	(276-315)	1	213,440
30	*Antidorcas marsupialis*	S. Africa	....	Mar-Aug	.....	....	171	1[3]	12
31	*Antilope cervicapra*	India	....	All year[5]	.....	....	180	(1-2)	48

/1/ From 1st day of last menses; 268(250-285)^c days after rise in basal body temperature [422]. /2/ Multiple pregnancies (mainly twins) = 1.0-1.5% [50]. /3/ Usually. /4/ Usually 2. /5/ Mainly February-March.

continued

41. PROPAGATION: MAMMALS

	Family and Species	Location	Age or Size at Puberty	Breeding Season	Estrus Cycle		Gestation Period da	Young per Litter	Reference
					Type	Duration da			
	(A)	(B)	(C)	(D)	(E)	(F)	(G)	(H)	(I)
				Artiodactyla					
	Bovidae								
32	*Bibos gaurus*	Malaya	....	All year	P	21	270	1[3]	159,319
33	*Bison bison*	N. America	2 yr	June-Sept	P	21	300	1	48,183,230, 262
34	*B. bonasus*	Europe	4 yr	All year	P	(21-26)	265	1	134,200
35	*Bos grunniens*	Russian Asia	24-30 mo	June-Nov	P	....	258	1	93
36	*B. indicus*	....	....	All year	P	23	285(276-295)	....	6,109
37	*B. taurus*	....	6-10 mo	All year	P	(14-23)	284(210-335)	1[3]	213,238,330
38	*Boselaphus tragocamelus*	India	....	All year	P	21	(240-274)	1	44,48,183, 440
39	*Bubalus bubalis*	Europe, Asia	2-3 yr	All year	P	21	(305-332)	(1-2)	141,209
40	*Budorcas bedfordi*	Asia (cen)	....	July-Aug	.....	....	240	1	410
41	*Capra falconeri*	Himalayas	....	Dec	M	....	153	(1-2)	239
42	*C. hircus*	....	8 mo	Sept-winter	P	21	151(135-160)	(1-5)	10,11
43	*C. ibex*	Europe (s)	....	Nov-Dec	M	....	(150-180)	(1-2)	183,373
44	*Capricornis sumatraensis*	Burma	....	Jan-Feb	.....	....	240	1	12
45	*Cephalophus caerulus*	Africa	....	June-July	.....	....	123	1	202
46	*Connochaetes gnou*	S. Africa	♀, 2 yr	Mar	.....	....	(240-276)	1	12
47	*C. taurinus*	Africa (cen & s)	♀, 2 yr	June	P	....	(240-270)	....	183
48	*Hemitragus jemlaicus*	Himalayas	....	Dec	M	....	180	1	239
49	*Kobus defassa*	Africa	....	All year	.....	....	283	1	310
50	*K. ellipsiprymnus*	Africa (cen)	....	May-July	P	21	240	1	183,310
51	*Oreamnos americanus*	N. America (w)	2 yr	Nov	.....	....	ca. 147	(1-2)	299,325
52	*Ovibos moschatus*	N. America	3 yr	July-Sept	.....	....	240	....	135,325
53	*Ovis ammon*	Siberia	....	Oct-Dec	M	....	150	(1-2)	34,335
54	*O. aries*	....	7-8 mo	Sept-late winter[6]	P	(14-20)	151(144-152)	(1-4)	238,330
55	*O. canadensis*	N. America	2.5-3.0 yr	Nov-Dec	M	....	180	1(1-2)	83,371
56	*O. musimon*	Zoo	3 yr	Autumn	P	....	150	....	183
57	*Pantholops hodgsoni*	Tibet	....	Winter	.....	....	180	1	34
58	*Pseudois nahoor*	Mongolia	....	Jan	M	....	160	....	12
59	*Raphicerus campestris*	Africa (cen & s)	....	Winter-spring	.....	....	210	1[3]	12
60	*Rhynchotragus kirki*	Africa (cen)	6 mo	June-July; Nov-Dec	P	....	(170-174)	1	211
61	*Rupicapra rupicapra*	Alps	....	Nov-Dec	.....	....	(150-160)	....	440
62	*Saiga tartarica*	Ural Steppes	....	Dec-Jan	.....	....	150	(1-3)	186
63	*Sylvicapra grimmia*	Zoo	....	All year	.....	....	120	1[3]	12
64	*Taurotragus oryx*	Africa (cen & s)	....	All year	P	21	260(255-270)	1	183,202
65	*Tetracerus quadricornis*	India	....	Rainy season	.....	....	183	(1-3)	34,202
66	*Tragelaphus scriptus*	Africa (cen & s)	....	All year	.....	....	(214-225)	1	202
	Antilocapridae								
67	*Antilocapra americana*	N. America	15-16 mo	Sept-Oct	.....	....	240	2[3]	104,269,361
	Giraffidae								
68	*Giraffa camelopardalis*	Africa (sw)	....	July-Sept	P	15	(400-480)	1[3]	44,92,183, 196
	Cervidae								
69	*Alces alces*	N. America, Eurasia (n)	1.5 or 2.5 yr	Sept-Oct	P	30	(240-250)	(1-2)	103,202,309
70	*Blastocerus dichotomus*	S. America	....	Oct-Nov	.....	....	365	1	14
71	*Capreolus capreolus*	....	2 yr	July-Aug	M	....	(140-280)	2[3]	183,317,375
72	*Cervus axis*	India	....	All year[7]	P	21	(210-248)	2(1-3)	44,183
73	*C. canadensis*	N. America (w)	1.5 or 2.5 yr	Sept-Oct	P	21.2	(247-262)	1	30,222,282, 283
74	*C. duvauceli*	India	....	Dec-Mar	M	....	(340-350)	1	202,440
75	*C. elaphus*	....	♂,3.5 yr; ♀,2.5 yr	Sept-Oct	P	....	234(225-246)	1[3]	55,183,316

/3/ Usually. /6/ Some all year. /7/ Mainly April-May.

continued

41. PROPAGATION: MAMMALS

	Family and Species	Location	Age or Size at Puberty	Breeding Season	Estrus Cycle Type	Estrus Cycle Duration da	Gestation Period da	Young per Litter	Reference
	(A)	(B)	(C)	(D)	(E)	(F)	(G)	(H)	(I)
	Artiodactyla								
	Cervidae								
76	*Cervus eldi*	Burma	18 mo	Mar-May	.....	....	183	1	34
77	*C. nippon*	Japan	....	Sept-Nov	.....	....	240	1	186
78	*C. porcinus*	Zoo	....	All year[8]	P	....	240	....	26
79	*C. unicolor*	India (cen)	....	All year	P	....	240	(1-2)	44,239
80	*Dama dama*	....	....	Sept-Oct	M	....	230(225-234)	1[3]	316,317
81	*Elaphurus davidianus*	China	....	June-July	.....	....	250	(1-2)	202
82	*Moschus moschiferus*	Asia (cen & ne)	<1 yr	Jan	M	....	160	1	34,202
83	*Muntiacus muntjak*	Asia (s)	....	All year[9]	P	....	183	(1-2)	202
84	*Odocoileus hemionus*	....	2-4 yr	Nov-Dec	M	....	(195-210)	(1-3)	17,230,269, 307
85	*O. virginianus*	U. S.	♂, 1.5 yr; ♀, 0.5-1.5 yr	Nov-Dec	P	28	199(189-222)	(1-2)[10]	60,61,387
86	*Rangifer tarandus*	Siberia	♂1.5 yr	Sept-Oct	P	....	240	1(1-2)	273,367
	Tragulidae								
87	*Tragulus javanicus*	Asia (se)	....	All year	.....	....	120+	1	339,440
88	*T. meminna*	India	....	June-July	.....	....	120	2	34
	Camelidae								
89	*Camelus bactrianus*	Asia	....	All year	P	(10-20)	(389-410)	1	22,38,310
90	*Lama glama*	S. America	2-3 yr	Summer, early autumn	.....	....	330	1[3]	14,55
91	*L. vicugna*	S. America	12 mo	All year	.....	....	300	1[3]	55
	Hippopotamidae								
92	*Choeropsis liberiensis*	Africa	....	All year	P	30	(201-210)	....	239,373
93	*Hippopotamus amphibius*	Africa	3-5 yr	All year	P	30	237(210-250)	1	248,331
	Tayassuidae								
94	*Tayassu tajacu*	Cen. & S. America	....	All year	.....	....	144	(2-6)	151,370
	Suidae								
95	*Phacochoerus aethiopicus*	Africa	....	All year	.....	....	(171-175)	4	197,202,331
96	*Potamochoerus larvatus*	S. Africa	....	Apr-Sept	.....	....	ca. 130	(5-8)	114,215
97	*P. porcus*	Africa (w)	....	All year	.....	....	120	(1-6)	272,331
98	*Sus cristatus*	India	....	Mar	.....	....	120	(4-6)	44,319
99	*S. scrofa*	....	7(5-8) mo	All year	P	(18-24)	114(101-130)	9(6-15)	213,238,263, 330,349
	Perissodactyla								
	Rhinocerotidae								
100	*Ceratotherium simus*	Africa	4-5 yr	All year	M	....	(510-578)	1	202
101	*Diceros bicornis*	Africa	....	Irregular	.....	....	(530-550)	1	12
102	*Didermocerus sumatraensis*	Sumatra	20 yr	July-Oct	.....	....	210	1	12
103	*Rhinoceros unicornis*	Asia	4.5 yr	Feb-Apr	.....	(40-50)	488	....	129,391
	Tapiridae								
104	*Tapirus bairdii*	Cen. America	....	Mar	.....	....	ca. 120	1	128
105	*T. indicus*	Asia	....	Oct-Nov	.....	....	390	1	45,340
106	*T. terrestris*	S. America	....	Seasonal[11]	.....	....	397(392-405)	....	18,55
	Equidae								
107	*Equus asinus*	....	1 yr	Mar-Aug	P	22	365	1	217
108	*E. caballus*	....	1 yr	All year[8]	P	(10-37)	336(264-420)	1[3]	238
109	*E. hemionus*	Asia (cen)	♂, 3-4 yr; ♀, 2-3 yr	Aug-Sept	.....	....	ca. 330	1	21,338,341, 440
110	*E. quagga*	S. Africa	....	Mar-Nov[12]	.....	....	(340-365)	1	12
111	*E. zebra*	Africa	....	All year?	.....	....	360	1	114,440

/3/ Usually. /8/ Mainly spring-autumn. /9/ Mainly January-February. /10/ Sometimes 3 or 4. /11/ Prior to rainy season. /12/ Mainly July-October.

continued

41. PROPAGATION: MAMMALS

	Family and Species	Location	Age or Size at Puberty	Breeding Season	Estrus Cycle		Gestation Period da	Young per Litter	Reference
					Type	Duration da			
	(A)	(B)	(C)	(D)	(E)	(F)	(G)	(H)	(I)
	Sirenia								
	Dugongidae								
112	*Dugong dugon*	Indian Ocean	...	Winter	...	...	365	1	12
	Hyracoidea								
	Procaviidae								
113	*Dendrohyrax arboreus*	Africa	...	All year	...	...	225	1	360,413
114	*Procavia capensis*	S. Africa	...	Mar-Apr	...	...	225	2(1-6)	401,423
	Proboscidea								
	Elephantidae								
115	*Elephas maximus*	India	8-16 yr	...	P	...	624(510-730)	1[3]	52,119,122, 248,360
116	*Loxodonta africana*	Africa (sw)	9-12 yr	Jan-Feb	...	42	(630-660)	1	118,301,302
	Tubulidentata								
	Orycteropodidae								
117	*Orycteropus afer*	Africa (cen)	...	Apr-May	...	...	210	1	398
	Carnivora								
	Phocidae								
118	*Erignathus barbatus*	Arctic	♂, 7 yr; ♀, 6 yr	Late May	M	...	345	1	265
119	*Halichoerus grypus*	Atlantic	2 yr	Sept-Oct	...	...	345	1	80,81
120	*Hydrurga leptonyx*	Antarctic	♂, 3 yr; ♀, 2-3 yr	Jan-Feb	P	...	240	1	154
121	*Leptonychotes weddelli*	Antarctic	2 yr	Dec-Jan	M	...	(300-310)	1[3]	235
122	*Lobodon carcinophagus*	Antarctic	1.5-2.5 yr	Dec	...	...	270	1	29
123	*Mirounga leonina*	Antarctic	♂, 4 yr; ♀, 2 yr	Oct	P	...	345	1	7,227
124	*Monachus schauinslandi*	Hawaii	...	Mar-July	...	...	330	1	214,329
125	*Phoca hispida*	Atlantic (n)	7 yr	Mar-mid-May	...	...	330	1	266
126	*P. vitulina*	N. Hemisphere	5-6 yr	June-Aug, (Atlantic); Sept (Pacific)	M	...	270	1	113,172
	Odobenidae								
127	*Odobenus rosmarus*	Arctic	♂, 5-6 yr; ♀, 4-5 yr	June	...	...	330	1	27
	Otariidae								
128	*Arctocephalus australis*	S. America	...	Nov-Jan	...	...	330	1	55
129	*A. pusillus*	Pacific (s)	1 yr	Nov-Dec	...	...	(330-360)	1	326
130	*Callorhinus ursinus*	Arctic	♂, 4 yr; ♀, 3-6 yr	July-Aug	M	...	...	1	24,106,291
131	*Otaria byronia*	Pacific	♂, 5 yr; ♀, 4 yr	Dec-Jan	...	...	345	1	153
132	*O. flavescens*	S. American coast	2 yr	Spring	...	...	330	1	12
133	*Zalophus californianus*	Pacific	...	June-July	M	...	330	1	48,334,440
	Felidae								
134	*Acinonyx jubatus*	Africa	...	Apr-Sept	...	...	95	(2-4)	202
135	*Felis bengalensis*	Asia (s & e)	...	May	...	...	56	(3-4)	34,213
136	*F. catus*	...	6-15 mo	Feb-July	P[13,14]	(15-28)	63(52-69)	4	25,143,147, 233,366
137	*F. chaus*	India	...	Mar-Sept	...	...	60	(3-4)	34,414
138	*F. concolor*	N. America	2-3 yr	All year[15]	P	22	(90-93)	2(1-4)	48,231,321
139	*F. libyca*	Africa	...	Sept-May	P	42	56	(2-5)	186,407,417
140	*F. sylvestris*	Europe, Asia	12 mo	Dec-Apr[16]	...	...	63	(3-9)	256,388
141	*Herpailurus jaguarondi*	S. America	...	End of year	...	...	270	(2-3)	55

/3/ Usually. /13/ Induced ovulation. /14/ Seasonally. /15/ Mainly January. /16/ Occasionally late autumn.

continued

	Family and Species	Location	Age or Size at Puberty	Breeding Season	Estrus Cycle Type	Estrus Cycle Duration da	Gestation Period da	Young per Litter	Reference
	(A)	(B)	(C)	(D)	(E)	(F)	(G)	(H)	(I)
	Carnivora								
	Felidae								
142	*Lynx canadensis*	N. America	....	Early Mar	.....	....	60	(1-5)	353
143	*L. lynx*	Europe, Asia	....	Early May	.....	....	63	(2-3)	14
144	*L. rufus*	N. America	....	Late Feb	.....	....	50	3(1-4)	159
145	*Panthera leo*	....	2 yr	All year	P	21	(105-113)	(1-6)	34,248
146	*P. onca*	Cen. America	....	Sept-Oct	.....	....	(93-110)	(2-4)	12
147	*P. pardus*	Asia, Africa	....	All year	.....	....	(90-105)	3(1-4)	48,360
148	*P. tigris*	Asia	1.5 yr	All year	.....	....	(105-112)	3(1-6)	34
	Hyaenidae								
149	*Crocuta crocuta*	Africa	....	All year	P	14	(91-110)	1[3]	213,255
	Viverridae								
150	*Herpestes auropunctatus*	Hawaii, Puerto Rico	♂, 4 mo	All year	P	20	50?	(2-4)	296,308
151	*H. edwardsi*	India	9 mo	All year	.....	....	60	2	12,125
152	*Mungos mungo*	Africa	1 yr or less	All year	.....	....	....	(2-6)	225,407
	Mustelidae								
153	*Enhydra lutris*	Pacific (n)	....	All year[17]	.....	....	(240-270)	1	14
154	*Gulo luscus*	United States (n), Canada	1 yr	Summer	?	?	270 or more	(2-4)	430
155	*Lutra canadensis*	N. America	♂, 5-6 yr; ♀, 2 yr	Winter, early spring	P	6	(300-360)	(2-4)	234
156	*L. lutra*	Europe	....	All year[18]	P	26	(61-63)	....	70
157	*Martes americana*	N. America	2 yr	July-Sept	M	....	(260-280)	3(1-4)	146,244
158	*M. foina*	England	2 yr	July-Aug	M	....	(255-285)	(3-5)	34,108
159	*M. martes*	Europe	....	July	P[14]	(3-7)	(270-285)	(1-4)	346
160	*M. pennanti*	N. America	1-2 yr	Apr	M	....	352(327-366)	3(1-5)	100,201
161	*M. zibellina*	Siberia	2 yr	June-Aug	P	(9-12)	(270-285)	(1-4)	312,346,436
162	*Meles meles*	Europe	2 yr	July-Aug	.....	....	210	(1-4)	173
163	*Mephitis mephitis*	N. America	10 mo	Mar	.....	(9-10)	62	(4-7)	159,354
164	*Mustela erminea*	United States (n), Canada, Eurasia	♂, 1 yr; ♀, 3 mo	Apr-June	P	30	300	(6-9)	85,87,145, 156,226
165	*M. frenata*	United States	♂, 1 yr; ♀, 3 mo	July	P[13]	ca. 30	279	(4-9)	427-429
166	*M. larvatus*	Himalayas	....	Feb	.....	....	63	(5-7)	34
167	*M. nivalis*	Europe	3 mo or 1 yr	Mar-Aug	P[13]	....	ca. 45	(6-7)	88,190,297
168	*M. putorius*	Europe	....	Mar-Aug	P[13]	....	(42-45)	9(5-13)	167,247
169	*M. vison*	N. America	1 yr	Mar-Apr	P[13]	(8-9)	53(39-76)	(4-10)	39,126,400
170	*Taxidea taxus*	America	....	Aug-Sept	M	....	(183-265)	3(1-7)	146,161
	Procyonidae								
171	*Ailurus fulgens*	Asia (cen)	....	Mar	.....	....	90	(1-2)	311,440
172	*Nasua narica*	S. America	....	Probably all year	.....	....	77	2	48,440
173	*Procyon lotor*	N. America	♂, 2 yr; ♀, 1 yr	Jan-June	P	....	63(60-73)	4(1-6)	32,379
	Ursidae								
174	*Euarctos americanus*	N. America	3 yr	June-July	M	....	210(208-225)	2(1-4)	146,163,230
175	*Melursus ursinus*	India	....	June	M	....	210	2	34
176	*Thalarctos maritimus*	Arctic	....	Feb-Mar	.....	....	240	2	202
177	*Ursus arctos*	Europe	6 yr	Apr-June	M	....	210(208-240)	(1-2)	34,314
178	*U. horribilis*	N. America	2-3 yr	June-July	M	....	208(180-225)	2(1-4)	230,353
	Canidae								
179	*Alopex lagopus*	N. America (n)	....	Feb	M	....	52(50-60)	6(4-8)	202
180	*Canis aureus*	Asia	....	Jan-Feb	.....	....	(60-63)	(2-6)	186,306,440
181	*C. familiaris*	....	6-8 mo	Spring-autumn	M[14]	9	63(53-71)	7(1-22)	130,238,249
182	*C. latrans*	N. America	2 yr	Feb-Aug	?	4	(60-65)	6(5-7)	164,415

/3/ Usually. /13/ Induced ovulation. /14/ Seasonally. /17/ Mainly late spring. /18/ In captivity.

continued

41. PROPAGATION: MAMMALS

	Family and Species	Location	Age or Size at Puberty	Breeding Season	Estrus Cycle: Type	Estrus Cycle: Duration da	Gestation Period da	Young per Litter	Reference
	(A)	(B)	(C)	(D)	(E)	(F)	(G)	(H)	(I)
	Carnivora								
	Canidae								
183	*Canis lupus*	Europe, Asia	2 yr	Dec-Apr	.....	....	63	(3-9)	34,319
184	*Cuon alpinus*	India	....	All year	.....	....	70	(3-5)	44,440
185	*Lycaon pictus*	Africa	....	All year	.....	....	(63-80)	(2-6)	48,360
186	*Nyctereutes procyonides*	Asia	....	Feb	.....	....	(61-63)	(5-12)	347
187	*Otocyon megalotis*	Africa	....	Oct-Feb	.....	....	(60-70)	(3-5)	12
188	*Thos adustus*	Africa	....	Early winter	.....	....	(57-60)	(3-7)	12
189	*Urocyon cinereoargenteus*	N. America	♀, 1 yr	Dec-Mar	M	....	63	4(1-7)	12,426
190	*Vulpes bengalensis*	Europe, Asia	....	Nov-Jan	M	....	....	4	34
191	*V. fulva*	....	10 mo	Dec-Mar[9]	M	(2-4)	52(49-56)	(4-9)	204,348,352
192	*V. vulpes*	England	10 mo	Jan-Feb	M	....	52(50-63)	5(1-8)	333,353
	Cetacea								
	Balaenidae								
193	*Eubalaena glacialis*	Atlantic Ocean (n)	....	Mar	.....	....	(276-365)	1	12
	Balaenopteridae								
194	*Balaenoptera borealis*	....	2 yr	May-Aug	P	....	360	1	212,254
195	*B. physalus*	....	3 yr	Nov-Mar[19]	.....	....	360	1	242,336,435
196	*Megaptera novaeangliae*	....	♂, 1120 cm; ♀, 1173 cm	Aug-Nov	P	....	360	1	63,64,252
197	*Sibbaldus musculus*	....	♂, 4-5 yr; ♀, 5 yr	Apr-June	P	....	360	1	224,242,337
	Phocaenidae								
198	*Phocaena phocaena*	Atlantic Ocean (n)	14 mo	July-Aug	.....	....	(300-330)	1	202,280,345
	Delphinidae								
199	*Delphinus delphis*	....	3 yr	Late summer	.....	....	276	1	213,362
200	*Tursiops truncatus*	....	4 yr	Feb-May	.....	....	360	1	259,386
	Physeteridae								
201	*Kogia breviceps*	S. Hemisphere	800-950 cm	Aug-Dec	P	....	270	1	5
202	*Physeter catodon*	S. Hemisphere	♂, 1200 cm; ♀, 900-950 cm[20]	Aug-Dec[21]	P	....	510	1	253
	Platanistidae								
203	*Platanista gangetica*	Indian rivers	....	July-Nov	.....	....	(240-270)	1[3]	12
	Rodentia								
	Capromyidae								
204	*Myocastor coypus*	S. America	8 mo	All year	P	(24-29)	(120-150)	10	293
	Chinchillidae								
205	*Chinchilla laniger*	S. America	4 mo	All year[22]	P	28	(105-115)	(1-4)	95,399
206	*Lagidium peruanum*	S. America	7 mo	Oct-Sept	P	....	90	....	293,294
207	*Lagostomus tridactylus*	S. America (s)	....	All year[18]	.....	....	145	2(2-3)	54,159
	Dasyproctidae								
208	*Dasyprocta aguti*	S. America	....	All year	.....	....	104	(1-2)	48,440
209	*D. punctata*	Cen.& S. America	....	All year	.....	....	(44-75)	2(2-4)	293
	Hydrochoeridae								
210	*Hydrochoerus isthmius*	Cen. America	....	Feb	.....	....	(104-111)	(3-4)	392
	Caviidae								
211	*Cavia porcellus*	....	55-70 da	All year	P	(16-19)	68(58-75)	3(1-8)	33,198,434
212	*Galea musteloides*	S. America	1st yr	July-Sept	.....	....	....	2(1-4)	295
	Erethizontidae								
213	*Erethizon dorsatum*	N. America	3rd yr	Nov-Dec	M	....	113	(1-4)	378

/3/ Usually. /9/ Mainly January-February. /18/ In captivity. /19/ N. Hemisphere; June-August in S. Hemisphere. /20/ Off Azores: ♂, 960 cm; ♀, 800-950 cm [67]. /21/ Off Azores, February-June [67]; off Japan, March [277]. /22/ Mainly late autumn and winter.

continued

41. PROPAGATION: MAMMALS

	Family and Species	Location	Age or Size at Puberty	Breeding Season	Estrus Cycle Type	Estrus Cycle Duration da	Gestation Period da	Young per Litter	Reference
	(A)	(B)	(C)	(D)	(E)	(F)	(G)	(H)	(I)
				Rodentia					
	Hystricidae								
214	*Hystrix cristata*	Zoos	....	All year	.....	....	112	1(1-2)	440
	Dipodidae								
215	*Dipus sagitta*	Europe (e), Asia (w)	1st year	Apr-Aug	.....	....	....	3(2-5)	12
216	*Jaculus orientalis*	Zoo	....	Most of year	.....	....	42	3	440
	Zapodidae								
217	*Sicista betulina*	Europe (e)	1 yr	May	.....	....	(28-35)	....	220
218	*Zapus hudsonicus*	N. America	1.5 mo	Spring-summer	.....	....	17.5	(2-8)	219,320
	Gliridae								
219	*Eliomys quercinus*	Europe	....		P	10	22	(3-6)	186,223
220	*Glis glis*	Europe	10-11 mo	Early spring	.....	....	(20-25)	(3-10)	186
221	*Muscardinus avellanarius*	Europe (n)	....	May-Oct	P	....	21	(2-7)	23
	Muridae								
222	*Acomys caharinus*	Zoos	....	All year	.....	....	12	4 or 5(2-11)	440
223	*A. dimidiatus*	Europe, Asia (w)	....	All year	P	....	42	....	12
224	*Apodemus sylvaticus*	Europe, Asia	80-90 da	Mar-Oct	P	6	(23-29)	5 or 6 (1-12)	186,213,328
225	*Chiropodomys gliroides*	Malaya	♂, 72+ gm; ♀, 139 gm	Jan-Mar	.....	....	....	(1-3)	171
226	*Cricetomys gambianus*	Africa	....	All year	.....	....	42	4	92
227	*Hydromys chrysogaster*	Australia	♂, 400-600 gm; ♀, 425 gm	Sept-Jan	.....	....	....	4 or 5 (1-7)	268
228	*Malacothrix typicus*	Africa	3 mo	Most of year	P	....	....	(4-5)	315
229	*Mastomys coucha*	Sierra Leone	3 mo	All year	P	6	23	12(7-17)	43,207
230	*Micromys minutus*	Europe, Asia	....	Summer	P	....	21	(5-9)	174
231	*Mus bactrianus*	Asia	150 da	All year	P	....	20	4	142
232	*M. musculus*	....	35 da	All year	P	4	(19-31)	6(1-12)	107,289
233	*Otomys irroratus*	Africa	4 mo	June-Aug	P	....	....	(3-5)	315,360
234	*Rattus conatus*	Australia	65 da	All year	P	4	22	(4-11)	12,261
235	*R. norvegicus*	....	40-60 da	All year	P	(4-5)	21	(6-9)	12
236	*R. rattus*	....	37-67 da	All year	P	(4-5)	(21-30)	12	35,213
237	*Rhabdomys pumilio*	Africa (e & s)	3 mo	Sept-Apr	P	....	....	(3-8)	12
238	*Thallomys namaquensis*	Africa	....	All year	.....	....	22	(2-5)	271,360
	Cricetidae								
239	*Arvicola amphibius*	Great Britain	3 mo	Mar-Sept	P	....	....	6	300
240	*Baiomys taylori*	United States (sw), Mexico	44 da	All year	P	....	20	3	12
241	*Clethrionomys gapperi*	N. America	120 mm	Late winter-early autumn	P	....	(17-19)	5(3-8)	79,381
242	*C. glareolus*	Europe	40 da	Apr-Oct	P	....	(17-18)	(2-8)	42,186
243	*Cricetulus barabensis*	China	8-12 wk	....	P	4	(20-21)	(4-8)	290,431
244	*C. triton*	Manchuria	2 mo	Mar-May	.....	....	(17-18)	(4-6)	12,397
245	*Cricetus cricetus*	Europe (cen), Russia, Asia Minor	....	Mar-Aug	.....	....	20	(4-18)	304
246	*Dicrostonyx groenlandicus*	Arctic	25-30 da	Mar-Sept	.....	....	(19-21)	(2-5)	91,168,243
247	*Dipodillus simoni*	Algeria	....	All year	P	....	20(20-21)	5(1-7)	223
248	*Lagurus lagurus*	Europe (e)	20-25 da	All year	.....	....	20(15-23)	6(2-11)	186
249	*Meriones libycus*	Africa (n)	....	All year	P	10	(20-25)	(4-7)	12,170
250	*Mesocricetus auratus*	....	5-8 wk	All year	P	4	16(15-18)	(1-12)	49,86,359
251	*Microtus agrestis*	Great Britain	♂, 6-8 wk; ♀, 3 wk	Feb-Oct	P	4	(21-29)	4	19,65,327

continued

	Family and Species	Location	Age or Size at Puberty	Breeding Season	Estrus Cycle: Type	Estrus Cycle: Duration da	Gestation Period da	Young per Litter	Reference
	(A)	(B)	(C)	(D)	(E)	(F)	(G)	(H)	(I)
	Rodentia								
	Cricetidae								
252	*Microtus californicus*	California	♂, 42 da; ♀, 20-22 da	Almost all year	P	....	21(20-22)	(4-8)	17,181
253	*M. pennsylvanicus*	....	♂, 45 da; ♀, 25 da	All year[18]	P	5	21	4(1-11)	15,136,158
254	*Neotoma albigula*	N. America (w)	....	All year	P	....	±30	2(1-6)	110
255	*N. floridana*	N. America (e)	5-6 mo	Feb-Aug	P	(3-8)	(31-36)	(1-6)	59,96,313, 322
256	*N. fuscipes*	United States (w)	240 g	Jan-Aug	P	....	33	3(2-4)	236,408,424
257	*Ondatra zibethica*	N. America	1 yr	Apr-Oct	P	(3-5)	30(19-42)	7(1-11)	267,364
258	*Onychomys leucogaster*	N. America (cen & w)	3 mo	Apr-Sept	P	....	33(32-47)	4(2-6)	12
259	*Oryzomys palustris*	United States (e)	50 da	Feb-Nov	P	(6-9)	25	3(1-5)	71,382
260	*Pachyuromys duprasi*	Africa (n)	2 mo	All year	P	(5-6)	20(19-22)	3(3-6)	223,440
261	*Peromyscus leucopus*	N. America	46 da	All year	P	(4-5)	23	5(3-7)	66,343,384
262	*P. maniculatus*	N. America	49 da	All year	P	(4-5)	(22-27)	(2-8)	66,159,288, 384
263	*P. truei*	N. America (w)	50 da	Spring-summer	P	....	26	3	66,384,412
264	*Phenacomys intermedius*	N. America (w)	....	Apr-Aug	P	....	....	(4-6)	12
265	*P. longicaudus*	N. America (w)	....	All year[23]	P	....	....	3(1-3)	12
266	*Pitymys pinetonum*	N. America	....	All year	P	....	21	(1-7)	28,133
267	*Reithrodontomys megalotis*	N. America	4-5 mo	All year[24]	P	....	(23-24)	3(1-7)	363,383
268	*Sigmodon hispidus*	N. America (s)	30-40 da	All year	P	± 9	27	5(2-10)	274,380
269	*Synaptomys cooperi*	N. America	....	Feb-Nov	P	....	23	3(1-5)	12,74
270	*Tatera brantsi*	S. Africa	55 gm	All year	P	(4-6)	22.5	3(1-4)	3,270
	Castoridae								
271	*Castor canadensis*	N. America	2 yr	Jan-Feb	.....	....	120(65-128)	4(1-6)	40,353
	Heteromyidae								
272	*Dipodomys merriami*	N. America (w)	Yr of birth	Spring, fall	P	25	(17-23)	(2-4)	1,62
273	*Perognathus fasciatus*	N. America (w)	....	Spring-summer	.....	....	28	(4-6)	151,412
274	*P. flavus*	N. America (sw)	....	Feb-Oct	P	....	....	(3-6)	16,193
	Geomyidae								
275	*Geomys breviceps*	N. America (s-cen)	....	Feb-Aug	P	....	....	3(1-9)	424
276	*G. bursarius*	N. America	3 mo	Mar-July	P	....	(40-50)	4(1-6)	99,342,425
277	*Thomomys quadratus*	United States (nw)	....	Mar-Dec	P	....	40	(2-3)[3]	12
278	*T. talpoides*	N. America (w)	6-7 mo	Feb-Mar	P	....	....	4-6	169,344,396, 416
279	*T. umbrinus*	N. America (w)	....	All year (little Aug-Jan)	P	....	18	6(3-13)	37,275,350
	Sciuridae								
280	*Callosciurus notatus*	Malaya	♂, 113+g; ♀, 200 g	Apr-June	.....	....	....	2(1-4)	171
281	*Citellus columbianus*	N. America (nw)	1 yr	Mar-May	P	(14-51)	24(23-28)	5(2-13)	194,358
282	*C. richardsoni*	Canada (sw), United States (nw)	....	Apr	.....	....	(17-18)	6(2-11)	94,353
283	*C. tridecemlineatus*	N. America (cen)	....	Apr-July	P[13]	(14-28)	28	(5-13)	123,194,205, 281
284	*Cynomys leucurus*	United States (w-cen)	1 yr	Mar-Apr	.....	....	(28-32)	6(2-10)	376

/3/ Usually. /13/ Induced ovulation. /18/ In captivity. /23/ Mainly spring-summer. /24/ Mainly April-October.

continued

41. PROPAGATION: MAMMALS

	Family and Species	Location	Age or Size at Puberty	Breeding Season	Estrus Cycle Type	Estrus Cycle Duration da	Gestation Period da	Young per Litter	Reference
	(A)	(B)	(C)	(D)	(E)	(F)	(G)	(H)	(I)
	Rodentia								
	Sciuridae								
285	*Cynomys ludovicianus*	N. America	....	Jan-Feb	.....	....	(30-35)	5(2-10)	8,409
286	*Eutamias quadrimaculatus*	N. America	11 mo	Apr	.....	....	31	....	332,389
287	*E. sibiricus*	Asia	....	End winter	.....	....	(35-40)	4 or 5 (3-12)	186
288	*Funambulus pennanti*	India	6-8 mo	All year	.....	....	42	3	20
289	*Glaucomys volans*	N. America	....	Feb-July	P	16	40	3(1-6)	368
290	*Marmota monax*	United States (e), Canada	1-2 yr	Mar-Apr	?	?	(32-34)	(1-8)	365
291	*Sciurus carolinensis*	N. America (e)	1-2 yr	Dec-Aug	.....	....	44	4(1-6)	89,138,230
292	*S. vulgaris*	Europe	11-12 mo	Dec-Sept	P	....	(28-40)	....	221
293	*Tamias striatus*	United States (e)	2.5-3.0 mo	Mar-July	P	....	31	(3-6)	54,159
294	*Tamiasciurus hudsonicus*	N. America (cen & e)	1 yr	Mar-Apr, Aug-Sept	.....	....	40	4(4-5)	157,159,228, 385
	Aplodontidae								
295	*Aplodontia rufa*	N. America (w)	2 yr	Feb	.....	....	(28-30)	(2-4)	305
	Lagomorpha								
	Leporidae								
296	*Lepus americanus*	N. America	1 yr	Mar-Aug	P	....	(30-38)	3(1-7)	2,230,353
297	*L. californicus*	N. America (w)	1 yr	All year	.....	....	43(41-47)	(1-4)	46,180
298	*L. europaeus*	Europe	8 mo	Mid-winter to mid-summer	.....	....	42	3	184,218
299	*Oryctolagus cuniculus*	....	5.5-8.5 mo	All year	P[13]	....	31(30-35)	8(1-13)	13,166,284
300	*Romerolagus diazi*	Mexico	....	Mar-Apr	.....	....	ca. 30	3(1-4)	82,231
301	*Sylvilagus auduboni*	N. America (sw)	Yr of birth	Jan-Aug	.....	....	(28-30)	(2-4)	97,369
302	*S. floridanus*	N. America (e)	4.5-7.0 mo	Jan-Aug	P	....	(26-30)	5(2-7)	31,185,230, 393
	Ochotonidae								
303	*Ochotona princeps*	Rocky Mountains (n)	....	Spring	P	....	31	(2-4)	12
	Edentata								
	Dasypodidae								
304	*Dasypus novemcinctus*	N. America (s)	1 yr	June-Aug	.....	....	(210-240)	4	385
	Bradypodidae								
305	*Bradypus griseus*	Cen. & S. America	....	All year	.....	....	(120-180)	4	12
	Myrmecophagidae								
306	*Myrmecophaga tridactyla*	S. America	....	....	.....	....	190	1	285,319
	Chiroptera								
	Molossidae								
307	*Tadarida cynocephala*	Florida	9 mo	Feb-Mar	M[25]	....	(77-84)	1	77,159
	Vespertilionidae								
308	*Antrozous pallidus*	N. America	....	Oct-Feb	.....	....	65	(1-3)	69,287
309	*Eptesicus fuscus*	N. America	....	Autumn	M[25]	....	35	2(1-4)	159,419,420
310	*Myotis lucifugus*	N. America (e)	♂, 2nd summer; ♀, end 1st summer	Autumn, spring	M[25]	....	(50-60)	1	144,150,159, 276
311	*M. myotis*	Europe	....	Autumn-spring	M[25]	....	(44-50)	1	78,421

/13/ Induced ovulation. /25/ Ovulation in spring.

continued

41. PROPAGATION: MAMMALS

	Family and Species	Location	Age or Size at Puberty	Breeding Season	Estrus Cycle		Gestation Period da	Young per Litter	Reference
					Type	Duration da			
	(A)	(B)	(C)	(D)	(E)	(F)	(G)	(H)	(I)
	Chiroptera								
	Vespertilionidae								
312	*Nyctalus noctula*	Europe	....	Sept	?[25]	......	49	(1-2)	23,148
313	*Pipistrellus pipistrellus*	Europe, Asia	2nd yr	Autumn, spring	M[25]	......	44	1	76,90
314	*Plecotus rafinesque*	N. America	4 mo	Sept-Apr	?[25]	......	73	1	298
315	*Scotophilus temmincki*	India	1st yr	Mar	.....	......	(105-111)	2	139,140
	Desmodontidae								
316	*Desmodus rotundus*	S. America	....	All year	P	......	ca. 150	1	111,421
	Phyllostomatidae								
317	*Glossophaga soricina*	S. America	....	Late spring	M	(14-21)	....	1	162,419
	Rhinolophidae								
318	*Rhinolophus ferrum-equinum*	Europe	15 mo	Oct-Apr	M[25]	......	(70-84)	1	23,251
	Megadermatidae								
319	*Megaderma lyra*	India	♂, 15 mo; ♀, 19 mo	Nov	.....	......	150	1	324
	Pteropodidae								
320	*Cynopterus sphinx*	India	....	Dec-Apr	P	......	150	1	279,323
321	*Pteropus giganteus*	India	....	Aug-Jan	.....	......	180	1	246,278
	Insectivora								
	Talpidae								
322	*Condylura cristata*	N. America	1st yr	Feb-May	.....	......	....	(2-7)	102
323	*Desmana moschata*	Europe	....	All year	.....	......	(45-60)	(3-5)	186
324	*Parascalops breweri*	N. America (e)	10-12 mo	Mar-Apr	M	......	(28-42)	4	101,159
325	*Scalopus aquaticus*	N. America	1 yr	Mar-Apr	.....	......	ca. 28	(3-5)	73
326	*Scapanus townsendi*	United States (nw)	....	Feb	M	......	....	3(2-4)	17
327	*Talpa europaea*	Europe	....	Feb-Aug	M	......	(28-42)	4(1-6)	250
	Soricidae								
328	*Blarina brevicauda*	N. America	6-8 wk	Feb-Sept	P[13]	33	(17-21)	5(3-7)	155,292
329	*Cryptotis parva*	N. America	....	All year in south	P	......	(21-23)	(2-6)	72,160
330	*Microsorex hoyi*	N. America	....	Spring, summer	P	......	....	(5-7)	159
331	*Neomys fodiens*	Europe	Yr after birth	Apr-Sept	.....	......	24	(5-11)	56,195,318
332	*Sorex araneus*	Europe	2nd yr	Mar-Sept	P	......	(13-19)	7	41
333	*S. fumeus*	N. America (e)	....	Mar-Aug	P	......	21	(4-6)	159
334	*S. vagrans*	N. America (w)	Mostly yr after birth	Feb-Apr	.....	......	ca. 20	(2-9)	68,206
	Macroscelididae								
335	*Elephantulus myurus*	S. Africa	5 wk	July-Jan	P	......	56	(1-2)	264,360,402
	Erinaceida								
336	*Erinaceus europaeus*	Europe	2nd yr	Mar-Sept	M	......	(35-49)	5(3-7)	84,187
	Tenrecidae								
337	*Setifer setosus*	Madagascar	....	Sept-Feb	P	(35-42)	....	(2-3)	112,210
	Marsupialia								
	Macropodidae								
338	*Bettongia cuniculus*	Tasmania	<1 yr	Mar-Dec	P	......	42	1	120
339	*Macropus giganteus*	Australia	....	Once a year	.....	......	(38-40)	1	208
340	*M. major*	....	....	Dec on	.....	......	(38-40)	1	357
341	*Setonyx brachyurus*	Australia (w)	18 mo	Jan-Oct	P	28	(24-28)	1	355,411
	Phalangeridae								
342	*Petaurus sciurus*	....	....	All year	.....	......	21	2	117
343	*Phascolarctos cinereus*	Australia	....	Sept-Jan	M	......	35	1	232,394,395
344	*Trichosurus vulpecula*	....	250-300 da	Mar-Aug	P	(21-30)	(15-24)	1	36,208,240, 356

/13/ Induced ovulation. /25/ Ovulation in spring.

continued

41. PROPAGATION: MAMMALS

	Family and Species	Location	Age or Size at Puberty	Breeding Season	Estrus Cycle Type	Estrus Cycle Duration da	Gestation Period da	Young per Litter	Reference
	(A)	(B)	(C)	(D)	(E)	(F)	(G)	(H)	(I)
	Marsupialia								
	Peramelidae								
345	*Thylacis macrourus*	....	1st yr	All year	P	....	<15	(1-7)	241
	Dasyuridae								
346	*Dasyurus viverrinus*	....	....	May-Aug	M	(4-12)	(8-14)	(20-35)	188,189
347	*Phascogale flavipes*	....	320 da	Aug	M	(2-7)	35	(8-12)	116,245
348	*Sarcophilus harrisi*	....	2nd yr	May	.....	....	31	(3-4)	115,213
	Didelphidae								
349	*Didelphis virginiana*	Texas	♂, 8 mo; ♀, 6 mo	Jan-Oct	P	28	(12.5-13.0)	9(5-13)	175-177
	Montremata								
	Ornithorhynchidae								
350	*Ornithorhynchus paradoxus*	Australia	1-2 yr	July-Oct	M	60	12 (incubation)	2[3]	53,127
	Tachyglossidae								
351	*Tachyglossus aculeatus*	Tasmania	....	July-Sept	M	60	(12-28)	1	47,121

/3/ Usually.

Contributors: (a) Asdell, S. A., (b) Blandau, Richard J., (c) McKenzie, Fred F., (d) Morris, Melvin S., (e) Wright, Philip L., (f) Tietze, Christopher, (g) van Wagenen, Gertrude

References: [1] Alcorn, J. R. 1941. J. Mammal. 22:88. [2] Aldous, C. M. 1937. Ibid. 18:46. [3] Allanson, M. 1958. Proc. Zool. Soc. (London) 130:373. [4] Allen, E. 1927. Contribs. Embryol. Carnegie Inst. Wash. 19:1. [5] Allen, G. M. 1941. Field Museum Nat. Hist., Zool. Ser., 27:17. [6] Anderson, J. 1944. J. Agr. Sci. 34:57. [7] Angot, M. 1954. Mammalia 18:1. [8] Anthony, A., and D. Foreman. 1951. Physiol. Zool. 24:242. [9] Arey, L. B. 1939. Am. J. Obstet. Gynecol. 37:12. [10] Asdell, S. A. 1926. J. Agr. Sci. 16:602. [11] Asdell, S. A. 1929. Ibid. 19:382. [12] Asdell, S. A. 1946. Patterns of mammalian reproduction. Comstock, Ithaca. [13] Asdell, S. A., and J. Hammond. 1933. Am. J. Physiol. 103:600. [14] Auge, P., ed. 1930. Librairie Larousse 3:775. [15] Bailey, V. 1924. J. Agr. Research 27:523. [16] Bailey, V. 1931. North Am. Fauna 53. [17] Bailey, V. 1936. Ibid. 55. [18] Baker, A. B. 1920. J. Mammal. 1:143. [19] Baker, J. R., and R. M. Ranson. 1933. Proc. Roy. Soc. (London), B, 113:486. [20] Banerji, A. 1957. J. Bombay Nat. Hist. Soc. 54:335. [21] Bannikov, A. G. 1958. Z. Säugetierk. 23:157. [22] Barmincev, J. 1939. Konevodstvo 1:42. [23] Barrett-Hamilton, G. E. H. 1910-12. A history of British mammals. Gurney and Jackson, London. [24] Bartholomew, G. A., and P. G. Hall. 1953. J. Mammal. 34:417. [25] Beard, J. 1897. The span of gestation and the cause of birth. G. Fischer, Jena. [26] Bedford, Duke of, and F. H. A. Marshall. 1942. Proc. Roy. Soc. (London), B, 130:396. [27] Belopoljskii, L. O. 1939. Zool. Zhur. 18:762. [28] Benton, A. H. 1955. J. Mammal. 36:52. [29] Bertram, G. L. C. 1940. Brit. Graham Land Exped. Sci. Rept. 1:1. [30] Beuchner, H. K., and C. V. Swanson. 1955. Trans. North Am. Wildlife Conf. 20:560. [31] Beule, J. D., and A. T. Studholme. 1942. Penna. Game News 13:6. [32] Bissonnette, T. H., and A. G. Csech. 1937. Proc. Roy. Soc. (London), B, 122:246. [33] Blandau, R. J., and W. C. Young. 1939. Am. J. Anat. 64:381. [34] Blanford, W. T. 1888-91. The fauna of British India, including Ceylon and Burma. London. v. 1 and 2. [35] Boling, J. L., et al. 1941. Anat. Record 79:313. [36] Bolliger, A., and A. L. Carrodus. 1940. J. Roy. Soc. N. S. Wales 73:218. [37] Bond, R. M. 1946. J. Mammal. 27:172. [38] Bosaev, J. 1938. Konevodstvo 4:44. [39] Bowness, E. R. 1942. Can. Silver Fox and Fur 8:12. [40] Bradt, C. W. 1939. J. Mammal. 20:486. [41] Brambell, F. W. R. 1935. Trans. Roy. Soc. (London), B, 225:1. [42] Brambell, F. W. R. 1936. Ibid., B, 226:71. [43] Brambell, F. W. R., and D. H. S. Davis. 1941. Proc. Zool. Soc. (London), B, 111:1. [44] Brander, A. A. D. 1923. Wild animals in Central India. E. Arnold, London. [45] Braun, C. E. 1936. J. Mammal. 17:10. [46] Bronson, F. H., and O. W. Tiemeier. 1958. J.

continued

Wildlife Management 22:409. [47] Broom, R. 1895. Proc. Linnean Soc. N. S. Wales 10:576. [48] Brown, C. E. 1936. J. Mammal. 17:10. [49] Bruce, H. M., and E. Hindle. 1934. Proc. Zool. Soc. (London), p. 361. [50] Bunle, H. 1954. Le mouvement naturel de la population dans le monde de 1906 à 1936. Institut National d'Études Démographiques, Paris. [51] Burger, K., and I. Korompai. 1939. Zentr. Gynäkol. 63:1290. [52] Burne, E. C. 1943. Proc. Zool. Soc. (London), A, 113:27. [53] Burrell, H. 1927. The platypus. Angus and Robertson, Sydney. [54] Burt, W. H. 1940. Univ. Mich. Misc. Publs. 45. [55] Cabrera, A., and J. Yepes. 1940. Historia natural ediar; mamiferos Sud Americanos. Compañia Argentina de Editores, Buenos Aires. [56] Cantuel, P. 1946. Mammalia 10:140. [57] Carpenter, C. R. 1941. Anat. Record 79:291. [58] Carpenter, C. R., and A. H. Schultz. 1940. Comp. Psychol. Monographs 16:1. [59] Chapman, A. O. 1951-52. Univ. Kansas Sci. Bull. 34:267. [60] Cheatum, E. L., and G. H. Morton. 1942. Trans. North Am. Wildlife Conf. 7:334. [61] Cheatum, E. L., and G. H. Morton. 1946. J. Wildlife Management 10(3):249. [62] Chew, R. M. 1958. J. Mammal. 39:597. [63] Chittleborough, R. G. 1954. Australian J. Marine and Freshwater Research 5:159. [64] Chittleborough, R. G. 1955. Ibid. 6:1. [65] Chitty, H. 1957. J. Endocrinol. 15:279. [66] Clark, F. H. 1938. J. Mammal. 19:230. [67] Clarke, R. 1955-57. Discovery Repts. 28:237. [68] Clothier, R. R. 1955. J. Mammal. 36:214. [69] Cockrum, E. L. 1955. Trans. Kansas Acad. Sci. 58:487. [70] Cocks, A. H. 1881. Proc. Zool. Soc. (London), p. 249. [71] Conaway, C. H. 1954. J. Mammal. 35:263. [72] Conaway, C. H. 1958. Ibid. 39:507. [73] Conaway, C. H. 1959. Ibid. 40:180. [74] Connor, P. F. 1959. Mich. State Univ. Museum Publs., Biol. Ser., 1:165. [75] Corner, G. W. 1923. Contribs. Embryol. Carnegie Inst. Wash. 15:73. [76] Courrier, R. 1922. Compt. rend. soc. biol. 87:1365. [77] Courrier, R. 1924. Ibid. 90:808. [78] Courrier, R. 1927. Arch. biol. (Liège) 37:173. [79] Coventry, A. P. 1937. J. Mammal. 18:489. [80] Davies, J. L. 1949-50. Proc. Zool. Soc. (London) 119:673. [81] Davies, J. L. 1956. Ibid. 127:161. [82] Davis, W. B. 1944. J. Mammal. 25:370. [83] Davis, W. B., and W. P. Taylor. 1939. Ibid. 20:440. [84] Deanesly, R. 1934. Trans. Roy. Soc. (London), B, 223:239. [85] Deanesly, R. 1935. Ibid., B, 225:459. [86] Deanesly, R. 1938. Proc. Zool. Soc. (London), A, 108:31. [87] Deanesly, R. 1943. Nature 151:365. [88] Deanesly, R. 1944. Proc. Zool. Soc. (London) 114:339. [89] Deanesly, R., and A. S. Parkes. 1933. Trans. Roy. Soc. (London), B, 222:47. [90] Deanesly, R., and T. Warwick. 1939. Proc. Zool. Soc. (London), A, 109:57. [91] Degerbøl, M., and U. Møhl-Hansen. 1943. Medd. Grønland 131(11):1. [92] Dekeyser, P. L. 1955. Les mammifères de l'Afrique noire Française. Institut Français d'Afrique Noire, Dakar. [93] Denisov, V. F. 1938. Izvest. Akad. Nauk S.S.S.R., Ser. Biol., p. 863. [94] Denniston, R. H. 1957. J. Mammal. 38:414. [95] Dennler, G. 1939. Deut. Pelztierzücht. 14:388. [96] Dice, L. R. 1923. J. Mammal. 4:107. [97] Dice, L. R. 1929. Ibid. 10:225. [98] Distout, W. L. 1897. Zoologist, Ser. 4, 1:29. [99] Dixon, J. 1929. J. Mammal. 10:327. [100] Douglas, W. O. 1943. Am. Fur Breeder 16:20. [101] Eadie, W. R. 1939. J. Mammal. 20:150. [102] Eadie, W. R., and W. J. Hamilton. 1956. Ibid. 37:223. [103] Edwards, R. Y., and R. W. Ritchey. 1958. J. Wildlife Management 22:261. [104] Einarsen, A. S. 1948. The pronghorn antelope and its management. Wildlife Management Institute, Washington, D. C. [105] Elder, J. H., and R. M. Yerkes. 1936. Proc. Roy. Soc. (London), B, 120:409. [106] Enders, R. K. 1945. Trans. North Am. Wildlife Conf. 10:92. [107] Enzmann, E. V., N. R. Saphir, and G. Pincus. 1932. Anat. Record 54:325. [108] Fairfoul, D. 1934. Brit. Fur Farmer, p. 84. [109] Federated Malay States Veterinary Dept. 1936. Ann. Rept., p. 40. [110] Feldman, H. W. 1935. J. Mammal. 16:300. [111] Felten, H. 1956. Senckenbergiana Biol. 37:341. [112] Feremutsch, K., and F. Strauss. 1949. Rev. suisse zool. 56 (suppl. 1):1. [113] Fisher, H. D. 1954. Nature 173:877. [114] FitzSimons, F. H. 1919. The natural history of South Africa. Longmans, London. [115] Fleay, D. 1935-36. Victorian Naturalist 62:100. [116] Fleay, D. 1948-49. Ibid. 65:273. [117] Fleay, D. 1953-54. Ibid. 70:208. [118] Flower, S. S. 1943. Proc. Zool. Soc. (London), A, 113:27. [119] Flower, W. H., and R. Lydekker. 1891. An introduction to the study of mammals living and extinct. A. and C. Black, London. [120] Flynn, T. T. 1930. Proc. Linnean Soc. N. S. Wales 55:506. [121] Flynn, T. T., and J. P. Hill. 1938. Trans. Zool. Soc. (London), 24:445. [122] Foot, A. E. 1935. J. Bombay Nat. Hist. Soc. 38:392. [123] Foster, M. A. 1934. Am. J. Anat. 54:487. [124] Foucher D'Obsonville. 1783. Essais philosophiques sur les moeurs de divers animaux étrangers. Paris. [125] Frene, A. G. 1929. J.

continued

Bombay Nat. Hist. Soc. 33:426. [126] Fritz, B. 1937. Deut. Pelztierzücht. 12:128. [127] Gatenby, J. B. 1922. Quart. J. Microscop. Sci. 66:475. [128] Gaumer, G. F. 1917. Monographia de los mamiferos de Yucatan. Secreteria de Fomento, Mexico City. [129] Gee, E. P. 1952-53. J. Bombay Nat. Hist. Soc. 51:341. [130] Gerlinger, H. 1925. Le cycle sexuel chez la femelle des mammiferes. Strasbourg. [131] Gilbert, C., and J. Gillman. 1951. S. African J. Med. Sci. 16:115. [132] Gillman, J., and C. Gilbert. 1946. Ibid. 11:1. [133] Glass, B. P. 1949. J. Mammal. 30:72. [134] Glover, R. 1947. Ibid. 28:333. [135] Glover, R. 1953. Oryx 2:76. [136] Goin, O. B. 1943. J. Mammal. 24:212. [137] Goodman, D. E., and G. B. Wislocki. 1935. Anat. Record 61:379. [138] Goodrum, P. D. 1940. Texas Agr. Expt. Sta. Bull. 591. [139] Gopalakrishna, A. 1947. Proc. Indian Acad. Sci. 26(B):219. [140] Gopalakrishna, A. 1949. Ibid. 30(B):17. [141] Gorbelik, V. I. 1935. Trudy Azerbaidzhan. Stanc. Zivotn. 4:5. [142] Green, C. V. 1932. J. Mammal. 13:45. [143] Greulich, W. W. 1934. Anat. Record 58:217. [144] Griffin, D. R. 1940. J. Mammal. 21:181. [145] Grigorjev, N. D. 1938. Zool. Zhur. 17:811. [146] Grinnell, J., J. S. Dixon, and J. M. Linsdale. 1937. Fur bearing mammals of California. Univ. California Press, Berkeley. [147] Gros, G. 1936. Thesis. Univ. Algiers. [148] Grosser, O. 1903. Verhandl. anat. Ges. 17:129. [149] Guthkelch, A. N., and S. Zuckerman. 1937. J. Physiol. (London) 91:269. [150] Guthrie, M. J. 1933. J. Mammal. 14:199. [151] Hall, E. R., and K. R. Kelson. 1959. Mammals of North America. Ronald Press, New York. [152] Haman, J. O. 1942. Am. J. Obstet. Gynecol. 43:870. [153] Hamilton, J. E. 1934. Discovery Repts. 8:269. [154] Hamilton, J. E. 1939. Ibid. 18:239. [155] Hamilton, W. J., Jr. 1929. J. Mammal. 10:124. [156] Hamilton, W. J., Jr. 1934. Am. Midland Naturalist 14:289. [157] Hamilton, W. J., Jr. 1939. Ibid. 22:732. [158] Hamilton, W. J., Jr. 1941. Cornell Agr. Expt. Sta. Mem. 237. [159] Hamilton, W. J., Jr. 1943. The mammals of eastern United States. Comstock, Ithaca. [160] Hamilton, W. J., Jr. 1944. J. Mammal. 25:1. [161] Hamlett, G. W. D. 1932. Anat. Record 53:283. [162] Hamlett, G. W. D. 1934. Ibid. 60:9. [163] Hamlett, G. W. D. 1935. Quart. Rev. Biol. 10:432. [164] Hamlett, G. W. D. 1938. U. S. Dept. Agr. Tech. Bull. 616. [165] Hamlett, G. W. D. 1939. Anat. Record 73:171. [166] Hammond, J., and F. H. A. Marshall. 1925. Reproduction in the rabbit. Oliver and Boyd, Edinburgh. [167] Hammond, J., and F. H. A. Marshall. 1930. Proc. Roy. Soc. (London), B, 105:607. [168] Hansen, R. M. 1957. Arctic 10:105. [169] Hansen, R. M. 1960. J. Mammal. 41:323. [170] Harrison, D. L. 1955. Ann. and Mag. Nat. Hist. 8(12):897. [171] Harrison, J. L. 1955. Proc. Zool. Soc. (London) 125:445. [172] Harrison, R. J. 1960. Mammalia 24:374. [173] Harrison, R. J., and E. G. Neal. 1956. Nature 177:977. [174] Harting, J. E. 1895. Zoologist, p. 421. [175] Hartman, C. G. 1921. Smithsonian Inst. Repts. 347. [176] Hartman, C. G. 1923. Anat. Record 32:353. [177] Hartman, C. G. 1928. J. Morphol. and Physiol. 46:143. [178] Hartman, C. G. 1931. J. Mammal. 12:129. [179] Hartman, C. G. 1932. Contribs. Embryol. Carnegie Inst. Wash. 23:1. [180] Haskell, H. S., and H. G. Reynolds. 1947. J. Mammal. 28:129. [181] Hatfield, D. M. 1935. Ibid. 16:261. [182] Heape, W. 1894. Trans. Roy. Soc. (London), B, 185:411. [183] Heape, W. 1901. Quart. J. Microscop. Sci. 44:1. [184] Hediger, H. 1948. Physiol. Comparata et Oecol. 1:46 [185] Hendrickson, G. O. 1943. J. Mammal. 24:273. [186] Heptner, V. G., L. G. Morosowa-Turowa, and V. I. Zalkin. 1956. Die Säugetiere in der Schutzwaldzone. Deutscher Verlag der Wissenschaften, Berlin. [187] Herter, K. 1933. Z. Säugetierk. 8:195. [188] Hill, J. P. 1910-11. Quart. J. Microscop. Sci. 56:1. [189] Hill, J. P., and C. H. O'Donoghue. 1913. Ibid. 59:133. [190] Hill, M. 1939. Proc. Zool. Soc. (London), B, 109:481. [191] Hill, W. C. O. 1939. Ceylon J. Sci., D, 5:21. [192] Hill, W. C. O. 1941. Nature 148:408. [193] Holdenried, R., and H. B. Morlan. 1956. Am. Midland Naturalist 55:369. [194] Howell, A. H. 1938. North Am. Fauna 56. [195] Hoyte, H. M. D. 1955. J. Animal Ecol. 24:412. [196] Hubback, T. H. 1937. J. Mammal. 18:267. [197] Hubbard, W. D. 1929. Ibid. 10:294. [198] Ibsen, H. L. 1928. J. Exptl. Zool. 51:51. [199] Israel, S. 1959. J. Obstet. Gynaecol. Brit. Empire 66:311. [200] Jaczewski, Z. 1958. Acta Theriologica 1:333. [201] James, C. S. 1941. Am. Fur Breeder 13(8):14. [202] Jennison, G. 1927. Natural history: animals. A. and C. Black, London. app., p. 1. [203] Joachimowitz, R. 1928. Biol. Generalis 4:447. [204] Johanssen, I. 1938. Lantbruks-Högskol. Ann. 5:179. [205] Johnson, G. E., M. A. Foster, and R. M. Coco. 1933. Trans. Kansas Acad. Sci. 36:250. [206] Johnson, R. F., and R. L. Rudd. 1957. J. Mammal. 38:157. [207] Johnston, H. L., and

continued

W. D. Oliff. 1954. Proc. Zool. Soc. (London) 124:605. [208] Jones, F. W. 1924. The mammals of South Australia. British Science Guild, Adelaide. pt. 2. [209] Kaleff, B. Z. 1932. Z. Zücht., B, 24:391. [210] Kaudern, W. 1914. Ark. Zool. 9 (1):1. [211] Kellas, L. M. 1954-55. Proc. Zool. Soc. (London) 124:751. [212] Kellog, R. 1940. Natl. Geograph. Mag. 77:35. [213] Kenneth, J. H. 1947. Imp. Bur. Animal Breeding Genet. Tech. Commun. 5. [214] Kenyon, K. W., and D. W. Rice. 1959. Pacific Sci. 13:215. [215] Kerbert, C. 1922. Bijdragen Dierk (Amsterdam), Festnumer, p. 185. [216] Kinsey, A. C., et al. 1953. Sexual behavior in the human female. W. B. Saunders, Philadelphia. [217] Koch, W. 1936. Deut. landwirtsch. Tierzucht 40:56. [218] Kolosov, A. M. 1941. Zool. Zhur. 20:154. [219] Krutsch, P. H. 1952-53. Univ. Kansas Publs. Museum Nat. Hist. 7:351. [220] Kubik, J. 1952. Ann. Univ. Mariae Curie-Sklodowska Lublin-Polonia, C, 7:1. [221] Labacev, S. V. 1934. Zool. Zhur. 13:280. [222] Lantz, D. E. 1910. U. S. Dept. Agr. Biol. Survey Bull. 36. [223] Lataste, F. 1886. Actes soc. linnéenne Bordeaux 40:295. [224] Laurie, A. H. 1937. Discovery Repts. 15:223. [225] Laveridge, A. J. 1922. E. Africa and Uganda Nat. Hist. Soc. 17:39. [226] Lavrov, N. P. 1944. People's Commisariat for Procurement (U.S.S.R.) 6:124. [227] Laws, R. M. 1956. Falkland Is. Dependency Survey Sci. Repts. 15:1. [228] Layne, J. N. 1954. Ecol. Monographs 24:227. [229] Lenner, A. 1944. Acta Obstet. Gynecol. Scand. 24:113. [230] Leopold, A. 1933. Game management. C. Scribner's Sons, New York. [231] Leopold, A. S. 1959. Wildlife of Mexico. Univ. California Press, Berkeley. [232] Lewis, F. 1934-35. Victorian Naturalist 51:73. [233] Liche, H. 1939. Nature 143:900. [234] Liers, E. 1951. J. Mammal. 32:1. [235] Lindsey, A. A. 1937. Ibid. 18:127. [236] Linsdale, J. M., and L. P. Tevis. 1951. The dusky-footed wood rat. Univ. California Press, Berkeley. [237] Lucas, N. S., E. M. Hume, and H. H. Smith. 1927. Proc. Zool. Soc. (London), p. 447. [238] Lush, J. L. 1945. Animal breeding plans. Iowa State College Press, Ames. [239] Lydekker, R. 1898. The deer of all lands. R. Ward, London. [240] Lyne, A. G., P. E. Pelton, and G. B. Sharman. 1959. Nature 183:622. [241] Mackerras, M. J., and R. H. Smith. 1960. Australian J. Zool. 8:371. [242] Mackintosh, N. A. 1942-43. Discovery Repts. 22:197. [243] Manning, T. H. 1954. Arctic 7:36. [244] Markley, M. H., and C. F. Bassett. 1942. Am. Midland Naturalist 28:604. [245] Marlow, B. J. 1961. Australian J. Zool. 9:203. [246] Marshall, A. J. 1947. Proc. Linnean Soc. 159:103. [247] Marshall, F. H. A. 1904. Quart. J. Microscop. Sci. 48:323. [248] Marshall, F. H. A. 1922. The physiology of reproduction. Longmans, Green; London. [249] Marshall, F. H. A., and W. A. Jolly. 1905. Trans. Roy. Soc. (London), B, 198:99. [250] Matthews, L. H. 1935. Proc. Zool. Soc. (London), p. 347. [251] Matthews, L. H. 1937. Trans. Zool. Soc. (London) 23:213. [252] Matthews, L. H. 1937-38. Discovery Repts. 17:7. [253] Matthews, L. H. 1938. Ibid. 17:93. [254] Matthews, L. H. 1938. Ibid. 17:183. [255] Matthews, L. H. 1939. Trans. Roy. Soc. (London), B, 230:1. [256] Matthews, L. H. 1941. Proc. Zool. Soc. (London), B, 111:57. [257] Matthews, L. H. 1946-47. Ibid. 116:339. [258] Matthews, L. H. 1953-56. Trans. Zool. Soc. (London) 28:543. [259] McBride, A. F., and H. Kritzler. 1951. J. Mammal. 322:251. [260] McCann, C. 1933. J. Bombay Nat. Hist. Soc. 36:618. [261] McDougall, W. A. 1946. Queensland J. Agr. Sci. 3:1. [262] McHugh, T. 1958. Zoologica 43:1. [263] McKenzie, F. F., and J. C. Miller. 1930. Missouri Agr. Expt. Sta. Research Bull. 285:43. [264] McKerrow, M. J. M. 1955. Trans. Roy. Soc. (London), B, 238:62. [265] McLaren, I. A. 1955. J. Fisheries Research Board Can. 15:219. [266] McLaren, I. A. 1958. Bull. Fisheries Research Board Can. 118:1. [267] McLeod, J. A., and G. F. Bondar. 1952. Can. J. Zool. 30:243. [268] McNally, J. 1960. Australian J. Zool. 8:170. [269] Mearns, E. A. 1907. U. S. Natl. Museum Bull. 56. [270] Meesrock, V. 1954-55. Proc. Zool. Soc. (London) 124:631. [271] Meester, J. 1958. J. Mammal. 39:302. [272] Menier, C. 1922. Rev. hist. nat. Mammalia 10:146. [273] Mertz, P. A. 1939. Trudy Biol. Inst. Tomsk Univ. 6:175. [274] Meyer, B. J., and R. K. Meyer. 1944. J. Mammal. 25:107. [275] Miller, M. A. 1946. Ibid. 27:335. [276] Miller, R. E. 1939. J. Morphol. 64:267. [277] Mizue, K., and H. Jimbo. 1950. Sci. Repts. Whales Research Inst. 3:119. [278] Moghe, M. A. 1951-52. Proc. Zool. Soc. (London) 121:703. [279] Moghe, M. A. 1956. Proc. Natl. Inst. Sci. India 22(B):48. [280] Møhl-Hansen, U. 1954. Videnskab. Medd. Dansk Naturhist. Forening, I, 116:369. [281] Moore, R. C., et al. 1934. Anat. Record 60:279. [282] Morrison, J. A. 1960. Behaviour 16:84. [283] Morrison, J. A., C. E. Trainer, and P. L. Wright. 1959. J. Wildlife Management 23:27. [284] Nachtsheim, H. 1935. Z. Zücht.,

continued

B, 33:343. [285] Newman, H. H. 1913. Am. Naturalist 47:513. [286] Noback, C. R. 1939. Anat. Record 73:209. [287] Orr, R. T. 1954. Proc. Calif. Acad. Sci. 28:165. [288] Osgood, F. L. Unpublished, 1945. [289] Parkes, A. S. 1926-27. Brit. J. Exptl. Biol. 4:93. [290] Parkes, A. S. 1931. Proc. Roy. Soc. (London), B, 108:138. [291] Pearson, A. K., and R. K. Enders. 1951. Anat. Record 111:695. [292] Pearson, O. P. 1944. Am. J. Anat. 75:39. [293] Pearson, O. P. 1948. J. Mammal. 29:345. [294] Pearson, O. P. 1949. Am. J. Anat. 84:143. [295] Pearson, O. P. 1951. Bull. Museum Comp. Zool. Harvard Univ. 106:115. [296] Pearson, O. P., and P. H. Baldwin. 1953. J. Mammal. 34:436. [297] Pearson, O. P., and R. K. Enders. 1944. J. Exptl. Zool. 95:21. [298] Pearson, O. P., M. R. Koford, and A. K. Pearson. 1952. J. Mammal. 33:273. [299] Pentfer, J. W. 1955. J. Wildlife Management 19:417. [300] Perry, J. S. 1942. Proc. Zool. Soc. (London), A, 112:118. [301] Perry, J. S. 1951. J. Endocrinol. 7:53. [302] Perry, J. S. 1954. Trans. Roy. Soc. (London), B, 237:93. [303] Peters, H., and S. M. Shrikande. 1957. Fertility and Sterility 8:355. [304] Petzsch, H. 1936. Kleintier u. Pelztier 12(1):1. [305] Pfeiffer, E. W. 1958. J. Mammal. 39:223. [306] Phillips, W. W. 1924-26. Ceylon J. Sci., B, 13:143. [307] Pickwell, G. 1941. Audubon Mag. 43:24. [308] Pimentel, D. 1955. J. Mammal. 36:62. [309] Pimlott, D. H. 1959. J. Wildlife Management 23:381. [310] Pocock, R. I. 1910. Proc. Zool. Soc. (London), p. 840. [311] Pocock, R. I. 1939-41. Fauna of British India, including Ceylon and Burma. Mammals. Taylor and Francis, London, v.1. [312] Ponomarev, A. L. 1938. Zool. Zhur. 17:482. [313] Poole, E. L. 1940. J. Mammal. 21:249. [314] Popoff, N. 1934. Compt. rend. assoc. anat. 29:471. [315] Powell, W. 1925. Rodents. Dept. of Public Health, South Africa. [316] Prell, H. 1938. Tharandt. forst. Jahrb. 89:696. [317] Prell, H. 1938. Züchtungskunde 13:325. [318] Price, M. 1953. Proc. Zool. Soc. (London) 123:599. [319] Przibram, H. 1927. Tabulae Biologicae 4:342. [320] Quimby, D. C. 1951. Ecol. Monographs 21:61. [321] Rabb, G. B. 1959. J. Mammal. 40:616. [322] Rainey, D. G. 1954-56. Univ. Kansas Publs. Museum Nat. Hist. 8:536. [323] Ramakrishna, P. A. 1947. Current Sci. (India) 16:186. [324] Ramakrishna, P. A. 1951. J. Mysore Univ., B, 11:107. [325] Rand, A. L. 1945. Bull. Natl. Museum Can. 100, Biol. Ser. 29. [326] Rand, R. W. 1954-55. Proc. Zool. Soc. (London) 124:717. [327] Ranson, R. M. 1934. J. Animal Ecol. 3:70. [328] Raynaud, A. 1956. Compt. rend. soc. biol. 144:938. [329] Rice, D. W. 1960. J. Mammal. 41:376. [330] Rice, V. A., et al. 1957. Breeding and improvement of farm animals. Ed. 5. McGraw-Hill, New York. [331] Rode, P. 1943. Mammifères ongulés de l'Afrique noire. Librairie Larose, Paris. [332] Ross, R. C. 1930. J. Mammal. 11:76. [333] Rowlands, I. W., and A. S. Parkes. 1935. Proc. Zool. Soc. (London), p. 823. [334] Rowley, J. 1929. J. Mammal. 10:1. [335] Rumjancev, B. S., W. S. Butarin, and V. F. Denisov. 1933-34. Trudy kirgiz. kompl. Eksp. 4(3):15. [336] Ruud, J. T. 1945. Hvalrådets Skr. 29. [337] Ruud, J. T., Å. Jonsgard, and P. Ottestad. 1950. Ibid. 33. [338] Salim, A. 1946. J. Bombay Nat. Hist. Soc. 46:472. [339] Sanborn, C. C. 1952. Fieldiana Zool. 33:89. [340] Sanborn, C. C., and A. R. Watkins. 1950. J. Mammal. 31:430. [341] Schäfer, E. 1937. Zool. Garten 9:122. [342] Scheffer, T. H. 1908. Kansas Agr. Expt. Sta. Bull. 152. [343] Scheffer, T. H. 1924. J. Mammal. 5:258. [344] Scheffer, T. H. 1938. Ibid. 19:220. [345] Scheffer, V. B., and J. W. Slepp. 1948. Am. Midland Naturalist 39:257. [346] Schmidt, F. 1934. Z. Säugetierk. 9:392. [347] Schmidt, F. 1937. Deut. Pelztierzücht. 12:235. [348] Schmidt, F. 1938. Der Silberfuchs und seine Zucht. Munich. [349] Schmidt, J., E. Lamprecht, and H. Staubesand. 1936. Z. Tierzücht. Züchtungsbiol. 36:55. [350] Schramm, P. 1961. J. Mammal. 42:167. [351] Schultz, A. H., and F. S. Snyder. 1935. Bull. Johns Hopkins Hosp. 57:193. [352] Schulze, G. 1938. Deut. Pelztierzücht. 13:97. [353] Seton, E. T. 1909. Life histories of northern animals. C. Scribner's Sons, New York. [354] Shadle, A. R. 1953. J. Wildlife Management 17:388. [355] Sharmon, G. B. 1954. Nature 173:302. [356] Sharman, G. B. 1954. West. Australian Naturalist 4:159. [357] Sharmon, G. B. 1959. Monographiae Biologicae 8:332. [358] Shaw, W. T. 1925. J. Mammal. 6:106. [359] Sheehan, J. F., and J. A. Bruner. 1945. Turtox News 23:65. [360] Shortridge, G. C. 1934. The mammals of South West Africa. W. Heinemann, London. [361] Skinner, M. P. 1922. J. Mammal. 3:82. [362] Sleptzov, M. M. 1940. Byull. Moskov. Obshchestva Ispytatelei Prirody, Otdel Biol., n.s. 49:50. [363] Smith, C. F. 1936. J. Mammal. 17:274. [364] Smith, F. R. 1938. U. S. Dept. Agr. Circ. 474. [365] Snyder, R. L., and J. J. Christian. 1900. Ecology 41:647. [366] Soame, E. B. H. 1936. Fur and Feather

continued

96:10. [367] Sokolov, I. I. 1935. Trudy Arkt. Inst. 24:67. [368] Sollberger, D. E. 1943. J. Mammal. 24:163. [369] Sowls, L. K. 1957. Ibid. 38:234. [370] Sowls, L. K. 1961. Ibid. 42:425. [371] Spencer, C. C. 1943. Ibid. 24:1. [372] Spiegel, A. 1931. Zentr. Gynäkol. 22:1762. [373] Steinmetz, H. 1937. Zool. Garten 9:255. [374] Stewart, H. C. 1952. J. Am. Med. Assoc. 148:1079. [375] Stieve, H. 1950. Z. mikroskop.- anat. Forsch. 55:427. [376] Stockard, A. H. 1929. Papers Mich. Acad. Sci. 11:471. [377] Stott, K. 1953. J. Mammal. 34:385. [378] Struthers, P. H. 1928. Ibid. 9:301. [379] Stuewer, F. W. 1943. J. Wildlife Management 7:60. [380] Svihla, A. 1929. J. Mammal. 10:352. [381] Svihla, A. 1930. Papers Mich. Acad. Sci. 11:485. [382] Svihla, A. 1931. J. Mammal. 12:238. [383] Svihla, A. 1931. Ibid. 12:363. [384] Svihla, A. 1932. Univ. Mich. Museum Zool. Misc. Publs. 24. [385] Talmage, R. V., and G. D. Buchanan. 1954. Rice Inst. Pamphl. 41:109. [386] Tavolga, M. C., and F. S. Essapian. 1957. Zoologica 42:11. [387] Taylor, W. P. 1956. The deer of North America. Stackpole, Harrisburg. [388] Tetley, H. 1941. Proc. Zool. Soc. (London), B, 111:13. [389] Tevis, L., Jr. 1955. Am. Midland Naturalist 53:71. [390] Thomas, W. D. 1958. Zoologica 43:95. [391] Tong, E. 1958. Proc. Zool. Soc. (London) 130:296. [392] Trapido, H. 1949. J. Mammal. 30:433. [393] Trippensee, R. E. 1936. Trans. 1st North Am. Wildlife Conf., p. 344. [394] Troughton, E. le G. 1947. Furred animals of Australia. C. Scribner's Sons, New York. [395] Troughton, E. le G. 1955. Australian Museum Mag. 11:396. [396] Tryon, C. A. 1947. Montana Agr. Expt. Sta. Bull. 448. [397] Tupikova, N. V., and S. M. Kulogin. 1952. Zool. Zhur. 31:476. [398] Urbain, A. 1954. Ann. Musee Congo Belge (Tervueren) Zool. 1:101. [399] U. S. Bureau of Biological Survey. 1940. Wildlife Leaflet BS-151. [400] U. S. Fish and Wildlife Service. 1941. (Reprint). Am. Fur Breeder 14(4):6. [401] Van der Horst, C. J. 1941. Science 93:430. [402] Van der Horst, C. J. 1955. Trans. Roy. Soc. (London), B, 238:27. [403] van Wagenen, G. 1950. The care and breeding of laboratory animals. J. Wiley and Sons, New York. [404] van Wagenen, G. 1952. Anat. Record 112:436. [405] van Wagenen, G. 1958. In W. F. Windle, ed. Neurological and psychological deficits of asphyxia neonatorum. C. C. Thomas, Springfield, Ill. p. 274. [406] van Wagenen, G., and M. E. Simpson. 1954. Anat. Record 118:231. [407] Verschuren, J. 1958. Exploration du parc national de la Garamba. Institut des Parcs Nationaux du Congo Belge, Bruxelles. [408] Vestal, E. H. 1938. J. Mammal. 19:1. [409] Wade, O. 1928. Ibid. 9:149. [410] Wallace, H. F. 1913. The big game of central and western China. Duffield, London. [411] Waring, H., et al. 1955. Australia J. Zool. 3:34. [412] Warren, E. R. 1942. The mammals of Colorado. Univ. Oklahoma Press, Stillwater. [413] Webb, C. S. 1954. The odyssey of an animal collector. Longmans, Green; London. [414] Webb-Peploe, C. G. 1947. J. Bombay Nat. Hist. Soc. 46:629. [415] Whiteman, E. E. 1940. J. Mammal. 21:435. [416] Wight, H. M. J. 1930. Ibid. 11:40. [417] Wilhelm, J. H. 1933. J. S. W. Africa Sci. Soc. 6:51. [418] Wilson, D. C., and I. Sutherland. 1950. Brit. Med. J. 2:862. [419] Wimsatt, W. A. 1942. Anat. Record 83:341. [420] Wimsatt, W. A. 1945. J. Mammal. 26:23. [421] Wimsatt, W. A., and H. Trapido. 1952. Am. J. Anat. 91:415. [422] Wislocki, G. B. 1930. Contribs. Embryol. Carnegie Inst. Wash. 22:173. [423] Wislocki, G. B., and O. P. van der Westhuysen. 1940. Ibid. 28:65. [424] Wood, F. D. 1935. J. Mammal. 16:105. [425] Wood, J. E. 1949. Ibid. 30:36. [426] Wood, J. E. 1958. Ibid. 39:74. [427] Wright, P. L. 1942. Anat. Record 83:341. [428] Wright, P. L. 1947. J. Mammal. 28:343. [429] Wright, P. L. 1948. Am. Midland Naturalist 39:338. [430] Wright, P. L., and R. Rausch. 1955. J. Mammal. 36:346. [431] Yergamian, G. 1958. J. Natl. Cancer Inst. 20:705. [432] Yerkes, R. M., and J. H. Elder. 1937. Yale J. Biol. Med. 10:41. [433] Young, W. C., and R. M. Yerkes. 1943. Endocrinology 33:121. [434] Young, W. C., et al. 1939. J. Comp. Psychol. 27:49. [435] Zenkavic, B. A. 1935. Doklady Akad. Nauk S.S.S.R. 2:337. [436] Zitkov, B. M. 1942. Zool. Zhur. 21:245. [437] Zuckerman, S. 1931. Proc. Zool. Soc. (London), p. 325. [438] Zuckerman, S. 1933. Ibid., p. 1059. [439] Zuckerman, S. 1937. Ibid., A, 107:315. [440] Zuckerman, S. 1952-53. Ibid. 122:827. [441] Zuckerman, S., and A. S. Parker. 1932. Ibid., p. 139.

42. PROPAGATION: BIRDS

Classification adapted from Wetmore, *A Classification for the Birds of the World*, Smithsonian Institution, 1960.

Part I: NEST BUILDING, INCUBATION, AND PARENTAL CARE OF YOUNG

In the case of those birds that take a number of incubation sessions on the eggs each day, the attentive period represents the range of averages at different nests, with the exclusion of the long nocturnal session; in the case of birds that take only one or a few incubation sessions each day, the extreme range of these sessions, often including the nocturnal period, seems usually to be given. Symbols in columns C, D, F, G, J, and K range from 0 (no time given to specified activity) to ++++ (one sex does all the work).

	Order and Family	Common Name	Nest Building		Incubation				Feeding and Care of Young			
					Duration	Parental Activity			Nestling Period[2]			Trips[3] per Hour[4]
			♂	♀	da	♂	♀	Attentive Period[1]	da	♂	♀	
	(A)	(B)	(C)	(D)	(E)	(F)	(G)	(H)	(I)	(J)	(K)	(L)
	Passeriformes											
1	Fringillidae	Finches, sparrows	+	+++	11-14	+	+++	14.6 min-continuous	8-17	++	++	1.3-21.3
2	Thraupidae	Tanagers	+	+++	12-16	0	++++	14-117 min	10-24	++	++	4.0-16.5
3	Icteridae	Blackbirds	0	++++	11-14	0	++++	9-63 min	9-34	+	+++	6.2-17.7
4	Ploceidae	Weaver finches	+++	+	12-16	+	+++	14 min	13-19	+	+++	4-20
5	Parulidae	Wood warblers	+	+++	11-17	0	++++	20-110 min	8-14	++	++	1.6-27.4
6	Coerebidae	Honeycreepers	+	+++	12-14	0	++++	19-61 min	13-19	+	+++	2.8-13.2
7	Vireonidae	Vireos	+	+++	12-16	+	+++	10-49 min	10-15	++	++	3.9-13.5
8	Zosteropidae	White-eyes	++	++	11-12	++	++	....	9-11	++	++	7
9	Dicaeidae	Flower-peckers	+	+++	.....	+	+++	....	.....	++	++	....
10	Nectariniidae	Sunbirds	+	+++	12-13	+	+++	....	.....	+	+++	20
11	Meliphagidae	Honey eaters	+	+++	13-18	+	+++	....	14-18	++	++	9
12	Sturnidae	Starlings	++	++	12	++	++	20 min	20-21	++	++	19-22
13	Prionopidae	Wood shrikes	++	++	.....	++	++	17-30 min	.....	++	++	7.0-10.9
14	Laniidae	Shrikes	++	++	16	+	+++	23 min	15-21	++	++	....
15	Artamidae	Wood swallows	+++	+	.....	+++	+	....	.....	++	++	....
16	Ptilogonatidae	Silky flycatchers	+++	+	15	++	++	9 min	18-19	+++	+	2.5-5.3
17	Bombycillidae	Waxwings	++	++	12	+	+++	37 min	16	++	++	3.0
18	Motacillidae	Pipits	+	+++	13-14	+	+++	19-48 min	10-15	+	+++	3.6-25.0
19	Prunellidae	Accentors, hedge sparrows	+	+++	12-15	+	+++	19-30 min	13	++	++	5.1
20	Muscicapidae	Old World flycatchers	++	++	12-20	+	+++	15-87 min	10-20	++	++	6.2-33.6
21	Regulidae	Kinglets	++	++	14-17	0	++++	....	18-20	++	++	17.5
22	Sylviidae	Old World warblers	+	+++	11-19	+	+++	11-80 min	9-15	++	++	10-33
23	Turdidae	Thrushes	+	+++	12-16	+	+++	12-120 min	12-18	++	++	5.5-38.5
24	Mimidae	Thrashers, catbirds	+	+++	12-13	+	+++	20.8-23.8 min	11-14	++	++	3.6-14.2
25	Troglodytidae	Wrens	++	++	13-19	0	++++	12-86 min	13-22	++	++	5.6-19.2
26	Cinclidae	Dippers	+	+++	16	+	+++	31 min	19-24	+	+++	8.8-25.9
27	Timaliidae	Babbling thrushes	+	+++	21±	+	+++	....	.....	+	+++	....
28	Chamaeidae	Wren-tits	++	++	15-16	++	++	47 min	15-16	++	++	8.8
29	Certhiidae	Creepers	+	+++	15	+	+++	....	15-20	++	++	....
30	Sittidae	Nuthatches	++	++	15	0	++++	31 min	22-24	++	++	11.9-18.4
31	Paridae	Titmice	++	++	13-15	+	+++	10-38 min	14-21	++	++	3.6-34.5
32	Paradisaeidae	Birds of paradise	0	++++	14-18	+	+++	16-36+ min	18-31	+	+++	12.9
33	Corvidae	Crows	++	++	16-20	+	+++	35-150 min	20-38	++	++	1.7-4.0
34	Oriolidae	Old World orioles	+	+++	14-15	+	+++	....	14-15	++	++	....
35	Hirundinidae	Swallows	++	++	14-19	+	+++	6-33 min	18-28	++	++	4-40
36	Alaudidae	Larks	0	++++	11-12	+	+++	....	9-12	++	++	5.9-8.0
37	Menuridae	Lyrebirds	0	++++	28	0	++++	....	42	0	++++	....
38	Tyrannidae	Tyrant flycatchers	+	+++	14-23	0	++++	6-69 min	14-28	+	+++	2.0-36.7
39	Pipridae	Manakins	0	++++	18-21	0	++++	34-156 min	13-15	0	++++	1.3-3.4
40	Cotingidae	Cotingas	+	+++	18-19	0	++++	12-114 min	20-28	+	+++	1.3-21.0
41	Formicariidae	Antbirds	++	++	14-20	++	++	68-188 min	9-19	++	++	1.8-5.3
42	Furnariidae	Ovenbirds	++	++	15-22	++	++	22-97 min	13-29	++	++	2-5
43	Dendrocolaptidae	Woodhewers	+	+++	15-21	+	+++	23-67 min	19-24	+	+++	2.0-8.5
	Piciformes											
44	Picidae	Woodpeckers	+++	+	11-18	+++	+	12 min-19.5 hr	19-36	++	++	1-30
45	Ramphastidae	Toucans	....	....	16	++	++	26-40 min	43-45	++	++	2.8-4.0

/1/ Time parent sits on eggs (1 sitting before leaving to feed and rest). /2/ Time from hatching until young birds leave nest. /3/ Range of averages for various nests. /4/ Unless otherwise specified.

continued

42. PROPAGATION: BIRDS

Part I: NEST BUILDING, INCUBATION, AND PARENTAL CARE OF YOUNG

	Order and Family	Common Name	Nest Building		Incubation				Feeding and Care of Young			
					Duration da	Parental Activity			Nestling Period[2] da	♂	♀	Trips[3] per Hour[4]
			♂	♀		♂	♀	Attentive Period[1]				
	(A)	(B)	(C)	(D)	(E)	(F)	(G)	(H)	(I)	(J)	(K)	(L)
	Piciformes											
46	Capitonidae	Barbets	++	++	13-15	++	++	37 min	.....	++	++	....
47	Bucconidae	Puffbirds	++	++	.....	++	++	58 min-16 hr	20	++	++	0.8-0.9
48	Galbulidae	Jacamars	+	+++	20-23	++	++	101 min	21-26	++	++	4.0-4.9
	Coraciiformes											
49	Bucerotidae	Hornbills	++	++	28-40	0	++++	Continuous	75	+++	+	1.6-2.0+
50	Phoeniculidae	Wood hoopoes	....	....	.....	....	....	....	.....	++	++	3
51	Upupidae	Hoopoes	....	....	16	0	++++	11.5 hr	29	++	++	1.9
52	Coraciidae	Rollers	....	....	18-19	++	++	....	26-28	++	++	....
53	Meropidae	Bee-eaters	++	++	22	++	++	15-30 min	30	++	++	....
54	Momotidae	Motmots	++	++	21	++	++	1-16 hr	28-32	++	++	4.9
55	Alcedinidae	Kingfishers	++	++	21-23	++	++	1.7-24.0 hr	24-35	++	++	1.9-3.8
	Trogoniformes											
56	Trogonidae	Trogons	++	++	17-19	++	++	1-18 hr	14-30	+++	+	0.8-3.1
	Apodiformes											
57	Trochilidae	Hummingbirds	0	++++	15-17	0	++++	5-99 min	19-25	0	++++	1.1-3.3
58	Apodidae	Swifts	++	++	17-21	++	++	32-75 min	20-42	++	++	0.7-2.5
	Caprimulgiformes											
59	Caprimulgidae	Goatsuckers	0	0	16-20	+	+++	1.4-14.0 hr	0	++	++	3.7
	Strigiformes											
60	Strigidae	Owls	++	++	27-35	+	+++	23.5 hr	21-35	++	++	1-8
61	Tytonidae	Barn owls	....	....	30-34	+	+++	....	56-64+	++	++	1.4-2.0
	Cuculiformes											
62	Cuculidae	Cuckoos	++	++	11-18	++	++	0.5-1.5 hr	6-22	++	++	2-12
	Psittaciformes											
63	Psittacidae	Parrots	+	+++	17-31	+	+++	Continuous	28-36	++	++	....
	Columbiformes											
64	Columbidae	Pigeons, doves	++	++	11-19	++	++	4-20 hr	10-35	++	++	0.2-1.0
65	Raphidae	Solitaires	....	....	49	++	++	....	.....	....	....	....
66	Pteroclididae	Sandgrouse	....	....	22-28	++	++	12 hr	.....	....	....	....
	Charadriiformes											
67	Alcidae	Murres, puffins, guillemots	++	++	24-42	++	++	12 hr	2-49	++	++	....
68	Rhynchopidae	Skimmers	....	....	.....	0	++++	....	0	++	++	....
69	Laridae	Gulls, terns	++	++	20-34	++	++	0.5-24.0 hr	0-several	++	++	0.2-7.0
70	Stercorariidae	Skuas, jaegers	....	....	23-26	++	++	....	0	++	++	....
71	Glareolidae	Pratincoles	....	....	.....	+	+++	....	.....	....	....	....
72	Burhinidae	Thick-knees	....	....	26-27	++	++	....	0	....	....	....
73	Phalaropodidae	Phalaropes	++++	0	20-21	+++	+	....	0	+++	+	....
74	Recurvirostridae	Avocets	++	++	23	++	++	10-66 min	0	....	....	....
75	Scolopacidae	Sandpipers	....	....	18-29	++	++	11-15 hr	0	++	++	....
76	Charadriidae	Plovers	++	++	23-28	++	++	0.5-2.3 hr	0	++	++	....
77	Haematopodidae	Oyster catchers	....	....	24-27	++	++	12 hr	0	++	++	....
78	Rostratulidae	Painted snipes	....	....	.....	+++?	?	....	.....	....	....	....
79	Jacanidae	Jacanas	....	....	23	++++	0	....	.....	++++	0	....
	Gruiformes											
80	Otidae	Bustards	....	....	20-25	0	++++	....	0	0	++++	....
81	Eurypygidae	Sun bitterns	++	++	27	++	++	....	21	++	++	....
82	Rhynochetidae	Kagus	++	++	36	++	++	....	.....	....	....	....
83	Rallidae	Rails	++	++	19-24	++	++	38 min	0-2	++	++	....
84	Gruidae	Cranes	++	++	29-32	++	++	44-165 min	0	++	++	....
85	Pedionomidae	Plain wanderers	....	....	.....	++++	0	....	0	++++	0	....
86	Turnicidae	Bustard quail	++	++	12-13	++++	0	....	0	++++	0	....
87	Mesitornithidae	Monias	....	....	.....	+++	+	....	.....	+++	+	....
	Galliformes											
88	Opisthocomidae	Hoatzins	++	++	.....	....	....	....	.....	....	....	....
89	Meleagrididae	Turkeys	0	++++	28	0	++++	23-24 hr	0	0	++++	....
90	Phasianidae	Quail, pheasants	++	++	21-28	+	+++	7-23+ hr	0	++	++	....

/1/ Time parent sits on eggs (1 sitting before leaving to feed and rest). /2/ Time from hatching until young birds leave nest. /3/ Range of averages for various nests. /4/ Unless otherwise specified.

continued

42. PROPAGATION: BIRDS

Part I: NEST BUILDING, INCUBATION, AND PARENTAL CARE OF YOUNG

	Order and Family	Common Name	Nest Building		Incubation				Feeding and Care of Young			
					Duration da	Parental Activity			Nestling Period[2] da	♂	♀	Trips[3] per Hour[4]
			♂	♀		♂	♀	Attentive Period[1]				
	(A)	(B)	(C)	(D)	(E)	(F)	(G)	(H)	(I)	(J)	(K)	(L)
	Galliformes											
91	Tetraonidae	Grouse, ptarmigan	0	++++	21-27	0	++++	6.0-11.5 hr	0	+	+++	....
92	Cracidae	Chachalacas	++	++	22-24	0	++++	....	0	....	....	....
93	Megapodiidae	Megapodes	++++	0	57-70	0	0	....	0	....	....	....
	Falconiformes											
94	Falconidae	Falcons	+	+++	28-29	+	+++	3 hr	25-35	++	++	0.3-5.8
95	Accipitridae	Hawks	+	+++	28-56	+	+++	1-20 hr	28-133	++	++	0.1-4.0
96	Cathartidae	Vultures	....	....	39-56	++	++	....	56-70	++	++	....
	Anseriformes											
97	Anatidae	Swans, geese, ducks	+	+++	21-35	+	+++	4.0-23.7 hr	0	+	+++	....
98	Anhimidae	Screamers	++	++	42	++	++	7-17 hr	0	....	....	....
	Ciconiiformes											
99	Phoenicopteridae	Flamingos	....	....	30-32	++	++	12 hr	3-4	++	++	....
100	Threskiornithidae	Ibis	++	++	21-24	++	++	6-18 hr	42+	++	++	12-20/da
101	Ciconiidae	Storks	++	++	30-38	++	++	1.0-4.5 hr	63	++	++	5-11/da
102	Scopidae	Hammerheads	++	++	21	++	++	....	42	++	++	....
103	Ardeidae	Herons, bitterns	++	++	18-28	++	++	1-6 hr	10-52	++	++	0.5-3.0
	Pelecaniformes											
104	Fregatidae	Man-o'-war birds	++	++	.....	++	++	....	.....	++	++	....
105	Anhingidae	Anhingas	....	....	.....	++	++	....	.....	++	++	....
106	Phalacrocoracidae	Cormorants	++	++	24-25	++	++	1-3 hr	35-42	++	++	1
107	Sulidae	Boobies	++	++	42-45	++	++	1 da	45+	++	++	1+/da
108	Pelecanidae	Pelicans	....	....	28-42	++	++	....	14-35	++	++	3+/da
109	Phaëthontidae	Tropic birds	....	....	28	++	++	....	62	++	++	2-3/da
	Procellariiformes											
110	Pelecanoididae	Diving petrels	++	++	56	++	++	1 da	54	++	++	1-2/da
111	Hydrobatidae	Storm petrels	++	++	38-50	++	++	1-5 da	56	++	++	1/da
112	Procellariidae	Fulmars, shearwaters	++	++	51-58	++	++	1-7 da	49-95	++	++	0.5-2.0/da
113	Diomedeidae	Albatrosses	++	++	63-80	++	++	5.3-21.8 da	150-251	++	++	2-5/wk
	Podicipediformes											
114	Podicipedidae	Grebes	++	++	21-27	++	++	0.5-5.0 hr	0	++	++	....
	Gaviiformes											
115	Gaviidae	Loons	....	....	28-30	++	++	....	0	++	++	....
	Tinamiformes											
116	Tinamidae	Tinamous	....	....	21	++++	0	....	0	++++	0	....
	Apterygiformes											
117	Apterygidae	Kiwis	++	++	75	++++	0	Up to 7 da	6	++++	0	....
	Casuariiformes											
118	Dromiceiidae	Emus	....	....	58-61	++++	0	Continuous	0	++++	0	....
	Rheiformes											
119	Rheidae	Rheas	....	....	35-42	++++	0	....	0	++++	0	....
	Struthioniformes											
120	Struthionidae	Ostriches	++++	0	42	+++	+	9-15 hr	0	++	++	....
	Sphenisciformes											
121	Spheniscidae	Penguins	++	++	38-56	++	++	1-5+ da	56-112	++	++	1-2/da

/1/ Time parent sits on eggs (1 sitting before leaving to feed and rest). /2/ Time from hatching until young birds leave nest. /3/ Range of averages for various nests. /4/ Unless otherwise specified.

Contributors: (a) Kendeigh, S. Charles, (b) Skutch, Alexander F.

References: [1] Kendeigh, S. C. 1952. Parental care and its evolution in birds. Univ. Illinois Press, Urbana.
[2] Skutch, A. F. Unpublished. San Isidro del General, Costa Rica, 1961.

continued

42. PROPAGATION: BIRDS

Part II: CLUTCH SIZE

Requirements for selection of data: (1) at least 25 clutches recorded within less than 10 years and within a limited geographical area, (2) proof that clutches were complete when counted, and (3) proof that only one female laid in nest.

	Order and Family	Species	Location	No. of Clutches	No. of Eggs per Clutch: Mean	No. of Eggs per Clutch: Standard Deviation	Observer and Year
	(A)	(B)	(C)	(D)	(E)	(F)	(G)
	Passeriformes						
1	Fringillidae	*Emberiza calandra*	England	92	3.98	0.84	Ryves, 1934
2		*E. citrinella*	England	946	3.31	0.77	Parkhurst, 1946
3			Germany	147	4.41	0.58	Haun, 1931
4		*Melospiza melodia*	Ohio	210	4.07	0.81	Nice, 1937
5		*Pheucticus melanocephalus*	United States	192	3.28	0.67	Weston, 1947
6		*Spinus tristis*	Wisconsin	150	4.63	0.90	Stokes, 1950
7		*Zonotrichia leucophrys nuttalli*	California	147	3.25	0.55	Blanchard, 1941
8		*Z. leucophrys pugetensis*	Washington	29	4.00	0.46	Blanchard, 1941
9	Icteridae	*Quiscalus quiscalus*	Wisconsin	55	4.87	0.74	Peterson, 1950
10		*Xanthocephalus xanthocephalus*	Utah	118	3.75	0.60	Fautin, 1941
11	Parulidae	*Seiurus aurocapillus*	Michigan	27	4.67	0.68	Hann, 1937
12		*Wilsonia citrina*	Michigan	62	5.01	0.85	Walkinshaw, 1941
13			Tennessee	44	4.55	0.62	Hann, 1937
14	Sturnidae	*Sturnus vulgaris*	Maryland	101	4.54	1.15	McAtee, 1940
15			England	105	4.85	1.08	Lack, 1948
16			Germany	95	4.44	0.99	Berndt, 1939
17			Holland	1785	5.14	1.11	Lack, 1948
18	Bombycillidae	*Bombycilla cedrorum*	Ohio	65	2.85	0.90	Putnam, 1949
19	Muscicapidae	*Muscicapa hypoleuca*	England	123	7.44	0.91	Campbell, 1950
20			Finland	275	6.43	1.09	Van Haartman, 1951
21			Germany	49	5.82	1.10	Berndt, 1939
22		*M. striata*	England	309	4.25	0.77	Summers Smith, 1952
23	Sylviidae	*Phylloscopus sibilatrix*	England	216	6.03	0.58	Lack, 1950
24	Turdidae	*Erythacus rubecula*	England (April)	534	4.97	0.65	Lack, 1946
25			England (May)	364	5.16	0.80	Lack, 1946
26		*Sialia sialis*	Tennessee	102	4.44	1.02	Laskey, 1939
27		*Turdus erecitorum*	England	179	4.13	0.67	Lack, 1949
28		*T. merula*	England	298	3.94	0.75	Lack, 1949
29		*T. migratorius*	New York	127	3.39	0.62	Howell, 1942
30	Troglodytidae	*Troglodytes aedon*	Maryland	98	5.46	1.10	McAtee, 1940
31	Chamaeidae	*Chamaea fasciata*	California	84	3.92	0.52	Erickson, 1938
32	Paridae	*Parus ater*	Holland	2759	8.69	1.65	Lack, 1950
33			Sweden	119	8.19	1.38	Lack, 1950
34		*P. atricapillus*	Holland	346	8.24	1.71	Lack, 1950
35		*P. caeruleus*	S. England	312	11.64	2.16	Lack, 1950
36			Holland	3455	10.65	2.16	Lack, 1950
37		*P. cristatus*	Holland	1143	7.07	1.27	Lack, 1950
38			Sweden	182	4.92	0.89	Lack, 1950
39		*P. major*	England	112	10.92	1.74	Gibb, 1950
40			S. England	339	10.27	1.81	Lack, 1950
41			Holland	8809	9.32	1.88	Lack, 1950
42			Sweden	174	9.83	1.43	Lack, 1950
43	Cracticidae	*Gymnorhina dorsalis*	Australia	46	3.46	0.62	Wilson, 1946
44	Corvidae	*Pica nuttalli*	California	70	6.50	0.92	Linsdale, 1937
45	Hirundinidae	*Iridoprocne bicolor*	Connecticut	68	5.20	0.84	Kuerzi, 1941
46		*Progne subis*	United States	84	4.94	0.74	Allen, 1952
47	Alaudidae	*Alauda arvensis*	Germany	55	3.87	0.70	Haun, 1931
48		*Galerida cristata*	Germany	68	4.18	0.84	Haun, 1931
49		*Lullula arborea*	Germany	99	4.17	0.70	Haun, 1931
	Piciformes						
50	Picidae	*Colaptes auratus*	United States	191	7.02	1.86	Burns, 1900
	Apodiformes						
51	Apodidae	*Apus apus*	England	170	2.24	0.48	Lack, 1951
52			Switzerland	79	2.76	0.52	Lack, 1951
53		*Micropus cafer*	Africa	93	2.00	0.00	Moreau, 1942
	Charadriiformes						
54	Laridae	*Larus argentatus*	New Brunswick	1011	2.38	0.71	Paynter, 1949
55			Holland	217	2.91	0.34	Paludan, 1951

continued

42. PROPAGATION: BIRDS

Part II: CLUTCH SIZE

	Order and Family	Species	Location	No. of Clutches	No. of Eggs per Clutch: Mean	No. of Eggs per Clutch: Standard Deviation	Observer and Year
	(A)	(B)	(C)	(D)	(E)	(F)	(G)
	Charadriiformes						
56	Laridae	*Larus fuscus*	Holland	242	2.75	0.56	Paludan, 1951
57		*Sterna dougalli*	Australia	2656	1.03	0.16	Serventy, 1951
58			England	373	1.43	0.50	Serventy, 1951
59		*S. paradisaea*	Germany	82	2.92	0.28	Dircksen, 1932
60		*S. sandvicensis*	Germany	3831	2.45	0.45	Dircksen, 1932
61	Scolopacidae	*Philohela minor*	Maine	122	3.96	0.20	Mendall, 1943
62	Haematopodidae	*Haematopus ostralegus*	Germany	84	3.01	0.68	Dircksen, 1932
	Gruiformes						
63	Rallidae	*Fulica americana*	California	256	8.7	...	Hunt, 1955
64			Iowa	37	8.84	1.27	Provost, 1947
65			Manitoba	169	9.90	1.30	Kiel, 1955
66		*Porzana carolina*	Minnesota	29	9.9	...	Popichal, 1954
67		*Rallus limicola*	Iowa	28	8.10	4.50	Tanner, 1954
68		*R. longirostris*	California	27	7.92	...	Zucca, 1954
69			New Jersey	104	9.97	2.10	Kozicky, 1949
70			Virginia	71	8.38	1.56	Stewart, 1951
	Galliformes						
71	Phasianidae	*Perdix perdix*	England	4051	14.60	2.38	Lack, 1947
72		*Phasianus colchicus*	Iowa	60	8.7	...	Kozicky, 1956
73			Pennsylvania	157	10.60	3.18	Randall, 1941
	Falconiformes						
74	Falconidae	*Falco sparverius*	Oregon	60	4.73	0.63	Roest, 1957
75	Accipitridae	*Circus cyaneus*	United States	60	5.05	0.76	Hammond, 1949
	Anseriformes						
76	Anatidae	*Aix sponsa*	Massachusetts	664	13.60	4.82	McLaughlin, 1952
77		*Anas acuta*	California	41	9.2	...	Miller, 1954
78			California	40	7.2	...	Hunt, 1955
79		*A. clypeata*	California	35	11.1	...	Miller, 1954
80		*A. cyanoptera*	California	32	10.7	...	Miller, 1954
81			California	76	9.3	...	Hunt, 1955
82		*A. discors*	Iowa	87	8.0	...	Glover, 1956
83		*A. platyrhynchos*	California	178	9.2	...	Miller, 1954
84			California	108	8.5	...	Hunt, 1955
85		*A. strepera*	California	344	11.1	...	Miller, 1954
86		*Aythya americana*	California	27	13.8	...	Miller, 1954
87		*A. collaris*	Maine	423	9.04	1.45	Mendall, 1958
88		*Branta* sp.	N. W. Territory	203	3.97	1.00	Barry, 1956
89		*B. canadensis*	California	158	5.13	1.35	Miller, 1953
90			Idaho	189	5.2	...	Steel, 1957
91			Montana	358	5.34	1.31	Geis, 1956
92		*Somateria mollissima*	Maine	110	3.25	1.05	Gross, 1938
93			New Brunswick	162	3.53	1.17	Paynter, 1951
94			St. Lawrence	1131	4.04	1.01	Lewis, 1939
	Pelecaniformes						
95	Phalacrocoracidae	*Phalacrocorax bouganvillii*	Peru	89	3.13	0.94	Vogt, 1942

Contributor: Davis, David E.

References: [1] Davis, D. E. 1955. In A. Wolfson, ed. Recent studies in avian biology. Univ. Illinois Press, Urbana. [2] Davis, D. E. 1960. In H. S. Mosby, ed. Manual of game investigational techniques. Edwards Brothers, Ann Arbor, Mich.

continued

42. PROPAGATION: BIRDS

Part III: HATCHING SUCCESS OF SOME PRECOCIAL SPECIES

Only studies that record at least 50 nests are included.

	Family and Species	Location	Nests		Eggs		Observer and Year
			No.	% Successful	No.	% Hatched	
	(A)	(B)	(C)	(D)	(E)	(F)	(G)
	Rallidae						
1	*Fulica americana*	California	163	96.5	......	...	Hunt, 1955
2		Manitoba	82	...	1394	99.0	Kiel, 1955
3	*Rallus longirostris*	New Jersey	56	89.3	513	87.3	Kozicky, 1949
	Phasianidae						
4	*Colinus virginianus*	Georgia-Florida	602	36	......	...	Stoddard, 1931
5		Texas	189	46	......	...	Lehmann, 1946
6		Texas	59	62.9	......	...	Parmalee, 1955
7		Wisconsin	53	50.9	......	...	Errington, 1933
8	*Lophortyx californica*	California	83	24.8	......	...	Glading, 1928
9		California	96	18	......	...	Glading, 1938
10	*Perdix perdix*	England	....	...	57,202	90.4	Lack, 1947
11		England	7251	78.0	......	...	Middleton, 1935
12		England	4090	...	59,825	93.0	Middleton, 1935
13		Michigan	143	32	......	...	Yeatter, 1934
14		Washington	113	37.1	......	...	Knott, 1943
15		Washington	68	32.5	......	...	Yocum, 1943
16		Wisconsin	435	32.0	......	...	McCabe, 1946
17	*Phasianus colchicus*	Colorado	333	65.0	......	...	Yeager, 1951
18		Iowa	533	25.5	1319	83.0	Baskett, 1947
19		Iowa	445	23.1	......	...	Hamerstrom, 1936
20		Iowa	64	...	723	82.3	Hamerstrom, 1936
21		Iowa	162	17.3	......	...	Kloglan, 1955
22		Iowa	72	18.0	......	...	Weston, 1953
23		Michigan	193	35.0	......	...	English, 1946
24		Minnesota	90	30.0	......	...	Carlson, 1946
25		Minnesota	241	28.6	......	...	Erickson, 1951
26		Ohio	563	58	......	...	Leedy, 1945
27		Ohio	358	72.0	......	...	Strode, 1946
28		Ontario	230	32.1	777	73.5	Ball, 1952
29		Oregon	145	44.8	......	...	Eklund, 1942
30		Pennsylvania	310	20.3	......	...	Randall, 1940
31		Utah	149	36	......	...	Rasmussen, 1945
32		Washington	63	27.0	......	...	Buss, 1950
33		Wisconsin	350	29.9	......	...	Buss, 1946
34		Wisconsin	126	71.3	1000	78.9	Errington, 1937
	Tetraonidae						
35	*Bonasa umbellus*	New York	1431	61.4	......	...	Darrow, 1947
36	*Centrocercus urophasianus*	Colorado	238	35	......	...	Keller, 1941
37		Utah	161	60	......	...	Rasmussen, 1938
38		Wyoming	134	34	......	...	Patterson, 1949
39		Wyoming	216	38.4	......	...	Patterson, 1952
40	*Lagopus lagopus*	Norway	107	80	......	...	Kristoffersen, 1937
41		Norway	125	63	......	...	Olstad, 1932
42	*Tympanuchus cupido*	Wisconsin	100	50	......	...	Hamerstrom, 1939
	Anatidae						
43	*Aix sponsa*	Iowa	63	...	868	80.0	Leopold, 1951
44		Massachusetts	1427	64.3	12,180	83.5	McLaughlin, 1952
45	*Anas acuta*	California	98	39.8	......	...	Hunt, 1955
46		Utah	135	65.0	969	82.0	Williams, 1937
47		United States	52	48.0	......	...	Kalmbach, 1937
48	*A. clypeata*	Montana	107	...	1135	69.7	Girard, 1941
49	*A. cyanoptera*	California	147	55.8	......	...	Hunt, 1955
50		Utah	326	62.0	2655	84.0	Williams, 1937
51	*A. discors*	Iowa	223	57.0	......	...	Bennett, 1938
52		Montana	107	...	888	71.8	Girard, 1941
53		United States	76	22.4	......	...	Kalmbach, 1937
54	*A. platyrhynchos*	California	510	12.7	......	...	Anderson, 1956
55		California	161	38.5	616	83.4	Anderson, 1957
56		California	60	52.0	417	49.4	Earl, 1950
57		California	206	51.5	......	...	Hunt, 1955

continued

42. PROPAGATION: BIRDS

Part III: HATCHING SUCCESS OF SOME PRECOCIAL SPECIES

	Family and Species	Location	Nests No.	Nests % Successful	Eggs No.	Eggs % Hatched	Observer and Year
	(A)	(B)	(C)	(D)	(E)	(F)	(G)
	Anatidae						
58	*Anas platyrhynchos*	California	209	85.2	1622	91.4	Miller, 1954
59		Montana	....	...	1793	71.2	Girard, 1941
60		Utah	185	59.0	1582	60.0	Williams, 1937
61		United States	188	55.7	......	...	Kalmbach, 1937
62	*A. strepera*	California	381	90.3	3834	94.2	Miller, 1954
63		Utah	660	71.0	6000	85.0	Williams, 1937
64	*Aythya affinis*	United States	94	47.8	......	...	Kalmbach, 1937
65	*A. americana*	California	60	45.0	......	...	Miller, 1954
66		Iowa	160	56.2	......	...	Low, 1945
67		Iowa	122	...	827	80.7	Low, 1945
68		Utah	212	62.0	2651	26.0	Williams, 1937
69	*A. collaris*	Maine	189	68.3	......	...	Mendall, 1958
70	*Branta canadensis*	California	201	17.8	......	...	Collins, 1954
71		California	248	60.0	......	...	Dow, 1943
72		California	201	78.6	810	87.0	Miller, 1953
73		California	360	68.5	1904	82.6	Naylor, 1953
74		California	117	71.0	432	85.2	Naylor, 1954
75		Illinois	96	...	927	56.6	Kossack, 1950
76		Montana	....	...	72	29.9	Atwater, 1959
77		Montana	383	57.5	1221	88.4	Geis, 1956
78		Utah	95	...	410	80.6	Williams, 1937
79		Wyoming	88	23.9	......	...	Craighead, 1949
80	*Oxyura jamaicensis*	Iowa	71	73.2	546	69.4	Low, 1941
81	*Somateria mollissima*	Maine	134	29.1	462	27.6	Paynter, 1951

Contributors: (a) Davis, David E., (b) Nice, Margaret Morse

References: [1] Davis, D. E. 1960. In H. S. Mosby, ed. Manual of game investigational techniques. Edwards Brothers, Ann Arbor, Mich. [2] Hickey, J. J. 1955. In A. Wolfson, ed. Recent studies in avian biology. Univ. Illinois Press, Urbana.

Part IV: HATCHING AND FLEDGING SUCCCESS OF OPEN-NEST ALTRICIAL SPECIES

For additional information, consult reference 15.

	Family and Species	Nests Total No.	Nests Successful No.	Nests Successful %	Eggs Total No.	Eggs Hatched No.	Eggs Hatched %	Eggs Fledged No.	Eggs Fledged %	Reference
	(A)	(B)	(C)	(D)	(E)	(F)	(G)	(H)	(I)	(J)
	Fringillidae									
1	*Emberiza calandra*	54	....	...	207	......	...	126	60.9	23
2		53	40	76.7	204	......	...	144	70.6	24
3	*Melospiza melodia*	147	77	52.4	585	389	66.5	243	41.5	14
4		76	30	39.5	321	147	45.8	80	24.9	14
5	*Rhynchophanus mccowni*	45	27	60.0	153	92	60.1	71	46.4	10
6	*Spinus tristis*	35	21	60.0	161	113	70.2	80	49.7	29
7		239	....	...	696	455	65.3	338	48.6	28
8	*Spizella passerina*	88	55	62.5	277	185	66.8	170	61.4	31
9	*S. pusilla*	593	226	38.1	1738	888	51.1	620	35.7	30
	Icteridae									
10	*Agelaius phoeniceus*	67	....	...	214	156	72.9	105	49.1	32
11		356	....	...	1140	823	72.2	675	59.2	26
12	*Euphagus cyanocephalus*	107	53	49.5	521	327	62.7	205	39.3	8
13	*Quiscalus versicolor*	62	34	54.8	288	209	72.6	135	46.9	18
14	*Xanthocephalus xanthocephalus*	128	....	...	443	314	70.9	99	22.4	4
	Bombycillidae									
15	*Bombycilla cedrorum*	60	46	76.7	245	189	77.1	171	69.8	22

continued

Part IV: HATCHING AND FLEDGING SUCCESS OF OPEN-NEST ALTRICIAL SPECIES

	Family and Species	Nests			Eggs					Reference
		Total No.	Successful No.	Successful %	Total No.	Hatched No.	Hatched %	Fledged No.	Fledged %	
	(A)	(B)	(C)	(D)	(E)	(F)	(G)	(H)	(I)	(J)
	Turdidae									
16	*Saxicola rubetra*	129	57	44.4	......	......	...	....	...	25
17	*Turdus migratorius*	136	78	57.3	259	157	60.6	131	54.4	5
18		64	49	76.6	......	......	...	....	...	7
19		176	86	48.8	548	316	57.8	246	44.9	34
	Alaudidae									
20	*Eremophila alpestris*	30	18	60.0	102	79	77.4	46	45.1	19
	Columbidae									
21	*Zenaidura macroura*	249	130	52.8	500	......	...	213	42.6	13
22		592	309	52.2	......	......	...	....	...	17
23		4273	2043	47.9	8018	4379	54.6	3734	46.6	9
24		235	122	52.0	......	......	...	....	...	11
25		204	142	69.6	398	310	77.8	274	68.8	3
	Unspecified									
26	6 species	121	57	47.0	421	257	61.0	170	40.4	33
27		113	....	...	428	295	68.9	248	55.6	27
28	7 species	43	18	41.9	......	......	...	....	...	20
29	8 species	240	99	41.2	......	......	...	....	...	21
30	10 species	30	20	66.6	145	93	64.1	70	48.3	2
31	11 species	71	....	...	265	160	60.4	124	46.7	1
32		....	....	...	2151	1299	60.4	1010	46.9	6
33	25 species	246	101	41.0	......	......	...	....	...	12
34	? species	156	....	...	687	420	61.1	300	43.7	16
	Summary									
35	Nest success, 25 studies	8034	3938	49.0	......	......	...	....	...	
36	Hatching success, 24 studies[1]	....	....	...	20,204	12,052	59.7	....	...	
37	Hatching success of passerine eggs, 22 studies[2]	....	....	...	11,788	7363	62.5	....	...	
38	Fledging success, 27 studies[3]	....	....	...	21,115	......	...	9728	46.1	

/1/ Frequency hatching success: 1 study in 40-49% range; 3 studies, 50-59%; 12 studies, 60-69%; 8 studies, 70-79%. Median is 64.7%, in contrast to the 59.7% average for the 20,204 eggs. The mean figure is biased by the low number (54.6%) of dove eggs hatched from 8018 laid (*Zenaidura macroura* builds extremely frail nests).
/2/ Omitting the *Zenaidura macroura* studies, hatching success of the 11,788 passerine (songbird) eggs is 62.5%.
/3/ Frequency of fledging success: 2 studies in 20-29% range; 2 studies, 30-39%; 14 studies, 40-49%; 4 studies, 50-59%; 3 studies, 60-69%; 2 studies, 70-79%. Median is 46.9%, and average 46.1%, for the 21,115 eggs.

Contributor: Nice, Margaret Morse

References: [1] Baron, S. 1934. Brit. Birds 28:77. [2] Clabaugh, E. D. 1925. Condor 27:114. [3] Cowan, J. B. 1952. Calif. Fish and Game 38:505. [4] Fautin, R. 1941. Auk 58:215. [5] Howell, J. C. 1942. Am. Midland Naturalist 28:529. [6] Kendeigh, S. C. 1942. J. Wildlife Management 6:19. [7] Koehler, A., and G. Koehler. 1945. Passenger Pigeon 7:15. [8] La Rivers, I. 1944. Am. Midland Naturalist 32:417. [9] McClure, H. E. 1946. Auk 63:24. [10] Mickey, F. W. 1943. Ibid. 60:181. [11] Monk, H. C. 1949. Migrant 20:1. [12] Nice, M. M. 1923. Proc. Oklahoma Acad. Sci. 3:61. [13] Nice, M. M. 1931. Univ. Oklahoma Biol. Survey 3(1):99. [14] Nice, M. M. 1937. Trans. Linnaean Soc. N. Y. 4:143. [15] Nice, M. M. 1957. Auk 74:305. [16] Nicholson, E. M. 1930. Encyclopedia Brit. 3:634. [17] Pearson, A. M., and G. C. Moore. 1939. Trans. 4th North Am. Wildlife Conf., p. 468. [18] Petersen, A., and H. Young. 1950. Auk 67:466. [19] Pickwell, G. B. 1931. Trans. Acad. Sci. St. Louis 27:1. [20] Potter, J. K. 1915. Cassinia 19:30. [21] Praeger, R. L. 1921. Irish Naturalist 30:25. [22] Putnam, L. S. 1949. Wilson Bull. 61:141. [23] Ryves, B. H. 1934. Brit. Birds 28:2. [24] Ryves, B. H. 1934. Ibid. 28:154. [25] Schmidt, K., and E. Hantge. 1954. J. Ornithol. 95:130. [26] Smith, H. M. 1943. Ecology 24:183. [27] Steuart, I. 1939. Brit. Birds 32:336. [28] Stokes, A. W. 1950. Wilson Bull. 62:107. [29] Walkinshaw, L. H. 1939. Jack-Pine Warbler 17:3. [30] Walkinshaw, L. H. 1952. Bird-Banding 23:101. [31] Walkinshaw, L. H. Unpublished, 1956. [32] Williams, J. F. 1940. Wilson Bull. 52:267. [33] Young, H. 1949. Ibid. 61:36. [34] Young, H. 1955. Am. Midland Naturalist 53:329.

continued

42. PROPAGATION: BIRDS

Part V: HATCHING AND FLEDGING SUCCESS OF HOLE-NESTING ALTRICIAL SPECIES

For additional information, consult reference 16.

	Family and Species	Years Observed	Nests No.	Eggs					Reference
				Total No.	Hatched		Fledged		
					No.	%	No.	%	
	(A)	(B)	(C)	(D)	(E)	(F)	(G)	(H)	(I)
	Ploceidae								
1	*Passer domesticus*	6	....	114	......	...	97	78.5	14
	Parulidae								
2	*Protonotaria citrea*	11	121	413	159	38.5	106	25.7	20
3		6	36	163	100	61.3	100	61.3	20
	Sturnidae								
4	*Sturnus vulgaris*	...	...	10,557	......	...	7923	75.1	8
5		6	...	472	......	...	410	84.5	14
	Turdidae								
6	*Sialia sialis*	11	1401	6260	3943	63.0	2786	44.5	9
7		2	86	377	302	80.1	274	72.7	11
8		3	301	1290	......	...	839	65.0	15
9		9	67	272	213	78.3	172	63.2	19
10		20	50	203	131	64.5	127	62.5	21
	Troglodytidae								
11	*Thryomanes bewickii*	15	21	129	......	...	79	56.8	10
12	*Troglodytes aedon*	19	1056	6673	5576	82.3	5351	79.0	4
13		3	34	211	135	64.0	118	55.2	7
14		6	...	469	......	...	339	83.7	14
15		21	64	333	199	59.7	161	48.3	21
	Paridae								
16	*Parus ater*	1	18	161	153	95.0	131	81.4	13
17	*P. atricapillus*	2	11	74	......	...	53	71.6	17
18	*P. caeruleus*	5	183	1887	1548	82.0	1453	77.0	2
19		2	...	247	185	75.0	168	68.0	3
20		4	37	286	187	65.0	128	44.7	5
21		2	46	413	366	88.6	327	79.2	13
22	*P. major*	5	202	1936	1653	85.4	1416	75.1	2
23		19	5011	45,466	......	...	29,529	64.9	6
24		2	66	460	425	92.4	340	72.4	13
25		2	623	6012	4579	76.2	3938	65.5	23
	Muscicapidae								
26	*Muscicapa hypoleuca*	8	221	1074	......	...	789	73.5	20
	Hirundinidae								
27	*Iridoprocne bicolor*	9	219	1123	928	83.4	679	61.0	1
28		3	352	1759	1424	81.0	857	48.7	12
29		3	80	430	310	72.1	303	70.5	7
30		2	37	184	163	88.6	123	66.8	18
31		8	60	363	358	98.6	340	93.7	22
32	5 unidentified species	2	...	755	......	...	500	66.2	23
	Summary								
33	Hatching success, 22 studies (7 species)	...	...	30,276	23,537	77.7	......	...	
34	Fledging success, 32 studies (14 species)	...	...	90,676	......	...	60,016	66.2	

Contributor: Nice, Margaret Morse

References: [1] Chapman, L. B. 1939. Bird-Banding 10:61. [2] Gibb, J. 1950. Ibis 92:507. [3] Huxley, J. S. 1938. Proc. Zool. Soc. (London), A, 108:445. [4] Kendeigh, S. C. 1942. J. Wildlife Management 6:19. [5] Kenrick, H. 1940. Brit. Birds 33:307. [6] Kluijver, H. N. 1951. Ardea 39:1. [7] Kuerzi, R. G. 1941. Proc. Linnaean Soc. N. Y. 52-53:1. [8] Lack, D. 1948. Evolution 2:95. [9] Laskey, A. R. 1943. Bird-Banding 14:39. [10] Laskey, A. R. 1946. Migrant 17:39. [11] Low, S. 1933. Bird-Banding 4:109. [12] Low, S. 1934. Ibid. 5:24. [13] Mackensie, J. M. D. 1950. Brit. Birds 43:393. [14] McAtee, W. L. 1940. Auk 57:333. [15] Musselman, T. E. 1935. Bird-Banding 6:117. [16] Nice, M. M. 1957. Auk 74:305. [17] Odum, E. P. 1941. Auk 58:518. [18] Shelley, L. O. 1937. Bird-Banding 8:80. [19] Thomas, R. T. 1946. Wilson Bull. 58:143.

continued

42. PROPAGATION: BIRDS

Part V: HATCHING AND FLEDGING SUCCESS OF HOLE-NESTING ALTRICIAL SPECIES

[20] Von Haartman, L. 1951. Acta Zool. Fennica 56:1. [21] Walkinshaw, L. H. 1941. Wilson Bull. 53:1. [22] Weydemeyer, W. 1935. Condor 37:216. [23] Wolda, G. 1929. Verslag Ornithol. Afdeel., Plantenziektenkundige Dienst, Wageningen, 1928, p. 1.

43. PROPAGATION: REPTILES

The manner of fertilization for all reptiles is internal (by copulation). Many of the ovoviviparous forms have a type of placentation verging on viviparity; however, to avoid confusion, the term "viviparous" is not used. Location (column B): (s) = southern, or south; (e) = eastern, or east; (w) = western, or west; (n) = northern, or north; (cen) = central. Gestation Time (column E) measured from copulation to parturition for ovoviviparous reptiles, Incubation Time from laying to hatching of eggs for oviparous reptiles. Manner of Birth (column F): O = oviparous, Ovo = ovoviviparous. Values in parentheses are ranges, estimate "c" or "d" (cf. Introduction). Classification adapted from Schmidt and Inger, *Living Reptiles of the World,* 1957.

	Family and Species	Location	Age at Sexual Maturity[1] yr	Breeding Season[2]	Gestation or Incubation Time[3]	Manner of Birth	Brood or Clutch[4] Size[5]	Brood or Clutch[4] No./yr	Reference
	(A)	(B)	(C)	(D)	(E)	(F)	(G)	(H)	(I)
	Serpentes								
	Crotalidae								
1	*Ancistrodon contortrix*	United States (se)	(2-4)	Apr-May	142 da	Ovo	(1-14)	1	11,12,27
2	*A. piscivorus*	United States (se)	....	Mar-Apr and fall	5 mo	Ovo	(3-15)	1	1,27,29
3	*Crotalus viridis*	N. America (w)	(3-4)	Apr-June	(4-5) mo	Ovo	(3-13)	0.5	17,22,38
	Colubridae								
4	*Coluber constrictor*	United States	....	May-June	(1-2) mo	O	(15-25)	1	27
5	*Farancia abacura*	United States (se)	....	July	110 da[6]	O	(22-104)	1	27
6	*Heterodon platyrhinos*	United States (e)	....	Apr-May	....	O	(8-40)	1	27
7	*Masticophis taeniatus*	United States (sw), Mexico	3	Apr-May	....	O	....	1	38
8	*Natrix erythrogaster*	United States (se)	....	Apr-May	....	Ovo	(8-27)	1	27
9	*Opheodrys vernalis*	United States, Canada (se)	....	May-June	1 mo	O	(3-11)	1	3
10	*Pituophis catenifer*	N. America	<3	Apr-May	70(64-77) da	O	(3-19)	1	9,16,17, 27,29
11	*Storeria dekayi*	N. America (e)	....	Mar-Apr	4 mo	Ovo	14(13-24)	1	6
12	*Thamnophis elegans*	United States (w)	....	Apr-May	90 da	Ovo	(10-23)	1	33
13	*T. radix*	N. America (cen)	....	Apr-June	63 da	Ovo	(6-26)	1	27
14	*T. sirtalis*	N. America	(2-3)	Mar-May and fall	(87-116) da	Ovo	28(6-51)	(1-2)	27
	Boidae								
15	*Charina bottae*	United States (w)	(2-3)	June	....	Ovo	(3-5)	1	34
	Sauria								
	Helodermatidae								
16	*Heloderma suspectum*	Arizona, New Mexico, Sonora	....	....	1 mo	O	(5-13)	1	35
	Anniellidae								
17	*Anniella pulchra*	United States (w)	(2-3)	....	....	Ovo	(1-4)	1	28
	Anguidae								
18	*Anguis fragilis*	Europe, Asia (w), Algeria	(3-4)	May-June	3 mo	Ovo	(7-19)	1	26,27
19	*Gerrhonotus coeruleus*	United States (w)	3 ?	Apr	4 mo	O	7(2-15)	1	7
20	*G. multicarinatus*	United States (w)	....	May	(51-60) da	O	(8-20)	1	7,30
21	*Ophisaurus ventralis*	United States (se & cen)	....	Apr-May	(56-61) da	O	(8-17)	1	28
	Lacertidae								
22	*Lacerta agilis*	Europe, Asia	(2-3)	May-June	(41-90) da	O	(5-8)	(1-2)	24,26

/1/ Males in some species mature before females. /2/ Varies with geographical location. /3/ Actual values expressed in days, approximations in weeks or months. /4/ Brood = young produced at one time; clutch = eggs laid at one time. /5/ Number of eggs or young. /6/ From one observation.

continued

43. PROPAGATION: REPTILES

	Family and Species	Location	Age at Sexual Maturity[1] yr	Breeding Season[2]	Gestation or Incubation Time[3]	Manner of Birth	Brood or Clutch[4]		Reference
							Size[5]	No./yr	
	(A)	(B)	(C)	(D)	(E)	(F)	(G)	(H)	(I)
	Sauria								
	Teiidae								
23	*Cnemidophorus tigris*	United States, Mexico	....	May-June	80 da[6]	O	(2-4)	(1-2)	28,30
	Scincidae								
24	*Eumeces fasciatus*	United States (e)	<2	May-June	(4-9) wk	O	(2-18)	1	10,28
	Xantusidae								
25	*Xantusia vigilis*	California, Nevada, Arizona	♀, 3	May-June	3 mo	Ovo	2(1-3)	1	19,20,28
	Iguanidae								
26	*Anolis carolinensis*	United States (se)	♂, 2; ♀, 1	Apr-Aug	(6-7) wk	O	(8-10)	1	14,28
27	*Crotaphytus collaris*	United States (w)	<(1-3)	May-June	(8-13) wk	O	(4-24)	(1-2)	10,28,30
28	*Gambelia wislizenii*	United States (w)	....	May-June	5 wk	O	(2-5)	1	28,30
29	*Holbrookia maculata*	United States (s), Mexico (n)	....	June-July	....	O	(6-8)	1	28
30	*Phrynosoma cornutum*	United States (sw)	....	Apr-May	(39-47) da	O	(23-37)	1	28
31	*P. douglassii*	United States (w)	....	May-June	(35-45) da	Ovo	(8-14)	1	21,28,32
32	*Sceloporus graciosus*	United States, Mexico	....	Apr-May	62 da	O	(2-7)	1	28
33	*S. grammicus*	United States, Mexico	....	Oct	(130-180) da	Ovo	(3-12)	1	28
34	*S. occidentalis*	United States, Mexico	<2	Mar-Apr	2 mo	O	9(6-13)	1	8,28,36
35	*S. undulatus*	United States (s & cen), Mexico	(2-3)	May-June	10 wk	O	(4-17)	1	2,28
36	*Uta stansburiana*	United States (sw)	....	Apr-May	(61-67) da	O	(3-4)	(2-4)	28,30
	Gekkonidae								
37	*Hoplodactylus maculatus*	New Zealand	....	Irregular	....	Ovo	2	....	4
38	*Ptychozoon homalocephalum*	India (e)	....	Nov	185 da[6]	O	2	....	13
	Crocodylia								
	Alligatoridae								
39	*Alligator mississipiensis*	United States (se)	(5-10)	Jan-Sept	(56-66) da	O	(29-88)	1	18,23
	Chelonia								
	Trionychidae								
40	*Amyda ferox*	United States (se)	....	Mar-July	64 da[6]	O	(17-22)	....	5
	Chelonidae								
41	*Caretta caretta*	Atlantic Ocean	....	Mar-July	(31-65) da	O	(120-130)	(2-3)	5
42	*Lepidochelys olivacea*	Pacific Ocean	....	Aug-Apr	50 da	O	(90-135)	(1-2)	5
	Testudinidae								
43	*Gopherus agassizii*	United States (sw)	(15-20)	May	(80-118) da	O	(2-13)	1	5,31,37
	Emydidae								
44	*Malaclemys terrapin*	United States coast (e)	(5-6)	Spring	3 mo	O	8	(1-3)	15
45	*Pseudemys floridana*	Florida	....	Nov-June	5 mo	O	(12-29)	2	5
46	*Terrapene carolina*	United States (e)	(4-5)	Apr-May	88(70-114) da	O	(2-7)	1	5
	Kinosternidae								
47	*Kinosternon subrubrum*	United States (e)	....	Apr-May	....	O	(2-5)	(1-2)	5
48	*Sternotherus odoratus*	N. America (e)	♂, (2-3); ♀, (9-11)	Apr-Oct	(60-75) da	O	(1-5)	(1-2)	5,25
	Chelydridae								
49	*Chelydra serpentina*	N. America	....	Apr-Nov	(81-90) da	O	25(8-80)	(1-2)	5

/1/ Males in some species mature before females. /2/ Varies with geographical location. /3/ Actual values expressed in days, approximations in weeks or months. /4/ Brood = young produced at one time; clutch = eggs laid at one time. /5/ Number of eggs or young. /6/ From one observation.

Contributors: (a) Altland, Paul D., (b) Fitch, Henry S., (c) Tanner, Vasco M.

References: [1] Allen, E. R., and D. Swindell. 1948. Herpetologica 4:1. [2] Altland, P. D. 1941. J. Elisha Mitchell Sci. Soc. 57:73. [3] Blanchard, F. N. 1933. Papers Mich. Acad. Sci. 17:493. [4] Boyd, M. M. M.

continued

43. PROPAGATION: REPTILES

1940-41. Quart. J. Microscop. Sci. 82:337. [5] Carr, A. 1952. Handbook of turtles. Comstock, Ithaca. [6] Clausen, H. J. 1936. Copeia (2):98. [7] Fitch, H. S. 1935. Trans. Acad. Sci. St. Louis 29:1. [8] Fitch, H. S. 1940. Univ. Calif. (Berkeley) Publs. Zool. 44:151. [9] Fitch, H. S. 1949. Am. Midland Naturalist 41:513. [10] Fitch, H. S. 1954. Univ. Kansas Publs. Museum Nat. Hist. 8:145. [11] Fitch, H. S. 1956. Ibid 8:269. [12] Fitch, H. S. 1960. Ibid. 13:272. [13] Gadow, H. 1901. In S. F. Harmer and A. E. Shipley, ed. Cambridge natural history. Macmillan, London. v. 8. [14] Hamlett, G. W. D. 1952. Copeia, p. 183. [15] Hildebrande, C. F. 1929. U. S. Fish Wildlife Service Fishery Bull. 45:25. [16] Imler, R. H. 1945. J. Wildlife Management 9:265. [17] Klauber, L. M. 1936. Trans. San Diego Soc. Nat. Hist. 8:20. [18] McIlhenny, E. A. 1935. The alligator's life history. Christopher, Boston. [19] Miller, M. R. 1948. Univ. Calif. (Berkeley) Publs. Zool. 47:197. [20] Miller, M. R. 1951. Copeia, p. 114. [21] Pack, H. J. 1918. Ibid. (63):91. [22] Rahn, H. 1942. Ibid., p. 233. [23] Reese, A. M. 1915. The alligator and its allies. G. P. Putnam and Sons, New York. [24] Regamey, J. 1935. Rev. suisse zool. 42:187. [25] Risley, P. L. 1933. Papers Mich. Acad. Sci. 17:685. [26] Sandars, E. 1943. A beast book for the pocket. Oxford Univ. Press, London. [27] Schmidt, K. P., and D. D. Davis. 1941. Field book of snakes of the United States and Canada. G. P. Putnam and Sons, New York. [28] Smith, H. M. 1946. Handbook of lizards. Comstock, Ithaca. [29] Smith, H. M. 1950. Univ. Kansas Museum Nat. Hist. Misc. Publ. 2. [30] Shaw, C. E. 1952. Herpetologica 8:71. [31] Stuart, G. R. 1954. Copeia, p. 61. [32] Tanner, V. M. 1942. Great Basin Naturalist 3:60. [33] Tanner, V. M. 1949. Ibid. 9:51. [34] Tanner, V. M. Unpublished, 1952. [35] Van Denburgh, J. 1922. The reptiles of western North America. California Academy of Sciences, San Francisco. v. 1. [36] Wilhoft, D. C. 1961. J. Morphol. 108:95. [37] Woodbury, A. M., and R. Hardy. 1948. Ecol. Monographs 18:145. [38] Woodbury, A. M., et al. 1951. Herpetologica 7:24.

44. PROPAGATION: AMPHIBIANS

The rate of growth and development of amphibians is influenced by temperature, moisture, and light to a much greater degree than is the rate of growth and development of homoiotherms. Manner of development is oviparous, unless otherwise specified. Fertilization (column D): Int = internal, Ext = external. Parental Care (column G): ♂ = male guards or transports eggs, ♀ = female guards or transports eggs, 0 = none. Classification adapted from Cochran, *Living Amphibians of the World*, 1961.

	Family and Species	Location	Breeding Season	Fertilization	Eggs or Young per Brood	Egg Development	Parental Care	Form at Hatching or Birth	Period of Growth: Egg da	Period of Growth: Larva da	Period of Growth: Sexual Maturity	Reference
	(A)	(B)	(C)	(D)	(E)	(F)	(G)	(H)	(I)	(J)	(K)	(L)
	Gymnophiona											
	Caeciliidae											
1	*Typhlonectes compressicauda*	S. America	....	Int[1]	6	In ♀	♀	Adult	....	....	......	12
	Salientia											
	Microhylidae											
2	*Breviceps gibbosus*	Africa	....	...	25-30	On land	0	Adult	....	....	......	30
3	*Microhyla carolinensis*	N. America	May-Sept	Ext	900-1200	In water	0	Embryo	1.5-3.0	20-70	......	21,34,35
	Rhacophoridae											
4	*Rhacophorus omeimontis*	China	Apr-May	Ext	100+	Above water[2]	0	Embryo	8	....	......	20
	Ranidae											
5	*Arthroleptella hewitti*	Africa	Oct	Ext	36	On land	...	Advanced tadpole	10		......	14,30
6	*Rana catesbeiana*	N. America	Feb-Aug	Ext	10,000-25,000	In water	0	Embryo	4-5	365-730	3-4 yr	32,34,35

/1/ Manner of birth is viviparous. /2/ On leaves.

continued

44. PROPAGATION: AMPHIBIANS

	Family and Species	Location	Breeding Season	Fertilization	Eggs or Young per Brood	Egg Development	Parental Care	Form at Hatching or Birth	Period of Growth: Egg da	Period of Growth: Larva da	Period of Growth: Sexual Maturity	Reference
	(A)	(B)	(C)	(D)	(E)	(F)	(G)	(H)	(I)	(J)	(K)	(L)
	Salientia											
	Ranidae											
7	*Rana pipiens*	N. America	Feb-Dec	Ext	3500-6500	In water	0	Embryo	9-20	60-80	3 yr	32,34,35
8	*R. sylvatica*	N. America	Mar-Apr	Ext	2000-3000	....	...	....	12 at 10oC	44-85	......	24,35
9	*R. temporaria*	Asia, Europe	Feb-Apr	Ext	1500-4000	In water	0	Embryo	14-21	90-180	4-5 yr	5,33
	Hylidae											
10	*Acris gryllus*	N. America	Feb-Oct	Ext	250	In water	0	Embryo	4	50-90	2 yr	34,35
11	*Gastrotheca ovifera*	S. America	....	Ext	100	In dorsal pouch of ♀	♀	Adult	....	....	......	13,26
12	*Hyla decipiens*	S. America	Feb	Ext	....	Above water[2]	0	Early tadpole	2	180	......	11,26
13	*H. regilla*	N. America	Jan-May	Ext	730-1250	....	...	....	6-14	50-80	2 yr	21,32,35
14	*H. versicolor*	N. America	Apr-Aug	Ext	1000-2000	In water	0	Embryo	4-5	45-65	1-2 yr	21,34,35
15	*Pseudacris nigrita*	N. America	Feb-May	Ext	500-1500	....	...	....	14	40-90	......	32,35
	Dendrobatidae											
16	*Hyloxalus granuliventris*	S. America	Sept	Ext	48	On land	♂[3]	Tadpole	12-14	5	......	13
	Rhinodermatidae											
17	*Rhinoderma darwinii*	S. America	....	Ext	....	In vocal sac of ♂	♂	Adult	....	....	......	23,25
	Bufonidae											
18	*Bufo americanus*	N. America	Mar-July	Ext	4,000-20,600	....	...	....	3-12	30-65	2-3 yr	6,18,31,35
19	*B. terrestris*	N. America	Feb-Sept	Ext	2500-3000	....	...	....	2-4	30-55	......	32,34,35
20	*B. woodhousei*	N. America	Apr-Aug	Ext	5,000-10,000	In water	0	Embryo	2-4	40-60	......	21,35
21	*Nectophrynoides tornieri*	S. Africa	....	Int[1]	....	In ♀	♀	Adult	....	....	......	1,28
	Leptodactylidae											
22	*Eleutherodactylus latrans*	N. America	Apr	Ext	67	On land	♂?	Adult	25-30		......	19
23	*E. ricordii*	N. America	May-Sept	...	3-26	....	...	....	13-20	None	1 yr	16
24	*Leptodactylus labialis*	N. America	June	Ext	86	On land	...	Embryo	2-3	30-35	......	25,35
25	*Zachaenus parvulus*	S. America	July	Ext	30	On land	0	Advanced tadpole	....	13	......	22,23
	Pelobatidae											
26	*Pelobates fuscus*	Europe	Mar-May	Ext	....	In water	0	Embryo	....	90-120	......	5
27	*Scaphiopus holbrookii*	N. America	Mar-Sept	Ext	100-2330	In water	0	Embryo	1.5-2.0	14-60	......	7,21,35
28	*S. hurteri*	N. America	Apr-June	Ext	100+	In water	0	Embryo	1.5-2.0	18-28	......	35
	Discoglossidae											
29	*Alytes obstetricans*	Europe	Apr-June	Ext	18-54	On land (legs of ♂)	♂	Tadpole	21	90-150	......	5
30	*Discoglossus pictus*	Europe	Jan-Oct	Ext	300-1000	In water	0	Embryo	2-4	30-60	......	5
	Pipidae											
31	*Pipa pipa*	S. America	....	Ext	....	In water (back of ♀)	♀	Adult	....	....	......	12
32	*Xenopus laevis*	Africa	Sept-Oct	Ext	<100-1000	In water	0	Embryo	3	35-300	♂, $\frac{1}{2}$; ♀, 2 yr	26,28

/1/ Manner of birth is viviparous. /2/ On leaves. /3/ Carries tadpoles to water.

continued

44. PROPAGATION: AMPHIBIANS

	Family and Species	Location	Breeding Season	Fertilization	Eggs or Young per Brood	Egg Development	Parental Care	Form at Hatching or Birth	Period of Growth: Egg da	Period of Growth: Larva da	Period of Growth: Sexual Maturity	Reference
	(A)	(B)	(C)	(D)	(E)	(F)	(G)	(H)	(I)	(J)	(K)	(L)
	Salientia											
	Leiopelmidae											
33	*Ascaphus truei*	N. America	May-Sept	Int	28-50	In water	0	Embryo	30	365	......	27,35
34	*Leiopelma hochstetteri*	New Zealand	Dec	Ext	6-18	On land	?[4]	Adult	30		......	2
	Caudata											
	Sirenidae											
35	*Siren intermedia*	N. America	....	...	224-706	In water	...	Larva	....	2 yr		4,9
	Proteidae											
36	*Necturus maculosus*	N. America	Sept-Nov[5]; May-June[7]	Int[6]	18-180	In water	...	Larva	38-63	5 yr		3
	Plethodontidae											
37	*Aneides aeneus*	N. America	May-June	Int[8]	10-26	On land	♀	Adult	84-91		......	17
38	*Ensatina eschscholtzii*	N. America	Feb-Apr	Int[8]	12-14	On land	♀	Adult	....	....	......	32
39	*Eurycea bislineata*	N. America	Autumn[5]; Apr-June[7]	Int[8]	12-41	In water	0	Larva	60-70	730-1100	......	4
40	*Hemidactylium scutatum*	N. America	Sept-Oct[5]; Apr-May[7]	Int[8]	22-64	On land	♀	Larva	38-60	48	2 yr	4
41	*Plethodon cinereus*	N. America	Oct-Dec[5] June-July[7]	Int[8]	3-13	On land	♀	Adult	60?	2 yr		4
	Amphiumidae											
42	*Amphiuma tridactylum*	N. America	Jan-May[5]; May-June[7]	Int[6]	42-131	In water	♀	Adult	2-3 yr			8
	Salamandridae											
43	*Salamandra salamandra*	Europe	July	Int[1]	12-72	In ♀	0	Larva or adult	90-150		4-5 yr	15
44	*Triturus viridescens*	N. America	Apr-June	Int[8]	200-376	In water	0	Larva	20-35	80+	2 yr	4,31
	Ambystomidae											
45	*Ambystoma maculatum*	N. America	Mar-Apr	Int[8]	Up to 250	In water	0	Larva	31-54	61-110	2 yr	4
46	*A. opacum*	N. America	Sept-Jan	Int[8]	25-200	On land	♀	Larva	30-180	180-240	14-17 mo	3,4
47	*A. tigrinum*	N. America	Jan-Mar	Int[8]	23-110	In water	0	Larva	24-30	180+	1 yr	4,31
	Cryptobranchidae											
48	*Cryptobranchus alleganiensis*	N. America	Aug-Dec	Ext	220-450	In water	♂	Larva	68-84	550-700	5-6 yr	3,4
	Hynobiidae											
49	*Hynobius chinensis*	China	May	Ext	35-70	In water	♂	Larva	....	60	......	10,23, 25,29

/1/ Manner of birth is viviparous. /4/ Sex of protector undetermined. /5/ Mating season. /6/ From spermatophore deposited by male in female cloaca. /7/ Time of oviposition. /8/ From spermatophore laid by male and picked up by female.

Contributors: (a) Cagle, Fred. R., (b) Blair, Albert P., (c) Tanner, Vasco M., (d) Fitch, Henry S.

References: [1] Angel, F., and M. La Motte. 1944. Ann. sci. nat. Zool. et biol. animale, Ser. 11, 6:63. [2] Archey, G. 1922. Records Canterbury Museum (New Zealand) 2(2):59. [3] Bishop, S. C. 1941. N. Y. State Museum Bull. 324. [4] Bishop, S. C. 1943. Handbook of salamanders. Comstock, Ithaca. [5] Boulenger, G. A. 1897. The tailless batrachians of Europe. Ray Society, London. [6] Bragg, A. N. 1940. Am. Midland Naturalist 24:322. [7] Bragg, A. N. 1944. Copeia, p. 230. [8] Cagle, F. R. 1948. Ecology 29(4):479. [9] Cagle, F. R., and P. E. Smith. 1939. Copeia, p. 232. [10] Chang, M. L. Y. 1936. Contribution à l'étude morphologique,

continued

biologique et systematique des amphibiens urodeles de la Chine. Librairie Picart, Paris. [11] Cochran, D. M. 1954. U. S. Natl. Museum Bull. 206. [12] Dunn, E. R. 1942. Bull. Museum Comp. Zool. Harvard Univ. 91(6):440. [13] Dunn, E. R. 1944. Caldasia 9:397. [14] Fitzsimons, V. 1947. Ann. Natal Museum 11(1):9. [15] Francis, E. T. B. 1934. The anatomy of the salamander. Oxford Univ. Press, London. [16] Goin, C. J. 1947. Univ. Florida Biol. Sci. Ser. 4(2):1. [17] Gordon, R. E. 1952. Am. Midland Naturalist 47(3):666. [18] Hamilton, J. W., Jr. 1934. Copeia, p. 88. [19] Jameson, D. L. 1950. Ibid., p. 44. [20] Liu, C.-C. 1950. Fieldiana Zool. Mem. 2. [21] Livezey, R. L., and A. H. Wright. 1947. Am. Midland Naturalist 37(1):179. [22] Lutz, B. 1944. Bol. museu nacl. (Rio de Janeiro) Zool. 17:1. [23] Lutz, B. 1948. Evolution 2(1):29. [24] Moore, J. A. 1939. Ecology 20:459. [25] Mulaik, S. 1937. Copeia, p. 72. [26] Noble, G. K. 1931. The biology of the amphibia. McGraw-Hill, New York. [27] Noble, G. K., and P. G. Putnam. 1931. Copeia, p. 97. [28] Orton, G. L. 1949. Ann. Carnegie Museum 31:257. [29] Parker, F., Jr., S. L. Robbins, and A. Loveridge. 1947. Am. Naturalist 81:38. [30] Rose, W. 1950. The reptiles and amphibians of southern Africa. M. Miller, Capetown. [31] Smith, H. M. 1950. Univ. Kansas Museum Nat. Hist. Misc. Publ. 2. [32] Stebbins, R. C. 1951. Amphibians of western North America. Univ. California Press, Berkeley. [33] Wilson, M. A. 1950. Brit. J. Herpetol. 1(3):66. [34] Wright, A. H. 1932. Life histories of the frog of Okefinokee Swamp, Georgia. Macmillan, New York. [35] Wright, A. H., and A. A. Wright. 1949. Handbook of frogs and toads. Comstock, Ithaca.

45. PROPAGATION: FISHES

Spawning activities vary with species, locale, and water temperature. The number of eggs produced varies (from a few to millions) with the species. The number of eggs may also differ greatly within a single species, depending chiefly on the size of the female. Classification adapted from Herald, *Living Fishes of the World*, 1961.

Part I: BONY FISHES

For additional information, consult references 45, 68, 77, 96, 97, 112, 134. Fertilization is external and development is oviparous, unless otherwise specified. Season (column C): spr = spring, sum = summer, aut = autumn, win = winter. Water (column D): S = salt; F = fresh; B = brackish; X = stagnant, swampy, or sluggish; V = fluviatile; L = lacustrine; (a) = anadromous. Egg type (column E): PB = pelagic or buoyant eggs, D = demersal. Parental care (column G): ♂ = male guards nest or eggs, ♀ = female guards next or eggs, ♂♀ = both parents guard nest or eggs, C = eggs covered by gravel or sand, 0 = none.

	Order and Family	Species	Spawning Season	Spawning Water	Egg Type	No. of Eggs or Young per Spawning Period	Parental Care	Reference
	(A)	(B)	(C)	(D)	(E)	(F)	(G)	(H)
	Pediculati							
1	Antennariidae	*Histrio histrio*	Sum,aut	S	PB	....	0	70,131
2	Lophiidae	*Lophius piscatorius*	Spr,sum,aut	S	PB	1,320,000	0	6
	Haplodoci							
3	Batrachoididae	*Opsanus tau*	Spr,sum	S	D	100	♂	6,7,56,63
4		*Porichthys notatus*	Spr	S	D	....	♂	34,78
	Plectognathi							
5	Molidae	*Mola mola*	Spr,sum	S	...	300,000,000	...	6,106
6	Tetraodontidae	*Sphaeroides maculatus*	Spr,sum	S	D	176,000	...	70,146
	Heterosomata							
7	Soleidae	*Trinectes maculatus*	Spr,sum	S,B	...	54,000	...	6,132
8	Pleuronectidae	*Hippoglossoides platessoides*	Spr	S	PB	30,000-60,000	0	6
9		*Hippoglossus hippoglossus*	Spr,sum	S	PB	2,182,773	...	6,60
10		*H. stenolepis*	Aut,win	S	PB	2,700,000	0	34
11		*Limanda ferruginea*	Spr,sum	S	PB	....	0	6
12		*Microstomus pacificus*	Win	S	PB	37,000-230,000	0	65
13		*Parophrys vetulus*	Win,spr	S	PB	....	0	23
14		*Platichthys stellatus*	Aut,win	S	PB	11,000,000	0	109
15		*Pleuronichthys decurrens*	Spr,sum	S	PB	....	0	23
16		*P. verticalis*	Spr,sum	S	PB	....	0	23,117

continued

45. PROPAGATION: FISHES

Part I: BONY FISHES

	Order and Family	Species	Spawning		Egg Type	No. of Eggs or Young per Spawning Period	Parental Care	Reference
			Season	Water				
	(A)	(B)	(C)	(D)	(E)	(F)	(G)	(H)
	Heterosomata							
17	Pleuronectidae	*Pseudopleuronectes americanus*	Win,spr	S	D	500,000-1,500,000	...	6
18	Bothidae	*Paralichthys dentatus*	Aut,win,spr	S	PB	...	...	6,59,70
19		*P. oblongus*	Spr,sum	S	PB	...	0	6
	Thoracostei							
20	Gasterosteidae	*Eucalia inconstans*	Spr,sum	F,V,L	...	...	♂	76,124
21		*Gasterosteus aculeatus*	Spr	F,B	...	100-150	♂	6,139
22		*G. wheatlandi*	Spr	F,B	...	100-150	♂	6
	Scleroparei							
23	Anoplopomatidae	*Anoplopoma fimbria*	Spr	S	PB	...	0	34
24	Hexagrammidae	*Hexagrammos decagrammus*	Aut	S	D	...	...	34
25	Ophiodontidae	*Ophiodon elongatus*	Win	S	D	170,000-476,000	♂[1]	34
26	Cyclopteridae	*Cyclopterus lumpus*	Win,spr	S	D	136,000	♂[1]	6,57
27	Cottidae	*Cottus bairdi bairdi*	Spr	F,V,L	D	...	♂	76
28		*C. bairdi punctulatus*	Spr	F,V	D	69-406	♂	2
29		*Hemitripterus americanus*	Aut,win	S	D	15,000-45,000	...	143
30		*Myoxocephalus octodecemspinosus*	Aut,win	S	D	8,000	...	6,101
31		*M. scorpius*	Aut,win	S	D	...	...	6,17
32		*Scorpaenichthys marmoratus*	Win	S	D	48,700-97,600	...	34,107
33	Triglidae	*Prionotus carolinus*	Sum	S	PB	...	0	6
34	Scorpaenidae[2]	*Sebastes marinus*	Spr,sum	S	...	25,000-40,000 yearly	0	6
35		*Sebastodes mystinus*	Aut,win	S	...	524,000	0	140
36		*S. pinniger*	Win	S	...	60,000	0	34
37		*S. ruberrimus*	...	S	...	2,700,000	0	34
	Percomorphi							
38	Atherinidae	*Atherinopsis affinis*	...	S,B	D	...	0	117,121
39		*A. californiensis*	Aut,win	S	D	...	0	32
40		*Leuresthes tenuis*	Spr,sum	S	D	1,000-3,000	0	142
41		*Menidia menidia*	Spr,sum	S,B	D	...	0	70
42	Sphyraenidae	*Sphyraena argentea*	Sum	S	...	42,000-484,000	...	3,141
43	Stromateidae	*Poronotus triacanthus*	Spr	S	PB	...	0	6
44	Zoarcidae	*Macrozoarces americanus*	Aut	S	...	1,800	...	6,7
45	Anarhichadidae	*Anarhichas lupus*	Win	S	D	40,000	...	17,58
46	Pholidae	*Pholis gunnellus*	Aut,win	S	D	...	...	17
47	Stichaeidae	*Anoplarchus purpurescens*	Win,spr	S	D	3,000	♀	34
48	Clinidae	*Heterostichus rostratus*	...	S	D	...	♂	3
49	Blenniidae	*Paraclinus marmoratus*	Spr	S	D	...	♂[1]	14
50	Gobiidae	*Bathygobius soporator*	Sum	S	D	...	♂	16
51		*Gillichthys mirabilis*	Win,spr	S	D	4,000-9,000	♂♀	145
52		*Gobiosoma robustum*	Spr	S	D	2-10	♂[1]	15
53	Xiphiidae	*Xiphias gladias*	Sum	S	PB	...	0	6,86
54	Scombridae	*Katsuwonus vagans*	Spr,sum	S	PB	...	0	3
55		*Scomber scombrus*	Spr,sum	S	PB	41,000-546,000	0	90
56		*Scomberomorus maculatus*	Spr,sum	S	PB	20,000	0	17
57	Kraemeriidae	*Ammodytes americanus*	Aut,win	S	D	...	...	6
58	Labridae	*Tautoga onitis*	Spr,sum	S	PB	...	0	6
59		*Tautogolabrus adspersus*	Spr,sum	S	PB	...	0	6
60	Pomacentridae	*Abudefduf saxatilis*	All year	S	D	...	♂	17
61		*Pomacentrus leucoris*	Spr,sum	S	D	400-500	♂♀[1]	10
62		*P. leucostictus*	Sum	S	D	...	♂	18
63	Embiotocidae[3]	*Hyperprosopon argenteum*	Spr,sum	S	...	5-12	0	115,117
64		*Taeniotoca lateralis*	Sum	S	...	44	0	34
65	Cichlidae	*Cichlasoma cyanoguttatum*	...	F,V,L	D	100-2000	♂♀[1]	80
66	Ephippidae	*Chaetodipterus faber*	Spr,sum	S	PB	...	0	17
67	Sparidae	*Stenotomus chrysops*	Spr,sum	S	PB	...	0	6

/1/ Eggs fanned. /2/ Fertilization is internal, and birth is ovoviviparous. /3/ Fertilization is internal, and birth is viviparous.

continued

45. PROPAGATION: FISHES

Part I: BONY FISHES

	Order and Family	Species	Spawning		Egg Type	No. of Eggs or Young per Spawning Period	Parental Care	Reference
			Season	Water				
	(A)	(B)	(C)	(D)	(E)	(F)	(G)	(H)
	Percomorphi							
68	Sciaenidae	*Aplodinotus grunniens*	Spr	F,L	...	200,000-400,000	...	38,76
69		*Cynoscion nobilis*	Spr,sum	S	...	...	0	34,129
70		*C. regalis*	Spr,sum	S	PB	...	0	147
71		*Micropogon undulatus*	Aut	S	...	180,000	...	111
72		*Pogonias cromis*	Win,spr	S	...	6,000,000	...	111
73		*Sciaenops ocellata*	Win,spr	S	...	3,410,000	...	111
74	Pomadasyidae	*Haemulon plumieri*	Sum,aut	S	D	...	0	113
75	Carangidae	*Trachurus symmetricus*	Win,spr,sum	S	...	...	...	117,118
76	Pomatomidae	*Pomatomus saltatrix*	Spr,sum	S	PB	...	0	6
77	Malacanthidae	*Lopholatilus chamaeleonticeps*	Sum	S	PB	...	0	6
78	Percidae	*Ammocrypta pellucida*	Sum	F,V,L	D	...	...	76,124
79		*Etheostoma exile*	Spr,sum	F,V,L	D	...	0	1,76,81
80		*E. nigrum*	Spr	F,V,L	D	...	♂	76
81		*Perca flavescens*	Spr	F,V,L	D	10,000-40,000	0	1,67
82		*Percina maculata*	Spr	F,V,L	D	...	...	1,76
83		*Stizostedion canadense*	Spr	F,V,L	D	50,000	0	132
84		*S. vitreum vitreum*	Spr	F,V,L	D	23,000-50,000	0	67
85	Centrarchidae	*Ambloplites rupestris*	Spr,sum	F,V,L	D	6,000-9,000	♂	1,12,67
86		*Archoplytes interruptus*	Spr,sum	F,V,L	D	84,000	0	102
87		*Enneacanthus chaetodon*	Spr,sum	F,V,L	D	...	♂	12
88		*Lepomis auritus*	Spr,sum	F,V,L	D	...	♂	12
89		*L. cyanellus*	Spr,sum	F,V,L	D	...	♂	12,113
90		*L. gibbosus*	Spr,sum	F,V,L	D	Several thousand	♂	67
91		*L. humilis*	Spr,sum	F,V,L	D	4,200	♂	12,30
92		*L. macrochirus*	Spr,sum	F,V,L	D	4,670-61,815	♂	67
93		*L. megalotis*	Spr,sum	F,V,L	D	...	♂	12,76,151
94		*Micropterus coosae*	Spr,sum	F,V,L	D	...	...	85,110
95		*M. dolomieu*	Spr,sum	F,V,L	D	1,000-10,000	♂	67,73
96		*M. salmoides*	Spr,sum	F,V,L	D	2,000-26,000	♂	1,44
97		*Pomoxis annularis*	Spr,sum	F,V,L	D	2,900-14,750	♂	67
98		*P. nigromaculatus*	Spr,sum	F,V,L	D	20,000-60,000	♂	44,67
99	Serranidae	*Centropristes striatus*	Spr,sum	S	PB	...	0	6,88
100		*Roccus americanus*	Spr,sum	F,V,L	D	40,000	0	6,17
101		*R. chrysops*	Spr	F,V,L	D	650,000-970,000	0	1,67,126
102		*R. mississippiensis*	Spr	F,V,L	D	...	0	76
103		*R. saxatilus*	Spr,sum	F,V(a),B	D	14,000-5,000,000	0	93,94,114
	Anacanthini							
104	Gadidae	*Brosme brosme*	Spr,sum	S	PB	2,000,000	0	6
105		*Gadus morhua*	Win,spr	S	PB	3,000,000-9,000,000	0	6
106		*Lota lota*	Win,spr	F,V,L	...	More than a million	0	44,76
107		*Melanogrammus aeglefinus*	Win,spr	S	PB	169,000-1,839,581	0	6
108		*Merluccius bilinearis*	Spr,sum	S	PB	...	0	6
109		*M. productus*	Win,spr	S	...	...	0	117
110		*Microgadus tomcod*	Aut,win	S,B	D	25,000-44,000	0	6
111		*Pollachius virens*	Aut,win	S	PB	225,000-4,000,000	0	6
	Solenichthys							
112	Syngnathidae	*Hippocampus hudsonius*	...	S	...	150	♂	6,54,119
113		*Syngnathus fuscus*	Spr,sum	S	...	104-570	♂	6,17,70
	Salmopercae							
114	Aphredoderidae	*Aphredoderus sayanus*	Spr	F,V,L	D	...	♂♀	76,113
115	Percopsidae	*Columbia transmontana*	Sum	F,V	D	4,748	...	42
116		*Percopsis omiscomaycus*	Spr	F,V,L	D	...	...	1,76
	Microcyprini							
117	Anablepidae[3]	*Anableps dovii*	...	F,V	D	...	0	82
118	Goodeidae[3]	*Neotoca bilineata*	...	F,V,L	...	5-40	0	80
119	Poeciliidae[3]	*Mollienisia latipunctata*	...	F	...	Few	0	72,80
120		*Xiphophorus helleri*	...	F	...	100-200	0	80
121	Cyprinodontidae	*Fundulus diaphanus*	Sum	F,V,B	D	200	0	113
122		*F. heteroclitus*	Spr,sum	F,V,B	D	460	0	70

/3/ Fertilization is internal, and birth is viviparous.

continued

45. PROPAGATION: FISHES

Part I: BONY FISHES

	Order and Family	Species	Spawning: Season	Spawning: Water	Egg Type	No. of Eggs or Young per Spawning Period	Parental Care	Reference
	(A)	(B)	(C)	(D)	(E)	(F)	(G)	(H)
	Microcyprini							
123	Cyprinodontidae	*Fundulus majalis*	Spr,sum	S,F,B	D	540	0	70
124		*F. notatus*	Spr,sum	F,V,L	D	....	0	28,51,76
	Synentognathi							
125	Exocoetidae	*Cypselurus californicus*	Sum	S	PB	....	0	75,99,117
126	Scomberosocidae	*Cololabis saira*	Win,spr,sum	S	...	....	0	117
127	Hemirhamphidae	*Hyporhamphus unifasciatus*	Sum	S	PB	....	0	70
128	Belonidae	*Strongylura marina*	Sum	S	...	....	0	17,70
	Apodes							
129	Congridae	*Conger oceanicus*	Sum	S	PB	3,000,000-7,900,000	0	46
130	Anguillidae	*Anguilla rostrata*	Win	S	PB	5,000,000-20,000,000	...	6,70
	Ostariophysi							
131	Ictaluridae	*Ictalurus catus*	Spr	F,V	D	2,000	♂♀	17,113
132		*I. furcatus*	Spr	F,V	D	....	...	67
133		*I. melas*	Spr	F,V,L	D	2,000-6,000	♂	67,113
134		*I. natalis*	Spr	F,V,L	D	2,000-7,000	♂	67
135		*I. nebulosus*	Spr	F,V,L	D	2,000-10,000	♂♀	11,47,67
136		*I. punctatus*	Spr,sum	F,V,	D	3,000-20,000	♂	67
137		*Noturus miurus*	Spr,sum	F,V,L	D	....	...	1,76
138		*Pilodictis olivaris*	Spr,sum	F,V,L	D	....	♂	67,113
139	Ariidae	*Bagre marinus*	Spr,sum	S	...	55	♂[4]	17,64
140		*Galeichthys felis*	Spr,sum	S	...	20-30	♂[4]	17
141	Catostomidae	*Catostomus commersonii*	Spr	F,V	D	20,000-100,000	0	1,67,113
142		*Chasmistes cujus*	Spr,sum	F,V,L	D	....	0	87
143		*Ictiobus cyprinellus*	Spr	F,V	D	400,000	0	67
144		*Xyrauchen texanus*	Spr	F,V,L	D	....	...	41,127
145	Cyprinidae	*Carassius auratus*	Spr	F,L	D	3,000	0	76,144
146		*Chrosomus erythrogaster*	Spr	F,V,L	D	....	...	130
147		*Cyprinus carpio*	Spr,sum	F,L	D	500,000-2,000,000	0	55
148		*Hesperoleucus symmetricus*	Spr,sum	F,V	D	250-900	0	48,52
149		*Lavinia exilicauda*	Spr	F,V	D	112,000	...	48,103
150		*Nocomis kentuckiensis*	Spr	F,V	D	....	...	30
151		*Notemigonus crysoleucas*	Spr,sum	F,V,L	D	....	0	35,76
152		*Notropis bifrenatus*	Spr,sum	F,V,L	D	135-2,110	...	1,27,69
153		*N. cornutus*	Spr	F,V,L	D	....	...	51,76
154		*N. girardi*	Sum	F,V	...	....	...	100
155		*N. whipplei spilopterus*	Spr,sum	F,V,L	D	....	...	49,66,74
156		*Pimephales notatus*	Spr,sum	F,V	D	2,500	♂	1,136,148
157		*P. promelas*	Spr,sum	F,V	D	4,144	...	67,74,91, 152
158		*Ptychocheilus oregonensis*	Spr	F,V	D	....	...	26
159		*Rhinichthys atratulus*	Spr	F,V	D	....	...	1
160		*Semotilus atromaculatus*	Spr,sum	F,V	D	4,100-4,671	♂	1,31,61,116
161		*S. corporalis*	Spr	F,V	D	....	♂	1
162		*Siphateles bicolor*	Spr	F,V,L	D	11,200	0	48,84
163		*Tinca tinca*	Spr	F,L	D	....	0	4,26
	Haplomi							
164	Dallidae	*Dallia pectoralis*	Spr	F,X,V,L	D	....	...	98
165	Umbridae	*Umbra limi*	Spr	F,X,V,L	D	425-450	...	1,27,53,76
166	Esocidae	*Esox lucius*	Spr	F,V,L	D	10,000-100,000	0	1,24,25,113
167		*E. masquinongy*	Spr	F,L	D	20,000-225,000	0	44,67,76,79, 124,149
168		*E. niger*	Spr	F,V,L	D	30,000	0	1,104
	Isospondyli							
169	Osmeridae	*Hypomesus pretiosus*	Spr,sum,aut	S	D	15,000-20,000	0	34
170		*Mallotus villosus*	Aut	S	D	3,000-6,000	0	34
171		*Osmerus mordax*	Spr	F,V	D	To 50,000	0	17,47,113
172		*Thaleichthys pacificus*	Spr	F,V	D	25,000	0	34
173	Thymallidae	*Thymallus signifer*	Spr	F,V	D	Average about 5,000	C	19,83

/4/ Eggs carried in mouth for protection.

continued

45. PROPAGATION: FISHES

Part I: BONY FISHES

	Order and Family	Species	Spawning		Egg Type	No. of Eggs or Young per Spawning Period	Parental Care	Reference
			Season	Water				
	(A)	(B)	(C)	(D)	(E)	(F)	(G)	(H)
	Isospondyli							
174	Coregonidae	*Coregonus artedii*	Aut	F,L	D	13,723-37,272	0	21,27,76, 137
175		*C. clupeaformis*	Aut	F,V,L	D	10,000-75,000	0	44,47,76, 113
176		*C. williamsoni*	....	F,V,L	D	1,426-24,143	0	20
177		*Stenodus leucichthys*	Aut	F,V	D	....	0	26,43,150
178	Salmonidae[5]	*Oncorhynchus gorbuscha*	Spr,sum	F,V(a)	D	2,000	C	135
179		*O. keta*	Spr,sum,aut	F,V(a)	D	3,000	C	135
180		*O. kisutch*	Sum,aut	F,V(a)	D	3,500	C	125,135
181		*O. nerka kennerlyi*	Spr	F,V	D	360-479	C	37,120,123
182		*O. nerka nerka*	Spr,sum	F,V(a)	D	3,500	C	50,135
183		*O. tshawytscha*	Spr,sum,win	F,V(a)	D	5,000	C	29,135
184		*Salmo aguabonita*	Sum	F,V	D	1,380-2,280	C	127
185		*S. clarki*	Aut,win,spr	F,V	D	226-2,100	C	41,83,122
186		*S. gairdneri*	Spr,sum,aut	F,V(a)	D	400-3,000	C	67,125
187		*S. salar salar*	Spr	F,V(a)	D	7,000	C	47,92,124
188		*S. salar sebago*	Spr	F,V	D	1,200	C	62
189		*S. trutta*	Aut,win	F,V	D	200-6,000	C	67
190		*Salvelinus alpinus*	Aut,win	F,L	D	....	C	40,124
191		*S. aureolus*	Aut	F,L	D	1,200	C	47
192		*S. fontinalis*	Aut	F,V	D	200-2,500	C	67
193		*S. malma*	Aut,win	F,V(a)	D	1,337-8,845	C	22,40,105
194		*S. namaycush*	Aut	F,L	D	6,000	0	47
195	Engraulidae	*Anchoviella mitchilli*	Spr,sum	S	PB	....	0	70
196		*Engraulis mordax*	All year	S	PB	....	0	34,117
197	Dorosomidae	*Dorosoma cepedianum*	Spr,sum,aut	F,B	D	22,000-544,000	0	8,51,70,124
198	Clupeidae	*Alosa pseudoharengus*	Spr	F,V(a)	D	10,000-102,800	0	70,89,108
199		*A. sapidissima*	Spr	F,V(a)	D	25,000-616,000	0	5,39,70
200		*Brevoortia tyrannus*	Spr,sum,aut	S	PB	Up to 140,000	0	6,7,70,83
201		*Clupea harengus*	Spr,sum,aut	S	D	20,000-40,000	0	6,70
202		*C. pallasi*	Win,spr	S	D	....	0	117
203		*Sardinops caerulea*	Spr,sum	S	PB	35,000	0	33,34,117
204	Elopidae	*Elops saurus*	....	S	PB	....	0	70
205		*Tarpon atlanticus*	Spr,sum	S	D	....	0	13
	Ginglymodi							
206	Lepisosteidae	*Lepisosteus osseus*	Spr	F,V,L	D	6,200-77,156	...	71,85,113
	Protospondyli							
207	Amiidae	*Amia calva*	Spr	F,V,L	D	23,000-64,000	♂	1,44,76
	Chondrostei							
208	Polyodontidae	*Polyodon spathula*	Spr,win	F,V	D	140,000	0	44,95,124, 133
209	Acipenseridae	*Acipenser fulvescens*	Spr,sum	F,V,L	D	182,000-1,000,000	0	36,67,76
210		*A. oxyrhynchus*	Spr,sum	F,V(a)	D	500,000-3,755,000	0	9,70,138
211		*A. transmontanus*	Spr,sum	F,V(a)	D	1,700,000	0	34,128

/5/ Eggs laid in clear, shallow, moving water on gravel nests or redds.

Contributors: (a) Migdalski, Edward C., (b) Katz, Max, (c) Carlander, Kenneth D.

References: [1] Adams, C. C., and T. L. Hankenson. 1928. Roosevelt Wild Life Ann. 1:241. [2] Bailey, J. E. 1952. Copeia, p. 243. [3] Barnhart, P. S. 1936. Marine fishes of southern California. Univ. Calif. Press, Berkeley. [4] Baughman, J. L. 1950. Texas J. Sci. 2:117. [5] Bean, T. H. 1902. N. Y. Forest Fish and Game Comm. Rept. 7:251. [6] Bigelow, H. B., and W. C. Schroeder. 1953. U. S. Fish Wildlife Service Fishery Bull. 74. [7] Bigelow, H. B., and W. W. Welsh. 1925. U. S. Bur. Fisheries Bull. 40. [8] Bodola, A. 1955. Ph. D. Thesis. Ohio State Univ., Columbus. [9] Borodin, N. 1925. Trans. Am. Fisheries Soc. 55:184. [10] Breder, C. M., Jr. 1933. Am. Museum Novitates 612. [11] Breder, C. M., Jr. 1935. Zoologica 19:143. [12] Breder, C. M., Jr. 1936. Ibid. 21:1. [13] Breder, C. M., Jr. 1939. Bull. N. Y. Zool. Soc. 42:99. [14] Breder, C. M., Jr. 1941.

continued

Zoologica 26:243. [15] Breder, C. M., Jr. 1942. Ibid. 27:61. [16] Breder, C. M., Jr. 1943. Bull. Bingham Oceanog. Collection 8(3). [17] Breder, C. M., Jr. 1948. Field book of marine fishes of the Atlantic Coast. G. P. Putnam's Sons, New York. [18] Brinley, F. J. 1939. Copeia, p. 185. [19] Brown, C. J. D. 1938. Ibid., p. 132. [20] Brown, C. J. D. 1952. Ibid., p. 109. [21] Brown, C. J. D., and J. Moffet. 1942. Ibid., p. 149. [22] Brunson, R. B. 1952. Ibid., p. 196. [23] Budd, P. L. 1940. Calif. Dept. Fish and Game Fish Bull. 56. [24] Carbine, W. F. 1942. Trans. Am. Fisheries Soc. 71:149. [25] Carbine, W. F. 1943. Papers Mich. Acad. Sci. 29:123. [26] Carl, C. G., and W. A. Clemens. 1948. Brit. Columbia Prov. Museum Handbook 5. [27] Carlander, K. D. 1950. Handbook of freshwater fishery biology. W. C. Brown, Dubuque, Iowa. [28] Carranza, J., and H. E. Winn. 1954. Copeia, p. 273. [29] Chapman, W. M. 1943. Ibid., p. 168. [30] Churchill, E. P., and W. H. Over. 1938. Fishes of South Dakota. South Dakota Dept. Game and Fish, Pierre. [31] Clark, C. F. 1943. Ohio Conservation Bull. 7:12. [32] Clark, F. N. 1929. Calif. Dept. Fish and Game Fish Bull. 16:1. [33] Clark, F. N. 1952. Calif. Fish and Game 38(3):467. [34] Clemens, W. A., and G. W. Wilby. 1946. Fisheries Research Board Can. Bull. 68. [35] Cooper, G. P. 1935. Papers Mich. Acad. Sci. 21:587. [36] Cuerrier, J. P. Unpublished, 1949. [37] Curtis, B., and J. C. Fraser. 1948. Calif. Fish and Game 34:111. [38] Daiber, F. C. 1953. Am. Midland Naturalist 50:159. [39] Davis, W. S. 1957. U. S. Fish Wildlife Service Research Rept. 49. [40] De Lacy, A. C., and W. M. Morton. 1942. Trans. Am. Fisheries Soc. 72:79. [41] De Witt, J. W., Jr. 1954. Calif. Fish and Game 40:329. [42] Donaldson, I. J. 1946. Bonneville Dam Yearbook, Portland, Oregon. [43] Dufresne, F. 1946. Alaska's animals and fishes. H. S. Barnes, New York. [44] Eddy, S., and T. Surber. 1947. Northern fishes. Univ. Minnesota Press, Minneapolis. [45] Eddy, S., and T. Surber. 1960. Ibid. Rev. ed. C. T. Branford, Newton Centre, Mass. [46] Eigenmann, C. H. 1901. Contribs. U. S. Fish Comm. Woods Hole Bull. 37. [47] Everhart, H. W. 1950. Fishes of Maine. Maine Dept. Inland Fisheries and Game, Augusta. [48] Evermann, B. W., and H. W. Clark. 1931. Calif. Dept. Fish and Game Fish Bull. 35. [49] Forbes, S. A., and R. E. Richardson. 1920. The fishes of Illinois. Ed. 2. Illinois Natural History Society, Danville. [50] Foerester, R. E. 1929. Contribs. Can. Biol. and Fisheries 5:39. [51] Fowler, H. W. 1945. Monographs Phila. Acad. Nat. Sci. 7. [52] Fry, D. H., Jr. 1936. Calif. Fish and Game 22:65. [53] Gill, T. 1904. Smithsonian Inst. Publs. Misc. Collections 45:295. [54] Gill, T. 1905. Proc. U. S. Natl. Museum 28:805. [55] Gill, T. 1905-07. Smithsonian Inst. Publs. Misc. Collections 48:195. [56] Gill, T. 1905-07. Ibid. 48:388. [57] Gill, T. 1907. Ibid. 50:175. [58] Gill, T. 1911. Proc. U. S. Natl. Museum 39:157. [59] Ginsburg, I. 1952. U. S. Fish Wildlife Service Fishery Bull. 71. [60] Goode, G. B., et al. 1884. The food fishes of the United States. U. S. Commission of Fish and Fisheries, Washington, D. C. Sect. 1(3). [61] Greeley, J. R. 1930. Abstract Thesis. Cornell Univ., Ithaca, N. Y. [62] Greeley, J. R. 1948. N. Y. State Conservation Dept. Fish and Wildlife Information Bull. 2. [63] Gudger, E. W. 1910. U. S. Bur. Fisheries Bull. 28:1071. [64] Gudger, E. W. 1916. Zoologica 2:125. [65] Hagerman, F. G. 1952. Calif. Fish and Game Comm. Fish Bull. 85. [66] Hankinson, T. L. 1930. Copeia, p. 73. [67] Harlan, J. R., and E. B. Speaker. 1951. Iowa fish and fishing. Iowa State Conservation Commission, Des Moines. [68] Harlan, J. R., and E. B. Speaker. 1956. Ibid. Rev. ed. Iowa State Conservation Commission, Des Moines. [69] Harrington, R. W. 1951. Copeia, p. 85. [70] Hildebrand, S. F., and W. C. Schroeder. 1927. U. S. Bur. Fisheries Bull. 43(1). [71] Holloway, A. 1954. J. Wildlife Management 18:438. [72] Hubbs, C. L. 1942. Aquarium J. 10:162. [73] Hubbs, C. L., and M. Bailey. 1938. Cranbrook Inst. Sci. Bull. 10. [74] Hubbs, C. L., and G. P. Cooper. 1936. Ibid. 8. [75] Hubbs, C. L., and E. M. Kampa. 1946. Copeia, p. 188. [76] Hubbs, C. L., and K. F. Lagler. 1947. Cranbrook Inst. Sci. Bull. 26. [77] Hubbs, C. L., and K. F. Lagler. 1957. Fishes of the Great Lakes region. Cranbrook Institute of Science, Bloomfield Hills, Mich. [78] Hubbs, C. L., and L. P. Schultz. 1939. Proc. U. S. Natl. Museum 86:473. [79] Huish, M. T. 1953. Trans. Am. Fisheries Soc. 83:176. [80] Innes, W. T. 1951. Exotic aquarium fishes. Innes, Philadelphia. [81] Jaffa, B. B. 1917. Copeia, p. 71 [82] Jordan, D. S. 1907. Fishes. H. Holt, New York. [83] Jordan, D. S., and B. W. Evermann. 1902. American food and game fishes. Doubleday Page, New York. [84] Kimsey, J. B. 1954. Calif. Fish and Game 40:395.

continued

45. PROPAGATION: FISHES

Part I: BONY FISHES

[85] Knapp, F. T. 1953. Fishes found in the fresh waters of Texas. Ragland and Litho Print, Brunswick, Georgia. [86] La Monte, F. 1944. Copeia, p. 258. [87] La Rivers, I., and T. J. Trelease. 1952. Calif. Fish and Game 38:113. [88] Lavenda, N. 1949. Copeia, p. 185. [89] Livingstone, D. A. 1951. Nova Scotia Inst. Sci. 23:1. [90] MacCay, C. 1929. Bull. Boston Soc. Nat. Hist. 53. [91] Markus, H. C. 1934. Copeia, p. 116. [92] MacFarland, W. L. 1925. Salmon of the Atlantic. Parke, Austin, and Lipscomb; New York. [93] Merriman, D. 1937. Copeia, p. 15. [94] Merriman, D. 1941. U. S. Fish Wildlife Service Fishery Bull. 35. [95] Meyer, F. P. 1960. Ph.D. Thesis. Iowa State Univ., Iowa City. [96] Migdalski, E. C. 1958. Salt water game fishes--Atlantic and Pacific. Ronald Press, New York. [97] Migdalski, E. C. 1962. Fresh water sport fishes of North America. Ronald Press, New York. [98] Migdalski, E. C. Unpublished, 1955. [99] Miller, D. J. 1952. Calif. Fish and Game 38:549. [100] Moore, G. A. 1944. Copeia, p. 209. [101] Morrow, J. E., Jr. 1951. Bull. Bingham Oceanog. Collection 13(2). [102] Murphy, G. I. 1948. Calif. Fish and Game 34:93. [103] Murphy, G. I. 1948. Ibid. 34:101. [104] Needham, J. G. 1920. Cornell Rural School Leaflet 13. [105] Needham, P. R., and T. M. Vaughan. 1952. Copeia, p. 197. [106] Norman, J. R., and F. C. Fraser. 1949. Field book of giant fishes. G. P. Putnam's Sons, New York. [107] O'Connell, C. P. 1953. Calif. Dept. Fish and Game Fish Bull. 93. [108] Odell, T. T. 1934. Trans. Am. Fisheries Soc. 64:118. [109] Orcutt, H. G. 1950. Calif. Div. Fish and Game Fish Bull. 78. [110] Parsons, J. W. 1953. Trans. Am. Fisheries Soc. 83:202. [111] Pearson, J. C. 1928. U. S. Bur. Fisheries Bull. 44:129. [112] Perlmutter, A. 1961. Guide to marine fishes. New York Univ. Press, New York City. [113] Raney, E. C. 1951. The Wise fisherman's encyclopedia. Wise, New York. [114] Raney, E. C., et al. 1952. Bull. Bingham Oceanog. Collection 14:5. [115] Rechnitzer, A., and C. Limbough. 1952. Copeia, p. 41. [116] Reighard, J. 1908. U. S. Bur. Fisheries Bull. 28. [117] Roedel, P. M. 1953. Calif. Dept. Fish and Game Fish Bull. 91. [118] Roedel, P. M. 1953. Calif. Fish and Game 39:45. [119] Ryder, J. A. 1881. Bull. U. S. Fisheries Comm. 1:191. [120] Scattergood, L. W. 1949. Copeia, p. 297. [121] Schultz, L. P. 1933. Univ. Wash. Publs. Biol. 2:49. [122] Schultz, L. P. 1946. U. S. Dept. Int. Conservation Bull. 22. [123] Schultz, L. P., et al. 1935. J. Pan-Pacific Research Inst. 10:365. [124] Scott, W. B. 1954. Freshwater fishes of eastern Canada. Univ. Toronto Press, Ontario. [125] Shapovalov, L., and A. C. Taft. 1954. Calif. Dept. Fish and Game Fish Bull. 98. [126] Sigler, W. F. 1949. Iowa State Coll. J. Sci. 23:311. [127] Simon, J. R. 1946. Wyoming Fish and Game Dept. Bull. 4. [128] Skinner, J. E. Unpublished, 1956. [129] Skogsberg, T. 1939. Calif. Dept. Fish and Game Fish Bull. 54. [130] Smith, B. G. 1908. Bull. Woods Hole Marine Biol. Sta. 15:9. [131] Smith, H. 1907. N. Carolina Geol. Econ. Survey Bull. 2. [132] Smith, H. M., and B. A. Bean. 1899. Bull. U. S. Fisheries Comm. 18:179. [133] Thompson, D. H. 1933. Copeia, p. 33. [134] Trautman, M. B. 1957. The fishes of Ohio. Ohio State Univ. Press, Columbus. [135] U. S. Fish and Wildlife Service. 1946. Fishery Leaflet 14. [136] Van Cleave, H. J., and H. C. Markus. 1929. Am. Naturalist 63:530. [137] Van Oosten, J. 1929. U. S. Bur. Fisheries Bull. 44:265. [138] Vladykov, V. D. 1955. Quebec Dept. Fisheries Album 5. [139] Vrat, V. 1949. Copeia, p. 252. [140] Wales, J. H. 1952. Calif. Fish and Game 38:485. [141] Walford, L. A. 1932. Calif. Dept. Fish and Game Fish Bull. 37. [142] Walker, B. W. 1952. Calif. Fish and Game 38:409. [143] Warfel, H. E., and D. Merriman. 1944. Copeia, p. 197. [144] Watson, F. R., and F. Perry. 1948. Fishponds and home aquaria. Collingridge, London. [145] Weisel, G. F. 1948. Calif. Fish and Game 34:81. [146] Welsh, W. W., and C. M. Breder, Jr. 1922. Zoologica 2:261. [147] Welsh, W. W., and C. M. Breder, Jr. 1923. U. S. Bur. Fisheries Bull. 39:141. [148] Westman, J. R. 1938. Copeia, p. 57. [149] Williams, J. E. 1948. Mich. Conservation 17:10. [150] Willimovsky, N. J. 1954. Stanford Ichthyol. Bull. 4:279. [151] Witt, A., Jr., and R. C. Marzolf. 1954. Copeia, p. 188. [152] Wynne-Edwards, V. C. 1933. Trans. Am. Fisheries Soc. 62:382.

continued

45. PROPAGATION: FISHES

Part II: CARTILAGINOUS AND JAWLESS FISHES

Manner of fertilization is internal and parental care is lacking, unless otherwise specified. Season (column C): spr = spring, sum = summer, aut = autumn, win = winter. Water (column D): S = salt, F = fresh, V = fluviatile, (a) = anadromous.

	Order and Family	Species	Spawning		Manner of Birth	No. of Eggs or Young per Spawning Period	Reference
			Season	Water			
	(A)	(B)	(C)	(D)	(E)	(F)	(G)
			Chondrichthyes				
	Chimaerae						
1	Rhinochimaeridae	*Harriotta raleighana*	Sum	S	Oviparous[1,2]	....	5
2	Chimaeridae	*Hydrolagus affinis*	....	S	Oviparous[1,2]	2	5
3		*H. colliei*	....	S	Oviparous[1,2]	2	5,17
	Batoidei						
4	Mobulidae	*Manta birostris*	....	S	Ovoviviparous	1	5
5		*Mobula hypostoma*	Sum	S	Ovoviviparous	1	5
6	Myliobatidae	*Aetobatus narinari*	....	S	Ovoviviparous	4	5
7		*Myliobatis freminvillei*	....	S	Ovoviviparous	6	5
8		*Rhinoptera bonasus*	Spr,sum,win	S	Ovoviviparous	6	5
9	Dasyatidae	*Dasyatis americana*	....	S	Ovoviviparous	3-5	5
10		*D. sayi*	Sum	S	Ovoviviparous	2-4	5
11		*Gymnura altavela*	Spr	S	Ovoviviparous	4	5
12		*Urolophus halleri*	Sum	S	Ovoviviparous	8	17
13	Rajidae	*Raja binoculata*	Jan-Oct	S	Oviparous[1]	2-7	8,17
14		*R. clavata*	May-July	S	Oviparous[1]	100	20
15		*R. erinacea*	All year	S	Oviparous[1]	6	5
16		*R. ocellata*	All year	S	Oviparous[1]	7	5
17	Pristidae	*Pristis pectinatus*	Spr,sum,aut	S	Ovoviviparous	15-20	5
18	Rhinobatidae	*Rhinobatos lentiginosus*	....	S	Ovoviviparous	6	5
19	Torpedinidae	*Narcine brasiliensis*	All year	S	Ovoviviparous	4-15	5
20		*Torpedo nobiliana*	Sum	S	Ovoviviparous	....	5
	Selachii						
21	Squatinidae	*Squatina dumerili*	Sum	S	Ovoviviparous	13-25	4
22	Dalatiidae	*Somniosus microcephalus*	....	S	Oviparous[2]	Up to 1½ barrels	4
23	Squalidae	*Centroscymnus coelolepis*	....	S	Ovoviviparous	13-16	4
24		*Squalus acanthias*	All year	S	Ovoviviparous	2-11	4
25		*S. suckleyi*	Aut	S	Ovoviviparous	3-14	1,8
26	Heterodontidae	*Heterodontus francisci*	....	S	Oviparous	....	18,22
27	Sphyrnidae	*Sphyrna tiburo*	Sum	S	Viviparous	8-9	3,4
28		*S. zygaena*	Sum	S	Viviparous	29-37	3,4
29	Carcharhinidae	*Carcharhinus acronotus*	Win,spr	S	Viviparous or ovoviviparous	3-6	4
30		*C. leucas*	Win,spr	S	Viviparous	5-6	4
31		*C. limbatus*	Spr	S	Viviparous or ovoviviparous	4-6	4
32		*C. maculipinnis*	Spr	S	Viviparous or ovoviviparous	10	4
33		*C. milberti*	Spr,sum	S	Viviparous	8-12	4
34		*C. obscurus*	Aut,win	S	Viviparous or ovoviviparous	10	4
35		*Galeocerdo cuvieri*	All year	S	Ovoviviparous	10-82	4
36		*Galeorhinus zyopterus*	....	S	Ovoviviparous	35	16,17
37		*Hypoprion signatus*	....	S	Viviparous	12	6
38		*Prionarce glauca*	All year	S	Viviparous	28-54	4,17
39		*Scoliodon terraenovae*	Spr,sum	S	Viviparous	12	4
40	Triakidae	*Mustelus canis*	Sum	S	Viviparous	10-20	4
41		*Triakis semifasciata*	....	S	Ovoviviparous	30-50	4
42	Orectolobidae	*Ginglymostoma cirratum*	....	S	Ovoviviparous	28	4
43	Rhincodontidae	*Rhincodon typus*	Sum	S	Oviparous	16	2,4
44	Alopiidae	*Alopias vulpinus*	Spr	S	Ovoviviparous	2-4	4,12
45	Isuridae	*Carcharodon carcharias*	Sum	S	Viviparous or ovoviviparous	9	6,14
46		*Lamna ditropis*	....	S	Viviparous or ovoviviparous	4	17

/1/ Eggs demersal. /2/ Parental care unspecified.

continued

45. PROPAGATION: FISHES

Part II: CARTILAGINOUS AND JAWLESS FISHES

	Order and Family	Species	Spawning		Manner of Birth	No. of Eggs or Young per Spawning Period	Reference
			Season	Water			
	(A)	(B)	(C)	(D)	(E)	(F)	(G)
	Chondrichthyes						
	Selachii						
47	Isuridae	*Lamna nasus*	All year	S	Ovoviviparous	1-4	4
48	Carchariidae	*Carcharias taurus*	....	S	Ovoviviparous	....	4
49	Hexanchidae	*Hexanchus griseus*	Spr,aut	S	Ovoviviparous	47-108	4
	Agnatha						
	Petromyzones						
50	Petromyzonidae[4]	*Ichthyomyzon gagei*	Spr	F,V	Oviparous[1,5]	1,000-3,264	9
51		*I. unicuspis*	Spr	F,V	Oviparous[1,5]	11,000-65,000	10,11,15
52		*Lampetra aepyptera*	Spr	F,V	Oviparous[1,5]	1,100	19
53		*L. lamottei*	Spr	F,V	Oviparous[1,5]	1,085-3,648	7,11,13
54		*Petromyzon marinus*	Spr	F,V(a)	Oviparous[1,5]	13,000-259,000	10,21,23
	Myxini						
55	Myxinidae	*Myxine glutinosa*	All year	S	Oviparous[1,3]	19-30	4

/1/ Eggs demersal. /3/ Manner of fertilization unspecified. /4/ Dig shallow pits for nests on gravelly riffles. /5/ Manner of fertilization external.

Contributors: (a) Migdalski, Edward C., (b) Katz, Max, (c) Carlander, Kenneth D.

References: [1] Barnhart, P. S. 1936. Marine fishes of southern California. Univ. California Press, Berkeley. [2] Baughman, J. L. 1955. Copeia, p. 54. [3] Baughman, J. L., and S. Springer. 1950. Am. Midland Naturalist 44:96. [4] Bigelow, H. B., and W. C. Schroeder. 1948. Fishes of the western North Atlantic. Sears Found. Marine Research, Yale University. pt. 1. [5] Bigelow, H. B., and W. C. Schroeder. 1953. Ibid. pt. 2. [6] Bigelow, H. B., and W. C. Schroeder. 1953. U. S. Fish Wildlife Service Fishery Bull. 74. [7] Carlander, K. D. 1950. Handbook of freshwater fishery biology. W. C. Brown, Dubuque, Iowa. [8] Clemens, W. A., and G. W. Wilby. 1949. Fisheries Research Board Can. Bull. 58. [9] Dendy, J. S., and D. C. Scott. 1953. Copeia, p. 152. [10] Gage, S. H. 1893. In Wilder Quarter century book. Comstock, Ithaca. p. 421. [11] Hubbs, C. L., and K. F. Lagler. 1947. Cranbrook Inst. Sci. Bull. 26. [12] Joseph, D. C. 1954. Calif. Fish and Game 40:433. [13] Legendre, V. 1954. The freshwater fishes of Quebec. Société Canadienne d'Ecologie, Quebec. v. 1. [14] Norman, J. R., and F. C. Fraser. 1949. Field book of giant fishes. G. P. Putnam's Sons, New York. [15] Raney, E. C. 1951. The Wise fisherman's encyclopedia. Wise, New York. [16] Ripley, W. E. 1946. Calif. Dept. Fish and Game Fish Bull. 64. [17] Roedel, P. M. 1953. Ibid. 91. [18] Roedel, P. M., and W. E. Ripley. 1950. Ibid. 75. [19] Seversmith, H. F. 1953. Copeia, p. 225. [20] Simpson, A. C. Unpublished, 1952. [21] Vladykov, V. D. 1951. Can. Fish Cult. 10:1. [22] Walford, L. A. 1935. Calif. Dept. Fish and Game Fish Bull. 45. [23] Wigley, R. L. 1959. U. S. Fish Wildlife Service Fishery Bull. 59:561.

V. INVERTEBRATE REPRODUCTION

46. SPERM DIMENSIONS: INVERTEBRATES

All values are from reference 2, unless otherwise indicated. Classification adapted from Lord Rothschild, *A Classification of Living Animals*, 1961.

	Phylum and Class	Species	Length, μ Head	Length, μ Middle Piece	Length, μ Tail	Length, μ Total	Time of Observation
	(A)	(B)	(C)	(D)	(E)	(F)	(G)
	Chordata						
1	Cephalochordata[1]	*Branchiostoma lanceolatum*	2.3		40	42	Mid-June to late July
2	Ascidiacea	*Ascidia obliqua*	4.5		33.5	38	Mid-April
3		*A. virginia*	5		60	65	Late April
4		*Ascidiella aspersa*	9		54	63	Late April to mid-May
5		*Ciona intestinalis*	3		27	30	Early January
6		*Clavelina lepadiformis*	5.5		36.5	42	Late July
7		*Corella parallelogramma*	5		27	32	Early July
8		*Molgula citrina*	8		40	48	Mid-April
9		*Polycarpa pomaria*	8.5		54	63	Mid-August
10		*Synoicum pulmonaria*	23		52	75	Early June
11	Enteropneusta	*Glossobalanus sarniensis*	3.3		64	68	Early August
12		*Protoglossus* sp.	3.7		62.5	66	Late August
	Annelida						
13	Archiannelida	*Dinophilus* sp.	13	120		133	Late May
14		*Nerilla antennata*	15	18	13	46	Mid-June to late July
15		*Protodrilus rubropharyngeus*	17	70	20	107	Mid-June to early September
16	Hirudinea	*Herpobdella octoculata*	26	66		92	Mid-June
17	Polychaeta	*Amphicteis gunneri*	4		50	54	Late July to early August
18		*Anobothrus gracilis*	2		50	52	Mid-June
19		*Apomatus globifer*	2		37	39	Mid-August
20		*Capitella capitata*	5.5	3.5	23	32	Mid-June to late July
21		*Chaetozone setosa*	3		48	51	Late July
22		*Enipo kinbergi*	3.5		60	64	Mid-June
23		*Ephesia gracilis*	5		90	95	Late July
24		*Euchone rubrocincta*	5		70	75	Mid-July
25		*Exogone gemmifera*	3		10	13	Late July
26		*Fabricia sabella*	3	70		73	Late June to late July
27		*Grubea clavata*	7.5		20	28	Mid-August
28		*Heteromastus filiformis*	2.3		50	52	Mid-December
29		*Hyalinoecia tubicola*	9.5		100	110	Mid-July
30		*Hydroides norvegica*	3		50	53	Mid-July to mid-August
31		*Leanira tetragona*	3		53	56	Mid-December
32		*Lepidonotus squamatus*	3		42	45	Mid-July to late August
33		*Manayunkia aestuarina*	3.5	13.5	10	27	Mid-June
34		*Miroserpula inflata*	6.3	2.6	34	43	Mid-August
35		*Notomastus latericeus*	3		50	53	Mid-June
36		*Onuphis conchylega*	6.5		66	73	Early to late July
37		*Owenia fusiformis*	2.7		38	41	Mid-June
38		*Platynereis dumerilio*	3.3		33	36	Late August
39		*Polydora ciliata*	5	4	46	55	Late April to early June
40		*Potamilla reniformis*	3.3		60	63	Early December
41		*Sabellides octocirrata*	4		50	54	Early July
42		*Serpula vermicularis*	3		63	66	Mid-August
43		*Sphaerosyllis hystrix*	23		50	73	Early August
44		*Spiochaetopterus typicus*	5		76	81	....
45		*Spirorbis borealis*	3	9	22	34	Mid-August
46		*S. granulatus*	3.4	6	16	25.4	Mid-July to early August
47		*S. pagenstecheri*	17	15	25	57	Early June to mid-August
48		*S. spririllum*	7	4.5	33	44.5	Late May to late August
49		*S. vitreus*	5.5	5.5	35	46	Mid-July and mid-February
50	Echiuroidea	*Echiurus echiurus*	3		51	54	Early February
51	Sipunculoidea	*Phascolosoma elongatum*	4		60	64	Early July
	Brachiopoda						
52	Articulata	*Waldheimia cranium*	3		55	58	Mid-August
53	Phoronida	*Phoronis pallida*	56		53	109	Mid- to late July

/1/ Subphylum.

continued

46. SPERM DIMENSIONS: INVERTEBRATES

	Phylum and Class	Species	Length, μ				Time of Observation
			Head	Middle Piece	Tail	Total	
	(A)	(B)	(C)	(D)	(E)	(F)	(G)
	Polyzoa						
54	Gymnolaemata	*Alcyonidium gelatinosum*	8	73	14	95	Late June to mid-July
55		*Berenicea patina*	7	9	6	22	Mid-July
56		*Bowerbankia* sp.	8	30	20	58	Early May to early August
57		*Caberea ellisii*	8	63	9	80	....
58		*Cryptosula pallasiana*	9	55	20	84	Early July
59		*Diplosolen obelia*	8.5	13	23.5	45	Mid-July
60		*Flustra foliacea*	10	50	8	68	Late April to mid-May
61		*F. securifrons*	10	36	5	51	Mid-July to mid-August
62		*Scrupocellaria scruposa*	10	40	9	59	Early July
63		*Triticella korenii*	16	53	33	102	Mid-August to late September
64		*Tubulipora liliacea*	8	8	17	33	Early to mid-August
65	Entoprocta	*Loxosoma annelidicola*	25	25	20	70	Mid-May to late August
66		*Pedicellina cernua*	25	22	30	77	Mid-May
	Nemertina						
67	Enopla	*Amphiporus lactifloreus*	13		30	43	Mid-February
68		*Carcinonemertes carcinophila*	24		20	44	Early July
69		*Emplectonema gracilis*	10		30	40	Mid-February
70		*Malacobdella grossa*	8		50	58	Late May
71	Anopla	*Cephalothrix rufifrons*	8		25	33	Late June to late August
72		*Hubrechtella dubia*	3		50	53	Mid-August
73		*Lineus bilineatus*	3		50	53	Mid-August
74		*L. ruber*	25		60	85	Mid-February
75		*Micrura fasciolata*	4		40	44	....
	Platyhelminthes						
76	Trematoda	*Fasciola hepatica*[2]	35-40	.....	60	ca. 100	April-November
77		*Haematoloechus medioplexus*[3]	25-30	.....	.....	ca. 400	....
	Ctenophora						
78	Tentaculata	*Pleurobrachia pileus*	3.5		40	44	Late April
	Cnidaria						
79	Anthozoa	*Caryophyllia smithii*	4		65	69	Mid- to late July
80		*Metridium senile*	5		50	55	Late July
81		*Sagartia troglodytes*	3.7		50	54	Late July
82		*Stenogorgia rosea*	4		70	74	Late July
83	Hydrozoa	*Dynamena pumila*	3		33	36	Mid-June
84		*Halammohydra schulzei*	2		35	37	Mid-August
85		*Sarsia tubulosa*	3.6		70	74	Late April
86		*Tima bairdii*	2.6		60	63	Mid-February

/2/ Values from reference 3. /3/ Values from reference 1.

Contributors: (a) Franzén, Åke, (b) Gresson, R. A. R.

References: [1] Burton, P. R. Unpublished, 1962. [2] Franzén, Å. 1956. Zool. Bidrag Uppsala 31:355. [3] Gresson, R. A. R. Unpublished. Queen's Univ., Belfast, Northern Ireland, 1962.

47. OVUM CHARACTERIZATION: INVERTEBRATES

The conditions listed are typical for the specified genera and are also typical for the class unless followed by an asterisk (*). Egg Type (column C): Hl = homolecithal, Tl = telolecithal, Cl = centrolecithal. Membrane (column D): Vm = vitelline membrane, Zr = zona radiata, Ch = chorion, Tm = tertiary membrane. Cleavage (column E): HO = holoblastic, Hr = radial holoblastic, Hd = disymmetrical or biradial holoblastic, Hb = bilateral holoblastic, Hs = spiral holoblastic, ME = meroblastic, Ms = superficial meroblastic, Md = discoidal meroblastic, IR = irregular. Blastulation (column F): Eq = equal coeloblastula, Un = unequal coeloblastula, St = stereoblastula, Mo = morula, So = stomoblastula, Su = superficial blastula, Di = discoblastula. Gastrulation (column G): EM = emboly, EP = epiboly, PI = polar ingression, Pu = unipolar ingression, Pc = many-celled polar ingression, Pm = multipolar ingression, DE = delamination, Ds = simple delamination, Dc = coeloblastic delamination, Dm = morula delamination, Dy = syncytial delamination. Mesoderm (column H): EC = ectomesoderm; endomesoderm abbreviations are Tb = teloblastic bands, Sb = secondary bands, En = enterocoele, Si = solid ingrowth, Me = mesenchyme. Coelom (column I): AC = acoelomate, PS = pseudocoelomate, CO = coelomate, Cs = schizocoele coelomate, Ce = enterocoele coelomate. Classification adapted from Lord Rothschild, *A Classification of Living Animals*, 1961.

	Phylum and Class[1]	Genus	Egg Type	Membrane	Cleavage	Blastulation	Gastrulation	Mesoderm	Coelom
	(A)	(B)	(C)	(D)	(E)	(F)	(G)	(H)	(I)
	Chordata								
1	Cephalochordata[2]	*Branchiostoma*	Tl	....	ME, Md	....	EM, EP	Si	......
2	Ascidiacea	*Cynthia, Ciona, Phallusia*	Tl	Ch	HO, Hb	Un	EP	Si	......
3	Enteropneusta	*Saccoglossus*	.....	Vm, Ch	HO, Hb, IR*	....	EP	En	......
	Echinodermata								
4	Ophiuroidea	*Amphiura*	Hl	Vm	Hr	Eq	EM	En	CO, Ce
5	Asteroidea	*Asterias*	Hl	Vm	Hr	Eq	EM	En	CO, Ce
6	Echinoidea	*Echinus*	Hl	Vm	Hr	Eq	EM	En	CO, Ce
7	Holothuroidea	*Synapta*	Hl	Vm	Hr, Ms*	Eq	EM	En	CO, Ce
8	Crinoidea	*Antedon*	Tl	Vm	Hr	Un	EM	Me, En	CO, Ce
9	Chaetognatha	*Sagitta*	Tl	....	Hr	Un	EP	En	CO, Ce
	Arthropoda								
10	Tardigrada	*Macrobiotus*	.....	....	....	Eq	EM	En	CO, Ce
11	Pycnogonida	*Pycnogonium*	.....	....	ME	....	....	....	CO, Cs
12	Acari[3]	*Trombidium*	Cl	....	ME, Ms	Su	....	....	CO, Cs
13	Araneae[3]	*Agelena, Argiope*	.....	....	ME, Ms	Su	....	Sb	CO, Cs
14	Scorpiones[3]	*Euscorpius*	Tl	....	ME, Md	Di	EM, Ds	Sb	CO, Cs
15	Decapoda[3]	*Gallinectes, Astacus*	Cl	Vm, Tm	ME, Ms	Su	Ds	Si	CO, Cs
16	Amphipoda[3]	*Gammarus*	Cl	Vm, Tm	ME, Ms	Su	Ds	....	CO, Cs
17	Mysidacea[3]	*Mysis*	Cl	Vm, Tm	ME, Ms	Su	Pm, Ds	Sb	CO, Cs
18	Cirripedia[4]	*Balanus, Lepas*	Cl	Vm, Tm	ME, Ms	Su	Pu	Sb	CO, Cs
19	Copepoda[4]	*Cyclops*	Cl	Vm, Tm	ME, Ms	Su	Pu	Sb	CO, Cs
20	Ostracoda[4]	*Cypris*	Cl	Vm, Tm	ME, Ms	Su	Pm	Sb	CO, Cs
21	Cladocera[3]	*Daphnia*	Cl	Vm, Tm	Ms	Su	Pc	Sb	CO, Cs
22	Anostraca[3]	*Branchipus, Artemia*	Cl	Vm, Tm	ME, Ms	Su	Pm	Sb	CO, Cs
23	Insecta	*Musca, Dytiscus*	Cl	Vm, Zr, Ch, Tm[5]	ME, Ms	Su	....	....	CO, Cs
24	Hymenoptera[3]	*Platygaster*	.....	Vm, Zr	HO, IR	....	....	....	CO, Cs
25	Epimorpha[4]	*Scolopendra*	Cl	Ch	ME, Ms	Su	Ds	Si	CO, Cs
26	Onychophora	*Peripatus*	Tl	....	ME, Ms	St, Su	EM, EP	Sb	CO, Cs
	Annelida								
27	Archiannelida	*Polygordius*	Tl	Vm	HO, Hs	Un, Pl	EP	EC, Tb	CO, Cs
28	Hirudinea	*Clepsine, Nephelis*	Tl	Vm	HO, Hs	Un	EP	EC, Tb	CO, Cs
29	Oligochaeta	*Criodrilus*	Tl	Vm	HO, Hs	Un, Mo	EM*, EP	EC, Tb	CO, Cs
30	Polychaeta	*Nereis, Eupomotus*	Tl	Vm, Zr[6]	HO, Hs	Un, St	EM*, EP	EC, Tb	CO, Cs
31	Echiuroidea	*Echiurus, Urechis*	Tl	....	HO, Hs	Un	EP	Tb	CO, Cs
32	Sipunculoidea	*Phascolosoma*	.....	Vm, Zr	HO, Hs	Un, St*	PI, Pu	EC, Tb	CO, Cs
	Mollusca								
33	Cephalopoda	*Loligo, Sepia*	Tl	Vm, Ch, Tm[7]	ME, Md	Di	EM	Sb	CO, Cs
34	Bivalvia	*Unio, Dreissensia*	Tl	Vm	HO, Hs	Un	EM, Pu, Pc	EC, Tb	CO, Cs
35	Scaphopoda	*Dentalium*	Tl	Ch	HO, Hs	Un	PI, EP, Pu	EC, Tb	CO, Cs
36	Gastropoda	*Patella, Crepidula*	Tl	Tm, Ch	HO, Hs	Un, St	EP, Pu, Pc	EC, Tb	CO, Cs
37	Polyplacophora	*Chiton, Ischnochiton*	Tl	Vm, Zr, Ch	HO, Hs	Un, St	EM, Pu	EC, Tb	CO, Cs
	Brachiopoda								
38	Articulata	*Terebratulina*	.....	....	HO, Hs*, IR	Eq	EM	En	CO, Ce
39	Phoronida	*Phoronis*	.....	....	....	Eq	EM, Pu	EC, Me	CO, Ce
	Polyzoa								
40	Gymnolaemata	*Bugula*	Hl	Zr*	HO, Hr	Un, Pl	PI, Pu	Me	CO
41	Entoprocta	*Loxosoma, Pedicellina*	Hl	....	HO, Hs	Un	EM	EC, Tb*	PS

/1/ Unless otherwise indicated. /2/ Subphylum. /3/ Order. /4/ Subclass. /5/ Chorion present in parasitic forms. /6/ Identified by some observers as zona radiata, by others as cortical cytoplasm. /7/ Fertilization membrane is formed as sperm enters egg.

continued

47. OVUM CHARACTERIZATION: INVERTEBRATES

	Phylum and Class[1]	Genus	Egg Type	Membrane	Cleavage	Blastu-lation	Gastru-lation	Meso-derm	Coelom
	(A)	(B)	(C)	(D)	(E)	(F)	(G)	(H)	(I)
42	Acanthocephala	*Macracanthorhynchus*	Tl	Vm	HO, Hs	St	Pu	....	PS
	Aschelminthes								
43	Phasmidia[4]	*Ascaris, Parascaris*	Hl	Vm, Tm	HO, Hb	Eq, Pl	EP	EC, Sb	PS
44	Nematomorpha	*Gordius, Paragordius*	Hl	....	HO, Hb	....	EM, Dc*	EC, Me*	PS
45	Priapulida	*Priapulus*	Hl	....	HO, IR	....	....	....	PS
46	Gastrotricha	*Neogossea*	Tl	....	HO, IR, Hs*	Un	Pu	....	PS
47	Rotifera	*Asplanchna*	Tl	Tm	HO, Hs*	....	Pu*	EC*	PS
	Nemertina								
48	Enopla	*Tetrastemma, Prostoma*	.....	....	....	Un*	Pc*	....	AC
49	Anopla	*Cerebratulus*	Tl	Vm, Zr	HO, Hs	Un	EM, Pu	EC, Tb	AC
	Platyhelminthes								
50	Cestoda	*Taenia*	Hl	Vm	IR	....	EP	....	AC
51	Trematoda	*Polystoma*	Hl	Vm	HO, Md, IR	Un, St	....	EC	AC
52	Turbellaria	*Planocera, Yungia*	Tl	Vm, Tm	Hs	Un, Mo	EP	....	AC
	Ctenophora								
53	Nuda	*Beroe*	Hl	....	Hd	Un	EP	EC	......
	Cnidaria								
54	Anthozoa	*Urticina, Actinia*	Hl, Cl*	Ch, Tm	HO	Eq, Mo	EM, Pm, Dc	....	......
55	Scyphozoa	*Aurelia*	Hl	Vm, Tm	HO	St, Mo	EM, Dm	....	......
56	Hydrozoa	*Tubularia*	Hl, Cl*	Tm	HO, Hs*	St, Mo, Su*	All except EP	....	......
	Porifera								
57	Calcarea	*Scypha*	Hl	....	HO	Eq, Un, Pl, So	EM, Dy	....	......

/1/ Unless otherwise indicated. /4/ Subclass.

Contributors: (a) Richards, A., (b) Afzelius, Björn A.

Reference: Richards, A. 1931. Outlines of comparative embryology. J. Wiley and Sons, New York.

48. PROPAGATION: AQUATIC INVERTEBRATES

Breeding habits of invertebrates may vary with changes in location, temperature, light, and, for marine forms, with changes in salinity. Type of Sexuality (column F): D = dioecious (separate sexes), M = monoecious (bisexual or hermaphroditic). Dimorphism (column G): + = sexual dimorphism, - = no sexual dimorphism. Values in parentheses are ranges, estimate "c" (cf. Introduction).

	Class and Species	Distribution[1]	Sexual Maturity: Age at Onset	Sexual Maturity: Size[2] mm	Breeding Season	Sexuality: Type	Sexuality: Dimorphism	Eggs or Young per Brood	Reference
	(A)	(B)	(C)	(D)	(E)	(F)	(G)	(H)	(I)
	Echinodermata[3]								
	Asteroidea								
1	*Asterias forbesi*	Mexico to Maine (Long Island Sound)	(1-2) yr	(60-210)[4]	July-Oct	D[5]	-	Several thousand	1,10,16, 26
	Arthropoda								
	Merostomata[3]								
2	*Limulus polyphemus*	Yucatan to Nova Scotia (Delaware Bay)	(9-11) yr	♂(178-258), ♀(243-351)[6]	May-June	D	+	3000	41

/1/ When data are for a specific area, that area is given in parentheses. /2/ Greatest dimension. /3/ All species listed are oviparous. /4/ Dependent on food supply. /5/ Protandrous hermaphrodite: male organs appear first, later replaced by female organs. /6/ Prosomal width.

continued

48. PROPAGATION: AQUATIC INVERTEBRATES

	Class and Species	Distribution[1]	Sexual Maturity: Age at Onset	Sexual Maturity: Size[2] mm	Breeding Season	Sexuality: Type	Sexuality: Dimorphism	Eggs or Young per Brood	Reference
	(A)	(B)	(C)	(D)	(E)	(F)	(G)	(H)	(I)
	Arthropoda								
	Crustacea[7]								
3	*Callinectes sapidus*	Uruguay to Nova Scotia (Chesapeake Bay)	♂♀ 13 mo	♂(135-215), ♀(134-185)	July-Aug	D	+	1,750,000	9,32
4	*Homarus americanus*	Newfoundland to N. Carolina	(4-5) yr	♂(170-600), ♀(180-480)	July-Sept	D	+	8500[8]	21,45
5	*Orconectes immunis*	Mississippi River & Great Lakes drainage (New York State)	♂♀15 mo	♂(40-60), ♀(44-90)	June-Oct	D	+	102(84-195)	34,36,43
6	*Cyclops viridis*	U. S. and Europe (Germany)	♂(41-132), ♀(36-128) da	♀(1.5-5.0)[9]	All year	D	+	75(20-160)[10]	5,47,50
7	*Daphnia longispina*	Asia, Europe, N. America (Florida)	♀(75-86) hr	♂1.2,♀1.9	All year except winter	D[11]	+	28(4-35)	2,3,5,22
	Mollusca[3]								
	Bivalvia								
8	*Crassostrea virginica*	Texas to Canada (Delaware Bay)	1 yr	(25-50)	June-Aug	M[5]	-	(500,000-1,000,000)	23;25,41
9	*Mya arenaria*	Arctic to N. Carolina; Pacific	(1-2) yr	....	May-Aug	D	-	....	25
10	*Siliqua patula*	Siberia to California	(2.0-4.2) yr	(10-14)	Spring-summer	D	-	....	29,49
11	*Tivela stultorum*	Eastern Pacific	5 yr	(10-12)	....	M[5]	-	750,000	48
12	*Mercenaria mercenaria*	Nova Scotia to Yucatan (Baja California)	(1-2) yr	(50-70)	July-Aug	M[5]	-	ca. 1,000,000	8,24
13	*Aequipecten irradians*	Maine to Mexico	12 mo	78	....	M	-	....	18
14	*Mytilus edulis*	World-wide	(1-2) yr	....	May-Sept	D	......	....	25
15	*Plactopecten magellanicus*	Newfoundland to Cape Hatteras	(3-4) yr	(50-70)	June-Oct	D	-	....	30
	Gastropoda								
16	*Helix pomatia*	Europe and U. S.	(33-39) mo	....	May-July	M[12]	-	(40-200)	4,31,35,37,39
17	*Lymnaea stagnalis*	World-wide (Wisconsin)	(4-14) mo	(50-60)	July-Oct	M[12]	-	6000	33,39
18	*Rostanga pulchra*	Monterey Bay to San Diego	....	....	Dec-Feb	M[12]	-	(9-156)	12,27
19	*Busycon canaliculatum*	Cape Cod to Mexico	....	....	....	D	+	(360-6240)	28,37,39
20	*Urosalpinx cinerea*	Mexico to Maine (Delaware Bay)	(4-12) mo	(15-24)	May-Oct	D	-	(300-960)	6,7,11,15,17,39
21	*Littorina littorea*	N. Atlantic to Florida	....	....	....	D	+	(1-3)	46
22	*Polynices duplicatus*	Massachusetts Bay to Mexico	2 yr	>12	June-Aug	D	+	....	37,39,40
23	*Haliotis tuberculata*	Channel Islands to Europe	3 yr	5	July-Sept	D	-	10,000	13,14,39,42
24	*Trochus niloticus*	Indo-Pacific	2 yr	(6-7)	....	D	+	....	38
	Polyplacophora								
25	*Ischnochiton magdalenensis*	California to Mexico	2 yr	(35-36)	....	D	...	57,970	19,20,37,39,44

/1/ When data are for a specific area, that area is given in parentheses. /2/ Greatest dimension. /3/ All species listed are oviparous. /5/ Protandrous hermaphrodite: male organs appear first, later replaced by female organs. /7/ All species listed are ovigerous. /8/ Under present fisheries conditions, average is difficult to obtain because females are not permitted to attain maximum egg-laying age. /9/ Male smaller. /10/ In early summer. /11/ Parthenogenetic reproduction during most of season. /12/ Cross-fertilization.

continued

48. PROPAGATION: AQUATIC INVERTEBRATES

Contributors: (a) Carriker, Melbourne R., (b) Abbott, R. Tucker, (c) Lochhead, John H., (d) Aldrich, Frederick A., (e) Shuster, Carl N., Jr., (f) Medcof, J. C., (g) Loosanoff, Victor L., (h) Sellmer, George P.

References: [1] Aldrich, F. A., and M. L. Aldrich. 1955. Notulae Naturae 276:1. [2] Banta, A. M. 1939. Carnegie Inst. Wash. Publ. 513:60. [3] Banta, A. M., and L. A. Brown. 1939. Ibid. 513:106. [4] Boycott, A. E. J. Ecol. 22(1):1. [5] Brown, F. A., Jr., ed. 1950. Selected invertebrate types. J. Wiley and Sons, New York. [6] Carriker, M. R. 1955. U. S. Fish Wildlife Service Spec. Sci. Rept. Fisheries 148. [7] Carriker, M. R. 1957. J. Elisha Mitchell Sci. Soc. 73(2):328. [8] Carriker, M. R. 1961. Ibid. 77(2):168. [9] Churchill, E. P. 1919. U. S. Bur. Fisheries Bull. 36:93. [10] Coe, W. R. 1912. Connecticut State Geol. Nat. Hist. Survey Bull. 19:1. [11] Cole, H. A. 1942. J. Marine Biol. Assoc. United Kingdom 25:477. [12] Costello, D. P. 1938. J. Morphol. 63(2):319. [13] Crofts, D. R. 1929. Liverpool Marine Biol. Commem. Mem. 29. [14] Crofts, D. R. 1937. Trans. Roy. Soc. (London), B, 228(552):219. [15] Federighi, H. 1931. U. S. Bur. Fisheries Bull. 47:83. [16] Galtsoff, P. S., and V. L. Loosanoff. 1939. Ibid. 49:75. [17] Galtsoff, P. S., H. F. Prytherch, and J. B. Engle. 1937. U. S. Bur. Fisheries Circ. 25. [18] Gutsell, J. S. 1931. U. S. Bur. Fisheries Bull. 46:569. [19] Heath, H. 1899. Zool. Jahrb. Anat. Ontog. Tiere 12:567. [20] Heath, H. 1906. Zool. Anz. 29:390. [21] Herrick, F. H. 1911. U. S. Bur. Fisheries Bull. 29:149. [22] Ingle, L., T. R. Wood, and A. M. Banta. 1937. J. Exptl. Zool. 76:325. [23] Korringa, P. 1952. Quart. Rev. Biol. 27:266. [24] Loosanoff, V. L. 1937. Biol. Bull. 72(3):389. [25] Loosanoff, V. L. Unpublished. U. S. Dept. of Interior, Milford, Conn., 1952. [26] Loosanoff, V. L., J. B. Engle, and C. A. Nomejko. 1955. Biol. Bull. 109(1):75. [27] MacFarland, F. M. 1906. U. S. Bur. Fisheries Bull. 25:109. [28] Magalhaes, H. 1948. N. Carolina Ecol. Monographs 18(3):377. [29] McMillin, H. C. 1924. 34th Ann. Rept. Dept. Fisheries Wash. State, p. 1. [30] Medcof, J. C. Unpublished. Fisheries Research Bd. of Canada, Ottawa, 1956. [31] Meisenheimer, J. 1907. Zool. Jahrb. Abt. system. Okol. Geog. Tiere 25:461. [32] Newcombe, C. L., F. Campbell, and A. M. Eckstine. 1949. Growth 13:71. [33] Noland, L. E., and M. R. Carriker. 1946. Am. Midland Naturalist 36(2):467. [34] Pearse, A. S. 1909. Am. Naturalist 43:746. [35] Pelseneer, P. 1935. Essai d'ethologie zoologique d'apres l'étude des mollusques. Bruxelles. [36] Pennak, R. W. 1953. Fresh-water invertebrates of the United States. Ronald Press, New York. [37] Pratt, H. S. 1948. A manual of the common invertebrate animals. Blakiston, Philadelphia. [38] Rao, H. S. 1939. Report on the shell-fisheries in the Andaman and Nicobar Islands during the years 1930-1935. Zool. Survey of India, Calcutta. [39] Rogers, J. E. 1951. The shell book. C. T. Branford, Boston. [40] Sawyer, D. B. 1951. M.S. Thesis. Univ. of Rhode Island, Providence. [41] Shuster, C. N., Jr. Unpublished. Univ. Delaware, Newark, 1955. [42] Stephenson, T. A. 1924. J. Marine Biol. Assoc. United Kingdom 13:480. [43] Tack, P. I. 1941. Am. Midland Naturalist 25:420. [44] Taki, I. 1940. Proc. Pacific Sci. Congr. Pacific Sci. Assoc. 3:487. [45] Templeman, W. 1940. Newfoundland Dept. Nat. Resources Service Bull. (Fisheries) 15. [46] Thorson, G. 1946. Medd. Komm. Danmarks Fisk.-Havun. Plankton 4(1). [47] Walter, E. 1922. Zool. Jahrb. Abt. system. Okol. Geog. Tiere 44:375. [48] Weymouth, F. W. 1923. Calif. Fish and Game Comm. Fish Bull. 7:5. [49] Weymouth, F. W., H. C. McMillin, and H. B. Holmes. 1925. U. S. Bur. Fisheries Bull. 41:201. [50] Yeatman, H. C. 1944. Am. Midland Naturalist 32:1.

49. PROPAGATION AND METAMORPHOSIS: INSECTS

Duration of stages varies with the season, geographic area, and climate. Where insects breed all year regardless of season, the cycle is continuous. Type of Metamorphosis (column B): C = complete (having internal development of wings until pupal stage), I = incomplete (having external development of wings). Overwintering Stage (column H): E = egg, L = larva, N = nymph, Pp = prepupa, P = pupa, A = adult, Cont = continuous. Insect Stage on, or in, host (column J): E = egg, L = larva, N = nymph, P = pupa, A = adult. Classification adapted from Borror and DeLong, *An Introduction to the Study of Insects*, 1954.

	Family and Species	Type of Metamorphosis	Eggs per Female	Duration of Stage, da: Egg	Larva or Nymph	Pupa	Adult	Overwintering Stage	Generations per Season	Host[1] (Insect Stage)	Reference
	(A)	(B)	(C)	(D)	(E)	(F)	(G)	(H)	(I)	(J)	(K)
	Hymenoptera										
	Apidae										
1	*Apis mellifera*	C	....	3[2]	8[2]	9[2]	35-40[2]	A	See Fn.[3]	Nectar (A)	55,116
2	*Xylocopa virginica*	C	....	6-8	23-30	58-65	30-45	A	2	Nectar (A)	91
	Braconidae										
3	*Apanteles militaris*	C	Hundreds	5-6	10-12	8-10	15-20	L in host body	Several	Armyworms (L)	122
4	*Macrocentrus ancylivorus*	C	700-800	3-13	11-15	8-10	5-8	L in host body	3	Oriental fruit moths (L)	2
	Cephidae										
5	*Cephus cinctus*	C	50	7-10	300	7-10	7	L	1	Wheat, grass (L)	6,34
	Chalcididae										
6	*Aphelinus mali*	C	ca. 150	3	10-12	6-7	40	L in host body	>6	Woolly apple aphides (L)	80
	Diprionidae										
7	*Diprion similis*	C	....	8-13	29-32	10-341	3-11	Pp	1-2	Conifers (L)	92
	Ichneumonidae										
8	*Bathyplectes curculionis*	C	....	Several	8-10	14	ca. 30	L in cocoon	2	Alfalfa weevils (L)	90
	Sphecidae										
9	*Sphecius speciosus*	C	16	1-2	4-10	270-300	60-70	Pp	1	Cicadas (A)	32
	Tiphiidae										
10	*Tiphia vernalis*	C	50-75	8-9	120-180	180-240	30-42	P	1	Japanese beetles (L)	49
	Vespidae										
11	*Vespula maculata*	C	25,000-35,000[4]	5-7	8-18	12	1 yr (queen)[5]	A (queen)	1	Soft-bodied insects (A)	91
	Siphonaptera										
	Pulicidae										
12	Many species	C	50-400	2-13	7-30	7-35	8-150	Cont	3-5	Animals (A)	61
13	*Ctenocephalides felis*	C	200-400	2-4	8-24	5-7	50-200	P	ca. 10	Mammals (A)	125
	Diptera										
	Anthomyiidae										
14	*Hylemyia cilicrura*	C	100	1-8	10-16	10-20	30-35	Cont	2-5	Vegetables (E, L)	42,60
	Calliphoridae										
15	*Callitroga hominivorax*	C	100-300	1-2	4-5	5-40	5-30	None	2-12	Animals (L)	40
	Culicidae										
16	Many species	C	100-1036	2-1800	5-15	2-5	5-300	E, L, A	1-17	Animals (A)	9
17	*Aedes aegypti*	C	....	2-365	6	2-3	15-60	Cont	.....	Man, monkeys, rodents (A)	110
	Drosophilidae										
18	*Drosophila melanogaster*	C	100	<1	3-11	2-8	14	L, A	5-6	Fruits, vegetables (L, A)	102

/1/ Host, or material affording subsistence or lodgment. /2/ Worker bees only. /3/ Not applicable to individual bee since colony is functioning unit; queen reproduces and can survive for several years, workers do not reproduce. /4/ Per queen. /5/ Worker, 21-35 days; male, 30 days.

continued

49. PROPAGATION AND METAMORPHOSIS: INSECTS

	Family and Species	Type of Metamorphosis	Eggs per Female	Duration of Stage, da				Overwintering Stage	Generations per Season	Host[1] (Insect Stage)	Reference
				Egg	Larva or Nymph	Pupa	Adult				
	(A)	(B)	(C)	(D)	(E)	(F)	(G)	(H)	(I)	(J)	(K)
	Diptera										
	Hippoboscidae										
19	*Melophagus ovinus*	C	....	7-14	0.5	19-35	80-120	....	3-5	Sheep, goats (E, L, P, A)	3,89, 119
	Hypodermatidae										
20	*Hypoderma* sp.	C	100-500	3-10	250-280	18-70	1-25	L	1	Cattle (E, L, A)	12
	Muscidae										
21	*Musca domestica*	C	75-200	1-3	4-10	4-18	10-50	Cont	4-18	Garbage, manure (L)	11,17, 44,63, 66,76, 85,86, 132
22	*Siphona irritans*	C	50-400	1-4	4-8	4-8	5-20	P	4-10	Cattle (A)	16,88
23	*Stomoxys calcitrans*	C	20-100	2-5	11-30	5-20	5-30	P	4-10	Animals (A)	61,123
	Tabanidae										
24	*Tabanus atratus*	C	100-400	2-5	100-600	5-20	5-20	L	1-2	Animals (A)	109
	Tachinidae										
25	*Compsilura concinnata*	C	90-120	Ovoviviparous	13	10-14	18-20	L in host body	3-4	Gypsy moths (E, L)	31
26	*Lydella stabulans grisescens*	C	....	Ovoviviparous	8-9	7-9	21	L in host body	2	European corn borers (E, L)	8
	Trypetidae										
27	*Rhagoletis pomonella*	C	....	3-10	13-48	....	....	P	>1	Fruits (L)	100
	Lepidoptera										
	Aegeriidae										
28	*Melittia cucurbitae*	C	150-200	7-14	30	All winter	....	L, P	1-2	Cucurbits (L)	22
29	*Sanninoidea exitiosa*	C	200-1200	7-48	270-380	16-25	4-24	L	1	Fruit trees (L)	51,115
	Bombycidae										
30	*Bombyx mori*	C	300-400	9-12	21-25	14-21	2-3	....	1-2	Mulberry leaves (L)	4,79, 89
	Danaidae										
31	*Danaus plexippus*	C	....	3-5	....	5-15	<180	A[6]	2-4	Milkweed (L)	126
	Gelechiidae										
32	*Pectinophora gossypiella*	C	200	4-10	14-21	12-18	14	L	3-6	Cotton (L)	46
33	*Sitotroga cerealella*	C	40-400	4-12	25-45	7-8	10-28	L	3	Grains (L)	78
	Lasiocampidae										
34	*Malacosoma americanum*	C	200-400	255-285	28-42	10-24	....	E	1	Fruit trees (L)	103
35	*M. disstria*	C	100-300	260-280	35-50	10-20	7-14	E	1	Broadleaf trees (L)	28
	Liparidae										
36	*Porthetria dispar*	C	400	270	65	15	15	E	1	Broadleaf trees (L)	28
	Olethreutidae										
37	*Carpocapsa pomonella*	C	6-300	4-14	15-72	7-40	3-20	L	>1 to >3	Fruits (L)	95,101, 127
38	*Grapholitha molesta*	C	100-200	3-28	6-26	5-35	2-34	L	4-7	Fruits (L)	97
39	*Polychrosis viteana*	C	9-23	3-14	19-63	8-24	4-23	P	2-3	Grapes (L)	73
40	*Rhyacionia buoliana*	C	100	10	322	18	15	L	1	Pines (L)	48
	Phalaenidae										
41	*Alabama argillacea*	C	400-600	3-20	7-21	7-21	10-24	None in U. S.	3-8	Cotton (L)	106
42	*Heliothis armigera*	C	1000	2-8	13-28	14	12	P	1-7	Corn, tomatoes, cotton (L)	6,38, 72,89, 98,99, 104

/1/ Host, or material affording subsistence or lodgment. /6/ Migratory.

continued

49. PROPAGATION AND METAMORPHOSIS: INSECTS

	Family and Species	Type of Meta-morphosis	Eggs per Female	Duration of Stage, da: Egg	Larva or Nymph	Pupa	Adult	Over-wintering Stage	Generations per Season	Host[1] (Insect Stage)	Reference
	(A)	(B)	(C)	(D)	(E)	(F)	(G)	(H)	(I)	(J)	(K)
	Lepidoptera										
	Pieridae										
43	*Pieris rapae*	C	200-500	7	14	7-14	....	P	3-6	Cole crops (L)	134
	Pyralidae										
44	*Diaphania nitidalis*	C	....	3	6-28	5-31	....	P	4-5	Cucurbits (L)	113
45	*Diatraea saccharalis*	C	200	4-9	20-30	6-7	7-14	L	4-5	Sugarcane (L)	6,71
46	*Ephestia kuhniella*	C	116-700	>3	40	5-7	3-4	....	>6	Milk products (L)	78
47	*Plodia interpunctella*	C	200-400	1-2	13-288	>8	18	L	5	Grains (L)	78
48	*Pyrausta nubilalis*	C	400	4-9	30-40	10-14	10-24	L	1-3	Corn, other plants (L)	6,7
	Sphingidae										
49	*Protoparce sexta*	C	200-300	7	21-28	14-28	....	P	1-3	Vegetables (L)	82,94
	Tineidae										
50	*Tinea pellionella*	C	>40	>6	30-100	10-90	7-28	....	1-2	Fabrics, furs (L)	78
51	*Tineola bisselliella*	C	40-160	>7	>28	8-40	7-14	L	1-4	Dry animal fabrics (L)	54,78
	Tortricidae										
52	*Argyrotaenia velutinana*	C	23-122	7-28	15-119	2-18	7-12	P	2-4	Fruits (L)	65
53	*Choristoneura fumiferana*	C	....	10-14	45	10	14	L	1	Firs, spruces (L)	28
	Coleoptera										
	Anobiidae										
54	*Lasioderma serricorne*	C	30	>6	>30	14-21	21	L	5-6	Dry food (L,A)	78
55	*Stegobium paniceum*	C	....	......	20-150	12-18	....	L	3-6	Dry food (L,A)	78
	Bostrichidae										
56	*Rhizopertha dominica*	C	300-500	......	....	....	....	....	8-12	Wood, books (L, A)	78
	Chrysomelidae										
57	*Acalymma vittata*	C	....	......	14-40	7	....	A[7]	1-4	Cucurbits (L, A)	24
58	*Epitrix tuberis*	C	500-900	5-8	14-21	10-14	....	A	2-3	Potatoes (L, A)	135
59	*Leptinotarsa decemlineata*	C	>500	4-9	10-21	5-10	....	A	1-3	Vegetables (L, A)	21,41
	Cleridae										
60	*Necrobia rufipes*	C	400-1000	>3	>17	>13	420	L	6-10	Meat, fish (L, A)	78
	Coccinellidae										
61	*Epilachna varivestis*	C	250-1200	5-14	20-35	10	....	A	3-4	Beans, cowpeas (L, A)	67,68
62	*Hippodamia convergens*	C	1000	5	16	6-7	30-275	A	1	Aphides (L, A)	33
	Curculionidae										
63	*Anthonomus grandis*	C	80-200	3-5	7-12	3-5	30-300	A	4-10	Cotton (L, A)	45,69, 70
64	*Caulophilus latenasus*	C	200-300	......	....	....	150	....	8-12	Grains (L, A)	78
65	*Conotrachelus nenuphar*	C	1-516	2-12	17-48	8-30	±365	A	>1	Fruits (L, A)	114
66	*Hypera postica*	C	200-800	13-17	17-21	7-14	14-21	E, A	1-2	Alfalfa (L)	6
67	*Pissodes strobi*	C	80-100	6-20	30-40	14	240-260	A	1	Pines, spruces (L)	81
68	*Sitophilus granarius*	C	50-250	4-8	19-34	5-16	210-250	Cont	8-12	Grains (L, A)	78
69	*S. oryza*	C	300-400	>3	>18	3-9	120-150	A	>8	Grains (L, A)	78

/1/ Host, or material affording subsistence or lodgment. /7/ Unmated.

continued

49. PROPAGATION AND METAMORPHOSIS: INSECTS

	Family and Species	Type of Meta-morphosis	Eggs per Female	Duration of Stage, da				Over-wintering Stage	Generations per Season	Host[1] (Insect Stage)	Reference
				Egg	Larva or Nymph	Pupa	Adult				
	(A)	(B)	(C)	(D)	(E)	(F)	(G)	(H)	(I)	(J)	(K)
	Coleoptera										
	Cyladidae										
70	*Cylas formicarius elegantulus*	C	1-319	4-56	12-154	5-49	3-416	Cont	6-8	Sweet potatoes (L, A)	25
	Dermestidae										
71	*Anthrenus flavipes*	C	37-96	>21	112-378	14-19	6-71	A	......	Fabrics (L)	78
72	*A. scrophulariae*	C	32	10-18	66	14	....	Cont	1-3	Fabrics (L)	78
73	*A. verbasci*	C	....	17-18	222-323	10-13	14-44	L	......	Fabrics (L)	78
74	*Attagenus piceus*	C	42-114	6-11	238-638	6-24	32-72	L	<1	Fabrics (L)	5,78
	Elateridae										
75	*Limonius canus*	C	50-300	20-30	120-1800	21	180-300	L, A	Overlap	Vegetables, field crops (L)	75
	Mylabridae										
76	*Acanthoscelides obtectus*	C	200	5-20	11-40	5-18	14-63	A	2-5	Beans (L)	78
77	*Bruchus pisorum*	C	300	5-18	28-42	14	<2 yr	A	1	Peas (L)	77
78	*Callosobruchus maculatus*	C	82-196	4-6	9-240	5-18	15	L, A	8-10	Dried peas (L)	78
	Nitidulidae										
79	*Carpophilus hemipterus*	C	>80	>3	28-120	>14	15	....	>8	Dry fruits (L)	78
	Ostomatidae										
80	*Tenebroides mauritanicus*	C	436-1000	7-10	39-414	8-25	365	L, A	3	Grains, cereals (L, A)	27,78
	Scarabaeidae										
81	*Cotinis nitida*	C	60-75	15-18	300	16-18	90-120	L	1	Decomposing vegetable matter (L); fruit juices, sap (A)	36
82	*Dynastes tityus*	C	....	>16	....	>51	240-300	A	1	Rotten wood (L); ash trees (A)	19
83	*Macrodactylus subspinosus*	C	24-36	12-21	244-290	10-30	21-28	L	1	Grapes, roses (A)	107
84	*Phyllophaga fusca*	C	....	21	>730	30	21-28	L, A	See Fn.[8]	Crops, trees (L, A)	6
85	*Popillia japonica*	C	40-60	14	275-300	8-20	30-45	L	1	Plants (A)	15,56, 89,108
	Scolytidae										
86	*Dendroctonus brevicomis*	C	65	7	20-155	8	30-214	E, L, A	1-4	Pines (L, A)	93
87	*D. engelmanni*	C	90	14	1 yr	2 wk	>1 yr	L, A	<1	Spruces, pines (L)	84
88	*D. frontalis*	C	20-50	3-9	25-38	8-10	15-30	Cont	3-6	Pines (L, A)	64
89	*D. monticolae*	C	70-100	9-12	33-260	9-12	40-245	E, L, A	2	Pines (L, A)	43
90	*D. ponderosae*	C	....	10-14	Aug-June	10-20	90	L	1	Pines (L, A)	13
91	*Scolytus multistriatus*	C	20-200	4-7	25-35	4-7	5-12	L	2	Elms (A)	26
	Silvanidae										
92	*Oryzaephilus surinamensis*	C	45-285	>8	>30	>6	180-1100	Cont	6-7	Grains, fruits (L, A)	78
	Tenebrionidae										
93	*Tenebrio molitor*	C	276	12-16	>600	18-20	60-90	L	<1	Grains (L)	78
94	*Tribolium confusum*	C	300-400	4-14	>22	5-18	1000	A	5-6	Grains, flours (L, A)	53,78, 89, 111

/1/ Host, or material affording subsistence or lodgment. /8/ 3 years per generation.

continued

49. PROPAGATION AND METAMORPHOSIS: INSECTS

	Family and Species	Type of Meta-morphosis	Eggs per Female	Duration of Stage, da				Over-wintering Stage	Generations per Season	Host[1] (Insect Stage)	Reference
				Egg	Larva or Nymph	Pupa	Adult				
	(A)	(B)	(C)	(D)	(E)	(F)	(G)	(H)	(I)	(J)	(K)
	Neuroptera										
	Corydalidae										
95	*Corydalus cornutus*	C	2000-3000	ca. 14	1065	7-19	4-13	L	See Fn.[8]	Small aquatic animals (L)	37
	Homoptera										
	Aphididae										
96	*Aphis gossypii*	I[9]	....	90-120	3-7	....	7-28	E, A	20	Cotton, melons (N, A)	106
97	*Macrosiphum pisi*	I[9]	50-100	90-120	10	....	....	E or Cont	7-20	Legumes (N, A)	35
98	*Myzus persicae*	I[9]	....	......	7-26	....	14-61	E	Up to 13	Fruits, vegetables (N, A)	89,120, 121, 129
99	*Toxoptera graminum*	I[9]	3-7	90-120	6-30	....	26-60	E, N, A[10]	5-20	Small grains (N, A)	6
	Cercopidae										
100	*Philaenus leucophthalmus*	I	2-20	All winter	42-48	....	Several mo	E	1	Hay crops (N)	6
	Cicadellidae										
101	*Aceratagallia sanguinolenta*	I	....	11	19-42	....	42-49	A	1-2	Clover, potatoes (N, A)	128
102	*Circulifer tenellus*	I	300-400	5-40	25-52	....	120-150	A	3-5	Beets, beans, etc. (N, A)	20,39
103	*Empoasca fabae*	I	60-90	10	14	....	30	Cont	2-4	Potatoes, beans (N, A)	57
	Cicadidae										
104	*Magicicada septendecim*	I	400-600	42-49	13 or 17 yr	....	30-40	N	See Fn.[11]	Deciduous trees and shrubs (A)	59,89, 124
	Hemiptera										
	Coreidae										
105	*Anasa tristis*	I	200-300	7-14	28-42	....	15-110	A	1	Cucurbits (N, A)	10,130
	Corizidae										
106	*Leptocoris trivittatus*	I	10	11-19	50-78	....	180-240	A	2	Box elder (L, N, P, A)	74
	Pentatomidae										
107	*Murgantia histrionica*	I	75-100	4-15	40-60	....	....	N, A	3-4	Cole crops (N, A)	29,133
	Reduviidae										
108	*Arilus cristatus*	I	42-172	130-160	28-40	....	140-160	E	1	Soft-bodied insects (L, N, P, A)	14
	Thysanoptera										
	Thripidae										
109	*Taeniothrips inconsequens*	C	99-155	4-16	60-240	30-120	50-200	A	1	Fruits (N, A)	47
110	*T. simplex*	I	150	4-12	4-12	3-8	26-32	A	6	Gladioli (N, A)	62,131
111	*Thrips tabaci*	I	50	4-10	5	4	20	L, A	Overlap	Onions, other crops (L, A)	23,50, 89, 112
	Anoplura										
	Pediculidae										
112	*Pediculus* sp.	I	50-300	5-21	7-10	None	10-30	Cont	10-12	Man (N, A)	18,61

/1/ Host, or material affording subsistence or lodgment. /8/ 3 years per generation. /9/ Parthenogensis. /10/ Egg in colder parts of country, nymph and adult in warmer parts. /11/ 13 or 17 years per generation.

continued

49. PROPAGATION AND METAMORPHOSIS: INSECTS

	Family and Species	Type of Metamorphosis	Eggs per Female	Duration of Stage, da				Overwintering Stage	Generations per Season	Host[1] (Insect Stage)	Reference
				Egg	Larva or Nymph	Pupa	Adult				
	(A)	(B)	(C)	(D)	(E)	(F)	(G)	(H)	(I)	(J)	(K)
	Mallophaga										
113	Trichodectidae *Bovicola* sp.	I	20-50	7-30	15-25	....	10-30	Cont	7-10	Cattle (N, A)	87
	Dermaptera										
114	Forficulidae *Forficula auricularia*	I	20-60	12-85	50-75	....	180-300	E, A	1	Flowers, vegetables, etc. (N, A)	30
	Isoptera										
115	Kalotermitidae *Kalotermes minor*	I	....	77	188-415	....	>12 yr (queen)	....	1 or less	Wood, wood products (all stages)	58,89
116	Rhinotermitidae *Reticulitermes flavipes*	I	Few to thousands	30	240-360 or more	None	3-5 yr or more	Cont	Cont	Dead wood, wood products (all stages)	117
	Orthoptera										
117	Acrididae *Melanoplus mexicanus*	I	300-400	90-120	40-60	....	>30	E	1	Crops, grass (N, A)	6,89, 96
118	Blattidae *Periplaneta americana*	I	200-1000	32-58	200-550	....	371-441	Cont	1 or less	Food, filth	52,83, 89
119	Mantidae *Stagmomantis carolina*	I	75-300	210-300	45-75	....	20-60	E	1	Carnivorous insects (N, A)	105
	Thysanura										
120	Lepismatidae *Thermobia domestica*	I	....	12-13	60-120	....	1-2.5 yr	....	2-5	Starchy substances	1,89, 118

/1/ Host, or material affording subsistence or lodgment.

Contributors: (a) Knipling, E. F., and Bishopp, Fred C., (b) Cutkomp, Laurence K., (c) Ritcher, Paul O., (d) Beal, James A., (e) Ewing, K. P., (f) Gardner, Theodore R., (g) Haeussler, G. J., (h) Lindquist, A. W., (i) Oman, Paul W., (j) Porter, B. A.

References: [1] Adams, J. A. 1933. Proc. Iowa Acad. Sci. 40:217. [2] Allen, H. W., J. K. Holloway, and G. J. Haeussler. 1940. U. S. Dept. Agr. Circ. 561. [3] Anonymous. 1941. Australia Council Sci. Ind. Research Rept. 14:16. [4] Anonymous. 1947. Gen. Headquarters Supreme Commander Allied Powers Rept. 76. [5] Back, E. A., and R. T. Cotton. 1938. J. Econ. Entomol. 31(2):280. [6] Baker, W. A. Unpublished. U. S. Dept. of Agriculture, Washington, D. C., 1954. [7] Baker, W. A., and W. G. Bradley. 1948. U. S. Dept. Agr. Farmers Bull. 1548. [8] Baker, W. A., W. G. Bradley, and C. A. Clark. 1949. U. S. Dept. Agr. Tech. Bull. 983. [9] Bates, M. 1949. The natural history of mosquitoes. Macmillan, New York. [10] Beard, R. L. 1940. Connecticut Agr. Expt. Sta. Bull. 440:598. [11] Bishopp, F. C., W. E. Dove, and D. C. Parman. 1915. J. Econ. Entomol. 8:54. [12] Bishopp, F. C., E. W. Laake, and R. W. Wells. 1957. U. S. Dept. Agr. Farmers Bull. 1596. [13] Blackman, M. W. 1931. N. Y. State Coll. Forestry Bull. 4(4). [14] Blatchley, W. S. 1926. Heteroptera or true bugs of eastern North America. Nature, Indianapolis. [15] Britten, W. E., and J. P. Johnson. 1938. Connecticut Agr. Expt. Sta. Bull. 411. [16] Bruce, W. G. 1940. U. S. Dept. Agr. Leaflet 205. [17] Bucher, G. E., J. W. M. Cameron, and A. S.

continued

West, Jr. 1948. Can. J. Research, D, 26:57. [18] Buxton, P. A. 1939. The louse. E. Arnold, London. [19] Calvert, P. P. 1930. Entomol. News 41:195. [20] Carter, W. 1930. U. S. Dept. Agr. Tech. Bull. 206. [21] Chittenden, F. H. 1907. U. S. Bur. Entomol. Circ. 87. [22] Chittenden, F. H. 1915. U. S. Dept. Agr. Farmers Bull. 668. [23] Chittenden, F. H. 1919. Ibid. 1007. [24] Chittenden, F. H. 1923. Ibid. 1322. [25] Cockerham, K. L., et al. 1954. Louisiana Agr. Expt. Sta. Tech. Bull. 483. [26] Collins, C. W., et al. 1936. J. Econ. Entomol. 29:169. [27] Cotton, R. T. 1923. J. Agr. Research 26:61. [28] Craighead, F. C. 1950. U. S. Dept. Agr. Misc. Publ. 657. [29] Crosby, C. R., and M. D. Leonard. 1918. Manual of vegetable-garden insects. Macmillan, New York. [30] Crumb, S. E., P. M. Eich, and A. E. Bonn. 1941. U. S. Dept. Agr. Tech. Bull. 766:1. [31] Culver, J. J. 1919. U. S. Dept. Agr. Bull. 766:1. [32] Dambach, C. A., and E. Good. 1943. Ohio J. Sci. 43:32. [33] Davidson, W. M. 1924. Trans. Am. Entomol. Soc. 50:163. [34] Davis, E. G., J. A. Callenbach, and J. A. Munro. 1950. U. S. Dept. Agr. Bur. Entomol. Plant Quarantine Leaflet EC-14. [35] Davis, J. J. 1915. U. S. Dept. Agr. Bull. 276. [36] Davis, J. J., and P. Luginbill. 1921. N. Carolina Agr. Expt. Sta. Bull. 242. [37] Davis, K. C. 1903. N. Y. State Museum Bull. 68:473. [38] Ditman, L. P., and E. N. Cory. 1931. Maryland Agr. Expt. Sta. Bull. 328:443. [39] Douglass, J. R., and W. C. Cook. 1954. U. S. Dept. Agr. Circ. 942. [40] Dove, W. E., and D. C. Parman. 1935. J. Econ. Entomol 28:765. [41] Dudley, J. E., Jr., B. J. Landis, and W. A. Shands. 1952. U. S. Dept. Agr. Farmers Bull. 2040. [42] Elmore, J. C. 1954. U. S. Dept. Agr. Leaflet 370. [43] Evenden, J. C., W. D. Bedard, and G. R. Struble. 1943. U. S. Dept. Agr. Circ. 664. [44] Feldman-Muhsam, B. 1944. Bull. Entomol. Research 35:53. [45] Fenton, F. A., and E. W. Dunnam. 1929. U. S. Dept. Agr. Tech. Bull. 112. [46] Fenton, F. A., and W. L. Owen, Jr. 1953. Texas Agr. Expt. Sta. Misc. Publ. 100. [47] Foster, S. W., and P. R. Jones. 1915. U. S. Dept. Agr. Bull. 173. [48] Friend, R. B., and A. S. West, Jr. 1933. Yale Univ. School Forestry Bull. 37. [49] Gardner, T. R. 1938. J. Econ. Entomol. 31:204. [50] Ghabn, A. A. A. 1949. Bull. soc. Fouad Ier entomol. 32. [51] Gossard, H. A., and J. L. King. 1918. Ohio Agr. Expt. Sta. Bull. 329:55. [52] Gould, G. E., and H. O. Deay. 1940. Purdue Univ. Agr. Expt. Sta. Bull. 451. [53] Gray, H. E. 1946. Ph.D. Thesis. Univ. Minnesota, Minneapolis. [54] Griswold, G. H. 1944. Cornell Univ. Agr. Expt. Sta. Mem. 262. [55] Grout, R. A. 1949. The hive and the honey bee. Dadant and Sons, Hamilton, Ill. [56] Hadley, C. H., and I. M. Hawley. 1934. U. S. Dept. Agr. Circ. 332. [57] Haeussler, G. J. Unpublished. U. S. Dept. of Agriculture, Washington, D. C., 1954. [58] Harvey, P. A. 1934. In C. A. Kofoid, ed. Termites and termite control. Univ. California Press, Berkeley. [59] Haseman, L. 1915. Missouri Agr. Expt. Sta. Bull. 137. [60] Hawley, I. M. 1922. Cornell Univ. Agr. Expt. Sta. Mem. 55. [61] Herms, W. B., and M. T. James. 1961. Medical entomology. Macmillan, New York. [62] Herr, E. A. 1934. Ohio Agr. Expt. Sta. Bull. 537. [63] Hewitt, C. G. 1914. The housefly. Cambridge Univ. Press, London. [64] Hopkins, A. D. 1909. U. S. Dept. Agr. Bull. 83(1). [65] Hough, W. S. 1927. Virginia Agr. Expt. Sta. Bull. 259. [66] Howard, L. O., and F. C. Bishopp. 1924. U. S. Dept. Agr. Farmers Bull. 1408. [67] Howard, N., and L. L. English. 1924. U. S. Dept. Agr. Bull. 1243. [68] Howard, N. F. 1924. U. S. Dept. Agr. Farmers Bull. 1407. [69] Hunter, W. D., and B. R. Coad. 1922. Ibid. 1262. [70] Hunter, W. D., and B. R. Coad. 1923. Ibid. 1329. [71] Ingram, J. W., et al. 1951. U. S. Dept. Agr. Circ. 878. [72] Isely, D. 1935. Univ. Arkansas Agr. Expt. Sta. Bull. 320. [73] Johnson, F., and A. G. Hammar. 1912. U. S. Bur. Entomol. Bull. 116(2):15. [74] Knowlton, G. F. 1950. Utah State Agr. Coll. Ext. Bull. 218. [75] Lane, N. C. 1941, rev. 1960. U. S. Dept. Agr. Farmers Bull. 1866. [76] Larsen, E. B., and M. Thomsen. 1940. Videnskab. Medd. Dansk Naturhist. Forening 104. [77] Larson, A. O., T. A. Brindley, and F. G. Hinman. 1938. U. S. Dept. Agr. Tech. Bull. 599. [78] Latta, R. Unpublished. U. S. Dept. of Agriculture, Washington, D. C., 1954. [79] Leggett, W. F. 1949. The story of silk. Lifetime Editions, New York. [80] Lundie, A. E. 1924. Cornell Univ. Agr. Expt. Sta. Mem. 79. [81] MacAloney, H. J. 1932. U. S. Dept. Agr. Circ. 221. [82] Madden, A. H., and F. S. Chamberlin. 1945. U. S. Dept. Agr. Tech. Bull. 896. [83] Mallis, A. 1945. Handbook of pest control. Buildings and Grounds Dept., Univ. California, Los Angeles. [84] Massey, C. L., and N. D. Wygant. 1954. U. S. Dept. Agr. Circ. 944. [85] Matheson, R. 1950. Medical entomology. Comstock, Ithaca. [86] Matthysse, J. G. 1945. J. Econ. Entomol. 39:743. [87] Matthysse, J. G. 1946. Cornell Univ. Agr. Expt. Sta. Bull. 832. [88] McLintock, J., and K. R. Depner.

continued

1954. Can. Entomologist 86(1):20. [89] Metcalf, C. L., W. P. Flint, and R. L. Metcalf. 1951. Destructive and useful insects. McGraw-Hill, New York. [90] Michelbacher, A. E. 1940. Hilgardia 13:81. [91] Michener, C. D., and M. H. Michener. 1951. American social insects. Van Nostrand, New York. ch. 8. [92] Middleton, W. 1923. U. S. Dept. Agr. Bull. 1182. [93] Miller, J. M., and F. P. Keen.. 1960. U. S. Dept. Agr. Misc. Publ. 800. [94] Morgan, A. C. 1923. U. S. Dept. Agr. Farmers Bull. 1356. [95] Newcomer, E. J., and W. D. Whitcomb. 1924. U. S. Dept. Agr. Bull. 1235. [96] Parker, J. R. 1957. U. S. Dept. Agr. Farmers Bull. 2064. [97] Peterson, A., and G. J. Haeussler. 1926. U. S. Dept. Agr. Circ. 395. [98] Phillips, W. J., and G. W. Barber. 1929. Virginia Agr. Expt. Sta. Tech. Bull. 40. [99] Phillips, W. J., and M. K. Kenneth. 1923. U. S. Dept. Agr. Farmers Bull. 1310. [100] Porter, B. A. 1928. U. S. Dept. Agr. Tech. Bull. 66. [101] Porter, B. A., and L. F. Steiner. 1928. Indiana Agr. Expt. Sta. Circ. 151. [102] Powsner, L. 1955. Physiol. Zool. 8:474. [103] Quaintance, A. L. 1915. U. S. Dept. Agr. Farmers Bull. 662. [104] Quaintance, A. L., and C. T. Brues. 1905. U. S. Dept. Agr. Bull. 50. [105] Rau, P., and N. Rau. 1913. Trans. Acad. Sci. St. Louis 22:1. [106] Riley, C. V. 1885. U. S. Entomol. Comm. Rept. 4. [107] Riley, C. V. 1890. Insect Life 2:295. [108] Schread, J. C. 1947. Connecticut Agr. Expt. Sta. Bull. 505. [109] Schwardt, H. H. 1932. Arkansas Agr. Expt. Sta. Bull. 280. [110] Shannon, R. C., and P. Putnam. 1934. Proc. Entomol. Soc. Wash. 36:185. [111] Shepard, H. H. 1943. Publ. Am. Assoc. Advance. Sci. 20:40. [112] Shirck, F. H. 1951. J. Econ. Entomol. 44:1020. [113] Smith, R. I. 1911. N. Carolina Agr. Expt. Sta. Bull. 214. [114] Snapp, O. I. 1930. U. S. Dept. Agr. Tech. Bull. 188. [115] Snapp, O. I., and J. R. Thomson. 1943. Ibid. 854. [116] Snodgrass, R. E. 1925. Anatomy and physiology of the honey bee. McGraw-Hill, New York. [117] Snyder, T. E. 1935. Our enemy the termite. Comstock, Ithaca. [118] Sweetman, H. L. 1938. Ecol. Monographs 8:285. [119] Swingle, L. D. 1913. Univ. Wyoming Agr. Expt. Sta. Bull. 99. [120] Taylor, E. P. 1908. J. Econ. Entomol. 1:83. [121] Theobald, F. V. 1926. The plant lice or aphididae of Great Britain. Headley Brothers, London. [122] Tower, D. G. 1915. J. Agr. Research 5:495. [123] U. S. Department of Agriculture. 1953. U. S. Dept. Agr. Leaflet 338. [124] U. S. Department of Agriculture. 1953. Ibid. 340. [125] U. S. Department of Agriculture. 1955. Ibid. 392. [126] Urquhart, F. A. 1960. The monarch butterfly. Univ. Toronto Press, Ontario. [127] Van Leeuwen, E. R. 1929. U. S. Dept. Agr. Tech. Bull. 90. [128] Watkins, T. C. 1941. Cornell Univ. Agr. Expt. Sta. Bull. 758. [129] Weed, A. 1927. J. Econ. Entomol. 20:150. [130] Weed, C. M., and A. F. Conradi. 1902. New Hampshire Agr. Expt. Sta. Bull. 89. [131] Weigel, C. A., et al. 1932. Florists Exchange Hort. Trade World 79:11, 40, 80B. [132] West, L. S. 1951. The housefly. Comstock, Ithaca. [133] White, W. H. and L. W. Brannon. 1933. U. S. Dept. Agr. Farmers Bull. 1712. [134] Wilson, H. F. 1919. Wisconsin Agr. Expt. Sta. Research Bull. 45. [135] Yearbook Committee. 1952. Insects. U. S. Dept. of Agriculture, Washington, D. C. opp. Pl. XLVI.

50. PROPAGATION AND DEVELOPMENT: INVERTEBRATES

Classification adapted from Lord Rothschild, *A Classification of Living Animals*, 1961.

Part I: METAZOA

Fertilization (column C): Ext = external fertilization of egg; Int = internal fertilization of egg. Sex (column F): D = dioecious, M = monoecious.

	Phylum and Class	Genus	Fertilization	Zygote	Development	Adult Sex	Adult Form	Reference
	(A)	(B)	(C)	(D)	(E)	(F)	(G)	(H)
	Chordata							
1	Cephalochordata[1]	*Branchiostoma*	Ext	Free	Direct	D	Amphioxus	3
2	Thaliacea	*Salpa*	Int	Placental	Direct	M[2]	Tunicate	3
3	Ascidiacea	*Ciona*	Ext	Free-floating	Appendicularia larva	M[2]	Sea squirt	3

/1/ Subphylum. /2/ Protogynous.

continued

50. PROPAGATION AND DEVELOPMENT: INVERTEBRATES

Part I: METAZOA

	Phylum and Class	Genus	Fertili-zation	Zygote	Development	Adult		Ref-er-ence
						Sex	Form	
	(A)	(B)	(C)	(D)	(E)	(F)	(G)	(H)
4	Enteropneusta	*Saccoglossus*	Ext	Free	Free larva, gradual change to adult	D	Acorn worm	6
	Echinodermata							
5	Ophiuroidea	*Ophiopholis*	Ext	Free	Dipleurula→ophiopluteus	D	Brittle star	9
6	Asteroidea	*Asterias*	Ext	Free	Dipleurula→bipinnaria→brachiolaria	D	Starfish	1
7	Echinoidea	*Arbacia*	Ext	Free	Dipleurula→echinopluteus	D	Sea urchin	1
8	Holothuroidea	*Cucumaria*	Ext	Free	Dipleurula→modified auricularia	D[3]	Sea cucumber	1
9	Crinoidea	*Antedon*	Ext	Attached to pinnules	Dipleurula→ciliated larva→stalked crinoid	D	Feather star	3
	Arthropoda							
10	Pycnogonida	*Nymphon*	Ext	Carried by male	Direct	D	Sea spider	3
11	Arachnida	*Centrurus*	Int	In female	Direct	D	Scorpion	3
12		*Ixodes*	Int	In sticky secretion	Larva (nymph-like)	D	Tick	3
13		*Pardosa*	Int	In cocoon	Direct	D	Spider	3
14	Merostomata	*Limulus*	Ext	In beach nests	Trilobite larva	D	King crab	3
15	Crustacea	*Cambarus*	Int	Fastened to swimmerets	Direct	D	Crayfish	14
16		*Eubranchipus*	Int	In shell	Metanauplius larva	D	Fairy shrimp	1
17	Insecta	*Apis*	Int	Laid in hive	Larva→pupa	D	Honeybee	3
18		*Ephemera*	Int	Laid in water	Aquatic nymph	D	May fly	3
19		*Melolontha*	Int	Laid in ground	Grub→pupa	D	Beetle	3
20		*Pieris*	Int	Laid on plants	Caterpillar→pupa	D	Butterfly	3
21		*Romalea*	Int	Laid in ground	Nymph stages	D	Grasshopper	11
22	Chilopoda	*Lithobius*	Int	Laid in ground	Direct	D	Centipede	3
23	Diplopoda	*Julus*	Int	Laid in ground	Direct	D	Millipede	3
24	Onychophora	*Peripatus*	Int	In parent	Direct	D	Peripatus	1
	Annelida							
25	Hirudinea	*Hirudo*	Int	In capsule	Direct	M[4]	Leech	1
26	Oligochaeta	*Lumbricus*	Int	In capsule	Direct	M[4]	Earthworm	1
27	Polychaeta	*Nereis*	Ext	Free	Trochophore larva	D	Sandworm	5
	Mollusca							
28	Cephalopoda	*Loligo*	Int	Encased in sticky secretion	Direct	D	Squid	3
29	Bivalvia	*Anodonta*	Int	In gills of parent	Glochidium parasitic on fish gill	M	Mussel	1
30		*Mercenaria*	Ext	Free	Trochophore larva→veliger larva→pediveliger larva	D	Quahog	4,12
31	Gastropoda	*Buccinum*	Int	In capsule	Trochophore larva→veliger larva	D	Whelk	1
32		*Helix*	Int	In ground	Direct	M[4]	Land snail	3
33	Aplacophora	*Neomenia*	Ext	Free	Trochophore larva	M	Solenogaster	11
34	Polyplacophora	*Ischnochiton*	Ext	Free	Trochophore larva	D	Chiton	3
35	Brachiopoda	*Lingula*	Ext	Free	Trochophore larva	D	Brachiopod	1
36	Phoronida	*Phoronis*	Ext or in coelom	Attached to adult tentacles	Actinotrocha larva	M	Phoronid	11
	Polyzoa							
37	Gymnolaemata	*Bugula*	Int	In body of parent	Trochophore larva	M[5]	Colony	1
38	Phylactolaemata	*Pectinatella*	Int	In body of parent	Ciliated hollow larva gemmates	M[5]	Colony	1
39	Acanthocephala	*Macracanthorhynchus*	Int	In capsule	Acanthor→acanthella in beetle larva	D	Spiny-headed worm (in swine)	7,8
	Aschelminthes							
40	Nematoda	*Ascaris*	Int	In shell	To juvenile stage in open; completion in host	D	Large roundworm (in mammals)	7,8

/3/ Also reproduce asexually. /4/ Cross-fertilization. /5/ Self-fertilization.

continued

50. PROPAGATION AND DEVELOPMENT: INVERTEBRATES

Part I: METAZOA

	Phylum and Class	Genus	Fertilization	Zygote	Development	Adult		Reference
						Sex	Form	
	(A)	(B)	(C)	(D)	(E)	(F)	(G)	(H)
	Aschelminthes							
41	Nematomorpha	*Gordius*	Int	Laid in strings	Larva free, then invades arthropod and develops to juvenile	D	Horsehair worm	7,8
42	Rotifera	*Philodina*	None	None	Direct	P[6]	Rotifer	7,8
	Nemertina							
43	Anopla	*Cerebratulus*	Ext	Free	Celoblastula→pilidium	D[3]	Ribbon worm	7,8
	Platyhelminthes							
44	Cestoda	*Taenia*	Int	In capsule	Oncosphere→hexacanth→cysticercus (all development in mammals)	M[5]	Tapeworm (in mammals)	13
45	Trematoda	*Fasciola*	Int	In capsule	Miracidium→sporocyst→rediae→cercariae[7]	M[4]	Liver fluke	7,8
46	Turbellaria	*Dugesia*	Int	In capsule	Direct	M[4]	Planarian	7,8
	Ctenophora							
47	Nuda	*Beroe*	Ext	Free	Cydippid larva	M	Comb jelly	7,8
	Cnidaria							
48	Anthozoa	*Metridium*	Ext	Free	Planula	D[3]	Polyp	3
49	Scyphozoa	*Aurelia*	Int	In folds of oral lobes	Planula→scyphistoma→ephyrae	D	Medusa	3
50	Hydrozoa	*Obelia*	Ext	Free	Planula→colony→medusa buds	D	Medusa	3
	Porifera							
51	Calcarea	*Scypha*	Int	In mesenchyme	Amphiblastula	M	Sponge	2
52	Mesozoa	*Dicyema*	Int	In body	Infusoriform larva→unknown stage→nematogen→rhombogen	M	Infusorigen	10

/3/ Also reproduce asexually. /4/ Cross-fertilization. /5/ Self-fertilization. /6/ Parthenogenetic female. /7/ Miracidia are free; sporocysts, rediae, and cercariae develop in snails; cercariae leave snails and are picked up by ruminant from water or grass.

Contributors: (a) Brown, Relis B., (b) Lochhead, John H., (c) Carriker, Melbourne R., (d) Shuster, Carl N., Jr.

References: [1] Borradaile, L. A., and F. A. Potts. 1932. The invertebrates. Macmillan, New York. [2] Brien, P. 1943. Bull. musée roy. hist. nat. Belg. (Brussels) 19(16):1. [3] Bullough, W. S. 1951. Practical invertebrate anatomy. Macmillan, New York. [4] Carriker, M. R. 1961. J. Elisha Mitchell Sci. Soc. 77(2):168. [5] Dales, R. P. 1951. J. Marine Biol. Assoc. United Kingdom 29:321. [6] Dawydoff, C. 1948. In P.-P. Grassé, ed. Traité de zoologie. Masson, Paris. v. 11, p. 367. [7] Hyman, L. H. 1940. The invertebrates. McGraw-Hill, New York. v. 1. [8] Hyman, L. H. 1951. Ibid. McGraw-Hill, New York. v. 2, 3. [9] Hyman, L. H. 1955. Ibid. McGraw-Hill, New York. v. 4. [10] McConnaughey, B. H. 1951. Univ. Calif. (Berkeley) Publs. Zool. 55(4):295. [11] Parker, T. J., and W. A. Haswell. 1940. A textbook of ecology. Ed. 6. Macmillan, New York. v. 1. [12] Pierce, M. E. 1950. In F. A. Brown, Jr., ed. Selected invertebrate types. J. Wiley and Sons, New York. p. 318. [13] Wardle, R. A., and J. A. McLeod. 1952. The zoology of tapeworms. Univ. Minnesota Press, Minneapolis. [14] Wolcott, R. H. 1946. Animal biology. Ed. 3. McGraw-Hill, New York.

continued

50. PROPAGATION AND DEVELOPMENT: INVERTEBRATES

Part II: PROTOZOA

	Class and Genus	Gametocytes	Gametes	Zygote	Development	Adult Form	Reference
	(A)	(B)	(C)	(D)	(E)	(F)	(G)
	Ciliata						
1	*Paramecium*	Conjugating pair	Pieces of micronuclei		Binary fission; each conjugant divides into four	Ciliate	3,4
2	*Podophrya*	Conjugating pair	Pieces of micronuclei		Budding of ciliated larva; each conjugant divides into four	Suctorian	2-4
	Sporozoa						
3	*Eimeria*	Megagametocyte, microgametocyte	One egg, many sperm	Encysted	Multiple fission; forms 4 smaller cysts, each with 2 sporozoites	Trophozoite	1,3,4
4	*Monocystis*	Megagametocyte, microgametocyte	Multiple fission into eggs and sperm	Encysted	Multiple fission into 8 sporozoites	Trophozoite	1,3,4
5	*Plasmodium*	Megagametocyte, microgametocyte	One egg, several sperm	Ookinete	Multiple fission into many sporozoites	Trophozoite	1,3,4
	Rhizopoda						
6	*Amoeba*				Binary fission	Ameba	3,4
7	*Endamoeba*				Binary fission	Endameba	3,4
8	*Patellina*[1]	Meiosis and mitosis into 16 gamonts	Each gamont forms 8 gametes		Two nuclear divisions without cell division	Schizont	5
	Mastigophora						
9	*Astasia*				Binary fission	Flagellate	3,4
10	*Trypanosoma*				Binary and multiple fission	*Trypanosoma* in vertebrates; *Leishmania* in invertebrates	3,4
11	*Volvox*	Megagametocyte, microgametocyte	Egg, sperm	Encysted	Budding, forming daughter colonies; a sphere of flagellated cells	Colony	3,4

/1/ Foraminifer.

Contributor: Brown, Relis B.

References: [1] Bullough, W. S. 1951. Practical invertebrate anatomy. Macmillan, New York. [2] Burbanck, W. D. 1950. In F. A. Brown, Jr., ed. Selected invertebrate types. J. Wiley and Sons, New York. p. 72. [3] Hyman, L. H. 1940. The invertebrates. McGraw-Hill, New York. v.1. [4] Hyman, L. H. 1951. Ibid. McGraw-Hill, New York. v. 2, 3. [5] Le Calvez, J. 1950. Arch. zool. exptl. et gén. 87:211.

51. CELL DIVISION FREQUENCY: PROTOZOA

	Class and Species	Culture Medium	Temp. °C	Cell Divisions per da	Reference
	(A)	(B)	(C)	(D)	(E)
	Ciliata				
1	*Didinium nasutum*	Hopkins' medium + paramecium	21	3.6	1
2	*Glaucoma pyriformis*	Yeast + yeast extract, or peptone	25.2	7.6-8.0	7
3		Yeast extract	24.2	6.9	7
4	*G. pyriformis* (Hetherington's strain)	Yeast extract	25	6.4	2
5	*G. pyriformis* (Phelps' strain)	Yeast extract	25	6.1	2
6	*Leucophrys patula*	*Glaucoma* sp.	25	3.7	2
7	*Paramecium aurelia*	Lettuce + bacteria	20±	0.72	10
8		Lettuce + bacteria	28	2.02	10
9	*P. caudatum*	Mineral salts + *Bacillus subtilis*	25-28	1.8	8
10		Oat medium + bacteria	26	2.3	4
11	*Stentor coeruleus*	Peter's medium + ciliates	19	0.6-0.9	6
12		Modified Peter's medium + ciliates	18-20	0.7-2.1	6
13		Hetherington's medium + *Blepharisma*	22	0.65	5
14	*Stylonychia pustulata*	....	25?	4.5-5.0	3
15	*Tetrahymena geleii*	Phelps' medium	24	5.7-10.9	14
	Mastigophora				
16	*Astasia longa*	Tryptophan + acetate	25	3.1	12
17	*Chilomonas paramecium*	Na-acetate + mineral salts	24	3.5	9
18	*Euglena gracilis*	Wheat infusion	25	3.5	13
19	*Polytomella uvella*	Aerated peptone	22	4.4	11
20		Non-aerated peptone	22	1.8	11

Contributor: Richards, Oscar W.

References: [1] Beers, C. D. 1929. Am. Naturalist 63:125. [2] Brown, M. G. 1940. Physiol. Zool. 13:277. [3] Darby, H. H. 1930. J. Exptl. Biol. 7:308. [4] Gause, G. F. 1934. The struggle for existence. Williams and Wilkins, Baltimore. [5] Gerstein, J. 1937. Proc. Soc. Exptl. Biol. Med. 37:210. [6] Hetherington, A. 1932. Arch. Protistenk. 76:118. [7] Hetherington, A. 1936. Biol. Bull. 70:426. [8] Johnson, W. H. 1936. Physiol. Zool. 9:1. [9] Mast, S. O., and D. M. Pace. 1933. Protoplasma 20:326. [10] Phelps, A. 1934. Arch. Protistenk. 82:134. [11] Rottier, P. B. 1936. Compt. rend. soc. biol. 122:776. [12] Schoenborn, H. W. 1949. J. Exptl. Zool. 111:437. [13] Sweet, H. E. 1939. Physiol. Zool. 12:173. [14] Wingo, W. J., and N. L. Anderson. 1951. J. Exptl. Zool. 116:571.

52. CROSS-FERTILIZATION DURING CONJUGATION: PARAMECIA

There are three sexual processes in paramecia: cross-fertilization during conjugation, self-fertilization during conjugation ("cytogamy") [3,4], and self-fertilization in unpaired animals (autogamy) [1-3]. Cross-fertilization during conjugation may result in nuclear changes in the paired animals, with no cytological or genetic evidence of cytoplasmic transfer (Part I); or, in prolonged union of the conjugants, cytoplasmic bridges may form, across which particles, such as kappa in *Paramecium aurelia*, may pass (Parts II and III). The genetic consequence of cross-fertilization is isogenicity of the exconjugants [3]. Conjugation has been reported for *P. aurelia*, *P. bursaria*, *P. calkinsi*, *P. caudatum*, *P. multimicronucleatum*, and *P. trichium* [4].

References: [1] Diller, W. F. 1934. Science 79:57. [2] Diller, W. F. 1954. J. Protozool. 1:60. [3] Sonneborn, T. M. 1947. Advances in Genet. 1:264. [4] Wichterman, R. 1953. The biology of *Paramecium*. Blakiston, New York.

continued

52. CROSS-FERTILIZATION DURING CONJUGATION: PARAMECIA

Part I: NUCLEAR CHANGES

Schematic drawing depicts conjugation between two animals having one macronucleus and one micronucleus. Normally the animals of each species contain a single macronucleus. The number of macronuclei may vary but is generally constant for any one species. [4]

Animal has "mated" with animal of complementary mating type. After initial ciliary adhesion (clumping, agglutination), establishment of a firm pellicular fusion occurs at one or more points about the oral region (conjugation). Macronucleus disintegrates.

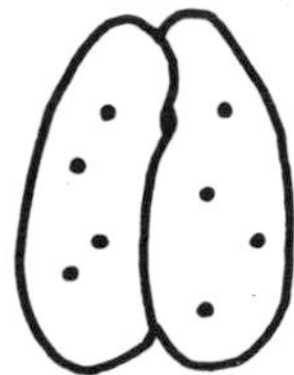

Each micronucleus undergoes meiosis, producing four haploid nuclei.

Three nuclei in each conjugant disintegrate. One persists and divides mitotically to form one stationary (female) and one migratory (male) gamete nucleus in each conjugant.

Migratory nuclei are exchanged through the paroral region and fertilize stationary nuclei. The diploid synkarya divide mitotically, and the macronucleus and micronucleus are differentiated from the division products of the synkarya [1-3]. Conjugants normally separate at this time and are termed exconjugants.

Contributors: (a) Hanson, Earl D., (b) Chen, T. T., (c) Wichterman, Ralph.

References: [1] Diller, W. F. 1936. J. Morphol. 59:11. [2] Hertwig, R. 1889. Abhandl. bayer. Akad. Wiss. Math.-Naturw. Abt. 17:150. [3] Maupas, E. 1889. Arch. zool. exptl. et gén., Ser. 2, 7:149. [4] Wichterman, R. 1953. The biology of *Paramecium*. Blakiston, New York.

continued

52. CROSS-FERTILIZATION DURING CONJUGATION: PARAMECIA

Part II: CYTOPLASMIC EXCHANGE DURING CONJUGATION BETWEEN KILLERS AND SENSITIVES

Present in the cytoplasm of certain paramecia (known as "killers") is a factor, given the name of kappa by Sonneborn, that is absent from the cytoplasm of other paramecia ("sensitives"). From cross-fertilization between killers and sensitives without exchange of cytoplasm, killers produce killer clones and sensitives produce sensitive clones (drawing at left). However, with the transfer of kappa particles during exchange of cytoplasm, both parents will produce killer clones (drawing at right). Adapted from Beale, 1954.

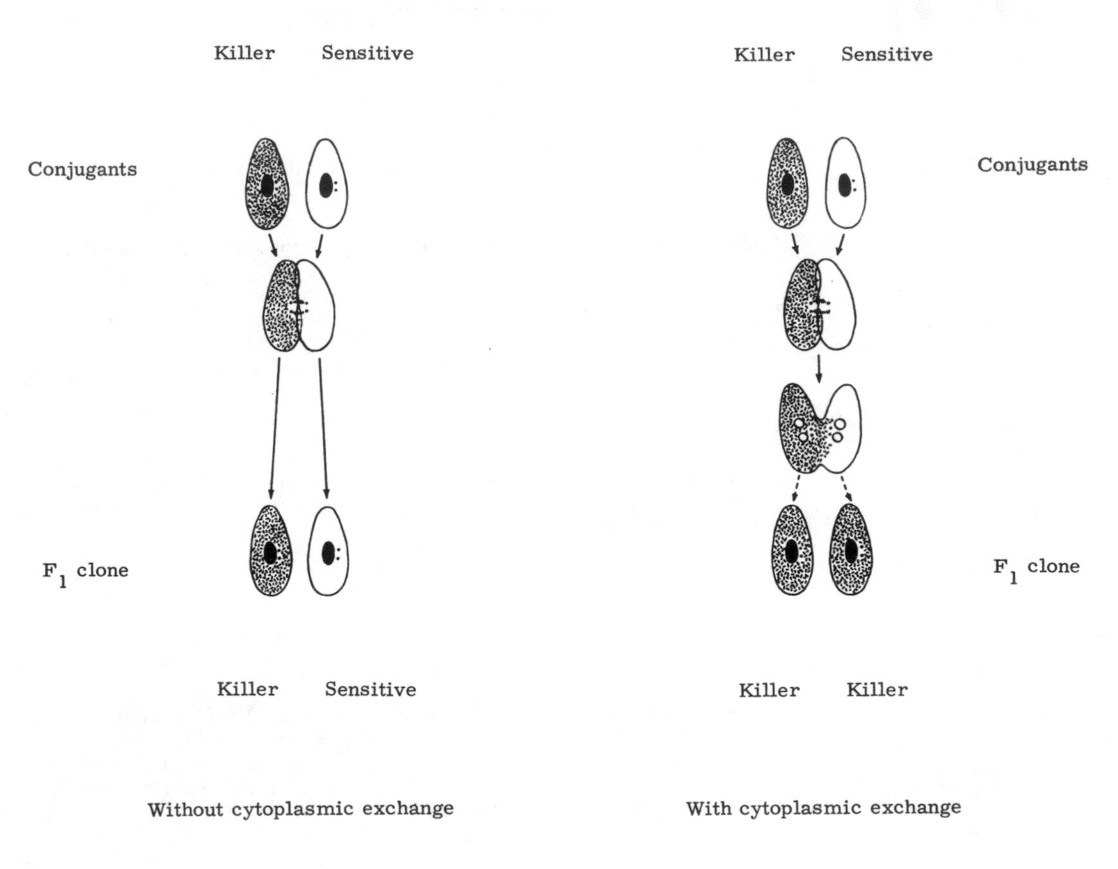

Contributor: Chen, T. T.

References: [1] Beale, G. H. 1954. The genetics of *Paramecium aurelia.* Cambridge Univ. Press, London. [2] Sonneborn, T. M. 1943. Proc. Natl. Acad. Sci. U. S. 29:329. [3] Sonneborn, T. M. 1946. Cold Spring Harbor Symposia Quant. Biol. 11:236.

continued

52. CROSS-FERTILIZATION DURING CONJUGATION: PARAMECIA

Part III: EFFECT OF CONJUGATION TIME ON CYTOPLASMIC EXCHANGE

The amount of cytoplasm exchanged is roughly proportional to the amount of time the paroral bridge persists after the conjugants have separated elsewhere. Adapted from Sonneborn, 1946.

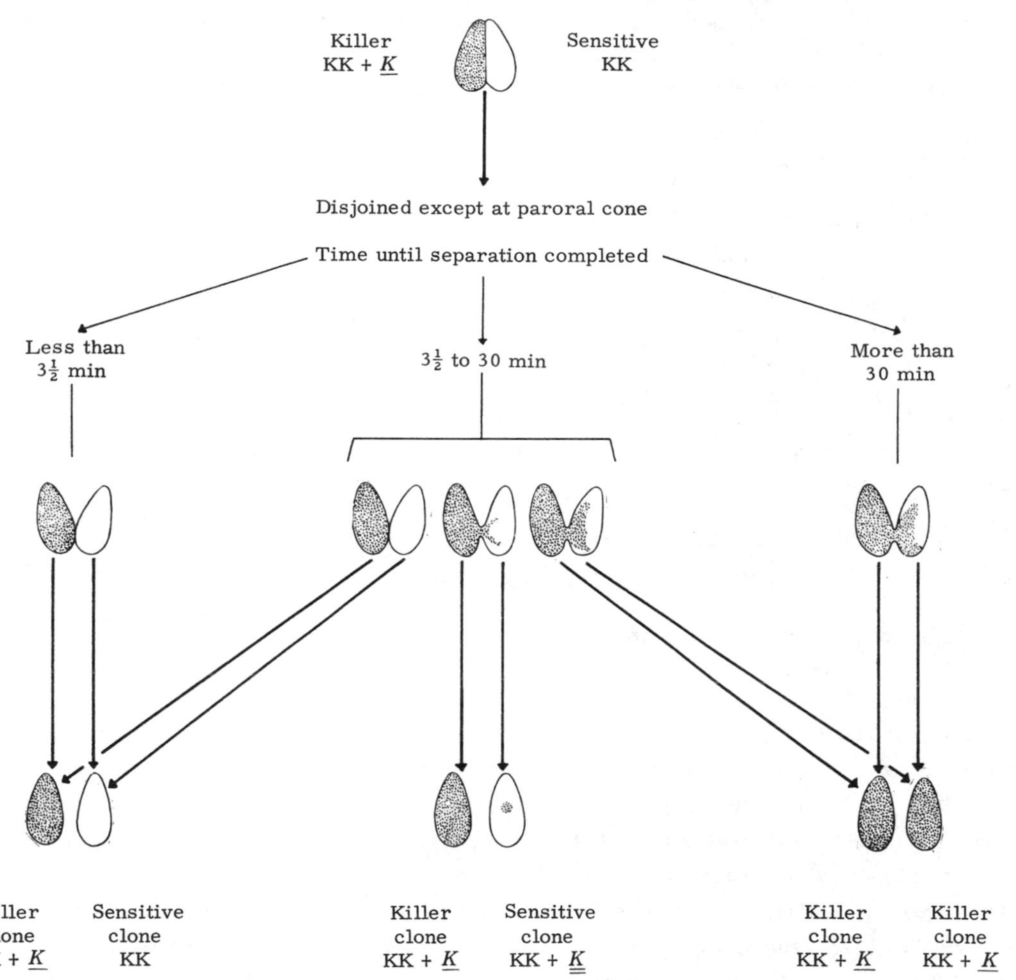

Contributor: Chen, T. T.

Reference: Sonneborn, T. M. 1946. Cold Spring Harbor Symposia Quant. Biol. 11:236.

53. MATING REACTIONS: PARAMECIUM AURELIA

Sixteen syngens (varieties)[1] of *Paramecium aurelia* can now be recognized [20]. Syngens 1, 3, 4, 5, 7, 8, 10, and 14 exhibit intervarietal reactions as shown in the table below [15, 17, 18, 22, 23], while syngens 2, 6, 9, 11, 12, 13, 15, and 16 have not been observed to react to each other [2, 5, 15, 17, 18, 22]. Two groups of syngens, A and B, are distinguished by their systems of mating type determination and inheritance. In group A (which includes syngens 1, 3, 5, 9, 11, and probably 7 and 15), mating type is inherited as a caryonidal trait; in group B (which includes syngens 2, 4, 6, 8, and probably 10, 12, and 14), mating type is inherited as a clonal trait [13, 20]. Nothing is known about mating type inheritance in syngen 16, and syngen 13 has not yet been assigned to either group A or B. Symbols: (+++) = maximum mating reaction, (++) = reduced mating reaction, (+) = weak mating reaction, (±) = barely detectable mating reaction, (-) = no mating reaction, C = conjugants formed, 0 = no conjugants formed. Symbols above the diagonal refer only to occurrence of mating reactions (adhesion, agglutination); symbols below the diagonal refer to occurrence of complete conjugation. For additional information on *P. aurelia*, consult references 1, 14, 20, and 21. For mating reactions of species other than *P. aurelia*, consult the following references: *P. bursaria*, 3, 4, 11, 12; *P. calkinsi*, 15, 24, 25; *P. caudatum*, 6-10; *P. trichium*, 15, 16, 26.

Syngen		1		3		4		5		7		8		10		14	
	Mating type	I	II	V	VI	VII	VIII	IX	X	XIII	XIV	XV	XVI	XIX	XX	XXVII	XXVIII
1	I	-	+++	-	-	-	-	-	++	-	-	-	±	-	-	-	-
	II	C	-	+	-	-	-	++	-	++	-	±	-	-	-	-	-
3	V	0	C	-	+++	-	-	-	-	-	-	-	++	-	-	-	-
	VI	0	0	C	-	-	-	-	-	±	-	-	-	-	-	-	-
4	VII	0	0	0	0	-	+++	-	-	-	-	-	+++	-	-	-	-
	VIII	0	0	0	0	C	-	-	-	-	-	++	-	+	-	+	-
5	IX	0	C	0	0	0	0	-	+++	-	-	-	-	-	-	-	-
	X	C	0	0	0	0	0	C	-	±	-	-	-	-	-	-	-
7	XIII	0	C	0	0	0	0	0	0	-	+++	-	±	-	-	-	-
	XIV	0	0	0	0	0	0	0	0	C	-	-	-	-	-	-	-
8	XV	0	0	0	0	0	C	0	0	0	0	-	+++	-	-	-	-
	XVI	0	0	C	0	C	0	0	0	0	0	C	-	+	-	+	-
10	XIX	0	0	0	0	0	0	0	0	0	0	0	0	-	+++	-	?
	XX	0	0	0	0	0	0	0	0	0	0	0	0	C	-	+	-
14	XXVII	0	0	0	0	0	0	0	0	0	0	0	0	0	0	-	+++
	XXVIII	0	0	0	0	0	0	0	0	0	0	0	0	0	0	C	-

/1/ Three of these syngens are those of the closely related species, *P. multimicronucleatum* [5, 19].

Contributors: (a) Austin, Mary L., (b) Butzel, Henry M., Jr., (c) Hanson, Earl D., (d) Ehret, Charles F., (e) Chen, T. T., (f) Wichterman, Ralph.

References: [1] Beale, G. H. 1954. The genetics of *Paramecium aurelia*. Cambridge Univ. Press, England. [2] Beale, G. H., and M. Schneller. 1954. J. Gen. Microbiol. 11:57. [3] Chen, T. T. 1945. Proc. Natl. Acad. Sci. U. S. 31:404. [4] Chen, T. T. 1946. Ibid. 32:173. [5] Giese, A. C. 1941. Anat. Record 81(suppl.):131. [6] Gilman, L. C. 1949. Biol. Bull. 97:239. [7] Gilman, L. C. 1950. Ibid. 99:348. [8] Gilman, L. C. 1954. J. Protozool. 1(suppl.):6. [9] Gilman, L. C. 1956. Ibid. 3(suppl.):4. [10] Hiwatashi, K. 1949. Science Repts. Tohoku Univ., Ser. 4, 18:137. [11] Jennings, H. S. 1939. Genetics 24:202. [12] Jennings, H. S., and P. Opitz. 1944. Ibid. 29:576. [13] Nanney, D. L. 1954. In D. H. Wenrich, ed. Sex in microorganisms. American Association for the Advancement of Science, Washington, D. C. [14] Rafalko, M., and T. M. Sonneborn. 1959. J. Protozool. 6(suppl.):30. [15] Sonneborn, T. M. 1938. Proc. Am. Phil. Soc. 79:411. [16] Sonneborn, T. M. 1939. Collecting Net 14:77. [17] Sonneborn, T. M. 1942. Anat. Record 84:92. [18] Sonneborn, T. M. 1956. Ibid. 125:566. [19] Sonneborn, T. M. 1957. Ibid. 128:626. [20] Sonneborn, T. M. 1957. In E. Mayr, ed. The species problem. American Association for the Advancement of Science, Washington, D. C. [21] Sonneborn, T. M. 1958. J. Protozool. 5(suppl.):17. [22] Sonneborn, T. M. Unpublished. Indiana Univ., Bloomington, 1957. [23] Sonneborn, T. M., and R. V. Dippell. 1946. Anat. Record 96:19. [24] Wichterman, R. 1950. Biol. Bull. 99:366. [25] Wichterman, R. 1951. Proc. Penna. Acad. Sci. 25:51. [26] Wichterman, R. 1953. The biology of *Paramecium*. Blakiston, New York.

VI. PLANT REPRODUCTION

54. GENERATION TIME: BACTERIA AND VIRUSES

Culture Medium (column C): MS = mineral salts, AM = allantoic membrane. Classification adapted from Bergey, *Manual of Determinative Bacteriology*, 1957.

	Order and Family	Species	Culture Medium	Temp. °C	Generation Time min	Reference
	(A)	(B)	(C)	(D)	(E)	(F)
			Bacteria[1]			
	Pseudomonadales					
1	Pseudomonadaceae	*Pseudomonas angulata*	Broth	23-25	76	43
2		*P. fluorescens*	Broth	30	40	30
3			Glucose broth	37	34.0-34.5	27
4		*P. pyocyanea*	Broth	37	34	27
5			Glucose broth	37	31	27
6			Lactose broth	37	34	27
7		*Xanthomonas* spp.	Broth	30	50-155	21
8		*X. campestris*	Broth	23-25	165	43
9			Glucose broth	25	74	27
10		*X. campsetre*	Broth	25	98	27
11		*X. glycineum*	Broth	23-25	95	43
12		*X. phaseoli*	Broth	25	150	27
13			Bean broth	25	160	27
14			Glucose broth	25	138	21
15		*X. sojae*	Broth	23-25	82	43
16		*X. tabacum*	Broth	23-25	81	43
17	Spirillaceae	*Vibrio comma*	Broth	37	21.2-38.0	4
18		*V. costatus*	Broth	27	42	25
	Eubacteriales					
19	Azotobacteraceae	*Azotobacter chroococcum*	Glucose broth	......	27-39	27
20			MS + sugar	25-30	240-348	27
21			Sugar + urea	28	74	5
22	Rhizobiaceae	*Rhizobium japonicum*	MS + yeast + mannitol	25	365	33
23		*R. leguminosarum*	MS + yeast + mannitol	25	79-187	6
24		*R. meliloti*	MS + yeast + mannitol	25	75-194	6
25		*R. trifolii*	MS + yeast + mannitol	25	101-174	27
26	Enterobacteriaceae	*Aerobacter aerogenes*	Broth or milk	37	18	27
27			Glucose + peptone	37	17.2-17.4	27
28			Peptone	37	22-30	27
29			Synthetic	37	29-44	11
30		*Erwinia amylovora*	Broth	30	71-94	21
31		*E. carotovora*	Broth	37	57	27
32			Glucose broth	37	42	27
33		*Escherichia coli*	Broth	37	16.5-17.0	37
34			Lactose broth	37	16	36
35			Milk	37	12.5	13
36		*E. coli communior*	Broth	37	16	17
37		*Proteus vulgaris*	Broth	37	21.5	27
38			Peptone + phosphate	37	40	8
39		*Salmonella enteritidis*	Broth	42	21.5	23
40		*S. paratyphi*	Broth	37	23	34
41			Peptone	37	28	27
42		*S. suipestifer*	Broth	37	26	42
43		*S. typhosa*	Bile + pus	37	24.5	32
44			Broth	37	23.5	29
45			Glucose broth	37	29	9
46			Glucose + peptone	37	33	31
47		*Serratia marcescens*	Milk	37	37	18
48		*Shigella dysenteriae*	Milk	37	23	18
49			Peptone + phosphate	37	37	8
50	Brucellaceae	*Pasteurella lepiseptica*	Broth + blood	37	24.5	41

/1/ Generation time: the average interval between cell divisions.

continued

54. GENERATION TIME: BACTERIA AND VIRUSES

	Order and Family	Species	Culture Medium	Temp. °C	Generation Time min	Reference
	(A)	(B)	(C)	(D)	(E)	(F)
	Bacteria[1]					
	Eubacteriales					
51	Micrococcaceae	*Staphylococcus albus*	Glucose broth	37	24-25	27
52		*S. aureus*	Broth	37	27	15
53			Glucose broth	37	32	27
54	Lactobacillaceae	*Diplococcus mucosus*	Milk	37	32	27
55		*D. pneumoniae I*	Broth	37	24.5	3
56			Serum	37	29	2
57			Serum + broth	37	20.5	7
58		*D. pneumoniae II*	Broth	37	33	7
59			Glucose broth	37	30	24
60			Serum + broth	37	23	3
61		*Lactobacillus acidophilus*	Milk	37	66-87	27
62		*L. bulgaricus*	Glucose milk	37	41-75	27
63			Milk	37	39-74	13
64			Peptone milk	37	50	27
65			Tomato juice + milk	37	38-40	27
66			Yeast extract	37	37	27
67		*L. casei*	Milk	25	38	27
68		*L. delbruckii*	Wort	45	83	38
69		*L. pentoaceticus*	Yeast extract	28	67	1
70		*Streptococcus fecalis*	Glucose-citrate broth	37	27	27
71			Milk	37	26.5	27
72		*S. hemolyticus*	Beef heart broth	37	32	27
73			Glucose broth	37	26	22
74			Serum + glucose broth	37	34	27
75		*S. lactis*	Glucose milk	37	26	27
76			Lactose broth	30	48	27
77			Milk	37	26	35
78			Peptone milk	37	37	27
79		*S. liquefaciens*	Milk	37	27	27
80		*S. mastitidis*	Glucose milk	37	35-37	27
81		*S. thermophilus*	Milk	37	27	13
82	Corynebacteriaceae	*Corynebacterium diphtheriae*	Serum + glucose broth	37	34	27
83		*C. pseudodiphtheriae*	Broth	37	37	20
84	Bacillaceae	*Bacillus cereus*	Broth	37	18.8	27
85			Glucose broth	37	17.0-24.5	27
86		*B. megatherium*	Broth	30	31	20
87		*B. mycoides*	Broth	37	28	40
88		*B. subtilis*	Glucose broth	......	26-32	27
89		*B. thermophilus*	Broth	55	18.3	27
90			Tryptophan + broth	54.5	16	16
91		*Clostridium amylobacter*	Corn mash	37	51	28
92		*C. botulinum*	Glucose broth	37	35	39
93		*C. welchii*	Milk	37	35	13
	Actinomycetales					
94	Mycobacteriaceae	*Mycobacterium tuberculosis*[2]	Synthetic	37	792-932	44
	Spirochaetales					
95	Spirochaetaceae	*Spirochaeta* spp.	Modified thioglycolate	37	528	14
96	Treponemataceae	*Treponema pallidum*	Rabbit skin	37	1800	26
97			Rabbit testes	37	1980	10
	Viruses[3]					
98	Virales	Influenza A (PR-8)	AM, chick embryo	37	330-510	12
99		Influenza A (5 strains)	AM, chick embryo	37	300-360	19
100		Influenza B (3 strains)	AM, chick embryo	37	480-600	19
101		Swine influenza	AM, chick embryo	37	360	19

/1/ Generation time: the average interval between cell divisions. /2/ Human strain H-37. /3/ Generation time: the time required for infected cells to release new virus.

Contributors: (a) Duca, Charles J., (b) Duggan, T. L.

continued

54. GENERATION TIME: BACTERIA AND VIRUSES

References: [1] Anderson, J. A., E. B. Fred, and W. H. Peterson. 1920. J. Infectious Diseases 27:281. [2] Barber, M. A. 1919. J. Exptl. Med. 30:569. [3] Blake, G. F. 1917. Ibid. 26:563. [4] Buchner, H., K. Longard, and G. Riedlin. 1887. Zentr. Bakteriol. Parasitenk. 2:1. [5] Burk, D., and H. Lineweaver. 1930. J. Bacteriol. 19:389. [6] Cameron, G. M., and J. M. Sherman. 1935. Ibid. 30:647. [7] Chesney, M. M. 1916. J. Exptl. Med. 24:387. [8] Cohen, B., and W. M. Clark. 1917. J. Bacteriol. 4:409. [9] Coulter, C. B., and M. L. Isaacs. 1929. J. Exptl. Med. 49:711. [10] Cumberland, M. C., and T. B. Turner. 1949. Am. J. Syphilis Gonorrhea Venereal Diseases 33:201. [11] Dean, A. C. R., and C. Hinshelwood. 1951. J. Chem. Soc. (London), p. 1157. [12] Fazekas de St. Groth, S. 1952. J. Immunol. 69:155. [13] Frazier, W. C., and E. O. Whittier. 1931. J. Bacteriol. 21:239. [14] Gelperin, A. 1949. Am. J. Syphilis Gonorrhea Venereal Diseases 33:101. [15] Graham-Smith, C. S. 1920. J. Hyg. 19:133. [16] Hansen, P. A. 1932. Arch. Mikrobiol. 4:23. [17] Hehewerth, F. H. 1901. Arch. Hyg. u. Bakteriol. 39:321. [18] Heinemann, D. G., and T. H. Glenn. 1908. J. Infectious Diseases 5:534. [19] Henle, W., and E. S. Rosenberg. 1949. J. Exptl. Med. 89:279. [20] Henrici, A. T. 1928. Morphologic variation and rate of growth of bacteria. C. C. Thomas, Springfield, Ill. [21] Hildebrand, E. M. 1938. J. Bacteriol. 35:487. [22] Kligler, H. 1919. J. Exptl. Med. 30:31. [23] Lane-Claypon, J. E. 1909. J. Hyg. 9:239. [24] Lord, F. T., and R. N. Nye. 1919. J. Exptl. Med. 30:389. [25] Lloyd, B., and J. A. Cranston. 1930. Biochem. J. (London) 24:529. [26] Magnuson, H. J., H. Eagle, and R. Fleischman. 1948. Am. J. Syphilis Gonorrhea Venereal Diseases 32:1. [27] Mason, M. M. 1935. J. Bacteriol. 29:103. [28] McCoy, E., et al. 1926. J. Infectious Diseases 39:457. [29] Muller, M. 1895. Z. Hyg. Infektionskrankh. 20:245. [30] Muller, M. 1903. Arch. Hyg. u. Bakteriol. 47:127. [31] Penfold, W. J., and D. Norris. 1912. J. Hyg. 12:527. [32] Pies, W. 1907. Arch. Hyg. u. Bakteriol. 62:107. [33] Porter, J. R. 1947. Bacterial chemistry and physiology. J. Wiley and Sons, New York. [34] Reichenbach, H. 1911. Z. Hyg. Infektionskrankh. 69:171. [35] Rogers, L. A., and G. L. Greenbank. 1930. J. Bacteriol. 19:181. [36] Saito, K. 1907. Arch. Hyg. u. Bakteriol. 63:215. [37] Sherman, J. M., and J. E. Holm. 1922. J. Bacteriol. 7:465. [38] Slator, A. 1916. J. Chem. Soc. (London) 109:2. [39] Wagner, E., K. F. Mayer, and C. C. Dozier. 1925. J. Bacteriol. 10:321. [40] Ward, H. M., and P. F. Frankland. 1895. Proc. Roy. Soc. (London), B, 58:265. [41] Webster, L. T. 1925. J. Exptl. Med. 41:571. [42] Wilson, G. S. 1922. J. Bacteriol. 7:405. [43] Wolf, F. A., and A. C. Foster. 1921. N. Carolina Agr. Expt. Sta. Tech. Bull. 20. [44] Youmans, G. P., and A. S. Youmans. 1950. J. Bacteriol. 60:569.

55. SPORE DISPERSAL: FUNGI

Part I: EJECTION DISTANCES

	Family	Species	Structure Dispersed	Distance Ejected Horizontal mm	Distance Ejected Vertical mm	Reference
	(A)	(B)	(C)	(D)	(E)	(F)
		Phycomycetes				
1	Peronosporaceae	*Sclerospora* sp.	Sporangium	1-2	....	19
2	Mucoraceae	*Pilobolus kleinii*	Sporangium	2451	1841	7,8
3		*P. Longipes*	Sporangium	2629	1841	7,8
4	Entomophthoraceae	*Basidiobolus ranarum*	Sporangium	10-20	....	13
5		*Conidiobolus villosus*	Conidium	5-40	....	13
6		*Empusa muscae*	Conidium	20-30	....	4,7
		Ascomycetes				
7	Pezizaceae	*Aleuria vesiculosa*	....	10-25	10-20	7,13
8		*Ascobolus immersus*	Ascospore	300	350	4,7
9		*Urnula geaster*	Ascospore	....	20-30	8
10	Geoglossaceae	*Geoglossum hirsutum*	....	5	....	13
11		*Trichoglossum hirsutum*	....	....	5	15
12	Taphrinaceae	*Taphrina communis*	Ascospore	12	....	20

continued

55. SPORE DISPERSAL: FUNGI

Part I: EJECTION DISTANCES

	Family	Species	Structure Dispersed	Distance Ejected: Horizontal mm	Distance Ejected: Vertical mm	Reference
	(A)	(B)	(C)	(D)	(E)	(F)
		Ascomycetes				
13	Sordariaceae	*Pleurage curvicolla*	Ascospore	....	>260-450	18,23
14		*Podospora fimiseda*	Ascospore	....	300	23
15		*Sordaria fimicola*	Ascospore	....	60-150	22,23
16		*S. tetraspora*	....	....	200	15
17	Diaporthaceae	*Endothia parasitica*	Ascospore	89	22	1,12
18	Xylariaceae	*Daldinia concentrica*	Ascospore	....	3-13	14
19	Hypocreaceae	*Hypomyces lactifluorum*	....	....	10	5
20	Clavicipitaceae	*Claviceps militaris*	Ascospore	....	0.2	15
21	Pleosporaceae	*Pleospora scirpicola*	Ascospore	....	0.2	15
22	Endomycetaceae	*Sporobolomyces* sp.	Sporidium	0.10-0.11	0.1	7,16
		Basidiomycetes				
23	Melampsoraceae	*Coleosporium* sp.	Basidiospore	0.6-0.9	0.3	5,11
24		*Cronartium asclepiadeum*	Basidiospore	....	0.6	11
25	Pucciniaceae	*Endophyllum euphorbiae-sylvaticae*	Basidiospore	0.4-0.5	....	5
26		*Gymnosporangium juniperi-virginianae*	Basidiospore	....	0.26-0.36	9
27		*Puccinia* spp.[1]	Basidiospore	0.6	0.3	6,11
28		*P. graminis*	Aeciospore	....	7.8	6
29		*P. pulverulenta*	Aeciospore	....	4-5	6
30		*Uromyces pisi*	Aeciospore	15-20	15-20	6,21
31		*U. poae*	Aeciospore	....	9	6
32	Tilletiaceae	*Tilletia tritici*	Basidiospore	1.4	0.5-1.0	7
33	Auriculariaceae	*Auricularia* sp.	....	0.4-0.5	....	5
34	Dacrymycetaceae	*Calocera cornea*	Basidiospore	0.2	....	5
35		*Dacrymyces deliquescens*	....	0.50-0.65	....	5
36	Tremellaceae	*Exidia alba*	....	0.4	....	5
37	Clavariaceae	*Clavaria formosa*	Basidiospore	0.1-0.2	....	5
38	Polyporaceae	*Polyporus conchifer*	Oidium	....	1220	3
39		*P. squamosus*	....	0.1	....	5
40	Agaricaceae	*Agaricus campestris*	Basidiospore	0.1	....	5,7
41		*Amanitopsis vaginata*	....	0.2	....	4
42		*Coprinus atramentarius*	....	0.05	....	6
43		*C. curtus*	....	0.10-0.12	....	5
44		*C. niveus*	....	0.1	....	5
45		*C. sterquilinus*	....	0.2	....	5
46		*Paneolus campanulatus*	....	0.10-0.12	....	5
47	Nidulariaceae	*Cyathus pallidus*	Peridiole	....	900-1200	2,10
48		*C. stercoreus*	Peridiole	....	2133	2
49		*C. striatus*	Peridiole	....	1220	2
50	Sphaerobolaceae	*Sphaerobolus iowensis*	....	5050	4000	17
51		*S. stellatus*	Peridiole	5664	4500	7,17

/1/ Species: *annularis, arenariae, glechomatis, malvacearum.*

Contributors: (a) Wolf, Frederick A., (b) Beneke, E. S., (c) Craigie, J. H.

References: [1] Anderson, P. J., and D. C. Babcock. 1931. Bull. Penna. Chestnut Blight Comm. 3:1. [2] Brodie, H. J. 1951. Can. J. Botany 29:224. [3] Brodie, H. J. 1951. Ibid. 29:593. [4] Buller, A. H. R. 1909. Researches on fungi. Longmans, Green; London. v. 1. [5] Buller, A. H. R. 1922. Ibid. v. 2. [6] Buller, A. H. R. 1924. Ibid. v. 3. [7] Buller, A. H. R. 1933. Ibid. v. 5. [8] Buller, A. H. R. 1934. Ibid. v. 6. [9] Coons, G. H. 1912. Nebraska Agr. Expt. Sta. Ann. Rept. 25:217. [10] Diehl, W. W. 1941. Mycologia 33:215. [11] Dietel, P. 1912. Mycol. Centr. 1:355. [12] Ingold, C. T. 1933. New Phytologist 32:178. [13] Ingold, C. T. 1939. Spore discharge in land plants. Clarendon Press, Oxford. [14] Ingold, C. T. 1957-1960. Friesia 6:148. [15] Ingold, C. T. 1960. Dispersal in fungi. Clarendon Press, Oxford. [16] Kluyver, A. J., and C. B. van Niel. 1924-25. Zentr. Bakteriol. Parasitenk., Abt. 2, 63:1. [17] Walker, L. B. 1927. J. Elisha Mitchell Sci. Soc. 42:151.

continued

55. SPORE DISPERSAL: FUNGI

Part I: EJECTION DISTANCES

[18] Weimer, J. L. 1920. Am. J. Botany 7:75. [19] Weston, W. H., Jr. 1923. J. Agr. Research 23:239. [20] Wolf, F. A. 1958. J. Elisha Mitchell Sci. Soc. 74:161. [21] Wolf, F. A., and F. T. Wolf. 1947. The fungi. J. Wiley and Sons, New York. v. 2. [22] Woronin, M. 1869. Abhandl. senckenberg. naturforsch. Ges. 7:325. [23] Ziegenspeck, H. 1926. Botan. Arch. 13:341.

Part II: MECHANISM

	Species	Projectile Size	Mechanism Analogue	Principal Mechanism of Dispersal	Special Feature of Projectile	Accessory Feature of Dispersal	Tropistic Responses	Reference
	(A)	(B)	(C)	(D)	(E)	(F)	(G)	(H)
1	*Pilobolus longipes*	0.5 mm (diameter)/1/	Squirt-gun/2/	Osmotic pressure in subsporangial swelling, plus elastic contractility of sporangium wall	Non-wettable sporangial wall basally ringed with wettable gelatin	Ocellus-like subsporangial swelling; light orients sporangiophore	Positive heliotropism of sporangiophore and subsporangial swelling	5
2	*Ascobolus immersus*	35-45 x 55-65μ/3/	Squirt-gun/2/	Osmotic pressure in epiplasm of ascus, plus elastic contractility of ascus wall	Gelatinous envelope covers 8-ascospore cluster	Asci protrude from paraphyses which hold bases of asci in position	Positive heliotropism of apothecium and asci	1,5
3	*Coprinus atramentarius*	5.5 x 10.0μ/4/	Balloon-gun/5/	Excretion of small drop of water at spore hilum	Spores describe a curved trajectory in falling, known as a "sporabola"	Cystidia hold gills apart; autodigestion clears cystidia and gills before spore fall	Negative geotropism of stipe	1-3, 5
4	*Sphaerobolus stellatus*	1.0-1.3 mm (diameter)/6/	Sling-shot/2/	Eversion of peridial layer by increase in osmotic pressure	Glebal mass adhesive because of high fat content	Air spaces between tooth-sinuses prevent formation of vacuum	Positive heliotropism of fruit body	4
5	*Lycoperdon perlatum*	3.7-4.4μ (diameter)	Puffing action/7/	Droplets of water strike peridium to eject spores	None	Basidiospores free inside basidiocarp as powdery mass	None	6
6	*Colletotrichum lindemuthianum*	13-32 x 3.5-5.3μ	Splash droplets/8/	Drop of water breaks up into 5200 splash droplets	Mass of conidia on an acervulus	Droplets force conidia horizontally 100-200 mm and vertically up to 700 mm from acervulus	None	7
7	*Leptodiscus terrestris*	24.0-34.8 x 4.4-7.0μ	Propelling action/8/	Seta unfold and propel spores outward	Seta against spore wall in mucus	Mucus on spore wall	None	8

/1/ Initial velocity = 14 m/sec. /2/ Spore-fall period is diurnal. /3/ Initial velocity = 10 m/sec. /4/ Initial velocity = 0.04 m/sec. /5/ Spore-fall period continuous for 24-48 hours. /6/ Initial velocity = 9 m/sec. /7/ Spore fall period during raindrop impact. /8/ Spore-fall period is continuous.

Contributors: (a) Bishop, Harlow, (b) Beneke, E. S.

References: [1] Buller, A. H. R. 1909. Researches on fungi. Longmans, Green; London. v. 1. [2] Buller, A. H. R. 1922. Ibid. v. 2. [3] Buller, A. H. R. 1924. Ibid. v. 3. [4] Buller, A. H. R. 1933. Ibid. v. 5. [5] Buller, A. H. R. 1934. Ibid. v. 6. [6] Gregory, P. H. 1949. Trans. Brit. Mycol. Soc. 32:11. [7] Gregory, P. H., E. J. Guthrie, and M. E. Bunce. 1959. J. Gen. Microbiol. 20:328. [8] McVey, D. V., and J. W. Gerdeman. 1960-61. Mycologia 52:193.

56. BREEDING SYSTEMS: ANGIOSPERMS

Species are those of economic importance. The systems listed indicate the usual breeding classification for a species; where variability exists within a species, only the predominant system (enclosed in parentheses) is given. System (column B): SC-S = self-compatible (predominantly self-fertilized), with no inbreeding degeneration; SC-M = self-compatible, monecious (staminate and pistillate flowers borne on same plant), but rarely self-fertilized under conditions of open pollination; SC-O = self-compatible, intermediate (between SC-S and SC-M), with perhaps a predominance of outcrossing; SI = self-incompatible (sterile to own pollen); D = dioecious (staminate and pistillate flowers borne on separate plants); A = apomictic (reproduction without fertilization); G = gynodioecious (hermaphrodite and female plants in about equal frequencies). Classification adapted from Engler and Diels, *Syllabus der Pflanzenfamilien*, 1936.

	Family and Species	System	Reference
	(A)	(B)	(C)
	Monocotyledoneae		
	Pandanaceae		
1	*Pandanus tectorius*	D	3
2	*P. utilis*	D	3
	Gramineae		
3	*Avena sativa*	SC-S	1
4	*Buchloe dactyloides*	D	3
5	*Coix lacryma-jobi*	SC-M	1
6	*Dactylis glomerata*	SI	1
7	*Eleusine coracana*	SC-S	1
8	*Euchlaena mexicana*	SC-M	1
9	*Festuca pratensis*	SI	1
10	*Hordeum sativum*	SC-S	1
11	*Lolium perenne*	SI	1
12	*Oryza sativa*	SC-S	1
13	*Panicum miliaceum*	SC-S	1
14	*Pennisetum glaucum*	SC-S	1
15	*Phleum pratense*	SI	1
16	*Saccharum officinarum*	SI	1
17	*Secale cereale*	SI	1
18	*Sorghum vulgare*	SC-S	1
19	*Triticum* spp.	SC-S	1
20	*Zea mays*	SC-M	1
21	*Zizania aquatica*	SC-M	1
	Cyperaceae		
22	*Cyperus papyrus*	SC-O	1
23	*C. tegetiformis*	SC-O	1
	Palmae		
24	*Arenga pinnata*	SC-O	1
25	*Borrassus flabellifer*	D	3
26	*Caryota urens*	SC-O	1
27	*Elaeis guineensis*	SC-O	1
28	*Phoenix dactylifera*	D	3
29	*Phytelephas macrocarpa*	D	3
30	*Sabal causiarum*	SC-O	1
31	*S. palmetto*	SC-O	1
	Cyclanthaceae		
32	*Carludovica palmata*	SI	1
	Araceae		
33	*Acorus calamus*	SI	1
	Bromeliaceae		
34	*Ananas sativus*	SI	1
	Juncaceae		
35	*Juncus effusus*	SC-O	1
	Liliaceae		
36	*Allium ascalonicum*	SC-O	1
37	*A. cepa*	(SC-O)[1]	1
38	*A. porrum*	SC-O	1
39	*A. sativum*	A	2
40	*A. schoenoprasum*	SI	1
41	*Aloe* spp.	SI	1
42	*Asparagus officinalis*	D	3
43	*Hyacinthus orientalis*	SC-O	1
44	*Lilium candidum*	SI	1
	Liliaceae		
45	*Lilium regale*	(SC-O)	1
46	*Smilax officinalis*	D	3
47	*Tulipa* spp.	SC-O	1
48	*Yucca* spp.	SI	1
	Amaryllidaceae		
49	*Agave* spp.	SI	1
50	*Narcissus* spp.	SI	1
	Dioscoreaceae		
51	*Dioscorea alata*	SC-O	1
	Iridaceae		
52	*Crocus* spp.	SC-O	1
53	*Iris* spp.	SC-O	1
	Musaceae		
54	*Musa paradisiaca*	SC-O	1
55	*M. textilis*	SC-O	1
	Zingiberaceae		
56	*Zingiber officinale*	SI	1
	Cannaceae		
57	*Canna edulis*	SC-O	1
	Marantaceae		
58	*Maranta arundinacea*	SC-O	1
	Dicotyledoneae		
	Piperaceae		
59	*Piper* spp.	D	3
	Salicaceae		
60	*Populus* spp.	D	3
61	*Salix* spp.	D	3
	Myricaceae		
62	*Myrica cerifera*	D	3
	Juglandaceae		
63	*Carya* spp.	SC-M	1
64	*Juglans* spp.	SC-M	1
	Betulaceae		
65	*Alnus* spp.	SC-M	1
66	*Betula* spp.	SC-M	1
67	*Carpinus* spp.	SC-M	1
68	*Corylus* spp.	SC-M	1
69	*Ostrya virginiana*	SC-M	1
	Fagaceae		
70	*Castanea* spp.	SC-M	1
71	*Fagus* spp.	SC-M	1
72	*Quercus* spp.	SC-M	1
	Ulmaceae		
73	*Celtis occidentalis*	SC-O	1
74	*Ulmus* spp.	SC-M	1
	Moraceae		
75	*Artocarpus incisus*	SC-O	1
76	*Broussonetia papyrifera*	D	3
77	*Cannabis sativa*	D	3
78	*Castilloa elastica*	SC-O	1
79	*Chlorophora tinctoria*	D	3
80	*Ficus* spp.[2]	SC-O	1
81	*F. carica*	D	3

/1/ Some are apomictic. /2/ Most species.

continued

56. BREEDING SYSTEMS: ANGIOSPERMS

	Family and Species	System	Reference
	(A)	(B)	(C)
	Dicotyledoneae		
	Moraceae		
82	*Humulus lupulus*	D	3
83	*Maclura pomifera*	D	3
84	*Morus alba*	D	3
85	*M. nigra*	D	3
	Proteaceae		
86	*Grevillea robusta*	SC-O	1
	Polygonaceae		
87	*Coccoloba uvifera*	SC-O	1
88	*Fagopyrum esculentum*	SI[3]	1
	Chenopodiaceae		
89	*Beta vulgaris*	SI	1
90	*Spinacia oleracea*	D	3
	Caryophyllaceae		
91	*Dianthus caryophyllus*	SC-O	1
92	*Saponaria officinalis*	SC-O	1
	Berberidaceae		
93	*Podophyllum peltatum*	SC-O	1
	Annonaceae		
94	*Annona* spp.	SC-O	1
	Myristicaceae		
95	*Myristica fragans*	D	3
	Lauraceae		
96	*Cinnamomum* spp.	SC-O	1
97	*Laurus nobilis*	D	3
98	*Nectandra rodioei*	SC-O	1
99	*Persea gratissima*	SC-O	1
100	*Sassafras albidum*	D	3
	Papaveraceae		
101	*Argemone mexicana*	SC-O	1
102	*Papaver somniferum*	SC-O	1
	Capparidaceae		
103	*Capparis spinosa*	SC-O	1
	Cruciferae		
104	*Brassica campestris*	SI	1
105	*B. juncea*	SC-O	1
106	*B. napus*	SC-O	1
107	*B. nigra*	SI	1
108	*B. oleracea*	(SI)	1
109	*Cakile maritima*	SI	1
110	*Cheiranthus cheiri*	SC-O	1
111	*Eruca sativa*	SI	1
112	*Lepidium sativum*	SC-S	1
113	*Matthiola incana*	SC-O	1
114	*Radicula armoracia*	SI	1
115	*R. nasturtium-aquaticum*	SC-O	1
116	*Raphanus sativus*	SI	1
117	*Sinapis alba*	SI	1
	Resedaceae		
118	*Reseda luteola*	SC-O	1
119	*R. odorata*	SI	1
	Moringaceae		
120	*Moringa oleifera*	SC-O	1
	Saxifragaceae		
121	*Ribes* spp.	SC-O	1
	Hamamelidaceae		
122	*Hamamelis virginiana*	SC-O	1
	Platanaceae		
123	*Platanus occidentalis*	SC-M	1
124	*P. orientalis*	SC-M	1
	Rosaceae		
125	*Cydonia oblonga*	SC-O	1
126	*Eriobotrya japonica*	SC-O	1
	Rosaceae		
127	*Fragaria chiloensis*	D	3
128	*F. vesca*	SC-O	3
129	*F. virginiana*	D[4]	3
130	*F. viridis*	SI	1
131	*Mespilus germanica*	SC-O	1
132	*Prunus americana*	SI	1
133	*P. armeniaca*	SC-O	1
134	*P. avium*	SI	1
135	*P. cerasus*	SC-O	1
136	*P. communis*	SI	1
137	*P. domestica*	(SI)	1
138	*P. persica*	SC-O	1
139	*P. salicina*	SI	1
140	*Pyrus communis*	SI	1
141	*P. malus*	SI	1
142	*Rosa* spp.[2]	SC-O	1
143	*R. rugosa*	SI	1
144	*Rubus* spp.[2]	SC-O	1
145	*R. calvatus*	A	2
146	*R. nitidiodes*	A	2
147	*R. thyrsiger*	A	2
	Leguminosae		
148	*Acacia* spp.	SC-O	1
149	*Arachis hypogaea*	(SC-S)	1
150	*Cajanus indicus*	SC-O	1
151	*Cassia* spp.	SC-O	1
152	*Crotalaria juncea*	SC-O	1
153	*Dolichos lablab*	SC-O	1
154	*Gleditsia triacanthos*	SC-O	1
155	*Glycine soja*	(SC-S)	1
156	*Gymnocladus dioicus*	D	3
157	*Haematoxylon* spp.	SC-O	1
158	*Indigofera tinctoria*	SC-O	1
159	*Lathyrus odoratus*	(SC-S)	1
160	*Lens esculenta*	SC-S	1
161	*Lespedeza striata*	SC-O	1
162	*Medicago sativa*	SI	1
163	*Phaseolus aureus*	SC-O	1
164	*P. lunatus*	SC-S	1
165	*P. multiflorus*	SC-O	1
166	*P. vulgaris*	SC-S	1
167	*Pisum sativum*	SC-S	1
168	*Robinia pseudoacacia*	SC-O	1
169	*Tamarindus indica*	SC-O	1
170	*Trifolium hybridum*	SI	1
171	*T. incarnatum*	SI	1
172	*T. pratense*	SI	1
173	*T. repens*	SI	1
174	*Vicia faba*	SC-O	1
	Geraniaceae		
175	*Pelargonium graveolens*	SC-O	1
176	*P. odoratissimum*	SC-O	1
	Linaceae		
177	*Linum usitatissimum*	SC-S	1
	Erythroxylaceae		
178	*Erythroxylon coca*	SI[3]	1
	Zygophyllaceae		
179	*Guaiacum officinale*	SC-O	1
	Rutaceae		
180	*Amyris elemifera*	SC-O	1
181	*Citrus* spp.	(SC-O)[1]	1
	Meliaceae		
182	*Swietenia mahagoni*	SC-O	1

/1/ Some are apomictic. /2/ Most species. /3/ Heterostyled, i.e., stigma and stamens inserted at different levels. /4/ Cultivated forms are selected intersexes.

continued

	Family and Species	System	Reference
	(A)	(B)	(C)
	Dicotyledoneae		
	Euphorbiaceae		
183	*Ricinus communis*	SC-M	1
	Buxaceae		
184	*Buxus sempervirens*	SC-M	1
	Anacardiaceae		
185	*Pistacia cabulica*	D	3
186	*P. lentiscus*	D	3
187	*P. vera*	D	3
	Aquifoliaceae		
188	*Ilex* spp.	D	3
189	*I. paraguariensis*	D	3
	Aceraceae		
190	*Acer* spp.	SC-O	1
	Rhamnaceae		
191	*Rhamnus cathartica*	D	3
192	*R. frangula*	SC-O	1
193	*R. infectoria*	D	3
194	*R. purshiana*	SC-O	1
	Vitaceae		
195	*Vitis vinifera*	SC-O	1
	Tiliaceae		
196	*Tilia* spp.	SC-O	1
	Malvaceae		
197	*Gossypium* spp.	SC-S	1
198	*Hibiscus cannabinus*	SC-O	1
	Bombacaceae		
199	*Adansonia digitata*	SC-O	1
200	*Bombax ceiba*	SI	1
201	*Ceiba casearia*	SC-O	1
202	*Durio zibethinus*	SC-O	1
	Sterculiaceae		
203	*Sterculia urens*	SC-O	1
204	*Theobroma cacao*	(SI)	1
	Dilleniaceae		
205	*Actinidia chinensis*	D	3
	Theaceae		
206	*Camellia sasanqua*	SC-O	1
207	*Thea sinensis*	SC-O	1
	Guttiferae		
208	*Garcinia mangostana*	A	2
	Bixaceae		
209	*Bixa orellana*	SC-O	1
210	*Cochlospermum gossypium*	SC-O	1
	Violaceae		
211	*Viola odorata*	SC-O	1
	Passifloraceae		
212	*Passiflora edulis*	SC-O	1
213	*P. ligularis*	SI	1
214	*P. quadrangularis*	SI	1
	Caricaceae		
215	*Carica papaya*	D	3
	Punicaceae		
216	*Punica granatum*	SC-O	1
	Lecythidaceae		
217	*Bertholletia excelsa*	SC-O	1
218	*Lecythis zabucajo*	SC-O	1
	Myrtaceae		
219	*Eucalyptus* spp.	SC-O	1
220	*Eugenia jambos*	SI	1
221	*Pimenta officinalis*	SC-O	1
222	*Psidium guajava*	SC-O	1
	Umbelliferae		
223	*Angelica archangelica*	SC-O	1
224	*Apium graveolens*	SC-O	1
	Umbelliferae		
225	*Carum carvi*	SC-O	1
226	*Daucus carota*	SC-O	1
227	*Foeniculum vulgare*	SC-O	1
228	*Pastinaca sativa*	SC-O	1
229	*Petroselinum hortense*	SC-O	1
	Ericaceae		
230	*Vaccinium* spp.	SC-O	1
	Sapotaceae		
231	*Achras zapota*	SC-O	1
232	*Mimusops balata*	SC-O	1
	Ebenaceae		
233	*Diospyros ebenum*	D	3
234	*D. kaki*	D	3
235	*D. virginiana*	D	3
	Oleaceae		
236	*Fraxinus* spp.	SC-O	1
237	*Olea europaea*	SC-O	1
	Loganiaceae		
238	*Strychnos nux-vomica*	SC-O	1
	Gentianaceae		
239	*Gentiana lutea*	SC-O	1
	Apocynaceae		
240	*Funtumia elastica*	SC-O	1
241	*Strophanthus* spp.	SC-O	1
	Convolvulaceae		
242	*Ipomoea batatas*	SI	1
	Boraginaceae		
243	*Borago officinalis*	SI	1
	Verbenaceae		
244	*Tectona grandis*	SC-O	1
	Labiatae		
245	*Lavandula officinalis*	SC-O	1
246	*Mentha* spp.	SC-O	1
247	*Nepeta cataria*	SC-O	1
248	*Origanum majorana*	G	1
249	*Salvia officinalis*	SC-O	1
250	*Thymus vulgaris*	G	1
	Solanaceae		
251	*Atropa belladonna*	SC-O	1
252	*Capsicum frutescens*	SC-O	1
253	*Datura stramonium*	SC-O	1
254	*Hyoscyamus niger*	SC-O	1
255	*Lycopersicon esculentum*	SC-O	1
256	*Nicotiana rustica*	SC-O	1
257	*N. tabacum*	SC-O	1
258	*Solanum melongena*	SC-O	1
259	*S. tuberosum*	SC-O	1
	Scrophulariaceae		
260	*Digitalis purpurea*	SC-O	1
	Bignoniaceae		
261	*Catalpa speciosa*	SC-O	1
	Rubiaceae		
262	*Cinchona* spp.	SI	1
263	*Coffea liberica*	SI	1
	Valerianaceae		
264	*Valeriana officinalis*	SC-O	1
	Cucurbitaceae		
265	Cultivated spp.	SC-M	1
	Compositae		
266	*Cichorium endivia*	SC-O	1
267	*C. intybus*	SI	1
268	*Dahlia pinnata*	SI	1
269	*Helianthus annuus*	SI	1
270	*H. tuberosus*	SI	1
271	*Lactuca sativa*	SC-S	1

continued

56. BREEDING SYSTEMS: ANGIOSPERMS

	Family and Species	System	Reference
	(A)	(B)	(C)
	Dicotyledoneae		
	Compositae		
272	*Parthenium argentatum*	(SI)[1]	1
	Compositae		
273	*Taraxacum* spp.[5]	A	2
274	*T. kok-saghyz*	SC-O	1
275	*Tragopogon porrifolius*	SC-O	1

/1/ Some are apomictic. /5/ Some species.

Contributor: Bateman, Angus J.

References: [1] East, E. M. 1940. Proc. Am. Phil. Soc. 82:449. [2] Gustafsson, A. 1947. Apomixis in higher plants. C. W. K. Gleerup, Lund. pt. 3. [3] Yampolsky, C., and H. Yampolsky. 1922. Bibliotheca Genet. 3:1.

57. PROPAGATION METHODS: CULTIVATED PLANTS

The methods listed for a genus are those most widely used in cultivation, but not all species of the genus can be propagated by each method. Horticultural varieties are not propagated by seed, as the new plants from seed may vary considerably from the parent plant. When propagation by seed is employed, the seed of species having no apparent rest period may be sown in the spring, while the seed of species having a definite rest period should be artificially stratified or sown in the autumn. Preferred Time (column C): spr = spring, sum = summer, aut = autumn, win = winter. Classification adapted from Engler and Diels, *Syllabus der Pflanzenfamilien,* 1936.

	Family and Species	Method	Preferred Time	Reference
	(A)	(B)	(C)	(D)
	Gymnospermae			
	Ginkgoaceae			
1	*Ginkgo biloba*	Seed	Spr	60
2		Cutting[1]	Spr	52
3		Whip graft	Early spr	42
4		Air layering	Spr	56,57
	Taxaceae			
5	*Taxus* spp.	Seed	Aut or spr	37,42
6		Cutting[2]	Aut-win	12,42,60
7		Cutting[1]	Sum	12,42,60
8		Air layering	Aut or spr	56,57
	Pinaceae			
9	*Abies* spp.	Seed	Aut or spr	25,26,60
10		Veneer graft	Win	41,42
11	*Cedrus* spp.	Seed	Aut or spr	42,50,60
12		Cutting[1]	Sum	42,50,60
13		Veneer or side graft	Aut-win	42,50,60
14	*Larix* spp.	Seed	Aut or spr	42,50,60
15		Whip graft	Spr	42
16	*Picea* spp.	Seed	Aut or spr	42,50,60
17		Cutting[1]	Sum	42
18		Veneer or side graft	Aut-win	33
19	*Pinus* spp.	Seed	Aut or spr	35
20		Veneer graft	Spr	35
21		Air layering	Spr-aut	35
22	*Pseudotsuga* spp.	Seed	Aut or spr	42,50
23		Veneer graft	Sum	42,60
24	*Tsuga* spp.	Seed	Aut or spr	42,50,60
25		Cutting[1]	Sum	42
26		Air layering	Early spr	56,57
	Cupressaceae			
27	*Chamaecyparis* spp.	Seed	Aut or spr	25,60
28		Cutting[2]	Aut	25,60
	Cupressaceae			
29	*Chamaecyparis* spp.	Cutting[1]	Sum	25,60
30		Veneer or side graft	Late sum	42
31	*Cupressus* spp.	Seed	Aut or spr	42,50,60
32		Cutting[1]	Sum	42,50,60
33		Veneer graft	Sum	42,50,60
34	*Juniperus* spp.	Seed	Spr or aut	42,60
35		Cutting[2]	Late win	42,60
36		Cutting[1]	Late sum	42,60
37		Veneer or side graft	Win	42,60
38		Simple layering	Spr	60
39	*Thuja* spp.	Seed	Aut or spr	3,42
40		Cutting[2]	Aut-win	42,60
41		Cutting[1]	Sum	42,60
42		Veneer or side graft	Aut-win	26
	Angiospermae (Monocotyledoneae)			
	Palmae			
43	*Phoenix dactylifera*	Shoots	Spr	29
	Araceae			
44	*Caladium* spp.	Tuber division	Spr	39
	Liliaceae			
45	*Convallaria majalis*	Crown division	Sum-aut	29
46	*Hyacinthus orientalis*	Scooping or notching bulb	Sum	22,29
47	*Lilium* spp.	Seed	Aut	4
48		Scales	Sum	29
49		Stem bulbils	Sum	26
	Iridaceae			
50	*Crocus* spp.	Cormels	Late spr-aut	29,39

/1/ Semi-hardwood. /2/ Hardwood.

continued

57. PROPAGATION METHODS: CULTIVATED PLANTS

	Family and Species	Method	Preferred Time	Reference
	(A)	(B)	(C)	(D)
	Angiospermae (Monocotyledoneae)			
	Iridaceae			
51	*Gladiolus hortulanus*	Cormels	Aut-spr	20
52	*Iris germanica*	Rhizome division	Aut	29
	Angiospermae (Dicotyledoneae)			
	Salicaceae			
53	*Populus* spp.	Cutting[2]	Aut	42
54		Root graft	Early win	42
55		Air layering	Early spr	56,57
	Juglandaceae			
56	*Carya* spp.	Veneer graft	Win-spr	40
57	*C. illinoensis*	Patch bud	Spr	1
58	*Juglans* spp.	Veneer graft	Early spr	13
59		Patch bud	Spr-sum	13
	Betulaceae			
60	*Alnus* spp.	Seed	Aut	42,50
61		Whip graft	Win	42
62	*Betula* spp.	Seed	Spr or aut	28,42,50
63		Cleft graft	Early spr	22,42
64		Air layering	Spr	56,57
65	*Carpinus* spp.	Seed	Aut or spr	42,50
66		Whip graft	Aut-win	42
67	*Corylus* spp.	Patch bud	Sum	40
68		Simple layering	Spr	40
	Fagaceae			
69	*Castanea* spp.	Patch bud	Spr	29
70	*Fagus* spp.	Seed	Aut or spr	42
71		Whip or cleft graft	Early spr	42
72	*Quercus* spp.	Seed	Aut or spr	23,42,50
73		Side graft	Early spr	42,60
	Ulmaceae			
74	*Ulmus* spp.	Seed	Aut or spr	42,50
75		Shoots	Early spr	22,42
76		Whip graft	Aut	22,42
	Moraceae			
77	*Ficus carica*	Cutting[2]	Win-spr	15
	Caryophyllaceae			
78	*Dianthus caryophyllus*	Cutting[3]	Spr-sum	34
	Ranunculaceae			
79	*Paeonia* spp.	Rough division	Aut	29,39
	Berberidaceae			
80	*Berberis* spp.	Seed	Aut	42,50,60
81		Cutting[2]	Aut-win	42
82		Cutting[1]	Sum	42
	Magnoliaceae			
83	*Liriodendron* spp.	Seed	Aut or spr	42,50,60
84		Whip graft	Win	42
85	*Magnolia* spp.	Seed	Spr or aut	2,42,50
86		Cutting[1]	Aut	42
87		Side graft	Sum	6,42
88		Air layering	Spr	56,57
	Lauraceae			
89	*Persea americana*	Patch bud	Spr	1
90		Whip graft	Win	1
	Saxifragaceae			
91	*Deutzia* spp.	Cutting[2]	Aut	42
92		Cutting[1]	Sum	42
	Saxifragaceae			
93	*Philadelphus* spp.	Seed	Spr	42
94		Cutting[1]	Sum	22,42
95		Cutting[2]	Win	22,42
96	*Ribes sativum*	Cutting[2]	Aut-win	51
97		Mound layering	Sum	1
	Rosaceae			
98	*Amelanchier* spp.	Seed	Aut or spr	42,50
99		Whip graft	Early spr	42
100		Simple layering	Spr	42
101		Mound layering	Early spr	42
102	*Chaenomeles* spp.	Seed	Aut or spr	30,42,50
103		Simple layering	Spr	42
104		Mound layering	Spr	42
105	*Cotoneaster* spp.	Seed	Aut or spr	24,42,50
106		Cutting[1]	Sum	22,42
107		Root graft	Early win	42
108	*Crataegus* spp.	Shield bud	Sum	42
109		Whip graft	Spr	42
110		Air layering	Spr	56,57
111	*Fragaria* spp.	Runners	Spr	17
112	*Malus pumila*	Shield bud	Spr-sum	1
113		Whip graft	Win	1
114	*Prunus* spp. (cherry)	Shield bud	Sum	22
115		Whip graft	Early spr	44
116	*P. amygdalus*	Shield bud	Sum	1
117	*P. armeniaca*	Shield bud	Spr-sum	1
118	*P. domestica*	Seed	Spr	1
119		Shield bud	Spr-sum	22
120		Top graft	Win	1
121	*P. persica*	Shield bud	June-sum	22
122	*Pyrus communis*	Shield bud	Sum	19
123		Whip graft	Win	49
124	*Rosa* spp.	Cutting[1]	Late spr	9,42,58,59
125		Shield bud	Spr-sum	39,49,58,59
126		Air layering	Spr-sum	56,57
127	*Rubus* spp. (blackberry)	Sucker plants	Spr	1
128		Root cutting	Late win	1
129	*Rubus* spp. (dewberry)	Tip layering	Sum-aut	1
130	*R. occidentalis*	Tip layering	Late sum	48
131	*R. strigosus*	Sucker plants	Aut-spr	14
132	*Spiraea* spp.	Cutting[2]	Aut	42
133		Cutting[1]	Sum	42
134		Rough division	Aut	42
135		Simple layering	Spr-sum	42
136		Mound layering	Spr	42
	Leguminosae			
137	*Caragana* spp.	Seed	Spr	2,42,50
138		Simple layering	Spr-sum	26,42
139	*Cercis* spp.	Seed	Aut	42
140		Root graft	Mid-win	42
141		Air layering	Spr	56,57
142	*Gleditsia* spp.	Seed	Aut or spr	38,42,50
143		Whip graft	Early spr	30,42
144	*Robinia* spp.	Seed	Aut or spr	42,50
145		Shoots	Aut	42
146		Cleft graft	Win	42
	Rutaceae			
147	*Citrus hybrida*	Inverted T-bud	Spr-sum	54
148	*Phellodendron* spp.	Cutting[1]	Sum	42
149		Root cutting	Win	42

/1/ Semi-hardwood. /2/ Hardwood. /3/ Softwood.

continued

57. PROPAGATION METHODS: CULTIVATED PLANTS

	Family and Species	Method	Preferred Time	Reference
	(A)	(B)	(C)	(D)
	Angiospermae (Dicotyledoneae)			
	Simarubaceae			
150	*Ailanthus* spp.	Seed	Spr	42,60
151		Root cutting	Early win	42,50
	Buxaceae			
152	*Buxus* spp.	Cutting[1]	Sum	42
153		Cutting[2]	Aut-win	42
154		Simple layering	Spr-sum	42
	Aquifoliaceae			
155	*Ilex* spp.	Cutting[1]	Sum	29,60
156		Shield bud	Spr	42
157		Simple layering	Spr-sum	42
158		Air layering	Spr	56,57
	Aceraceae			
159	*Acer* spp.	Seed	Aut-spr	41,42,50
160		Cutting[2]	Win	42,45
161		Shield bud	Late sum	47
162		Side graft	Win	33,42
163		Air layering	Spr	56,57
	Hippocastanaceae			
164	*Aesculus* spp.	Seed	Aut	42,50
165		Root cutting	Win	42
166		Shield bud	Sum	42
167		Whip graft	Early spr	42
168		Air layering	Spr	56,57
	Vitaceae			
169	*Vitis* spp.	Cutting[2]	Win	1,55
170		Whip graft	Late win	1
171		Chip bud	Spr	44
	Tiliaceae			
172	*Tilia* spp.	Seed	Aut or spr	43,51
173		Whip graft	Early spr	42
174		Simple layering	Spr	42
175		Air layering	Early spr	56,57
	Theaceae			
176	*Camellia* spp.	Cutting[1]	Spr-sum	39,42
177		Air layering	Spr	44
	Begoniaceae			
178	*Begonia* spp.	Cutting[3]	Yr-round	29
179		Leaf cutting	Yr-round	29
	Elaeagnaceae			
180	*Elaegnus* spp.	Seed	Aut or spr	42,50
181		Cutting[1]	Late sum	42
182		Cutting[2]	Aut-win	42
183		Simple layering	Spr-sum	5,42
184		Mound layering	Spr	30,42
	Nyssaceae			
185	*Nyssa* spp.	Seed	Aut or spr	42,50
	Myrtaceae			
186	*Eucalyptus* spp.	Seed	Spr	50
	Cornaceae			
187	*Cornus* spp.	Seed	Aut or spr	18,42,50
188		Cutting[2]	Sum-aut	22,42
	Cornaceae			
189	*Cornus* spp.	Simple layering	Spr	42
190		Air layering	Spr	56,57
	Ericaceae			
191	*Kalmia* spp.	Seed	Early spr	42,50
192		Cutting[1]	Aut	42
193	*Rhododendron* spp.	Seed	Spr	36,50,61
194		Cutting[1]	Mid-sum	7,43,61
195		Veneer graft	Win	32,42,61
196		Simple layering	Spr-sum	22,42,61
197		Air layering	Spr-sum	16
198	*Vaccinium corymbosum*	Cutting[2]	Early spr	27
199		Cutting[3]	Early sum	44
200	*V. macrocarpum*	Cutting[2]	Aut	31
	Ebenaceae			
201	*Diospyros* spp.	Whip graft	Win	1
202		Inverted T-bud	Spr	1
	Oleaceae			
203	*Olea europaea*	Cutting[2]	Win	29
204		Whip graft	Early spr	29
205	*Forsythia* spp.	Cutting[1]	Sum	8
206		Cutting[2]	Aut	42,60
207		Simple layering	Spr-sum	52
208	*Fraxinus* spp.	Seed	Aut or spr	42,46,50
209	*Ligustrum* spp.	Cutting[4]	Sum-win	11,42
210		Simple layering	Spr-sum	42
211	*Syringa vulgaris*	Seed	Spr	42
212		Cutting[3]	Early sum	44
213		Shield bud	Spr	39,42
214		Simple layering	Early spr	30,42
215		Air layering	Early spr	56,57
	Labiatae			
216	*Coleus blumei*	Cutting[3]	Yr-round	10
	Bignoniaceae			
217	*Catalpa* spp.	Seed	Spr	21,50
	Caprifoliaceae			
218	*Abelia grandiflora*	Cutting[2]	Aut	42,53
219		Cutting[3]	Sum	42,53
220		Simple layering	Spr-sum	42
221	*Lonicera* spp.	Seed	Spr or aut	30,42
222		Cutting[3]	Sum	22,42
223		Cutting[2]	Win	22,42
224	*Viburnum* spp.	Seed	Spr	44
225		Cutting[3]	Late spr	42
226		Cutting[1]	Sum	42
227		Side graft	Sum	42
228		Simple layering	Spr-sum	42
	Compositae			
229	*Chrysanthemum* spp.	Cutting[3]	Yr-round	34
230		Rough division	Aut	29
231	*Dahlia* spp.	Cutting[3]	Spr	26
232		Root division	Spr	22
233		Leaf-bed cutting	Spr	39

/1/ Semi-hardwood. /2/ Hardwood. /3/ Softwood. /4/ Softwood or hardwood.

Contributors: (a) Mahlstede, John P., (b) Wyman, Donald, (c) Brase, Karl D., (d) Slate, George L.

References: [1] Adriance, G. W., and F. R. Brison. 1939. Propagation of horticultural plants. McGraw-Hill, New York. [2] Afanasiev, M. 1937. N. Y. State Agr. Expt. Sta. (Ithaca) Mem. 208. [3] Barton, L. V. 1930. Am.

continued

J. Botany 17:88. [4] Barton, L. V. 1936. Contribs. Boyce Thompson Inst. 8:297. [5] Barton, L. V. 1939. Ibid. 10:221. [6] Beilman, A. P. 1932. Bull. Missouri Botan. Garden 20. [7] Bridgers, B. T. 1952. Quart. Bull. Am. Rhododendron Soc. 6:184. [8] Bryant, L. R., and G. Beach. 1941. Colo. Agr. Expt. Sta. Bull. 468. [9] Buck, G. J. Unpublished, 1953. [10] Calma, V. C., and H. W. Richey. 1930. Proc. Am. Soc. Hort. Sci. 27:457. [11] Chadwick, L. C. 1930. Florists Rev. 66:20. [12] Chadwick, L. C. 1933. N. Y. State Agr. Expt. Sta. (Ithaca) Bull. 571. [13] Chase, S. 1947. Proc. Am. Soc. Hort. Sci. 49:175. [14] Colby, A. S., H. W. Anderson, and W. P. Flint. 1946. Illinois Agr. Expt. Sta. Circ. 508. [15] Condit, I. J. 1941. Univ. Calif. Coll. Agr. Ext. Serv. Circ. 77. [16] Creech, J. 1950. Horticulture 10:86. [17] Darrow, G. M. 1929. U. S. Dept. Agr. Tech. Bull. 122. [18] Davis, O.H. 1926. Florists Exchange Hort. Trade World 63:917. [19] Day, L. H. 1947. Calif. Agr. Expt. Sta. Bull. 700. [20] Denny, F. E. 1930. Contribs. Boyce Thompson Inst. 2:523. [21] Engstrom, H. E., and J. H. Stoeckeler. 1941. U. S. Dept. Agr. Misc. Publ. 434. [22] Gardner, F. E. 1932. Maryland Agr. Expt. Sta. Bull. 335. [23] Gardner, R. C. B. 1937. Quart. J. Forestry 31:32. [24] Giersbach, J. 1934. Contribs. Boyce Thompson Inst. 6:323. [25] Griffiths, D. 1920. Flower Grower 7(12):199. [26] Hottes, A. C. 1922. Practical plant propagation. A. T. Dela Mare, New York. [27] Johnston, S. 1930. Mich. State Coll. Agr. Expt. Sta. Spec. Bull. 202. [28] Joseph, H. C. 1929. Botan. Gaz. 87:127. [29] Kains, M. G., and L. M. McQuesten. 1949. Propagation of plants. Orange Judd, New York. [30] Laurie, A., and L. C. Chadwick. 1931. Modern nursery. Macmillan, New York. [31] Mahlstede, J. P. Unpublished. Iowa State College, Ames, 1956. [32] Mallinson, J. W. 1926. Florists Exchange Hort. Trade World 61:749. [33] Mallinson, J. W. 1926. Ibid. 61:1139. [34] Maxon, M. A., B. S. Pickett, and H. W. Richey. 1940. Iowa Agr. Expt. Sta. Bull. 280. [35] Mergen, F., and H. Rossoll. 1954. Southeastern Forest Expt. Sta. Paper 46. [36] Morrison, B. Y. 1929. U. S. Dept. Agr. Circ. 68. [37] Nichols, G. E. 1934. Ecology 15:364. [38] Pammel, L. H., and C. M. King. 1922. Proc. Iowa Acad. Sci. 29:257. [39] Post. K. C. 1950. Florist crop production and marketing. Orange Judd, New York. [40] Reed, C. A. 1926. U. S. Dept. Agr. Farmers Bull. 1501. [41] Roe, E. T. 1941. J. Forestry 39:413. [42] Sheat, W. G. 1948. Propagation of trees, shrubs and conifers. Macmillan, London. [43] Skinner, H. T. 1937. Proc. Am. Soc. Hort. Sci. 35:830. [44] Slate, G. L., and K. D. Brase. Unpublished. Cornell Univ., Geneva, 1953. [45] Snow, A. G. 1941. J. Forestry 39:395. [46] Steinbauer, G. P. 1937. Plant Physiol. 12:813. [47] Stewart, L. B. 1924. Trans. Proc. Botan. Soc. Edinburgh 29:43. [48] Sudds, R. H. 1934. Proc. Am. Soc. Hort. Sci. 32:401. [49] Tukey, H. B., and K. D. Brase. 1934. N. Y. State Agr. Expt. Sta. (Geneva) Bull. 649. [50] U. S. Forest Service. 1948. U. S. Dept. Agr. Misc. Publ. 654. [51] Van der Lek, H. A. A. 1930. Rept. Proc. 9th Intern. Hort. Congr., p. 66. [52] Wardin, R. W. Unpublished. 1952. [53] Watkins, J. V. 1952. Univ. Florida Coll. Agr. Ext. Serv. Bull. 150. [54] Webber, H. J. 1920. Calif. Agr. Expt. Sta. Bull. 317. [55] Winkler, A. J. 1927. Hilgardia 2:230. [56] Wyman, D. 1951. Arnoldia 11(7). [57] Wyman, D. 1951. Ibid. 11(8). [58] Yerkes, G. E. 1928. Propagation of roses. U. S. Dept. of Agriculture, Bureau of Plant Industry, Washington, D. C. [59] Yerkes, G. E. 1939. Rose propagation by cuttings. U. S. Dept. of Agriculture, Bureau of Plant Industry, Washington, D. C. [60] Yerkes, G. E. 1945. U. S. Dept. Agr. Farmers Bull. 1657. [61] Yerkes, G. E., and B. Y. Morrison. 1925. Propagation of rhododendrons and azaleas. U. S. Dept. of Agriculture, Bureau of Plant Industry, Washington, D. C.

58. SEED GERMINATION: HERBACEOUS PLANTS

	Family and Species	Substratum	Germination Temp.[1] °C	Germination Time[2] da	Special Requirements
	(A)	(B)	(C)	(D)	(E)
	Monocotyledoneae				
	Gramineae				
1	*Agropyron cristatum*	Closed petri dish with cotton, blotter, or filter paper; top of blotters	15-25	5-14	Light; 0.2% KNO_3 solution; prechill at 5 or 10°C for 7 days
2	*Agrostis alba*	Top of blotters; closed petri dish with cotton, blotter, or filter paper	20-30	5-10	Light; 0.2% KNO_3 solution
3	*A. tenuis*	Closed petri dish with cotton, blotter, or filter paper	15-30	7-28	Light; 0.2% KNO_3 solution
4	*Avena sativa*	Between folded paper toweling; soil or sand	15	5-10	Prechill at 5 or 10°C for 5 days and conclude test on 7th day
5	*Cynodon dactylon*	Closed petri dish with cotton, blotter, or filter paper	20-35	7-21	Light; 0.2% KNO_3 solution
6	*Dactylis glomerata*	Closed petri dish with cotton, blotter, or filter paper; soil or sand	20-30	7-21	Light
7	*Festuca arundinacea*	Closed petri dish with cotton, blotter, or filter paper	20-30	5-14	Light and 0.2% KNO_3 optional
8	*F. elatior*	Closed petri dish with cotton, blotter, or filter paper	15-25	5-14	Light and 0.2% KNO_3 optional
9	*Hordeum vulgare*	Between folded paper toweling; soil or sand	15	4-7	Prechill at 5 or 10°C for 5 days
10	*Lolium multiflorum*	Closed petri dish with cotton, blotter, or filter paper; top of blotters	20-30	5-14	Light; 0.2% KNO_3 solution; prechill at 5°C for 5 days
11	*Oryza sativa*	Between blotters; between folded toweling; soil or sand	20-30	5-14	None
12	*Paspalum dilatatum*	Closed petri dish with cotton, blotter, or filter paper	20-35	7-21	Light; 0.2% KNO_3 solution
13	*Phalaris canariensis*	Between blotters or toweling	20-30	3-7	None
14	*Phleum pratense*	Closed petri dish with cotton, blotter, or filter paper; top of blotters	20-30	5-10	Light; prechill at 5 or 10°C for 5 days
15	*Poa pratensis*	Closed petri dish with cotton, blotter, or filter paper	10-30	10-28	Light; 0.1% KNO_3 solution; prechill dormant seeds at 10°C for 5 days
16	*Secale cereale*	Between folded paper toweling; soil or sand	15	4-7	Prechill at 5 or 10°C for 5 days
17	*Sorghum halepense*	Closed petri dish with cotton, blotter, or filter paper	20-35	7-35	Light; 0.2% KNO_3 solution
18	*S. vulgare*	Between blotters; soil or sand	20-30	4-10	Prechill at 5 or 10°C for 5 days
19	*Triticum* spp.	Between folded paper toweling; soil or sand	15	4-7	Prechill at 5 or 10°C for 5 days
20	*Zea mays*	Rolled towel; soil or sand	25	4-7	None
	Liliaceae				
21	*Allium cepa*	Between blotters or toweling	20	6-10	None
22	*Asparagus officinalis*	Between blotters; between folded paper toweling; soil or sand	20-30	7-21	None
	Dicotyledoneae				
	Moraceae				
23	*Cannabis sativa*	Between blotters or toweling	20-30	3-7	None
	Polygonaceae				
24	*Fagopyrum esculentum*	Between blotters; between folded paper toweling	20-30	3-6	None
25	*Rheum rhaponticum*	Top of blotters; top of soil	20-30	7-21	Light
	Chenopodiaceae				
26	*Beta vulgaris*	Between blotters; soil or sand	20-30	3-14	Soak in water for 2 hours; rinse, blot surface dry
27	*Spinacia oleracea*	Top of blotters	10	7-21	Keep substratum drier than for average kind of seed

/1/ When a range is given, a daily fluctuating temperature is preferred for germination: 16 hours at the lower temperature and 8 hours at the higher temperature. /2/ Maximum germination is usually obtained during the given time limits; for hard-coated seeds an additional 5 days is recommended.

continued

58. SEED GERMINATION: HERBACEOUS PLANTS

	Family and Species	Substratum	Germination Temp.[1] °C	Germination Time[2] da	Special Requirements
	(A)	(B)	(C)	(D)	(E)
	Dicotyledoneae				
	Caryophyllaceae				
28	*Dianthus caryophyllus*	Top of blotters	20	8	None
	Ranunculaceae				
29	*Delphinium* spp.	Top of blotters	15	10-21	None
	Papaveraceae				
30	*Papaver orientale*	Top of blotters	20	6-12	Light; 0.2% KNO_3 solution
	Cruciferae				
31	*Brassica napobrassica*	Between blotters	20-30	3-14	None
32	*B. nigra*	Closed petri dish with cotton, blotter, or filter paper	20-30	3-7	Light; 0.2% KNO_3 solution; prechill at 10°C for 3 days
33	*B. oleracea acephala*	Between blotters; closed petri dish with cotton, blotter, or filter paper	20-30	3-10	Dormant seed: light; 0.2% KNO_3 solution; prechill at 5 or 10°C for 3 days
34	*B. oleracea capitata*	Between blotters; closed petri dish with cotton, blotter, or filter paper	20-30	3-10	Dormant seed: light; 0.2% KNO_3 solution; prechill at 5 or 10°C for 3 days
35	*B. rapa*	Between blotters	20-30	3-7	None
36	*Cheiranthus allioni*	Top of blotters	20-30	4-10	Light; 0.2% KNO_3 solution
37	*Matthiola incana*	Top of blotters	20-30	7	Light
38	*Raphanus sativus*	Between blotters	20	4-6	None
	Leguminosae				
39	*Arachis hypogaea*	Rolled towel; soil or sand	20-30	5-10	Remove shells
40	*Crotalaria* spp.	Between blotters; soil or sand	20-30	4-10	None
41	*Glycine soja*	Rolled towel; soil or sand	20-30	5-8	None
42	*Lathyrus odoratus*	Rolled towel	18	12	None
43	*Lespedeza stipulacea*	Between blotters; soil or sand	20-35	5-14	None
44	*Lupinus angustifolius*	Rolled towel; soil or sand	20	4-10	None
45	*Medicago sativa*	Between blotters; soil or sand	20	4-7	None
46	*Phaseolus coccineus*	Rolled towel; soil or sand	20-30	5-9	None
47	*P. lunatus macrocarpus*	Rolled towel; soil or sand; creped cellulose paper wadding	20-30	5-9	None
48	*P. vulgaris*	Rolled towel; soil or sand	20-30	5-8	None
49	*Pisum sativum*	Rolled towel; soil or sand	20	5-8	None
50	*P. sativum arvense*	Rolled towel; soil or sand	20	3-8	None
51	*Trifolium* spp.[3]	Between blotters; soil or sand	20	3-7	Dormant seed: 15°C
52	*Vicia faba*	Soil or sand; creped cellulose paper wadding	20	4-14	Prechill at 10°C for 3 days
53	*Vigna sinensis*	Rolled towel; soil or sand	20-30	5-8	None
	Tropaeolaceae				
54	*Tropaeolum* spp.	Rolled towel	18	14	None
	Linaceae				
55	*Linum usitatissimum*	Between blotters; soil or sand	20-30	3-7	None
	Balsaminaceae				
56	*Impatiens balsamina*	Top of blotters	20	8	Light; 0.2% KNO_3 solution
	Malvaceae				
57	*Althaea rosea*	Between blotters	20	5-18	None
58	*Gossypium* spp.	Rolled towel; soil or sand	20-30	4-12	None
59	*Hibiscus esculentus*	Rolled towel; between blotters	20-30	4-14	None
	Violaceae				
60	*Viola tricolor*	Top of blotters	20-30	12	None
	Umbelliferae				
61	*Apium graveolens dulce*	Closed petri dish with cotton, blotter, or filter paper; top of blotters	15-25	10-21	Light
62	*Daucus carota*	Between blotters	20-30	6-21	None
63	*Pastinaca sativa*	Between blotters	20-30	6-28	None
64	*Petroselinum hortense*	Between blotters	20-30	11-28	None
	Boraginaceae				
65	*Myosotis* sp.	Top of blotters	20	5-12	None

/1/ When a range is given, a daily fluctuating temperature is preferred for germination: 16 hours at the lower temperature and 8 hours at the higher temperature. /2/ Maximum germination is usually obtained during the given time limits; for hard-coated seeds an additional 5 days is recommended. /3/ Species: *alexandrinum, fragiferum, hybridum, lappaceum, repens, resupinatum.*

continued

58. SEED GERMINATION: HERBACEOUS PLANTS

	Family and Species	Substratum	Germination Temp.[1] °C	Germination Time[2] da	Special Requirements
	(A)	(B)	(C)	(D)	(E)
	Dicotyledoneae				
	Labiatae				
66	*Salvia splendens*	Top of blotters	20-30	4-12	Light
	Solanaceae				
67	*Capsicum* spp.	Top of blotters	20-30	6-14	Light; 0.2% KNO_3 solution
68	*Lycopersicon esculentum*	Between blotters or toweling; closed petri dish with cotton, blotter, or filter paper	20-30	5-14	Dormant seed: light; 0.2% KNO_3 solution
69	*Nicotiana tabacum*	Closed petri dish with cotton, blotter, or filter paper; top of blotters	20-30	7-14	Light
70	*Petunia* spp.	Closed petri dish with cotton, blotter, or filter paper	20-30	6-14	Light; 0.2% KNO_3 solution
71	*Solanum melongena esculentum*	Closed petri dish with cotton, blotter, or filter paper; top of blotters	20-30	7-14	Dormant seed: light; 0.2% KNO_3 solution
	Scrophulariaceae				
72	*Antirrhinum* spp.	Closed petri dish with cotton, blotter, or filter paper	20-30	5-12	Light; fresh and hybrid seed may require prechilling at 3 or 5°C for 10-20 days
	Pedaliaceae				
73	*Sesamum orientale*	Closed petri dish with cotton, blotter, or filter paper	20-30	3-6	None
	Cucurbitaceae				
74	*Citrullus vulgaris*	Between folded paper toweling; soil or sand	20-30	4-14	Keep substratum drier than for other seeds
75	*Cucumis melo*	Between blotters; between folded paper toweling; soil or sand	20-30	4-10	Keep substratum drier than for other seeds
76	*C. sativus*	Between folded paper toweling; soil or sand; between blotters	20-30	3-7	None
77	*Cucurbita* spp.	Between folded paper toweling; soil or sand	20-30	4-7	Keep substratum drier than for other seeds
	Campanulaceae				
78	*Campanula* spp.	Top of blotters	20-30	6-16	Light
	Compositae				
79	*Aster* sp. (annual)	Top of blotters	20	8	None
80	*Centaurea cyanus*	Top of blotters	15	4-8	None
81	*Chrysanthemum maximum*	Top of blotters	20-30	8	Light
82	*Cichorium endivia*	Closed petri dish with cotton, blotter, or filter paper; top of soil	20-30	5-14	None
83	*Cosmos* spp.	Top of blotters	20-30	3-8	Light; 0.2% KNO_3 solution
84	*Dahlia* spp.	Top of blotters	15	4-14	None
85	*Helianthus annuus*	Between folded paper toweling; between blotters	20-30	3-7	None
86	*Lactuca sativa*	Closed petri dish with cotton, blotter, or filter paper	20	7	Light; prechill at 10°C for 3 days or test at 15°C
87	*Tagetes* spp.	Top of blotters	20-30	7	Light
88	*Taraxacum officinale*	Closed petri dish with cotton, blotter, or filter paper; top of blotters	20-30	7-21	Light
89	*Zinnia* spp.	Top of blotters	20-30	3-7	Light

/1/ When a range is given, a daily fluctuating temperature is preferred for germination: 16 hours at the lower temperature and 8 hours at the higher temperature. /2/ Maximum germination is usually obtained during the given time limits; for hard-coated seeds an additional 5 days is recommended.

Contributors: (a) Justice, O. L., and Rollin, S. F., (b) Allen, George S., (c) Rogers, C. B. W.

Reference: Justice, O. L., et al. 1960. Proc. Assoc. Offic. Seed Analysts 49(2):21.

59. SEED GERMINATION: FOREST

Dormancy (column D): E = embryo, SC = seed coat. Storage Method (column E): D = dry; M = moist (% indicates
P = moist peat; S = moist sand. Pretreatment Method (column H): P = stratify in moist peat; S = stratify in moist

	Species	Common Name	Seed-bearing Age, yr[1]	Dormancy[2]	Storage		
					Method	Temp. °C	Interval[3]
	(A)	(B)	(C)	(D)	(E)	(F)	(G)
	Gymnospermae						
1	*Abies amabilis*	Pacific silver fir	30-300	E[5]	D, C	2-4	>3 yr
2	*A. balsamea*	Balsam fir	20->60	E[5]	D, C	2-4	5 yr
3	*A. concolor*	White fir	40-200	E[5]	D, C	2-4	>3 yr
4	*A. fraseri*	Fraser fir	30-	E[5]	D, C	2-4	>3 yr
5	*A. grandis*	Grand fir	20-300	E[5]	D, C	4-5	11 yr
6	*A. magnifica*	California red fir	50->200	E[5]	D, C	2-4	>3 yr
7	*A. procera*	Noble fir	30-300	E[5]	D, C	2-4	5 yr
8	*Chamaecyparis lawsoniana*	Port Orford cedar	8-200	E?	D, C	0-5	>1 yr
9	*C. nootkatensis*	Alaska cedar	15-300	E?	D, C	0-5	>1 yr
10	*C. thyoides*	Atlantic white cedar	4->100	E?	D, C	0-5	>1 yr
11	*Cupressus arizonica*	Arizona cypress	....	E?	D, C	5	10 yr
12	*Juniperus scopulorum*	Rocky Mountain juniper	10-300	E+SC	C	0-5	>3 yr
13	*J. virginiana*	Eastern red cedar	10-175	E+SC	D, C	-7	>2 yr
14	*Larix laricina*	Tamarack	40->150	E	D, C	2-15	>3 yr
15	*L. occidentalis*	Western larch	40-400	E[5]	D, C	5	>2 yr
16	*Libocedrus decurrens*	Incense cedar	20->200	E[5]	D, C	5	>1 yr
17	*Picea engelmannii*	Engelmann spruce	16->200	E[9]	D, C	5-20	>3 yr
18	*P. glauca*	White spruce	30->100	E	M(5%), C	2-5[10]	10 yr
19	*P. mariana*	Black spruce	30-250	E	D, C	5-20	5 yr
20	*P. rubens*	Red spruce	30->100	E	D, C	5-10	10 yr
21	*P. sitchensis*	Sitka spruce	35-300	E[5]	D, C	5	5 yr
22	*Pinus banksiana*	Jack pine	5->80	E[9]	D, C	0-5	>5 yr
23	*P. contorta*	Lodgepole pine	5->200	E[9]	D, C	0-5	>9 yr
24	*P. echinata*	Shortleaf pine	16->280	E?	M(9%), C	0-5[10]	>7 yr
25	*P. elliottii*	Slash pine	12->150	E[9]	M(9%), C	0-5[10]	6->9 yr
26	*P. jeffreyii*	Jeffrey pine	8->150	E[9]	D, C	0-5	>10 yr
27	*P. lambertiana*	Sugar pine	40-300	E[5]	D, C	0-5	>10 yr
28	*P. monticola*	Western white pine	15-300	E?+SC[5]	D, C	5	>8 yr
29	*P. palustris*	Longleaf pine	20->350	E[12]	M(6%), C	0-5[10]	>2 yr
30	*P. ponderosa*	Ponderosa pine	20-350	E[9]	M(2%), C	0-5[10]	4->20 yr
31	*P. resinosa*	Red pine	25->200	None	M(5%), C	0-10[10]	>10 yr
32	*P. strobus*	Eastern white pine	15-250	E	M(6%), C	0-5	>10 yr
33	*P. taeda*	Loblolly pine	12-150	E?	M(6%), C	0-5[10]	>7 yr
34	*Pseudotsuga menziesii*	Douglas fir	9-600	E+SC[5]	D, C	5	>4 yr
35	*Sequoia gigantea*	Giant sequoia	50->300	E[5]	D, C	-3 to -1	8-24 yr
36	*S. sempervirens*	Redwood	20->300	E[5]	D, C	-3 to -1	1-10 yr
37	*Taxodium distichum*	Bald cypress	....	E+SC?	D, C	5	>1 yr
38	*Thuja occidentalis*	Northern white cedar	20->100	E[5]	D, C	2-5	5 yr
39	*T. plicata*	Western red cedar	16->200	E[5]	D, C	0-5	>2 yr
40	*Tsuga canadensis*	Eastern hemlock	30->400	E[5]	D, C	2-5	4 yr
41	*T. heterophylla*	Western hemlock	25-300	E[5]	D, C	2-5	>3 yr
	Angiospermae (Dicotyledoneae)						
42	*Acer negundo*	Box elder	30-	E	M, C	5	18 mo
43	*A. rubrum*	Red maple	35-	E[5]	M, C	5	2 yr
44	*A. saccharinum*	Silver maple	35-	None	M, C	5	2 yr
45	*A. saccharum*	Sugar maple	40->200	E	M, C or O	0-5	>1 yr
46	*Alnus rubra*	Red alder	10-100	E?	D, C	0-5	>1 yr
47	*Betula alleghaniensis*	Yellow birch	40->70	E?	D, C	5	12 yr
48	*B. lenta*	Sweet birch	40-	E?	D	5-7	18 mo
49	*B. papyrifera*	Paper birch	15->70	E?	D	5-7	18 mo
50	*B. populifolia*	Gray birch	8-50	E?	D	5-7	18 mo
51	*Carya cordiformis*	Bitternut hickory	30-175	E	C(>90%)	5	3->5 yr
52	*C. glabra*	Pignut hickory	30-300	E	C(>90%)	5	3->5 yr
53	*C. illinoensis*	Pecan	20-300	E	C(90%)	5	3->5 yr
54	*C. laciniosa*	Shellbark hickory	40-350	E	C(90%)	5	3->5 yr

/1/ Age of most abundant production. /2/ Dormancy may be general, variable (dormant and non-dormant seeds in
/4/ Lower limit of range is night temperature, upper limit is day temperature. /5/ Variable. /6/ Plus 120 days at
7-10 days at 5°C. /9/ Occasional. /10/ Or -15 to -5°C. /11/ Or soak in water for 14 days at 5°C. /12/ Rare.

moisture content); C = in sealed containers (% indicates relative humidity); O = in open; V = under partial vacuum; sand; H_2SO_4 = soak in concentrated sulfuric acid.

Pretreatment			Sowing to Conclusion of Germination, da		Germination			Reference	
Method	Temp. °C	Duration	Pretreated	Untreated	Temp.[4] °C	Field %	Lab %		
(H)	(I)	(J)	(K)	(L)	(M)	(N)	(O)	(P)	
Gymnospermae									
P or S	5	60-90 da	30	100	20-30	15	22	9,10	1
S	5	>90 da	60-120	210	20-30	15	22	8,10	2
S	5	60-90 da	30	>100	20-30	15	34	10	3
P	5	>40 da	30-45	>100	20-30	15	42	9,10	4
P	5	30 da	30	100	20-30	15	28	10	5
S	5	60 da	30-45	>100	20-30	15	25	10	6
P or S	5	60 da	30	100	20-30	15	24	10	7
S	5	30-60 da	60	60-110	20-30	25	52	9,10	8
S	5	60-90 da	60	>300	20-30	5	10	10	9
S	5	30-60 da	60	60-110	20-30	40	84	10	10
S	5	60 da	30	75	20-30	15	26	10	11
P or S	20-30	120 da[6]	20-30	>200	20-30	20	22	10	12
H_2SO_4	......	30 min[7]	20-30	>180	10-25	30	42	1,10	13
S	5	30-60 da[8]	30-50	110	20-30	30	47	9,10	14
S	5	30 da	20-30	60	20-30	20	27	2,10	15
S	2-5	60-90 da	20-30	>60	15-27	25	50	9,10	16
None	......	....	.....	50	20-27	45	69	10	17
S	5	60-90 da[11]	30-45	50-140	20-30	35	50	4,5,8-10	18
S	5	30-60 da[8]	20-30	30-80	20-30	40	64	8-10	19
S	5	30-45 da	20-30	30-50	20-30	40	60	9,10	20
S	5-10	60-90 da	50	60	25-25	40	60	10	21
None	......	....	.....	15-60	20-30	45	68	9,10	22
None	......	....	30	60	15-27	40	64	9,10	23
P or S	2-4	30-45 da	35-45	60-120	15-27	35	68	9,10	24
P or S	2-5	15-45 da	20-40	45	20-30	30	61	9,10	25
None	......	....	.....	60-90	15-27	50	68	9,10	26
P or S	2-5	90 da	40	120	15-20	35	56	9,10	27
P or S	2-5	90 da	60-90	200	15-27	30	48	9,10	28
None	......	....	35	30-40	13-25	35	54	9,10	29
None	......	....	30	60	20-30	45	59	9,10	30
None	......	....	.....	30	20-30	55	75	9,10	31
P or S	10	30 da[8]	30-40	60-100	20-30	50	64	8-10	32
P or S	2-4	30-90 da	35-45	70	20-30	30	60	9,10,12	33
S	5	30-60 da	15-30	60-90	15-35	55	85	9,10	34
None	......	....	.....	40-60	15-20	15	25	9-11	35
None	......	....	.....	40-60	15-20	5	10	9,10	36
P or S	5	30-60 da	30-50	60-110	20-30	8	12	10	37
S	0-10	30-60 da	30	50	20-30	30	46	10	38
S	0-10	30-60 da	20	40	20-30	35	51	9,10	39
S	5	60-120 da	60	200	20-30	20	38	10	40
S	5	90 da	30	>90	10-15	30	56	10	41
Angiospermae (Dicotyledoneae)									
S	5	90 da	50-60	300	10-25	15	33	9,10	42
S	5	60-75 da	30-40	>90	10-25	58	46	10	43
None	......	....	.....	20-30	25-30	18	76	10	44
P or S	3-5	60-90 da	30	>150	20-30	15	39	10	45
S	5	30-60 da	30-40	60	20-30	14	27	9,10	46
P or S	5	30-60 da	30-40	120	15-32	15	27	9,10	47
P or S	0-5	40-70 da	30	90	15-32	15	43	10	48
P or S	5	60-75 da	30-40	>100	15-32	15	34	10	49
P or S	0-10	60->90 da	40	>120	20-30	25	64	10	50
P or S	0-7	90-120 da	30-45	250-300	20-30	55	55	10	51
P or S	0-7	90-120 da	30-45	250-300	20-30	40	85	10	52
P or S	2-7	30-90 da	45-60	200-300	20-30	50	50	10	53
P or S	0-7	120-150 da	45-60	300-350	20-30	55	...	10	54

same sample), occasional, or rare; type is general unless otherwise indicated. /3/ Without serious loss in viability. 5°C. /7/ Or stratify in moist soil for 30 days at 25°C, then stratify for 90 days at 5°C. /8/ Or soak in water for

continued

	Species	Common Name	Seed-bearing Age, yr[1]	Dormancy[2]	Storage		
					Method	Temp. °C	Interval[3]
	(A)	(B)	(C)	(D)	(E)	(F)	(G)
	Angiospermae (Dicotyledoneae)						
55	*Carya ovata*	Shagbark hickory	40-300	E	C(>90%)	5	3->5 yr
56	*C. tomentosa*	Mockernut hickory	25-200	E	C(>90%)	5	3->5 yr
57	*Castanea dentata*	American chestnut	20->150	E	P or S	0-5	6 mo
58	*Catalpa speciosa*	Northern catalpa	20-	None?	D, C	0-5	>2 yr
59	*Celtis occidentalis*	Hackberry	25-	E+SC?	D, C	2-5	>5 yr
60	*Fagus grandifolia*	American beech	40-100	E	D, C	1-5	>6 mo
61	*Fraxinus americana*	White ash	20-175	E	D, C	2-5	>3 yr
62	*F. pennsylvanica*	Green ash	20-	E	D, C	5	5 yr
63	*Gleditsia triacanthos*	Honey locust	10-100	SC	C	0-7	3 yr
64	*Gymnocladus dioicus*	Kentucky coffee tree	20->100	SC	D, C	0-5	>1 yr
65	*Juglans cinerea*	Butternut	20-80	E+SC?	D, C	2-5	>4 yr
66	*J. nigra*	Black walnut	12-130	E+SC?	D, C	2-5	>1 yr
67	*Liquidambar styraciflua*	Sweet gum	20-150	E?	D, C	5	>1 yr
68	*Liriodendron tulipifera*	Yellow poplar	15->200	E+SC?	D, C	0-5	>1 yr
69	*Nyssa sylvatica*	Black tupelo	....	E	S	5	6 mo
70	*Platanus occidentalis*	Sycamore	25-250	E?	D, C	2-5	>1 yr
71	*Populus deltoides*	Eastern cottonwood	10-death	None	V	5	8 mo
72	*P. tremuloides*	Quaking aspen	20->70	None	D, C	5	>1 yr
73	*Prunus serotina*	Black cherry	10-180	E+SC?	C	5	>2 yr
74	*Quercus alba*	White oak	20-300	None	D, C (80-90%)	0-2	>1 yr
75	*Q. coccinea*	Scarlet oak	20-150	E	D, C (80-90%)	0-2	>1 yr
76	*Q. falcata*	Southern red oak	25-125	E	D, C (80-90%)	0-2	>1 yr
77	*Q. macrocarpa*	Bur oak	35-400	E[5, 14]	D, C (80-90%)	0-2	>1 yr
78	*Q. michauxii*	Swamp chestnut oak	25->100	None	D, C (80-90%)	0-2	>1 yr
79	*Q. prinus*	Chestnut oak	20-150	None	D, C (80-90%)	0-2	>1 yr
80	*Q. rubra*	Northern red oak	25-200	E	D, C (80-90%)	0-2	>1 yr
81	*Q. velutina*	Black oak	20-100	E	D, C (80-90%)	0-2	>1 yr
82	*Robinia pseudoacacia*	Black locust	6-60	SC	D, C	0-5	>10 yr
83	*Tilia americana*	American basswood	15->100	E+SC	D, C	5	>2 yr
84	*Ulmus americana*	American elm	15-300	E[5]	D, C	5	>2 yr
85	*U. rubra*	Slippery elm	15-200	E[15]	D, C	5	>1 yr
86	*U. thomasii*	Rock elm	20-250	None	D, C	5	>1 yr

/1/ Age of most abundant production. /2/ Dormancy may be general, variable (dormant and non-dormant seeds in
/4/ Lower limit of range is night temperature, upper limit is day temperature. /5/ Variable. /13/ Plus 60-90 days
/15/ In northern regions.

Contributor: Rudolf, Paul O.

References: [1] Barton, L. V. 1951. Contribs. Boyce Thompson Inst. 16:387. [2] Boe, K. N. 1958. U. S. Forest Service Central States Forest Expt. Sta. Misc. Release 22. [4] Cram, W. H. 1951. Forestry Chron. [6] Hough, A. F. 1960. U. S. Forest Service Northeastern Forest Expt. Sta. Paper 139. [7] Johnson, L. P. V. [10] Rudolf, P. O., et al. 1948. U. S. Dept. Agr. Misc. Publ. 654. [11] Schubert, G. H. 1957. U. S. Forest Southeastern Forest Expt. Sta. Paper 98.

Pretreatment			Sowing to Conclusion of Germination, da		Germination			Reference	
Method	Temp. °C	Duration	Pretreated	Untreated	Temp.[4] °C	Field %	Lab %		
(H)	(I)	(J)	(K)	(L)	(M)	(N)	(O)	(P)	
Angiospermae (Dicotyledoneae)									
P or S	2-7	90-150 da	45-60	300-350	20-30	55	80	10	55
P or S	-1 to +2	90-150 da	45-60	300-350	20-30	65	66	10	56
P or S	0-5	90 da	30-45	100	15-25	55	72	10	57
None	......	....	.....	60	20-30	70	75	10	58
S	5	60-90 da	60	60-100	20-30	20	41	9,10	59
S	5	90 da	60	150-160	20-30	40	85	10	60
P or S	5	60-90 da	40-60	>60	20-30	20	38	9,10	61
P or S	5	60-90 da	40-60	60->90	20-30	20	42	10	62
H_2SO_4	25-36	1-2 hr	15-40	120-180	20-30	50	50	10	63
P or S	18-30	60->120 da[13]	60-90	200	20-30	50	75	10	64
P or S	2-7	90-120 da	45-60	>110	20-30	50	65	10	65
P or S	1-10	60-120 da	15-40	100-300	20-30	55	75	3,10	66
S	5	30-90 da	20-60	120-200	20-30	50	70	9,10	67
P	0-10	70 da	50-70	90-180	20-30	3	5	9,10	68
S	0-5	60-90 da	30-60	>150	20-30	20	30	9,10	69
P or S	2-5	45-60 da	15-20	30-60	20-30	20	35	9,10	70
None	......	....	.....	2-6	20-30	80	88	9,10	71
None	......	....	.....	7	20-30	50	59	9,10	72
P or S	5	90-120 da	30	>190	15-30	30	63	6,9,10	73
None	......	....	.....	30-50	20-30	66	78	10	74
S	0-5	30-60 da	60	>240	20-30	60	62	9,10	75
S	0-4	30-45 da	30-40	>240	15-25	65	<90	9,10	76
S	5	30-45 da	40	130->225	20-30	45	45	9,10	77
None	......	....	.....	110	15-25	80	87	9,10	78
None	......	....	.....	60	18-27	80	82	10	79
S	0-4	30-45 da	40-60	>300	20-30	70	58	10	80
S	1-5	30-60 da	30-50	>240	18-27	>50	47	10	81
H_2SO_4	17-27	20-120 min	10-25	40-70	15-27	25	68	9,10	82
P or S	2-5	110-130 da	30-60	200-1000	18-29	20	34	7,10	83
S	5	60 da	15-60	90	20-30	15	63	9,10	84
S	5	60-90 da	50-70	90->120	20-30	10	17	9,10	85
None	......	....	.....	4-10	20-30	35	85	9,10	86

same sample), occasional, or rare; type is general unless otherwise indicated. /3/ Without serious loss in viability. at 1-5°C. /14/ No embryo dormancy in species proper, but general embryo dormancy in variety *olivaeformis*.

Forest Service Intermountain Forest and Range Expt. Sta. Misc. Publ. 16. [3] Brinkman, K. A. 1957. U. S. 27:349. [5] Crossley, D. I., and L. Skov. 1951. Can. Dept. Resources and Develop. Silvicultural Leaflet 59. 1946. Forestry Chron. 22:182. [8] Rudolf, P. O. 1950. J. Forestry 48:31. [9] Rudolf, P. O. Unpublished, 1961. Service Calif. Forest and Range Expt. Sta. Tech. Paper 20. [12] Wenger, K. F. 1958. U. S. Forest Service

VII. PRENATAL VERTEBRATE DEVELOPMENT

60. EARLY PRENATAL DEVELOPMENT: MAN

Diagrams illustrate the development of the embryonic germ layers and their derivatives but are not meant to show size relationships between various stages.

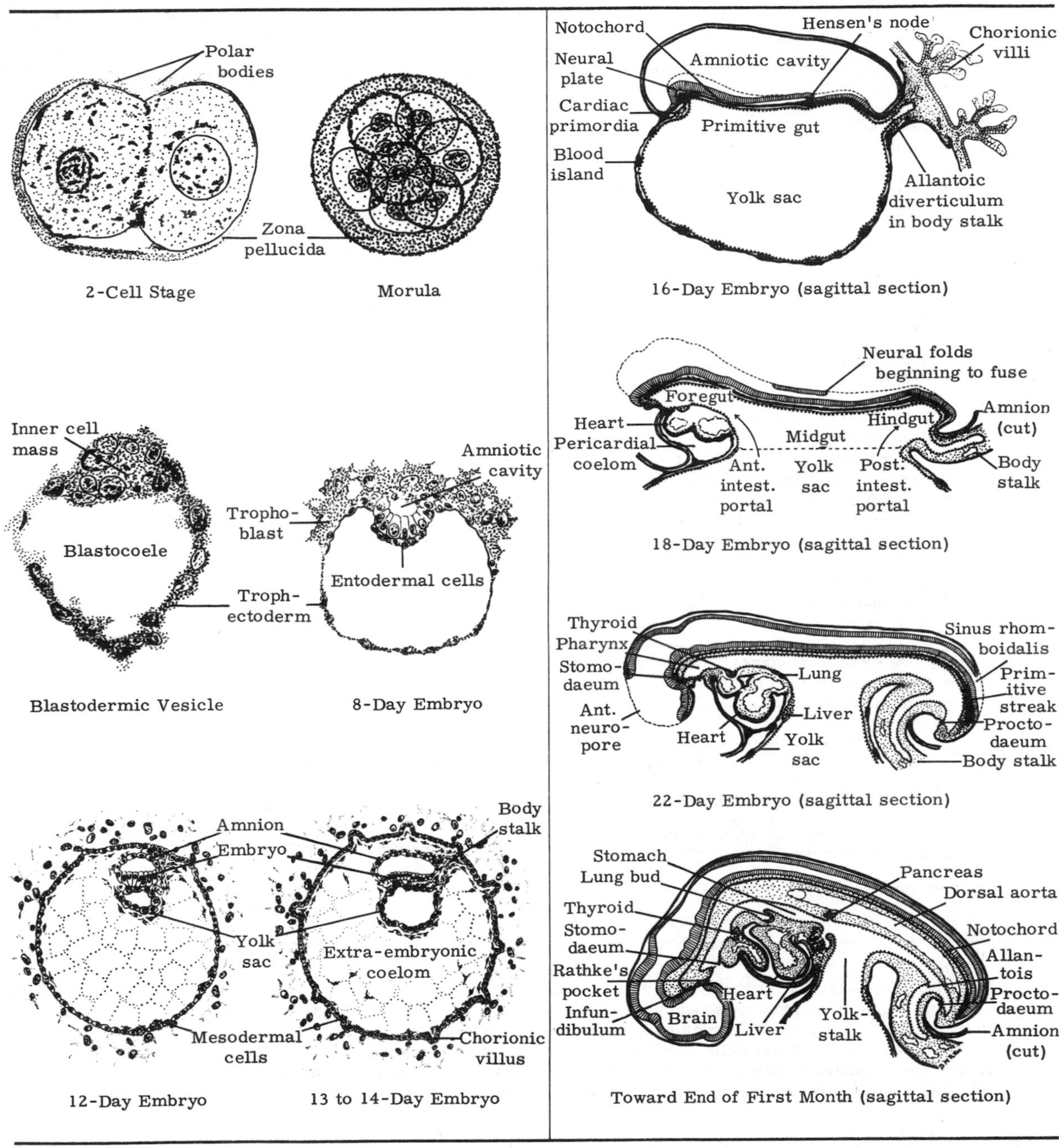

Contributors: (a) Hertig, Arthur T., (b) Patten, Bradley M.

References: [1] Hertig, A. T., et al. 1954. Contribs. Embryol. Carnegie Inst. Wash. 35:199. [2] Patten, B. M. 1953. Human embryology. Ed. 2. Blakiston, New York.

Adapted from B. M. Patten, *Human Embryology*, Blakiston,

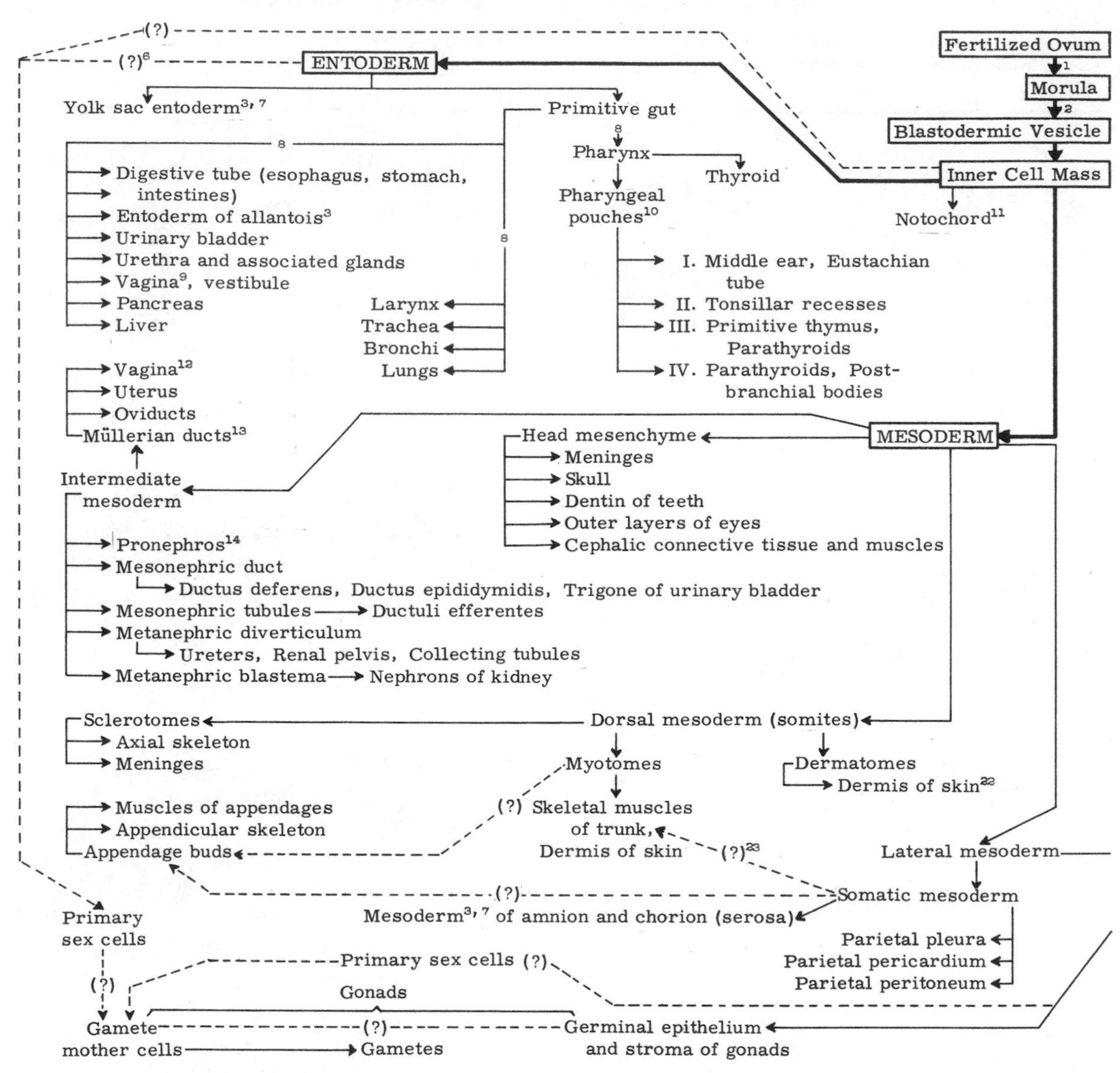

/1/ By cleavage divisions. /2/ By hollowing out and expansion. /3/ Extra-embryonic. /4/ Not present in all mammals. from entoderm, remainder from mesoderm. /9/ Lower part. /10/ Between visceral arches I-IV. /11/ Embryonic of peritoneum. /14/ Embryonic structure (disappears). /15/ Epithelial portion of structures from ectoderm, ectoderm along with neural crest cells. /18/ Probably in part only; remainder of pia, and all of dura and arachnoid, be derived from ectodermal placodes. /20/ Derivation from neural crest still disputed. /21/ Pars anterior, pars from chick only). /24/ Not all from splanchnic mesoderm; some from somatic mesoderm or head mesenchyme.

Contributors: (a) Patten, Bradley M., (b) Reyer, Randall W., (c) Hertig, Arthur T., (d) Arey, Leslie B.

DERIVATIVES: EUTHERIAN MAMMALS

New York, 1953. Broken line indicates disputed origin.

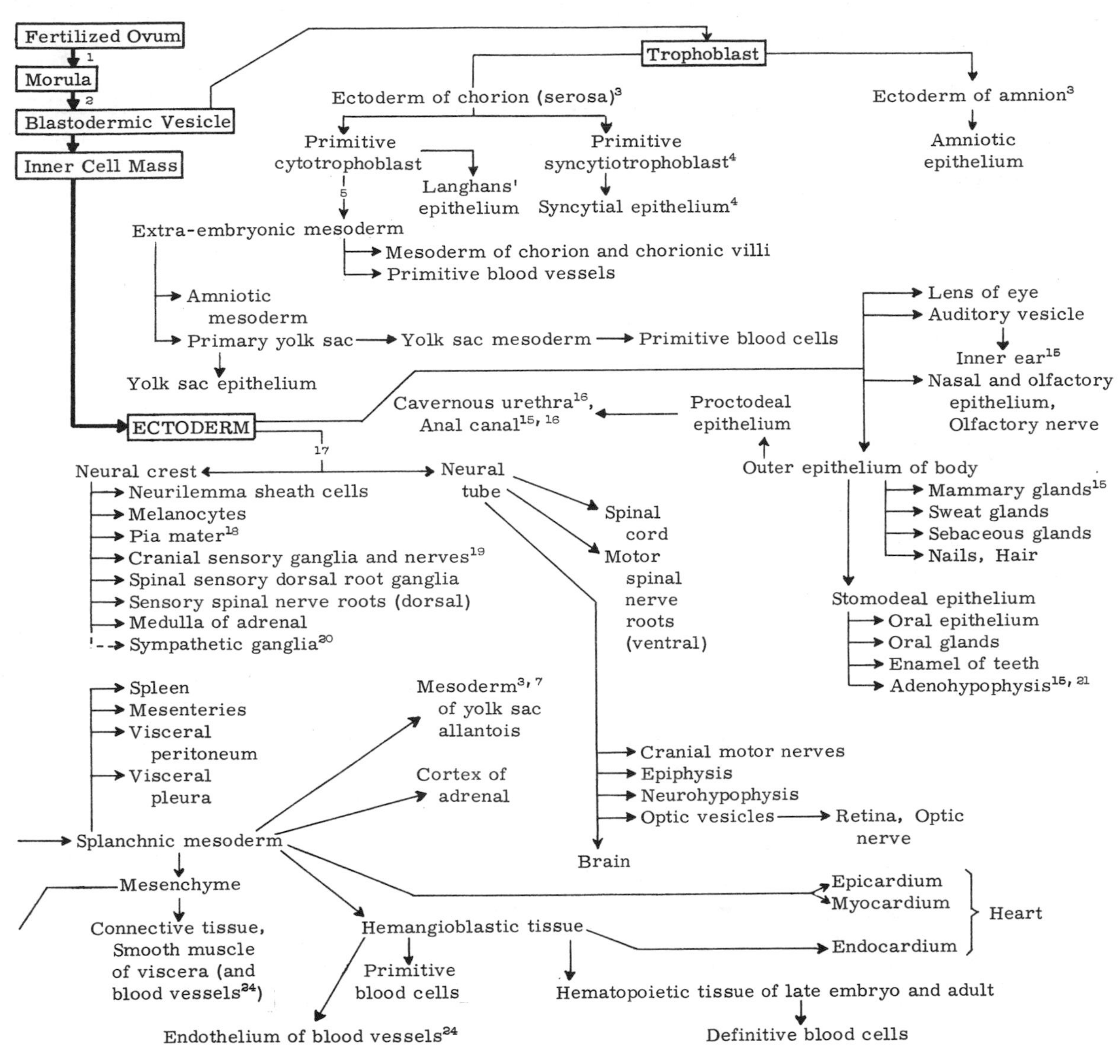

/5/ In primates only. /6/ In man. /7/ Probably not in primates. /8/ Epithelial and glandular portion of structure structure; may form nucleus pulposus of intervertebral discs. /12/ Upper part. /13/ Or from splanchnic mesoderm remainder from mesoderm. /16/ In part only. /17/ In rostral areas of head, some mesenchyme comes in from the from mesenchyme. /19/ Evidence from lower vertebrates indicates that a portion of these ganglia and nerves may tuberalis, and pars intermedia of pituitary. /22/ In region of somites only. /23/ Ventral and lateral part (evidence

62. TIME VARIATIONS IN PRENATAL DEVELOPMENT: MAMMALS AND BIRDS

In mammals, hours and days were counted from time of fertilization. In birds, one day was allowed for intrauterine development and added to the incubation age (lines 4-10). Sex differentiation most often occurs at Stage 30 but varies between Stages 28 (rat) and possibly 35 (opossum).

	Standard Stages (Witschi)	Identification of Stages	Man	Rhesus Monkey	Sheep	Swine	Hamster	Rat	Rabbit	Opossum	Chick	Hawk	Sparrow
	(A)	(B)	(C)	(D)	(E)	(F)	(G)	(H)	(I)	(J)	(K)	(L)	(M)
1	2	2 cells	38 hr	24 hr	30 hr	30 hr	16 hr	24 hr	8 hr	40 hr	3 hr	......	......
2	3	4 cells	48 hr	36 hr	34 hr	40 hr	40 hr	48 hr	11 hr	56 hr	$3\frac{1}{4}$ hr	......	......
3	7-8	Beginning of implantation	$6\frac{1}{2}$ da	9 da	10 da	.....	$4\frac{1}{2}$ da	6 da	7 da	6 da	.....	......	......
4	12	Primitive streak	19 da	19 da	13 da	11 da	$6\frac{1}{2}$-7 da	$8\frac{1}{2}$ da	$6\frac{1}{2}$ da	$6\frac{1}{2}$ da	$1\frac{1}{2}$ da	......	$1\frac{1}{2}$ da
5	16	13-20 somite embryo	27 da	25 da	17 da	16 da	8 da	$10\frac{1}{2}$ da	9 da	9 da	3 da	$4\frac{1}{2}$ da	$2\frac{1}{2}$ da
6	18	Formation of tail bud	29 da	26 da	18 da	17 da	$8\frac{1}{2}$ da	$11\frac{1}{2}$ da	$9\frac{1}{2}$ da	$9\frac{1}{2}$ da	$3\frac{1}{4}$ da	......	$3\frac{1}{4}$ da
7	25	End of embryonic period	36 da	28 da	21 da	20 da	9 da	$12\frac{1}{2}$ da	10 da	10 da	5 da	9 da	5 da
8	33-34	End of metamorphosis	60 da	40 da	32 da	35 da	$13\frac{1}{2}$ da	$16\frac{1}{2}$ da	14 da	12 da	$8\frac{1}{2}$ da	$13\frac{1}{2}$ da	8 da
9	35	Closed eyelids	70 da	48 da	42 da	50 da	......	18 da	19 da	$12\frac{1}{4}$ da	13 da	23 da	11 da
10	36	Open eyelids	140 da	......	84 da	90 da	......	38 da[1]	42 da[2]	72 da[3]	21 da	......	20 da[4]
	Birth or hatching												
11	Age		267 da	164 da	150 da	112 da	16 da	22 da	32 da	$12\frac{1}{2}$ da	22 da	36 da	14 da
12	Standard Stages (Witschi)		36	36	36	36	35	35	35+	35	36	35-36	35
13	Weight		3.2 kg	450 g	5 kg	2.5 kg	2.2 g	4.5 g	57 g	0.13 g	34 g	12 g	1.7 g
14	Weight relative to mother		5.5%	7.5%	8%	2.5%	2.3%	2.25%	3%	0.01%	3%	......	6%

/1/ 16 days after birth. /2/ 10 days after birth. /3/ 60 days after birth. /4/ 6 days after hatching.

Contributor: Witschi, Emil

Reference: Witschi, E. 1956. Development of vertebrates. W. B. Saunders, Philadelphia. Also see references appended to tables 64, 66-68.

63. EQUIVALENT NUMERICAL DESIGNATIONS FOR STAGING SYSTEMS: AMPHIBIANS AND FISHES

	Phase	Standard Stages (Witschi)	*Rana pipiens*[1]	*Rana fusca*	*Bufo valliceps*	*Xenopus laevis*	*Ambystoma maculatum*[2]	*Triturus vulgaris*	*Ambystoma mexicanum*[3]	*Salmo irideus*
	(A)	(B)	(C)	(D)	(E)	(F)	(G)	(H)	(I)	(J)
1	Cleavage	1-6	2-7	1-2	1-7	1-6	1-6	0-5	1-6	1-6
2	Blastula	7	8, 9	3	8, 9	7-9	7, 8	6	7	7
3	Gastrula	8-11	10-12	4-5	10-13	10-12	9-12	7-12	8-11	8-11
4	Primitive streak	12	13	6	13	12.5	13	13	12	12
5	Neurula	13-17	14-17	7-10	14-17	13-23	14-22	14-20	13-17	13-17
6	Tail bud	13-24	18-24	11-17	18-24	24-44	23-39	21-36	18-24	18-24
7	Larva	25	25, I	18	25-27	47	40	37	25	25[4]
	Metamorphosis									
8	Incipient	26-29	II-XVII	19-25	28-40	48-57	41-46	38-52	26-29	
9	Climactic I	30	XVIII, XIX	26	41	58	St. 30	53-55		
10	Climactic II	31	XX	27	42	59-61	St. 31	56		
11	Climactic III	32	XXI, XXII	28, 29	43	62-64	St. 32			
12	Climactic IV	33	XXIII, XXIV	30	44-46	65-66				
	Reference	11	8, 9	3	4	6	2, 11	1	11	11

/1/ Arabic numbers after Shumway [8], Roman after Taylor and Kollros [9]. A complete table for *Rana pipiens* is given in reference 11; other species of frogs are considered in references 5, 7, 10. /2/ Harrison's series, being incomplete, is extended by standard stages (St. 30 to 32). /3/ The primitive perennibranchiate salamanders (e.g. *Necturus, Proteus, Cryptobranchus*), much like *Ambystoma mexicanum*, stop development at about stage 29, without entering climactic metamorphosis. /4/ Adult fish.

Contributor: Witschi, Emil

continued

63. EQUIVALENT NUMERICAL DESIGNATIONS FOR STAGING SYSTEMS: AMPHIBIANS AND FISHES

References: [1] Glaesner, L. 1925. In F. Keibel, ed. Normentafeln. G. Fischer, Jena. v. 14. [2] Harrison, R. G. Unpublished, 1955. [3] Kopsch, F. 1952. Die Entwicklung des braunen Grasfrosches *Rana fusca* (Roesel). G. Thieme, Stuttgart. [4] Limbaugh, B. A., and E. P. Volpe. 1957. Am. Museum Novitates 1842. [5] Mangold, O. 1929. Ergeb. Biol. 5:290. [6] Nieuwkoop, P. D. 1956. Normal table of *Xenopus laevis* (Daudin). North Holland Publ. Co., Amsterdam. [7] Pollister, A. W., and J. A. Moore. 1937. Anat. Record 68:489. [8] Shumway, W. 1940. Ibid. 78:139. [9] Taylor, A., and J. J. Kollros. 1946. Ibid. 94:7. [10] Tschernoff, N. D. 1907. Anat. Anz. 30:593. [11] Witschi, E. 1956. Development of vertebrates. W. B. Saunders, Philadelphia.

64. CHARACTERIZATION OF DEVELOPMENTAL STAGES: MAN

Age (column C) = fertilization or ovulation age, usually calculated from last menstruation age (minus 14 days). Size (column D) = greatest diameter, or crown-to-rump length (approximate chorionic size given in parentheses). Identification (column E) is for standard stages, and therefore Streeter's horizons are not always comparable to the information given.

	Standard Stages (Witschi)	Streeter's Horizons	Age da	Size mm	Identification of Stages	Reference
	(A)	(B)	(C)	(D)	(E)	(F)
					Cleavage and Blastula	
1	1	I	1	0.125	1 cell; in the tubes of the oviducts	18,23
2	2	II	2	0.115	2 cells; in the tubes of the oviducts	6,23
3	3	II		0.115	4 cells; in the tubes of the oviducts	6,23
4	4	II	3	0.100	8-12 cells (morula), entering the uterus	6
5	5	III	4	0.101	Early blastocyst (58 cells), in lumen of uterus	6
6	6	III	5	0.095	Free blastocyst (107 cells), in lumen of uterus	6
7	7	III			Blastocyst beginning of implantation	6
					Gastrula	
8	8	IV	7-8	0.05(0.3)	Bilaminar disc (embryoblast) amniotic cavity	5,27
9	9	V	9	0.1(0.5)	Embryonic disc and exoembryonic envelopes; exoem ryonic mesoderm	5
10	10	VI	11-13	0.15(1.0)	Beginning primitive streak; yolk sac; exocoelem	4,27
11	11	VII	14-17	0.3(2.5)	Median primitive streak; syn- and cytotrophoblast	10,15,27
					Primitive Streak	
12	12	VIII	19	0.7(8.0)	Complete primitive streak; villous chorion	14,15,27
					Neurula	
13	13	IX	20	1.5(12.0)	Presomite neurula; spreading neural plate	8,21
14	14	X	21	2(13)	Occipital somites 1-4; neural folds; invagination canal	9,16,22,24
15	15	X	24	2.8(16.0)	Cervical somites 5-12; neural tube starts forming	1,9,15,17,20,21
16	16	XI	27	3.3(22.0)	Thoracal somites 13-20; two visceral arches; upper and lower neuropores; germ cells start leaving yolk sac	7,25-27
17	17	XII	28	3.5	Thoracal somites 21-24; three visceral arches; oral membrane ruptures	2,13,25
					Tail Bud Embryo	
18	18	XII	29	3.8(24.0)	Lumbar somites 25-27; oral membrane resorbed; germ cells in hindgut and ventral mesentery	19,25,26
19	19	XII	30	4(25)	Lumbar somites 28-29; appendicular ridges	25,27
20	20	XIII	31	4.3(26.0)	Sacral somites 30-32; arm and leg buds appear; germ cell migration reaches borders of mesonephric ridges	25-27
21	21	XIII	32	4.6(27.0)	Sacral somites 33-34; four visceral arches	25
22	22	XIII	33	4.8(28.0)	Caudal somites 35-36; otic vesicles detach	12,25
23	23	XIII	34	5(29)	Caudal somites 37; slender yolk stalk	15,25
24	24	XIII	35	5.4(30.0)	Caudal somites 38; lens placode; germ cells from hindgut to median mesonephric ridges	25,26

continued

64. CHARACTERIZATION OF DEVELOPMENTAL STAGES: MAN

	Standard Stages (Witschi)	Streeter's Horizons	Age da	Size mm	Identification of Stages	Reference
	(A)	(B)	(C)	(D)	(E)	(F)
					Complete Embryo	
25	25	XIV	35-37	6(28-35)	End of somite formation; arm and leg buds fully formed; regression of tail bud; germ cells in genital ridges, end of migration	3,11,25, 27
					Metamorphosing Embryo	
26	26	XV	38	8(32)	Differentiation of hand plate; beginning of umbilical hernia	11,25
27	27	XVI	40	8-10(35)	Visceral arches III and IV disappear under cervical fold and operculum; eyes pigmented; yolk sac separates from gut	25
28	28	XVII	42	12	Pentadactyl rudiments; closing of cervical sinus	25
29	29	XVII	44	12.5-14.0(40.0)	Median processes of maxillaries advancing; chorionic villi longer where umbilicus attaches; cartilage formation in vertebrae	19,22,25, 27
30	30	XVIII	46	14.6	Premaxillary processes; beginning sexual differentiation of gonads	19,26,29
31	31	XVIII	48	15.6	Closing of facial clefts; hands and feet lateral to body wall	25,27
32	32	XIX	50	17	Phalanges, first links; hands, far apart, bending over heart; first ossification centers in mandible and clavicle	25
33	33	XX-XXII	56	22-25(47)	Closed facial clefts; auricles rising; large umbilical hernia; arms and feet growing, fingers from left and right touch nose	25,27
					Fetus	
34	34	XXIII+	56-70	26-45	1st fetal stage: growth of eyelids; gut withdrawal from hernia; palatine raphe; differentiation of male and female external genitalia	11,15,25, 27,28
35	35		70-140	45-180	2nd fetal stage: periderm sealed eyelids; ossification of vertebral column begins; first ovocytes in ovaries; hair follicles; disc placenta	19,27,29
36	36		140-266	180-340	3rd fetal stage: resorption of periderm; cornification and separation of eyelids; lanugo; uterovaginal differentiation	19,27,28

Contributor: Witschi, Emil

References: [1] Corner, G. W. 1929. Contribs. Embryol. Carnegie Inst. Wash. 20:81. [2] Davis, C. L. 1923. Ibid. 15:1. [3] Hamilton, W. J., J. D. Boyd, and H. W. Mossman. 1952. Human embryology. Ed. 2. Williams and Wilkins, Baltimore. p. 87. [4] Hertig, A. T., and J. Rock. 1941. Contribs. Embryol. Carnegie Inst. Wash. 29:127. [5] Hertig, A. T., and J. Rock. 1945. Ibid. 31:65. [6] Hertig, A. T., et al. 1954. Ibid. 35:199. [7] Heuser, C. H. 1930. Ibid. 22:135. [8] Heuser, C. H. 1932. Ibid. 23:251. [9] Heuser, C. H., and G. W. Corner. 1957. Ibid. 36:29. [10] Heuser, C. H., J. Rock, and A. T. Hertig. 1945. Ibid. 31:85. [11] His, W. 1880-85. Anatomie menschlicher Embryonen. Atlas. Vogel, Leipzig. [12] Ingalls, N. W. 1907. Arch. mikroskop. Anat. u. Entwicklungsmech. 70:506. [13] Johnson, F. P. 1917. Contribs. Embryol. Carnegie Inst. Wash. 6:125. [14] Jones, H. O., and J. I. Brewer. 1941. Ibid. 29:157. [15] Keibel, F. 1910. In F. Keibel and F. P. Mall, ed. Manual of human embryology. v. 1, pp. 59-90. [16] Ludwig, E. 1928. Morphol. Jahrb. 59:41. [17] Ludwig, E. 1929. Compt. rend. assoc. anat. 24me réunion (Bordeaux), p. 580. [18] Mankin, M. F., and J. Rock. 1948. Am. J. Obstet. Gynecol. 55:440. [19] Patten, B. M. 1953. Human embryology. Ed. 2. Blakiston, Philadelphia. ch. 5 and 7. [20] Payne, F. 1925. Contribs. Embryol. Carnegie Inst. Wash. 16:115. [21] Politzer, G., and F. Hann. 1935. Z. Anat. Entwicklungsgeschichte 104:670. [22] Sensenig, E. C. 1957. Contribs. Embryol. Carnegie Inst. Wash. 36:141. [23] Shettles, L. B. 1953. Am. J. Obstet. Gynecol. 66:235. [24] Sternberg, H. 1927. Z. Anat. Entwicklungsgeschichte 82:747. [25] Streeter, G. L. 1951. Contribs. Embryol. Carnegie Inst. Wash., Embryol. reprint

continued

64. CHARACTERIZATION OF DEVELOPMENTAL STAGES: MAN

vol. 2. [26] Witschi, E. 1948. Ibid. 32:67. [27] Witschi, E. 1956. Development of vertebrates. W. B. Saunders, Philadelphia. [28] Witschi, E. 1959. Ann. N. Y. Acad. Sci. 75:412. [29] Witschi, E. 1962. In H. G. Grady and D. E. Smith, ed. The ovary. Williams and Wilkins, Baltimore.

65. DEVELOPMENT OF TISSUES AND ORGANS: MAN

Data must be considered with discretion because of certain discrepancies between embryological terminology and fact. The changes which constitute development are continuous but can only be described as stages, in discontinuous units of time, and as anatomical or functional events. Also, since many of the changes are essentially unmeasurable, data may have been estimated, qualified, or given different interpretations by different authors. Size (column D) = crown-to-rump length.

Part I: NERVOUS SYSTEM

	Standard Stages (Witschi)	Streeter's Horizons	Age	Size mm	Structural Development	Reference
	(A)	(B)	(C)	(D)	(E)	(F)
1	12	VIII	ca. 18 da	1.0-1.5	Elongated neural plate	24
2	13	IX	ca. 19 da	1-2	Neural folds wider in brain region than caudally	21
3	14-15	X	ca. 22 da	2	Groove deepens; neural folds begin to close at 4th to 5th somite level. Midbrain cranial flexure. Four distinct rhombomeres. Optic primordium begins at 8 somite stage. Neural crest proliferates from mid- and hindbrain for cranial nerve V.	1,2,5, 14
4	16	XI	24±1 da	3-5	Optic vesicle formed. Neural tube begins to close anteriorly and posteriorly, except for small area--anterior neuropore. Ventricle IV begins to enlarge. Neural crest from rhombomere 4 reaches epibranchial placode of nerve VII; neural crest for nerves IX and X. Spinal flexure sometimes present.	3,6
5	17-19	XII	26±1 da	3.8-4.9	Anterior neuropore closed. Midbrain flexure present. Beginning evagination of corpus mamillare and tuber cinereum. Three brain vesicles present. Rhombomeres 1 to 5 recognizable as related to neural crest for nerves V to X.	24
6	20-24	XIII	27±1 da	4-6	Posterior neuropore closed (from 24 hours to 5 days after closure of anterior neuropore). Spinal flexure disappears; cervical flexure present. Sulcus limitans present in spinal cord; ventral horn neuroblasts differentiated; mantle zone in alar plate. Fovea isthmi appear; rapid expansion of ventricle IV with thinning of roof. Mesencephalic tegmentum differentiated. Neural layer of retina and lens plate appear.	25
7	25	XIV	29±1 da	5.5-7.3	Afferent and efferent roots of cranial nerves V to X present; beginning of nerves III, IV, and XII. Rhombomeres are folds of entire wall of hindbrain; cerebellar lamina present. Cerebral vesicle arises; telencephalon medium distinct from diencephalon roof plate. Thickening of walls of hypothalamus.	3,25
8	26	XV	31±1 da	7-9	Afferent and efferent root fibers of spinal nerves developed; long tracts in tegmentum of mid- and hindbrain, also in hypothalamus. Epiphysis and velum transversum differentiated. Commissure bed and chiasma thicken in embryonic lamina terminalis; optic stalk prominent. Rhombomeres well-defined; telencephalic vesicle present as single evagination (i.e., 4 brain vesicles). Beginning of thickening of anterior lip of lateral recess. Olfactory placode present.	12,18, 26
9	27	XVI	33±1 da	7-11	Sympathetic components of spinal nerves present. Five cerebral vesicles present; beginning of 2 telencephalic vesicles; 4 parts of diencephalon distinct. Corpus striatum present; hippocampal primordium, earliest differentiation of cerebral cortex, appears.	3,15,26

continued

65. DEVELOPMENT OF TISSUES AND ORGANS: MAN

Part I: NERVOUS SYSTEM

	Standard Stages (Witschi)	Streeter's Horizons	Age	Size mm	Structural Development	Reference
	(A)	(B)	(C)	(D)	(E)	(F)
10	28-29	XVII	35±1 da	10.8-14.2	Rhombic grooves obliterated by developing nuclei and fiber systems. Cerebellar lamina grows. Appearance of pontine flexure. Choroid plexuses well-defined; vascularization of those of lateral ventricle; thinning of ependyma in roof of diencephalon and rhombencephalon. Lamina terminalis divided into 2 parts; posterior commissure present. Epiphyseal evagination thinned; nuclei of hypothalamus and ventral thalamus differentiated. Sulcus limitans and sulcus hypothalamicus prominent. Postophthalmic commissure fibers in chiasma; olfactory lobe present. Nerve fibers extend between corpus striatum and neopallium.	3,15, 19, 26
11	30-31	XVIII	37±1 da	11.7-17.0	Few nerve fibers in optic chiasma and anterior commissure; optic recess closed; olfactory evagination prominent. Lateral choroid plexus evagination at level of paraphysis; pars crassa of lamina terminalis thickens. Evagination of posterior lobe of hypophysis hollow; epiphysis well-evaginated; ridge between dorsal and ventral thalamus prominent. Major tract of brain stem recognizable; superior and inferior colliculi outlined.	15,17, 26
12	32	XIX	39±1 da	16.3-19.1	Alar plate of spinal cord thickens. Cerebral vesicle lies rostral to lamina terminalis and caudal to midlevel of diencephalon; lateral choroid plexus and paraphysis vascularized. Commissure bed and chiasma expanding. Olfactory fibers enter olfactory bulb; internal capsule fibers, stria medullaris thalami, and fasciculus retroflexus present.	3,15,17
13	33	XX	41±1 da	18-23	Earliest reflex responses obtained. Differentiation of roof of ventricle IV; site of foramen of Magendie can be recognized in roof of ventricle IV. Posterior growth of telencephalic vesicle reaches level of posterior commissure; habenular commissure appears. First optic fibers in chiasma.	3,10,20
14		XXII	45±1 da	24-27	Rapid enlargement of lateral choroid plexus; cerebral pedicles indicated; internal capsule prominent. "Cortical plate" appears in neopallium in wall overlying corpus striatum. Folding of roof of diencephalon begins; lamination of nerve cells in colliculi; neuroblasts cluster in habenula; superior colliculus has appeared. Grouping of nuclei in ventral thalamus.	3,7,15 19
15	34	XXIII	47±1 da	28.0-32.1	Evagination of olfactory bulb. Plexus of ventricle III formed anteriorly. Great enlargement in midthalamic region; lateral limb of caudate larger than medial. Dorsal part of lamina terminalis thickens. Pontine and cervical flexures less marked; midbrain flexure remains. Neuroblasts in posterior lip of lateral recess migrate to form nuclei of pons and nerve cells in inferior olive. Anterior commissure present; sulcus limitans of spinal cord a shallow groove; spinal cord ends at caudal 4. Neopallium shows 3 cell layers and the primordium, an intermediate cell layer; tip of temporal lobe well-defined; fascia dentata differentiated as far as temporal tip.	3,7-9, 15
16			9 wk	40-43	Almost complete vascularization of choroid plexus of ventricle III; hippocampal and posterior commissures present; anterior commissure and fornix system well-developed; fascia dentata well-developed along margin of medial wall of telencephalon. Cerebellum bilaterally a large ball of neuroblasts in anterior lip of lateral recess. Cervical and pontine flexures less marked.	15
17	35		10 wk	53-60	Pontine flexure gone at 53 mm. Vascularization of choroid plexus of ventricle III completed. Corpus callosum present at 60 mm.	15

continued

65. DEVELOPMENT OF TISSUES AND ORGANS: MAN

Part I: NERVOUS SYSTEM

	Standard Stages (Witschi)	Streeter's Horizons	Age	Size mm	Structural Development	Reference
	(A)	(B)	(C)	(D)	(E)	(F)
18	35		11 wk	65-75	Adult shape and organization of posterior lobe of hypophysis achieved; habenular commissure present at 63 mm; 2 halves of cerebellum fuse (may be delayed until 12th wk).	23
19			12-14 wk	80-102	No sulcus limitans in spinal cord; adult cell columns present in spinal cord. Septum pellucidum present. Fissures formed in midline of cerebellum.	22,23
20			4 mo	180	Superior and inferior colliculi separated in midbrain tectum. Cavity of olfactory bulb closed.	16
21	36		5 mo	225	First fissures of cerebral cortex appear. Spinal cord ends at lumbar 3; myelination of spinal cord begins.	13
22			6 mo	300	Adult cerebral fissures and gyri can be recognized; cellular layers of cerebral cortex typical of adult, except in prefrontal area. Beginning myelination of fiber tracts within brain.	4,11

Contributors: (a) Hines, Marion, (b) Bartelmez, George W.

References: [1] Bartelmez, G. W. 1923. J. Comp. Neurol. 26:79. [2] Bartelmez, G. W., and H. M. Evans. 1926. Contribs. Embryol. Carnegie Inst. Wash. 17:1. [3] Bartelmez, G. W., and A. S. Dekaban. 1962. Ibid. 35:12. [4] Bolton, J. S. 1914. The brain in health and disease. E. Arnold, London. [5] Corner, G. W. 1929. Contribs. Embryol. Carnegie Inst. Wash. 20:81. [6] Davis, C. L. 1923. Ibid. 15:1. [7] Dekaban, A. S. 1954. J. Comp. Neurol. 100:63. [8] Essick, C. R. 1909. Anat. Record 3:254. [9] Essick, C. R. 1912. Am. J. Anat. 13:2. [10] Fitzgerald, J. E., and W. F. Windle. 1941. J. Comp. Neurol. 76:159. [11] Flechsig, P. E. 1876. Die Leitungsbahnen im Gehirn und Rüchenmark. W. Engelmann, Leipzig. [12] Gilbert, M. S. 1935. J. Comp. Neurol. 62:81. [13] Hamilton, W. J., J. D. Boyd, and H. W. Mossman. 1952. Human embryology. Ed. 2. Williams and Wilkins, Baltimore. [14] Heuser, C. H., and G. W. Corner. 1957. Contribs. Embryol. Carnegie Inst. Wash. 36:29. [15] Hines, M. 1922. J. Comp. Neurol. 34:73. [16] Hines, M. Unpublished, 1917. [17] His, W. 1887. Arch. Anat. u. Entwicklungsgeschichte, p. 368. [18] His, W. 1904. Die Entwicklung des menschlichen Gehirns. S. Hirzel, Leipzig. [19] Hochstetter, F. 1929. Beiträge zur Entwicklungsgeschichte des menschlichen Gehirns. F. Deuticke, Leipzig. [20] Hooker, D. 1942. Psychosomat. Med. 4:199. [21] Ingalls, N. W. 1920. Contribs. Embryol. Carnegie Inst. Wash. 11:61. [22] Larsell, O. 1947. J. Comp. Neurol. 87:85. [23] Streeter, G. L. 1907. Ibid. 17:183. [24] Streeter, G. L. 1942. Contribs. Embryol. Carnegie Inst. Wash. 30:211. [25] Streeter, G. L. 1945. Ibid. 31:27. [26] Streeter, G. L. 1948. Ibid. 32:133.

Part II: SENSE ORGANS

	Standard Stages (Witschi)	Streeter's Horizons	Age	Size mm	Structural Development	Reference
	(A)	(B)	(C)	(D)	(E)	(F)
					Eye	
1	14-15	X	21-24 da	2.0-2.8	Primordium of optic vesicle	5
2	16	XI	27 da	3.3	Preoptic condensations	4,16,18
3	17-24	XII-XIII	28-35 da	3.5-5.4	Primordium of lens	4,16,18
4	20-24	XIII	31-35 da	4.3-5.4	Differentiation of optic vesicle	4,16,18
5	20-29	XIII-XVII	31-44 da	4.3-14.0	Extrinsic premuscle masses appear	10
6	25	XIV	35-37 da	6	Ingrowth of lens; primordium of posterior corpus vitreum and hyaloid artery	4,12,13,16,18
7	26	XV	38 da	8	Primordium of cornea and anterior corpus vitreum	4,16,18
8	27	XVI	40 da	8-10	Differentiation of lens; vascularization of posterior corpus vitreum	4,12,13,16,18
9	28-29	XVII	42-44 da	12-14	Differentiation of retina	4,16,18

continued

65. DEVELOPMENT OF TISSUES AND ORGANS: MAN

Part II: SENSE ORGANS

	Standard Stages (Witschi)	Streeter's Horizons	Age	Size mm	Structural Development	Reference
	(A)	(B)	(C)	(D)	(E)	(F)
					Eye	
10	30-31	XVIII	46-48 da	14.6-15.6	Nerve fibers appear in retina; tunica vascular lentis appears; primordium of eyelid	4,16,18
11	32	XIX	50 da	17	Differentiation of cornea	4,16,18
12	33	XX	56 da	22-25	Extrinsic muscle myofibrillae appear; primordium of iris and ciliary body	4,11,16,18
13		XXI	56 da	22-25	Vascularization of anterior corpus vitreum; primordium of lacrimal gland	4,16,18
14		XXII	56 da	22-25	Extrinsic muscle cross-striations appear; iris differentiation	4,11,16,18
15	34	XXIII	56-70 da	26-45	Ciliary body differentiation; primordium of choroidea sclera	4,16,18
16			8 wk	40	Differentiation and closure of eyelid	
17	34-35		8-16 wk	40-142	Differentiation of choroidea sclera	4,16,18
18	35		12 wk	87	Differentiation of retinal cones and rods; major retinal channels formed; vascularization of ciliary body	4,13,16,18
19			16 wk	142	Differentiation of iris muscles and sphincter iridis muscle	4,16,18
20	35-36		16-36 wk	142-341	Fovea of retina	4,16,18
21	36		20 wk	186	Full function of anterior corpus vitreum	4,16,18
22			20-32 wk	186-302	Degeneration of hyaloid artery	
23			24 wk	228	Vascularization of iris muscles; differentiation of dilator iridis muscle	
24			32 wk	302	Function of anterior corpus vitreum ceases and degeneration begins	
25	Infancy		1 yr		1/2 of final growth of choroidea sclera attained	4,16,18
26	Early childhood		5 yr		4/5 of final growth of choroidea sclera attained	4,16,18
					Ear	
27	14-18	X-XII	21-29 da	2.0-3.7	Open otic vesicle	3
28	19	XII	30 da	4	Closure of otic sac	3
29	25	XIV	35-37 da	6	Otic sac separates from ectoderm	3
30		XIV	35-37 da	6.5	Appearance of fold I which differentiates otic (endolymphatic) duct and sac from rest of vesicle	1,8
31	26-29	XV-XVII	38-44 da	8-13	Semicircular ducts appear as ridges	8,9
32	29	XVII	44 da	13.5	Appearance of superior semicircular duct	8,9
33		XVII	44 da	14	Appearance of posterior semicircular duct; folds II and III separate utriculo-semicircular duct portion of vesicle from sacculo-cochlear part; formation of $\frac{1}{2}$ turn of cochlear duct	1,8,9
34	30-31	XVIII	46-48 da	15	Appearance of lateral semicircular duct	8,9
35	32	XIX	50 da	17	Transition from mesenchyme to precartilage of middle ear ossicles	8
36	32-33	XIX-XX	50-56 da	17-20	Precartilage stage of otic capsule	8
37		XIX-XX	50-56 da	20	True cartilage appears in otic capsule; formation of 1 turn of cochlear duct; dedifferentiation of precartilage to a loose mesenchymal tissue begins in periotic labyrinth	8,17
38	34	XXIII	56-70 da	27.5-30.0	Transition from precartilage to true cartilage of middle ear ossicles	8
39		XXIII	56-70 da	28	Ossification of anterior process of malleus	14,15
40			7 wk	30	Formation of $1\frac{1}{2}$ turns of cochlear duct	8
41			7.0-7.5 wk	30-35	Fluid space formation in vestibule begins	8
42			7.5 wk	36	Ossification in anterosuperior part of tympanic ring or head of ring	2
43	34		8 wk	40	Fluid space formation begins in scala tympani and periotic duct, and shortly in scala vestibuli	7,8
44			9 wk	50	Small areas of periotic spaces found in relation to all 3 semicircular canals; 3-4 separate ossification centers appear in body of tympanic ring; formation of $2\frac{1}{2}$ turns of cochlear duct	2,8
45			9.5 wk	55	All ossification centers in tympanic ring fuse	2
46	35		14 wk	117	Ossification of incus	14,15
47			14 wk+	120	Ossification of malleus; earliest ossification center in otic capsule appears	6,8,14,15

continued

65. DEVELOPMENT OF TISSUES AND ORGANS: MAN

Part II: SENSE ORGANS

	Standard Stages (Witschi)	Streeter's Horizons	Age	Size mm	Structural Development	Reference
	(A)	(B)	(C)	(D)	(E)	(F)
					Ear	
48	35		18 wk	160	Superior semicircular duct reaches approximate adult size; ossification of stapes	8,14,15
49	36		20 wk	180	Posterior semicircular duct reaches approximate adult size	8
50			21 wk	180-190	Cochlear duct reaches maximum size; periotic tissue and space formation essentially completed; ossicles attain adult size (bony rebuilding continues even into old age)	8,15
51			21 wk	183	Last of approximately 14 ossification centers in otic capsule appears	6,8
52			22 wk	200	Lateral semicircular duct reaches approximate adult size	8
53			23 wk	220	Ossification of otic capsule essentially completed	6,8
54	Postnatal		After birth		Bony canal of external auditory meatus begins to develop from tympanic ring by exostoses from anterosuperior and posteroventral parts of ring	2
55			After 1st yr		Bony processes meet to form bony annulus	

Contributors: (a) Bartelmez, George W., (b) Anson, Barry J., and Bast, T. H., (c) Böving, Bent G.

References: [1] Anson, B. J. 1934. Anat. Record 59:15. [2] Anson, B. J., T. H. Bast, and S. F. Richany. 1955. Quart. Bull. Northwestern Univ. Med. School 29:21. [3] Anson, B. J., and W. T. Black, Jr. 1934. Anat. Record 58:127. [4] Bach, L., and R. Seefelder. 1911-12. Atlas zur Entwicklungsgeschichte des menschlichen Auges. W. Engelmann, Leipzig. [5] Bartelmez, G. W., and H. M. Evans. 1926. Contribs. Embryol. Carnegie Inst. Wash. 17:1. [6] Bast, T. H. 1930. Ibid. 21:53. [7] Bast, T. H. 1946. Ann. Otol. Rhinol. & Laryngol. 55:278. [8] Bast, T. H., and B. J. Anson. 1949. The temporal bone and the ear. C. C. Thomas, Springfield, Ill. [9] Bast, T. H., B. J. Anson, and W. D. Gardner. 1947. Anat. Record 99:60. [10] Gilbert, P. 1952. J. Morphol. 90:149. [11] Gilbert, P. Unpublished, 1954. [12] Keibel, F. 1912. In F. Keibel and F. P. Mall, ed. Manual of human embryology. J. B. Lippincott, Philadelphia. v. 2, p. 218. [13] Mann, I. 1928. The development of the human eye. Cambridge Univ. Press, England. [14] Richany, S. F., B. J. Anson, and T. H. Bast. 1954. Ann. Otol. Rhinol. & Laryngol. 63:399. [15] Richany, S. F., B. J. Anson, and T. H. Bast. 1954. Quart. Bull. Northwestern Univ. Med. School 28:29. [16] Scammon, R. E., and E. L. Armstrong. 1924. J. Comp. Neurol. 38:165. [17] Streeter, G. L. 1918. Contribs. Embryol. Carnegie Inst. Wash. 7:5. [18] Streeter, G. L. 1951. Ibid., Embryol. reprint vol. 2.

Part III: DIGESTIVE SYSTEM

	Standard Stages (Witschi)	Streeter's Horizons	Age	Size mm	Structural Development	Reference
	(A)	(B)	(C)	(D)	(E)	(F)
					Chewing Structure (Exclusive of Teeth)	
1	14-15	X	21-24 da	2.0-2.8	Primordium of mandible and lower jaw as protrusion	2,19, 24-28
2	14-16	X-XI	21-27 da	2.0-3.3	Crosswise subdivision of mandible and lower jaw to form primordium of maxilla and upper jaw	
3	20-24	XIII	31-35 da	4.3-5.4	Fusion of mandibular and lower jaw elements begins	
4	25-27	XIV-XVI	35-40 da	6-10	Primordium of tongue	
5	26	XV	38 da	8	Fusion of mandibular and lower jaw elements completed; nerve supply to mandible and lower jaw, and to maxilla and upper jaw	
6	27	XVI	40 da	8-10	Completion of basic plan of mandible and lower jaw	
7	28-29	XVII	42-44 da	12-14	Primordium of palate as evagination	

continued

65. DEVELOPMENT OF TISSUES AND ORGANS: MAN

Part III: DIGESTIVE SYSTEM

	Standard Stages (Witschi)	Streeter's Horizons	Age	Size mm	Structural Development	Reference
	(A)	(B)	(C)	(D)	(E)	(F)
					Chewing Structure (Exclusive of Teeth)	
8	28-32	XVII-XIX	42-50 da	12-17	Muscle formation of tongue	2,19, 24-28
9	32	XIX	50 da	17	Fusion of maxillary and upper jaw elements begins	
10	33	XX-XXI	56 da	22-25	Transposition of tongue	
11		XXI	56 da	22-25	Separation of gums from lips begins	
12		XXII	56 da	22-25	Fusion of maxillary and upper jaw elements completed; ossification of mandible and lower jaw	
13	34	XXIII	56-70 da	26-45	Completion of basic plan of maxilla and upper jaw	
14			7 wk	30	Palate increases in size	
15			8 wk	40	Ossification of maxilla, upper jaw, and palate; taste buds in tongue	
16			8.5 wk	45	Bones of maxilla and upper jaw begin to fuse; fusion of palate	
17			9 wk	50	Separation of gums from lips completed	
18	35		11 wk	74	Partial function of mandible and lower jaw	
19			12 wk	87	Bones of maxilla and upper jaw completely fused; partial function of tongue	
20	Birth to infancy		Neonatal to 1 yr		Bones of mandible and lower jaw begin to fuse	
21	Early childhood		1-2 yr		Bones of mandible and lower jaw completely fused	
					Teeth	
22	27-29	XVI-XVII	40-44 da	8-14	Oral epithelium proliferation of deciduous upper and lower 1st and 2nd incisors, 1st molars and canines	18
23	28-31	XVII-XVIII	42-48 da	12.0-15.6	Dental lamina of deciduous upper and lower 1st and 2nd incisors, 2nd molars, and canines	1,7,8
24	28-33	XVII-XX	42-56 da	12-22	Dental lamina of deciduous upper and lower 1st molars	8
25	32-33	XIX-XX	50-56 da	17-22	Enamel organ buds of deciduous upper and lower canines, 1st and 2nd incisors	7,22
26	33	XXII	56 da	25	Enamel organ buds of deciduous upper and lower 1st molars; enamel organ caps of deciduous upper and lower 1st and 2nd incisors	7,21
27	33-34	XXII-XXIII	56-70 da	25-45	Enamel organ caps of deciduous upper and lower canines	22
28	34		7 wk	30	Enamel organ caps of deciduous upper and lower 1st molars; enamel organ knots of deciduous upper and lower 1st and 2nd incisors; dental papillae of deciduous upper and lower 1st and 2nd incisors, canines, and 1st molars	8,22
29			7-8 wk	30-40	Enamel organ buds of deciduous upper and lower 2nd molars	7,21
30	35		10 wk	61	Enamel organ knots of deciduous upper and lower canines; enamel niches of deciduous upper and lower canines and 2nd molars	22
31			10-11 wk	10-74	Enamel organ caps and knots, and enamel niches of deciduous upper and lower 2nd molars	8
32			13-14 wk	102-116	Enamel organ bells of deciduous upper and lower 1st incisors	18
33			14 wk	116	Enamel organ bells of deciduous upper and lower 2nd incisors; dentin calcification of diciduous upper and lower 1st incisors. Enamel organ bud of permanent upper and lower 1st molars.	1,4,5,7
34			14-15 wk	116-129	Enamel organ bells of deciduous upper and lower canines and 1st molars; dentin calcification of deciduous upper and lower 2nd incisors; enamel formation of deciduous upper and lower 1st incisors. Dental lamina of permanent upper and lower canines, 1st and 2nd incisors and premolars.	4,5,7,8
35			15-16 wk	129-142	Enamel organ bells of deciduous upper and lower 2nd molars; dentin calcification of deciduous upper and lower canines and 1st molars; enamel formation of deciduous upper and lower 2nd incisors	4,5,7,8
36			18 wk	164	Dentin calcification of deciduous upper and lower 2nd molars; enamel formation of deciduous upper and lower canines and 1st molars. Enamel organ caps of permanent upper and lower 1st molars.	4,5,7

continued

65. DEVELOPMENT OF TISSUES AND ORGANS: MAN

Part III: DIGESTIVE SYSTEM

	Standard Stages (Witschi)	Streeter's Horizons	Age	Size mm	Structural Development	Reference
	(A)	(B)	(C)	(D)	(E)	(F)
					Teeth	
37	36		23 wk	218	Enamel formation of deciduous upper and lower 2nd molars. Enamel organ bud of permanent upper and lower canines, 1st and 2nd premolars.	1,4,5,7
38			26 wk	247	Enamel dentin on all cusps of deciduous upper and lower 1st molars	8
39			30 wk	283	Enamel organ buds of permanent upper and lower 1st and 2nd incisors	1,7
40			32 wk	302	Cusps of deciduous upper and lower 1st molars completely fused; enamel dentin on all cusps of deciduous upper and lower 2nd molars. Enamel organ buds of permanent upper and lower canines.	1,4,5
41			35 wk	331	Dentin calcification of permanent upper and lower 1st molars	4,5
42			36 wk	341	Enamel formation of permanent upper and lower 1st molars	4,5
43	Birth		At birth		Cusps of deciduous upper and lower 2nd molars completely fused. Enamel organ caps of permanent upper and lower 1st premolars; enamel dentin on mesial cusps of permanent upper and lower 1st molars.	4,5,21
44	Infancy		1.5 mo		Crown of deciduous upper 1st incisor completed	15
45			2.5 mo		Crowns of deciduous lower 1st and upper 2nd incisors completed	15
46			3 mo		Crown of deciduous lower 2nd incisor completed	15
47			3-4 mo		Dentin calcification of permanent upper and lower 1st incisors and lower 2nd incisor	14
48			4-5 mo		Dentin calcification of permanent upper and lower canines	14
49			6 mo		Crown of deciduous upper and lower 1st molars	15
50			7 mo		Eruption of deciduous lower 1st incisor	15,20
51			9 mo		Eruption of deciduous upper 1st incisor; crowns of deciduous upper and lower canines completed	15,20
52			10-11 mo		Eruption of deciduous upper 2nd incisor. Dentin calcification of permanent upper 2nd incisor.	14,15, 18,20
53			11-12 mo		Crowns of deciduous upper and lower 2nd molars completed	15
54	Early childhood		1.0-1.5 yr		Eruption of deciduous lower 2nd incisor, upper and lower 1st molars	20
55			1.5 yr		Roots of deciduous upper and lower 1st incisors, lower 2nd incisor completed	15,18
56			1.5-2.0 yr		Eruption of deciduous upper and lower canines; root of deciduous upper 2nd incisor completed. Dentin calcification of permanent upper and lower 1st premolars.	14,15,18
57			2.0-2.5 yr		Eruption of deciduous upper and lower 2nd molars; root of deciduous lower 1st molar. Dentin calcification of permanent upper 2nd premolar.	14,15, 18,20
58			2-3 yr		Crowns of permanent upper and lower 1st molars completed	14
59			2.5 yr		Root of deciduous upper 1st molar completed	15,20
60			2.5-3.0 yr		Dentin calcification of permanent upper and lower 2nd molars	14
61			3 yr		Roots of deciduous upper and lower 2nd molars completed	15,18
62			3.0-3.5 yr		Roots of deciduous upper and lower canines completed	15,18
63			4-5 yr		Crowns of permanent upper and lower 1st and 2nd incisors completed	14
64	Middle childhood		5 yr		Enamel organ bud of permanent upper and lower 3rd molars	1,7
65			5-6 yr		Root degeneration of deciduous upper and lower 1st incisors. Crowns of permanent upper and lower 1st premolars completed.	14
66			6-7 yr		Deciduous upper and lower 1st incisors shed. Eruption of permanent lower 1st incisor, upper and lower 1st molars; crowns of permanent upper and lower canines and 2nd premolars completed.	12,14, 15,18
67			7-8 yr		Deciduous lower 2nd incisor shed. Eruption of permanent upper 1st incisor and lower 2nd incisor; crowns of permanent upper and lower 2nd molars completed.	12,14, 15,18

continued

65. DEVELOPMENT OF TISSUES AND ORGANS: MAN

Part III: DIGESTIVE SYSTEM

	Standard Stages (Witschi)	Streeter's Horizons	Age	Size mm	Structural Development	Reference
	(A)	(B)	(C)	(D)	(E)	(F)
					Teeth	
68	Late child-		7-9 yr		Deciduous upper 2nd incisor shed. Dentin calcification of permanent upper 3rd molar.	14,15,18
69	hood		8-10 yr		Roots of permanent upper and lower 1st molars completed; dentin ossification of permanent lower 3rd molar	14,18
70			9-11 yr		Deciduous lower canine, upper and lower 1st molars shed	14,15,18
71			10 yr		Root of permanent lower 2nd incisor completed	14,18
72			10-11 yr		Eruption of permanent lower canine, upper and lower 1st premolars	12,14
73			10-12 yr		Deciduous upper canine, upper and lower 2nd molars shed. Eruption of permanent upper 2nd premolar.	12,14, 15,18
74			11 yr		Root of permanent upper 2nd incisor completed	14,18
75	Puberty		12-13 yr		Roots of permanent upper and lower 1st premolars completed; eruption of permanent upper and lower 2nd molars	14,18
76			12-14 yr		Roots of permanent lower canine and upper 2nd premolar completed	14,18
77			12-16 yr		Crowns of permanent upper and lower 3rd molars completed	14
78			13-14 yr		Root of permanent lower 2nd premolar completed	14,18
79			13-15 yr		Root of permanent upper canine completed	14,18
80			14-15 yr		Root of permanent lower 2nd molar completed	14,18
81			14-16 yr		Root of permanent upper 2nd molar completed	14,18
82	Adolescence to		17-21 yr		Eruption of permanent upper and lower 3rd molars	11,14,18
83	maturity		18-25 yr		Roots of permanent upper and lower 3rd molars completed	14,18
					Alimentary Tract	
84	16	XI	27 da	3.3	Ingrowth of pharyngeal pouches begins; appearance of cloaca	2,19, 24-26, 28
85	16-19	XI-XII	27-30 da	3.3-4.0	Opening of mouth	
86	17-19	XII	28-30 da	3.5-4.0	Differentiation of pharynx; esophagus present; primordium of stomach	
87	20-24	XIII	31-35 da	4.3-5.4	Lamination of esophagus; constriction of stomach	
88	20-25	XIII-XIV	31-37 da	4.3-6.0	Ingrowth of pharyngeal pouches completed; constriction of esophagus; lengthwise subdivision of cloaca begins	
89	25	XIV	35-37 da	6	Transposition of stomach begins; duodenum, jejunum, ileum begin to bend	
90	26	XV	38 da	8	Vascularization of pharynx; completion of basic plan of esophagus; primary intestinal loop of duodenum, jejunum, ileum; primordium of cecum, constriction of cecum	
91	26-27	XV-XVI	38-40 da	8-10	Rotation of stomach begins	
92	28-29	XVII	42-44 da	12-14	Completion of basic plan of stomach and duodenum; umbilical hernia with gut in cord; appendix present	
93	28-32	XVII-XIX	42-50 da	12-17	Completion of basic plan of pharynx	
94	30-31	XVIII	46-48 da	14.6-15.6	Constriction of appendix	
95	30-33	XVIII-XX	46-56 da	14.6-22.0	Rotation of stomach completed	
96	30-32	XVIII-XIX	46-50 da	16.5	Perforation of anus	
97	33	XX	56 da	22	Lumen appears in duodenum	
98	33	XX-XXI	56 da	22-25	Inner (circular) muscles of esophagus, stomach, duodenum, jejunum, ileum, cecum, colon	
99		XXI	56 da	22-25	Gums begin to separate from lips; lengthwise subdivision of cloaca completed	
100	34	XXIII	56-70 da	26-45	Transposition of stomach completed; completion of basic plan of rectum	
101	34-35		7-11 wk	30-74	Formation of cardiac glands in esophagus begins	
102	34		7.5 wk	35	Glands invade stomach	
103			8 wk	40	Completion of basic plan of anus	
104			8.5 wk	45	Gut returned to abdominal cavity	
105			9 wk	50	Gums completely separated from lips	
106			9.5 wk	55	Glands in duodenum and jejunum	
107	35		10 wk	61	Outer (longitudinal) muscles of esophagus, duodenum, jejunum, ileum, cecum, colon	
108			12 wk	87	Lobulation of duodenal glands	

continued

65. DEVELOPMENT OF TISSUES AND ORGANS: MAN

Part III: DIGESTIVE SYSTEM

	Standard Stages (Witschi)	Streeter's Horizons	Age	Size mm	Structural Development	Reference
	(A)	(B)	(C)	(D)	(E)	(F)
					Alimentary Tract	
109	35		13 wk	102	Completion of basic plan of colon	2,19, 24-26, 28
110			14 wk	116	Lobulation of stomach glands; formation of cardiac glands in esophagus completed	
111			14-16 wk	116-142	Fusion of duodenum and colon to body wall	
112			16 wk	142	Partial function of stomach muscles	
113	36		20 wk	186	Partial function of stomach glands	
114			26 wk	247	Completion of esophageal glands	
					Glands	
115	14-16	X-XI	21-27 da	2.0-3.3	Primordium of liver	10,19
116	16	XI	27 da	3.3	Liver diverticulum	13,24
117	16-19	XI-XII	27-30 da	3.3-4.0	Proliferation at liver diverticulum; primordium of gallbladder	3,24
118	17-19	XII	28-30 da	3.5-4.0	Differentiation of liver; gallbladder is hollow sacculation. Primordium of dorsal bud of pancreas.	2,10,13, 23,24
119	20-24	XIII	31-35 da	4.3-5.4	Sinusoids of liver formed; separation of gallbladder from liver diverticulum. Primordium of ventral bud of pancreas; ingrowth of dorsal bud of pancreas.	2,6,10, 23,24
120	20-25	XIII-XIV	31-37 da	4.3-6.0	Gallbladder without lumen; primordium of bile duct	2,16
121	26	XV	38 da	8	Lobulation of liver; lumen in bile duct. Ingrowth of ventral bud of pancreas.	2
122	27-29	XVI-XVII	40-44 da	8-14	Primordium of submandibular gland. Fusion of dorsal and ventral primordia of pancreas.	2,17
123	28-31	XVII-XVIII	42-48 da	12.0-15.6	Primordium of parotid gland. Fusion of pancreatic ducts.	2,10,19
124	30-32	XVIII-XIX	46-50 da	14.6-17.0	Ingrowth of submandibular and parotid glands	2,19
125	30-33	XVIII-XXI	46-56 da	14.6-22.0	Lumen appears in gallbladder	2,23
126	32-33	XIX-XX	50-56 da	17-22	Primordium of sublingual glands. Fusion of pancreas to body wall.	2,10
127	33	XXI	56 da	22-25	Branching of submandibular gland into primordial cell cords	10,19,28
128	33-34	XXI-XXIII+	6-7 wk	26-45	Lumen appears in parotid gland	2
129	34		7 wk	30	Vascularization of submandibular gland	2
130			8-9 wk	40-50	Differentiation of islets of Langerhans in pancreas	2,9,10
131	34-35		8-12 wk	40-87	Bile secretion in liver	2
132	35		10 wk	61	Branching of parotid gland into primordial cell cords	10,19
133			10-12 wk	61-87	Branching of sublingual glands into primordial cell cords	
134	35-36		14-20 wk	116-186	Differentiation of parotid gland completed	2
135			16-20 wk	142-186	Bile pigment in liver	10
136			18-24 wk	164-228	Lumina of parotid and sublingual glands completed	10

Contributors: (a) Böving, Bent G., (b) Chase, Samuel W., (c) Avery, James K., (d) Singer, Ronald

References: [1] Ahrens, H. 1913. Anat. Hefte 48:167. [2] Arey, L. B. 1946. Developmental anatomy. Ed. 5. W. B. Saunders, Philadelphia. [3] Atwell, W. 1930. Contribs. Embryol. Carnegie Inst. Wash. 21:1. [4] Avery, J. K. Ph.D. Thesis. Univ. Rochester, N. Y. [5] Avery, J. K. Unpublished. Univ. Michigan, Ann Arbor, 1955. [6] Bremer, J. L. 1906. Am. J. Anat. 5:456. [7] Chase, S. W. Unpublished. Western Reserve Univ., Cleveland, Ohio, 1955. [8] Churchill, H. R. 1935. Histology and histogenesis of the human teeth. J. B. Lippincott, Philadelphia. p. 292. [9] Frazer, J. E. 1940. A manual of embryology. Baillière, Tindall, and Cox; London. [10] Hamilton, W. J., J. D. Boyd, and H. W. Mossman. 1952. Human embryology. W. Heffer, Cambridge. [11] Hellman, M. 1936. Dental Cosmos 76:750. [12] Hurme, V. O. 1949. J. Dentistry 16:11. [13] Krafka, J. 1942. Human embryology. P. B. Hoeber, New York. [14] Kronfeld, R. 1935. Bur, p. 3. [15] Kronfeld, R., and I. Schour. 1939. J. Am. Dental Assoc. 26:18. [16] Nelson, W., et al. 1949. Surgery 25:916. [17] Odgers, P. N. B. 1930. J. Anat. 65:1. [18] Orban, B. 1953. Oral histology and embryology. C. V. Mosby. St. Louis. [19] Patten, B. M. 1953. Human embryology. Ed. 2. Blakiston, New York. [20] Robinow, M., T. W. Richards, and M. Anderson. 1942. Growth 6:127. [21] Röse, E.

continued

65. DEVELOPMENT OF TISSUES AND ORGANS: MAN

Part III: DIGESTIVE SYSTEM

1891. Arch. mikroskop. Anat. u. Entwicklungsmech. 38:447. [22] Schour, I. 1929. J. Dental Research 9:700. [23] Simkins, C. S. 1931. Textbook of human embryology. F. A. Davis, Philadelphia. [24] Streeter, G. L. 1942. Contribs. Embryol. Carnegie Inst. Wash. 30:211. [25] Streeter, G. L. 1945. Ibid. 31:27. [26] Streeter, G. L. 1948. Ibid. 32:133. [27] Streeter, G. L. 1949. Ibid. 33:149. [28] Streeter, G. L. 1951. Ibid. 34:165.

Part IV: RESPIRATORY SYSTEM

	Standard Stages (Witschi)	Streeter's Horizons	Age	Size mm	Structural Development	Reference
	(A)	(B)	(C)	(D)	(E)	(F)
					Lungs	
1	16	XI	27 da	3.3	Lung primordia first appear	7,11,18,23
2	20-25	XIII-XIV	31-37 da	4.3-6.0	Pinching off of trachea and primary bronchi	11,18,23
3	25-26	XIV-XV	35-38 da	6-8	Lobar bronchi	7,11,14,19,23
4	27-29	XVI-XVII	40-44 da	8-14	Muscle fibers of trachea, primary and lobar bronchi	24
5	28-31	XVII-XVIII	42-48 da	12.0-15.6	Segmental bronchi	8,11,14,19, 23-25
6	31-32	XVIII-XIX	48-50 da	15.6-17.0	Subsegmental bronchi; muscle fibers of segmental bronchi	8,11,24,25
7	32-33	XIX-XX	50-56 da	17-22	Muscle fibers of subsegmental bronchi	24
8	33	XX-XXI	56 da	22-25	Chondrification of trachea	11,24
9		XXI-XXII	56 da	22-25	Chondrification of primary bronchi	11,24
10	33-34	XXII-XXIII	56-70 da	25-45	Chondrification of lobar bronchi	24
11	34-35		8-10 wk	40-61	Tracheal glands and cilia	24
12			9-11 wk	50-74	Glands and cilia of primary bronchi; chondrification of segmental bronchi	12,24
13			10-13 wk	61-102	Glands and cilia of lobar bronchi	24
14			11-14 wk	74-117	Elastic tissues of trachea, primary bronchi; lobar and segmental bronchi; glands and cilia of segmental bronchi; chondrification of subsegmental bronchi	1,3,12,13,24
15	36		20-24 wk	180-228	Alveolar ducts and their elastic tissues	4,24
16	36 to post-natal		34 wk fetal-4 wk postnatal	321+	Alveolar sacs and terminal alveoli	4,17,24
					Larynx	
17	25	XIV	35-37 da	6	Larynx becomes increasingly distinct	5,6,23
18	26-29	XV-XVII	38-44 da	8-14	Obliteration of lumen	6,24
19	28-31	XVII-XVIII	42-48 da	12.0-15.6	Primordium of epiglottis	5
20	30-34	XVIII-XXIII	46-70 da	14.6-45.0	Lumen reopens	5,6,24
21	32-33	XIX-XXI	50-56 da	17-25	Chondrification of larynx	5,11,15,24
22	33	XX-XXI	56 da	22-25	Muscle fibers of larynx	5,11,15,24
23	34		7-8 wk	30-40	Completion of laryngeal basic plan	5,6
24			8-9 wk	40-50	Cilia of larynx	6,24
25	35		11-12 wk	74-87	Glands of larynx and epiglottis	15,24
26			16-18 wk	142-164	Chondrification of epiglottis	10
27	36		22-26 wk	208-247	Formation of laryngeal joint-cavities	15
					Nose and Accessory Sinuses	
28	20-24	XIII	31-35 da	4.3-5.4	Nasal fields first become identifiable	11,23
29	26	XV	38 da	8	Olfactory pit	11,21,23
30	27	XVI	40 da	8-10	Differentiation of nasal epithelium	23,24
31	27-29	XVI-XVII	40-44 da	8-14	Vomeronasal organ	11,16,21,22,24
32	27-32	XVI-XIX	40-50 da	8-17	Maxilloturbinal	11,16,21,22
33	28-34	XVII-XXIII	42-70 da	12-45	Ethmoturbinals 1, 2, 3 in order	11,16,21,22
34	30-31	XVIII	46-48 da	14.6-15.6	Innervation of nasal epithelium; nasolacrimal duct appears as a groove	22,23
35	30-32	XVIII-XIX	46-50 da	14.6-17.0	Opening of choanae	9,11,23

continued

65. DEVELOPMENT OF TISSUES AND ORGANS: MAN

Part IV: RESPIRATORY SYSTEM

	Standard Stages (Witschi)	Streeter's Horizons	Age	Size mm	Structural Development	Reference
	(A)	(B)	(C)	(D)	(E)	(F)
					Nose and Accessory Sinuses	
36	32-33	XIX-XX	50-56 da	17-22	Closure of external nares	11,21,24
37	33	XX-XXI	56 da	22-25	Nasal chondrification	11,22
38	34	XXIII+	7-9 wk	30-50	Chondrification of maxilloturbinal	22
39	34+	XXIII+	7 wk+	30+	Atrophy of vomeronasal organ is continuous from Streeter's Horizon XXIII onward	11,21,23
40	34		8-9 wk	40-50	Glands and cilia of nasal epithelium	24
41	34-35		8-10 wk	40-61	Maxillary sinus; chondrification of ethmoturbinals 1, 2, 3 in order	16,20-22
42	35		10-14 wk	61-116	Opening of external nares	16,24
43			13-17 wk	102-153	Sphenoidal sinus	21,22
44			15-19 wk	129-175	Ethmoidal sinus	21,22
45	35-36		17-22 wk	153-208	Frontal sinus; ossification of maxilloturbinal	21,22
46	36 to post-natal		22 wk fetal-4 wk postnatal	208+	Opening of nasolacrimal duct	16,21,22
47	36		26-34 wk	247-321	Ossification of ethmoturbinals 1, 2, 3 in order	22
48			34-38 wk	321-362	Bone excavation of maxillary and ethmoidal sinuses	2
49	Post-natal		1-2 mo postnatal		Bone excavation of sphenoidal sinus	2
50	Infancy to early childhood		1-3 yr		Bone excavation of horizontal part of frontal sinus	2
51	Early to middle childhood		3-7 yr		Bone excavation of vertical part of frontal sinus	2

Contributors: (a) Towers, Bernard, (b) Böving, Bent G.

References: [1] Amprino, R. 1937. Arch. ital. anat. embriol. 38:447. [2] Coffin, L. 1905. Am. J. Med. Sci. 129:297. [3] De Leonardis, L. 1950. Arch. ital. anat. embriol. 55:383. [4] Dubreuil, G., A. Lacoste, and R. Raymond. 1936. Bull. histol. appl. et tech. microscop. 13:235. [5] Frazer, J. E. 1910. J. Anat. Physiol. 44:156. [6] Grosser, O., F. T. Lewis, and J. P. McMurrich. 1912. In F. Keibel and F. P. Mall, ed. Manual of human embryology. J. B. Lippincott, Philadelphia. v. 2. [7] Heiss, R. 1919. Arch. Anat. u. Physiol. Anat. Abt., p. 1. [8] His, W. 1887. Ibid., p. 89. [9] Hochstetter, F. 1892. Verhandl. anat. Ges., p. 181. [10] Kallius, E. 1897. Anat. Hefte 9:301. [11] Keibel, F., and C. Elze. 1908. Normentafeln zur Entwicklungsgeschichte des Menschen. G. Fischer, Jena. [12] Lenzi, L. 1898. Monit. zool. ital. 9:213. [13] Linser, P. 1900. Anat. Hefte 13:307. [14] Lopez, A. R. 1954. Arch. españ. morfol. 11:123. [15] Nicolas, A. 1894. Bibliographie anat. (Paris) 2:176. [16] Peter, K. 1913. Atlas des Entwicklung der Nase und des Gaumens beim Menschen, mit Einschluss der Entwicklungsstorungen. G. Fischer, Jena. [17] Potter, E. L., and C. G. Loosli. 1951. Am. J. Diseases Children 82:226. [18] Puiggros-Sala, J. 1936. Z. Anat. Entwicklungsgeschichte 106:209. [19] Quenu, L., and P. Quereux. 1955. Congr. fédération intern. anat., p. 185. [20] Schaeffer, J. P. 1910. Am. J. Anat. 10:313. [21] Schaeffer, J. P. 1910. J. Morphol. 21:613. [22] Schaeffer, J. P. 1920. The embryology, development and anatomy of the nose, paranasal sinuses, nasolacrimal passageways and olfactory organ in man. Blakiston, Philadelphia. [23] Streeter, G. L. 1951. Contribs. Embryol. Carnegie Inst. Wash., Embryol. reprint vol. 2. [24] Towers, B. Unpublished, 1955. [25] Wells, L. J., and E. Boyden. 1954. Am. J. Anat. 95:163.

continued

65. DEVELOPMENT OF TISSUES AND ORGANS: MAN

Part V: CIRCULATORY SYSTEM

	Standard Stages (Witschi)	Streeter's Horizons	Age	Size mm	Structural Development	Reference
	(A)	(B)	(C)	(D)	(E)	(F)
					Blood Forming Loci	
1	12	VIII	19 da	0.7	Vascularization of yolk sac	1-3,8,11, 12,14, 18,27,29
2	13	IX	20 da	1.5	Yolk sac hemopoiesis begins; vascularization of chorion	
3	14-24	X-XIII	21-35 da	2.0-5.4	Chorion hemopoiesis begins	
4	16	XI	27 da	3.3	Chorion hemopoiesis maximal	
5	25	XIV	35-37 da	6	Yolk sac hemopoiesis maximal	
6	27	XVI	40 da	8-10	Chorion hemopoiesis markedly decreased; liver hemopoiesis begins; hemopoiesis in intra-embryonic mesenchyme, especially in head and mediastinum, begins and continues through embryonic and greater part of fetal life	
7	34		7.5 wk	35	Humerus marrow formation begins (defines onset of fetal stage)	
8	34-35		9.5-18.0 wk	55-164	Yolk sac hemopoiesis markedly decreased; marrow formation begins in scapula, pelvic bones, occipital bone, and ribs during 3rd fetal month and continues throughout life	
9	35-36		16-32 wk	142-302	Erythrocyte formation in spleen; lymphocyte and monocyte production begins in lymph nodes in 3rd fetal mo	
10	35		17 wk	153	Spleen hemopoiesis begins	
11			19 wk	175	Spleen hemopoiesis maximal	
12			20 wk	186	Hemopoiesis in sternum from 5th fetal month throughout life	
13	36		22 wk	208	Spleen hemopoiesis markedly decreased	
14			28 wk	265	Liver hemopoiesis maximal	
15			32 wk	302	Liver hemopoiesis markedly decreased	
16	Post-natal		Newborn		Hemopoiesis in flat bones of cranium and ascending ramus of mandible from childhood on; hemopoiesis in proximal epiphyses of humerus and femur from time of ossification	
					Heart	
17	14-15	X	21-24 da	2.0-2.8	Primordium of atrial myocardium; bulboventricular loop formed; ventricle begins to function	2,5,6,9,11, 19,21, 24-26, 29,31
18	16	XI	27 da	3.3	Primordium of ventricular myocardium	
19	17-19	XII	28-30 da	3.5-4.0	Separation of septum primum begins	
20	20-24	XIII	31-35 da	4.3-5.4	Primordium of atrioventricular valve	
21	26	XV	38 da	8	Lengthwise subdivision of ventricle begins; differentiation of conducting tissue	
22	27	XVI	40 da	8-10	Separation of septum primum completed; separation of septum secundum begins	
23	30-31	XVIII	46-48 da	14.6-15.6	Lengthwise subdivision of ventricle completed; primordium of semilunar valve	
24	33	XX	56 da	22-25	Growth of atrioventricular valve completed	
25		XXI	56 da	22-25	Growth of semilunar valve completed	
26	35		14 wk	116	Growth of conducting tissue completed	
27	Post-natal		6 mo post-natal		Separation of septum secundum completed	
					Blood Vessels	
28	14-15	X	21-24 da	2.0-2.8	Embryonic blood vessels, a paired symmetrical system; aortic arch I	1,2,4,11, 17,19, 22,29
29	16	XI	27 da	3.3	Aortic arch II	
30	20-24	XIII	31-35 da	4.3-5.4	Aortic arches III and IV; paired aortas fuse; cardinal veins completed	
31	25	XIV	35-37 da	6	Aortic arch VI; primordia of ductus arteriosus and pulmonary artery	
32	26	XV	38 da	8	Primitive vessels extend into head and limbs; vitelline and umbilical veins transforming	
33	27	XVI	40 da	8-10	Branching of truncus arteriosus begins	
34	28-29	XVII	42-44 da	12-14	Branching of truncus arteriosus and basic plan of aorta and pulmonary artery completed; left umbilical vein and ductus venosus become important	

continued

65. DEVELOPMENT OF TISSUES AND ORGANS: MAN

Part V: CIRCULATORY SYSTEM

	Standard Stages (Witschi)	Streeter's Horizons	Age	Size mm	Structural Development	Reference
	(A)	(B)	(C)	(D)	(E)	(F)
					Blood Vessels	
35	30-31	XVIII	46-48 da	14.6-15.6	Appearance of the subcardinal and supracardinal veins	1,2,4,11, 17,19, 22,29
36	32	XIX	50 da	17	Cardinal veins transforming; stem of pulmonary vein absorbed into left atrium; beginning of transformation of hepatic, subcardinal, and supracardinal veins into inferior vena cava	
37	33	XX-XXII	56 da	22-25	Sinus venosus absorbed into right atrium	
38	34	XXIII+	56-70 da	26-45	Main blood vessels assume final plan	
39	35		70-140 da	45-180	Blood vessels acquire accessory coats	
40	36		140-266 da	180-340	First venous valves begin to form at 3.5 months of intrauterine life, and full quota is acquired during next 2 months	
41	Postnatal		Newborn		Some of fetal blood passages cease to function; ductus arteriosus, ductus venosus, and stems of umbilical vessels.	
					Lymph Vessels	
42	26-27	XV-XVI	38-40 da	8.5-9	Prelymphatic jugular venous plexus (represents a vestigial stage corresponding to anterior lymph hearts in amphibians)	15,16,27
43	29-32	XVII-XIX	45-50 da	14-17	Replacement of jugular venous plexuses by mesenchymal lymphatic spaces to form jugular lymph sacs	
44	31-34	XVIII-XXIII+	48-60 da	16-29	Formation of thoracic duct (prevertebral lymphatic) and cisterna chyli by replacement of antecedent venous plexus with mesenchymal lymphatic spaces	
45	32-33	XIX-XX	50-56 da	20.5	Formation of posterior iliac sacs begins	
46	34		7-8 wk	30-40	Continuity of main lymph passages completed; jugular sacs have attained greatest relative size immediately prior to establishment of permanent outlet into veins in jugulo-subclavian angle; valves begin to form in immediate, smaller tributaries of jugular lymph sacs	
47			9.5 wk	55	Lateral and greater portion of jugular lymph sac enters into formation of cervical lymph nodes, and medial and smaller portion composes proximal stretches of jugular and subclavian lymphatics and outlet of thoracic duct; lymph vessels from jugular region have almost reached vertex and those from posterior iliac region have reached base of toes	
48	35		12 wk	87	Lymph vessels in retro-peritoneal region have probably reached intestinal mucosa; formation of valves in peripheral lymphatics begins and continues throughout remaining fetal period	
49			14 wk	116	Beginning formation of valves in thoracic duct and their numerical completion and regression during later fetal months	
50	35-36		16-20 wk	142-186	Thoracic duct and its main tributaries begin differentiation of their accessory coats	
					Lymph Nodes[1]	
51	34		7.0-8.5 wk	30-45	Primordium in jugular region	7,13,18
52			7.0-9.5 wk	30-55	Primordium in posterior iliac region	
53			9.5 wk	55	Lymphocytes present in tissue	
54	35		11 wk	72	Primordium in retro-peritoneal region	
55	35-36		19-26 wk	175-247	Primitive nodules present in jugular region	
56	36		32 wk	302	Growth completed in jugular region	
57	Postnatal		After birth		Secondary follicles in jugular region	
					Lymphatic Tissues	
58	19-27	XII-XVI	30-40 da	4-10	Primordium of thymus	1,10,13,20, 23,27, 28,30,32
59	26-27	XV-XVI	38-40 da	8.5	Primordium of spleen	

/1/ Applies to earliest appearing nodes only; lymph nodes are found in various primitive conditions well after birth.

continued

65. DEVELOPMENT OF TISSUES AND ORGANS: MAN

Part V: CIRCULATORY SYSTEM

	Standard Stages (Witschi)	Streeter's Horizons	Age	Size mm	Structural Development	Reference
	(A)	(B)	(C)	(D)	(E)	(F)
					Lymphatic Tissues	
60	32-34	XIX-XXIII	50-70 da	20.5-29.0	Ectodermal and entodermal components fuse	1,10,13,20, 23,27,28, 30,32
61	33	XX-XXI	56 da	23.5	Cortex-medulla differentiation of thymus	
62		XXI	56 da	24	Vascularization of thymus begins	
63		XXI-XXII	56 da	24.5	Primordium of palatine tonsil	
64	34		7-8 wk	30-40	Appearance of lymphoid cells in thymus	
65			9 wk	50	Hassall's corpuscles appear in thymus	
66	35		13-16 wk	102-142	Pharyngeal tonsil primordium, lymphocytes present in tissue	
67			14-16 wk	116-142	Appearance of lymphoid cells in palatine tonsil	
68	35-36		16-32 wk	142-302	Erythrocyte formation in spleen	
69	36		20 wk	186	Lingual tonsil primordium, lymphocytes present in tissue	
70			20-26 wk	186-247	Primordium of Peyer's patches	
71			24 wk	228	Secondary nodules present in palatine tonsil	
72	Postnatal		After birth		Malpighian bodies in spleen; pit formation in lingual tonsil	

Contributors: (a) Kampmeier, Otto F., (b) Clark, Eliot R., (c) Neill, Catherine A., (d) Böving, Bent G.

References: [1] Arey, L. B. 1946. Developmental anatomy. Ed. 5. W. B. Saunders, Philadelphia. [2] Bartelmez, G. W., and H. M. Evans. 1926. Contribs. Embryol. Carnegie Inst. Wash. 17:1. [3] Bloom, W., and G. W. Bartelmez. 1940. Am. J. Anat. 67:21. [4] Congdon, E. D. 1922. Contribs. Embryol. Carnegie Inst. Wash. 14:47. [5] Davis, C. L. 1927. Ibid. 19:245. [6] Ebert, J. 1953. Proc. Natl. Acad. Sci. U. S. 39:333. [7] Ehrich, W. 1929. Am. J. Anat. 43:385. [8] Gilmour, J. R. 1941. J. Pathol. Bacteriol. 52:25. [9] Goss, C. M. 1942. Am. J. Physiol. 13:146. [10] Grosser, O. 1912. In F. Keibel and F. P. Mall, ed. Manual of human embryology. J. B. Lippincott, Philadelphia. v. 2, p. 446. [11] Heuser, C. H. 1923. Contribs. Embryol. Carnegie Inst. Wash. 15:121. [12] Jägeroos, B. H. 1934. Acta Soc. Med. Duodecim, B, 19:1. [13] Jolly, J. 1923. Traité technique d'hematologie. Maloine et Fils, Paris. v. 2. [14] Kampmeier, O. F. 1928. Am. J. Anat. 42:181. [15] Kampmeier, O. F. 1931. Morph. Jahrb. 67:157. [16] Kampmeier, O. F. 1960. Am. J. Anat. 107:153. [17] Kampmeier, O. F., and C. L. Birch. 1927. Ibid. 38:451. [18] Kling, C. A. 1904. Arch. mikroskop. Anat. u. Entwicklungsmech. 63:575. [19] Kramer, T. C. 1942. Am. J. Anat. 71:342. [20] Lewis, F. T. 1912. In F. Keibel and F. P. Mall, ed. Manual of human embryology. J. B. Lippincott, Philadelphia. v. 2, p. 390. [21] Marcell, M. P., and J. P. Exchaquet. 1938. Arch. maladies coeur et vaisseaux 31:504. [22] McClure, C. F. W., and E. G. Butler. 1925. Am. J. Anat. 35:331. [23] Norris, E. H. 1938. Contribs. Embryol. Carnegie Inst. Wash. 27:191. [24] Odgers, P. N. B. 1937. J. Anat. 72:247. [25] Odgers, P. N. B. 1939. Ibid. 73:643. [26] Robb, J. S., C. T. Kaylor, and W. G. Trumers. 1948. Am. J. Med. 5:324. [27] Sabin, F. R. 1912. In F. Keibel and F. P. Mall, ed. Manual of human embryology. J. B. Lippincott, Philadelphia. v. 2, p. 709. [28] Snook, T. 1934. Am. J. Anat. 55:321. [29] Streeter, G. L. 1951. Contribs. Embryol. Carnegie Inst. Wash., Embryol. reprint vol. 2. [30] Tonkoff, W. 1900. Arch. mikroskop. Anat. u. Entwicklungsmech. 56:392. [31] Walls, E. W. 1947. J. Anat. 81:93. [32] Weller, G. L. 1933. Contribs. Embryol. Carnegie. Inst. Wash. 24:93.

continued

65. DEVELOPMENT OF TISSUES AND ORGANS: MAN

Part VI: EXCRETORY SYSTEM

	Standard Stages (Witschi)	Streeter's Horizons	Age	Size mm	Structural Development	Reference
	(A)	(B)	(C)	(D)	(E)	(F)
1	14-16	X-XI	21-27 da	2.0-3.3	Differentiation of nephrogenic cord; primordium of pronephros	17
2	16	XI	27 da	3.3	Branching of nephric duct	17
3	16-25	XI-XIV	27-37 da	3.3-6.0	Differentiation of mesonephros	1,2,5,14
4	18-19	XII	29-30 da	3.8-4.0	Nephric duct joins cloaca	3,15,17
5	18-24	XII-XIII	29-35 da	3.8-5.4	Nephric duct acquires lumen	17
6	20-25	XIII-XIV	31-37 da	4.3-6.0	Degeneration of mesonephros; primordium of ureter	5,14,16
7	25	XIV	35-37 da	6	Primordium of kidney pelvis and blastema; subdivision of cloaca begins	3,14-16
8	26	XV	38 da	8	Separation of bladder and urachus	6,8,18
9	27-31	XVI-XVIII	40-48 da	8.0-15.6	Subdivision of kidney pelvis begins	16
10	32	XIX	50 da	17	1st or vestigial generation of metanephric tubules laid down; subdivision of cloaca completed	3,11,12,15,16
11	32-34	XIX-XXIII	50-70 da	17-45	Development and differentiation of provisional 2nd, 3rd, and 4th generations of metanephric tubules, including their glomeruli	4,11,12,16
12	34	XXIII	56-70 da	26-45	Constriction of male and female urethra	5,10,13
13	34-36		7-20 wk	30-186	Degeneration of vestigial and provisional generations of metanephric tubules	11,12
14	34		9 wk	50	Degeneration of nephric duct in female begins; maximum number of mesonephric tubules; dilation of bladder	1,2,5-7,14,18
15	34-36		9-20 wk	50-186	Development of permanent metanephric tubules	11,12
16	35		12 wk	87	Basic plan of male urethra completed	5
17			14 wk	116	Degeneration of nephric duct in female completed; basic plan of bladder completed	5,7,18
18			16 wk	142	Degeneration of mesonephros completed, except for epigonadal and paragonadal elements	1,2,5,14
19	36		20 wk	186	Subdivision of kidney pelvis completed; basic plan of female urethra completed	9,10,13
20	Postnatal		Newborn		Final generations of metanephric tubules laid down	11,12

Contributors: (a) Torrey, Theodore W., (b) Kampmeier, Otto F., (c) Böving, Bent G.

References: [1] Altschule, M. D. 1930. Anat. Record 46:81. [2] Bremer, J. L. 1916. Am. J. Anat. 19:179. [3] Chwalla, R. 1927. Z. Anat. Entwicklungsgeschichte 83:615. [4] Edwards, J. G. 1951. Anat. Record 169:495. [5] Felix, W. 1912. In F. Keibel and F. P. Mall, ed. Manual of human embryology. J. B. Lippincott, Philadelphia. v. 2, p. 752. [6] Frazer, J. E. 1935. J. Anat. 69:445. [7] Gyllensten, L. 1949. Acta Anat. 7:305. [8] Hammond, G., et al. 1941. Anat. Record 80:271. [9] Huber, G. C. 1932. In E. V. Cowdry, ed. Special cytology. Ed. 2. P. B. Hoeber, New York. [10] Johnson, F. P. 1920. J. Urol. 4:447. [11] Kampmeier, O. F. 1924. Z. Anat. Entwicklungsgeschichte 73:31. [12] Kampmeier, O. F. 1926. Anat. Record 33:115. [13] Politzer, G. 1952. Z. mikroskop. anat. Forsch. 58:6. [14] Shikinami, J. 1926. Contribs. Embryol. Carnegie Inst. Wash. 18:49. [15] Streeter, G. L. 1948. Ibid. 32:133. [16] Streeter, G. L. 1951. Ibid. 34:165. [17] Torrey, T. W. 1954. Ibid. 35:175. [18] Wesson, M. B. 1920. J. Urol. 4:279.

Part VII: REPRODUCTIVE SYSTEM

	Standard Stages (Witschi)	Streeter's Horizons	Age	Size mm	Structural Development	Reference
	(A)	(B)	(C)	(D)	(E)	(F)
					Common Primordia	
1	14-15	X-XI	21-24 da	2.3	Germ cells in yolk sac	20
2	17-19	XII	28-30 da	3.5-4.0	Germ cells in hindgut	20
3	17-24	XII-XIII	28-35 da	3.5-5.4	Germ cells from gut to coelomic angle	20
4	20-24	XIII	31-35 da	4.3-5.4	Germ cells from gut to mesonephric folds	20

continued

65. DEVELOPMENT OF TISSUES AND ORGANS: MAN

Part VII: REPRODUCTIVE SYSTEM

	Standard Stages (Witschi)	Streeter's Horizons	Age	Size mm	Structural Development	Reference
	(A)	(B)	(C)	(D)	(E)	(F)
					Common Primordia	
5	25	XIV	35-37 da	6	Germ cells from mesentery to mesonephric folds	20
6	25-26	XIV-XV	35-38 da	6-8	Germ cells from mesentery to gonadal folds	20
7	26-27	XV-XVI	38-40 da	8-10	Germ cells mainly in cortex of gonadal folds	20
8	27	XVI	40 da	8-10	Primordium of gonad; germ cells in cortex and medulla of primitive gonad	8,20
9	28-29	XVII	42-44 da	12-14	Primordia of müllerian duct, gubernaculum, and genital tubercle	4,7
10	33	XXI	56 da	22-25	Fusion of müllerian ducts	4
11	34	XXIII	56-70 da	26-45	End of müllerian duct downgrowth	4,7
12			7 wk	30	Degeneration of wolffian duct in female begins; degeneration of müllerian duct in male begins; differentiation of gubernaculum in male	2,4,14,19
13	35		12 wk	87	Degeneration of müllerian duct in male completed	2,4
14			14 wk	116	Degeneration of wolffian duct in female completed	4
					Male	
15	28-29	XVII	42-44 da	12-14	Primordium of penis	1,10,15,17
16	30-31	XVIII	46-48 da	14.6-15.6	Differentiation of gonad into testis	8
17	32	XIX	50 da	17	Descent of testes within body begins; differentiation of penis; perforation of urogenital membrane	9,19
18	34	XXIII	56-70 da	26-45	Genital swelling (scrotum)	1,10,15,18
19			7-8 wk	30-40	Primordium of prostate, bulbo-urethral gland, and prepuce; closure of penile urethra	2,3,19
20			8-9 wk	40-50	Fusion of testes with tubules of epididymides	4
21	34-35		8-11 wk	40-74	Ingrowth of inguinal canal into scrotum	1,10,15
22	35		12 wk	87	Descent of testes within body completed	14
23			16-18 wk	142-164	Interstitial cells in testes	
24	36		21 wk	197	Degeneration of interstitial cells begins	1,10,15
25			22-28 wk	208-265	Descent of testes into scrotum begins	
26			30-32 wk	283-302	Descent of testes into scrotum completed	
27	Birth		At birth		Degeneration of interstitial cells completed	1,10,15
28	Late childhood		9 yr		Growth of definitive forms of reproductive structures	1,10,15
29	Late childhood to puberty		9-16 yr		Spermatogenesis begins	1,10,15
30	Puberty		12-17 yr		Interstitial cells redevelop; full function of reproductive organs attained	1,10,15
31	Transitional		40-60 yr		Degeneration and functional decrease in reproductive system	1,10,15
					Female	
32	27	XVI	40 da	8-10	Invasion of primary sex cords	5,17
33	28-29	XVII	42-44 da	12-14	Appearance and caudad growth of tube, and corpus and cervix of uterus; primordium of clitoris	11,16,17
34	30-31	XVIII	46-48 da	14.6-15.6	Differentiation of gonad into ovary; differentiation of germinal epithelium and follicles begins	5,8,17
35	32	XIX	50 da	17	Differentiation of clitoris; perforation of urogenital membrane	16-19
36	32-35	XIX+	6-11 wk	17-74	Descent of ovary within body; ingrowth of secondary germinal cords	6,9
37	34	XXIII	56-70 da	26-45	Fusion begins in tube, corpus and cervix of uterus, and upper 4/5 of vagina; genital swelling (labium majus); degeneration of epoophoron begins	11,12,16,18
38			7-8 wk	30-40	Caudad growth of tube, and corpus and cervix of uterus completed; appearance of müllerian tubercle	1,10,15
39			8 wk	40	Differentiation of germinal epithelium and follicles completed	5
40			8-9 wk	40-50	Primordium of vestibular gland	1,10,15
41	34-35		9-10 wk	50-61	Differentiation of muscle wall of uterus and vagina; fusion completed in tube, corpus and cervix of uterus, and upper 4/5 of vagina; replacement of müllerian epithelium by sinus epithelium; evagination and caudad growth of vestibular gland; primordium of prepuce	4,5,11-13,19

continued

65. DEVELOPMENT OF TISSUES AND ORGANS: MAN

Part VII: REPRODUCTIVE SYSTEM

	Standard Stages (Witschi)	Streeter's Horizons	Age	Size mm	Structural Development	Reference
	(A)	(B)	(C)	(D)	(E)	(F)
					Female	
42	35		10-12 wk	61-87	Completion of müllerian tubercle; evagination of lower 1/5 of vagina	12,13
43			12 wk	87	Differentiation of labium majus	16
44			12-14 wk	87-116	Fusion and trabeculation of vagina begins	12
45			14-16 wk	116-142	Fusion and trabeculation of vagina completed; appearance of pregranulosa cells; proliferation of stroma of ovary begins	5,12
46			16-18 wk	142-164	Primary follicles in ovary; appearance of lumen in vagina	5,12
47	35-36		18-20 wk	164-186	Lumen completed in lower 1/5 of vagina	12
48	36		20-24 wk	186-228	Lumen completed in upper 4/5 of vagina; definitive sex cords	8,12
49			28-32 wk	265-302	Graafian follicles (antrum present)	
50			32-36 wk	302-341	Completion of pregranulosa cells and of stroma of ovary	
51	Late childhood		8 yr		Growth of definitive forms of reproductive structures	1,10,15
52	Puberty		11-15 yr		Full function of reproductive organs attained	1,10,15
53	Climac-		40-50 yr		Degeneration and functional decrease in reproductive system	1,10,15
54	teric		50-55 yr		Termination of function in reproductive system	

Contributors: (a) Gruenwald, Peter, (b) Ramsey, Elizabeth M., (c) Böving, Bent G.

References: [1] Arey, L. B. 1946. Developmental anatomy. Ed. 5. W. B. Saunders, Philadelphia. [2] Chwalla, R. 1927. Z. Anat. Entwicklungsgeschichte 83:615. [3] Eggerth, A. H. 1915. Anat. Record 9:191. [4] Felix, W. 1911. In F. Keibel and F. P. Mall, ed. Handbuch der Entwicklungsgeschichte des Menschen. S. Hirzel, Leipzig. v. 2, p. 732. [5] Gillman, J. 1948. Contribs. Embryol. Carnegie Inst. Wash. 32:81. [6] Gruenwald, P. 1934. Z. Anat. Entwicklungsgeschichte 103:259. [7] Gruenwald, P. 1941. Anat. Record 81:1. [8] Gruenwald, P. 1942. Am. J. Anat. 70:359. [9] Gruenwald, P. 1943. Anat. Record 85:163. [10] Hamilton, W. J., J. D. Boyd, and H. W. Mossman. 1952. Human embryology. W. Heffer, Cambridge. [11] Hunter, R. H. 1930. Contribs. Embryol. Carnegie Inst. Wash. 22:91. [12] Koff, A. K. 1933. Ibid. 24:59. [13] Meyer, R. 1938. Arch. Gynäkol. 165:504. [14] Moszkowicz, L. 1935. Z. Anat. Entwicklungsgeschichte 105:37. [15] Patten, B. M. 1953. Human embryology. Ed. 2. Blakiston, New York. [16] Spaulding, M. H. 1921. Contribs. Embryol. Carnegie Inst. Wash. 13:67. [17] Streeter, G. L. 1948. Ibid. 32:133. [18] Streeter, G. L. 1951. Ibid. 34:165. [19] Szenes, A. 1924. Morphol. Jahrb. 54:65. [20] Witschi, E. 1948. Contribs. Embryol. Carnegie Inst. Wash. 32:67.

Part VIII: MUSCULAR SYSTEM

	Standard Stages (Witschi)	Streeter's Horizons	Age	Size mm	Structural Development	Reference
	(A)	(B)	(C)	(D)	(E)	(F)
					Appendicular and Axial	
1	17-24	XII-XIII	28-35 da	3.5-5.4	Primordium of upper limb (mesenchymal origin, no myotome precursor)	1,4,13,14
2	20-24	XIII	31-35 da	4.3-5.4	Primordium of lower limb (mesenchymal origin, no myotome precursor); myotome primordium of deep muscles of back, thoracico-abdominal (ventrolateral), and prevertebral muscles	1,3,4,14, 15,19,20
3	20-25	XIII-XIV	31-37 da	4.3-6.0	Eruption of upper limb myotome and migration of its cells	1,4,13,14
4	25	XIV	35-37 da	6	Eruption of myotomes (and migration of their cells) of lower limb, deep muscles of back, thoracico-abdominal, and prevertebral muscles	1,3,4,14, 15,19,20
5	26	XV	38 da	8	Primordium of neck (ventrolateral) muscles	1,4,13,14
6	26-27	XV-XVI	38-40 da	8-10	Final position outgrowth of myotomes of upper and lower limbs, deep muscles of back, thoracico-abdominal, and prevertebral muscles	1,3,4,13-15,19,20

continued

65. DEVELOPMENT OF TISSUES AND ORGANS: MAN

Part VIII: MUSCULAR SYSTEM

	Standard Stages (Witschi)	Streeter's Horizons	Age	Size mm	Structural Development	Reference
	(A)	(B)	(C)	(D)	(E)	(F)
					Appendicular and Axial	
7	27	XVI	40 da	8-10	Anlage of diaphragm on inner surface of coelom wall	1,5,14
8	27-32	XVI-XIX	40-50 da	8-17	Differentiation of neck muscles	1,4,14
9	28-29	XVII	42-44 da	12-14	Fusion of muscle lamella with cutis lamella of deep muscles of back, thoracico-abdominal, and prevertebral muscles	1,4,14,15
10	28-31	XVII-XVIII	42-48 da	12.0-15.6	Differentiation of upper and lower limb muscles, and thoracico-abdominal muscles	1,3,4,13-15,19,20
11	30-31	XVIII	46-48 da	14.6-15.6	Growth of prevertebral muscles completed	1,4,14
12	30-32	XVIII-XIX	46-50 da	14.6-17.0	Differentiation of diaphragm completed	1,5,14
13	30-33	XVIII-XX	46-56 da	14.6-22.0	Differentiation of deep muscles of back completed	1,4,14
14	32	XIX	50 da	17	Differentiation of thoracico-abdominal muscles completed	1,4,14,15
15		XIX-XX	50-56 da	17-22	Differentiation of upper and lower limb muscles completed	1,3,4,13, 14,19,20
16	33	XX	56 da	22	Growth of thoracico-abdominal muscles and diaphragm completed	1,4,5,14, 15
17		XXI	56 da	22-25	Growth of upper and lower limb muscles, deep muscles of back, and neck muscles completed	1,3,4,13, 14,19,20
18	34		7-8 wk	30-40	Primordium of perineal muscles (mesenchymal origin, no myotome precursor)	1,7,14,18
19	34-35		8.5-17.0 wk	45-175	Differentiation of perineal muscles	1,7,14,18
20	35-36		18-20 wk	164-186	Growth of perineal muscles completed	1,7,14,18
					Cranial	
21	26	XV	38 da	8	Primordium of extrinsic eye muscles (mesenchymal origin, no myotome precursor)	1,2,9,16, 17, 22
22	27-29	XVI-XVII	40-44 da	8-14	Primordium of facial muscles	1,6,14
23	27-31	XVI-XVIII	40-48 da	8.0-15.6	Differentiation of extrinsic eye muscles	1,2,9,16, 17,22
24	28-29	XVII	42-44 da	12-14	Primordium of orbicularis oculi (mesenchymal origin, no myotome precursor)	1,2,9,16, 17,22
25	30-31	XVIII	46-48 da	14.6-15.6	Differentiation of orbicularis oculi	1,2,9,16, 17,22
26	30-34	XVIII-XXIII	46-70 da	14.6-45.0	Differentiation of facial muscles	1,6,14
27	32	XIX	50 da	17	Differentiation of extrinsic eye muscles completed; growth of orbicularis oculi completed	1,2,9,16, 17,22
28	33	XX	56 da	22	Growth of extrinsic eye muscles completed	1,2,9,16, 17,22
29	34		7-8 wk	30-40	Differentiation of facial muscles completed	1,6,14
30			8-9 wk	40-50	Primordium of meridional ciliary muscle	1,2,9,11, 16,17,22
31	34-36		9.5-22.0 wk	55-208	Differentiation of meridional ciliary muscle	1,2,9,11, 16,17,22
32	35		11-12 wk	74-87	Primordium of sphincter muscle of iris	1,2,9,12, 16,17,22
33	35-36		13-26 wk	102-247	Differentiation of sphincter muscle of iris	1,2,9,12, 16,17,22
34	35		16-18 wk	142-164	Primordium of circular ciliary muscle	1,2,9,11, 16,17,22
35	35-36		19-22 wk	175-208	Differentiation of circular ciliary muscle	1,2,9,11, 16,17,22
36	36		22 wk	208	Primordium of dilator muscle of iris	1,2,8,9,12, 16,17,22
37			26 wk	247	Differentiation of dilator muscle of iris	1,2,8,9,12, 16,17,22
38			26-34 wk	247-321	Differentiation of meridional and circular ciliary muscles completed	1,2,9,11, 16,17,22
39			30 wk	283	Differentiation of sphincter and dilator muscles of iris completed	1,2,8,9,12, 16,17,22
40			37 wk	351	Growth of meridional ciliary muscle completed	1,2,9,11, 16,17,22
41	Post-natal		After birth		Development of circular ciliary muscle continued	1,2,9,11, 16,17,22

continued

Part VIII: MUSCULAR SYSTEM

	Standard Stages (Witschi)	Streeter's Horizons	Age	Size mm	Structural Development	Reference
	(A)	(B)	(C)	(D)	(E)	(F)
					Visceral	
42	26-27	XV-XVI	38-40 da	8-10	Primordium of tongue (mesenchymal origin, no myotome precursor)	1
43	27	XVI	40 da	8-10	Primordium of pharynx (mesenchymal origin, no myotome precursor)	1,10
44	28-31	XVII-XVIII	42-48 da	12.0-15.6	Differentiation of pharynx	1,10
45	28-33	XVII-XX	42-56 da	12-22	Differentiation of tongue	1
46	30-32	XVIII-XIX	46-50 da	14.6-17.0	Differentiation of larynx	1,21,23
47	32	XIX	50 da	17	Differentiation of pharynx completed	1,10
48	33	XX	56 da	22	Differentiation of larynx completed; growth of pharynx completed	1,10,21,23
49		XX-XXI	56 da	22-25	Primordium of inner, circular intestinal muscles	1
50		XXI	56 da	22-25	Differentiation of tongue completed	1
51	34-35		10 wk	61	Primordium of outer, longitudinal intestinal muscles	1
52	35		12 wk	87	Basic plan of intestinal musculature completed	1
					Integumentary	
53	36		22 wk		Primordia of hair and sweat gland muscles	1
54			26 wk		Differentiation of hair and sweat gland muscles	
55			30 wk		Growth of hair and sweat gland muscles completed	

Contributors: (a) Zechel, Gustav, (b) Böving, Bent G.

References: [1] Arey, L. B. 1946. Developmental anatomy. Ed. 5. W. B. Saunders, Philadelphia. p. 106. [2] Bach, L., and R. Seefelder. 1911-14. Atlas zur Entwicklungsgeschichte des menschlichen Auges. W. Engelmann, Leipzig. [3] Bardeen, C. R. 1907. Am. J. Anat. 6:259. [4] Bardeen, C. R., and W. H. Lewis. 1901. Ibid. 1:1. [5] Bremer, J. L. 1943. Arch. Pathol. 36:539. [6] Futamura, R. 1906. Anat. Hefte 30:433. [7] Graefenberg, E. 1904. Ibid. 23:429. [8] Heerfordt, C. F. 1900. Ibid. 14:487. [9] Henckel, F. 1898. Ibid. 10:485. [10] Kingsbury, B. F. 1915. Am. J. Anat. 18:329. [11] Lange, O. 1901. Klin. Monatsbl. Augenheilk. 39:1. [12] Lauber, H. 1908. Albrecht von Graefe's Arch. Ophthalmol. 68:1. [13] Lewis, W. H. 1901. Am. J. Anat. 1:145. [14] Lewis, W. H. 1910. In F. Keibel and F. P. Mall, ed. Manual of human embryology. J. B. Lippincott, Philadelphia. v. 1, p. 454. [15] Mall, F. P. 1898. J. Morphol. 14:347. [16] Mann, J. C. 1928. The development of the human eye. Cambridge Univ. Press, London. [17] Neal, H. V. 1918. J. Morphol. 30:433. [18] Popowski, J. 1899. Anat. Hefte 12:13. [19] Ruge, G. 1878. Morphol. Jahrb., Suppl. 4, p. 117. [20] Schomburg, H. 1900. Untersuchung der Entwicklungen der Muskeln und Knochen des menschlichen Fusses. W. F. Kaestner, Göttingen. [21] Soulié, A., and E. Bardier. 1907. J. anat. physiol. (Paris) 43:137. [22] Steiner, K. 1926. Z. Anat. Entwicklungsgeschichte 78:83. [23] Strazza. 1899. Mitt. embryol. Inst. Univ. Wien, Folge 2, Heft 3.

Part IX: SKELETAL SYSTEM

	Standard Stages (Witschi)	Streeter's Horizons	Age	Size mm	Structural Development	Reference
	(A)	(B)	(C)	(D)	(E)	(F)
					Axial	
1	14-16	X-XI	21-27 da	2.0-3.3	Cartilage centers of notochord appear	22,25
2	28-29	XVII	42-44 da	13	Cartilage centers of ribs appear	15
3	28-32	XVII-XIX	42-50 da	11-20	Cartilage centers of vertebrae and sacrum appear	15,25
4	30-31	XVIII	46-48 da	15	Cartilage centers of sternum appear	15

continued

65. DEVELOPMENT OF TISSUES AND ORGANS: MAN

Part IX: SKELETAL SYSTEM

	Standard Stages (Witschi)	Streeter's Horizons	Age	Size mm	Structural Development	Reference
	(A)	(B)	(C)	(D)	(E)	(F)
					Axial	
5	30-32	XVIII-XIX	46-50 da	14-21	Cartilage centers of basicranium, visceral arches, and bony derivatives appear	14,16
6	30-34	XVIII+	47-63 da	15-45	Primary ossification centers of facial bones appear	2,17,18
7	32	XIX	50 da	20	Cartilage centers of coccyx appear	15
8	34		7.0-8.5 wk	29-45	Primary ossification centers of calvaria appear	2,17,18
9			7-9 wk	29-50	Primary ossification centers of ribs appear	17,18
10	34-35		7-12 wk	34-90	Primary ossification centers of vertebrae appear	17,18,22
11	34 to early childhood		7 wk fetal-1 yr post-partum	32+	Primary ossification centers of basicranium appear	2,17,18
12	34-36		9-24 wk	52-230	Primary ossification centers of sacrum appear	18,22
13	35 to early childhood		10 wk fetal-1.5 yr post-partum	65+	Fusion of basicranium	1,11-13,21,23, 24,26
14			18 wk fetal-2 yr post-partum	161+	Primary ossification centers of visceral arches and bony derivatives appear	2
15	36 to middle childhood		26 wk fetal-6 6 yr	250+	Primary ossification centers of sternum appear	7
16	Early childhood to puberty		1-13 yr		Primary ossification centers of coccyx appear	2,4,9,12,13,17, 18,21,26
17	Infancy		2 mo-2 yr		Fusion of fontanelles	27
18	Early to middle childhood		2-6 yr		Fusion of sacral diaphyses	1,11-13,21,23, 24,26
19			3-6 yr		Fusion of vertebral diaphyses	
20	Puberty		10-15 yr		Secondary ossification centers of ribs appear	1,11-13,20,21, 26
21			11-16 yr		Secondary ossification centers of vertebrae appear	
22			12-16 yr		Secondary ossification centers of sacrum appear	
23	Puberty to middle age		12-40 yr		Fusion of sternum	1,11-13,21,23, 24,26
24	Puberty to maturity		14-30 yr		Fusion of calvaria	27
25			15-25 yr		Fusion of sacral epiphyses	1,11-13,21,23, 24,26
26	Adolescence to maturity		18-25 yr		Fusion of vertebral epiphyses	1,11-13,21,23, 24,26
27	Maturity		20-25 yr		Fusion of ribs	1,11-13,21,23, 24,26
28	Maturity to climacteric		30-50 yr		Secondary ossification centers of costal cartilage appear	1,11-13,20,21, 26
29	Middle age to climacteric		40-60 yr		Fusion of visceral arches and bony derivatives	1,11-13,21,23, 24,26
30	Old age		70+ yr		Fusion of coccyx	1,11-13,21,23, 24,26
					Appendicular	
31	28-29	XVII	42-44 da	11-14	Cartilage centers of scapula, long bones of upper and lower limbs, and hipbone appear	3,15
32	30-32	XVIII-XIX	46-50 da	14-20	Cartilage centers of carpus, tarsus, metatarsus, and phalanges of foot appear	3,15
33	30-33	XVIII-XX	46-56 da	14-23	Cartilage centers of metacarpus and phalanges of hand appear	3,15
34	31-32	XVIII-XIX	48-50 da	15-20	Primary ossification centers of clavicle appear	17,18
35	32-34	XIX+	50-70 da	18-35	Primary ossification centers of scapula and long bones of upper and lower limbs appear	11,17,18
36	34		7 wk	30	Marrow formation begins in humerus by periosteal penetration of primary osseous shell (defines end of embryonic period--horizons--and start of fetal period, according to Streeter)	25
37	34-35		7-11 wk	29-70	Primary ossification centers of metacarpus and phalanges of hand appear	17,18
38			7.0-18.5 wk	29-170	Primary ossification centers of hipbone appear	
39	34 to birth		7.5-38.0 wk	34-362	Primary ossification centers of metatarsus and phalanges of foot appear	17,18

continued

65. DEVELOPMENT OF TISSUES AND ORGANS: MAN

Part IX: SKELETAL SYSTEM

Standard Stages (Witschi)	Streeter's Horizons	Age	Size mm	Structural Development	Reference
(A)	(B)	(C)	(D)	(E)	(F)
				Appendicular	
40	36 to middle childhood	20 wk fetal-4 yr	186+	Primary ossification centers of tarsus appear	19
41	36 to puberty	30 wk fetal-14 yr	283+	Secondary ossification centers of long bones of lower limb appear	5,6,10
42		32 wk fetal-13 yr	302+	Secondary ossification centers of scapula and long bones of upper limb appear	5,6,10,19
43	Infancy to middle child-hood	6 mo-4 yr		Secondary ossification centers of metacarpus and phalanges of hand appear	5,6,10,19
44		1-6 yr		Secondary ossification centers of metatarsus and phalanges of foot appear	
45	Infancy to late childhood	8 mo-10 yr		Primary ossification centers of carpus appear	11,19
46	Middle to late childhood	5-10 yr		Secondary ossification centers of tarsus appear	5,6,10,19
47	Late childhood to puberty	10-15 yr		Secondary ossification centers of hipbone appear	1,11-13,20,21, 26
48	Late childhood to maturity	10-25 yr		Fusion of hipbone	1,11-13,21,23, 24,26
49	Puberty to adolescence	12-18 yr		Fusion of metatarsus and phalanges of foot	1,11-13,21,23, 24,26
50		13-18 yr		Fusion of metacarpus and phalanges of hand	
51	Puberty to maturity	13-20 yr		Fusion of lower extremity	1,11-13,21,23, 24,26
52		15-20 yr		Fusion of tarsus	
53		15-25 yr		Fusion of upper extremity	
54	Adolescence	17-21 yr		Secondary ossification centers of clavicle appear	8
55		18-25 yr		Fusion of clavicle	1,11-13,21,23, 24,26

Contributors: (a) Noback, Charles R. (b) Böving, Bent G.

References: [1] Appleton, A., W. Hamilton, and G. Simon. 1949. Surface and radiological anatomy for students and general practitioners. W. Wood, Baltimore. [2] Augier, M. 1931. In P. Poirier and A. Charpy, ed. Traité d'anatomie humaine. G. Masson, Paris. v. 1, p. 89. [3] Bardeen, C. R. 1905. Am. J. Anat. 4:265. [4] Bardeen, C. R. 1910. In F. Keibel and F. P. Mall, ed. Manual of human embryology. J. B. Lippincott, Philadelphia. v. 1, p. 292. [5] Borovansky, L., and O. Hnevkovsky. 1929. Anthropologie (Prague) 7:169. [6] Borovansky, L., and O. Hnevkovsky. 1929. Bull. intern. acad. sci. Boheme, Oct. 18. [7] Borovansky, L. 1931. Rozpravy II Trudy Ceske Akad. 40:1. [8] Cave, A., and N. Green. 1954. J. Anat. 88:545. [9] De Beer, G. 1937. The development of the vertebrate skull. Clarendon Press, Oxford. [10] Elgenmark, O. 1946. Acta Paediat. 33(suppl. 1). [11] Flecker, H. 1942. Am. J. Roentgenol. Radium Therapy Nuclear Med. 47:97. [12] Goss, C., ed. 1954. Gray's Anatomy of the human body. Lea and Febiger, Philadelphia. pp. 119-316. [13] Inkster, R. G. 1951. In J. C. Brash, ed. Cunningham's Textbook of anatomy. Oxford Univ. Press, London. [14] Kernan, J. D. 1916. J. Morphol. 27:605. [15] Lewis, W. H. 1902. Am. J. Anat. 2:145. [16] Lewis, W. H. 1920. Contribs. Embryol. Carnegie Inst. Wash. 8:299. [17] Mall, F. 1906. Am. J. Anat. 5:433. [18] Noback, C., and G. Robertson. 1951. Ibid. 89:1. [19] Pyle, S., and L. Sontag. 1943. Am. J. Roentgenol. Radium Therapy Nuclear Med. 49:795. [20] Sawtell, R. 1929. Am. J. Diseases Children 37:61. [21] Scammon, R. 1953. In J. P. Schaeffer, ed. Morris' Human anatomy. Blakiston, New York. pp. 11-60. [22] Sensenig, E. C. 1949. Contribs. Embryol. Carnegie Inst. Wash. 33:21. [23] Stevenson, P. 1924. Am. J. Phys. Anthropol. 7:53. [24] Stewart, T. 1934. Ibid. 19:433. [25] Streeter, G. L. 1942. Contribs. Embryol. Carnegie Inst. Wash. 30:211. [26] Terry, R., and M. Trotter. 1953. In J. P. Schaeffer, ed. Morris' Human anatomy. Blakiston, New York. pp. 89-287. [27] Todd, T. 1924. Am. J. Phys. Anthropol. 7:325.

continued

65. DEVELOPMENT OF TISSUES AND ORGANS: MAN

Part X: INTEGUMENTARY SYSTEM

	Standard Stages (Witschi)	Streeter's Horizons	Age	Size mm	Structural Development	Reference
	(A)	(B)	(C)	(D)	(E)	(F)
					Skin	
1	14-16	X-XI	21-27 da	2.0-3.3	Primordium of epidermis	1,6,7, 9-12
2	16-19	XI-XII	27-30 da	3.3-4.0	Primordium of corium	
3	20-25	XIII-XIV	31-37 da	4.3-6.0	Periderm present	
4	26-31	XV-XVIII	38-48 da	8.0-15.6	Periderm becomes increasingly distinct	
5	30-32	XVIII-XIX	46-50 da	14.6-17.0	Differentiation of epidermis	
6	34		7.5 wk	35	Completion of epidermal basic plan	
7			9.5 wk	55	Melanocytes become distinct; differentiation of corium; definitive periderm	
8	35		10 wk	61	Primordium of ridge pattern	
9			14 wk	116	Completion of melanocyte basic plan	
10			14-16 wk	116-142	Stratification of epithelium	
11			15 wk	129	Degeneration of periderm; differentiation of ridge pattern	
12			18 wk	164	Completion of ridge pattern basic plan; definitive epidermis	
13	36		21 wk	197	Degeneration of periderm completed	
14			23 wk	218	Periderm absent; completion of corium basic plan	
					Glands	
15	30-31	XVIII	46-48 da	14.6-15.6	Appearance of nipples	1,6,7,11
16	35		11 wk	74	Differentiation of mammary glands and nipples	
17			16 wk	142	Primordium of sweat glands	
18			16-17 wk	142-153	Invagination of sweat glands	
19			19 wk	175	Primordium of sebaceous glands	
20	36		20 wk	186	Evagination of sebaceous glands	
21			24 wk	228	Sweat gland loop formed	
22			28 wk	265	Sweat gland lumen acquired; completion of basic plan of mammary glands and nipples	
23	Birth		At birth		Protrusion of nipples	
24	Late childhood		9 yr		Growth of mammary glands and nipples in females	
25	Puberty		12-16 yr		Definitive mammary glands and nipples	
26	Climacteric		40-50 yr		Decrease to termination of function of mammary glands and nipples	
					Hair	
27	33-34		6-8 wk	23.5-40.0	Primordium of facial hair	1-5,8,13
28	34-35		8.5-12.0 wk	45-87	Primordium of axillary and pubic hair	
29	34		9 wk	50	Slight evagination of facial hair cells followed by ingrowth of stratum germinativum	
30	35		10 wk	61	Formation of prospective facial hair papillae, and a splitting or separation of epithelial column from peripheral cells	
31			11 wk	74	Outgrowth or evagination again as shaft of facial hair grows towards surface	
32			12 wk	87	Facial hair shaft erupts through stratum corneum as epithelial cells move aside; primordium of scalp and body hair	
33			13 wk	102	Slight evagination of axillary, pubic, scalp, and body hair cells, followed by ingrowth of stratum germinativum	
34			14 wk	116	Formation of prospective axillary, pubic, scalp, and body hair papillae, and a splitting or separation of epithelial column from peripheral cells	
35			15 wk	129	Outgrowth or evagination again as shafts of axillary, pubic, scalp, and body hair grow towards surface	
36			16 wk	142	Axillary, pubic, scalp, and body hair shafts erupt through stratum corneum as epithelial cells move aside	
37	35-36		16-20 wk	142-186	Cornification and pigmentation of facial hair	
38	35		17 wk	153	Lanugo hair appears on axillary and pubic regions, scalp, and body	
39	36		21-22 wk	197-208	Cornification and pigmentation of axillary, pubic, scalp, and body hair	
40			26-32 wk	247-302	Vellus hair appears on axillary and pubic regions, face, scalp, and body	
41	Infancy		7-8 mo postnatal		Most lanugo has been gradually shed, leaving vellus hair	

continued

65. DEVELOPMENT OF TISSUES AND ORGANS: MAN

Part X: INTEGUMENTARY SYSTEM

	Standard Stages (Witschi)	Streeter's Horizons	Age	Size mm	Structural Development	Reference
	(A)	(B)	(C)	(D)	(E)	(F)
					Hair	
42	Early childhood		1.5-3.0 yr		Terminal scalp hair appears, gradually replacing all but 5-25% of vellus hair; cycle for individual hair follicle on scalp is 2-4 years	1-5,8,13
43	Puberty		11-14 yr		Terminal axillary and pubic hair appears in females, replacing vellus hair	
44	Puberty		12.5-15.5 yr		Terminal facial, axillary, and pubic hair appears in males, replacing vellus hair; cycle for individual hair follicle on face is 4-6 months	
					Nails	
45	34		9 wk	50	Primordium of nails	1,6,7
46			12 wk	87	Differentiation of nails	
47			17 wk	153	Primordium of neuromyo-arterial glomus	
48			18 wk	164	Completion of basic plan of nails	
49			30 wk	283	Differentiation of neuromyo-arterial glomus	
50	Birth		At birth		Nails of definitive type	
51	Newborn		Postnatal		Completion of basic plan of neuromyo-arterial glomus	

Contributors: (a) Böving, Bent G., (b) Duggins, Oliver H.

References: [1] Arey, L. B. 1946. Developmental anatomy. Ed. 5. W. B. Saunders, Philadelphia. [2] Butcher, E. O. 1951. Ann. N. Y. Acad. Sci. 53:508. [3] Cowdry, E. V. 1950. Textbook of histology. Ed. 4. Lea and Febiger, Philadelphia. [4] Danforth, C. H. 1925. Hair with special reference to hypertrichosis. American Medical Association, Chicago. [5] Duggins, O. H., and M. Trotter. 1951. Ann. N. Y. Acad. Sci. 53:569. [6] Hamilton, W. J., J. D. Boyd, and H. W. Mossman. 1952. Human embryology. W. Heffer, Cambridge. [7] Patten, B. M. 1953. Human embryology. Blakiston, New York. [8] Reynolds, E. L. 1951. Ann. N. Y. Acad. Sci. 53:576. [9] Streeter, G. L. 1942. Contribs. Embryol. Carnegie Inst. Wash. 30:211. [10] Streeter, G. L. 1945. Ibid. 31:27. [11] Streeter, G. L. 1948. Ibid. 32:133. [12] Streeter, G. L. 1951. Ibid. 34:165. [13] Trotter, M. 1924. Am. J. Phys. Anthropol. 7:427.

Part XI: ENDOCRINE GLANDS

	Standard Stages (Witschi)	Streeter's Horizons	Age	Size mm	Structural Development	Reference
	(A)	(B)	(C)	(D)	(E)	(F)
					Thyroid	
1	15-16	X-XI	24-27 da	3	Outgrowth of median thyroid	13,14, 26
2	19	XII	30 da	4	Primordium of median thyroid	
3	21-25	XIII-XIV	32-37 da	4.5-6.8	Branching of median thyroid	
4	26-28	XV-XVII	38-42 da	8-11	Primordium of lateral thyroid	
5	27-28	XVI-XVII	40-42 da	11	Separation of primordium of median thyroid	
6	32-33	XIX-XX	50-56 da	20-21	Separation of lateral thyroid	
7	33-34	XX-XXIII	56-70 da	24-30	Early mature stage of median thyroid	
8	34-35		8-10 wk	40-65	Early mature stage of lateral thyroid	
					Parathyroid	
9	25-26	XIV-XV	35-38 da	6-8	Early outgrowth	13,14, 26
10	27	XVI	40 da	9	Primordium	
11	32-33	XIX-XX	50-56 da	18-20	Separation	
12	35		13-17 wk	100-150	Sinusoids formed	
13	35-36		18.5-24.0 wk	170-230	Cytologic differentiation	

continued

65. DEVELOPMENT OF TISSUES AND ORGANS: MAN

Part XI: ENDOCRINE GLANDS

	Standard Stages (Witschi)	Streeter's Horizons	Age	Size mm	Structural Development	Reference
	(A)	(B)	(C)	(D)	(E)	(F)
					Hypophysis (Pituitary)	
14	19-23	XII-XIII	30-34 da	4-5	Primordium of anterior lobe	3,7,16, 23
15	23	XIII	34 da	5	Primordium of posterior lobe	
16	27-28	XVI-XVII	40-42 da	11	Primordium of pars intermedia	
17	30-32	XVIII-XIX	46-50 da	15-16	Stalk of anterior lobe becomes solid	
18	33	XX-XXII	56 da	24-25	Separation of anterior lobe; differentiation of pars intermedia	
19	34		7.0-9.5 wk	30-55	Sinusoids formed in anterior lobe	
20	34-35		8-10 wk	40-60	Cytologic differentiation of beta cells of anterior lobe	
21	35		10.5-11.5 wk	70-80	Cytologic differentiation of alpha cells of anterior lobe	
					Suprarenal (Adrenal)	
22	23	XIII	34 da	5	Primordium of medulla	8,9,11, 17,20, 21,24
23	23-26	XIII-XV	34-38 da	5-7	Coelomic thickening of fetal cortex	
24	27	XVI	40 da	9.0-9.5	Separation of fetal cortex	
25	27-28	XVI-XVII	40-42 da	11-12	Increase in number of cells in medulla	
26	27-29	XVI-XVII	40-44 da	11-14	Second proliferation of permanent cortex	
27	28-29	XVII	42-44 da	12-14	Capsule forms around fetal cortex	
28	29	XVII	44 da	13	Sinusoids formed in fetal cortex	
29	29	XVII	44 da	13-14	Ingrowth of medulla into cortex	
30	33-34	XX+	6-9 wk	23-50	Lipids appear in fetal cortex	
31	34-36		9-21 wk	50-200	Lipids appear in permanent cortex	
32	35		12 wk	87	Early function of medulla	
33	36		22 wk	208	Chromaffin reaction of medulla	
34	Post-natal		Birth-1 mo		Zona glomerulosa	
35			Birth-1 yr		Degeneration of fetal cortex	
36			1 mo		Zona fasciculata	
37			3.5-6.0 mo		Zona reticularis	
					Pancreas	
38	15-19	X-XII	24-30 da	3-4	Primordium of dorsal, then ventral, buds	2,4,6, 10,15, 18,19, 22,25
39	20-24	XIII	31-35 da	4.3-5.4	Ingrowth of dorsal bud; duct formation commences in ventral bud	
40	27-28	XVI-XVII	38-42 da	11	Fusion of ventral and dorsal primordia	
41	28	XVII	42 da	12	Fusion of ducts	
42	32	XIX	50 da	17	Pancreas becomes retroperitoneal	
43	32-33	XIX-XX	56 da	20	Lumina become confluent	
44	35		12-14 wk	87-116	Differentiation of islets of Langerhans	
45	36		20 wk	186	Proteolytic pancreatic enzyme produced	
					Testes	
46	14	X	21 da	2	Germ cells in yolk sac	1,5,12, 27
47	24-25	XIII-XIV	35-37 da	5.5-5.7	Primordial outgrowth	
48	25-26	XIV-XV	37-38 da	6.7-8.0	Mesenchymal proliferation; ingrowth of sex cords	
49	29-31	XVII-XVIII	44-48 da	14-16	Sex differentiation	
50	35		16-18 wk	140-160	Interstitial cells present	
51	36 to birth		21 wk-birth	200-362	Interstitial cells regress	
52	Late childhood to puberty		9-16 yr		Spermatogenesis	
53	Puberty		12-17 yr		Interstitial cells redevelop	
					Ovaries	
54	14	X	21 da	2	Germ cells in yolk sac	1,5,12, 27
55	24-26	XIII-XV	35-38 da	5.5-7.5	Primordial outgrowth	
56	25-26	XIV-XV	37-38 da	6.7-8.0	Proliferation of mesenchyme and sex cords	
57	35		13-15 wk	100-130	Secondary proliferation	
58	36		28.5-32.0 wk	270-300	Primary follicles form	
59	Middle to late childhood		7 yr		Graafian follicles form	
60	Puberty		11-15 yr		Growth of graafian follicles completed	

Contributors: (a) Gardner, William U., (b) Singer, Ronald, (c) Böving, Bent G.

continued

65. DEVELOPMENT OF TISSUES AND ORGANS: MAN

Part XI: ENDOCRINE GLANDS

References: [1] Albert, A., et al. 1953. Proc. Staff Meetings Mayo Clinic 28:409. [2] Arey, L. B. 1946. Developmental anatomy. Ed. 5. W. B. Saunders, Philadelphia. [3] Atwell, W. J. 1926. Am. J. Anat. 37:159. [4] Frazer, J. E. 1940. A manual of embryology. Baillière, Tindall, and Cox; London. [5] Gillman, J. 1948. Contribs. Embryol. Carnegie Inst. Wash. 32:81. [6] Hamilton, W. J., J. D. Boyd, and H. W. Mossman. 1952. Human embryology. W. Heffer, Cambridge. [7] Herring, P. T. 1908. Quart. J. Exptl. Physiol. 1:161. [8] Hett, J. 1925. Z. mikroskop. anat. Forsch. 3:179. [9] Keene, M. F. L., and E. E. Hewer. 1927. J. Anat. 61:302. [10] Krafka, J. 1942. Human embryology. P. B. Hoeber, New York. [11] Lanman, J. T. 1953. Medicine 32:389. [12] Lynch, K. M., and W. W. Scott. 1950. J. Urol. 64:767. [13] Norris, E. H. 1916. Am. J. Anat. 20:411. [14] Norris, E. H. 1937. Contribs. Embryol. Carnegie Inst. Wash. 26:248. [15] Odgers, P. N. B. 1930. J. Anat. 65:1. [16] Pearre, A. G. E. 1953. J. Pathol. Bacteriol. 65:355. [17] Politzer, G. 1936. Z. Anat. Entwicklungsgeschichte 106:40. [18] Simkins, C. S. 1931. Textbook of human embryology. F. A. Davis, Philadelphia. [19] Streeter, G. L. 1942. Contribs. Embryol. Carnegie Inst. Wash. 30:211. [20] Swinyard, C. A. 1943. Anat. Record 87:41. [21] Tähkä, H. 1951. Acta Paediat. 40(suppl. 81). [22] Thyng, F. W. 1908. Am. J. Anat. 7:489. [23] Tilney, F. 1945. Bull. Neurol. Inst. N. Y. 5:387. [24] Uotila, U. U. 1940. Anat. Record 76:133. [25] Võlker, O. 1902. Arch. mikroskop. Anat. u. Entwicklungsmech. 59(1):62. [26] Weller, G. L., Jr. 1933. Contribs. Embryol. Carnegie Inst. Wash. 24:93. [27] Witschi, E. 1948. Ibid. 32:67.

66. DEVELOPMENT: SWINE

Part I: CHARACTERIZATION OF STAGES

Size (column C) = greatest length, neck (spine) length, or crown-to-rump length of embryo.

	Standard Stages (Witschi)	Age da	Size mm	Identification of Stages	Reference
	(A)	(B)	(C)	(D)	(E)
				Cleavage and Blastula	
1	1		0.11-0.14	1 cell	11
2	2	1.0-1.5		2 cells	9,11
3	3	2		4 cells; passes into uterus	4,5,9,11
4	4	3		8-12 cells	4,5,9,11
5	5	3.5		16 cells (morula)	9,11
6	6	4.75		Blastocyst	6,9
7	7	5-7		Late blastocyst still free in uterus	5,11
				Gastrula	
8	8	7-8	0.49-1.36[1]	Bilaminar disc begins elongation	4,9-11
9	9	8-9	2.5-3.0[1]	Proliferation of mesoderm	4,9,11
10	10	8-9		Beginning primitive streak	9-11
11	11	10		Medium primitive streak	9,11
				Primitive Streak	
12	12	11-12	10-65[1]	Completed primitive streak; notochord; becomes attached to endometrium	5,9,11
				Neurula	
13	13	13		Presomite neurula	11
14	14	14-15	2.5-3.0	Occipital somites 1-4; 1st somite not delimited anteriorly	2,7,10, 11
15	15	15-16	3.2-5.2	Cervical somites 5-12	1,7
				Tail Bud	
16	16	15-17	5.2-6.5	Thoracic somites 13-20; spiral torsion; heart bulge	1,7
17	17	17	4.9	Thoracic somites 21-24	1,7
18	18	16.5-18.0	4.5	Thoracic somites 25-26; head and tail meet; anterior limb bud	1,7

/1/ Extra-embryonic length.

continued

66. DEVELOPMENT: SWINE

Part I: CHARACTERIZATION OF STAGES

	Standard Stages (Witschi)	Age da	Size mm	Identification of Stages	Reference
	(A)	(B)	(C)	(D)	(E)
				Tail Bud	
19	19	16.5-17.5	3.6	Lumbar somites 27-29; hind limb bud	1,7
20	20	17.5	6.8	Lumbar somites 30, 31; spiraling completed	1,7
21	21	17.5	5.2	Lumbar somites 32, 33; uncoiling; mandibular and maxillary processes	7
22	22	19	5.8-8.0	Sacral somites 34, 35	7
23	23	20	6.4	Sacral somites 36, 37	7
24	24	20		Caudal somites 38-40	7
				Embryo	
25	25	20	8.0-8.6	Caudal somites 41-43	7
26	26	20-21	9-10	Caudal somites 44-46; beginning of umbilical hernia	7, 9
27	27	21-22	11	Caudal somites 47-47	7, 9
28	28	22	11.6-14.4	Caudal somites 50-52; end of somite formation; cervical sinus closing; handplate	3, 7
29	29	22	16.4-18.6	Cervical sinus closed; lateral palatine processes; pentadactyl rudiments	7,9
30	30	28	19.4-24.0	Median (premaxillary) palatine processes; sex differentiation; eyelids and plica semilunaris	7,9
31	31	30	25	Facial clefts closing; palate developing	9
32	32	32.5	26.5-29.5	Phalanges 3 and 4 most prominent; fusion of palatine processes	3,9
33	33	34.5	35	Facial clefts closed; palate completed	7,11
				Fetus	
34	34	36-50	35-55	1st fetal stage: growth of eyelids, gut withdrawal from umbilical cord	3,8
35	35	50-90	55-130	2nd fetal stage: sealed eyelids	3,8
36	36	90-113[2]	130-280	3rd fetal stage: separation of eyelids	3,8

/2/ Duration of pregnancy is usually given as 110-116 days, with extreme deviations for certain breeds. Young are born with open eyelids and open external ear ducts.

Contributor: Kemp, Norman E.

References: [1] Boyden, E. A. 1936. A laboratory atlas of the 13-mm. pig embryo. Wistar Institute Press, Philadelphia. [2] Boyden, E. A. 1940. Contribs. Embryol. Carnegie Inst. Wash. 28:157. [3] Carey, E. J. 1922. J. Morphol. 37:1. [4] Green, W. W., and L. M. Winters. 1946. Ibid. 78:305. [5] Heuser, C. H. 1927. Contribs. Embryol. Carnegie Inst. Wash. 19:229. [6] Heuser, C. H., and G. L. Streeter. 1929. Ibid. 20:1. [7] Keibel, F. 1897. Normentafeln zur Entwicklungsgeschichte der Wirbelthiere. G. Fischer, Jena. pt. 1. [8] MacCallum, J. B. 1901. Bull. Johns Hopkins Hosp. 12:102. [9] Patten, B. M. 1948. Embryology of the pig. Ed. 3. Blakiston, New York. [10] Streeter, G. L. 1927. Contribs. Embryol. Carnegie Inst. Wash. 19:73. [11] Waterman, A. J. 1948. A laboratory manual of comparative vertebrate embryology. H. Holt, New York.

Part II: TISSUES AND ORGANS

Size (column C) = greatest length, neck (spine) length, or crown-to-rump length of embryo.

	Standard Stages (Witschi)	Age da	Size mm	Structural Development	Reference
	(A)	(B)	(C)	(D)	(E)
				Nervous System	
1	13	13		Neural plate and groove	13
2	15	15-16	3.2-5.2	Neural tube; fusion of neural crest primordia	8,13
3	16	15-17	4.6	Prosencephalon, mesencephalon, rhombencephalon	8,13
4	17	17	4.9	Telencephalon and diencephalon, metencephalon and myelencephalon; closure of anterior neuropore	8,13

continued

66. DEVELOPMENT: SWINE

Part II: TISSUES AND ORGANS

	Standard Stages (Witschi)	Age da	Size mm	Structural Development	Reference
	(A)	(B)	(C)	(D)	(E)
				Nervous System	
5	18	16.5-18.0	4.5	Epithelial hypophysis	8
6	19	16.5-17.5	3.6	Gasserian and acoustico-facialis ganglia	8
7	22	19	5.8-7.8	Cranial ganglia IX and X; cranial nerves 3-12 present	8,16
8	26	20-21	9.6-10.0	Ependymal, mantle, and marginal layers of neural tube; neuroblasts; cerebral hemispheres	8,13
9	28	22	11.6-15.0	Olfactory nerve	8,13
10	29		16.4	Pia mater and arachnoid layer; sympathetic ganglia, ramus anastomoticus	8,12
11	30	28	19.4-24.0	Epiphysis	12
12	33	34.5	35	Cerebellum	13
13	35	46	70	Neuroglia present	13
14		54.5	100	Corpora quadrigemina	
15	36	92	200	Sulci and gyri in cerebrum	13
				Sense Organs	
16	15	15-16	3.2-5.2	Auditory placode; optic vesicle	8,13
17	16	15-17	4.6	Auditory pit	8,13
18	18	16.5-18.0	4.5	Auditory vesicle	8
19	22	19	5.8-7.8	Optic cup and lens	8,16
20	25	20	8.0-8.6	Olfactory pits; endolymphatic duct	8
21	26	20-21	9.6-10.0	Retinal differentiation, sacculus, utriculus	8,13
22	28	22	11.6-15.0	Olfactory lobe; vitreous body	8,13
23	29		16.4	Semicircular canals; cochlea	8,12
				Digestive System	
24	12	11-12	10-65[1]	Primitive gut	13
25	13	13		Hindgut	13
26	14	14-15	3	Foregut, preoral gut, stomodeum, oral plate; allantois	8
27	15	15-16	5.2	1st and 2nd visceral pouches; pharynx	8
28	16	15-17	5.8	3rd and 4th visceral pouches, liver diverticula	8
29	18	16.5-18.0	4.5	Esophagus, stomach, postcloacal gut, proctodeum, anal plate, intestine	8,13
30	19	16.5-17.5	3.6	Dorsal and ventral pancreas	8
31	20	17.5	6.8	Oral plate ruptures; gallbladder	8
32	22	19	7	Tongue primordia	13
33	26	20-21	10	Thymus	8
34	29	22	16.4-18.6	Cecum	10
35	30	28	19.5-24.0	Dental lamina, enamel organs; coils of small intestine, anus opens	8,13
36	33	34.5	35	Coils of large intestine	13
37	35	61	120	Ameloblasts, odontoblasts	13
38		63	130	Dentin and enamel	
				Respiratory System	
39	19	16.5-17.5	3.6	Laryngotracheal groove, lung buds	8
40	20	17.5	6.8	Trachea	8
41	22	19	7	Epiglottis	13
42	25	20	8.6	Olfactory pits, lateral and median nasal processes	8
43	26	20-21	9.6	Bronchi branching	8,13
44	28	22	11.6	Jacobson's organ	8
45	33	34.5	35	Nasal chamber, nasal septum complete	17
				Circulatory System	
46	14	14-15	2.5	Pericardial cavity, endocardium, epimyocardium	8
47			2.5-3.0	Anlagen of blood vessels	
48	15	15-16	3.2-5.2	Ventral aorta; fusion of paired cardiac tubes; blood in yolk sac; blood finally in heart and blood vessels	8
49	16	15-17	4	Omphalomesenteric arteries; allantoic arteries and veins; subintestinal artery; arteries of pronephros; posterior cardinal vein; duct of Cuvier; umbilical veins	14
50			4.15	1st pair of aortic arches; dorsal aortas	5
51			4.0-6.5	Truncus arteriosus, bulbus arteriosus, ventricle, atrium, sinus venosus; septum primum	8,13

/1/ Extra-embryonic length.

continued

66. DEVELOPMENT: SWINE

Part II: TISSUES AND ORGANS

	Standard Stages (Witschi)	Age da	Size mm	Structural Development	Reference
	(A)	(B)	(C)	(D)	(E)
				Circulatory System	
52	17	17	6.0-6.5	Longitudinal neural artery; lateral cardinal vein	14
53	18	16.5-18.0	3.8-4.5	Aortic arch II; endocardial cushions	5,8
54	19	16.5-17.5	3.6-4.6	Aortic arch III; interventricular septum	5,8
55	20	17.5	4.5-7.0	Aortic arch IV; mesial cardinal vein; venous valves	5,8,14
56	22	19	6	Aortic arch VI; primitive head vein	5,14
57	23	20	6.4	Foramen II in septum I	8
58	25	20	8.0-8.6	Septum II; external carotid	5,8
59	26	20-21	9.5-10.0	Bulbus dividing into aortic and pulmonary trunks; inferior vena cava; spleen	3,7,8
60	27	21-22	11	Thymus	1
61	28	22	12-14	Pulmonary, subclavian, basilar, and vertebral arteries	5
62	30	28	20.7	Brachiocephalic and left common carotid arteries	5
63	35	52	90	Tonsil	9
				Excretory System	
64	15	15-16	3.7	Duct of pronephros and mesonephros	8
65			5	Mesonephros	
66	16	15-17	4.0-6.5	Glomeruli in mesonephros	
67	17	17	4.9	Wolffian duct attains a lumen	
68	23	20	6.4	Metanephric duct	
69	26	20-21	10	Pelvis	
70	29	22	17.6	Calyces	
71	30	28	19.5	Glomeruli and convoluted tubules in metanephros	
				Reproductive System	
72	26	20-21	9.6	Indifferent gonads; anlagen of external genitalia (genital tubercle, genital folds, genital swellings)	8
73	28	22	12.4	Müllerian duct	8
74	30	28	24	Testes differentiated	8
75	34	39	44.5	Raphe penis	13
76	35	44	60	Prepuce, scrotum in male; labia majora, clitoris in female	13
77		51	85	Seminal vesicles, prostate, and Cowper's glands in male; oviducts, uteri, and vagina in female	
78		58.5	113	Nymphae (labia minora)	
79		62.5	128	Testes descending	
80	36	95	210	Testes enter inguinal canal	13
				Muscular System	
81	21	17.5	5	Elongation of smooth muscle nuclei of mesenchyme cells in region of circular muscle layer of esophagus at level of laryngotracheal groove	11
82	25	20	8	Dermomyotome differentiates	2
83			8.5	Skeletal muscle myoblasts elongate	
84	26	20-21	9	Smooth muscle myofibrillae in myoblasts of esophagus	11
85	29	22	18	Cross striations of skeletal muscle	2
86	31	30	25	Heart myoblasts become spindle-shaped	20
87	32	32.5	30	Elongation of smooth muscle nuclei in longitudinal muscle layer of esophagus and stomach	11
88	33	34.5	35	Skeletal muscle bundles	2
89	34	36.5	40	Muscularis mucosae of smooth muscle	11
90	35	48	76	Intercalated discs of cardiac muscle appear	20
91		52	89	Intercalated discs of cardiac muscle extend across fibers	
				Skeletal System	
92	12	11-12	10-65[1]	Notochord	13
93	22	19	7	Notochordal sheath	19
94	29	22	16.4	Chondrification of vertebrae; appearance of sternum	4,8
95	30	28	24	Appearance of presternum	4
96	32	32.5	28	Mandible ossified	6
97	33	34.5	35	Humerus ossified; femur ossified	6
98			38	Ribs start to ossify	

/1/ Extra-embryonic length.

continued

66. DEVELOPMENT: SWINE

Part II: TISSUES AND ORGANS

	Standard Stages (Witschi)	Age da	Size mm	Structural Development	Reference
	(A)	(B)	(C)	(D)	(E)
				Skeletal System	
99	34	36.5	40	Bodies and arches of vertebrae start to ossify	6
100	35	48	75	Odontoid process ossified	6
101		62	125	Sternebrae start to ossify	
102		63	130	Petrous portion of temporal bone ossifies	
103	36		135	Spinous processes of vertebrae ossify	6
104			240	Carpale II ossifies	
105			280	Tarsale II ossifies	
				Integumentary System	
106	28	22	12.4	Milk line	8
107	29	22	17.6	Milk hillocks	
108	30	28	19.5	Mammary gland primordia; hair follicles in head	
				Endocrine Glands (Appearance of Primordia)	
109	18	17	4.5	Epithelial hypophysis; thyroid	8
110	19	16.5-17.5	3.6	Dorsal and ventral pancreas anlagen	8
111	25	20	8	Adrenal cortex	18
112	27	21-22	11	Thymus	1
113	28	22	11.7	Neurohypophysis	8
114			15	Parathyroids	13
115	30	28	19.4-24.0	Pineal	12
116			24	Testis	8,15
117		28-30	20-25	Ovary	15
118	33	34.5	30-35	Adrenal medulla	18

Contributor: Kemp, Norman E.

References: [1] Badertscher, J. A. 1915. Am. J. Anat. 17:317. [2] Bardeen, C. R. 1900. Bull. Johns Hopkins Hosp. 9:367. [3] Davis, D. M. 1910. Am. J. Anat. 10:461. [4] Hanson, F. B. 1919. Anat. Record 17:1. [5] Heuser, C. H. 1923. Contribs. Embryol. Carnegie Inst. Wash. 15:121. [6] Hodges, P. C. 1953. Anat. Record 116:315. [7] Holyoke, E. A. 1936. Ibid. 65:333. [8] Keibel, F. 1897. Normentafeln zur Entwicklungsgeschichte der Wirbelthiere. G. Fischer, Jena. pt. 1. [9] Levin, P. M. 1930. Anat. Record 45:189. [10] MacCallum, J. B. 1901. Bull. Johns Hopkins Hosp. 12:102. [11] McGill, C. 1907-08. Intern. Monatsschr. Anat. u. Physiol. 24:209. [12] Minot, C. S. 1903. A laboratory textbook of embryology. Blakiston, Philadelphia. [13] Patten, B. M. 1948. Embryology of the pig. Ed. 3. Blakiston, New York. [14] Sabin, F. R. 1917. Contribs. Embryol. Carnegie Inst. Wash. 6:61. [15] Thomson, J. D. 1942. Proc. Iowa Acad. Sci. 49:475. [16] Thyng, F. W. 1910. Anat. Record 5:17. [17] Waterman, A. J. 1948. A laboratory manual of comparative vertebrate embryology. H. Holt, New York. [18] Whitehead, R. H. 1903. Am. J. Anat. 2:349. [19] Williams, L. W. 1908. Ibid. 8:251. [20] Witte, L. 1919. Ibid. 25:333.

67. DEVELOPMENT: RAT

Part I: CHARACTERIZATION OF STAGES

Age (column B) = days after fertilization, i.e., copulation age minus 8 hours (corresponding ages of mouse embryos of the same stage, based chiefly on references 7 and 8, are given in parentheses). Size (column C) = largest dimension of embryo in natural position (largest and smallest dimensions of blastocysts and chorionic vesicles are given in parentheses).

	Standard Stages (Witschi)	Age da	Size mm	Identification of Stages
	(A)	(B)	(C)	(D)
				Cleavage and Blastula
1	1	1	0.07	1 cell (in oviduct)
2	2	2 (1)	0.08 x 0.06	2 cells (in oviduct)
3	3	3		4 cells (in oviduct)
4	4	3.25 (2)	0.08 x 0.05	8-12 cells (in oviduct)
5	5	3.5	0.08 x 0.04	Morula (in uterus)
6	6	4	(0.08 x 0.03)	Early blastocyst (in uterus)
7	7	5 (4)	(0.12 x 0.05)	Free blastocyst (in uterus)
				Gastrula
8	8	6 (4.5)	(0.28 x 0.07)	Implanting blastocyst, with trophoblastic cone and inner cell mass; outgrowth of endoderm (hypoblast)
9	9	6.75 (5)		Diplotrophoblast; inner cell mass (pendant), covered with endoderm
10	10	7.25 (5.5)	(0.3 x 0.1)	Near complete implantation; pendant begins differentiation into embryonic and extra-embryonic parts
11	11	7.75 (6.5)	(0.5 x 0.1)	Completion of implantation; primary amniotic cyst; ectoplacental cone
				Primitive Streak
12	12	8.5 (7)	(1.04 x 0.26)	Connecting ectochorionic and amniotic cavities; rudiments of amniotic folds; primitive streak; start of 3rd layer formation; blastemas of heart and pericardium
				Neurula
13	13	9 (7.5)	1.0 (1.40 x 0.45)	Presomite neurula; fusion of chorio-amniotic folds, chorio-amniotic stalk; neural plate; embryo bent dorsally; bud of allantoic stalk
14	14	9.5 (7.75)	1.5 (1.8 x 1.1)	Somites 1-4 (occipital); pendant with 3 cavities: ectochorionic cyst, exocoelom, and amniotic cavity; ectochorionic cyst collapsing; allantoic stalk projects into exocoelom; embryo bent dorsally
15	15	10 (8.0-8.5)	2	Somites 5-12 (cervical); 1st visceral arch; ectochorionic cyst fused with ectoplacenta and with allantoic stalk; regression of peripheral (distal) yolk sac and trophectoderm (diplotrophoblast); Reichert's membrane; gonia in endoderm; embryo bent dorsally
16	16	10.5 (8.5-9.0)	2.4 (2.2 x 3.4)	Somites 13-20 (upper thoracic); 2 visceral arches; disc and yolk-sac placentas; appendicular folds; embryo reverses, curves ventrally
17	17	11 (9.5)	3.3	Somites 21-25 (lower thoracic); yolk stalk closes at level of 15th somite; primary gonia in mesentery; primitive streak disappears; tail bud becomes organized; arm and leg buds recognizable
				Tail Bud Embryo
18	18	11.5 (10)	3.8	Somites 26-28 (upper lumbar); 3 visceral arches; arm buds recognizable
19	19	11.75 (10.25)	4.2	Somites 29-31 (lower lumbar); visceral arches I-IV; cervical folds; appendicular folds and buds
20	20	11.875	5 (4.7 x 5.2)	Somites 32-33 (upper sacral)
21	21	12	5.1	Somites 34-35 (lower sacral); deep cervical sinuses
22	22	12.125 (10.5)	5.2	Somite 36 (1st caudal); olfactory pits
23	23	12.25	5.6 (4.5 x 5.8)	Somites 37-38 (caudal); start of umbilical herniation
24	24	12.375	6	Somites 39-40 (caudal)
				Complete Embryo
25	25	12.5 (11)	6.2	Somites 41-42 (caudal); occipital somites dispersing; 4 visceral arches; deep cervical sinuses; arm buds at somite levels 8-14, about as high as long; leg buds at somite levels 28-31, smaller; body forms a spiral of about $1\frac{1}{2}$ turns, the left face and trunk applied to yolk sac, the right side turned toward placenta; tail and allantoic stalk rise to the placenta

continued

67. DEVELOPMENT: RAT

Part I: CHARACTERIZATION OF STAGES

	Standard Stages (Witschi)	Age da	Size mm	Identification of Stages
	(A)	(B)	(C)	(D)
	Metamorphosing Embryo			
26	26	12.75	7	Somites 43-45 (caudal); mandibular, maxillary, and frontonasal processes; cervical sinuses closing; mammary welts; differentiation of handplates; arm buds vascularized, brachial nerves entering; beginning of umbilical hernia
27	27	13 (12)	8	Somites 46-48 (caudal); prominent facial processes and clefts; nose-snout projecting; cervical sinuses closed; primordia of mammary glands; round handplates and footplates; larger umbilical hernia
28	28	13.5 (12.5)	8.5	Somites 49-51 (caudal); 1st visceral cleft transforms into external ear duct; precartilaginous condensations in handplates
29	29	14	9.5	Somites 52-55 (caudal); auricular hillocks on visceral arches I and II
30	30	14.5 (13)	10.5	Somites 56-60 (caudal); body uncoils; mandibular precartilage; nearly round opening of external ear duct; pleuroperitoneal canal has become very narrow
31	31	15	12	Somites 61-63 (caudal); facial clefts closed; pleuroperitoneal canal closed; complete diaphragm
32	32	15.5 (14.5)	14.2 (14.3 x 8.0)	Somite 64 (caudal); pinna turns forward; maximal size of umbilical hernia
33	33	16 (15)	15.5	Somite 65 (usually this is last caudal); snout lifts off chest; last stage of metamorphosis
	Fetus			
34	34	17-18 (16.0-16.5)	16-20	1st fetal stage: rapid growth of eyelids (eyes entirely covered at end of 18th day); palate complete; pinna covers ear duct; umbilical hernia withdraws
35	35 antenatal	19-22 (17-19)	20-40	2nd fetal stage: sealed eyelids; fetal membranes and placentas reach peak of development; tail grows to 10 mm; birth occurs (22nd day in rat, 19th day in mouse)
36	35 postnatal	1-16 (1-20) postpartum	40-100[1]	After birth, fetus becomes a breathing and suckling nestling[2]; during 1st 16 days (22 to 38 days total age), eyelids remain sealed and external ear ducts plugged with periderm
37	36 postnatal	17+ (21+) postpartum	100+[1]	Periderm seals of ears and eyelids vanish; active feeding begins within next 3 days and weaning after 1 week (total weaning age, 45-48 days for rats and mice)

/1/ Body length from nose to root of tail. During preimplantation stages mouse development gains a lead of $1\frac{1}{2}$ to 2 days and maintains it until birth; its nestling period is correspondingly longer so that the average weaning age is nearly the same in the two species. /2/ Developmentally, nestling period belongs to 2nd fetal stage.

Contributor: Witschi, Emil

References: [1] Butcher, E. O. 1929. Am. J. Anat. 44:381. [2] Henneberg, B. 1937. Normentafel zur Entwicklungsgeschichte der Wanderratte (*Rattus norvegicus* Erxleben). G. Fischer, Jena. [3] Huber, G. C. 1915. J. Morphol. 26:1. [4] Long, J. A., and P. L. Burlingame. 1938. Univ. Calif. (Berkeley) Publs. Zool. 43:143. [5] MacDowell, E. C., E. Allen, and C. G. MacDowell. 1927. J. Gen. Physiol. 11:57. [6] Nicholas, J. S., and D. Rudnick. 1938. J. Exptl. Zool. 78:205. [7] Otis, E. M., and R. Brent. 1954. Anat. Record 120:33. [8] Snell, G. D. 1941. The early embryology of the mouse. Blakiston, Philadelphia. pp. 1-54. [9] Witschi, E. 1956. The development of vertebrates. W. B. Saunders, Philadelphia.

continued

67. DEVELOPMENT: RAT

Part II: TISSUES AND ORGANS

Age (column B) = days after fertilization, i.e., copulation age minus 8 hours. Size (column C) = longest dimension of embryo in natural postion; nose to anus in postnatal animals

	Standard Stages (Witschi)	Age da	Size mm	Structural Development	Reference
	(A)	(B)	(C)	(D)	(E)
				Nervous System	
1	13	9	1	Neural groove in neural plate without definite borders	1,4,9,
2	14	9.5	1.5	Neural plate with limiting neural folds; expansion of otic (5th) rhombomere; preotic transverse sulcus	14,16, 21,28,
3	15	10	2	Partly closed neural tube; neural crest condensations, spreading ventrolaterally, are primordia of cranial ganglia V, VII-VIII, and IX-X; cranial neural crest continues into spinal neural crest	30,31
4	16	10.5	2.4	3 primordial brain vesicles: forebrain, midbrain (cranial flexure), and hindbrain with 6 (7) rhombomeres; upper neuropore closes (at 17 somites); cranial ganglia separate from neural tube and surface ectoderm; 5th ganglion with ophthalmic ramus	
5	17	11	3.3	Roof of rhombencephalon becomes thin; neural crest cells are loosely arranged alongside spinal cord; some condensations indicated in cervical region but no distinct spinal ganglia; terminal lamina of prosencephalon; lower neuropore closes (24 somites)	
6	18	11.5	3.8	5 divisions of brain: telencephalon, diencephalon, mesencephalon, metencephalon, myelencephalon; trigeminal ganglion (V) has developed 3 branches, partly fibrous (ophthalmic, maxillary, mandibular); complexes VII-VIII and IX-X dividing into the 4 pairs of separate ganglia; acoustic ganglia establish close contact with otic vesicle	
7	19	11.75	4.2	Floor of diencephalon with beginning infundibular depression; marginal white zone appears in myelencephalon, mostly in 4th and 5th rhombomeres; 1st fibers of VIIth nerve enter brain; cervical spinal ganglia are definite metameric condensations	
8	22	12.125	5.2	Cerebral hemispheres; lamina terminalis well defined; cranial nerves V, VII, VIII, IX, X enter brain with heavy roots; also distal nerve fibers developed	
9	23	12.25	5.6	1st cervical ganglion has completely regressed; ganglion of 2nd cervical nerve (6th somite) may serve as convenient landmark in counting somites	
10	25	12.5	6.2	Cervical flexure; roof of 4th ventricle extremely thin	
11	28	13.5	8.5	Choroid plexus starts in 4th ventricle; start of pontine flexure; thickening of metencephalic dorsal plate (cerebellum); olfactory nerves enter brain; rhinencephalon begins to project from forebrain hemispheres; spinal ganglion chain extends to 40th somite (last 2 later regress)	
12	29	14	9.5	Cerebral hemispheres grow posteriorly over about 1/4 of diencephalon; choroid plexuses in 1st and 2nd ventricles; corpora striata; 1st elevation of pineal primordium; optic thalamus; spinal cord reaches to near tip of tail	
13	30	14.5	10.5	Rhinencephalon, a shallow lobe of each hemisphere, receives olfactory nerve; connections between hemispheric ventricles (1, 2) and diencephalic (3) become fairly narrow (foramens of Monro); pineal outgrowth	
14	31	15	12	Optic nerve fibers grow into brain	
15	32	15.5	14.2	Foramens of Monro reduced to small pores; choroid plexus in 3rd ventricle; maximal curvature of pontine flexure; spinal tube ends some distance from end of tail	
16	34	17-18	16-20	Body of metencephalon rapidly enlarging laterally, followed by recesses of 4th ventricle; pontine flexure straightens	
17	35a antenatal	19	20	Mesencephalon with upper and lower colliculi; spinal cord abruptly becomes a fine thread at root of tail	
18	35b newborn	22	40	Rhinencephalon with projecting olfactory bulbs; cerebellum with 5 transverse deep folds and 2 shallow ones	
				Sense Organs	
19	15	10	2	Optic sulci. Otic placodes.	9,14,
20	16	10.5	2.4	Olfactory pads. Optic bulbs. Otic cups.	16,21,
21	17	11	3.3	Olfactory placodes. Optic bulbs and stalks. Closing otic cups.	28,30,
22	18	11.5	3.8	Olfactory placodes. Lens placodes; optic bulbs contact epidermis; stalks short. Otic vesicles closed.	31

continued

67. DEVELOPMENT: RAT

Part II: TISSUES AND ORGANS

	Standard Stages (Witschi)	Age da	Size mm	Structural Development	Reference
	(A)	(B)	(C)	(D)	(E)
				Sense Organs	
23	19	11.75	4.2	Olfactory saucers. Beginning invagination of optic bulbs and lens placodes. Otic vesicles with short endolymphatic duct.	9,14, 16,21, 28,30, 31
24	22	12.125	5.2	Simple olfactory cups. Lens cups begin to close; optic bulbs with choroid fissure; nervous layer of retina thicker than pigment layer. Otic vesicles with endolymphatic duct.	
25	23	12.25	5.6	Olfactory pits. Lens sacs with fairly large pore. Endolymphatic duct turns dorsally.	
26	24	12.375	6	Deep olfactory pits flattening. Lens sacs with closing pore; optic stalks elongate.	
27	25	12.5	6.2	Deep olfactory pouches with median evaginations (vomeronasal organ); nerve fibers growing out from olfactory epithelia. Lens sacs closed, detach from epidermis; lenses differentiate into epithelial and fibrous parts; optic cups and stalks with deep choroid fissure; hyaloid vessels and plexus; vitreous mesenchyme; nervous layer of retina 4 times as thick as pigment layer. Otic vesicles laterally compressed, utricular and saccular parts recognizable.	
28	26	12.75	7	Narrow olfactory pouches; elongating tube-shaped vomeronasal organs. Lenses with small round cavity. Cochlear rudiment projects from saccule.	
29	27	13	8	Bucconasal membranes; olfactory nerves approach brain; primordial welts of 2 conchae. Lens cavity slit-like; vitreous body. Semicircular primordial pouches of utricle.	
30	28	13.5	8.5	Olfactory nerves reach brain; primordial welts of 3 conchae. Lens cavity disappears, fiber part 8 times as high as epithelial cells; invasion of mesenchyme between lens and epidermis; choroid fissure closed; hyaloid canal. Endolymphatic duct projects dorsally far beyond otic vesicle; semicircular pouches project further.	
31	29	14	9.5	Bucconasal membranes of choanae rupture; precartilaginous condensations of nasal capsule and septum. Vertical diameter of lens larger than horizontal; nervous layer of retina 8 times as thick as pigment layer; optic nerve fibers grow into stalk; eyelids; condensations of ocular muscles. Anterior semicircular canals with ampulla and primordial crista; posterior and lateral semicircular canals just forming; ampullary branches of vestibular nerves; opening of external ear ducts by changes from irregular visceral groove to round pore; precartilaginous condensation of otic capsules.	
32	31	15	12	Partly cartilaginous nasal septum and capsule. Anterior eye chamber; iris folds at free border of retina; lumen of eye stalks disappearing; fibers of optic nerve reach brain; ocular muscles innervated. All semicircular ducts well-differentiated, slender, with ampullae; cochlear process has accomplished 1st spiral turn; tympanic cavity from distal recess of 1st pharyngeal pouch; cartilaginous development of otic capsule and of auditory ossicles; external acoustic meatus partly covered by folding pinna (from visceral arch II).	
33	32	15.5	14	Slit-shaped choanae (1 mm long); 3 conchae as high as thick; vomeronasal organs long (0.8 mm), thick-walled tubes in septum; some periderm growth in nares; nasolacrimal duct. Cornea and sclera attain condition of mesenchyme layer around eyeball. Chondrification of otic capsule progressing; utriculosaccular duct constriction; cochlear duct 1-1/4 turns; starting condensation of spiral ganglion; pinna bent over outer opening of acoustic meatus.	
34	33	16	15.5	Palatine processes meet mesially, dividing each primary choana into an anterior pore (nasopalatine duct) and a longer posterior (secondary) choana. Eyelids slowly growing. Perilymphatic mesenchyme within cartilaginous otic capsules; external acoustic meatus closing, periderm fills deepest recess.	
35	34	17-18	16-20	Completion of palate (except incisive foramen) adds a long nasopharyngeal meatus to olfactory cavity of nose; secondary choanae open into this duct; nares plugged with periderm. Eyelids growing, rapidly closing; cornea and sclera are stratified epithelia; single, nucleated neuroblast layer; fibrous layer measures up to 1/8 thickness of nervous	

continued

67. DEVELOPMENT: RAT

Part II: TISSUES AND ORGANS

	Standard Stages (Witschi)	Age da	Size mm	Structural Development	Reference
	(A)	(B)	(C)	(D)	(E)
				Sense Organs	
	34	17-18	16-20	retina. Endolymphatic sac expanding; cochlea, 1-3/4 turns; vestibular nerve, spiral ganglion; proximal 1st pharyngeal pouch reduced to short auditive tube; otic capsule extensively chondrified; external acoustic meatus filled with periderm, opening covered by partly attached pinna.	9,14, 16,21, 28,30, 31
36	35a antenatal	19	20-40	Progressive development of conchae; lateral nasal mucus glands; nares plugged. Eyelids closed with periderm seal; retina with outer and inner nuclear layers and innermost fibrous layer; primordial ciliary ring. Cartilage of otic capsule sharply delineated from perilymphatic loose mesenchyme; wide endolymphatic sac; endolymphatic-utricular-saccular-reunient duct system slender, essentially adult condition; cochlear duct with 2-1/4 turns; middle ear cavities complete, with tympanic cavity, auditive tube, and nasopharyngeal ostium; cartilaginous auditory ossicles embedded in mesenchyme; external acoustic meatus solidly filled with periderm.	
37	35b newborn	22	40	Nares open, periderm sloughed off, epithelium cornified. Eyelids sealed; cornea 3 times as thick as sclera, stratified folds of ciliary body project inside, rumpling base of iris. Otic capsules partly ossified; perilymphatic duct system; external meatuses completely plugged with periderm and covered with sealed-on pinnae.	
38	35c postnatal	1-17 postpartum	40-100	Rapid functional development of sense organs enables young to leave nest at stage 36, 17 days postpartum, with eyelids and external ear ducts open	
				Digestive System	
39	14	9.5	1.5	Start of foregut formation	1,4,9, 16,20, 21,25, 26,28, 30,31
40	15	10	2	Oral membrane ruptures	
41	16	10.5	2.4	Liver primordium; yolk stalk narrows to slender tube	
42	17	11	3.3	Laryngotracheal groove; liver; dorsal pancreas; vitelline duct closes; cloaca; tailgut	
43	18	11.5	3.8	Longitudinal stomach; liver trabeculae; endoderm of vitelline duct resorbed; mesodermal stalk and vitelline vessels persist; cloacal membrane	
44	22	12.125	5.2	1st pharyngeal pouch touches ectoderm, 2nd ruptured into visceral groove, 3rd touches ectoderm; epithelial ultimobranchial body starts forming in 4-6 pouch complex. Stomach; duodenum; hepatopancreatic duct. Small ventral pancreas; larger dorsal pancreas with duct.	
45	25	12.5	6.2	Tongue starts; trachea separated from esophagus; stomach oblique; liver with deep cut lobes. Cloaca separates into rectal and urogenital parts. Tailgut starts regression; early stage of umbilical hernia.	
46	27	13	8	Dorsal and ventral pancreas fuse, primary dorsal duct disappears. Single intestinal loop forms umbilical hernia. Cloaca halfway separated into urogenital and intestinal parts; tailgut disappears.	
47	30	14.5	10.5	Placode-like dental lamina. Salivary glands (epithelial cords); free tip of tongue; cloaca divided into urogenital sinus and rectum.	
48	31	15	12	Ingrowth of dental laminas; long gap between molar and incisor parts. Salivary glands with secretory buds; large umbilical hernia. Pancreatic tubules and islets spread loosely in abundant connective tissue, highly vascularized. Thin anal membrane rupturing.	
49	33	16	15.5	Molar laminas with trough-shaped rim; papillary blastema cord fills cavity; incisor germs about as long as their diameters	
50	34	17-18	16-20	Umbilical hernia withdraws	
51	35a antenatal	19	20	Each molar lamina with 2 concentrations of enamel organ and papillary blastema; upper and lower incisor germs about twice as long as thick; tall ameloblast epithelia; papillae well vascularized. Rapid increase in liver glycogen. Pancreas a more compact body of acini, ducts, and islets; connective tissue reduced; gut completely withdrawn from umbilicus. For nutrition, fetus depends on fetal membranes and placenta.	
52	35b newborn	22	40	Pre-eruptive incisors with thin dentin and enamel layers; 1st and 2nd molars with crosswise ridges. Intestinal organs attain functional state; pancreas, very compact, shows acinar cells crowded with secretion granules; start of secretion.	

continued

67. DEVELOPMENT: RAT

Part II: TISSUES AND ORGANS

	Standard Stages (Witschi)	Age da	Size mm	Structural Development	Reference
	(A)	(B)	(C)	(D)	(E)
				Digestive System	
53	35c post-natal	8-10 post-partum	ca. 70	Eruption of incisors	1,4,9, 16,20, 21,25, 26,28, 30,31
54	36 post-natal	19 post-partum	ca. 100	Eruption of 1st molars	
55		22 post-partum	Young adult	Eruption of 2nd molars	
56		35 post-partum	Young adult	Eruption of 3rd molars	
				Respiratory System	
57	15	10	2	1st pharyngeal pouch	9,16, 21,25, 28,30, 31
58	17	11	3.3	2nd pharyngeal pouch; beginning laryngotracheal groove	
59	18	11.5	3.8	3rd pharyngeal pouch; laryngotracheal groove; paired lung buds	
60	19	11.75	4.2	Trachea begins separation from esophagus	
61	22	12.125	5.2	4th to 6th pharyngeal pouch complex; larynx; trachea partly free; primary lung buds, larger right one grows downward	
62	23	12.25	5.6	Larynx differentiation; arytenoid swellings compress larynx laterally; entrance to trachea a longitudinal cleft; lung buds turn downward	
63	25	12.5	6.2	Upper part of larynx completely compressed; lower part still an open entrance into trachea; left and right bronchus; simple lung buds; swelling right bud larger than left	
64	26	12.75	7	Pharyngeal pouches regressing; cervical sinus narrowing; arytenoid and epiglottis swellings; tracheal opening in pharyngeal cleft reduced to fine pore; right bronchus with 3, left bronchus with 2 secondary buds; pleuroperitoneal folds (septa)	
65	28	13.5	8.5	Cervical sinus closed; entrance to trachea occluded; right bronchus with 4 secondary and tertiary buds, left with 2 only; pleural cavity still widely open toward peritoneal cavity	
66	29	14	9.5	Crosswise furrow in anterior larynx separates epiglottis from arytenoid bodies	
67	30	14.5	10.5	Epiglottis grows in height, separated from lower larynx by deep cross-furrow; lower larynx occluded; bronchial tree with about 20 branches and buds of higher order; narrow pleuroperitoneal canals	
68	32	15.5	14.2	Larynx same as at stage 30 but larger; cross furrow becomes ventricle of larynx; greater branching of bronchial tree; lungs highly vascularized; major lobes of lungs indicated; hyoid cartilage, but no laryngeal or tracheal cartilages; complete diaphragm separates pleural and peritoneal cavities	
69	34	17-18	16-20	Epiglottis projects into opening of nasopharyngeal meatus; 1st set of laryngeal and tracheal cartilages; ventricle of larynx with several secondary grooves	
70	35a antenatal	19	20	Epiglottis still in nasopharyngeal duct (with precartilage); ventricle of larynx expanding; lung tissue compact, highly differentiated	
71	35b newborn	22	40	Lumen of trachea and lower larynx becomes continuous with ventricle of upper part; in resting condition epiglottis (with cartilage) rests on root of tongue, covered by soft palate; with nares also wide open, a continuous air passage leads now to lungs; lungs are inflated with air	
				Circulatory System	
72	12	8.5	0.6	Paired cardiogenic primordia (mesoderm)	3,5,6, 9,13, 16,17, 21,28, 30,31
73	13	9	1	Cardiogenic primordia fusing; crescent-shaped pleuropericardial cavity; endothelial cells between splanchnic mesoderm and endoderm	
74	14	9.5	1.5	Partly fused tubular hearts; initiation of myocardial contractions	
75	15	10	2	S-shaped single tubular heart; atrial and bulboventricular zones (latter beating); aortic arch I	
76	16	10.5	2.4	Aortic arches I and II; cardinal veins, sinus venosus, umbilical veins, atrium, ventricular loop, arterial bulb and trunk; circulation established	
77	17	11	3.3	Aortic arches I, II, and III; interventricular sulcus	
78	18	11.5	3.8	3 aortic arches, I regressing, IV in preparation; 1st indication of separation of left and right heart chambers	
79	19	11.75	4.2	4 aortic arches, I regressing, IV still small	

continued

67. DEVELOPMENT: RAT

Part II: TISSUES AND ORGANS

	Standard Stages (Witschi)	Age da	Size mm	Structural Development	Reference
	(A)	(B)	(C)	(D)	(E)
				Circulatory System	
80	20	11.875	5	Aortic arches II regressing, III and IV well-developed, V very slender and irregular	3,5,6, 9,13, 16,17, 21,28, 30,31
81	21	12		Aortic arches III and IV large; sometimes one or both arches V well-developed; atrial septum starts forming; atrioventricular canal	
82	22	12.125	5.2	4 aortic arches, III and IV large, V and VI very slender; I and II have disappeared	
83	23	12.25	5.6	Addition of arch VII (pulmonary); starting interventricular septum	
84	24	12.375	6	In heart, atrioventricular cushions and septa in evidence (primordia); small pulmonary vein opens into left atrium	
85	25	12.5	6.2	Aortic arches III and IV well-developed, V very irregular and regressing, VII (pulmonary) consolidating; common cardinal veins; hepatic vein collects vitelline and umbilical veins through liver; atrial septum still incomplete; dorsal and ventral atrioventricular cushions fused	
86	26	12.75	7	Aortic arches III and IV well-developed, symmetric, dorsal longitudinal connection narrowing; V disappears; VI asymmetric, right narrowed to half; pulmonary (VII) roots branching off arches VI; atrial septum nearly complete, oval foramen forming	
87	27	13	8	Cervical sinus closing; aortic arches same as at stage 26, but aortic trunk partly divided into systemic and pulmonary stems; increased size of lingual (ventral carotid) and pulmonary arteries; beginning of auricle formation; oval foramen	
88	28	13.5	8.5	Aortic arches same as at stage 26; in aortic trunk and heart, left-right separation nears completion; inferior cardinal veins intact	
89	29	14	9.5	Aortic arches III only symmetric pair; IV *left*, large (systemic arch); IV *right*, small (supplies vertebral and subclavian arteries of right side); VI *left*, a large arterial duct to dorsal aorta; VI *right*, disappeared except for contribution to paired pulmonary arteries; dorsal aortas reduced between arches III and IV, right aorta very thin below root of vertebral artery; aortic trunks completely separated; inferior vena cava collects renal, vitelline, umbilical veins, and incorporates hepatic vein; right inferior cardinal vein interrupted, left reduced	
90	31	15	21	Aortic arches III only symmetric pair, with lingual and carotid branches; IV *right*, no longer connected with dorsal aorta, relatively short, supplies right subclavian and vertebral arteries; IV *left*, systemic arch, receives arterial duct from VI *left*, and after giving off left subclavian and vertebral arteries becomes descending aorta; interventricular septum nearly complete, but an interatrial foramen still persists	
91	32	15.5	14.2	Fetal circulatory system is established; differs from that in man mainly by persistence of a capacious vitelline circuit in addition to allantoic (umbilical) circuit	
92	35 postnatal	22-38 (1-16 postpartum)	40-100	Immediately following birth, with discard of fetal membranes and placentas, vitelline and allantoic (umbilical) veins collapse and degenerate, oval and interatrial foramens close, and arterial duct (VI *left*) shrinks	
				Excretory System	
93	15	10	2	Nephric blastema cord	7,9,15, 16,21, 28,30
94	17	11	3.3	Rudiments of nephric ducts and tubules	
95	18	11.5	3.8	Nephric duct approaches cloacal region	
96	19	11.75	4.2	Growing tips of nephric ducts apposed to wall of cloaca; mesonephric tubules begin to organize at upper pole	
97	22	12.125	5.2	Primitive mesonephric tubules, mostly solid; nephric ducts (lumen not continuous) fused with cloacal nephric papillae	
98	23	12.25	5.6	Mesonephros consists of a series of densely crowded nephrons, histologically not fully differentiated; only uppermost of tubules attached to nephric ducts; no renal corpuscles; primitive metanephric ureter buds from dorsal wall of lower nephric ducts	
99	24	12.375	6	Cloaca begins dividing	
100	25	12.5	6.2	2 rudimentary nephrostomes at upper end of funnel field; ureter buds, as long as wide, imbedded in metanephric blastema	
101	26	12.75	7	Single tubular ureter buds 4 times as long as wide; capped by dense nephric blastema	

continued

67. DEVELOPMENT: RAT

Part II: TISSUES AND ORGANS

	Standard Stages (Witschi)	Age da	Size mm	Structural Development	Reference
	(A)	(B)	(C)	(D)	(E)
				Excretory System	
102	27	13	8	Metanephric ducts end in pelvis with 2 branches (calyces); cloaca halfway separated in urogenital and intestinal parts	7,9,15, 16,21, 28,30
103	28	13.5	8.5	Mesonephric tubules scattered; only top few join mesonephric duct; others consist of isolated curved tubules with a vestigial renal capsule; mesonephroi shorter than gonads; common nephric ducts short, open into urogenital part of cloaca; 3rd pelvic bud indicated; no differentiation of renal tubes; perineum and external urethral papilla forming	
104	29	14	9.5	Upper cloaca divided in rectum and urogenital sinus; cloacal membrane long and narrow, loose-celled in anal region; metanephros: rapid multiplication of pelvic branches and participation of blastema in histologic differentiation	
105	31	15	12	Mesonephros regressed, except epididymal part; metanephroi ascend behind gonads, contact adrenals; sprouting tubules; numerous ampullae; nephrons; meso- and meta-nephric ducts open separately into urogenital sinus; anus still attached to urogenital sinus by a tissue bridge	
106	32	15.5	14.2	Tips of metanephroi on same level with those of gonads and epididymides; ureters acquire direct openings into neck of bladder; anus still attached to urogenital sinus; cloacal membrane forms a narrow lamina on underside of urethral papilla	
107	34	17	16	Rectum and urogenital sinus completely separated; perineal development	
108	35a antenatal	19	20	For excretion, fetuses depend almost entirely on fetal membranes and placentas	
109	35b newborn	22	40	Kidneys attain functional state; perineal distance (anus to urethral papilla) of newborn is greater in males than in females	
				Reproductive System	
110	14	9.5	1.5	Germ cells in yolk-sac epithelium	7,9,16, 18,19, 21-23, 28-32
111	16	10.5	2.4	Germ cell migration into hindgut and mesenteries of lower body region	
112	18	11.5	3.8	Germ cells in dorsal mesentery and left and right coelomic angles	
113	19	11.75	4.2	Gonadal folds begin to form; first germ cells arrive	
114	22	12.125	5.2	Indifferent gonadal folds; rapid increase in number of germ cells	
115	26	12.75	7	Fully-developed indifferent gonads; end of germ-cell migration	
116	28	13.5	8.5	Sex differentiation: 1st indication of cortical or medullary prevalence in gonad development; funnels of oviducts organize	
117	29	14	9.5	Oviducts (solid) reach gonad level	
118	30	14.5	10.5	Sex differentiation: testes and ovaries clearly identifiable; germ cells now are either spermatogonia or ovogonia; oviducts end below mesonephros, do not enter pelvis	
119	31	15	12	Oviducts cross over nephric duct, end in pelvis	
120	32	15.5	14.2	Oviducts reach urogenital sinus	
121	34	17-18	16-20	In ovary, many germ cells enter maturation phase (synaptic ovocytes); oviducts still of same size and shape in both sexes	
122	35a antenatal	19-22	20-40	Differentiation of male and female secondary sex characters: seminal vesicles and prostate gland in male, uterovaginal canal in females; regression of heterologous gonaducts	
123	35b newborn	22	40	Perineal distance from anus to urethral papilla greater in males than in females	
				Muscular System	
124	12	7.25	0.6	Paired mesodermal cardiogenic primordia	2,3,4, 5,6,9, 10,16, 17,21, 28,30, 31
125	13	9	1	Cardial myoblasts from fused primordia arrange into primitive bulboventricular rudiment	
126	14	9.5	1.5	Start of myocardial contractions	
127	16	10.5	2.4	At 16 somites, myotomes become organized in cervical region	
128	19	11.75	4.2	At 30 somites, myotomes consist of longitudinally elongated myoblasts	
129	25	12.5	6.2	Same type of short spindle-shaped myoblasts; myotomes with ventral processes	
130	30	14.5	10.5	Rapid multiplication of myoblasts resumed	
131	32	15.5	14.2	Differentiation of somitic muscle fibrils; some are birefringent	
132	33	16	15.5	Birefringence of skeletal muscles; step up in myosin synthesis; contractility	
133	34	17-18	16-20	Cross-striated myofibrils; rapid development of musculature	

continued

67. DEVELOPMENT: RAT

Part II: TISSUES AND ORGANS

	Standard Stages (Witschi)	Age da	Size mm	Structural Development	Reference
	(A)	(B)	(C)	(D)	(E)
				Skeletal System	
134	29	14	9.5	Early stages of vertebral condensation; cartilage deposition starts in humerus	11,16, 21,26, 30,31
135	31	15	12	Precartilaginous nasal capsules; cartilaginous otic capsules; condensation of auditory ossicle primordia	
136	32	15.5	14.2	Active chondrification; periosteal membranes; multiple foci of ossification (e.g., clavicle)	
137	34	17-18	16-20	Ossification of many skeletal parts now in progress	
				Integumentary System	
138	22	12.125	5.2	Mammary welts	9,16, 21,28, 30,31
139	29	14	9.5	Cup-shaped mammary glands; primary whisker papillae	
140	30	14.5	10.5	Whisker papillae more elevated	
141	31	15	12	Invaginated whisker papillae; eyelid-folds	
142	32	15.5	14.2	Flask-shaped mammary glands; periderm proliferation in external nares	
143	34	17-18	16-20	Periderm thickens in nostrils, on eyelids and in external meatus of ear; cornification within deep whisker follicles; papillae of body hair	
144	35a antenatal	19	20	More papillae of body hair	
145	35b newborn	22	40	Periderm of nares sloughs off; seals of eyelids and periderm plugs of ears persist until 17th day postnatal; surface layer of epidermis cornified, hair not erupted	
				Endocrine Glands (Endodermal Origin)	
146	15	10	2	Primitive thyroid depression in floor of pharyngeal cavity at level of 1st pharyngeal pouches	8,9,12, 24,25, 27,31
147	16	10.5	2.4	Thyroid pit with thick epithelium	
148	17	11	3.3	Thyroid a deep pit	
149	18	11.5	3.8	Thyroid vesicle with constricting opening	
150	19	11.75	4.2	Thyroid thick-walled, neck opening into upper pharyngeal cavity	
151	20	11.875	5	Thyroid with pore opening into oral cavity	
152	21	12	5.1	Thyroid vesicle closed but still attached to oral epithelium	
153	22	12.125	5.2	Thyroid separating from oral epithelium. Buds of ventral and dorsal pancreas.	
154	23	12.25	5.6	Thyroid connected with site of origin by slender cord of cells	
155	24	12.375	6	Thyroid a solid body, shifting from foramen cecum. Thymus primordia. Pancreatic ducts.	
156	25	12.5	6.2	Thyroid with several lobes has moved down to anterior surface of arterial trunk. Thymus primordium: epithelium of ventral diverticle of 3rd pharyngeal pouch. Parathyroid primordium: epithelium of dorsal diverticle of 3rd pharyngeal pouch. 4-6 pouch complex contains epithelial primordium of ultimobranchial body.	
157	26	12.75	7	Ultimobranchial bodies are thick-walled vesicles at left and right ends of 4-6 pharyngeal pouch complex	
158	27	13	8	Thymus and parathyroid detaching from 3rd pouch; vesicular ultimobranchial body (lateral thyroid) detaching. Fusion of ventral with dorsal pancreas; sprouting tubules, acini, and islets.	
159	28	13.5	8.5	Thymus and parathyroid primordia separated from 3rd pharyngeal pouch. Ultimobranchial vesicles detached from pharynx.	
160	29	14	9.5	Thyroid a crescent bar around ventral surface of lower larynx, with lobular differentiation	
161	32	15.5	14.2	Separation of parathyroid and thymus components (latter grows downward with lymphocyte and connective tissue invasion). Ultimobranchial vesicles attached to wings of thyroid. Pancreas: loosely branching trees of acini and attached islets in abundant mesenchyme.	
162	34	17-18	16-20	Thyroid consists of 2 highly-lobulated and vascularized bodies at left and right of upper trachea, connected by isthmus ventrally around 3rd tracheal ring. Parathyroids attached to left and right wings of thyroid. Ultimobranchial bodies embedded in thyroids, scattering and regressing.	
163	35a antenatal	19	20	Thyroid gland encapsulated, now a body of compact follicles without colloid; approximate starting time of hypophyseal control (by TSH). Pancreas now a more compact gland with scattered islets.	

continued

67. DEVELOPMENT: RAT

Part II: TISSUES AND ORGANS

	Standard Stages (Witschi)	Age da	Size mm	Structural Development	Reference
	(A)	(B)	(C)	(D)	(E)
				Endocrine Glands (Endodermal Origin)	
164	35b newborn	22	40	Thyroid follicles with small amounts of colloid. Thymus glands with cortex and medulla, both crowded with rapidly multiplying small lymphocytes. Ultimobranchial bodies do not form thyroid follicles nor colloid; no storage of radio iodine. Pancreas: highly granular acini and chromophobe islets; possible initiation of insulin production by β cells.	8,9,12, 24,25, 27,31
				Endocrine Glands (Neural and Nephroblastemic Origin)	
165	16	10.5	2.4	Hypophysis placode contacts base of diencephalon	9,12, 16,21, 22,28, 30-32
166	17	11	3.3	Hypophysis a shallow cup	
167	19	11.75	4.2	Hypophysis a pouch as deep as long; somewhat narrower, distal part closely adheres to short infundibulum	
168	22	12.125	5.2	Hypophysis closely applied to frontal wall of infundibulum with lateral embracing lobes	
169	25	12.5	6.2	Hypophysis posteriorly caved in by lobular development of neurohypophysis. Adrenal cortical blastema.	
170	26	12.75	7	Hypophyseal pouch opening narrows	
171	27	13	8	Hypophyseal pouch closed; walls of pouch and of infundibulum folded. Gonads: cortex and medulla established, probably assume inductive functions.	
172	28	13.5	8.5	Hypophysis with solid stalk. Sympathoblasts begin associating with adrenal cortex. Gonads start sexual differentiation.	
173	30	14.5	10.5	Hypophysis: sprouting anterior lobe connected with oral roof by a fine stalk only; neural hypophysis with highly lobular development, infundibular lumen reduced short pit. Pineal cup-shaped evagination in roof of diencephalon. Adrenal bodies consolidating, loose cords of cortical cells, some scattered nests or strands of medullary cells; no capsule. Ovary: blood vessels spreading between cortex and medulla. Testis: albuginea with peripheral spread of blood vessels.	
174	32	15.5	14.2	Hypophyseal stalk still passes through pore in cartilaginous base of skull, but cells disperse near roof of mouth. Pineal tubular evagination. Testes with primitive seminal tubules and some interstitial cells.	
175	34	17-18	16-20	Hypophysis: trabecular anterior lobe and stalk have disappeared, wide cavity separates intermediate lobe; compact trabecular posterior lobe. Pineal hollow tube with smooth walls.	
176	35a antenatal	19	20	Hypophysis from this stage on gives evidence of endocrine activity. Pineal with lobular fragmentation of distal half. Adrenal cortical cells in strands and medullary cells scattered or in nests, dispersed; adrenals start control of liver glycogenesis by release of corticoids.	
177	35b newborn	22	40	Hypophysis same as at stage 34, but cavity between anterior and intermediate lobes narrowed. Adrenal medulla becomes arranged in center of cortical columns. Primary ovarian follicles. Testes with seminal tubules imbedded in stroma and interstitial cells.	

Contributor: Witschi, Emil

References: [1] Adelmann, H. B. 1925. J. Comp. Neurol. 39:19. [2] Aoto, T. 1957. J. Fac. Sci. Hokkaido Univ. 13:364. [3] Burlingame, P. L., and J. A. Long. 1939. Univ. Calif. (Berkeley) Publs. Zool. 43:249. [4] Butcher, E. O. 1929. Am. J. Anat. 44:381. [5] Goss, C. M. 1952. Anat. Record 112:761. [6] Hall, E. K. 1954. Ibid. 118:175. [7] Hall, K. 1936. J. Anat. 70:413. [8] Harland, M. 1940. Anat. Record 77:247. [9] Henneberg, B. 1937. Normentafel zur Entwicklungsgeschichte der Wanderratte (*Rattus norvegicus* Erxleben). G. Fischer, Jena. [10] Herrmann, H., J. S. Nicholas, and M. E. Vosgian. 1949. Proc. Soc. Exptl. Biol. Med. 72:454. [11] Johnson, M. L. 1933. Am. J. Anat. 52:241. [12] Jost, A. 1961. Harvey Lectures, Ser. 55, p. 201. [13] Krehbiel, R. H. 1937. Physiol. Zool. 10:212. [14] Long, J. A., and P. L. Burlingame. 1938. Univ. Calif. (Berkeley) Publs. Zool. 43:143. [15] Ludwig, E. 1947. Acta Anat. 4:193. [16] MacDowell, E. C., E. Allen, and C. G. MacDowell. 1927. J. Gen. Physiol. 11:57. [17] Marit, C. 1959. Bull. acad. roy. méd. Belg. 24:451. [18] Mintz, B. 1959. Arch.

continued

67. DEVELOPMENT: RAT

Part II: TISSUES AND ORGANS

anat. microscop. (Paris) 48:155. [19] Mintz, B. 1957. J. Embryol. Exptl. Morphol. 5:396. [20] Morse, A., and R. O. Greep. 1947. Anat. Record 99:379. [21] Otis, E. M., and R. Brent. 1954. Ibid. 120:33. [22] Price, D. 1936. Am. J. Anat. 60:79. [23] Raynaud, A. 1942. Bull. biol. France et Belg., Suppl. 29:1. [24] Rogers, W. M. 1927. Am. J. Anat. 38:349. [25] Rogers, W. M. 1929. Ibid. 44:283. [26] Schour, I., and M. Massler. 1942. In J. Q. Griffith and E. J. Farris, ed. The rat in laboratory investigation. J. B. Lippincott, Philadelphia. [27] Sehe, C. T. 1957. Ph. D. Thesis. State Univ. Iowa, Iowa City. pp. 1-45. [28] Snell, G. D. 1941. The early embryology of the mouse. Blakiston, Philadelphia. pp. 1-54. [29] Thomson, J. D. 1942. Proc. Iowa Acad. Sci. 49:475. [30] Witschi, E. 1956. The development of vertebrates. W. B. Saunders, Philadelphia. [31] Witschi, E. Unpublished. Embryology of the rat. State Univ. Iowa, Iowa City, 1961. [32] Witschi, E., and E. Dale. 1961. Gen. & Comp. Endocrinol. 1(suppl. 1).

68. DEVELOPMENT: CHICK

Part I: CHARACTERIZATION OF STAGES

Data adapted from Hamilton [2]. Times at which stages occur are approximate and are based on incubation temperature of 38°C.

	Standard Stages (Witschi)	Chick Stages[1]	Age	Identification of Stages
	(A)	(B)	(C)	(D)
				Before Laying
1	3,4	Early cleavage	3.5-4.5 hr[2]	Shell membrane of egg formed in isthmus of oviduct
2	5,6	During cleavage		Germ wall formed from marginal periblast
3	7	Late cleavage	4.5-24.0 hr[2]	Shell of egg formed in uterus
				After Laying
4	8,9	1		Preprimitive streak (embryonic shield)
5	10	2	6-7 hr	Initial primitive streak, 0.3-0.5 mm long
6	11	3	12-13 hr	Intermediate primitive streak
7	12	4	18-19 hr	Definitive primitive streak, ±1.88 mm long
8	13a	5	19-22 hr	Head process (notochord)
9	13b	6	23-25 hr	Head fold
10	14a	7	23-26 hr	1 somite; neural folds
11	14b	7 to 8-	ca. 23-26 hr	1-3 somites; coelom
12	14c	8	26-29 hr	4 somites; blood islands
13	15a	9	29-33 hr	7 somites; primary optic vesicles
14	15b	9+ to 10-	ca. 33 hr	8-9 somites; anterior amniotic fold
15	15c	10	33-38 hr	10 somites; 3 primary brain vesicles
16	16a	11	40-45 hr	13 somites; 5 neuromeres of hindbrain
17	16b	12	45-49 hr	16 somites; telencephalon
18	16c	13	48-52 hr	19 somites; atrioventricular canal
19	17a	13+ to 14-	ca. 50-52 hr	20-21 somites; tail bud
20	17b	14	50-53 hr	22 somites; trunk flexure; visceral arches I and II, clefts 1 and 2
21	17c	14+ to 15-	ca. 50-54 hr	23 somites; premandibular head cavities
22	17d	15	50-55 hr	24-27 somites; visceral arch III, cleft 3
23	18	16	51-56 hr	26-28 somites; wing bud; posterior amniotic fold
24	19	17	52-64 hr	29-32 somites; leg bud; epiphysis
25	20	18	3 da	30-36 somites extending beyond level of leg bud; allantois
26	21	19	3.0-3.5 da	37-40 somites extending into tail; maxillary process
27	22	20	3.0-3.5 da	40-43 somites; rotation completed; eye pigment
28	23	21	3.5 da	43-44 somites; visceral arch IV, cleft 4
29	24	22	3.5-4.0 da	Somites extend to tip of tail
30	25	23	4 da	Dorsal contour from hindbrain to tail is a curved line
31	26	24	4.5 da	Toe plate

/1/ As described by Hamburger and Hamilton [1]. /2/ After ovulation.

continued

68. DEVELOPMENT: CHICK

Part I: CHARACTERIZATION OF STAGES

	Standard Stages (Witschi)	Chick Stages[1]	Age	Identification of Stages
	(A)	(B)	(C)	(D)
				After Laying
32	27	25	4.5-5.0 da	Elbow and knee joints
33	28	26	5 da	1st 3 toes
34	29	27	5.0-5.5 da	Beak
35	30	28	5.5-6.0 da	3 digits, 4 toes
36	31	29	6.0-6.5 da	Rudiment of 5th toe
37	32	30	6.5-7.0 da	Feather germs; scleral papillae; egg tooth
38	33a	31	7.0-7.5 da	Web between 1st and 2nd digits
39	33b	32	7.5 da	Anterior tip of mandible has reached beak
40	34a	33	7.5-8.0 da	Web on radial margin of wing and 1st digit
41	34b	34	8 da	Nictitating membrane
42	34c	35	8.5-9.0 da	Phalanges in toes
43	34d	36	10 da	Length of 3rd toe from tip to middle of metatarsal joint = 5.4±0.3 mm; length of beak from anterior angle of nostril to tip of bill = 2.5 mm; primordium of comb; labial groove; uropygial gland
44	34e	37	11 da	Length of 3rd toe = 7.4±0.3 mm; length of beak = 3.0 mm
45	34f	38	12 da	Length of 3rd toe = 8.4±0.3 mm; length of beak = 3.1 mm
46	35a	39	13 da	Length of 3rd toe = 9.8±0.3 mm; length of beak = 3.5 mm
47	35b	40	14 da	Length of beak = 4.0 mm; length of 3rd toe = 12.7±0.5 mm
48	35c	41	15 da	Length of beak from anterior angle of nostril to tip of upper bill = 4.5 mm; length of 3rd toe = 14.9±0.8 mm
49	35d	42	16 da	Length of beak = 4.8 mm; length of 3rd toe = 16.7±0.8 mm
50	35e	43	17 da	Length of beak = 5.0 mm; length of 3rd toe = 18.6±0.8 mm
51	35f	44	18 da	Length of beak = 5.7 mm; length of 3rd toe = 20.4±0.8 mm
52	36a	45	19-20 da	Yolk sac half enclosed in body cavity; chorio-allantoic membrane contains less blood and is "sticky" in living embryo
53	36b	46	20-21 da	Newly-hatched chick

/1/ As described by Hamburger and Hamilton [1].

Contributor: Hamilton, Howard L.

References: [1] Hamburger, V., and H. L. Hamilton. 1951. J. Morphol. 88:49. [2] Hamilton, H. L. 1952. Lillie's Development of the chick. H. Holt, New York.

Part II: TISSUES AND ORGANS

Chick Stages (column B) adapted from Hamburger and Hamilton [1]; number of somites is given in parentheses.

	Standard Stages (Witschi)	Chick Stages	Age	Structure	Origin	Reference (Page)
	(A)	(B)	(C)	(D)	(E)	(F)
				Nervous System		
1	14	7 (1)	23-26 hr	Neural folds	Anterior end of medullary plate	2(79)
2		8 (4)	26-29 hr	Neural tube	Fusion of neural folds at level of future midbrain	2(79)
3	15	9- to 9 (6-7)	ca. 29-33 hr	Neural crest	In head	2(198)
4	16	11 to 11+ (13-14)	ca. 40-45 hr	Trigeminus, neural crest component	Neural crest at level of metencephalon	2(201)
5		12- (15)	ca. 45 hr	Acousticofacialis ganglion, facial component	Neural crest and posterodorsal epibranchial placode of 1st visceral furrow	2(203)
6		12+ (17)	ca. 45-49 hr	Glossopharyngeal ganglion	Neural crest and epibranchial placode of 2nd visceral furrow	2(204,205)

continued

68. DEVELOPMENT: CHICK

Part II: TISSUES AND ORGANS

	Standard Stages (Witschi)	Chick Stages	Age	Structure	Origin	Reference (Page)
	(A)	(B)	(C)	(D)	(E)	(F)
				Nervous System		
7	16-17	13- to 13+ (18-20)	ca. 48-52 hr	Diencephalon (delimitation)	Primitive forebrain	2(191)
8				Parencephalon	Anterior portion of diencephalon	2(193)
9				Synencephalon	Hindmost third of diencephalon	2(193)
10				Velum transversum	Indentation in roof of forebrain	2(191)
11	17	13+ (20)		Rathke's pouch	Ectoderm of roof of stomodeum immediately anterior to oral plate	2(195,311)
12				Vagus nerve, neural crest component	Indistinct aggregation of neural crest cells immediately in front of level of duct of Cuvier	2(204)
13		14 (21)		Acousticofacialis ganglion, acoustic component	Wall of auditory vesicle	2(203)
14	17-18	15 (25-27)		Trigeminus, component from epibranchial placode	Ectodermal placode in front of and above 1st visceral cleft	2(201)
15	19	17 (30-35)	3 da	Epiphysis	Roof of diencephalon	2(81,194)
16	20	18	3 da	Abducens nerve	Floor of myelencephalon beneath nerve VII	2(333)
17			3 da	Spinal cord, mantle layer	Middle zone of neural tube	2(299)
18			3 da	Spinal nerves, motor component	Medullary neuroblasts of ventral horn, spinal cord	2(317)
19	20-25	18 to 23	3-4 da	Facial nerve	Anteroventral portion of acousticofacialis complex	2(334)
20	21-22	19 to 20	78 hr	Hypoglossus, cranial nerve XII	Ventral part of neural tube opposite somites 3-4	2(336)
21	24	22	End of 3rd da	Trochlear nerve	Dorsal surface of brain in region of isthmus	2(331)
22			End of 3rd or beginning of 4th da	Sympathetic nervous system	Aggregation of neural crest cells at dorsolateral angle of dorsal aorta	2(318)
23	25	23	97 hr	Epithalamus	Dorsolateral wall of diencephalon	2(195)
24			97 hr	Hypothalamus	Ventral wall of diencephalon	
25			97 hr	Mesothalamus	Lateral wall of diencephalon	
26	26	24	$4\frac{1}{2}$ da	Paraphysis	Roof of telencephalon just in front of velum transversum	2(310)
27	26-34	24 to 34	$4\frac{1}{2}$-8 da	Preganglionic column, visceral motor nucleus	Neuroblasts of ventrolateral motor column that migrate to dorsolateral angle of central canal, spinal cord	2(322)
28	33	32	$7\frac{1}{2}$ da	Spinal cord, glycogenic body	Roof plate of spinal cord, level of spinal nerves 26-29	2(304)
29	34	34 to 38	8-12 da	Neostriatum	Telencephalic cortex	2(310)
30		36 to 37	10-11 da	Cerebellar fissures	External surface of cerebellum	2(312)
				Sense Organs		
31	14-15	8 to 9	26-33 hr	Optic vesicles	Lateral wall of forebrain	2(79)
32	16	11- (12)		Otocyst	Thickened ectoderm on dorsal surface of head opposite posteriormost neuromeres of hindbrain	2(212)
33	17	13+ to 14- (20-21)		Lens (invagination)	Ectoderm overlying optic vesicle	4
34	18	16 (28)		Olfactory epithelium	Ectoderm of head in front of eyes	2(214)
35	19	17 (28-30)		Oculomotor nerve	Ventral zone of midbrain, near median line	2(330)
36				Otocyst (closure)		2(212)
37	21-22	19 to 20	3-3.5 da	Eye pigment		2(83)
38	25	23	4 da	Cornea propria	Beneath corneal epithelium	2(346)
39			4 da	Retinal neuroblasts	Fundus of retina	2(352)
40			100 hr	Cornea, inner epithelium (Bowman's membrane)	Mesenchyme on inner face of cornea propria	2(346)
41			Middle of 4th da	Retinal pigment	Outer wall of retina	2(342)
42	25-31	23 to 29	4-6 da	Olfactory nerve	Olfactory epithelium	2(328)

continued

68. DEVELOPMENT: CHICK

Part II: TISSUES AND ORGANS

	Standard Stages (Witschi)	Chick Stages	Age	Structure	Origin	Reference (Page)
	(A)	(B)	(C)	(D)	(E)	(F)
				Sense Organs		
43	28	26	5 da	Pecten	Lips of optic cup growing over mesodermal keel of choroid fissure	2(350)
44	28-31	26 to 29	5-6 da	Auditory ossicles	Mesoderm above dorsal extremity of tubotympanal cavity	2(370)
45	28-34	26 to 38	5-12 da	Inner ear, semicircular canals	Pars superior of otocyst	2(361)
46	31	29	6 da	Perilymph	Mesenchyme surrounding otocyst	2(366,367)
47	31-33	29 to 31	6-7 da	Sacculus	Median surface of uppermost part of pars inferior of otocyst	2(363)
48	33	31	7 da	Conjunctival sac	Within folds of eyelids	2(348)
49			7 da	Nictitating membrane	Semilunar fold of integument within eyelid on side next beak	2(348)
50			7 da	Scleral papillae	Conjunctiva surrounding iris, at some distance peripheral to margin	2(349)
51	33-34	31 to 34	7-8 da	Stapes	Mesenchyme adjacent to bottom of external auditory meatus	2(371)
52	34	33	End of 7th da	Choroidal pigment	Neural crest cells that invade at early stage	2(342)
53		34	8 da	Canal of Schlemm	Margin of anterior chamber of eye	2(347)
54			8 da	Ciliary processes	Ciliary region of lenticular zone of optic cup	2(341)
55			8 da	Harderian gland	Conjunctival sac at innermost angle of nictitating membrane	2(348)
56			8 da	Sclerotic cartilage	Sclerotic (outer) coat of eye	2(348)
57			8 da	Nose, septal gland	Solid cord of cells from inner wall of vestibulum opposite base of vestibular turbinal	2(357)
58	35	39 to 41	13-15 da	Cornea, Descemet's membrane	Beneath Bowman's membrane	2(346)
				Digestive System		
59	13	6	23-25 hr	Pharynx (foregut)	Entoderm of head fold	2(79,127)
60	16	11- (12)		Stomodeum	Expansion of embryonic parts surrounding oral plate	2(217)
61	17	14- (21)		Hindgut	Splanchnopleure, with appearance of tail fold	2(172)
62		14 (22)		Liver	Diverticula of entoderm of anterior intestinal portal	2(226,398)
63	19	17 (30)		Oral plate (rupture)		2(218)
64		17	60 hr	Accessory mesenteries	Mesenchymatous outgrowth of splanchnic mesodermal covering of lateral wall of esophagus	2(416)
65	20	18	68 hr	Ductus choledochus	Depression of ventral wall of duodenum	2(394)
66			68 hr	Gallbladder	Hindmost part of posterior liver bud	
67		18 (35)		Pancreas, dorsal diverticulum	Dorsal wall of intestine immediately above posterior liver bud	2(227)
68				Visceral pouch IV	Branchial region; no cleft develops	2(223)
69		18 (ca. 36)		Esophagus	Gut immediately behind pharynx	2(224)
70	25	23	4 da	Pancreas, ventral diverticulum	Common hepatic diverticulum near junction with duodenum	2(398)
71			4 da	Tongue, tuberculum impar	Slight, rounded swelling between lower ends of 1st and 2nd visceral arches	2(376)
72	28	26	5 da	Gizzard	Posterior part of stomach	2(386)
73			5 da	Proventricular glands	Evaginations of entoderm of stomach	
74	31	29	6 da	Crop	Esophageal dilation at base of neck	2(385)
75			6 da	Teeth, vestige of dental ridge	Thickened ridge of ectoderm just inside margin of jaw	2(376)

continued

68. DEVELOPMENT: CHICK

Part II: TISSUES AND ORGANS

	Standard Stages (Witschi)	Chick Stages	Age	Structure	Origin	Reference (Page)
	(A)	(B)	(C)	(D)	(E)	(F)
				Digestive System		
76	33	31	7 da	Intestine, cecal processes	Junction of small and large intestines	2(384)
77	34	34	8 da	Mandibular glands	Mucosa near mandibular symphysis to base of tongue	2(378)
78		37	11 da	Lingual glands	Oral epithelium beneath lateral margin of tongue	2(378)
79	34-35	38+	After 11th da	Palatine glands	Oral epithelium near choanae	2(378)
80	35	39 to 40	13-14 da	Gizzard glands	Lining epithelium of gizzard	2(386,387)
81		42	16 da	Esophageal glands	Entodermal epithelial lining of esophagus	2(385,386)
				Respiratory System		
82	17	14+ to 15- (23)		Laryngotracheal groove	Postbranchial floor of pharynx	2(224)
83				Lungs	Postbranchial floor of pharynx	
84	19	17	52-64 hr	Nasal (olfactory) pits	Ectoderm of ventrolateral sides of head opposite telencephalon	2(81)
85	25	23	96 hr	Trachea	Hind portion of laryngotracheal groove	2(407)
86			4 da	Lung air sacs, primary bronchi and mesobronchi	Posterior end of trachea	2(401)
87	25-28	23 to 26	4-5 da	Nares, external and internal	By fusion of median and lateral frontonasal processes with maxillary processes of visceral arch I	2(271)
88	31	29	6 da	Lung air sacs, entobronchi (secondary bronchi)	Mesial wall of anterior part of mesobronchus	2(402,403)
89			6 da	Lung air sacs, ectobronchi (secondary bronchi)	Dorsal surface of middle part of mesobronchus	2(403)
90	34	34 to 37	8-11 da	Lung air sacs, parabronchi (tertiary bronchi)	Secondary bronchi	2(403)
				Circulatory System		
91	14	8- to 8+ and onward[1]		Vascular system	Blood islands at posterior margin of area opaca	2(154)
92		8- to 8+ (3-5)		Epimyocardium	Thickening of splanchnopleure of amniocardiac vesicles	2(156,158)
93				Ventral aorta	Hemangioblasts continuous anteriorly with primordia of heart	2(157,158)
94	15	8+ (5)		Dorsal aorta	Hemangioblasts at ventrolateral margin of somites	2(159)
95		10- to 10 (9-10)		Aortic arch I	Anterior to hyomandibular cleft	2(253)
96		10 (10)		Lateral mesocardia	At point of contact of somatopleure with proximal part of vitelline veins	2(260,261)
97	16	11- (12)		Blood cells, macrophages	Endothelium or mesenchyme	2(257-260)
98				Anterior cardinal vein	Intersegmental capillary sprouts of dorsal aorta	2(162)
99		12- (15)		Duct of Cuvier (common cardinal vein)	Capillary plexus between root of anterior cardinal vein and omphalomesenteric vein at level of somite 4	2(254)
100	17	13 to 15 (19-24)		Aortic arch II	Posterior to hyomandibular cleft	2(253)
101		13+ (20)		Pulmonary vein	Proliferation of hemangioblasts from dorsal wall of sinus venosus at level of lung buds	2(255,257)
102		15	50-55 hr	Interatrial septum	Vault of atrium between openings of sinus venosus and pulmonary vein	2(432)
103		15 (26)		Aortic arch III	Between visceral clefts 2 and 3	2(253)

/1/ 3-5 and onward in later stages.

continued

68. DEVELOPMENT: CHICK

Part II: TISSUES AND ORGANS

	Standard Stages (Witschi)	Chick Stages	Age	Structure	Origin	Reference (Page)
	(A)	(B)	(C)	(D)	(E)	(F)
				Circulatory System		
104	20	18	70 hr	Subcardinal vein	Series of venous islands on median surface of mesonephros	2(453)
105			3 da	Blood cells, granulocytes		2(257-260)
106			3 da	Subintestinal vein	Plexus of capillaries around gut	2(451)
107		18 (35)		Pulmonary artery	Network of hemangioblasts extending caudally from ventral aorta	2(253)
108		18 (36)		Aortic arch IV	Between visceral clefts 3 and 4	2(253)
109	20-25	18 to 23	3-4 da	Blood cells, thrombocytes		2(257-260)
110			3-4 da	Atrioventricular canal, endocardial cushions	Floor and roof of atrioventricular canal	2(433)
111			3-4 da	Umbilical vein	Capillary plexus in somatopleure extending back from duct of Cuvier	2(255)
112	25	23	4 da	Aortic arch V	Just anterior to aortic arch VI and attached to base and summit of that arch	2(439)
113			4 da	Aortic arch VI	Behind 4th visceral cleft	2(439)
114			4 da	Interventricular septum	Along sulcus from bulbo-atrial angle towards apex of heart	2(430)
115			4 da	Subclavian artery	Segmental artery of 18th intersomitic space	2(445)
116	27	25	2nd half of 4th da	Spleen	Proliferation of peritoneum of left side of dorsal mesentery, just above dorsal pancreas	2(422)
117	28	26	5 da	Blood cells, granulocytes (neutrophils)		2(257-260)
118			5 da	Hepatic portal vein, definitive vessel	Mesenteric vein in dorsal mesentery	2(450)
119			5 da	Mesenteric vein	Dorsal mesentery, near level of dorsal pancreas	2(450)
120			5 da	Pelvic lymph sac	Hemangioblasts from intersegmental veins of pelvic region	2(462)
121	28-31	26 to 29	5-6 da	Bursa of Fabricius	Posterodorsal wall of cloaca	2(390-393)
122			5-6 da	Septum aorticopulmonale	Within truncus and bulbus arteriosus	2(428,429)
123	31-33	29 to 31	6-7 da	Thoracic duct of lymphatic system	Intramesenchymal spaces along ventrolateral side of dorsal aorta	2(463)
124			6-7 da	Vertebral artery	1st 5 or 6 segmental arteries and plexus they form around secondary sympathetic ganglia	2(443)
125	31-34	29 to 34	6-8 da	Thymus	From dorsal part of visceral pouches III, IV, and possibly V	2(380,381)
126	33	31	7 da	Blood cells, granulocytes (eosinophils)	Spleen ?	2(257-260)
127			7 da	Jugular lymph sac	Fusion of lymphatic vessels near anterior cardinal vein	2(463)
128	35	40	14 da	Blood cells, granulocytes (basophils)	Spleen ?	2(257-260)
129		43	17 da	Blood cells, lymphocytes	Spleen and other lymphatic areas	2(257-260)
				Excretory System		
130	19	17 (29-30)		Mesonephric tubules	Nephrotome between somites 13-14 and 30	2(242,243, 469)
131	27	25	End of 4th da	Ureter	Broad diverticulum of mesonephric duct at convexity of its terminal bend to cloaca	2(473)
132	28	26	5 da	Renal portal system	Through substance of mesonephros	2(453)
133	33-34	31 to 34	7-8 da	Metanephric tubules	Metanephrogenous blastema just behind level of umbilical arteries	2(477)
				Reproductive System		
134	21	19 (38)		Germinal epithelium (primordium of gonad)	Coelomic epithelium at level of somites 20-27	2(482)

continued

68. DEVELOPMENT: CHICK

Part II: TISSUES AND ORGANS

	Standard Stages (Witschi)	Chick Stages	Age	Structure	Origin	Reference (Page)
	(A)	(B)	(C)	(D)	(E)	(F)
	Reproductive System					
135	25	23	4 da	Oviduct	Thickened peritoneum on dorsolateral surface of anterior end of mesonephros	2(498)
136	28	26	5 da	Ostium tubae abdominale	Anterior end of tubal ridge (primordium of oviduct)	2(498)
137			5 da	Gonad, rete cords	In stroma between genital primordium and mesonephros	2(485,487)
138	33	31	7 da	Oviduct, junction with cloaca		2(499)
139	33-34	31 to 34	7-8 da	Oogonia	Germ cells in secondary sexual cords of ovarian cortex	2(494)
140	34	38	12 da	Uterus, shell-gland	Posterior end of left oviduct	2(500,501)
141	35	39	13 da	Testis, interstitial cells	In stroma of testis	2(491)
142		39+	13th da onward	Spermatogonia	Primordial germ cells within sexual cords of testis	2(489)
143	After hatching		Shortly after hatching	Oocytes	Ovarian cortex	2(494)
	Muscular System					
144	34	36	10th da	Pulmonary diaphragm muscles		2(418,419)
	Skeletal System					
145	25-28	23 to 26	4-5 da	Upper jaw	Fusion of frontonasal and maxillary processes	2(271)
146			4-5 da	Scapula	Base of wing bud	2(536)
147	25-34	23 to 34	4-8 da	Nasal turbinals	Folds of lateral wall of nasal cavity	2(355)
148	26	24	$4\frac{1}{2}$ da	Acrochordal cartilage	Anterior tip of notochord	2(529)
149	27-28	25 to 26	Beginning of 5th da	Middle nasal turbinals	Ventral part of lateral nasal wall	2(355)
150	28	26	5th da	Costal processes (ribs)		2(516)
151	28-31	26 to 29	5-6 da	Auditory ossicles	Mesoderm above dorsal extremity of tubotympanic cavity	2(370)
152			5-6 da	Superior nasal turbinals	Immediately above middle turbinal	2(355)
153	31-34	29 to 34	6-8 da	Vestibular nasal turbinals		2(355)
154	32	30	End of 6th da	Coracoid (chondrification)	Near union of coracoid with scapula	2(536)
155	33-34	31 to 34	7-8 da	Vertebrae (chondrification)	Within membranous parts of vertebrae	2(518)
156	34	34	8th da	Femur (ossification)		3
157		34 to 35	8-9 da	Clavicle (ossification)		2(537)
158		35	9th da	Jugal bone	Skull	2(534)
159			9th da	Mandible (ossification)		
160			9th da	Maxilla		
161			9th da	Nasal bone		
162		35 to 36	End of 9th da	Premaxilla	Skull	2(534)
163			End of 9th da	Pterygoid bone	Skull	
164			End of 9th da	Quadrate bone, otic process	Skull	
165			End of 9th da	Quadratojugal bone	Skull	
166			End of 9th da	Squamosal bone	Skull	
167		38	12th da	Parasphenoid bone	Skull	2(534)
168	35	39	13th da	Parietal bone	Skull behind squamosal bone	2(534)
169			13th da	Patella	Anterior face of knee joint	2(545)
170		40+	After 13 da	Basioccipital bone	Skull	2(534)
171	36	45	Day before hatching	Uncinate processes	Membranous ossifications along sternal ends of ribs ?	3
	Integumentary System					
172	28	26	5 da	Beak		2(85)
173	33	31	7th da	Eyelids	Circular fold of integument around eyeball	2(348)
174			$7\frac{1}{4}$ da	Wing feathers	Along outer margin of wing	2(550)

continued

68. DEVELOPMENT: CHICK

Part II: TISSUES AND ORGANS

	Standard Stages (Witschi)	Chick Stages	Age	Structure	Origin	Reference (Page)
	(A)	(B)	(C)	(D)	(E)	(F)
	Integumentary System					
175	34	36	10 da	Claws		2(88)
176			10 da	Comb	Dorsal midline of beak	2(88)
177			10 da	Spur	Medial surface of leg, just proximal to base of 1st toe	2(547)
178		37	11 da	Scales of leg	Anterior surfaces of lower leg and toes	2(548)
179			11 da	Wattles	Throat	
180		38	12 da	Dermis (differentiation of fibers)	Within mesenchyme next to ectoderm	2(546)
	Endocrine Glands					
181	16	11- (12)		Thyroid	Thickened epithelium of median floor of pharynx between levels of visceral arches II and III	2(223,379)
182	19	17 (30-35)		Pineal	Roof of diencephalon	2(81,194)
183	20	18 (35)		Pancreas, dorsal diverticulum	Dorsal wall of intestine, immediately above posterior liver bud	2(227)
184	21	19	78 hr	Adrenal gland, cortical component	Coelomic epithelium at level of somites 17-22	2(501)
185	25-33	23 to 31	4-7 da	Adrenal gland, medullary component	Migratory cells of neural crest and sympathetic ganglia	2(502,503)
186	31-34	29 to 34	6-8 da	Parathyroid	Ventral portion of visceral pouches III and IV	2(380,381)
187			6-8 da	Thymus	From dorsal part of visceral pouches III, IV, and possibly V	
188	34	34 to 35	8-9 da	Islets of Langerhans	Within pancreatic diverticula	2(399,400)
189		35 to 37	9-11 da	Ovary	Proliferation from germinal epithelium	2(492)
190	35	39	13 da	Testis, interstitial cells	In stroma of testis	2(491)

Contributor: Hamilton, Howard L.

References: [1] Hamburger, V., and H. L. Hamilton. 1951. J. Morphol. 88:49. [2] Hamilton, H. L. 1952. Lillie's Development of chick. Ed. 3. H. Holt, New York. [3] Landauer, W. Unpublished. Storrs Agr. Expt. Sta., Univ. Connecticut, 1956. [4] McKeehan, M. S. 1951. J. Exptl. Zool. 117:31.

69. DEVELOPMENT: FROG

Data are principally for *Rana pipiens*. At a given stage, age and size can be expected to vary widely with differences in geographic strains and culture conditions.

Part I: CHARACTERIZATION OF STAGES

Frog Stages (column B) designated by Arabic numerals are for the embryo at 18°C, and are adapted from Shumway [18]; those designated by Roman numerals are for the larva at 20°C, and are adapted from Taylor and Kollros [22].

	Standard Stages (Witschi)	Frog Stages	Age[1]	Size mm	Identification of Stages	Reference
	(A)	(B)	(C)	(D)	(E)	(F)
	Cleavage and Blastula					
1	0	1	0	1.5-2.0	Unfertilized egg	18
2	1	2	1 hr	1.5-2.0	Fertilized egg; gray crescent	
3	2	3	3.5 hr		2 cells	

/1/ Comparable ages in hours at 20°C for frog stages 2 through 20: 0.5, 2.3, 3.2, 4.0, 4.8, 5.6, 7, 17, 22, 28, 30, 38, 43, 49, 52, 61, 76, 88, and 96, respectively.

continued

69. DEVELOPMENT: FROG

Part I: CHARACTERIZATION OF STAGES

	Standard Stages (Witschi)	Frog Stages	Age[1]	Size mm	Identification of Stages	Reference
	(A)	(B)	(C)	(D)	(E)	(F)
					Cleavage and Blastula	
4	3	4	4.5 hr		4 cells	18
5	4	5	5.7 hr		8 cells	
6	5	6	6.5 hr		16 cells	
7	6	7	7.5 hr		32 cells	
8	7a	8	16 hr		Middle blastula	
9	7b	9	21 hr		Late blastula	
					Gastrula	
10	8	10	26 hr		Early gastrula; dorsal lip stage	18
11	9, 10	11	34 hr		Middle gastrula; blastopore C- or U-shaped	18
12	11	12	42 hr		Late gastrula; yolk plug; primitive gut	16,18
					Neurula	
13	12	13	50 hr		Early neurula; medullary plate defined	10,16,18
14	13	14	62 hr		Midneurula; well-defined neural folds approaching each other; oral plate; anal pit; postanal gut	9,18
15	14, 15	15	67 hr		Late neurula; neural folds touch each other over most of their length; neurenteric canal; embryo rotates in jelly	9,18
16	16	16	72 hr	3	Neural tube, ectoderm fused over tube; oral sucker	18,19
					Tail Bud	
17	17	17	84 hr	3.5	Tail bud; nasal pit; dorsal aorta	10,14,18
18	18	18	96 hr	4	Muscular response to stimulation of myotome; lens placode	18,19
19	19	19	118 hr	5	Heart beats; pronephros functional; Rohon-Beard cells; thyroid evagination	12,14,15, 18
20	20	20	140 hr	6	Embryo hatched; gill circulation; lens vesicle	18,19
21	21	21	162 hr	7	Mouth open; free swimming; cornea becoming transparent; olfactory nerve; 2 rudiments of ventral pancreas; lung rudiments	14,18
22	22	22	192 hr	8	Circulation in tail fin; cartilaginous trabeculae; 2 gill slits are perforate; trabeculae carneae	14
23	23	23	216 hr	8-9	Opercular folds and labial teeth appear; spontaneous respiratory activity of mouth begins; basal plate	6,14,18
24	24	24	240 hr	9-10	Operculum closed on right side; adrenal cortex rudiment; respiratory rhythm begins	6,18,20
25	25a	25	284 hr	10-11	Operculum closed except for spiracle; rods and cones; germinal ridge; sucker regressed; rudiments of mesonephric tubules	4,16,18, 19
					Metamorphosis	
26	25b	I	3 da	13	Feeding begins; rudiments of adrenal medulla and of hindlimb appear	17,22
27	25c	II	6 da	17	Lagena; neural lobe of hypophysis	1,23
28	25d	III	11 da	23	Limb bud of equal length and diameter; lateral motor column	3,22
29	26a	IV	19 da	33	Ovarial sac; cartilage in synotic tectum	4,14
30	26b	V	23 da	39	Limb bud twice as long as it is broad; distal half of bud is bent ventrad	22
31	26c	VI	26 da	43	Flattened paddle at distal end of limb bud; scapular cartilage; gonads distinguishable	14,22,24
32	27a	VII	31 da	50	Foot paddle indented between toes 4 and 5	22
33	27b	VIII	34 da	53	Urinary bladder rudiment; measurable thyroid hormone output	2,12,14
34	27c	IX	36 da	56	Separation of fat body from gonad; spontaneous limb twitches	14,22
35	27d	X	40 da	58	Indentations delimit toe margins; rudiments of fungiform papillae of tongue	7,22
36	28a	XI	43 da	61	Margin of 5th toe web directed toward toe 2	22
37	28b	XII	47 da	64	Margin of 5th toe web directed toward toe 1	22
38	28c	XIII	52 da	67	Margin of 5th toe web directed toward prehallux	22
39	28d	XIV	58 da	70	Rudiments of harderian glands; rudiments of skin glands	13,14
40	29a	XV	62 da	72	1st toe pads; hindlimbs take part in swimming	12,22
41	29b	XVI	64 da	73	Nictitating membrane a low fold anterior to eyeball	12
42	29c	XVII	67 da	73	Some skin glands patent; peritoneal thickening presages oviduct	4,13

/1/ Comparable ages in hours at 20°C for frog stages 2 through 20: 0.5, 2.3, 3.2, 4.0, 4.8, 5.6, 7, 17, 22, 28, 30, 38, 43, 49, 52, 61, 76, 88, and 96, respectively.

continued

69. DEVELOPMENT: FROG

Part I: CHARACTERIZATION OF STAGES

	Standard Stages (Witschi)	Frog Stages	Age	Size mm	Identification of Stages	Reference
	(A)	(B)	(C)	(D)	(E)	(F)
					Metamorphosis	
43	30a	XVIII	70 da	74[2]	Cloacal tail piece resorbed; corneal reflex	11,22
44	30b	XIX	72 da	73	Tail regression begins; skin windows form	5,22
45	31	XX	74 da	70	Skin windows perforate; forelimbs emerge; oral beaks lost	5,22
46	32a	XXI	76 da	63	Upper lid forms; 1st molt	5,8
47	32b	XXII	79 da	44	Conjunctival sac complete; lateral lines regressing	8,22
48	33a	XXIII	81 da	33	Labial fringes completely lost; vasa efferentia	22,24
49	33b	XXIV	84 da	26	Tympanic membrane outlined; tail stub of 1-2 mm	22
50	33c	XXV	88 da	25[3]	Tail stub fully resorbed; oviduct extends nearly to cloaca	4,22
51	Juvenile	Juvenile	90+ da	25-70	Fully metamorphosed; gonads immature; urostyle	21,22
52	Adult	Adult	1-3 yr	60-110	Sexually mature	22

/2/ Maximum size highly variable; tadpoles over 100 mm long have been collected. /3/ Size upon completion of metamorphosis highly variable, ranging from 16-30 mm.

Contributor: Kollros, Jerry J.

References: [1] Atwell, W. J. 1918. Anat. Record 15:73. [2] Barch, S. H. 1953. Physiol. Zool. 26:223. [3] Beaudoin, A. R. 1955. Anat. Record 121:81. [4] Christensen, K. 1930. Am. J. Anat. 45:159. [5] Etkin, W. 1932. Physiol. Zool. 5:275. [6] Fribourgh, J. H. 1949. M.S. Thesis. State Univ. Iowa, Iowa City. [7] Helff, O. M., and M. C. Mellicker. 1941. Am. J. Anat. 68:371. [8] Holbert, M. 1952. M.S. Thesis. State Univ. Iowa, Iowa City. [9] Huettner, A. F. 1949. Fundamentals of comparative embryology of the vertebrates. Macmillan, New York. [10] Knouff, R. A. 1935. J. Comp. Neurol. 62:17. [11] Kollros, J. J. 1942. J. Exptl. Zool. 89:37. [12] Kollros, J. J. Unpublished. State Univ. Iowa, Iowa City, 1956. [13] Kollros, J. J., and J. C. Kaltenbach. 1952. Physiol. Zool. 25:163. [14] Kopsch, F. 1952. Die Entwicklung des braunen Grasfrosches *Rana fusca* Roesel. G. Thieme, Stuttgart. [15] Rappaport, R., Jr. 1955. J. Exptl. Zool. 128:481. [16] Rugh, R. 1951. The frog: its reproduction and development. Blakiston, Philadelphia. [17] Segal, S. 1953. Anat. Record 115:205. [18] Shumway, W. 1940. Ibid. 78:139. [19] Shumway, W. 1942. Ibid. 83:309. [20] Stenger, A. H., and H. A. Charipper. 1946. J. Morphol. 78:27. [21] Stokeley, P. S., and J. C. List. 1955. Trans. Am. Microscop. Soc. 74:112. [22] Taylor, A. C., and J. J. Kollros. 1946. Anat. Record 94:7. [23] Villy, F. 1890. Quart. J. Microscop. Sci. 30:522. [24] Witschi, E. 1929. J. Exptl. Zool. 52:235.

Part II: TISSUES AND ORGANS

Frog Stages (column B) designated by Arabic numerals are for the embryo at 18°C, and are adapted from Shumway [35]; those designated by Roman numerals are for the larva at 20°C, and are adapted from Taylor and Kollros [40].

	Standard Stages (Witschi)	Frog Stages	Age	Size mm	Structural Development	Reference
	(A)	(B)	(C)	(D)	(E)	(F)
					Nervous System	
1	12	13	50 hr		Neural groove, neural plate, and adjacent placodal thickenings	21,35
2	13	14	62 hr		Placodal thickenings developed maximally	21
3	14	15	67 hr		Neural folds closing; forebrain walls evaginate laterad	21
4	16	16	72 hr	3	Neural tube closed; forebrain, midbrain, hindbrain, infundibulum; placodal thickenings caudad to level of prospective ganglion X have disappeared	21,33
5	17	17	84 hr	3.5	Neural crest withdraws from spinal cord; subotic ganglion	21

continued

69. DEVELOPMENT: FROG

Part II: TISSUES AND ORGANS

	Standard Stages (Witschi)	Frog Stages	Age	Size mm	Structural Development	Reference
	(A)	(B)	(C)	(D)	(E)	(F)
					Nervous System	
6	18	18	96 hr	4	Ganglia V, VII, IX, X; epibranchial placodes; white matter in spinal cord; torus transversus	21,27,33, 36
7	19	19	118 hr	5	Lateral line ganglia send fibers to primitive lateral lines; lateral lines elongating; epiphysis; Rohon-Beard cells	21,24,27
8	21	21	162 hr	7	Cerebral hemispheres; olfactory nerve; nerve fibers in optic chiasma	27,33,35, 36
9	22	22	192 hr	8	Cerebellar rudiment; macula acustica; Rohon-Beard cells along entire length of spinal cord	27,36
10	23	23	216 hr	8-9	Optic nerve fibers reach anterior pole of optic lobe; choroid plexus in forebrain	27,36
11	25	25	284 hr	10-11	Choroid plexus in hindbrain	27,36
12		I	3 da	13	First appearance of mesencephalic V nucleus cells	26
13	26	IV	19 da	33	First appearance of lateral motor column; optic nerve fibers reach posterior pole of optic tectum	4,23,30, 32
14	27	VIII	34 da	53	Spinal ganglia 3, 8-10 are largest; opercular rudiment in fenestra vestibuli	27
15	31-33	XX-XXV	74-88 da	70-25[1]	Regression of Mauthner's cells, lateral lines, and lateral line centers in cerebellum	2,28
					Sense Organs	
16	14	15	67 hr		Auditory placode distinguishable from adjacent placodes	21,41
17	16	16	72 hr	3	Eye vesicle in contact with lateral ectoderm; otic placode cup-shaped; nasal placode	15,21,29
18	17	17	84 hr	3.5	Slight nasal pit	21
19	18	18	96 hr	4	Lens placode; pigmentation in pigment layer of retina completed; optic stalk; otic vesicle and endolymphatic duct rudiment	21,27,33, 36
20	19	19	118 hr	5	Lens pit	21,24,27
21	20	20	140 hr	6	Lens vesicle	36
22	21	21	162 hr	7	Lens detached from epidermis; cornea transparent	27,33,35, 36
23	22	22	192 hr	8	Lens fibers; cavity of lens nearly obliterated	27,36
24	23	23	216 hr	8-9	Retina with 2 cellular layers; nasal pit opens into oral cavity	15,23
25	24	24	240 hr	9-10	Lens cavity obliterated; inner and outer nuclear layers of retina incipient; horizontal semicircular duct	36
26	25	25	284 hr	10-11	Rods and cones; vomeronasal organ	15,27,36
27	25	I-	3 da	13	Utricular and saccular chambers	41
28		II-	6 da	17	Anterior semicircular duct; lagena; early bronchial columella	41,44
29	27	VII	31 da	50	Bronchial columella completely within dorsal aorta	44
30		VIII	34 da	53	Endolymph sac extends caudad to level of 8th vertebra	27
31	28	XIV	58 da	70	Rudiments of harderian glands	27
32	29	XV	62 da	72	Nictitating membrane rudiment	24
33	30	XVIII	70 da	74[2]	Corneal reflex; fusion of cornea and Descemet's membrane; very short conjunctival sac	22,24,29
34	31-33	XX-XXV	74-88 da	70-25[1]	Regression of bronchial columella; completion of conjunctival sacs and lids	29,44
					Digestive System	
35	11	12	42 hr		Primitive gut	33
36	12	13	50 hr		Liver diverticulum	33
37	13	14	62 hr		Oral plate; anal pit or proctodeum; postanal gut	17
38	14	15	67 hr		Neurenteric canal; fore-, mid-, and hind-guts	17
39	16	16	72 hr	3	Stomodeal depression; pharynx; gill pouches 1 and 2; subnotochordal rod	17,33
40	17	17+	84 hr	3.5	Rudiment of dorsal pancreas; 4 gill pouches (2, 3, and 4 fused to epidermis)	27
41	18	18	96 hr	4	Anus perforates	17
42	19	19	118 hr	5	Thyroid evagination; 5 gill pouches	27
43	21	21	162 hr	7	Thymus rudiment (pouch 2); 2 rudiments of ventral pancreas; mouth open; rudiment of eustachian tube is short stump	27,35

/1/ Size upon completion of metamorphosis highly variable, ranging from 16-30 mm. /2/ Maximum size highly variable; tadpoles over 100 mm long have been collected.

continued

69. DEVELOPMENT: FROG

Part II: TISSUES AND ORGANS

	Standard Stages (Witschi)	Frog Stages	Age	Size mm	Structural Development	Reference
	(A)	(B)	(C)	(D)	(E)	(F)
					Digestive System	
44	22	22	192 hr	8	Thyroid separated from pharyngeal epithelium; gallbladder; dorsal pancreas fuses to ventral pancreas; midgut begins to coil; postanal gut no longer present	27
45	23	23	216 hr	8-9	Short oral papillae; pharyngo-esophageal and midgut plugs have disappeared; postbranchial body; gastric glands are short tubes	27
46	25	25	284 hr	10-11	Thymus separate from gill pouch epithelium; long tubular gastric glands; thyroid gland develops isthmus	27
47		I	3 da	13	Subnotochordal rod disappears; tongue papillae	13,17
48		III	11 da	23	Tongue rudiment with 4 filiform papillae	13,27
49	26	VI	26 da	43	Rudiments of tongue musculature	27
50	27	X	40 da	58	Rudiments of fungiform papillae of tongue	14
51	29	XVI	64 da	73	Maximum length of digestive tract; anal sphincter	27
52	31	XX	74 da	70	Tip of tongue is free, bifurcate, with papillae and glands	27
53	33	XXIII	81 da	33	Fungiform papillae first assume mushroom shape	14
54		XXIV	84 da	26	Filiform papillae no longer present in mouth or pharynx	27
					Respiratory System	
55	13	14	62 hr		Faint gill elevation	27,35
56	16	16	72 hr	3	2 gill furrows; onset of gill pouch formation	27
57	17	17	84 hr	3.5	4 gill pouches	27
58	19	19	118 hr	5	5 gill pouches; 1st 2 gill arches possess blood vessels (aortic arches)	27
59	20	20	140 hr	6	Circulation in external gills; external gills branched	35
60	21	21	162 hr	7	Lung rudiments; 1st gill slit nearly open; aortic arches III and IV present	27
61	22	22	192 hr	8	2 gill slits open; laryngotracheal rudiment sealed secondarily; internal gill rudiment present on all arches; larynx sealed, but trachea re-forms its cavity	27
62	23	23	216 hr	8-9	Larynx and trachea both open; opercular fold	27,35
63	24	24	240 hr	9-10	Opercular cavity closed on left	27,35
64	25	25	284 hr	10-11	Complete opercular cavity; spiracle opening	35
65		II-	6 da	17	Early bronchial columella	44
66		III	11 da	23	External gill "twigs" fully regressed	27
67	26	IV	19 da	33	Precartilage stage of arytenoid cartilage	27
68	27	VII	31 da	50	Bronchial columella within dorsal aorta	44
69		VIII	34 da	53	Arytenoid cartilage	27
70	31-33	XX-XXV	74-88 da	70-25[1]	Bronchial columella regresses	44
71	33	XXIV	84 da	26	Cricotracheal cartilage	27
					Circulatory System	
72	15	15	67 hr		Heart rudiment lies within heart bulge	27
73	16	16	72 hr	3	Pericardial cavity indicated by split in mesoderm; temporary ventral mesocardium	27
74	17	17	84 hr	3.5	Dorsal mesocardium; heart a straight tube; truncus arteriosus branched; blood island within first aortic arch; dorsal aorta	27
75	18	18	96 hr	4	Rudiments of vitelline veins	33
76	19	19	118 hr	5	Heart S-shaped; truncus arteriosus connects to aortic arch I, and thus to dorsal aorta; blood islands in aortic arch II, and numerous islands below posterior yolk mass; blood in heart; heart beats; common cardinal veins and hepatic veins empty into sinus venosus	27,35
77	20	20	140 hr	6	Anterior lymph hearts; pulmonary vein rudiments	33
78	21	21	162 hr	7	Interatrial septum; sino-atrial constriction; atriobulbar constriction; circulation through aortic arches I and II; anterior cardinal veins, arteries of brain formed; suprabranchial aortas fuse to single dorsal aorta medial to pronephros	27,33
79	22	22	192 hr	8	A few blood cells weakly ellipsoidal--most are spherical; trabeculae carneae in ventricle; partitioning of heart complete; circulation in tail fin	27,33,35

/1/ Size upon completion of metamorphosis highly variable, ranging from 16-30 mm.

continued

69. DEVELOPMENT: FROG

Part II: TISSUES AND ORGANS

	Standard Stages (Witschi)	Frog Stages	Age	Size mm	Structural Development	Reference
	(A)	(B)	(C)	(D)	(E)	(F)
					Circulatory System	
80	23	23	216 hr	8-9	Atrioventricular constriction; truncus arteriosus has thick endothelial cushions at level of its branching; blood cells ellipsoidal	27
81	25	25	284 hr	10-11	Truncus arteriosus divided by median septum; erythrocytes free of yolk granules; spleen rudiment	27,33
82		I	3 da	13	Lymphocytes appear in spleen	9
83		III	11 da	23	Thoracic ducts	33
84	32-33	XXI-XXV	76-88 da	63-25[1]	Reorganization of aortic arches at metamorphosis	33
					Excretory System	
85	14	15	67 hr		Pronephric swelling	27
86	16	16	72 hr	3	Pronephric swelling extends caudad to somite 7	27
87	17	17	84 hr	3.5	1st 2 peritoneal funnels; pronephric tubules and anterior pronephric duct patent; pronephric capsule extending	27
88	19	19	118 hr	5	All 3 peritoneal funnels; pronephric capsule completed; pronephric duct opens into cloaca; tubules surrounded by sinus spaces; rudiment of glomus contains blood cells; onset of pronephric function	18,31
89	20	20	140 hr	6	Glomus larger; tubules more convolute	18,27
90	23	23	216 hr	8-9	Epithelial cells of pronephros free of yolk granules	18,27
91	25	25	284 hr	10-11	Rudiments of mesonephric (opisthonephric) tubules	27,33
92		I	3 da	13	Nephroblast vesicles of mesonephros; maximal development of pronephros	12,17
93		II	6 da	17	Lymphocyte islands in intertubular spaces	18
94		III	11 da	23	Primary mesonephric tubules, glomeruli, and their peritoneal funnels well developed; pronephric peritoneal funnels fused to single opening; regression of pronephros begins	12,18,33
95	26	IV	19 da	33	Onset of formation of secondary mesonephric units	12
96	27	VIII	34 da	53	Pronephros largely gone; rudiment of urinary bladder	27
97		IX	36 da	56	Rostral part of pronephric duct completely regressed	27
98	29	XVI	64 da	73	Ligaments of urinary bladder distinguishable	27
99	32	XXI	76 da	63	Only traces of pronephros remain; glomus somewhat less fully regressed	27
					Reproductive System	
100	23	23	216 hr	8-9	Primary germ cells migrated dorsad to root of mesentery	6,43
101	25	25	284 hr	10-11	Primary germ cells migrating laterad and aggregating in germ ridge; cells of genital ridges retain yolk granules	6,27
102		III	11 da	23	Genital ridges round in cross-section; germ cells surrounded by follicle	27,43
103	26	IV	19 da	33	Ovarial sac; a few ovocytes in growth stages; rete cords	6,43
104		V	23 da	39	End of germ cell migration; medulla and cortex of gonad	6,27
105		VI	26 da	43	Primordial seminiferous tubules	43
106	27	IX	36 da	56	Fat body separates from gonad	27
107	29	XVII	67 da	73	Peritoneum thickens to begin oviduct formation	6
108	31	XX	74 da	70	Rete tubules	43
109	32	XXI	76 da	63	A few spermatocytes have entered synapsis	6
110	33	XXIII	81 da	33	Vasa efferentia	43
111		XXV	88 da	25[1]	Oviduct extends nearly to cloaca, ends blindly	6
112	Juvenile	Juvenile	90+ da	25-70	Oviduct opens into cloaca, becomes wavy and later convolute; peritoneal cilia	6,33
					Muscular System	
113	14	15	67 hr		3-4 somites	36
114	16	16	72 hr	3	6-8 somites; cells of medial lamella of most rostral somites have several nuclei	27,36
115	17	17	84 hr	3.5	12-13 somites; medial lamella of most rostral somites with muscle fibers	27,36
116	18	18	96 hr	4	18-19 somites; rostral myotomes bend head to either side (head flexure stage)	27,36

/1/ Size upon completion of metamorphosis highly variable, ranging from 16-30 mm.

continued

69. DEVELOPMENT: FROG

Part II: TISSUES AND ORGANS

	Standard Stages (Witschi)	Frog Stages	Age	Size mm	Structural Development	Reference
	(A)	(B)	(C)	(D)	(E)	(F)
					Muscular System	
117	19	19	118 hr	5	23-25 somites; muscle fibers through segment 19; coil and S stages of movement; mesenchyme aggregations represent unseparated rudiments of muscles of jaws and hyoid arch	21,27,36
118	21	21	162 hr	7	35 somites; muscle fibers through segments 25-33; swimming movements	27
119	22	22	192 hr	8	37-45 somites; muscles in belly wall	27
120	23	23	216 hr	8-9	45 somites; muscles of upper jaw segregating from common mass; muscles of lower jaw "strongly" developed; muscle fibrillae in pharyngeal musculature; twitching activity of mouth begins	10,11,27
121	24	24	240 hr	9-10	Cross striations in submaxillary muscle; rhythmic respiratory movements	10,11
122	25	25	284 hr	10-11	50-55 segments; onset of function of extrinsic ocular muscles	24,27
123		II	6 da	17	Muscle fibers free of yolk granules	27
124	26	IV	19 da	33	Major muscle groups of hindlegs represented as mesenchymal aggregations	39
125		V	23 da	39	Rudiments of extensor and flexor muscles of hip and knee joints; faint cross striations in retractor bulbi muscle	22,39
126		VI	26 da	43	Cross striations in muscle masses of middle of thigh; elsewhere leg myoblasts are spindle-shaped	39
127	27	IX	36 da	56	Some movements of thigh muscles	39
128	29	XV-XVI	62-64 da	72-73	Hindlimbs participate in swimming movements	24
129		XVII	67 da	73	Forelimb movements visible within branchial cavity	27
130	30-31	XIX-XX	72-74 da	73-70	Regression of tail musculature	7,40
					Skeletal System	
131	14	15	67 hr		Notochord not completely separated from adjacent cells	27
132	16	16	72 hr	3	Anterior end of notochord free from adjacent cells but still attached caudally; rudiment of hypochordal rod	27
133	17	17	84 hr	3.5	Sclerotome formation from rostral somites; visceral arches I and II show mesenchymal condensations; vacuolated cells in rostral part of notochord	27
134	19	19	118 hr	5	Vacuolated cells through levels of head and trunk; rudiments of certain visceral cartilages appear as vague local thickenings in mesenchyme	27
135	21	21	163 hr	7	Vacuolated cells throughout all but caudal tip of notochord; mesenchymal rudiments of trabecular cartilages and visceral arches III and IV	27
136	22	22	192 hr	8	Trabeculae fuse to suprarostral cartilages; connective tissue joins trabecular cartilages across midline; copula cartilaginous; notochord surrounded by perichordal connective tissue; hypochordal rod begins regression in tail	27
137	23	23	216 hr	8-9	Cartilaginous basal plate	27
138	25	25	284 hr	10-11	Vacuolated cells throughout notochord	27
139	26	IV	19 da	33	Cartilage in synotic tectum and in most rostral neural arches; precartilage stage of arytenoid cartilages; tip of notochord begins to regress; mesenchyme thickenings presage femur, fibula, tibia	27,39
140		VI	26 da	43	Cartilage present in scapula, humerus, ulna, radius, femur, tibia, and fibula; ilium and ischium of precartilage	27
141	27	VIII	34 da	53	All neural arches cartilaginous in part; arytenoid cartilage; suprascapula of precartilage; radiale, ulnare, tibiale, and fibulare cartilaginous in part	27
142		IX	36 da	56	Some cartilage in nasal capsule, suprascapula, metacarpals, tarsals, and metatarsals; transverse processes on vertebrae 2-6	27
143	28	XIV	58 da	70	Phalanges partly cartilaginous; perichondral ossification of shaft of femur and humerus; ossification of tibia, fibula, tarsals	20,27
144	29	XVII	67 da	73	Cartilage in clavicle coracoid	27
145	31	XX	74 da	70	Perichondral ossification in both jaws, in roof and floor of cranium, in neural arches and transverse processes; endochondral ossification in scapula, humerus, coracoid	27

continued

69. DEVELOPMENT: FROG

Part II: TISSUES AND ORGANS

	Standard Stages (Witschi)	Frog Stages	Age	Size mm	Structural Development	Reference
	(A)	(B)	(C)	(D)	(E)	(F)
					Skeletal System	
146	32	XXI	76 da	63	Endochondral ossification in neural arches	27
147	33	XXIV	84 da	26	Endochondral ossification of centrum of most rostral vertebrae	27
148	Juvenile	Juvenile	90+ da	25-70	Fusion of separate bony elements of urostyle	38
					Integumentary System	
149	13	14	62 hr		Epidermis 2-layered, thicker near blastopore	27
150	15	15	67 hr		Oral sucker rudiment darker than adjacent epidermis	27
151	16	16	72 hr	3	Edges of oral suckers raised; epidermal cilia vibrate; lateral line primordia	21,27,36
152	17	17	84 hr	3.5	Oral sucker produces mucus	27
153	19	19	118 hr	5	Maximal development of oral suckers; lateral lines extend caudad to level of somites 4-5	27,36
154	21	21	162 hr	7	Suckers regressing; cornea transparent	35,36
155	22	22	192 hr	8	Rudiments of oral fringes and their horny teeth; fin transparent	27
156	23	23	216 hr	8-9	Opercular fold forming; figures of Eberth present	35,42
157	25	25	284 hr	10-11	Operculum complete; suckers absent except for traces of pigment; horny jaws present; horny teeth on labial fringes; guanophores; epidermal cilia disappearing	27,35
158	26	IV	19 da	33	Epidermal ridge around external nares	27
159	27	X	40 da	58	Interdigital webs begin to form; figures of Eberth begin to regress	40,42
160	28	XIII	52 da	67	Rudiments of plical glands in epidermis	5
161		XIV	58 da	70	All interdigital webs present; rudiments of harderian glands; 1st plical gland nests in dermis; nasolacrimal duct	5,25,27, 40
162	29	XV	62 da	72	1st hollow serous glands	5
163		XVI	64 da	73	Low fold anterior to eye presages nictitating membrane	24
164		XVII	67 da	73	Some skin glands patent; a thin stratum spongiosum near largest glands; traces of dorsal spotting pattern; 1st hollow mucous glands	5,22,25
165	30	XVIII	70 da	74[2]	Loss of cloacal tail piece; short conjunctival sac	16,40
166		XIX	72 da	73	Stratum spongiosum a continuous layer; skin window	8,25,40
167	31	XX	74 da	70	Skin window ruptures; conjunctival sac 90° of arc or more; beaks lost; labial teeth and fringes regressing; rapid tail resorption begins; figures of Eberth essentially absent; epidermal gland nests no longer present	5,8,40,42
168	32	XXI	76 da	63	Upper lid forms; 1st molting	8,16
169		XXII	79 da	44	Conjunctival sac complete; regression of lateral lines of head and trunk	16
170	33	XXIV	84 da	26	Tympanic membrane outlined	40
171		XXV	88 da	25[1]	Tail completely lost; all plical glands now hollow	5,40
					Endocrine Glands	
172	13	14	62 hr		Nasohypophyseal placode	21
173	16	16	72 hr	3	Separate hypophyseal pouch	21
174	17	17	84 hr	3.5	Dorsal pancreas rudiment	27
175	19	19	118 hr	5	Thyroid evagination	27
176	21	21	162 hr	7	Rudiments of ventral pancreas	27
177	22	22	192 hr	8	Islets of Langerhans rudiments; hypophyseal placode detaches from epidermis	19
178	24	24	240 hr	9-10	Rudiment of adrenal cortex	37
179	25	25	284 hr	10-11	Adrenal cortex rudiments paired: pars anterior, pars intermedia, pars lateralis of hypophysis; germinal ridge	27,37
180		I	3 da	13	Adrenal medulla rudiments	34
181		II	6 da	17	Neural lobe of hypophysis	1
182	26	V	23 da	39	Secondary islets of Langerhans forming from walls of pancreatic ducts	19
183		VI	26 da	43	Gonads distinguishable	6,43
184	27	VIII-IX	34-36 da	53-56	Onset of measurable thyroid secretion	3,24

/1/ Size upon completion of metamorphosis highly variable, ranging from 16-30 mm. /2/ Maximum size highly variable; tadpoles over 100 mm long have been collected.

continued

69. DEVELOPMENT: FROG

Part II: TISSUES AND ORGANS

Contributor: Kollros, Jerry J.

References: [1] Atwell, W. J. 1918. Anat. Record 15:73. [2] Baffoni, G. M., and G. Catte. 1951. Riv. biol. (Perugia) 43:373. [3] Barch, S. H. 1953. Physiol. Zool. 26:223. [4] Beaudoin, A. R. 1955. Anat. Record 121:81. [5] Bovbjerg, A. M. 1961. Ph.D. Thesis. State Univ. Iowa, Iowa City. [6] Christensen, K. 1930. Am. J. Anat. 45:159. [7] Clausen, H. J. 1930. Biol. Bull. 59:199. [8] Etkin, W. 1932. Physiol. Zool. 5:275. [9] Fabrizio, M., and H. A. Charipper. 1941. J. Morphol. 68:179. [10] Fribourgh, J. H. 1949. M.S. Thesis. State Univ. Iowa, Iowa City. [11] Fribourgh, J. H. 1952. Proc. Arkansas Acad. Sci. 5:43. [12] Gray, P. 1930. Quart. J. Microscop. Sci. 73:507. [13] Helff, O. M., and M. C. Mellicker. 1941. Am. J. Anat. 68:339. [14] Helff, O. M., and M. C. Mellicker. 1941. Ibid. 68:371. [15] Hinsberg, V. 1901. Arch. mikroskop. Anat. u. Entwicklungsmech. 58:411. [16] Holbert, M. 1952. M.S. Thesis. State Univ. Iowa, Iowa City. [17] Huettner, A. F. 1949. Fundamentals of comparative embryology of the vertebrates. Macmillan, New York. [18] Jaffe, O. C. 1954. J. Morphol. 95:109. [19] Janes, R. G. 1938. Ibid. 62:375. [20] Kaltenbach, J. C. 1953. J. Exptl. Zool. 122:21. [21] Knouff, R. A. 1935. J. Comp. Neurol. 62:17. [22] Kollros, J. J. 1942. J. Exptl. Zool. 89:37. [23] Kollros, J. J. 1953. Ibid. 123:153. [24] Kollros, J. J. Unpublished. State Univ. Iowa, Iowa City, 1956. [25] Kollros, J. J., and J. C. Kaltenbach. 1952. Physiol. Zool. 25:163. [26] Kollros, J. J., and V. M. McMurray. 1955. J. Comp. Neurol. 102:47. [27] Kopsch, F. 1952. Die Entwicklung des braunen Grasfrosches *Rana fusca* Roesel. G. Thieme, Stuttgart. [28] Larsell, O. 1923. J. Comp. Neurol. 36:89. [29] Petersen, H. 1924. Ergeb. Anat. u. Entwicklungsgeschichte 25:623. [30] Race, J., Jr. 1961. Gen. & Comp. Endocrinol. 1:322. [31] Rappaport, R., Jr. 1955. J. Exptl. Zool. 128:481. [32] Reynolds, W. A. K. 1962. Ph.D. Thesis. State Univ. Iowa, Iowa City. [33] Rugh, R. 1951. The frog: its reproduction and development. Blakiston, Philadelphia. [34] Segal, S. 1953. Anat. Record 115:205. [35] Shumway, W. 1940. Ibid. 78:139. [36] Shumway, W. 1942. Ibid. 83:309. [37] Stenger, A. H., and H. A. Charipper. 1946. J. Morphol. 78:27. [38] Stokeley, P. S., and J. C. List. 1955. Trans. Am. Microscop. Soc. 74:112. [39] Taylor, A. C. 1943. Anat. Record 87:379. [40] Taylor, A. C., and J. J. Kollros. 1946. Ibid. 94:7. [41] Villy, F. 1890. Quart. J. Microscop. Sci. 30:522. [42] Weed, I. G. 1934. J. Morphol. 56:213. [43] Witschi, E. 1929. J. Exptl. Zool. 52:235. [44] Witschi, E. 1955. J. Morphol. 96:497.

70. CHARACTERIZATION OF DEVELOPMENTAL STAGES: SALMONID FISHES

Age (columns B-D) = days after fertilization (differences in the data of Witschi (W.), Pasteels (P.), and Lagler (L.), are due to the fact that speed of development varies widely according to temperature and other environmental factors). Size (column E) = length of embryo or fry (diameter of blastopore is given in parentheses). Size and Identification of Stages compiled mostly from data in the references of Kopsch [2] and Witschi [12]. For information on development of other teleost species, consult references 1, 4, 5, 9-11.

	Standard Stages (Witschi)	Age days W.[1]	P.	L.	Size mm	Identification of Stages
	(A)	(B)	(C)	(D)	(E)	(F)
	Cleavage					
1	1					1 cell, fertilized
2	2	0.5		0.5		2 cells
3	3					4 cells
4	4			1		8 cells
5	5					16-32 cells
6	6	1				Blastodisc up to 500 cells
7	7	4		5	(1.5)	Disc blastula, hypoderm largely syncytial; blastocoele

/1/ Approximates natural conditions near $5^{\circ}C$.

continued

70. CHARACTERIZATION OF DEVELOPMENTAL STAGES: SALMONID FISHES

	Standard Stages (Witschi)	Age days W.[1]	Age days P.	Age days L.	Size mm	Identification of Stages
	(A)	(B)	(C)	(D)	(E)	(F)
						Gastrula
8	8		3		(1.6)	Start of invagination around dorsal blastopore lip; prospective prechordal mesoblast
9	9		3.2		(1.8)	Prospective upper notochord invaginated, small gastrocoele
10	10	5	3.5		(2.0)	Prospective mid-notochord and first somites invaginating
11	11		3.7		0.4 (2.2)	Prospective trunk notochord and somites invaginating; primitive node forming
						Primitive Streak
12	12		4	12	0.7 (2.5)	Prospective lower notochord and median neuroblast form primitive node (axial rudiment); prospective lateral neuroblasts and left and right mesoblasts meet in germ wall (lateral folds of primitive streak)
						Neurula
13	13	10	5	12	1.0 (3.1)	Presomite neurula; lateral primitive folds start concrescing
14	14		5.5		1.5 (3.7)	1-4 somites; neural plate narrowing, forming central solid cord of blastemic brain; upper notochord distinctly differentiated; hindgut vesicle
15	15	15	6	22	2.0 (4.5)	5-9 somites; forebrain and midbrain not separated, optic rudiments protruding; hindbrain narrow, imbedded between somitic mesoderm
16	16		6	68	2.5 (4.5)	10-15 somites; optic vesicles; forebrain and midbrain with slit-shaped cavity; otic vesicles with small cavity; concrescence constantly progresses, while yolk-sac epithelia spread over surface of yolk (in teleosts with small eggs, the yolk becomes much earlier engulfed by the yolk sac epithelia; the yolk-sac blastopore may close even before any somites have become externally noticeable)
17	17	20	6.5		3.0 (3.5)	16-25 somites; indication of lens placodes over optic vesicles; 2 or 3 visceral arches externally recognizable
						Tail Bud Embryo
18	18		7	83	3.5 (0.01)	26-30 somites; yolk-sac blastopore closes, embryo measures $\frac{1}{4}$ of entire egg circumference and is in full length attached to yolk-sac epithelium; brain cavity prolongating into upper spinal cord; flat lens placodes over optic vesicles; otic vesicles with small cavity that opens at surface; flat solid pharynx with 2 "pouches" reaching surface epithelium, 2nd one breaking through; nephrotomes in pronephric region begin to organize
19	19	30			4.0	31-40 somites; short, free tail bud; rhombencephalic roof becomes thin and broad; widening of ventricle
20	20			86	4.5	40-50 somites; optic vesicles start invagination; lens placodes thicken
21	21	40			5.2	50-55 somites; foregut with pharyngeal pouches; olfactory placodes thicken; deep optic cups; plug-shaped lens rudiments; nephric blastema-nephrostomes; nephric ducts get lost in lower mesonephric blastema cords; primordial germ cells widely scattered on both sides in mesodermal blastema; hindgut vesicle
22	22	50			6.0	55-58 somites; 2nd and 3rd pharyngeal pouches open on surface; pectoral limb buds; olfactory placodes saucer-shaped; free lenses in eye cups; round otic vesicle develops a thick neural epithelium ventrally; acoustic ganglion. Embryo begins to separate from yolk sac, especially the forehead; liver diverticles forming; tubular midgut; anus forming; nephric tubules and corpuscles; nephric ducts with free ends left and right of rectum.
23	23	60		86	10.0	58-60 somites; all somites have formed; pectoral fins fairly large and differentiated; buds of pelvic fins are present but not externally noticeable; eyes now heavily pigmented; otic vesicles become labyrinths; cartilaginous skeleton of head and upper body; germ cells still free in peritoneum or mesenchyme near nephric ducts and blastema; renal corpuscles; nephric ducts unite caudal to rectum
24	24	70			15.0	Hatching fish (fry); pelvic fin bud below caudal end of yolk sac (about 30th somite); anus at about 40th somite; total number of somites varies normally from about 56 to 60. Swimbladder has grown out from dorsal wall of esophagus; undifferentiated gonads; skin pigment appearing.
						Young Adult Fish
25	25	80			20+	General appearance as at preceding stage, but pelvic and all unpaired fins are now well-differentiated. Skin heavily pigmented. Yolk sac shrinks and eventually disappears.

/1/ Approximates natural conditions near 5°C.

Contributor: Witschi, Emil

continued

70. CHARACTERIZATION OF DEVELOPMENTAL STAGES: SALMONID FISHES

References: [1] Armstrong, P. B. In press, 1962. [2] Kopsch, F. 1898. Arch. mikroskop. Anat. u. Entwicklungsmech. 51:181. [3] Lagler, K. F. 1952. Freshwater fishery biology. W. C. Brown, Dubuque, Iowa. [4] Oppenheimer, J. M. 1937. Anat. Record 68:1. [5] Outram, D. 1957. Turtox News 35:16. [6] Pasteels, J. 1936. Arch. biol. (Liège) 47:206. [7] Schmidt, J. 1921. Compt. rend. trav. lab. Carlsberg 14(15):1. [8] Schmidt, J. 1921. Ibid. 14(16):1. [9] Solberg, A. N. 1938. Progressive Fish Culturist 40. [10] Swarup, H. 1958. J. Embryol. Exptl. Morphol. 6:373. [11] Wilson, H. V. 1889. Bull. U. S. Fisheries Comm. 9:209. [12] Witschi, E. 1956. The development of vertebrates. W. B. Saunders, Philadelphia.

71. PRENATAL DEVELOPMENT OF MOTOR ACTIVITIES: MAMMALS

Data are for induced exteroceptive reflexes (spontaneous activity given in parentheses). Gestation period, in italics, was measured from time of insemination. % GP = percent of gestation period elapsed at time motor activity appears.

	Motor Activity	Appearance									
		Man *(266 da)*		Sheep *(157 da)*		Cat *(66 da)*		Guinea Pig *(67 da)*		Rat *(21 da)*	
		Da	% GP	Da	% GP	Da	% GP	Da	% GP	Da	% GP
	(A)	(B)	(C)	(D)	(E)	(F)	(G)	(H)	(I)	(J)	(K)
	Earliest appearance										
1	First exteroceptive reflex	52.5	19.7	40	25.7	22	33.3	26	38	15.8	75
2	Last exteroceptive reflex	224	84.3	90	57.3	49	74.2	51	76	19	90.5
3	Spontaneous activity	(63)	(23.7)	(35)	(22.3)	(24)	(36.4)	(26.5)	(39.5)	...	...
	Head										
4	Extension	52.5	19.7	40	25.7	28	42.4	32	47.8	16.0-16.6	76-79
5	Lateral flexion at neck	42	15.8	45 (36)	28.6 (22.9)	24-25	36.7-37.8	32	47.8	15.9	75.6
6	Ventral flexion	56	21.1	55	35	24-28	36.4-42.4	35	52.2	...	...
7	Rotation	42	15.8	40 (39)	25.7 (24.8)	24-28	36.4-42.4	34	50.7	16	76
	Face										
8	Forehead movements	70	26.3	...	...	...	...	40	59.7	...	...
9	Palpebral muscle movements	63	23.7	...	...	...	...	36	53.7	...	...
10	Eyes, movement of globus oculi	70	26.3	(50)	(31.8)	...	...	39	58.2	...	...
11	Oronasal muscle movements	49[1]; 60[2]	18.4[1]; 22.6[2]	50	31.8	26	39.4	39	58.2	19	90.5
12	Lip movements	49	18.4	...	...	...	...	36	53.7	...	...
13	Mouth closing	49	18.4	41	26.1	...	...	36	53.7	19	90.4
14	Mouth opening	49	18.4	50 (40)	31.8 (25.7)	...	...	35	52.2	16.2	77
15	Mouth pursing	154	57.9	...	...	...	...	...	...	...	...
16	Tongue movements	84	31.6	...	...	29-37	44-56	37	55.2	16.2	77
17	Sucking	203[3]	76.3	49	31.2	49	74.2	37	55.2	...	...
18	Swallowing	73	27.4	80	50.9	...	...	...	...	...	...
19	Phonation	164.5[3]	61.8	...	...	49	74.2	...	...	...	...
	Neck										
20	Extension	53	19.9	55 (38)	35 (24.2)	...	...	26	38.8	...	...
21	Lateral flexion	42	15.8	45	28.6	...	...	26	38.8	15.9	75.6
22	Ventral flexion	56	21.1	40	25.7	...	...	26	38	...	...
	Trunk										
23	Rotation or twisting	84	31.6	...	...	26-27	39.4-40.9	36	53.7	17	81
24	Chest contractions, respiratory	91	34.2	38-49 (40)	24.2-31.2 (25.7)	33	50	...	...	...	...
25	Diaphragmatic contractions, respiratory	154	57.9	(38)	(24.2)	44	66.6	...	...	...	...
26	Effective respiration	164.5	61.8	...	...	...	...	...	...	...	...
27	Abdominal muscle contractions	105	39.5	...	...	28-33	42.4-50.0	39 (31)	58.2 (46.2)	17	81
28	Cremasteric reflex	224	84.3	78	49.7	...	...	51	76.1	...	...
29	Tail movements	...	...	...	...	28-31	42.4-47.0	...	...	17	85.7
	Upper trunk[4]										
30	Extension	56	21.1	...	...	28	42.4	29.5	45	...	...
31	Lateral flexion	56	21.1	40 (36)	25.7 (22.9)	24-26	36.4-39.4	27 (31)	39.8 (46.2)	15.8-16.0[5]	75-76
32	Ventral flexion	63	23.7	(38)	(24.2)	25	37.8	29	43.3	16.2	77

/1/ Oral muscle movements. /2/ Nasal muscle movements. /3/ Human fetus viable at 189 days (71.1% of gestation period). /4/ Data for guinea pig do not distinguish between movements of upper and lower segments of trunk. /5/ Direction of movement not specifically indicated.

continued

71. PRENATAL DEVELOPMENT OF MOTOR ACTIVITIES: MAMMALS

	Motor Activity	Appearance									
		Man (266 da)		Sheep (157 da)		Cat (66 da)		Guinea Pig (67 da)		Rat (21 da)	
		Da	% GP	Da	% GP	Da	% GP	Da	% GP	Da	% GP
	(A)	(B)	(C)	(D)	(E)	(F)	(G)	(H)	(I)	(J)	(K)
	Lower trunk[4]										
33	Extension	56	21.1	......	......	28	42.4	29.5	45	16	76.1
34	Lateral flexion	56	21.1	......	......	26	39.4	27 (31)	39.8 (46.2)	15.8	75
35	Ventral flexion	63	23.7	(38)	(24.2)	25	37.8	29	43.3	16.2	77
	Rump										
36	Extension	73.5	27.6	......	......	34	51.6	37	55.2	17	81
37	Lateral flexion	56	21.1	......	......	27	40.9	32	49.2	16	76.2
38	Ventral flexion	63	23.7	......	......	26[5]-32	39.4-48.5	......	......	16.2	77
39	Rotation	42	15.8	......	......	31	47	......	......	17	81
	Upper extremity										
40	Movement with trunk	42	15.8	......	......	24.5	37.1	......	......	16	76.2
41	Adduction at shoulder	49	18.4	......	......	33	50	32	47.8	......	......
42	Abduction at shoulder	42	15.8	40 (36)	25.7 (22.9)	......	......	......	......	......	......
43	Extension at shoulder	42	15.8	40	25.7	26	39.4	26	39	15.7[5]	74.8
44	Flexion at shoulder	......	......	40	25.7	23-26	34.8-39.4	26	38.8	......	......
45	Rotation, medial	52	19.5	......	......	......	......	......	......	......	......
46	Elbow extension	52	19.5	(39)	(24.8)	25	37.8	......	......	......	......
47	Elbow flexion	56	21.1	44 (39)	28 (24.8)	26	39.4	32	47.8	17	81
48	Forearm pronation	63	23.7	......	......	......	......	......	......	......	......
49	Wrist extension	73	27.4	......	......	38[5]	57.5	......	......	18	85.7
50	Wrist flexion	52	19.5	......	......	25-32	37.8-48.5	32	47.8	15.8[5]-17.0	75-81
51	Pollex flexion	63	23.7	......	......	......	......	......	......	......	......
52	Pollex opposition	70	26.3	......	......	......	......	......	......	......	......
53	Finger flexion	60	22.6	......	......	......	......	36	53.7	......	......
54	Finger closure, maintained	105	39.5	......	......	......	......	......	......	......	......
55	Grasp, light	84	31.6	......	......	......	......	......	......	......	......
56	Grasp, tight	175	65.8	......	......	......	......	......	......	......	......
	Lower extremity										
57	Movement with trunk	56	21.1	......	......	......	......	......	......	16.8	77
58	Scratch reflex	......	......	90	57.3	......	......	56	83.5	......	......
59	Adduction at hip	78	29.3	......	......	......	......	45	67.2	......	......
60	Abduction at hip	67	25.2	......	......	25[5]-30	37.8-45.4	......	......	......	......
61	Extension at hip	63	23.7	......	......	31-40 (38)	47.0-60.6 (57.5)	34	50.7	17	81
62	Flexion at hip	56	21.1	40	25.7	28-30	42.4-45.4	32	47.8	18	85.7
63	Rotation, lateral	67	25.2	......	......	......	......	......	......	......	......
64	Rotation, medial	67	25.2	......	......	......	......	......	......	......	......
65	Knee extension	63	23.7	(39)	(24.8)	......	......	......	......	......	......
66	Knee flexion	60	22.6	(39)	(24.8)	31-38	47.0-57.5	......	......	......	......
67	Ankle adduction	......	......	......	......	45[5]	68.1	......	......	......	......
68	Ankle dorsiflexion	60	22.6	(39)	(24.8)	......	......	......	......	......	......
69	Ankle plantar flexion	72	27.1	(39)	(24.8)	40	60.6	......	......	......	......
70	Ankle rotation	......	......	......	......	45[5]	68.1	......	......	......	......
71	Hallux dorsiflexion	70	26.3	......	......	......	......	......	......	......	......
72	Toe fanning	70	26.3	......	......	......	......	......	......	......	......
73	Toe dorsiflexion	70	26.3	......	......	48[5]	72.7	......	......	......	......
74	Toe plantar flexion	60	22.6	......	......	48[5]	72.7	......	......	......	......
	Reference	6, 7		2		5, 8, 9		3, 4		1, 10	

/4/ Data for guinea pig do not distinguish between movements of upper and lower segments of trunk. /5/ Direction of movement not specifically indicated.

Contributor: Hooker, Davenport

References: [1] Angulo, A. W. 1932. J. Comp. Neurol. 55:395. [2] Barcroft, J., and D. H. Barron. 1939. Ibid. 70:477. [3] Bridgman, C. S., and L. Carmichael. 1935. J. Genet. Psychol. 47:247. [4] Carmichael, L. 1934. Genet. Psychol. Monographs 16:337. [5] Coronios, J. D. 1933. Ibid. 14:283. [6] Hooker, D. 1952. The prenatal origin of behavior. Univ. Kansas Press, Lawrence. [7] Hooker, D. Unpublished. Yale Univ. School of Medicine, New Haven, 1961. [8] Windle, W. F., and A. M. Griffin. 1931. J. Comp. Neurol. 52:149. [9] Windle, W. F., J. E. O'Donnell, and F. E. Glasshagle. 1933. Physiol. Zool. 6:521. [10] Windle, W. F., et al. 1935. Ibid. 8:156.

VIII. POSTNATAL VERTEBRATE DEVELOPMENT

72. DIMENSIONS OF BODY STEM AND EXTREMITIES: MAN, NORTH AMERICAN

Part I: PRENATAL, BIRTH, AND POSTNATAL

Values are for white subjects.

	Type of Measurement and Structure	Region of Measurement	Dimensions, cm							
			Prenatal		Birth	Postnatal				
			2 mo[1] ♂♀	4.5 mo[2] ♂♀	♂♀	3 yr ♂♀	8 yr ♂♀	13 yr ♂♀	18 yr ♂	18 yr ♀
	(A)	(B)	(C)	(D)	(E)	(F)	(G)	(H)	(I)	(J)
	Circumference									
1	Head	Glabella	4.1	18.0	34.2	49.8	52.2	54.4	56.4	55.1
2	Chest	Xiphisternal level	1.9	15.0	32.3	50.5	59.1	69.9	83.9	72.8
3	Abdomen	Umbilicus	...	12.9	30.5	50.2	57.0	65.0	73.0	67.0
4	Arm	Biceps at deltoid insertion	...	4.0	10.4	15.5	18.4	21.9	26.4	24.4
5	Leg	Maximum cross-section of calf	...	4.3	11.3	20.6	25.6	30.9	35.3	33.3
	Breadth									
6	Head	Biparietal	1.2	4.8	9.4	13.8	14.4	14.7	15.3	14.8
7	Face	Bizygomatic	...	3.4	7.3	11.0	12.1	12.8	13.9	13.2
8	Shoulders	Biacromial	0.9	5.5	11.3	21.8	27.8	33.4	39.0	36.1
9	Chest	Thorax at xiphisternal level	0.6	5.0	10.5	17.1	19.5	23.5	28.2	24.8
10	Hips	Bitrochanteric	0.5	4.0	8.9	17.8	22.4	28.4	32.3	32.3
	Length									
11	Head and neck	Vertex to suprasternale	1.8	7.7	12.8	21.5	26.6	29.7	32.3	30.5
12	Trunk	Vertex-rump minus vertex-suprasternale	1.6	8.9	21.0	35.0	42.8	50.8	58.5	55.6
13	Upper limb	Acromion to dactylion	1.4	10.2	22.2	40.0	53.6	67.2	77.6	71.1
14	Lower limb	Vertex-heel minus vertex-rump	0.9	7.8	16.6	39.8	59.7	75.3	83.5	76.5
15	Foot	Acropodion to pternion	0.6	3.5	8.0	15.3	20.1	23.5	26.3	23.8

/1/ 2 months after fertilization. /2/ Middle of prenatal period.

Contributor: Meredith, Howard V.

References: [1] Bakwin, H., and R. M. Bakwin. 1934. Human Biol. 6:612. [2] Cates, H. A., and J. C. Goodwin. 1936. Ibid. 8:433. [3] Meredith, H. V. 1939. Child Develop. 10:129. [4] Meredith, H. V. 1946. Ibid. 17:1. [5] Meredith, H. V. 1944. Human Biol. 16:207. [6] Meredith, H. V. 1947. Growth 11:1. [7] Meredith, H. V., and B. Boynton. 1937. Human Biol. 9:366. [8] Scammon, R. E., and L. A. Calkins. 1929. Development and growth of the external dimensions of the human body in the fetal period. Univ. Minnesota Press, Minneapolis. [9] Schultz, A. H. 1926. Quart. Rev. Biol. 1:465. [10] Schwartz, L., R. H. Britten, and L. H. Thompson. 1928. U. S. Public Health Bull. 179. [11] Simmons, K. 1944. Monographs Soc. Research in Child Develop. 9(1):19. [12] Vickers, V. S., and H. C. Stuart. 1943. J. Pediat. 22:155.

Part II: SEX DIFFERENCES FROM CHILDHOOD TO ADOLESCENCE

	Structure and Region of Measurement	Specification	Age, yr											Reference
			7	8	9	10	11	12	13	14	15	16	17	
	(A)	(B)	(C)	(D)	(E)	(F)	(G)	(H)	(I)	(J)	(K)	(L)	(M)	(N)
	Body stem (vertex to	Males												4
1	rump in erect sit-	No. of subjects	210	200	171	170	178	201	184	164	128	98	60	
2	ting position)	Length, cm	67.7	70.3	72.4	74.3	76.2	78.3	80.8	84.6	88.6	90.4	91.8	
		Females												4
3		No. of subjects	242	212	191	182	201	194	171	143	111	69	28	
4		Length, cm	67.5	69.8	71.9	74.2	76.9	80.1	83.6	86.1	87.3	87.9	88.0	
		Sex difference, cm												
5		Alternating relationship	0.2	0.5	0.5	0.1	-0.7	-1.8	-2.8	-1.5	1.3	2.5	3.8	

continued

72. DIMENSIONS OF BODY STEM AND EXTREMITIES: MAN, NORTH AMERICAN

Part II: SEX DIFFERENCES FROM CHILDHOOD TO ADOLESCENCE

	Structure and Region of Measurement	Specification	Age, yr											Reference
			7	8	9	10	11	12	13	14	15	16	17	
	(A)	(B)	(C)	(D)	(E)	(F)	(G)	(H)	(I)	(J)	(K)	(L)	(M)	(N)
	Thorax (mid-respiration measurements taken at level of xiphisternal junction)	Males												1
6		No. of subjects	108	98	95	79	72	74	91	102	113	123	126	
7		Circumference, cm	57.4	60.0	62.4	63.5	65.7	67.4	70.3	73.6	77.4	80.6	82.5	
		Females												1
8		No. of subjects	86	72	86	91	85	98	109	123	135	129	101	
9		Circumference, cm	56.1	58.1	59.6	61.2	64.3	66.4	69.5	70.9	72.3	73.0	72.3	
		Sex difference, cm												
10		♂ larger than ♀	1.3	1.9	2.8	2.3	1.4	1.0	0.8	2.7	5.1	7.6	10.2	
	Thigh (right leg at level of gluteal fold)	Males												3
11		No. of subjects	4627	5495	6067	6444	6567	6550	6433	5516	4739	4359	3394	
12		Circumference, cm	34.8	36.2	37.8	39.4	41.0	42.7	44.4	46.2	48.4	50.4	51.6	
		Females												3
13		No. of subjects	4963	5560	5964	6213	6192	5998	5499	4383	3812	3660	2722	
14		Circumference, cm	35.8	37.4	39.0	40.8	42.7	44.8	46.9	49.0	51.3	52.8	53.4	
		Sex difference, cm												
15		♀ larger than ♂	1.0	1.2	1.2	1.4	1.7	2.1	2.5	2.8	2.9	2.4	1.8	
	Arm tissue (skin and subcutaneous tissue anterior to biceps and posterior to triceps muscles)	Males												2
16		No. of subjects	142	107	115	104	97	91	117	116	147	128	103	
17		Thickness, mm	4.9	5.0	5.1	5.1	5.4	5.4	5.3	5.1	4.7	4.4	4.4	
		Females												1
18		No. of subjects	73	58	70	72	71	77	92	108	118	112	90	
19		Thickness, mm	5.6	6.0	6.3	6.4	6.4	6.4	6.5	6.6	7.1	7.4	7.5	
		Sex difference, mm												
20		Divergence[1]	0.7	1.0	1.2	1.3	1.0	1.0	1.2	1.5	2.4	3.0	3.1	

/1/ After 12 years of age, adipose tissue of arm decreases in males and increases in females.

Contributor: Meredith, Howard V.

References: [1] Boynton, B. 1936. Univ. Iowa Studies in Child Welfare 12(4):24. [2] Meredith, H. V. 1935. Ibid. 11(3):31. [3] O'Brien, R., et al. 1941. U. S. Dept. Agr. Misc. Publ. 366:64. [4] Simmons, K. 1944. Monographs Soc. Research in Child Develop. 9(1):19.

73. BODY MEASUREMENTS: MAN, NORTH AMERICAN

Part I: BIRTH TO CHILDHOOD

Values were derived from repeated determinations on a group of white subjects, of North European ancestry, living in or near Boston, Massachusetts. Values in parentheses are the 10th and 90th percentiles.

	Age	Weight kg	Length cm	Pelvic Breadth cm	Head Circumference cm	Chest Circumference cm	Abdominal Circumference cm
	(A)	(B)	(C)	(D)	(E)	(F)	(G)
				Males			
1	Birth	3.4(2.9-4.1)	50.6(48.1-53.3)	8.1(7.4-8.7)	35.3(33.5-37.0)	33.2(30.6-35.7)	....
2	3 mo	5.7(5.0-6.6)	60.4(57.8-62.8)	10.6(10.0-11.5)	40.9(39.2-42.1)	40.6(38.3-42.9)	38.5(35.5-41.4)
3	6 mo	7.6(6.7-8.7)	66.4(63.9-69.3)	11.6(10.8-12.4)	43.9(42.7-45.4)	43.7(41.6-46.3)	41.4(38.4-45.0)
4	9 mo	9.1(8.1-10.4)	71.2(68.6-74.2)	12.3(11.5-13.1)	46.0(44.5-47.1)	46.0(43.7-48.9)	43.3(40.1-47.6)
5	12 mo	10.1(8.9-11.5)	75.2(72.4-78.1)	12.8(11.9-13.7)	47.3(45.5-48.4)	47.6(45.1-50.7)	44.6(41.1-48.9)
6	15 mo	10.8(9.5-12.3)	78.5(75.6-81.5)	13.3(12.4-14.2)	48.0(46.3-49.2)	48.6(46.1-51.7)	45.1(43.5-49.3)
7	18 mo	11.4(10.1-13.2)	81.8(78.8-85.0)	13.7(12.8-14.7)	48.7(47.0-49.9)	49.5(47.0-52.6)	45.5(42.2-49.6)
8	2 yr	12.6(11.2-14.5)	87.5(84.2-91.1)	14.4(13.5-15.5)	49.7(48.0-51.0)	50.8(48.4-53.9)	46.2(43.4-50.2)
9	2.5 yr	13.6(12.1-15.7)	92.1(88.5-96.2)	15.1(14.2-16.2)	50.2(48.5-51.6)	51.7(49.3-54.9)	46.7(44.0-50.7)
10	3 yr	14.6(13.0-16.7)	96.2(92.3-100.5)	15.8(14.8-16.9)	50.4(48.9-51.9)	52.4(49.9-55.8)	47.2(44.6-51.1)
11	3.5 yr	15.6(13.8-17.7)	99.8(96.0-104.5)	16.3(15.3-17.4)	....	53.1(50.5-56.6)	....
12	4 yr	16.5(14.6-18.8)	103.4(99.3-108.5)	16.9(15.8-18.0)	....	53.7(51.1-57.2)	....
13	4.5 yr	17.4(15.3-19.9)	106.7(102.4-112.3)	17.3(16.2-18.5)	....	54.4(51.7-58.0)	....

continued

73. BODY MEASUREMENTS: MAN, NORTH AMERICAN

Part I: BIRTH TO CHILDHOOD

	Age	Weight kg	Length cm	Pelvic Breadth cm	Head Circumference cm	Chest Circumference cm	Abdominal Circumference cm
	(A)	(B)	(C)	(D)	(E)	(F)	(G)
				Females			
14	Birth	3.4(2.8-3.9)	50.2(47.8-51.9)	7.7(7.2-8.5)	34.7(33.4-36.0)	32.9(30.8-35.0)	....
15	3 mo	5.6(4.9-6.4)	59.5(56.9-61.7)	10.4(9.6-11.4)	40.0(38.5-41.7)	39.8(37.6-42.0)	38.4(34.4-41.7)
16	6 mo	7.3(6.4-8.4)	65.2(62.5-67.8)	11.3(10.5-12.4)	42.8(41.4-44.5)	43.0(40.6-45.4)	41.4(37.9-45.0)
17	9 mo	8.7(7.5-10.2)	70.1(67.0-72.9)	12.0(11.3-13.1)	44.6(43.2-46.3)	45.4(42.7-47.9)	43.4(39.9-47.7)
18	12 mo	9.8(8.4-11.3)	74.2(70.6-77.1)	12.4(11.7-13.6)	45.8(44.3-47.7)	47.0(44.2-49.5)	44.5(40.9-49.2)
19	15 mo	10.4(9.0-12.1)	77.6(73.7-80.8)	12.9(12.1-14.1)	46.5(44.9-48.4)	47.9(45.1-50.5)	45.0(41.5-49.8)
20	18 mo	11.1(9.6-12.8)	80.9(76.8-84.5)	13.3(12.4-14.5)	47.1(45.5-49.0)	48.8(46.0-51.4)	45.5(42.1-50.3)
21	2 yr	12.3(10.7-14.4)	86.6(82.0-91.0)	14.1(13.1-15.3)	48.1(46.4-50.1)	50.1(47.4-53.0)	46.3(42.8-51.4)
22	2.5 yr	13.4(11.6-15.7)	91.4(86.3-96.4)	14.8(13.7-16.1)	48.8(47.0-50.8)	51.2(48.4-54.3)	47.0(43.6-52.6)
23	3 yr	14.4(12.5-17.0)	95.7(90.5-101.1)	15.4(13.8-16.8)	49.3(47.5-51.1)	51.9(49.3-55.1)	47.7(44.5-53.6)
24	3.5 yr	15.4(13.4-18.3)	99.5(94.2-105.4)	16.0(14.9-17.4)	....	52.5(50.1-55.8)	....
25	4 yr	16.4(14.2-19.7)	103.2(97.6-109.6)	16.5(15.4-17.9)	....	53.1(50.7-56.5)	....
26	4.5 yr	17.5(14.9-21.2)	106.8(100.9-113.5)	17.0(15.9-18.5)	....	53.7(51.3-57.3)	....

Contributor: Stuart, Harold C.

References: [1] Stuart, H. C., et al. Unpublished. Harvard Univ. School of Public Health, Dept. of Maternal and Child Health, Cambridge, 1952. [2] Vickers, V. S., and H. C. Stuart. 1943. J. Pediat. 22:155.

Part II: CHILDHOOD TO ADOLESCENCE

Values were derived from repeated determinations on white subjects, of predominantly Northwest European ancestry and from predominantly professional and managerial classes, living in or near Iowa City, Iowa. Values in parentheses are the 10th and 90th percentiles.

	Age yr	No. of Subjects	Weight kg	Height cm	Hip Width cm	Chest Circumference cm	Leg Girth cm
	(A)	(B)	(C)	(D)	(E)	(F)	(G)
				Males			
1	5	235	19.4(16.6-22.5)	111.3(105.3-116.7)	18.3(17.0-19.6)	54.5(51.6-57.5)	22.6(21.0-24.6)
2	6	218	21.9(18.6-25.6)	117.5(111.2-123.5)	19.1(17.7-20.5)	56.1(53.2-59.5)	23.6(21.8-25.7)
3	7	169	24.5(20.8-29.2)	124.1(116.9-130.5)	19.9(18.5-21.4)	57.8(54.9-61.6)	24.6(22.6-26.9)
4	8	142	27.3(23.2-33.1)	130.0(123.1-137.3)	20.7(19.2-22.3)	59.8(56.7-64.1)	25.7(23.6-28.2)
5	9	120	29.9(25.5-36.7)	135.5(128.3-142.6)	21.4(19.9-23.0)	61.8(58.4-66.7)	26.8(24.5-29.5)
6	10	117	32.6(27.7-40.8)	140.3(132.8-147.5)	22.0(20.4-23.9)	63.9(60.1-69.4)	27.7(25.3-30.7)
7	11	101	35.2(30.1-45.0)	144.2(137.3-151.8)	22.6(21.1-24.8)	65.9(61.7-71.9)	28.5(26.0-32.0)
8	12	95	38.3(32.7-49.7)	149.6(142.4-157.9)	23.5(21.9-25.8)	67.8(63.3-74.2)	29.5(26.8-33.5)
9	13	100	42.2(35.0-55.9)	155.0(146.6-165.3)	24.6(22.7-27.2)	70.3(65.0-77.4)	30.8(27.8-34.8)
10	14	118	48.8(39.7-62.1)	162.7(152.1-172.4)	25.8(23.6-28.3)	74.5(67.6-81.4)	32.3(29.1-35.8)
11	15	144	54.5(45.1-67.0)	167.8(157.8-176.7)	26.7(24.6-29.1)	78.0(71.1-84.8)	33.4(30.4-36.6)
12	16	137	58.8(50.3-71.4)	171.6(162.8-179.7)	27.4(25.6-29.6)	80.7(74.4-87.8)	34.2(31.3-37.3)
13	17	117	61.8(53.3-74.7)	173.7(165.5-181.6)	27.8(26.1-29.9)	82.5(76.4-89.7)	34.6(31.7-37.8)
14	18	86	63.1(54.4-76.7)	174.5(166.3-182.4)	28.0(26.5-30.1)	83.4(77.5-90.7)	34.9(31.9-38.1)
				Females			
15	5	210	18.8(16.4-21.9)	109.7(105.0-115.4)	18.0(17.0-19.4)	52.9(50.2-56.5)	22.8(21.1-24.7)
16	6	169	21.1(18.1-24.6)	115.9(110.6-122.3)	18.8(17.7-20.5)	54.5(51.5-58.2)	23.8(21.9-25.8)
17	7	130	23.7(20.2-27.8)	122.3(116.8-128.9)	19.6(18.4-21.6)	56.1(52.8-60.1)	24.8(22.7-27.0)
18	8	115	26.4(22.0-31.7)	128.0(122.1-134.6)	20.5(19.1-22.6)	57.8(54.2-62.3)	25.8(23.5-28.3)
19	9	110	28.9(23.9-35.9)	132.9(127.0-140.4)	21.3(19.7-23.5)	59.6(55.5-64.7)	26.8(24.2-29.5)
20	10	112	31.9(25.9-40.7)	138.6(131.7-146.0)	22.2(20.5-24.6)	61.4(56.9-67.4)	27.7(25.1-30.9)
21	11	113	35.7(28.4-45.5)	144.7(137.0-153.4)	23.5(21.4-26.0)	64.2(58.6-70.5)	28.9(26.0-32.6)
22	12	112	39.7(31.5-50.6)	151.5(142.6-160.6)	24.9(22.4-27.6)	66.7(60.6-73.8)	30.1(27.1-33.8)

continued

73. BODY MEASUREMENTS: MAN, NORTH AMERICAN

Part II: CHILDHOOD TO ADOLESCENCE

	Age yr	No. of Subjects	Weight kg	Height cm	Hip Width cm	Chest Circumference cm	Leg Girth cm
	(A)	(B)	(C)	(D)	(E)	(F)	(G)
	Females						
23	13	120	45.0(36.2-56.5)	157.1(149.1-164.8)	26.0(23.6-29.0)	68.6(62.9-76.7)	31.2(28.2-34.8)
24	14	134	49.2(41.3-60.5)	159.6(153.0-167.0)	26.9(24.8-29.9)	69.9(64.6-78.6)	32.0(29.2-35.4)
25	15	169	51.5(44.2-62.6)	161.1(155.2-168.1)	27.5(25.6-30.6)	70.9(65.5-79.8)	32.6(29.9-35.9)
26	16	151	53.1(45.8-64.0)	162.2(156.1-169.0)	28.0(26.1-31.0)	71.6(66.1-80.5)	33.1(30.3-36.3)
27	17	140	54.0(46.6-65.0)	162.5(156.3-169.4)	28.3(26.3-31.2)	72.1(66.4-80.9)	33.4(30.6-36.5)
28	18	87	54.4(46.9-65.5)	162.5(156.3-169.4)	28.4(26.4-31.3)	72.3(66.6-81.1)	33.6(30.8-36.8)

Contributors: Stuart, Harold C., and Meredith, Howard V.

Reference: Stuart, H. C., and H. V. Meredith. 1946. Am. J. Public Health 36:1365.

74. REGRESSION OF STANDING AND SITTING HEIGHTS ON BODY WEIGHT: MAN

Curves were plotted from five large groups of measurements made on males from infancy to old age. The curve for standing height was based on a total of 17,523 values, for sitting height on 14,992 values. In each of the five groups, care was taken to exclude persons not in good health. Curves representing the ordinary range limits (95% range) are not available but would be expected to lie above and below, and parallel to, each of the curves shown. The upper of such curves for standing height would represent the ordinarily encountered limit in the direction of slenderness, the lower the ordinarily encountered limit in the direction of heaviness of build. Evidence indicates that curves for females (not represented) are identical in slope and position with those for males, but the means for females of the same age simply do not extend as far to the right along the curve. The line slopes for the standing height curve are 34, 63, and 35%, with the breaks at 10 and 22 kg. For sitting height the comparable slopes are 34, 41, and 30%. The relationships between standing height and weight for the three weight ranges are expressed by the formulas $H/W^{0.34}$, $H/W^{0.63}$, and $H/W^{0.35}$.

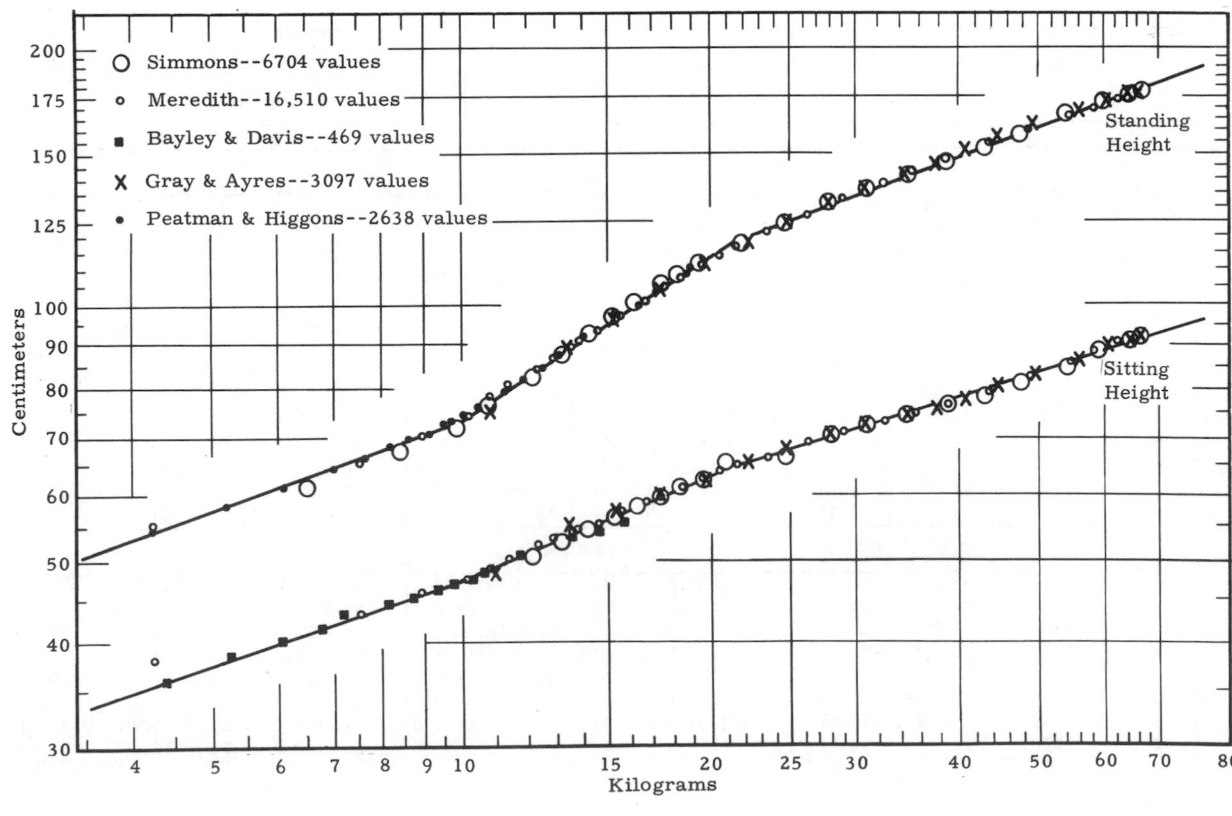

continued

74. REGRESSION OF STANDING AND SITTING HEIGHTS ON BODY WEIGHT: MAN

Contributor: Zucker, Theodore F.

References: [1] Bayley, N., and F. C. Davis. 1935. Biometrika 27:26. [2] Gray, H., and J. G. Ayres. 1931. Growth in private school children. Univ. Chicago Press, Chicago. [3] Meredith, H. V. 1935. Univ. Iowa Studies in Child Welfare 11(3). [4] Peatman, J. G., and R. A. Higgons. 1938. Am. J. Diseases Children 55:1233. [5] Simmons, K. W. 1944. Monographs Soc. Research in Child Develop. 9(1).

75. BODY WEIGHT AND HEIGHT: MAN, NORTH AMERICAN

Values for individuals and for specific groups of individuals vary widely from average weight-height values. Variations are particularly great for boys ages 12-17 years and for girls 10-15 years. For additional information, consult Hathaway, Milicent L., 1957, *Heights and Weights of Children and Youth in the United States,* Home Economics Research Report No. 2, U. S. Dept. of Agriculture, Washington, D. C.

Part I: RELATED TO RATE OF MATURING

Values are for subjects living in California. Weights and heights were interpolated from a large graph based on mean values calculated at 2% intervals of mature height.

	Age yr	Males						Females					
		Accelerated (38 subjects)		Average (106 subjects)		Retarded (31 subjects)		Accelerated (27 subjects)		Average (108 subjects)		Retarded (25 subjects)	
		Weight kg	Height cm	Weight kg	Height cm	Weight kg	Height cm	Weight kg	Height cm	Weight kg	Height cm	Weight kg	Height cm
	(A)	(B)	(C)	(D)	(E)	(F)	(G)	(H)	(I)	(J)	(K)	(L)	(M)
1	1	10.8	78.5	10.4	78.0	10.6	74.4	10.9	77.7	9.8	73.9	9.6	71.9
2	2	14.1	89.4	13.3	87.9	12.4	83.3	13.7	87.4	12.7	87.4	11.7	84.6
3	3	16.1	98.0	15.7	96.5	13.9	91.7	15.7	96.0	14.7	95.2	13.9	93.2
4	4	18.8	105.4	17.7	103.6	16.2	100.6	19.1	104.9	17.0	103.1	15.3	100.1
5	5	20.8	113.0	19.4	111.0	18.3	107.4	21.8	112.8	18.7	109.5	17.2	105.9
6	6	23.5	119.9	21.6	116.3	20.0	114.0	24.1	119.1	21.2	116.6	19.5	113.0
7	7	25.8	127.0	24.0	123.7	22.0	119.4	26.0	125.0	24.0	122.2	21.6	119.9
8	8	29.5	133.4	26.4	129.3	24.8	125.5	30.3	132.1	27.2	128.0	23.2	125.0
9	9	33.8	139.4	30.3	134.9	27.3	131.6	35.6	140.0	30.1	133.9	27.1	130.8
10	10	39.0	145.5	33.6	141.5	30.0	137.4	41.8	145.5	34.5	140.0	29.4	135.4
11	11	44.1	151.4	37.3	146.0	33.3	141.7	49.4	153.4	39.3	146.0	31.7	141.0
12	12	49.8	157.0	41.4	150.1	36.6	146.6	56.6	160.3	45.0	154.2	35.4	146.6
13	13	56.7	166.6	46.0	156.0	40.9	150.0	59.5	163.3	51.0	160.0	39.4	151.9
14	14	61.0	174.0	52.6	164.1	45.4	156.7	61.2	164.6	54.9	163.1	44.9	158.5
15	15	67.1	179.6	60.7	173.0	50.9	163.1	62.9	165.1	58.4	164.6	49.2	162.1
16	16	69.9	182.1	64.7	178.1	59.4	172.0	63.2	165.6	59.7	165.6	52.0	163.8
17	17	70.7	182.1	67.9	179.1	64.9	176.5	62.4	165.6	60.0	165.9	54.1	164.6
18	18	...	.....	69.9	180.1	68.4	179.1	61.0	165.6	59.8	165.9	54.0	164.8

Contributors: (a) Hathaway, Milicent L., (b) Bayley, Nancy

Reference: Bayley, N. 1956. J. Pediat. 48:187.

continued

75. BODY WEIGHT AND HEIGHT: MAN, NORTH AMERICAN

Part II: RELATED TO AGE AT MAXIMUM GROWTH INCREASE

Values are for subjects, dressed in indoor clothing but without shoes, from three towns near Boston, Massachusetts. Ancestry: 63% North European, 24% Italian, 7% Jewish, 4% South European, 1% Negro and mixed. MGI = maximum growth increase.

	Age yr	No. of Subjects	Weight kg	Height cm	No. of Subjects	Weight kg	Height cm	No. of Subjects	Weight kg	Height cm
	(A)	(B)	(C)	(D)	(E)	(F)	(G)	(H)	(I)	(J)
		Males								
		MGI at 12.5-13.5 yr			MGI at 14.0-15.5 yr			MGI at 16.0-17.0 yr		
1	7	77	24.0	120.7	317	22.9	118.9	98	21.6	117.4
2	8	97	27.1	126.6	387	25.5	124.6	127	23.9	122.7
3	9	109	30.1	132.1	429	28.2	130.0	135	26.3	127.9
4	10	112	33.3	137.3	452	31.0	135.1	139	28.8	132.8
5	11	112	37.1	142.6	453	34.1	139.9	141	31.3	137.3
6	12	112	42.5	149.4	454	37.6	144.8	141	34.0	141.7
7	13	112	50.4	159.8	454	41.6	150.1	141	36.8	146.0
8	14	112	57.2	166.8	454	48.3	158.3	141	39.9	150.3
9	15	111	61.8	170.0	449	55.8	166.4	141	45.0	156.4
10	16	102	64.4	171.2	426	60.7	170.5	141	52.5	165.0
11	17	76	66.1	171.9	336	63.5	172.3	114	58.3	170.5
12	18	32	67.3	172.3	144	65.5	173.0	44	62.1	173.0
		Females								
		MGI at 10.5-11.5 yr			MGI at 12.0-13.0 yr			MGI at 13.5-14.5 yr		
13	7	109	23.1	119.0	259	21.7	116.9	112	20.8	115.8
14	8	140	25.9	124.8	339	24.2	122.6	145	23.1	121.1
15	9	153	29.0	130.6	383	26.9	127.9	170	25.4	126.2
16	10	155	33.3	137.3	407	29.7	133.1	175	27.8	131.0
17	11	155	39.4	146.0	413	33.2	138.5	177	30.6	135.8
18	12	155	45.9	152.4	413	38.3	145.7	177	33.8	140.7
19	13	155	50.2	155.6	413	44.3	153.0	177	38.8	147.5
20	14	153	52.9	157.0	411	49.1	156.8	177	44.7	154.2
21	15	145	54.4	157.7	400	52.0	158.5	173	49.2	157.4
22	16	128	55.0	158.0	374	53.5	159.2	157	51.5	158.9
23	17	90	55.3	158.2	294	54.4	159.6	109	53.1	159.5
24	18	26	55.1	158.4	130	54.6	159.9	49	53.9	159.8

Contributor: Hathaway, Milicent L.

Reference: Shuttleworth, F. K. 1939. Monographs Soc. Research in Child Develop. 4(3).

Part III: RELATED TO AGE AT PUBESCENCE

Values are for subjects, weighed in the nude, from well-to-do professional classes, living in or near Chicago, Illinois.

	Age yr	No. of Subjects	Weight kg	Height cm	No. of Subjects	Weight kg	Height cm	No. of Subjects	Weight kg	Height cm
	(A)	(B)	(C)	(D)	(E)	(F)	(G)	(H)	(I)	(J)
		Males								
		Pubescence before 14 yr			Pubescence at 14-15 yr			Pubescence at 15 yr or later		
1	6	35	22.4	119.9	9	20.4	115.3	8	19.7	115.8
2	7	46	24.9	125.5	15	23.1	121.9	12	21.9	120.9
3	8	60	27.4	130.8	18	25.4	127.3	18	23.8	125.7
4	9	65	30.5	136.1	19	28.6	133.6	25	25.7	130.6
5	10	81	34.1	141.7	22	32.1	138.7	24	28.4	135.1
6	11	89	37.6	147.1	29	34.3	143.5	25	30.8	140.0
7	12	96	42.1	152.9	40	36.7	147.1	29	33.8	144.3
8	13	105	47.4	159.8	54	41.1	152.4	35	37.0	148.6
9	14	112	53.3	167.1	87	46.7	159.5	50	40.8	153.2

continued

75. BODY WEIGHT AND HEIGHT: MAN, NORTH AMERICAN

Part III: RELATED TO AGE AT PUBESCENCE

	Age yr	No. of Subjects	Weight kg	Height cm	No. of Subjects	Weight kg	Height cm	No. of Subjects	Weight kg	Height cm
	(A)	(B)	(C)	(D)	(E)	(F)	(G)	(H)	(I)	(J)
		Males								
		Pubescence before 14 yr			Pubescence at 14-15 yr			Pubescence at 15 yr or later		
10	15	90	58.9	173.5	86	53.1	167.1	70	46.7	160.5
11	16	79	63.0	176.3	73	58.4	173.0	79	52.4	167.1
12	17	42	65.8	176.5	53	61.9	176.3	55	57.3	171.7
13	18	9	66.5	176.5	20	63.9	177.8	20	61.0	179.1
		Females								
		Menarche before 13 yr			Menarche at 13-14 yr			Menarche at 14 yr or later		
14	6	19	22.5	119.4	7	20.0	112.8	5	19.6	113.0
15	7	33	24.6	123.4	12	23.7	122.4	13	21.4	117.9
16	8	44	27.4	129.5	15	25.6	126.5	13	24.0	124.2
17	9	58	31.2	135.4	19	29.2	131.3	18	25.8	128.0
18	10	62	35.9	141.7	21	32.1	137.4	19	28.3	133.8
19	11	75	40.7	148.3	27	36.6	143.0	25	31.4	137.9
20	12	85	46.3	155.4	37	41.5	151.1	36	35.1	144.3
21	13	93	51.8	160.0	53	47.1	156.7	48	39.4	151.6
22	14	115	54.8	162.1	91	50.8	160.8	70	44.6	157.2
23	15	108	56.4	162.8	105	53.5	162.6	84	49.4	161.8
24	16	98	57.4	163.6	96	54.4	163.3	74	52.1	163.3
25	17	61	47.7	163.3	74	54.5	162.6	58	52.9	163.3

Contributor: Hathaway, Milicent L.

Reference: Richey, H. G. 1937. Monographs Soc. Research in Child Develop. 2(1).

76. BODY WEIGHT AND HEIGHT FOR TWO SOCIO-ECONOMIC GROUPS: MAN, NORTH AMERICAN

Socio-economic classification was determined by the occupation of the principal wage earner supporting the child's family. Values are for white subjects wearing light underclothing. Values in parentheses are ranges, estimate "b" (cf. Introduction).

	Age yr	Professional or Skilled			Semiskilled or Unskilled		
		No. of Subjects	Weight kg	Height cm	No. of Subjects	Weight kg	Height cm
	(A)	(B)	(C)	(D)	(E)	(F)	(G)
		Males					
1	4.5	306	18.0(13.2-22.8)	106.2(95.6-116.8)	492	17.3(13.3-21.3)	104.3(93.7-114.9)
2	7.5	2466	24.4(17.8-31.0)	123.9(112.9-124.9)	2544	23.5(17.3-29.7)	122.6(111.2-134.0)
3	10.5	3230	32.9(22.1-43.7)	139.5(126.7-152.3)	3258	31.2(21.4-41.0)	137.6(125.0-150.2)
4	13.5	3430	44.3(27.9-60.7)	155.1(138.3-171.9)	2684	42.0(26.4-57.6)	152.9(136.7-169.1)
5	16.5	2534	61.3(43.7-78.9)	172.3(159.3-185.3)	1372	59.3(42.3-76.3)	170.9(156.7-185.1)
		Females					
6	4.5	388	17.5(12.9-22.1)	105.5(95.9-115.1)	587	16.8(12.6-21.0)	103.6(93.0-114.2)
7	7.5	2464	24.0(16.4-31.6)	122.9(111.5-134.3)	2838	23.0(16.0-30.0)	121.5(110.3-132.7)
8	10.5	2967	32.6(20.4-44.8)	138.9(125.7-152.1)	3179	31.3(20.1-42.5)	137.6(124.2-151.0)
9	13.5	2696	45.8(30.2-61.4)	155.6(143.4-168.8)	2361	44.0(28.6-59.4)	154.3(140.7-167.9)
10	16.5	2135	53.2(40.0-66.4)	161.2(149.6-172.4)	1106	52.7(38.9-66.5)	160.9(149.5-172.3)

Contributor: Garn, Stanley M.

Reference: O'Brien, R., M. A. Girshick, and E. P. Hunt. 1941. U. S. Dept. Agr. Misc. Publ. 366.

77. STATURE AT DIFFERENT HISTORICAL PERIODS: MAN, NORTH AMERICAN

Part I: BIRTH TO MATURITY: 1860-1900 AND 1930-1950

At each of the given ages, subjects for the two periods were white males from similar ethnic and socio-economic backgrounds.

	Age yr	1860-1900			1930-1950			Height Difference cm
		No. of Subjects	Height cm	Investigator (Year)	No. of Subjects	Height cm	Investigator (Year)	
	(A)	(B)	(C)	(D)	(E)	(F)	(G)	(H)
1	Birth	951	50.4	Stockton-Hough (1885), Holt (1897), Riggs (1904)	1352	50.7	Bakwin & Bakwin (1934), Meredith & Brown (1937)	0.3
2	1	ca. 70	73.8	Holt (1897)	114	77.1	Meredith (1940)	3.3
3	2	ca. 100	81.6	Peckham (1880), Holt (1897)	235	86.9	Rhoads et al. (1941), Peatman & Higgons (1938)	5.3
4	4	ca. 80	96.5	Bowditch (1880), Holt (1897)	198	103.4	Vickers & Stuart (1934), Meredith & Knott (1938)	6.9
5	7	171	114.3	Barnes (1892-93)	4529	122.4	Lloyd-Jones (1941)	8.1
6	10	2380	129.6	Peckham (1881), West (1894), Porter (1894)	192	139.2	Steggerda & Densen (1936)	9.6
7	14	533	151.8	Bowditch (1877), MacDonald (1897-98)	303	163.7	Simmons (1944), Stuart & Meredith (1946)	11.9
8	17	253	166.3	Bowditch (1877), Porter (1894)	3259	172.9	Lloyd-Jones (1941)	6.6
9	19[1]	5200	172.1	Hitchcock (1892), Seaver (1909)	3058	175.6	Chenoweth (1937), Mills & Chenoweth (1938)	3.5
10	25[2]	315,620	171.8	Gould (1869)	42,661	173.5	Randall (1948)	1.7

/1/ College freshmen. /2/ Army separatees.

Contributor: Meredith, Howard V.

References: [1] Meredith, H. V. 1941. Am. J. Phys. Anthropol. 28:1. [2] Meredith, H. V. 1943. Univ. Iowa Studies in Child Welfare 19:11. [3] Meredith, H. V. 1944. Human Biol. 16:126.

Part II: MILITARY MEN: 1861-1952

	Date	Type of Personnel	Age yr	No. of Subjects	Weight kg	Height cm	Investigator (Year)
	(A)	(B)	(C)	(D)	(E)	(F)	(G)
1	1861-63	U. S. volunteers	18-45	25,878	...	173.2	Elliott (1863)
2	1862-63	Army of the Potomac	24	1700	67.0	170.4	
3	1892-97	Army recruits (native white)	20-24	20,636	65.2	172.0	Sternberg (1893-98)
4			25-29	10,136	66.6	171.7	
5	1901-16	Army officers	21-45	8790	70.2	175.5	Reed (1932)
6	1917-18	Army recruits	21-30	872,931	64.3	171.5	Davenport (1921)
7	1919	Army separatees	21-30	83,573	65.9	172.0	
8	1940-45	Army inductees and separatees	18-19	6206	67.1	173.7	Randall (1949)
9			20-24	5985	70.2	174.0	
10			25-29	13,145	71.7	173.7	
11	1943-44	Selective Service registrants (white)	18-19	110,251	65.3	172.9	Karpinos (1958)
12			20-24	97,795	67.9	173.2	
13			25-29	69,905	70.4	172.9	
14		Selective Service registrants (Negro)	18-19	16,139	64.5	171.8	
15			20-24	21,131	67.2	172.5	
16			25-29	16,107	69.1	172.5	
17	1946	Army separatees	15-40	24,554	70.4	173.7	Newman (1951)
18	1952	Naval recruits	17-25	2173	69.3	174.2	Gibbons (1953)

Contributors: (a) Hathaway, Milicent L., (b) Karpinos, Bernard D.

References: [1] Hathaway, M. L., and E. D. Foard. 1960. U. S. Dept. Agr. Home Econ. Research Rept. 10. [2] Karpinos, B. D. 1958. Human Biol. 30:292.

78. BODY WEIGHT AND HEIGHT FOR DIFFERENT RACIAL STOCKS: MAN, NORTH AMERICAN

Part I: MALES

Data are for the years 1930-1940.

	Subject	Age yr	No. of Subjects	Weight kg	Height cm	Reference
	(A)	(B)	(C)	(D)	(E)	(F)
1	Dutch	7	220	22.9	123.3	3
2		11	189	33.8	144.3	
3		15	149	50.5	168.6	
4	Finnish	7	83	23.5	121.2	1
5		11	100	33.4	141.6	
6		15	100	52.1	164.4	
7	Italian	7	50	22.7	119.3	1
8		11	79	32.1	139.1	
9	Italian	15	93	50.9	161.4	1
10	Navaho Indian	7	101	21.6	120.8	3
11		11	153	30.3	138.9	
12		15	133	45.2	160.5	
13	Pueblo Indian	7	211	20.0	114.1	2
14		11	213	29.1	133.7	
15		15	54	43.0	153.5	

Contributor: Meredith, Howard V.

References: [1] Matheny, W. D., and H. V. Meredith. 1947. Am. J. Phys. Anthropol., n.s. 5:343. [2] Pitney, E. H. 1940. Ph. D. Thesis. Yale Univ., New Haven. [3] Steggerda, M., and P. Densen. 1936. Child Develop. 7:115.

Part II: FEMALES

Data are for the years 1920-1940.

	Subject	Age yr	Weight		Height		Reference
			No. of Subjects	kg	No. of Subjects	cm	
	(A)	(B)	(C)	(D)	(E)	(F)	(G)
1	White	6	3577	20.0	3577	113.9	4
2		8	5560	24.6	5560	125.0	
3		10	6213	30.2	6213	135.4	
4		12	5998	38.1	5998	147.1	
5		14	4382	46.5	4382	156.4	
6		16	3660	52.4	3660	160.8	
7	Negro	6	190	19.7	258	113.9	1-3
8		8	193	24.5	279	125.0	
9		10	201	30.7	334	135.4	
10		12	181	39.5	428	147.3	
11		14	207	48.6	702	156.1	
12		16	211	52.4	546	159.3	
13	Mexican	6	1043	19.0	1043	111.8	7
14		8	1412	23.1	1412	122.2	
15		10	1719	28.2	1719	132.2	
16	Mexican	12	1576	35.9	1576	143.7	7
17		14	1093	44.5	1093	152.0	
18		16	689	49.8	689	155.2	
19	Indian	6	204	18.6	203	111.2	5,9
20		8	298	22.1	298	121.0	
21		10	320	27.3	319	131.7	
22		12	275	34.4	277	142.6	
23		14	234	42.8	236	150.8	
24		16	129	48.4	129	154.0	
25	Japanese	6	139	18.6	139	109.3	2,6,8, 10
26		8	265	22.8	298	119.0	
27		10	275	27.8	295	129.6	
28		12	271	35.7	291	142.0	
29		14	252	43.3	252	150.6	
30		16	166	46.7	166	152.8	

Contributor: Meredith, Howard V.

References: [1] Herskovits, M. J. 1930. Columbia Univ. Contribs. Anthropol. 11:101. [2] Lloyd-Jones, O. 1941. Research Quart. 12:83. [3] Michelson, N. 1943. Am. J. Phys. Anthropol., n.s. 1:193. [4] O'Brien, R., M. A. Girshick, and E. P. Hunt. 1941. U. S. Dept. Agr. Misc. Publ. 366:65. [5] Pitney, E. H. 1940. Ph. D. Thesis. Yale Univ., New Haven. [6] Preston, M. I. 1936. Am. J. Diseases Children 51:1324. [7] Priani, A., et al. 1952. In H. V. Meredith and M. S. Goldstein. Child Develop. 23:91. [8] Spier, L. 1929. Univ. Wash. Publs. Anthropol. 3:1. [9] Steggerda, M., and P. Densen. 1936. Child Develop. 7:115. [10] Suski, P. M. 1933. Biometrika 25:323.

79. BODY WEIGHT AND HEIGHT FOR VARIOUS NATIONALITIES: MAN

	Subject	Date	Age yr	Males		Females		Reference
				Wt kg	Ht cm	Wt kg	Ht cm	
	(A)	(B)	(C)	(D)	(E)	(F)	(G)	(H)
1	African Pygmy	1935	Birth	3.6	45.9	3.9	47.0	3
2			1	....	71.0	7.0	65.0	
3			5	13.5	100.4	13.5	98.1	
4			7	17.6	103.9	....	102.8	
5			9	....	113.3	....	113.0	
6			11	23.0	.....	18.5	.....	
7	Argentine	1931	9	28.1	123	27.6	122	3
8			11	33.1	136	33.9	132	
9			13	40.6	147	41.9	145	
10			15	44.9	153	46.6	153	
11	Austrian	1932	1	10.3	76	9.8	75	3
12			3	14.5	95	14.0	94	
13			5	18.5	108	18.0	107	
14			7	22.5	119	22.0	118	
15			9	26.7	128	26.0	127	
16			11	31.8	137	31.5	138	
17			13	38.5	148	38.5	149	
18			15	48.0	.....	47.5	....	
19	Briton	1935	Birth	3.4	51.2	3.3	50.8	3
20			1	9.3	70.8	8.8	69.8	
21			3	13.7	96.3	13.2	96.0	
22		1926	5	15.5	108.2[1]	15.9	107.9[1]	3
23			7	19.8	118.1[1]	19.3	117.9[1]	
24			9	23.4	128.0[1]	22.0	127.8[1]	
25			11	26.8	136.7[1]	27.2	137.9[1]	
26			13	32.9	148.1[1]	32.4	149.6[1]	
27		1943	14	42.7	155.2	45.5	154.4	2
28			15	45.9	158.5	47.7	156.0	
29			16	50.9	163.8	50.0	157.5	
30			17	54.5	167.4	51.4	157.7	
31			18	56.4	168.4	51.8	158.0	
32			20	59.5	169.9	52.7	158.2	
33			22	61.8	170.9	53.2	158.5	
34	Canadian	1953	2	13.6	88.1	12.7	85.3	4
35			3	14.5	93.0	14.0	91.4	
36			4	16.8	99.6	16.3	99.6	
37			5	18.1	106.4	18.6	106.2	
38			6	20.8	113.3	19.9	112.3	
39			7	22.7	119.4	22.2	118.1	
40			8	25.8	124.7	25.8	124.2	
41			9	28.5	130.8	28.1	129.5	
42			10	31.7	135.9	31.3	135.4	
43			11	34.9	140.7	34.9	140.5	
44			12	38.1	145.8	41.7	147.8	
45			13	42.6	150.6	46.2	153.4	
46			14	48.9	158.0	48.5	155.7	
47			15	53.9	164.3	50.7	158.0	
48			16-17	61.6	169.4	54.4	158.7	
49			18-19	65.2	172.7	56.2	159.0	
50			20-24	69.8	172.5	56.2	159.5	
51	Chinese	1935	Birth	3.1	48.2	3.0	48.2	3
52			1	....	73.5	....	71.4	
53			3	....	92.0	....	89.7	
54		1927	5	14.9	104.4	14.0	108.0	
55			7	18.4	114.6	20.1	117.2	
56			9	22.2	123.7	23.4	126.6	
57			11	26.5	131.3	28.7	135.4	
58			13	32.3	141.1	37.0	145.7	
59			15	41.7	152.7	45.0	150.0	
60			17	48.3	162.4	47.5	154.3	
61			19	52.6	165.0	44.4	152.0	
62			21	53.8	166.0	49.0	156.0	
63	Czecho-slovakian	1931	3	....	89.7	....	87.7	3
64			5	17.1	103.5	16.8	102.7	
65		1934	7	21.7	115.6	21.3	115.0	
66			9	26.0	125.9	25.8	124.9	
67			11	30.2	133.4	30.2	133.4	
68			13	35.5	142.9	38.0	144.7	
69		1929	15	52.1	156.0[1]	....	.....	
70			17	61.3	159.0[1]	....	.....	
71	Dane	1930	Birth	3.4	.....	3.3	.....	3
72			7	21.8	118.5	21.5	117.9	
73			9	26.2	127.9	26.2	127.5	
74			11	31.8	137.5	32.3	137.5	
75			13	38.1	146.5	40.8	148.6	
76			15	49.2	160.1	49.6	158.0	
77	Frenchman	1935	Birth	3.1	49.9	3.1	49.2	3
78			5	18.4	107.9	17.8	106.9	
79			7	22.2	117.7	21.2	116.4	
80			9	27.0	127.9	26.8	127.7	
81			11	32.6	137.8	33.9	138.6	
82	German	1928	Birth	3.5	51.0	3.3	50.5	3
83			1	9.7	75.0	9.5	74.5	
84			3	14.1	93.0	13.7	92.5	
85			5	18.6	107.0	17.8	106.5	
86			7	22.2	119.5	21.6	118.5	
87			9	26.7	129.0	25.9	128.5	
88			11	31.5	137.5	31.4	139.0	
89			13	37.5	147.0	40.2	151.0	
90			15	48.1	160.5	49.5	160.0	
91			17	59.8	170.5	56.3	164.0	
92			19	64.5	174.0	59.0	165.0	
93	Japanese	1949	Birth	3.1	50.2	3.0	49.3	7
94		1960	1	10.3	77.9	9.6	76.0	1
95			2	12.2	85.7	11.5	84.3	
96			3	14.0	93.4	13.6	92.6	
97			4	15.5	99.6	15.0	98.5	
98			5	17.1	104.7	16.5	104.0	
99			6	19.0	110.8	18.4	109.7	
100			7	21.0	116.7	20.6	115.5	
101			8	22.9	121.5	22.6	120.6	
102			9	25.6	126.6	25.1	126.0	
103			10	27.6	130.8	28.1	131.7	
104			11	30.5	135.9	32.1	138.0	
105			12	34.2	141.0	36.5	143.7	
106			13	39.1	147.6	40.7	147.9	
107			14	43.9	153.6	44.4	149.4	
108			15	49.4	158.7	47.9	151.5	
109			16	52.8	159.9	48.6	152.1	
110			17	54.9	163.2	50.1	151.8	
111			18	56.0	162.9	49.8	152.4	
112			19	55.4	163.2	50.6	152.7	
113	Roumanian	1937	5	17.5	104.5	17.0	103.7	3
114			7	21.2	115.8	20.6	115.4	
115			9	24.6	123.0	23.8	122.8	
116			11	28.7	131.2	28.7	131.6	
117			13	33.8	139.1	34.7	140.2	
118			15	39.8	146.8	41.8	148.1	
119	Russian	1935	Birth	3.4	48.6	3.3	48.6	3
120		1931	9	....	125.3	....	124.5	
121	Spaniard	1934	7	21.6	117.0	21.5	116.0	3
122			9	24.7	123.0	26.0	124.6	
123			11	29.0	132.7	31.5	134.0	
124			13	35.7	139.6	38.0	143.7	

/1/ Date of measurement, 1933.

continued

79. BODY WEIGHT AND HEIGHT FOR VARIOUS NATIONALITIES: MAN

	Subject	Date	Age yr	Males Wt kg	Males Ht cm	Females Wt kg	Females Ht cm	Reference
	(A)	(B)	(C)	(D)	(E)	(F)	(G)	(H)
125	Swiss	1935	Birth	3.3	......	3.1	......	3
126		1933	7	22	118	19	110	
127			9	26	126	23	118	
128			11	30	136	30.5	136	
129			13	36	146	40	147	
130			15	47	157	44.5	152	
	U. S.							
131	Navaho	1936	6	20.2	116.1	19.0	113.4	3
132	Indian		7	21.7	120.8	21.2	119.0	
133			8	24.0	125.7	23.1	123.9	
134			9	26.2	131.1	25.6	129.9	
135			10	28.4	135.3	28.3	134.9	
136			11	30.4	138.9	31.2	140.2	
137			12	32.8	143.0	34.6	143.9	
138			13	36.6	149.2	39.0	150.2	
139			14	41.2	153.8	43.6	153.1	
140			15	45.3	160.5	47.7	155.3	
141			16	50.0	165.5	51.1	156.3	
142			17	54.0	167.5	52.3	157.4	
143			18	56.3	169.5	54.0	157.5	
144	Negro	1961	Birth	3.2	49.6	3.3	49.6	5
145			1	10.4	76.1	9.9	74.9	
146		1925	2	....	89.1	....	85.9	3
147			3	....	95.2	....	95.8	
148			4	....	102.0	....	100.6	
149			5	....	110.0	....	109.9	
150			6	....	116.2	....	116.2	
151			7	....	120.3	....	120.8	
152			8	....	125.8	....	124.6	
153			9	....	130.8	....	131.3	
154			10	....	135.3	....	135.2	
	U. S.							
155	Negro	1925	11	....	140.9	....	141.2	3
156			12	37.0	144.8	40.0	149.0	
157			13	43.9	150.1	43.9	153.7	
158			14	48.0	156.5	47.7	154.7	
159			15	53.0	161.0	53.0	158.1	
160			16	57.0	163.6	57.0	157.8	
161			17	....	167.0	....	158.5	
162			18	....	170.1	....	159.2	
163			19	....	172.0	....	159.9	
164	White	1934-59	Birth	3.5	50.8	3.4	50.0	6
165			1	10.5	75.4	9.5	74.4	
166			2	12.7	87.6	12.3	86.6	
167			3	14.5	96.0	14.1	95.3	
168			4	16.8	103.6	16.4	103.1	
169			5	19.1	111.0	18.6	111.3	
170			6	21.4	117.1	20.5	116.1	
171			7	24.5	122.4	22.7	121.7	
172			8	27.3	128.0	26.4	127.8	
173			9	30.0	134.1	29.1	132.3	
174			10	33.2	138.4	32.7	138.7	
175			11	37.3	144.3	37.3	145.0	
176			12	39.5	148.1	42.3	151.4	
177			13	45.0	154.2	46.4	156.0	
178			14	51.4	161.5	50.9	159.5	
179			15	58.2	168.4	53.2	161.0	
180			16	62.3	172.0	54.5	162.3	
181			17	65.0	173.5	55.5	162.8	
182			18	67.7	174.0	55.9	162.8	
183			19	69.5	174.2	56.4	162.8	
184			20-24	71.8	174.5	56.8	162.6	

Contributors: (a) Krogman, W. M., (b) Arimoto, Kunitaro, (c) Pett, L. Bradley, (d) Scott, Roland B., (e) Damon, Albert

References: [1] Arimoto, K. Unpublished. Natl. Institute of Nutrition, Tokyo, 1960. [2] Kemsley, W. F. F. 1950. Ann. Eugenics 15:161. [3] Krogman, W. M. 1941. Tabulae Biologicae 20. [4] Pett, L. B. 1954. Survey, 1953. Nutrition Div., Dept. of Natl. Health and Welfare, Ottawa, Canada. [5] Scott, R. B., et al. Unpublished. Freedmen's Hosp., Washington, D. C. 1962. [6] Stoudt, H. W., A. Damon, and R. A. McFarland. 1960. Human Biol. 32:331. [7] Yanagi, K., et al. 1949. Studies on dietary allowances for Japanese. Natl. Council of Food and Nutrition, Tokyo. p. 1.

80. ADULT BODY WEIGHT, HEIGHT, AND SURFACE AREA FOR VARIOUS NATIONALITIES AND SUBGROUPS: MAN

Unless otherwise indicated, body surface area was calculated from the formula 71.84 x weight$^{0.425}$ x height$^{0.725}$. Values in parentheses are ranges, estimate "b" (cf. Introduction).

	Subject	Sex	Weight kg	Height cm	Surface Area sq m	Reference
	(A)	(B)	(C)	(D)	(E)	(F)
1	Aeta (Bataan)	♂	41(31-52)	148(137-158)	1.29(1.09-1.49)	18
2		♀	37(29-44)	138(130-146)	1.17(1.05-1.29)	18
3	Aeta (Zambales)	♂	41(32-50)	148(139-157)	1.28(1.14-1.42)	18
4		♀	34(26-43)	139(129-148)	1.14(0.98-1.30)	18
5	Akka (Congo)	♂	40(31-49)	144(134-154)	1.26(1.08-1.44)	8
6		♀	37(27-47)	137(132-141)	1.17(1.01-1.33)	8
7	Albanian (southern Italy)	♂	61(49-73)	164(152-175)	1.65(1.47-1.83)	19,20

continued

80. ADULT BODY WEIGHT, HEIGHT, AND SURFACE AREA FOR VARIOUS NATIONALITIES AND SUBGROUPS: MAN

	Subject	Sex	Weight kg	Height cm	Surface Area sq m	Reference
	(A)	(B)	(C)	(D)	(E)	(F)
8	American, white	♂	70(54-86)	177(163-191)	1.85(1.61-2.09)	25
9		♀	56(40-72)	163(153-173)	1.57(1.33-1.81)[1]	1
10	Andamanese (Indian Ocean)	♂	45(36-54)	148(135-161)	1.35(1.17-1.53)	19,20,22
11		♀	43(30-55)	138(130-146)	1.24(1.08-1.40)	19,20,22
12	Antumba (Mozambique)	♂	55(41-70)	165(153-177)	1.57(1.35-1.79)	5
13	Arab (Yemen)	♂	59(48-70)	163(150-175)	1.57(1.41-1.73)	19,20,22
14	Asheraf (Somaliland)	♂	60(48-73)	171(159-183)	1.69(1.49-1.89)	30
15	Australian aborigine	♂	59(40-78)	169(160-179)	1.64(1.38-1.90)	29
16	Babinga (Bangui, Africa)	♂	48(38-57)	155(143-168)	1.41(1.26-1.56)	15
17		♀	42(36-49)	144(137-153)	1.28(1.20-1.40)	15
18	Baga (French West Africa)	♂	64(51-77)	169(157-181)	1.71(1.49-1.93)	15
19	Bambara (French West Africa)	♂	66(53-78)	170(158-183)	1.74(1.52-1.96)	15
20	Baoubé (French West Africa)	♂	62(50-73)	167(156-178)	1.67(1.47-1.87)	15
21	Bassari (French West Africa)	♂	59(48-70)	166(157-176)	1.64(1.46-1.82)	15
22	Basua (Congo)	...	40(30-50)	144(133-155)	1.27(1.07-1.47)	8
23	Berber (Giado)	♂	59(48-70)	170(160-180)	1.66(1.48-1.84)	19,20
24	Bété (French West Africa)	♂	63(54-73)	167(155-179)	1.69(1.51-1.87)	15
25	Bobo-Fing (French West Africa)	♂	67(59-74)	172(164-181)	1.77(1.63-1.91)	15
26	Bobo-Oulé (French West Africa)	♂	67(55-80)	172(160-183)	1.76(1.54-1.98)	15
27	Boussanga (French West Africa)	♂	62(51-73)	169(157-182)	1.69(1.49-1.89)	15
28	Bozo (French West Africa)	♂	65(55-74)	174(162-186)	1.75(1.57-1.93)	15
29	Brahman (southern India)	♂	51(38-82)	163(157-169)	1.52(1.32-1.72)	14
30	Chinese (Canton)	♀	54(36-72)	148(138-159)	1.43(1.19-1.67)	9
31	Daouad (Fezzan)	♂	54(41-68)	166(153-180)	1.58(1.36-1.80)	19,20
32	Darod (Somaliland)	♂	59(46-72)	172(159-185)	1.69(1.47-1.91)	19,20
33	Dir (Somaliland)	♂	57(48-67)	173(163-183)	1.67(1.49-1.85)	19,20
34	Dogon (French West Africa)	♂	67(56-78)	172(160-183)	1.77(1.57-1.97)	15
35		♀	62(50-74)	170(157-183)	1.74(1.56-1.92)	15
36	Efe (Congo)	♀	37(29-45)	138(129-146)	1.18(1.04-1.32)	8
37	English convict	♂	65(49-81)	167(153-181)	1.70(1.44-1.96)	19,20
38	English student (London)	♂	69(56-82)	179(170-188)	1.85(1.67-2.03)	26
39	Eskimo (Angmassalik)	♂	64(54-74)	164(156-172)	1.68(1.52-1.84)	6
40		♀	58(48-67)	156(148-165)	1.55(1.39-1.71)	6
41	Eskimo (Canada)	♂	66(49-83)	163(152-174)	1.68(1.44-1.92)	2
42		♀	56(46-66)	152(141-163)	1.49(1.33-1.65)	2
43	Finn (northern Finland)	♂	67(55-79)	169(157-180)	1.75(1.57-1.93)	16
44	Fon (French West Africa)	♂	65(56-75)	170(161-179)	1.73(1.59-1.89)	15
45	Foula (French West Africa)	♂	60(49-71)	169(158-181)	1.66(1.48-1.84)	15
46	French soldier	♂	66(51-80)	166(154-179)	1.71(1.49-1.93)	19,20
47	French worker	♂	66(53-79)	168(157-180)	1.73(1.53-1.93)	19,20
48		♀	56(41-71)	158(149-168)	1.54(1.34-1.74)	19,20
49	German soldier	♂	71(51-91)	171(154-189)	1.82(1.50-2.14)	11
50	Gobaween (Somaliland)	♂	57(43-72)	168(154-183)	1.63(1.39-1.87)	19,20
51		♀	59(51-68)	157(148-166)	1.57(1.41-1.73)	19,20
52	Gouro (French West Africa)	♂	62(50-75)	166(157-175)	1.71(1.51-1.91)	15
53	Gourounsi (French West Africa)	♂	66(54-78)	172(160-184)	1.76(1.56-1.96)	15
54	Guéré (French West Africa)	♂	63(51-74)	166(155-178)	1.68(1.48-1.88)	15
55	Guerzé (French West Africa)	♂	65(51-79)	169(159-178)	1.72(1.52-1.92)	15
56	Haouiya (Somaliland)	♂	57(46-68)	170(158-182)	1.63(1.45-1.81)	19,20
57	Harijan (southern India)	♂	48(33-63)	162(150-174)	1.47(1.25-1.69)	14
58	Indochinese (Cambodia)	♀	53(37-69)	149(134-159)	1.44(1.20-1.68)	9
59	Indochinese (Hué)	♀	43(31-54)	146(136-156)	1.28(1.10-1.46)	9
60	Indochinese (Tonkin)	♂	57(49-66)	160(150-170)	1.55(1.35-1.75)	19,20
61	Irish (northern Ireland)	♂	68(51-85)	172(159-185)	1.77(1.53-2.01)	12,13
62	Italian	♂	63(44-82)	168(155-181)	1.81(1.49-2.13)[1]	4
63		♀	53(39-67)	159(148-169)	1.51(1.29-1.73)	4
64	Italian soldier (Sicily)	♂	65(54-75)	169(164-174)	1.72(1.60-1.84)	19,20
65	Japanese	♂	53(37-68)	159(149-169)	1.55(1.31-1.79)[2]	24
66	Kassena (French West Africa)	♂	62(50-73)	169(158-181)	1.69(1.49-1.89)	15
67	Kissi (French West Africa)	♂	63(49-76)	165(153-177)	1.67(1.45-1.89)	15
68	Korana (South Africa)	♂	50(39-61)	160(152-168)	1.48(1.32-1.64)	7
69	Kung bushman (Kalahari)	♂	40(31-50)	157(143-170)	1.33(1.13-1.53)	23
70	Lapp (northern Finland)	♂	63(52-74)	164(154-174)	1.69(1.53-1.85)	16

/1/ Measured by surface integrator. /2/ Measured by coating method.

continued

80. ADULT BODY WEIGHT, HEIGHT, AND SURFACE AREA FOR VARIOUS NATIONALITIES AND SUBGROUPS: MAN

	Subject	Sex	Weight kg	Height cm	Surface Area sq m	Reference
	(A)	(B)	(C)	(D)	(E)	(F)
71	Lebou (French West Africa)	♂	62(54-70)	171(159-183)	1.71(1.53-1.89)	15
72	Macouah (southern India)	♂	52(43-61)	162(152-174)	1.53(1.37-1.69)	14
73	Malinké (French West Africa)	♂	64(52-76)	169(157-181)	1.72(1.54-1.90)	15
74	Mapuches (Andes)	♂	67(51-84)	164(154-173)	1.71(1.49-1.93)	17
75	Marka civilian (French West Africa)	♂	61(47-74)	171(156-186)	1.69(1.47-1.91)	15
76	Marka soldier (French West Africa)	♂	66(55-78)	171(161-182)	1.76(1.58-1.94)	15
77	Maya Quiche (Guatemala)	♂	58(48-67)	158(148-168)	1.56(1.40-1.72)	3
78	Minianka (French West Africa)	♂	66(55-77)	171(160-181)	1.75(1.57-1.93)	15
79	Moroccan	♂	64(50-78)	169(156-182)	1.71(1.47-1.95)	28
80	Mossi (French West Africa)	♂	67(56-78)	173(162-183)	1.77(1.59-1.95)	15
81	Muslim (southern India)	♂	55(37-73)	163(149-177)	1.57(1.31-1.83)	14
82	Nhungüè (Mozambique)	♂	60(47-73)	168(157-179)	1.64(1.44-1.84)	5
83		♀	55(42-69)	157(146-168)	1.56(1.36-1.76)	5
84	Nigerian	♂	57(42-72)	167(148-186)	1.61(1.33-1.89)	10
85	Nyaturu (Tanganyika)	♂	52(41-63)	165(154-177)	1.54(1.34-1.74)	27
86	Ouobé soldier (French West Africa)	♂	64(52-76)	167(156-178)	1.70(1.50-1.90)	15
87	Otomi Indian (Mexico)	♂	53(42-64)	158(148-167)	1.52(1.34-1.70)	19-21
88	Rahanwein (Somaliland)	♂	58(45-70)	169(156-183)	1.64(1.44-1.84)	19,20
89		♀	61(49-72)	157(146-168)	1.59(1.41-1.77)	19,20
90	Russian (northern)	♀	58(44-72)	158(147-168)	1.56(1.34-1.78)	9
91	Russian (southern)	♀	55(36-75)	157(145-168)	1.52(1.24-1.80)	9
92	Samogo (French West Africa)	♂	67(55-79)	171(161-182)	1.76(1.58-1.94)	15
93	Sandawe (Tanganyika)	♂	49(40-59)	165(153-176)	1.50(1.32-1.68)	27
94	Semang (Malaya)	♂	41(29-54)	164(140-167)	1.32(1.10-1.54)	18
95		♀	33(24-42)	144(133-155)	1.14(0.96-1.32)	18
96	Sénoufo (French West Africa)	♂	65(51-79)	170(161-180)	1.73(1.53-1.93)	15
97	Shanar (southern India)	♂	47(36-57)	160(146-174)	1.46(1.26-1.66)	14
98	Somba (French West Africa)	♂	72(61-84)	171(161-181)	1.81(1.63-1.99)	15
99	Soussou (French West Africa)	♂	60(50-71)	168(157-179)	1.66(1.48-1.84)	15
100	Toma (French West Africa)	♂	64(50-77)	166(155-177)	1.69(1.47-1.91)	15
101	Tunisian	♂	62(53-71)	173(163-184)	1.70(1.54-1.86)	28
102	Vania (southern India)	♂	49(38-60)	163(153-173)	1.51(1.31-1.71)	14
103	Vellaya (southern India)	♂	56(32-80)	165(152-178)	1.59(1.23-1.95)	14
104	Wolof (French West Africa)	♂	63(51-75)	172(160-183)	1.72(1.52-1.92)	15
105	Yakoba (French West Africa)	♂	63(51-75)	165(155-175)	1.67(1.49-1.85)	15

Contributor: Schreider, Eugène

References: [1] Bradfield, H. S. 1927. Univ. Mississippi Agr. Expt. Sta. Research Bull. 109. [2] Crile, G. W., and D. P. Quiring. 1939. J. Nutrit. 18:361. [3] Crile, G. W., and D. P. Quiring. 1939. Ibid. 18:369. [4] Curci, C. 1940. Endocrinol. patol. costituz. 15:30. [5] Dos Santos, Jr. 1944. Contribução para o estudo da antropologia de Moçambique. Porto. [6] Gessain, R. Unpublished, 1958. [7] Grobbelaar, C. S. 1956. S. African J. Sci. 53(suppl):97. [8] Gusinde, M. Individual measurements. Microfilm. 1958. [9] Laboratoire d'Anthropologie Physique, Paris. Unpublished, 1958. [10] Ladell, W. S. 1949. Interim Rept. Oshodi (Nigeria), Appendix E. [11] Ling, W. S. M., and H. Spring. 1948. Am. J. Med. Sci. 215:555. [12] Mogey, J. M. 1942. Ulster J. Archeol. 6:126. [13] Mogey, J. M. 1942. Ibid. 9:118. [14] Olivier, G. 1961. Anthropologie des Tamouls du Sud de l'Indè. Ecole Française d'Extrème Orient, Paris. [15] Pales, L. Unpublished, 1958. [16] Pelosse. Unpublished, 1962. [17] Pi-Suñer, J. 1933. Am. J. Physiol. 105:384. [18] Schebesta, P. 1952. Die Negrito Asiens. Vienna. v. 1. [19] Schreider, E. 1950. Anthropologie (Paris) 54:68. [20] Schreider, E. 1951. Rev. sci. 89:110. [21] Schreider, E. 1955. Anthropologie (Paris) 59:254. [22] Schreider, E. 1957. Biotypologie (Paris) 18:168. [23] Seiner, F. 1912. Z. Ethnol. 44:275. [24] Takeya, K., and H. Takahira. 1935. In E. Boyd, ed. The growth of the surface area of the human body. Univ. Minnesota Press, Minneapolis. pp. 70-71. [25] Tanner, J. M. 1949. J. Clin. Invest. 28:572. [26] Tanner, J. M. 1951. J. Physiol. (London) 115:371. [27] Trevor, J. C. Unpublished, 1958. [28] Vallois, H. V. Unpublished, 1958. [29] Wardlaw, H. S., and W. J. Lawrence. 1932. Australian J. Exptl. Biol. Med. Sci. 10:157. [30] Zonchello, S. A. Unpublished, 1958.

81. PRENATAL AND POSTNATAL ORGAN WEIGHT INCREASE: MAN

Values are multiples and were obtained by dividing the weight at the end of a specified time period by the weight at the beginning of that period (e.g., the adrenal cortex was 25 times heavier at 12 weeks than it was at 8 weeks).

	Organ	Weight Increase: Prenatal 8th to 12th wk	Prenatal 12th to 16th wk	Prenatal 20th to 24th wk	Birth to Maturity	Reference
	(A)	(B)	(C)	(D)	(E)	(F)
1	Adrenal cortex	25	5	1.7	......	2, 6
2	Brain	15	4.5	1.7	3.7	1-3
3	Heart	6.5	4.3	1.9	15	1-3
4	Kidney	75	6.7	1.6	10	1-3
5	Liver	17	3.6	1.8	18	1-3
6	Muscle, striped	...	...	...	30-40	2
7	Ovary	...	...	...	37	6
8	Pancreas	16[1]	16[1]	1.6	20-40	2, 5
9	Hypophysis	2.5	3	1.7	3-6	4, 5
10	Thymus	400	3.7	1.9	......	2, 3
11	Thyroid	...	6.6	2.2	14	3, 4
12	Uterus	...	...	...	27	2, 3

/1/ Average.

Contributor: O'Connor, R. J.

References: [1] Coppoletta, J. M., and S. B. Wolbach. 1933. Am. J. Pathol. 9:55. [2] Jackson, C. M. 1909. Am. J. Anat. 9:119. [3] Johnston, T. B., and J. Whillis, ed. 1942. Gray's Anatomy. Ed. 28. Longmans, Green; London. [4] Lucien, M., and A. George. 1927. Compt. rend. assoc. anat. 22me réunion, p. 176. [5] Maximow, A. A., and W. Bloom. 1944. A textbook of histology. W. B. Saunders, New York. [6] Wehefritz, E. 1923. Z. Konstitutionslehre 9:2.

82. ORGAN WEIGHTS FROM BIRTH TO MATURITY: MAN, NORTH AMERICAN

No. = number of specimens.

Part I: BRAIN AND LUNGS

	Age	Males Brain No.	Males Brain Wt g	Males Lungs No.	Males Lungs Wt g	Females Brain No.	Females Brain Wt g	Females Lungs No.	Females Lungs Wt g
	(A)	(B)	(C)	(D)	(E)	(F)	(G)	(H)	(I)
1	Newborn	137	353	92	51.7	122	347	71	50.9
2	0-3 mo	272	435	46	68.8	237	411	47	63.6
3	3-6 mo	149	600	53	94.1	150	534	52	93.3
4	6-9 mo	...	....	72	128.5	...	...	55	114.7
5	6-12 mo	174	877	...	.....	167	726	...	.....
6	9-12 mo	...	....	49	142.4	...	...	63	142.1
7	1-2 yr	167	971	78	170.3	143	894	84	175.3
8	2-3 yr	90	1076	76	245.9	86	1012	62	244.3
9	3-4 yr	64	1179	51	304.7	58	1076	34	265.5
10	4-5 yr	56	1290	32	314.2	44	1156	21	311.7
11	5-6 yr	49	1275	18	260.6	33	1206	27	319.9
12	6-7 yr	26	1313	8	399.5	31	1225	17	357.5
13	7-8 yr	28	1338	15	365.4	24	1265	10	404.4
14	8-9 yr	26	1294	5	405.0	23	1208	7	382.1
15	9-10 yr	15	1360	5	376.4	8	1226	5	358.4
16	10-11 yr	23	1378	15	474.5	10	1247	4	571.2
17	11-12 yr	22	1348	8	465.6	8	1259	4	535.0
18	12-13 yr	18	1383	4	458.8	13	1256	3	681.7
19	13-14 yr	16	1382	6	504.5	16	1243	4	602.3
20	14-15 yr	28	1356	12	692.8	16	1318	6	517.0
21	15-16 yr	18	1407	12	691.7	15	1271	13	708.8
22	16-17 yr	10	1419	9	747.3	19	1300	6	626.5
23	17-18 yr	18	1409	12	776.9	23	1254	13	694.5
24	18-19 yr	18	1426	20	874.7	16	1312	15	654.9
25	19-20 yr	22	1430	19	1035.6	16	1294	12	785.2
26	20-21 yr	...	....	13	953.0	...	....	28	792.8

Contributor: Boyd, Edith

Reference: Boyd, E. 1952. An introduction to human biology and anatomy for first year medical students. Child Research Council, Denver.

continued

82. ORGAN WEIGHTS FROM BIRTH TO MATURITY: MAN, NORTH AMERICAN

Part II: HEART, KIDNEYS, LIVER, AND SPLEEN

	Age yr	Males								Females							
		Heart		Kidneys		Liver		Spleen		Heart		Kidneys		Liver		Spleen	
		No.	Wt g	No.	Wt g	No.	Wt g	No.	Wt g	No.	Wt g	No.	Wt g	No.	Wt g	No.	Wt g
	(A)	(B)	(C)	(D)	(E)	(F)	(G)	(H)	(I)	(J)	(K)	(L)	(M)	(N)	(O)	(P)	(Q)
1	Birth	58	19	55	24	63	124	58	8	31	20	28	24	36	125	33	6
2	0.5-0.9	37	41	41	60	37	300	36	26	5	36	5	52	5	240	5	25
3	1-1.9	31	54	31	72	34	400	33	35	15	48	13	65	14	390	15	34
4	2-2.9	24	63	24	85	24	460	24	42	8	62	10	75	11	450	9	41
5	3-3.9	26	73	25	93	27	510	24	48	12	71	13	84	12	500	12	47
6	4-4.9	27	83	27	100	26	555	27	53	11	80	10	93	13	550	12	52
7	5-5.9	27	95	28	106	27	595	29	58	8	90	10	102	9	590	10	57
8	6-6.9	20	103	18	112	20	630	18	62	8	100	7	112	8	635	8	62
9	7-7.9	16	110	13	120	16	665	17	64	5	113	6	123	6	685	5	67
10	8-8.9	13	122	13	128	13	715	11	68	8	126	7	135	9	745	8	71
11	9-9.9	14	132	14	138	16	770	14	73	5	140	5	148	5	810	5	77
12	10-10.9	9	144	9	150	8	850	8	82	6	154	5	163	5	880	5	85
13	11-11.9	4	157	3	164	4	950	4	91	8	168	8	180	8	960	7	93
14	12-12.9	12	180	12	178	14	1050	14	101	9	188	9	195	8	1080	6	103
15	13-13.9	8	202	7	196	8	1150	8	111	2	207	2	210	3	1180	3	112
16	14-14.9	8	238	7	212	8	1240	8	121	4	226	3	222	4	1270	3	120
17	15-15.9	11	258	9	229	12	1315	11	135	9	238	7	230	7	1330	6	127
18	16-16.9	6	282	7	244	7	1380	7	145	9	243	6	236	7	1360	5	134
19	17-17.9	18	300	17	260	19	1450	19	152	8	247	8	240	7	1380	8	140
20	18-18.9	13	310	14	270	14	1510	14	157	9	250	10	244	9	1395	9	146
21	19-19.9	24	318	23	282	24	1580	24	160	11	251	11	247	9	1405	10	151
22	20-20.9	29	322	28	290	9	1630	29	162	7	252	8	248	7	1415	7	155

Contributor: Boyd, Edith

Reference: Boyd, E. 1952. An introduction to human biology and anatomy for first year medical students. Child Research Council, Denver.

Part III: MALE REPRODUCTIVE ORGANS

	Age yr	Testes		Testes and Epididym-ides		Seminal Vesicles		Prostate Gland	
		No.	Wt g	No.	Wt g	No.	Wt g	No.	Wt g
	(A)	(B)	(C)	(D)	(E)	(F)	(G)	(H)	(I)
1	Birth	91	0.85	25	0.91	2	0.050	7	0.82
2	0-1	31	1.03	66	1.33	21	0.052	8	0.9
3	1-3	8	1.48	13	1.82	...	.....	3	1.2
4	3-5	9	1.64	11	1.76	...	.....	8	1.1
5	5-10	18	1.67	20	2.24	11	0.099	6	1.3
6	10-12	8	2.00	10	4.00	3	0.120	4	1.9
7	12-14	14	6.96	6	8.15	...	.....	6	3.3
8	14-16	5	15.56	7	19.3	5	0.900	10	4.3
9	16-18	...	.....	7	32.0	...	.....	10	8.8
10	20-30	528	34.66	...	.....	...	.....	18	16.6

Part IV: FEMALE REPRODUCTIVE ORGANS

	Age yr	Ovaries		Uterine Tubes		Uterus	
		No.	Wt g	No.	Wt g	No.	Wt g
	(A)	(B)	(C)	(D)	(E)	(F)	(G)
1	Birth	58	0.33	2	0.29	24	3.90
2	0-1	25	0.62	4	0.26	55	1.42
3	1-2	6	0.84	2	0.29	31	1.50
4	2-4	13	1.12	...	....	25	2.30
5	4-7	9	1.90	...	....	22	2.80
6	7-14	9	3.30	5	0.49	32	4.30
7	14-20	7	6.03	1	1.05	14	32.50
8	20-30	34	10.71	4	2.13	48	49.50

Contributor: Boyd, Edith

Reference: Boyd, E. 1952. An introduction to human biology and anatomy for first year medical students. Child Research Council, Denver.

continued

82. ORGAN WEIGHTS FROM BIRTH TO MATURITY: MAN, NORTH AMERICAN

Part V: ADRENALS, HYPOPHYSIS, AND THYMUS

Values are for both sexes.

	Age	Adrenals		Hypophysis		Thymus	
		No.	Wt g	No.	Wt g	No.	Wt g
	(A)	(B)	(C)	(D)	(E)	(F)	(G)
1	Birth	516	9.04	...	.....	...	....
2	Birth-24 hr	...	....	...	.....	56	10.9
3	Birth-6 mo	...	....	19	0.113	...	....
4	24 hr-1 yr	...	....	...	.....	11	19.5
5	2-14 da	48	5.19	...	.....	...	....
6	14 da-3 mo	83	3.95	...	.....	...	....
7	3-6 mo	78	3.91	...	.....	...	....
8	6 mo-1 yr	115	4.73	11	0.127	...	....
9	1-2 yr	177	3.56	17	0.148	...	....
10	1-3 yr	...	....	...	.....	17	23.0
11	2-5 yr	112	4.71	20	0.194	...	....
12	3-5 yr	...	....	...	.....	19	28.0
13	5-10 yr	44	5.19	16	0.257	52	28.5
14	10-15 yr	35	7.00	20	0.380	40	29.5
15	15-20 yr	71	10.00	19	0.556	20	21.0
16	20-25 yr	...	....	...	.....	50	18.6

Contributor: Boyd, Edith

Reference: Boyd, E. 1952. An introduction to human biology and anatomy for first year medical students. Child Research Council, Denver.

Part VI: PANCREAS AND THYROID

Values are for both sexes.

	Age	Pancreas		Thyroid	
		No.	Wt g	No.	Wt g
	(A)	(B)	(C)	(D)	(E)
1	Newborn	35	2.77	377	2.09
2	0-1 mo	27	2.42	...	.....
3	0-3 mo	...	....	37	1.71
4	1-2 mo	10	2.63	...	.....
5	2-3 mo	7	4.46	...	.....
6	3-6 mo	60	5.38	30	2.11
7	6-12 mo	87	9.24	39	2.04
8	1-2 yr	88	13.54	42	2.53
9	2-3 yr	...	....	16	3.40
10	2-4 yr	77	19.44	...	.....
11	4-6 yr	13	22.44	25	5.24
12	6-8 yr	8	28.46	14	7.05
13	8-10 yr	9	26.53	19	9.30
14	10-12 yr	3	29.25	12	8.69
15	12-14 yr	...	....	15	14.82
16	13-14 yr	1	35.00	...	.....
17	14-16 yr	...	....	11	14.48
18	14-20 yr	34	68.33	...	.....
19	16-18 yr	...	....	20	16.62
20	18-20 yr	...	....	17	18.33

Contributor: Boyd, Edith

Reference: Boyd, E. 1941. Outline of physical growth and development. Burgess, Minneapolis.

83. HEMATOPOIETIC TISSUES FROM INFANCY TO MATURITY: MAN

	Specification	Measurement										
		1.2 mo	3 mo	6 mo	9 mo	1 yr	6 yr	8 yr	10 yr	15 yr	Adult ♂	Adult ♀
	(A)	(B)	(C)	(D)	(E)	(F)	(G)	(H)	(I)	(J)	(K)	(L)
1	Stature, cm	53	60	68	73	76	112	124	135	160	175	165
	Weight											
2	Body, kg	4.0	5.74	7.58	8.91	10.0	20.5	23.9	32.0	54.2	70.0	60.0
3	Liver, g	130.0	185.0	242	283	320	642.0	750	940	1400	1700	1450
4	Spleen, g	11.0	16.3	22	25	28	57.5	67	83	130	160	160
5	Thymus, g	15.0	20.0	25	25	25	25.0	25	25	25	25[1]; 15[2]	25[1]; 15[2]
	Blood values											
6	Blood volume, ml	370	500	650	725	800	1640	1900	2400	3850	5000	4200
7	Total erythrocyte volume, ml	140	190	230	260	280	600	760	960	1600	2300	1750
8	Total hemoglobin, g	58	70	80	87	95	205	240	320	540	790	580
	Erythrocytes											
9	Total no. in blood x 10^{-12}	1.7	2.30	2.90	3.4	3.6	7.5	9.0	12.0	19.0	27.0	20.0
10	Nucleated no. in marrow x 10^{-11}	0.6	0.65	0.75	0.8	0.9	1.6	1.9	2.5	4.4	6.0	4.5
	Neutrophils											
11	Total no. in marrow x 10^{-11}	0.70	1.00	1.3	1.50	1.70	3.60	4.6	6.50	13.0	18.0	15.0
12	Outside marrow x 10^{-11}	0.44	0.65	0.9	1.10	1.20	2.40	3.0	4.30	8.6	12.0	10.0
13	Total neutrophils x 10^{-11}	1.16	1.65	2.2	2.60	2.90	6.00	7.6	10.80	21.6	30.0	25.0
14	In blood (absolute count x 10^{-9})	1.20	1.60	2.0	2.30	2.50	6.50	8.0	10.00	15.0	20.0	17.0
15	Ratio, outside marrow:blood	1:37	1:40	1:45	1:48	1:48	1:38	1:38	1:43	1:58	1:60	1:60
	Lymphocytes											
16	Total no. in marrow x 10^{-11}	0.30	0.60	0.8	0.80	0.80	0.80	0.9	1.50	3.0	4.0	3.5

/1/ At 20 years. /2/ At 60 years.

continued

83. HEMATOPOIETIC TISSUES FROM INFANCY TO MATURITY: MAN

	Specification	Measurement										
		1.2 mo	3 mo	6 mo	9 mo	1 yr	6 yr	8 yr	10 yr	15 yr	Adult ♂	Adult ♀
	(A)	(B)	(C)	(D)	(E)	(F)	(G)	(H)	(I)	(J)	(K)	(L)
	Lymphocytes											
17	Total no. in spleen, lymph nodes, etc., x 10^{-11}	1.00	2.00	3.0	3.00	3.00	3.00	3.1	3.28	3.8	4.0	3.4
18	No. outside hematopoietic tissues x 10^{-11}	4.80	10.00	22.2	22.20	22.20	22.20	24.0	30.00	44.0	52.0	40.0
19	In blood x 10^{-9}	2.10	3.10	4.7	5.60	5.60	5.60	6.0	7.00	10.0	12.0	10.0
20	Ratio, blood:outside blood-forming organs	1:240	1:300	1:500	1:400	1:400	1:400	1:400	1:400	1:400	1:400	1:400
21	Total no. lymphocytic series in body x 10^{-11}	6.00	13.60	26.0	26.00	26.00	26.00	28.0	36.00	50.0	60.0	50.0
	Leukocytes[3]											
22	Total no. in marrow x 10^{-11}	1.20	1.80	2.2	2.50	2.70	4.40	5.6	8.10	16.2	24.0	20.0
23	Total no. in blood x 10^{-9}	3.80	5.60	7.5	8.00	9.50	13.00	14.0	18.00	29.0	34.0	29.0
24	Total hemic cells in marrow x 10^{-11}	1.80	2.40	2.9	3.40	3.60	6.00	7.5	10.60	20.6	32.0	27.0

/3/ Hemic cells only; does not include disintegrated cells.

Contributor: Osgood, Edwin E.

Reference: Osgood, E. E. 1955. Pediatrics 15:733.

84. BODY MEASUREMENTS: MONKEY

Part I: BODY WEIGHT AND SITTING HEIGHT: RHESUS

Measurements are for *Macaca mulatta*, born and reared in the laboratory of the Department of Obstetrics and Gynecology, Yale University School of Medicine, New Haven, Connecticut. Values in parentheses are ranges, estimate "c" (cf. Introduction).

	Age	Males				Females			
		Weight		Sitting Height[1]		Weight		Sitting Height[1]	
		No. of Subjects	kg	No. of Subjects	cm	No. of Subjects	kg	No. of Subjects	cm
	(A)	(B)	(C)	(D)	(E)	(F)	(G)	(H)	(I)
1	Birth	28	0.49(0.39-0.67)	22	19.6(17.5-22.5)	50	0.47(0.33-0.64)	37	19.4(15.7-21.0)
2	3 mo	28	0.96(0.76-1.30)	24	25.2(22.5-29.2)	50	0.92(0.54-1.16)	41	25.5(21.0-28.3)
3	6 mo	28	1.45(1.07-1.88)	24	29.9(26.3-32.0)	50	1.42(0.89-1.80)	43	29.8(23.7-32.8)
4	9 mo	28	1.84(1.25-2.33)	24	32.6(28.9-36.0)	50	1.82(1.18-2.28)	43	32.7(24.8-36.5)
5	12 mo	28	2.20(1.48-2.98)	24	35.0(30.4-38.2)	50	2.19(1.45-2.68)	43	34.9(26.4-38.6)
6	18 mo	22	2.88(2.01-3.76)	19	38.8(35.4-41.5)	45	2.83(1.86-3.44)	39	38.6(30.1-42.3)
7	2 yr	17	3.45(2.70-4.76)	15	41.3(38.0-44.0)	43	3.41(2.40-4.35)	37	41.2(33.9-44.4)
8	3 yr	12	5.27(4.19-7.22)	14	46.4(41.1-48.5)	34	4.82(3.72-5.94)	37	45.8(40.7-48.9)
9	4 yr	10	7.52(5.74-10.76)	12	51.5(47.0-53.7)	31	5.95(4.80-7.21)	30	48.5(45.2-51.1)
10	5 yr	9	8.71(6.83-10.29)	9	54.1(50.4-57.5)	28	6.66(5.28-9.60)	28	49.9(46.7-52.4)
11	6 yr	7	9.97(8.78-11.10)	4	56.0(54.0-58.0)	25	7.29(5.65-10.90)	25	50.7(47.8-53.0)
12	7 yr	6	10.97(8.80-12.13)	3	57.0(54.8-58.3)	21	8.01(6.31-12.20)	21	51.2(47.8-53.1)

/1/ Crown-rump length.

Contributor: van Wagenen, Gertrude

Reference: van Wagenen, G., and H. R. Catchpole. 1956. Am. J. Phys. Anthropol. 14:245.

continued

84. BODY MEASUREMENTS: MONKEY

Part II: BODY WEIGHT: HOWLER, SPIDER, AND CAPUCHIN

Values in parentheses are ranges, estimate "c" (cf. Introduction).

	Age	*Alouatta palliata* No. of Subjects	*Alouatta palliata* Weight kg	*Ateles fussiceps* No. of Subjects	*Ateles fussiceps* Weight kg	*Ateles geoffroyi* No. of Subjects	*Ateles geoffroyi* Weight kg	*Cebus capucinus* No. of Subjects	*Cebus capucinus* Weight kg
	(A)	(B)	(C)	(D)	(E)	(F)	(G)	(H)	(I)
	Males								
1	Infant	7	1.05(0.57-1.59)	1	1.59	1	1.14	1	0.23
2	Juvenile	5	2.62(2.16-2.95)	...	....	...	....	4	1.48(1.36-1.82)
3	Young adult	3	4.62(3.18-5.68)	1	5.45	1	3.86	12	2.71(2.27-3.41)
4	Old adult	60	7.07(4.77-10.91)	3	8.71(7.73-9.55)	2	8.52(8.41-8.64)	27	4.13(3.18-5.45)
	Females								
5	Infant	15	1.13(0.68-2.05)	...	....	...	....	4	0.63(0.45-0.91)
6	Juvenile	5	1.91(1.36-2.25)	...	....	1	2.95	6	1.63(1.36-2.05)
7	Young adult	40	4.45(3.18-6.36)	...	....	2	3.41	26	2.82(1.59-3.41)
8	Old adult	117	6.10(4.55-9.09)	2	7.61(6.59-8.64)	9	8.56(6.59-10.00)	7	3.57(3.18-4.09)

Contributor: Clark, Herbert C.

Reference: Clark, H. C. Unpublished. Gorgas Memorial Laboratory, Panama, 1952.

Part III: TRUNK, LIMB, AND TAIL DIMENSIONS: SPIDER, CAPUCHIN, AND MACAQUE

Values in parentheses are ranges, estimate "c" (cf. Introduction).

	Species	Age	No. of Speci-mens	Trunk Height	Knee Height	Thigh Length	Leg Length	Foot Length	Upper Arm Length	Forearm Length	Hand Length	Tail Length	Refer-ence
				Dimensions, mm									
	(A)	(B)	(C)	(D)	(E)	(F)	(G)	(H)	(I)	(J)	(K)	(L)	(M)
1	*Ateles geof-*	Infant	8	123.1(106-138)	93.3	87.9	82.3	94.4	92.1	85.8	72.4	398.4	2
2	*froyi*[1]	Juvenile	16	215.7(173-249)	148.6	139.3	132.2	141.8	146.6	142.4	114.5	598.9	
3		♂ Adult	27	289.9(229-324)	196.9	187.8	178.1	170.3	193.4	196.3	137.7	724.4	
4		♀ Adult	50	301.8(258-340)	203.1	194.8	182.9	174.2	199.6	202.0	141.7	757.2	
5	*Cebus capu-*	Infant	2	139.5(129-150)	89.0	83.0	78.5	88.5	69.0	63.8	54.0	352.5	2
6	*cinus*[1]	Juvenile	7	205.9(178-233)	126.0	122.0	113.6	118.1	98.6	91.1	74.1	435.7	
7		♂ Adult	14	251.6(219-285)	150.4	144.1	135.4	130.6	115.9	112.1	83.1	482.6	
8		♀ Adult	11	233.7(198-246)	142.0	133.5	126.3	122.5	109.5	104.8	78.6	466.4	
9	*Macaca mu-*	Infant	10	175.5(130-230)	97.0	92.2	85.6	96.8	81.6	77.2	62.3	152.0	1
10	*latta*[2]	Juvenile	7	262.6(242-300)	144.4	138.7	128.3	135.0	117.0	112.1	82.1	201.0[3]	
11		♂ Adult	7	363.9(327-396)	181.9	178.1	163.0	161.3	150.7	148.7	107.1	264.9	
12		♀ Adult	17	337.8(308-367)	168.4	166.9	151.2	147.5	144.4	136.9	94.8	227.9	
13	*M. philip-*	Infant	2	145.0(110-180)	83.5	78.5	74.0	82.0	75.5	67.5	51.5	314.0	1
14	*pinensis*[2]	Juvenile	16	236.3(202-263)	126.1	122.9	112.6	115.9	110.8	104.8	75.3	455.0[4]	
15		♂ Adult	4	260.0(234-270)	142.3	141.0	129.3	128.0	124.5	120.5	82.8	527.0[5]	
16		♀ Adult	3	263.3(256-276)	135.3	132.7	119.7	118.0	119.3	114.0	80.0	505.5[6]	

/1/ Fresh specimens. /2/ Preserved specimens. /3/ 6 specimens. /4/ 13 specimens. /5/ 3 specimens. /6/ 2 specimens.

Contributor: Schultz, Adolph H.

References: [1] Lumer, H., and A. H. Schultz. 1941. Human Biol. 13:283. [2] Lumer, H., and A. H. Schultz. 1947. Ibid. 19:53.

85. BODY MEASUREMENTS AND ORGAN WEIGHTS: CATTLE

No. = number of subjects.

Part I: WEIGHT, HEIGHT, AND LENGTH

	Breed	Age mo	Body Weight		Height at Withers		Height at Hooks		Height at Pinbones		Diagonal Length		Body Length		Rump Length	
			No.	kg	No.	cm	No.	cm	No.	cm	No.	cm	No.	cm	No.	cm
	(A)	(B)	(C)	(D)	(E)	(F)	(G)	(H)	(I)	(J)	(K)	(L)	(M)	(N)	(O)	(P)
	Males [2]															
1	Ayrshire	Birth	58	36.8	58	69.5	58	72.2	43	69.5	43	67.3	43	56.1	43	19.3
2		3	23	74.5	23	79.8	23	82.9	16	81.1	16	82.9	16	70.2	16	23.8
3		6	12	140.9	12	92.7	12	95.3	9	91.2	9	99.7	9	85.6	9	28.4
4		9	4	205.9	4	103.1	4	105.6	3	100.0	3	115.7	3	99.2	3	33.4
5		12	3	289.1	3	112.7	3	114.7	2	111.4	2	129.2	2	111.1	2	38.6
6	Guernsey	Birth	25	35.5	25	71.5	25	74.8	14	71.5	14	67.7	14	56.9	14	19.3
7		3	14	69.1	14	81.4	14	84.3	9	84.2	9	86.3	9	78.6	9	24.2
8		6	8	129.1	8	95.5	8	98.3	5	97.2	5	105.4	5	92.2	5	28.9
9		8	3	204.5	3	105.5	3	109.7	1	104.5	1	123.0	1	100.0	1	35.0
10	Holstein	Birth	220	45.5	220	75.5	220	78.7	137	76.1	136	72.1	136	61.2	136	21.2
11		3	145	99.1	144	87.8	144	91.3	75	90.8	75	92.7	75	78.9	75	26.8
12		6	104	190.5	104	102.9	104	106.4	54	106.1	54	115.1	54	98.2	54	33.4
13		9	65	287.3	65	114.4	65	117.9	33	116.6	33	131.1	33	112.3	33	38.5
14		12	25	370.5	25	122.0	25	125.4	11	122.7	11	141.5	11	121.1	11	41.4
15		18	4	526.8	4	133.6	4	136.2	3	131.3	3	157.6	3	135.9	3	46.1
16		24	2	640.9	2	142.0	2	142.5	2	135.5	2	165.6	2	143.8	2	47.7
17	Jersey	Birth	95	26.4	95	65.2	95	67.9	51	64.5	51	62.3	51	52.2	51	18.5
18		3	57	59.1	57	76.9	57	79.1	30	78.3	30	81.2	30	68.7	30	23.4
19		6	31	114.1	31	89.6	31	91.9	21	89.6	21	98.2	21	84.0	21	28.2
20		9	8	184.1	8	101.0	8	103.4	4	99.3	4	114.4	4	98.4	4	33.1
21		12	1	290.9	1	112.0	1	115.0	1	112.5	1	126.5	1	113.5	1	38.5
	Females [1]															
22	Ayrshire	Birth	100	35.9	99	68.5	99	71.8	77	68.6	79	66.8	77	56.5	77	19.6
23		3	81	84.1	81	83.3	81	86.6	60	84.9	60	88.4	60	75.0	60	25.6
24		6	91	155.9	91	96.3	91	99.8	71	97.4	69	109.9	71	92.0	71	30.8
25		9	75	222.7	75	105.9	75	109.1	56	106.6	56	120.3	56	104.1	56	35.1
26		12	86	266.4	86	110.9	86	113.7	69	111.0	69	127.3	69	108.8	69	37.2
27		18	76	354.5	76	119.0	76	121.2	62	117.8	62	139.6	62	120.6	62	41.2
28		24	72	448.6	72	123.6	72	125.0	62	121.8	62	147.4	62	127.9	62	43.8
29		36	56	501.4	56	126.6	56	127.3	50	123.2	50	154.7	50	134.4	50	45.1
30		48	32	525.9	32	127.5	32	127.6	31	122.9	31	157.4	31	136.6	31	45.8
31		60	18	550.9	18	128.8	18	127.5	18	122.0	18	158.4	18	137.6	18	45.6
32		72	8	543.2	8	129.4	8	128.4	8	121.1	8	157.4	8	140.0	8	45.7
33		84	4	589.5	4	129.9	4	128.4	4	123.2	4	159.6	4	141.0	4	46.9
34	Guernsey	Birth	78	32.7	78	69.6	78	72.7	64	69.8	64	65.9	64	55.5	64	18.5
35		3	59	69.5	59	81.9	59	85.7	46	82.4	46	85.5	46	72.1	46	24.5
36		6	69	138.2	69	95.7	69	99.4	57	98.3	57	103.8	57	90.0	57	29.7
37		9	56	201.4	58	105.6	56	108.2	44	107.1	44	118.6	44	101.8	44	34.3
38		12	68	246.4	68	111.5	68	114.0	57	112.8	57	125.8	57	108.5	57	37.0
39		18	54	330.0	54	119.4	54	122.1	47	119.5	47	137.6	47	118.6	41	41.0
40		24	58	414.5	58	124.0	58	125.3	53	123.6	53	146.7	53	127.0	53	43.8
41		36	34	469.5	34	126.9	34	127.5	32	125.7	32	153.4	32	134.1	32	45.9
42		48	21	506.4	21	127.1	21	127.2	20	125.0	20	156.7	20	136.2	21	46.2
43		60	12	519.5	12	126.5	12	125.7	12	123.9	12	158.0	12	137.3	12	46.9
44		72	2	586.8	2	131.5	2	132.0	2	128.2	2	167.0	2	143.2	2	48.2
45		84	2	526.4	2	128.7	2	129.0	2	126.5	2	162.2	2	140.5	2	47.7
46	Holstein	Birth	262	40.0	261	74.0	261	77.1	170	74.7	170	68.2	170	59.3	170	20.5
47		3	256	97.7	214	89.2	214	92.2	127	91.9	127	93.7	127	79.6	127	26.6
48		6	247	181.4	225	103.4	225	106.6	144	105.2	144	114.1	144	97.5	144	32.0
49		9	244	258.2	201	113.1	201	116.4	126	113.8	125	126.9	126	109.1	126	36.5
50		12	242	320.0	229	119.5	229	122.2	156	119.2	156	135.1	156	116.1	156	39.1
51		18	233	420.0	192	128.3	192	130.6	126	126.5	126	146.6	126	126.6	126	42.6
52		24	215	522.3	185	133.3	183	134.7	134	130.4	134	154.3	134	133.7	134	45.0
53		36	158	587.3	130	137.8	130	138.7	98	133.3	98	162.7	98	142.8	98	47.3
54		48	110	628.2	90	138.7	90	139.1	72	133.5	72	166.0	72	145.9	72	48.4
55		60	77	653.2	64	139.2	64	139.3	56	133.7	56	167.2	56	147.8	56	48.4
56		72	53	673.6	41	139.8	41	139.6	36	133.3	37	168.7	36	147.7	36	49.3
57		84	34	679.1	21	139.8	21	138.5	21	133.1	20	167.8	21	149.3	23	48.6

continued

85. BODY MEASUREMENTS AND ORGAN WEIGHTS: CATTLE

Part I: WEIGHT, HEIGHT, AND LENGTH

	Breed	Age mo	Body Weight		Height at Withers		Height at Hooks		Height at Pinbones		Diagonal Length		Body Length		Rump Length	
			No.	kg	No.	cm	No.	cm	No.	cm	No.	cm	No.	cm	No.	cm
	(A)	(B)	(C)	(D)	(E)	(F)	(G)	(H)	(I)	(J)	(K)	(L)	(M)	(N)	(O)	(P)
	Females [1]															
58	Jersey	Birth	105	24.5	105	64.6	105	67.3	72	64.5	71	60.7	72	51.6	72	18.3
59		3	82	62.3	82	79.1	82	81.6	53	80.2	53	84.1	54	70.8	54	23.8
60		6	97	129.1	97	93.3	97	95.7	70	94.3	70	104.9	71	90.1	70	29.9
61		9	76	188.2	76	102.7	76	104.7	50	102.6	50	117.8	50	101.9	50	34.6
62		12	89	231.8	89	108.0	89	109.7	63	106.9	63	125.2	64	108.2	63	37.4
63		18	78	301.8	78	114.8	78	116.5	53	112.9	53	135.5	54	117.1	53	40.3
64		24	80	365.5	80	119.1	80	119.3	57	115.8	57	142.4	59	123.3	57	42.9
65		36	47	406.8	47	121.4	47	120.9	33	116.7	33	147.4	34	129.4	33	44.5
66		48	37	441.4	37	122.7	37	121.7	29	118.2	29	150.8	28	132.3	29	45.5
67		60	22	464.5	22	122.5	22	121.4	19	117.1	19	151.4	19	132.9	19	45.2
68		72	7	441.8	8	122.4	8	120.7	8	117.1	8	152.2	6	134.7	8	45.3
69		84	4	482.3	4	124.1	4	119.9	4	116.2	4	152.7	4	135.2	4	45.4

Contributor: Swett, Walter W.

References: [1] Davis, H. P., and I. L. Hathaway. 1956. Nebraska Agr. Exp. Sta. Res. Bull. 179. [2] Davis, H. P., and I. L. Hathaway. 1959. Ibid. 189.

Part II: WIDTH AND GIRTH

	Breed	Age mo	Width of Chest		Width at Hooks		Width at Pinbones		Chest Depth		Barrel Depth		Chest Girth		Barrel Girth	
			No.	cm	No.	cm	No.	cm	No.	cm	No.	cm	No.	cm	No.	cm
	(A)	(B)	(C)	(D)	(E)	(F)	(G)	(H)	(I)	(J)	(K)	(L)	(M)	(N)	(O)	(P)
	Males [2]															
1	Ayrshire	Birth	58	16.6	58	16.0	57	10.7	57	27.4	58	27.4	58	75.2	58	78.8
2		3	23	19.9	23	20.7	22	13.3	22	34.4	23	36.6	23	91.6	23	107.5
3		6	12	25.2	12	27.1	11	17.2	11	43.1	12	47.8	12	114.7	12	143.0
4		9	4	30.2	4	32.6	4	20.5	4	50.5	4	55.2	4	133.3	4	167.0
5		12	3	34.5	3	37.9	3	23.4	3	56.6	3	60.1	3	151.7	3	184.3
6	Guernsey	Birth	25	15.8	25	15.3	24	9.9	24	27.6	25	27.0	25	74.3	25	76.6
7		3	14	18.6	14	19.7	13	12.4	13	34.5	14	35.8	14	90.3	14	104.7
8		6	8	24.2	8	26.0	7	16.1	7	43.8	8	47.3	8	113.8	8	138.8
9		8	3	29.7	3	30.7	3	18.8	3	50.2	3	53.8	3	127.7	3	160.7
10	Holstein	Birth	220	18.2	212	17.1	193	12.0	192	29.5	220	28.7	219	80.2	220	81.7
11		3	144	22.9	137	22.8	120	15.6	119	38.0	144	39.4	144	101.1	144	116.9
12		6	104	29.6	97	30.0	81	20.2	82	47.5	104	51.0	104	127.7	104	154.3
13		9	65	35.7	60	35.6	45	24.4	46	55.0	65	58.8	65	149.2	65	178.5
14		12	25	40.1	22	39.8	13	27.7	14	60.7	25	63.9	25	164.7	25	193.9
15		18	4	47.0	4	47.2	3	32.9	3	71.2	4	71.2	4	192.2	4	218.9
16		24	2	50.5	2	51.2	2	35.9	2	76.2	3	74.4	2	206.8	2	233.0
17	Jersey	Birth	95	13.7	92	13.9	83	8.6	83	24.7	95	24.3	95	67.3	95	70.0
18		3	57	16.6	57	19.0	50	11.1	50	32.9	57	34.1	57	85.2	57	100.7
19		6	31	21.3	31	25.0	26	14.4	25	41.2	31	45.0	31	108.0	31	131.4
20		9	8	26.6	8	30.8	5	18.1	5	49.5	8	52.9	8	129.6	8	156.0
21		12	1	31.5	1	37.5	1	22.0	3	57.0	1	58.0	1	151.0	1	181.0
	Females [1]															
22	Ayrshire	Birth	99	15.9	97	15.9	90	10.5	89	27.5	99	27.2	99	75.2	99	78.7
23		3	81	21.2	79	22.5	73	14.6	72	37.1	81	39.5	81	99.5	81	118.2
24		6	91	26.5	89	29.4	83	18.9	82	45.1	91	49.5	91	121.6	91	149.8
25		9	75	30.6	73	34.7	68	22.6	68	51.6	75	55.9	75	138.8	75	172.3
26		12	86	32.6	84	38.1	79	24.2	79	55.3	86	59.0	86	149.6	86	180.8
27		18	76	36.7	74	43.8	69	27.5	69	60.9	76	64.7	76	166.5	76	200.5

continued

85. BODY MEASUREMENTS AND ORGAN WEIGHTS: CATTLE

Part II: WIDTH AND GIRTH

	Breed	Age mo	Width of Chest No.	Width of Chest cm	Width at Hooks No.	Width at Hooks cm	Width at Pinbones No.	Width at Pinbones cm	Chest Depth No.	Chest Depth cm	Barrel Depth No.	Barrel Depth cm	Chest Girth No.	Chest Girth cm	Barrel Girth No.	Barrel Girth cm
	(A)	(B)	(C)	(D)	(E)	(F)	(G)	(H)	(I)	(J)	(K)	(L)	(M)	(N)	(O)	(P)
	Females [1]															
28	Ayrshire	24	72	39.6	70	48.5	67	29.9	67	65.4	72	69.7	72	180.2	72	220.5
29		36	56	41.2	56	52.2	55	31.8	55	67.7	56	71.4	56	185.2	56	227.0
30		48	32	42.0	32	54.0	32	33.0	32	68.9	32	72.9	32	189.2	32	232.8
31		60	18	43.5	18	54.7	18	33.5	18	69.7	18	75.7	18	192.2	18	238.4
32		72	8	43.8	8	55.0	8	32.4	8	70.4	8	76.0	8	193.4	8	237.2
33		84	4	42.6	4	55.2	4	33.5	4	70.5	4	76.6	4	194.2	4	239.5
34	Guernsey	Birth	78	14.8	75	15.0	70	10.0	70	27.5	78	27.3	78	73.6	78	76.6
35		3	59	19.0	56	20.5	52	13.5	52	36.4	59	37.5	59	94.4	59	107.6
36		6	69	24.2	69	25.9	63	17.6	63	45.1	69	47.8	69	117.7	69	140.4
37		9	56	28.3	53	32.3	50	21.0	50	51.1	56	54.3	56	135.7	56	162.5
38		12	68	31.0	65	35.9	62	23.2	62	55.1	68	57.9	68	147.6	68	174.7
39		18	54	34.9	49	42.8	49	26.4	49	60.5	54	62.8	54	164.1	54	194.5
40		24	58	38.4	54	45.8	53	29.0	54	64.7	58	67.8	58	176.8	58	213.6
41		36	34	40.0	33	49.9	32	30.9	32	67.7	34	70.3	34	184.9	34	222.4
42		48	21	41.0	20	51.6	20	31.4	20	69.2	21	72.5	21	189.7	21	240.3
43		60	12	42.8	12	52.9	12	32.4	12	69.9	12	72.7	12	190.2	12	232.4
44		72	2	46.7	2	54.2	2	35.2	2	72.0	2	76.0	2	201.0	2	230.5
45		84	2	51.5	2	53.5	2	31.7	2	75.0	2	77.0	2	191.5	2	229.5
46	Holstein	Birth	261	17.2	253	17.0	227	12.0	227	28.7	261	28.0	261	78.7	261	80.5
47		3	214	22.4	204	23.5	191	16.4	190	38.6	214	40.1	214	102.6	224	120.2
48		6	225	28.3	215	30.8	218	21.1	218	47.4	225	50.7	225	127.6	249	153.7
49		9	201	32.8	191	36.3	174	24.7	174	54.0	201	56.9	201	146.2	205	175.9
50		12	229	35.9	219	40.4	205	27.2	207	58.1	229	61.2	229	158.6	237	188.6
51		18	192	40.2	182	46.3	166	31.5	168	65.0	192	66.9	192	176.8	198	207.6
52		24	185	43.3	177	51.1	164	34.1	164	69.9	185	71.1	185	189.9	192	225.5
53		36	130	45.1	115	55.9	104	36.7	105	73.1	130	75.0	130	199.0	130	237.7
54		48	90	46.5	84	58.2	77	37.6	78	74.6	90	76.8	90	203.6	94	244.0
55		60	64	47.5	60	59.1	54	38.5	55	75.7	64	78.4	64	206.0	66	248.0
56		72	35	48.1	35	59.9	36	38.7	38	76.3	41	79.8	41	208.9	44	250.3
57		84	20	49.6	20	60.0	24	38.6	25	76.7	23	80.5	21	211.1	28	251.9
58	Jersey	Birth	105	13.3	99	13.9	89	8.9	88	25.4	105	24.1	105	67.6	105	70.3
59		3	82	17.1	75	20.2	66	12.5	65	34.9	82	36.2	82	89.4	82	104.8
60		6	97	22.3	91	27.3	83	16.7	81	44.1	97	46.8	97	114.1	97	138.7
61		9	76	26.2	71	32.7	63	19.6	60	50.1	76	52.9	76	131.7	76	161.1
62		12	89	28.7	84	36.0	76	21.5	75	54.4	89	56.8	89	141.7	89	173.6
63		18	78	33.3	72	41.2	65	24.5	64	59.7	78	61.9	78	158.1	78	191.3
64		24	80	34.7	76	45.4	69	26.6	68	63.1	80	65.6	80	169.2	80	206.0
65		36	47	36.1	44	48.3	39	27.9	39	65.8	47	68.2	47	175.0	47	215.3
66		48	37	37.3	35	50.6	29	29.1	30	66.9	37	69.5	37	180.0	37	222.8
67		60	22	38.2	21	51.3	19	29.8	19	67.8	22	71.6	22	182.7	22	228.6
68		72	8	39.2	7	52.2	4	29.2	8	67.8	8	69.9	8	182.0	8	218.5
69		84	4	42.2	4	52.4	4	29.1	4	66.2	4	72.5	4	188.5	4	232.0

Contributor: Swett, Walter W.

References: [1] Davis, H. P., and I. L. Hathaway. 1956. Nebraska Agr. Expt. Sta. Research Bull. 179. [2] Davis, H. P., and I. L. Hathaway. 1959. Ibid. 189.

continued

85. BODY MEASUREMENTS AND ORGAN WEIGHTS: CATTLE

Part III: ORGAN WEIGHTS

Values are for males.

	Age	Holstein						Jersey					
		No.	Body Weight kg	Brain g	Heart g	Adrenals g	Thyroid g	No.	Body Weight kg	Brain g	Heart g	Adrenals g	Thyroid g
	(A)	(B)	(C)	(D)	(E)	(F)	(G)	(H)	(I)	(J)	(K)	(L)	(M)
1	<6 mo	6	90	299	422	6.4	14.3	3	52	304	304	5.4	6.4
2	6-12 mo	3	241	386	998	10.1	30.2	5	214	356	744	9.8	19.4
3	1-3 yr	5	520	408	1905	19.8	41.4	2	367	384	1270	14.5	29.1
4	3-5 yr	2	861	471	3243	22.5	45.5	2	591	444	1987	18.3	47.0
5	>5 yr	5	888	462	3357	41.6	95.3	10	597	447	2186	27.5	82.2

Contributor: Swett, Walter W.

Reference: Swett, W. W., et al. 1937. J. Agr. Research 55:239.

86. BODY WEIGHT: GOAT

Values in parentheses are ranges, estimate "b" (cf. Introduction).

	Age	Angora		British Alpine	Saanen[1]		Toggenburg[2]	
		♂	♀	♂♀	♂	♀	♂	♀
	(A)	(B)	(C)	(D)	(E)	(F)	(G)	(H)
1	Birth	3.03(2.08-3.97)	2.75(1.90-3.61)	3.75	3.60(2.36-4.84)	3.14(1.64-4.64)	3.49(2.31-4.67)	3.08(2.00-4.16)
2	1 mo	....	....	9.55	7.17(4.75-9.59)	6.71(4.11-9.31)	6.76(4.48-9.04)	6.35(4.41-8.29)
3	2 mo	....	....	14.5	11.3(7.5-15.1)	11.0(7.3-14.7)	11.2(7.9-14.4)	10.2(7.5-13.0)
4	3 mo	....	....	25.9[3]	15.0(9.2-20.7)	14.6(9.1-20.1)	15.0(10.1-19.9)	13.7(10.2-17.3)
5	6 mo	17.0(11.3-22.7)	15.4(10.5-20.3)	33.2	24.6(14.9-34.5)	24.5(15.4-33.5)	23.3(16.8-29.8)	20.8(14.8-26.8)
6	9 mo	....	....	.....	30.6(20.8-40.3)	29.9(18.9-40.8)	27.2(18.7-35.7)	25.4(18.3-32.4)
7	12 mo	27.5(18.1-36.9)	21.1(15.8-26.4)	49.1	40.7(28.1-54.3)	35.3(21.6-49.1)	34.8(25.8-43.8)	29.0(21.0-36.9)
8	18 mo	....	....	62.0	52.2(34.7-69.6)	44.9(28.9-60.9)	42.6(31.9-53.3)	38.1(26.7-49.4)
9	2 yr	36.6(24.7-48.5)	26.1(20.2-32.0)	65.5[4]	58.2(29.8-86.6)	53.7(34.1-73.4)	47.9(30.9-65.0)	45.0(28.6-61.4)
10	3 yr	45.3(29.6-61.0)	29.4(24.0-34.8)	.....	67.8(33.5-102.1)	58.4(32.9-83.9)	58.2(39.7-76.8)	51.6(31.0-72.1)
11	4 yr	55.4(39.3-71.5)	31.7(25.6-37.9)	.....	81.7	60.3(37.1-83.6)	70.9(52.3-89.4)	51.6(33.9-69.4)
12	5 yr	63.1	33.2(26.5-39.9)	.....	76.7	70.1(37.5-102.7)	66.5(31.2-101.8)	54.2(39.7-68.6)
	Reference	3		2	1		1	

/1/ Born between 1930 and 1942. /2/ Born between 1938 and 1947. /3/ At 4 months. /4/ At 21 months.

Contributors: (a) Eaton, Orson N., (b) Shelton, Maurice, (c) Asdell, S. A.

References: [1] Eaton, O. N. Unpublished. U. S. Dept. of Agriculture, Beltsville, Md., 1952. [2] Plimpton, A. A. 1940. Brit. Goat Soc. Yearbook, p. 24. [3] Shelton, M. Unpublished. Texas Agricultural Experiment Station, Sonora, 1961.

87. BODY AND ORGAN WEIGHTS: SHEEP

Part I: BODY WEIGHT

	Age	Type of Birth	Weight, kg							
			Corriedale		Hampshire		Shropshire		Southdown	
			♂	♀	♂	♀	♂	♀	♂	♀
	(A)	(B)	(C)	(D)	(E)	(F)	(G)	(H)	(I)	(J)
1	Birth	Single	4.4	4.0	5.1	4.5	4.4	3.8	3.9	3.6
2		Twin	3.7	3.3	4.5	4.1	3.5	3.2	3.6	3.0
3	3 mo	Single	24.7	20.9	30.1	27.0	22.4	20.6	20.8	18.4
4		Twin	20.5	17.8	26.5	23.1	20.0	17.5	19.0	15.5
5	6 mo	Single	36.6	30.5	42.2	36.5	30.4	28.9	29.0	25.4
6		Twin	32.9	26.9	37.2	32.6	28.6	25.7	26.4	22.6
7	1 yr	Single	56.0	46.0	66.3	57.7	55.1	48.3	47.3	40.8
8		Twin	55.9	43.3	64.5	54.2	53.2	42.8	43.3	38.4

Contributor: Potts, Carl G.

Reference: Potts, C. G. Unpublished. U. S. Dept. of Agriculture, Beltsville, Md., 1952.

Part II: ORGAN WEIGHTS

Values in parentheses are ranges, estimate "b" (cf. Introduction).

	Breed	Age da	No. of Subjects	Body Weight kg	Organ Weight, g							Reference
					Brain	Alimentary Tract	Lungs and Trachea	Heart	Kidneys	Liver	Spleen	
	(A)	(B)	(C)	(D)	(E)	(F)	(G)	(H)	(I)	(J)	(K)	(L)
1	Border Leicester-Merino x Suffolk and Romney-Merino x Suffolk	1	2	5.7	....	262	109	61	36	157	15	3
2		7	2	7.8	....	384	170	74	54	179	19	
3		14	2	12.1	....	424	196	90	64	280	32	
4		30	2	14.4	....	757	227	108	75	249	42	
5		42	2	19.7	....	1104	251	111	81	343	34	
6		56	2	21.5	....	1366	387	139	90	389	53	
7		70	2	23.4	....	1559	300	143	97	413	40	
8		91	2	33.3	....	2425	435	184	126	564	68	
9		112	2	38.9	....	2469	555	232	157	720	85	
10	Border Leicester-Cheviot x Suffolk	62	2♂, 2♀	27.7	....	1601	340	128	102	556	55	2
11		112	4♂, 4♀	38.3	....	2184	398	168	110	730	61	
12		200	3♂, 3♀	53.2	....	2024	405	191	109	702	60	
13		332	1♂, 1♀	61.8	....	2207	463	208	108	773	66	
14	Rambouillet-Merino	28-34	3♀	10 (8-12)	53 (49-57)	....	162 (84-240)[1]	71 (35-107)	26 (20-32)[2]	231 (127-335)	26 (16-36)	1
15	Hampshire, Rambouillet-Merino, and Suffolk	92-132	3♂, 3♀	17 (15-19)	75 (69-81)	....	229 (185-273)[1]	99 (87-111)	39 (31-47)[2]	366 (306-426)	28 (24-32)	1
16	Rambouillet and Rambouillet-Merino	288-296	6♂	51 (43-59)	90 (82-98)	....	613 (507-719)[1]	244 (200-288)	84 (76-92)[2]	816 (700-932)	81 (73-89)	1

/1/ Lungs only. /2/ 1 kidney.

Contributor: Smith, Arthur H.

References: [1] Smith, A. H., et al. 1952. J. Animal Sci. 11:638. [2] Wallace, L. R. 1948. J. Agr. Sci. 38:243. [3] Wardrop, I. D., and J. B. Coombe. 1960. Ibid. 54:140.

88. BODY AND ORGAN WEIGHTS: SWINE

Part I: BODY WEIGHT: BERKSHIRE AND DUROC-JERSEY

Values in parentheses are ranges, estimate "c" (cf. Introduction).

	Age wk	Weight, kg Berkshire (7 subjects)	Weight, kg Duroc-Jersey (2 subjects)
	(A)	(B)	(C)
1	Birth	1.84(1.34-2.17)	(2.73-2.76)
2	1	2.58(2.17-3.10)	(2.96-3.64)
3	2	4.32(3.76-4.91)	(4.75-5.74)
4	3	7.02(5.78-8.14)	(6.84-8.03)
5	4	9.85(8.43-12.60)	(8.55-9.12)
6	5	14.02(12.30-17.00)	(12.80-13.45)
7	6	18.31(16.14-21.36)	(16.50-17.45)
8	7	23.16(21.02-27.04)	(20.43-21.45)
9	8	27.45(24.32-31.36)	(23.86-24.55)
10	9	....	(31.0-32.0)
11	10	....	(36.8-38.0)
12	11	....	(43.4-44.5)
13	12	....	(50.0-51.5)
14	13	....	(56.7-58.5)

Contributor: Johnson, B. Connor

Reference: Johnson, B. C. Unpublished. College of Agriculture, Univ. of Illinois, Urbana, 1952.

Part II: BODY WEIGHT: YORKSHIRE

	Age wk	No. of Observations	Weight kg
	(A)	(B)	(C)
1	Birth	154	1.23
2	8	127	11.8
3	10	191	16.3
4	12	64	20.4
5	14	142	27.2
6	16	85	35.8
7	18	97	46.2
8	20	61	47.6
9	22	220	65.2
10	24	80	78.8
11	26	136	79.3
12	28	64	87.9

Contributors: Crown, R. M., and Rusoff, Louis L.

Reference: Crampton, E. W. 1939. Sci. Agr. 19:736.

Part III: ORGAN WEIGHTS

	Structure	Weight Birth	4 wk	8 wk	16 wk	20 wk	24 wk	28 wk
	(A)	(B)	(C)	(D)	(E)	(F)	(G)	(H)
1	Body weight, kg[1]	1.34	5.93	13.21	36.10	52.06	71.44	100.00
2	Esophagus, g	1.6	4.6	15	29	40	54	61
3	Stomach, g	5.9	39.0	138	370	449	598	574
4	Pancreas, g	1.55	14.7	31	94	129	110	140
5	Small intestine, g	21.7	219	313	1009	1292	1579	1397
6	Cecum, g	0.9	5.3	14	76	113	123	129
7	Large intestine and rectum, g	7.5	4.0	189	618	879	897	1021
8	Caul, g	0.15	1.75	3.0	34	64	101	252
9	Mesentery, g	7.25	37.5	107	367	594	822	1705
10	Lungs and trachea, g	25.8	88.3	193	446	553	627	778
11	Heart, g	10.2	48.5	62	165	199	254	266
12	Pericardium, blood vessels, g	2.6	11.4	20	83	114	173	181
13	Kidneys, g	10.8	40.9	76	170	212	222	225
14	Bladder, g	2.6	3.0	10	17	24	41	50
15	Diaphragm, g	6.5	24.3	53	166	236	344	408
16	Hoofs, g	2.9	7.1	17	41	51	71	96
17	Gallbladder, g	0.35	1.85	12	16	27.5	36	43
18	Liver, g	46.40	190	435	1017	1398	2098	1745

/1/ Empty live weight.

continued

88. BODY AND ORGAN WEIGHTS: SWINE

Part III: ORGAN WEIGHTS

	Structure	Weight						
		Birth	4 wk	8 wk	16 wk	20 wk	24 wk	28 wk
	(A)	(B)	(C)	(D)	(E)	(F)	(G)	(H)
19	Spleen, g	1.4	9.2	21	37	60	77	99
20	Neck thymus, g	1.8	13.6	30	38	65	109	84
21	Heart thymus, g	1.8	5.5	10	29	40	44	61
22	Leaf and kidney fat, g	1.4	20.7	50	238	520	1004	2295

Contributor: Kraybill, H. F.

Reference: McMeekan, C. P. 1940. J. Agr. Sci. 30:301.

89. BODY AND ORGAN WEIGHTS: HORSE

Values are for thoroughbreds.

	Age	No. of Subjects	Body Weight kg	Organ Weight, g								
				Brain	Eyes	Lungs	Heart	Kidneys	Adrenals	Liver	Spleen	Thyroid
	(A)	(B)	(C)	(D)	(E)	(F)	(G)	(H)	(I)	(J)	(K)	(L)
	Males											
1	54.4 da[1]	5	27.30	273.9	51.5	1374	275.9	257.4	4.66	699.5	162.5	12.28
2	16 da[1]	15	38.91	317.3	46.0	1179	458.2	275.6	6.26	1266	235.8	14.80
3	3.1 da	18	52.45	370.1	48.5	1366	565	323.5	9.34	1592	319.0	17.57
4	33.5 da	3	93.89	425.3	56.8	1427	970	859.3	14.43	3386	610.3	15.23
5	9 mo	8	285.13	582.8	71.1	2996	1999	767.7	18.77	4193	1700	26.55
6	Yearling	5	306.35	602.4	79.1	3110	2708	970.2	22.20	4821	5494	26.81
7	2-3 yr	3	433.92	621.4	89.9	3659	3488	1297	27.71	3931	4190	26.50
8	4.3 yr	11[2]	445.76	639.0	97.2	3963	3444	1404	34.30	5354	4239	29.91
	Females											
9	91 da[1]	3	13.00	150.0	....	444.3	111.3	99.0	2.21	702.0	82.5	4.18
10	46.4 da[1]	5	26.47	254.4	37.1	895.7	331.5	245.0	14.89	902.2	139.0	13.23
11	14.6 da[1]	11	47.68	333.9	42.8	1526	472.0	321.3	8.10	1634	335.1	17.54
12	5.6 da	19	54.32	366.5	54.8	1414	606.4	405.7	10.38	1651	306.6	16.80
13	83 da	4	116.77	470.2	67.5	1393	1125	812.2	15.20	3704	838.5	22.60
14	Yearling	1	354.00	570.0	93.3	3280	3010	1520	21.90	.....	.....	28.90
15	12 mo	2	380.11	616.0	81.5	2970	2653	1168	32.30	3452	3379	36.90
16	2-3 yr	7	408.50	632.0	98.8	4588	3237	1653	38.41	5350	3438	30.56

/1/ Premature. /2/ Geldings.

Contributor: Walker, Henry

Reference: Quiring, D. P. 1950. Functional anatomy of the vertebrates. McGraw-Hill, New York.

90. BODY AND ORGAN MEASUREMENTS: CAT

Part I: BODY WEIGHT

Values are for six males and six females. Values in parentheses are ranges, estimate "c" (cf. Introduction).

	Age wk	Weight, g Males	Females		Age wk	Weight, g Males	Females
	(A)	(B)	(C)		(A)	(B)	(C)
1	Birth	97.75(82.7-107.4)	103.92(97.0-119.5)	8	7	641.69(514.7-766.8)	622.30(520.5-701.4)
2	1	129.22(82.7-195.9)	144.21(97.0-212.2)	9	8	713.92(558.7-820.4)	683.80(644.8-760.0)
3	2	213.10(145.6-282.3)	230.22(162.4-295.8)	10	9	810.98(589.0-963.0)	762.53(715.3-817.1)
4	3	296.52(259.0-365.0)	323.68(266.5-377.1)	11	10	1005.58(872.4-1159.0)	891.35(790.0-1032.0)
5	4	363.73(266.4-486.7)	402.42(330.2-475.4)	12	11	997.90(789.0-1218.9)	1008.60(897.3-1104.7)
6	5	446.03(346.0-577.8)	467.02(387.2-562.7)	13	12	1280.25(1200.0-1347.0)	1010.65(902.0-1216.0)
7	6	541.01(420.0-624.5)	540.30(466.7-522.6)	14	13	1440.33(1271.0-1550.0)	1202.10(1024.0-1361.0)

Contributor: Latimer, Homer B.

Reference: Latimer, H. B., and H. L. Ibsen. 1932. Anat. Record 52:1.

Part II: ORGAN MEASUREMENTS

Values in parentheses are ranges, estimate "b" (cf. Introduction).

	Structure	Measurement: Newborn (35 subjects)	Adult: Male (52 subjects)	Female (52 subjects)	Reference
	(A)	(B)	(C)	(D)	(E)
1	Body weight, g	148.7(100.7-201.7)	2821.9(1410.3-4233.5)	2445.2(1414.7-3475.6)	B,16;C,D,3
2	Body length, mm	180.4(163.3-197.4)	521.2(449.0-593.4)	509.1(460.4-557.8)	B,16;C,D,3
3	Brain, g	5.369(3.616-7.122)	27.555(22.959-32.151)	26.542(22.386-30.698)	B,5;C,D,6
4	Spinal cord, g	0.487(0.335-0.652)	7.961(5.213-10.709)	7.657(5.691-9.623)	B,5;C,D,6
5	Eyeballs, g	1.029(0.716-1.355)	9.787(7.707-11.867)	9.716(7.858-11.574)	B,5;C,D,6
6	Digestive tube, g	7.54(4.02-11.71)	131.15(81.47-180.83)	120.47(73.24-167.70)	B,1;C,D,4
7	Digestive tube, mm	631(498-764)	2031.2(1696.9-2365.4)	1924.6(1548.5-2300.7)	B,1;C,D,4
8	Pancreas, g	0.360(0.137-0.636)	6.745(3.281-10.209)	6.520(3.726-9.314)	B,2;C,D,4
9	Lungs and trachea, g	3.763(2.170-6.047)	21.912(12.870-30.954)	19.637(13.187-26.087)	13
10	Heart, g	1.37(0.607-1.701)	11.120(4.920-17.320)	9.777(5.468-14.086)	12
11	Kidney, g	1.569(0.883-2.495)	21.118(9.262-37.974)	16.890(7.706-26.074)	7
12	Testes, g	0.028(0.011-0.070)	2.016(0.505-4.266)	....	7
13	Ovaries, g	0.028(0.017-0.056)	....	0.220(0.040-0.400)	7
14	Uterus, g	0.133(0.040-0.223)	....	1.525(0.205-2.845)	7
15	Musculature, g	44.42(28.33-60.51)	1400.2(618.2-2182.3)	1247.3(649.8-1844.9)	15
16	Skeleton, g	17.70(11.22-24.18)	378.69(217.36-540.03)	325.47(238.67-412.27)	14
17	Integument, g	29.91(22.05-37.77)	383.12(139.46-626.78)	311.50(190.70-432.30)	11
18	Adrenals, g	0.038(0.023-0.053)	0.389(0.155-0.623)	0.359(0.147-0.571)	B,8;C,D,9
19	Liver, g	6.063(3.550-9.199)	101.49(54.49-148.49)	88.61(54.78-122.44)	B,2;C,D,4
20	Hypophysis, g	0.006(0.004-0.008)	0.0362(0.0228-0.0496)	0.0333(0.0203-0.0463)	B,8;C,D,9
21	Spleen, g	0.255(0.112-0.398)	7.570(2.780-14.976)	5.672(1.174-10.170)	10
22	Thyroid, g	0.033(0.019-0.052)	0.235(0.095-0.375)	0.218(0.108-0.330)	B,8;C,D,9

Contributor: Latimer, Homer B.

References: [1] Latimer, H. B. 1934. Anat. Record 60:23. [2] Latimer, H. B. 1934. Scritti biol. 9:313. [3] Latimer, H. B. 1936. Am. J. Anat. 58:329. [4] Latimer, H. B. 1937. Anat. Record 68:469. [5] Latimer, H. B. 1938. J. Comp. Neurol. 68:381. [6] Latimer, H. B. 1938. Ibid. 68:395. [7] Latimer, H. B. 1939. Growth 3:89. [8] Latimer, H. B. 1939. Ibid. 3:337. [9] Latimer, H. B. 1939. Ibid. 3:435. [10] Latimer, H. B. 1940. Ibid. 4:259. [11] Latimer, H. B. 1941. Ibid. 5:285. [12] Latimer, H. B. 1942. Ibid. 6:341. [13] Latimer, H. B. 1943. Ibid. 7:239. [14] Latimer, H. B. 1944. Ibid. 8:149. [15] Latimer, H. B. 1944. Ibid. 8:205. [16] Latimer, H. B., and J. M. Aikman. 1931. Anat. Record 48:1.

91. BODY WEIGHT: DOG

Values in parentheses are ranges, estimate "b" for columns B-D, F, G, and estimate "c" for column E (cf. Introduction).

	Age wk	Weight, kg					
		Basenji (23♂, 27♀)	Beagle (39♂, 31♀)	Cocker Spaniel (31♂, 37♀)	German Shepherd (22♂, 15♀)	Shetland Sheepdog (15♂, 14♀)	Wirehaired Fox Terrier (21♂, 23♀)
	(A)	(B)	(C)	(D)	(E)	(F)	(G)
	Males						
1	Birth	0.29(0.20-0.38)	0.31(0.17-0.45)	0.24(0.17-0.31)	0.49(0.34-0.68)	0.21(0.14-0.28)	0.19(0.10-0.28)
2	1	0.49(0.27-0.71)	0.55(0.37-0.73)	0.41(0.27-0.61)	0.87(0.57-1.02)	0.39(0.23-0.55)	0.37(0.22-0.52)
3	2	0.73(0.45-1.01)	0.80(0.35-1.35)	0.62(0.40-0.84)	1.43(1.14-1.70)	0.58(0.32-0.84)	0.57(0.35-0.79)
4	3	0.93(0.60-1.26)	1.08(0.67-1.49)	0.80(0.51-1.09)	2.06(1.59-2.39)	0.76(0.35-1.17)	0.77(0.46-1.06)
5	4	1.12(0.72-1.52)	1.30(0.52-2.08)	1.04(0.64-1.44)	2.95(2.39-3.52)	1.04(0.42-1.66)	1.01(0.58-1.44)
6	5	1.29(0.81-1.77)	1.67(1.00-2.34)	1.35(0.79-1.91)	3.88(3.30-4.66)	1.47(0.60-2.34)	1.26(0.79-1.73)
7	6	1.51(0.85-2.17)	2.05(1.24-2.86)	1.82(1.14-2.50)	5.00(3.86-5.91)[1]	1.92(0.68-3.16)	1.59(1.06-2.12)
8	7	1.83(0.86-2.80)	2.51(1.48-3.54)	2.28(1.63-2.93)	....	2.42(0.88-3.96)	1.94(1.36-2.52)
9	8	2.30(1.16-3.44)	2.95(1.62-4.28)	2.83(1.90-3.76)	(7.0-16.0)[2]	2.92(0.95-4.89)	2.25(1.49-3.01)
10	9	2.79(1.42-4.16)	3.31(1.71-4.91)	3.27(2.20-4.34)	....	3.44(1.10-5.78)	2.55(1.59-3.51)
11	10	3.29(1.69-4.89)	3.81(1.95-5.67)	3.78(2.71-4.85)	(9.5-22.5)[2]	3.92(1.18-6.66)	2.94(1.83-4.05)
12	12	4.49(2.55-6.43)	4.80(2.60-7.00)	4.88(3.55-6.21)	(10.5-29.5)[2]	4.96(1.56-8.36)	3.73(2.26-5.20)
13	14	5.66(3.58-7.74)	5.71(3.32-8.10)	5.93(4.36-7.50)	(12.0-37.0)[2]	5.93(1.72-10.14)	4.45(2.93-5.97)
14	16	6.57(4.34-8.80)	6.52(3.54-9.50)	6.82(5.02-8.62)	(13.5-43.0)[2]	6.96(1.92-12.00)	5.14(3.50-6.78)
	Females						
15	Birth	0.27(0.22-0.32)	0.30(0.21-0.39)	0.24(0.15-0.33)	....	0.20(0.11-0.29)	0.19(0.14-0.24)
16	1	0.43(0.23-0.63)	0.52(0.32-0.72)	0.41(0.24-0.58)	0.50(0.34-0.64)	0.36(0.16-0.56)	0.38(0.22-0.54)
17	2	0.65(0.41-0.89)	0.77(0.43-1.11)	0.63(0.41-0.85)	0.89(0.57-1.02)	0.55(0.24-0.86)	0.56(0.35-0.77)
18	3	0.82(0.52-1.12)	1.02(0.61-1.43)	0.80(0.54-1.06)	1.46(1.02-1.70)	0.73(0.36-1.10)	0.74(0.48-1.00)
19	4	0.96(0.60-1.32)	1.26(0.77-1.75)	1.05(0.66-1.44)	2.02(1.48-2.27)	0.97(0.42-1.52)	0.96(0.63-1.29)
20	5	1.14(0.71-1.57)	1.50(0.93-2.07)	1.33(0.86-1.80)	2.84(2.39-3.18)	1.27(0.47-2.07)	1.20(0.78-1.62)
21	6	1.37(0.87-1.87)	1.82(1.14-2.50)	1.74(0.91-2.57)	3.77(3.30-4.09)	1.67(0.57-2.77)	1.48(0.92-2.04)
22	7	1.72(1.14-2.30)	2.24(1.46-3.02)	2.14(1.45-2.83)	4.52(3.98-5.34)	2.06(0.72-3.40)	1.79(1.06-2.52)
23	8	2.13(1.39-2.87)	2.63(1.67-3.59)	2.56(1.86-3.26)	(8.0-18.0)[2]	2.44(0.72-4.16)	2.10(1.24-2.96)
24	9	2.51(1.97-3.05)	2.98(1.87-4.09)	2.95(2.12-3.78)[3]	....	2.83(0.70-4.96)	2.37(1.36-3.38)
25	10	2.96(1.87-4.05)	3.36(2.15-4.57)	3.39(2.50-4.28)	(9.5-24.5)[2]	3.23(0.81-5.65)	2.71(1.58-3.84)
26	12	3.97(2.65-5.29)	4.34(2.87-5.81)	4.27(3.33-5.21)[3]	(15.5-28.0)[2]	4.04(0.98-7.10)	3.42(2.22-4.62)
27	14	4.97(3.71-6.23)	5.10(3.55-6.65)	5.08(3.90-6.26)	(16.5-31.5)[2]	4.86(1.20-8.44)	4.02(2.66-5.38)
28	16	5.51(4.08-6.94)	5.75(3.64-7.86)	5.77(4.39-7.15)	(16.5-38.0)[2]	5.67(1.48-9.86)	4.59(3.23-5.95)
	Reference	2	2	2	1, 3	2	2

/1/ 20 pups. /2/ Number of pups not given. /3/ 36 pups.

Contributors: (a) Scott, J. P., (b) Light, Amos E., (c) Weagley, John L.

References: [1] Light, A. E. Unpublished. Wellcome Research Laboratories, Tuckahoe, N. Y., 1954. [2] Scott, J. P. Unpublished. Roscoe B. Jackson Memorial Laboratory, Bar Harbor, Maine, 1961. [3] Weagley, J. L. Unpublished, 1955.

92. BODY MEASUREMENTS AND ORGAN WEIGHTS: GUINEA PIG

Part I: BODY WEIGHT: INBRED AND RANDOM-BRED LINES

All values are for males. Values in parentheses are ranges, estimate "b" (cf. Introduction).

	Age da	Weight, g	
		Inbred Line No. 2 (112 subjects)	Random-bred Line (68 subjects)
	(A)	(B)	(C)
1	Birth	77(55-99)	94(56-132)
2	13	127(87-167)	168(102-232)
3	23	165(107-223)	227(143-311)
4	33	192(114-270)	268(172-364)
5	53	266(166-366)	345(211-479)
6	83	381(239-523)	456(280-632)

continued

92. BODY MEASUREMENTS AND ORGAN WEIGHTS: GUINEA PIG

Part I: BODY WEIGHT: INBRED AND RANDOM-BRED LINES

	Age da	Weight, g Inbred Line No. 2 (112 subjects)	Weight, g Random-bred Line (68 subjects)
	(A)	(B)	(C)
7	113	474(336-612)	571(389-753)
8	143	540(406-674)	658(460-856)
9	173	585(455-715)	719(525-913)
10	233	648(516-780)	813(599-1027)
11	293	689(555-823)	872(668-1076)
12	353	709(581-837)	910(686-1134)
13	413	729(597-861)	938(714-1162)
14	473	744(612-876)	952(742-1162)
15	533	759(631-887)	985(777-1193)
16	593	764(642-886)	992(774-1210)
17	653	775(647-903)	1001(805-1197)
18	713	778(656-900)	1022(780-1264)

Contributor: Wright, Sewall

Reference: McPhee, H. C., and O. N. Eaton. 1931. U. S. Dept. Agr. Tech. Bull. 222.

Part II: BODY SURFACE AREA

	Age	Males No. of Observations	Males Body Weight[1] g	Males Surface Area[2] sq cm	Females No. of Observations	Females Body Weight[1] g	Females Surface Area[2] sq cm
	(A)	(B)	(C)	(D)	(E)	(F)	(G)
1	Birth-1 wk	4	104	192	14	98	185
2	1-3 wk	43	134	226	43	131	223
3	3-5 wk	30	189	282	39	186	279
4	5-7 wk	36	258	344	33	259	345
5	7-9 wk	22	296	376	18	314	390
6	9-11 wk	15	386	445	15	380	441
7	11-13 wk	15	411	464	29	400	456
8	3-4 mo	43	507	530	51	483	514
9	4-5 mo	31	596	588	62	564	568
10	5-6 mo	36	676	638	54	609	596
11	6-7 mo	31	722	665	45	655	625
12	7-8 mo	31	723	666	44	687	644
13	8-9 mo	26	710	658	29	789	704
14	9-10 mo	19	790	704	19	861	744
15	10-11 mo	30	765	690	30	873	751
16	11-12 mo	21	777	697	32	814	718

/1/ Values are for successive measurements on 4 subjects. /2/ Calculated from the formula 9.85 x $weight^{0.64}$, which was derived from measurements on 19 males and females; the 95% range of values lies between -9.7% and +10.7% of the given values.

Contributor: Kibler, H. H.

Reference: Kibler, H. H., S. Brody, and D. Worstell. 1947. J. Nutrition 33:33.

continued

92. BODY MEASUREMENTS AND ORGAN WEIGHTS: GUINEA PIG

Part III: ORGAN WEIGHTS

Values are for males and females. Values in parentheses are ranges, estimate "c" (cf. Introduction).

	Nominal Weight Group g	No. of Subjects	Organ Weight, g		No. of Subjects	Organ Weight, g		
			Lungs	Heart		Kidneys	Liver	Spleen
	(A)	(B)	(C)	(D)	(E)	(F)	(G)	(H)
1	75	20	1.09(0.79-1.45)	0.39(0.24-0.54)	20	0.78(0.61-0.99)	3.68(2.75-6.02)	0.11(0.07-0.22)
2	150	5	1.42(1.15-1.52)	0.77(0.60-0.88)	20	1.65(1.10-2.13)	6.86(4.05-11.28)	0.27(0.14-0.48)
3	250	5	1.94(1.79-2.10)	1.07(0.92-1.23)	20	2.65(2.11-3.51)	11.82(9.21-16.72)	0.45(0.27-1.13)
4	350	9	2.40(1.86-2.94)	1.31(1.07-1.48)	20	3.09(2.47-3.83)	16.18(10.77-20.27)	0.56(0.35-0.79)
5	450	5	3.04(2.69-3.37)	1.58(1.29-1.87)	20	3.63(2.31-4.39)	19.25(12.67-24.92)	0.72(0.47-1.10)
6	550	8	3.55(2.85-4.18)	1.93(1.50-2.27)	20	4.25(3.26-4.90)	23.86(19.29-31.85)	0.78(0.48-1.42)
7	650	6	4.84(3.71-5.54)	2.22(2.04-2.44)	20	4.56(3.61-5.20)	28.07(18.22-42.85)	0.95(0.43-1.88)
8	750	10	5.04(3.92-6.08)	2.22(1.93-2.40)	20	5.02(4.00-6.57)	29.74(24.26-37.44)	0.99(0.50-1.82)
9	850	9	5.39(4.58-6.47)	2.61(2.29-3.03)	20	5.77(3.90-8.21)	31.67(23.16-38.93)	0.93(0.50-1.48)
10	950	11	5.80(4.75-6.99)	2.78(2.51-3.33)	20	5.77(4.59-8.64)	33.07(23.45-45.42)	1.06(0.45-1.70)
11	1050	8	6.22(4.90-7.18)	2.92(2.60-3.19)	15	6.32(5.35-8.05)	33.75(29.80-43.74)	0.80(0.31-1.20)
12	1150	4	6.29(5.00-7.23)	2.96(2.77-3.16)	12	6.51(5.45-7.36)	36.92(31.01-41.13)	1.05(0.67-1.61)
13	1250	6	6.56(5.56-7.31)	3.20(2.64-3.46)	8	6.73(5.37-8.49)	40.75(34.25-47.70)	0.90(0.66-1.14)
14	1350	3	6.12(5.78-6.33)	2.98(2.66-3.31)	4	7.40(6.42-8.33)	40.54(33.28-48.03)	0.75(0.41-0.92)

Contributor: Webster, Stewart H.

Reference: Webster, S. H., and E. J. Liljegren. 1949. Am. J. Anat. 85:199.

93. BODY MEASUREMENTS: HAMSTER

Values were derived from representative points on a median curve plotted from data for 111 golden hamsters *(Mesocricetus auratus)* [2]. Animals were interbred from a single pair and sacrificed at various ages from birth to two years. Values in parentheses are ranges, estimate "c" (cf. Introduction).

	Age da	Body Weight[1] g	Length, cm		
			Total	Tail	Right Hindfoot
	(A)	(B)	(C)	(D)	(E)
1	3	3.3(2-5)	4.6(4.0-5.8)	0.51(0.39-0.81)	0.59(0.48-0.75)
2	7	7.0(4-10)	6.1(4.9-7.0)	0.75(0.51-1.15)	0.81(0.59-0.99)
3	18	23(9-33)	9.3(7.3-10.7)	1.20(0.98-1.70)	1.31(0.88-1.50)
4	25	40(17-51)	11.8(9.1-12.9)	1.40(1.10-1.84)	1.53(1.13-1.66)
5	45	79(65-88)	14.3(13.1-15.4)	1.59(1.23-1.95)	1.68(1.51-1.85)
6	90	103(94-112)	16.0(14.4-16.5)	1.63(1.25-2.03)	1.78(1.58-1.92)
7	180	112(103-121)	16.3(14.7-16.9)	1.68(1.30-2.13)	1.83(1.62-1.99)
8	730	105(97-113)	16.5(14.8-16.9)	1.70(1.30-2.15)	1.83(1.65-2.00)

/1/ For additional information on body weight, consult references 1 and 3.

Contributor: DuBois, R. Callery

References: [1] Bond, C. R. 1945. Physiol. Zool. 18:56. [2] DuBois, R. C. Unpublished, 1950. [3] Poiley, S. M. 1950. In E. J. Farris, et al., ed. The care and breeding of laboratory animals. J. Wiley and Sons, New York. pp. 142-143.

94. BODY MEASUREMENTS AND ORGAN WEIGHTS: MOUSE

Part I: BODY WEIGHT: WHITE AND PIEBALD

Values in parentheses are ranges, estimate "b" for column C and estimate "c" for columns E and G (cf. Introduction).

	Age wk	Males				Female Piebald[1]	
		White		Piebald[1]			
		No. of Subjects	Weight g	No. of Subjects	Weight g	No. of Subjects	Weight g
	(A)	(B)	(C)	(D)	(E)	(F)	(G)
1	Birth	...	....	81	1.25(0.80-1.68)	78	1.26(0.89-1.68)
2	1	...	....	81	4.03(2.67-5.69)	78	4.04(2.93-5.90)
3	2	...	....	81	6.54(4.61-9.28)	78	6.52(4.74-8.65)
4	3	50	8.16(7.34-8.98)	81	8.76(6.48-11.90)	78	8.72(6.00-11.52)
5	4	50	12.44(11.58-13.30)	81	12.13(7.88-16.80)	78	11.94(8.46-15.50)
6	5	50	17.10(16.20-18.00)	81	14.94(9.90-21.35)	78	14.73(9.70-17.70)
7	6	50	19.56(18.66-20.46)	81	17.60(10.15-24.25)	78	16.77(8.75-21.20)
8	7	50	21.06(20.00-22.12)	81	20.06(12.10-25.65)	78	18.42(11.40-21.40)
9	8	50	22.22(20.96-23.48)	81	21.59(15.35-26.60)	78	19.81(13.90-23.15)
10	12	43	25.27(24.19-26.35)	81	24.78(18.70-31.30)	78	22.99(16.75-27.75)
11	16	42	27.19(25.69-28.69)	81	27.70(20.70-38.95)	78	26.11(18.77-35.20)
12	20	42	27.81(26.39-29.23)	81	29.91(22.83-41.62)	78	29.03(20.08-42.68)
13	24	38	27.58(26.36-28.80)	81	31.68(22.83-44.43)	78	31.41(20.50-45.35)
14	28	24	28.04(26.38-29.70)	81	33.07(23.70-45.45)	78	33.00(21.43-46.97)
15	32	22	29.36(28.22-30.50)	81	34.07(22.68-46.67)	78	34.52(22.42-49.85)
16	36	...	....	81	35.49(24.53-50.93)	78	36.38(22.58-50.68)
	Reference	2		1		1	

/1/ Black predominant.

Contributors: (a) Latyszewski, M., (b) Mills, Clarence A.

References: [1] Kopeć, S. 1930. Mém. inst. natl. polon. écon. rurale 11:2. [2] Ogle, C. 1934. Am. J. Physiol. 107:635.

Part II: ORGAN WEIGHTS: PIEBALD

Values are for mice of a piebald (black predominant) inbred strain of unknown origin, bred at the National Institute for Agricultural Research at Pulawy, Poland, between 1931 and 1933. For paired organs, data are for the right member only, unless otherwise specified. The average weight difference in paired organs (i.e., right minus left) is as follows: eyeballs, no difference in either sex; kidneys, +0.038% for ♂, +0.025% for ♀; testes, +0.018%; vesicular glands, -0.007%; ovaries, +0.0006%; uteri, +0.004%; adrenals, -0.0006% for ♂, -0.0014% for ♀. Values in parentheses are ranges, estimate "b" unless otherwise indicated (cf. Introduction).

	Structure	Measurement					
		Birth (20 subjects)	2 wk (20 subjects)	4 wk (20 subjects)	6 wk (25 subjects)	12 wk (21 subjects)	24 wk (20 subjects)
	(A)	(B)	(C)	(D)	(E)	(F)	(G)
		Males					
1	Tail length, mm	11.73 (9.75-13.71)	39.70 (32.76-46.64)	63.70 (54.58-72.82)	72.68 (65.34-80.02)	83.43 (75.57-91.29)	83.35 (76.11-90.59)
2	Body weight, g	1.38 (1.09-1.67)	6.06 (4.44-7.68)	12.25 (9.83-14.67)	19.11 (15.31-22.91)	25.86 (22.24-29.48)	33.10 (25.70-40.50)
	Percent body weight						
3	Brain	6.34(5.12-7.57)	5.87(5.33-6.41)	3.21(2.95-3.47)	2.25(2.02-2.49)	1.71(1.51-1.91)	1.33(1.18-1.48)
4	Eyeball	0.277 (0.196-0.358)	0.180 (0.151-0.208)	0.118 (0.104-0.131)	0.089 (0.079-0.098)	0.077 (0.069-0.085)	0.068 (0.059-0.077)
5	Stomach	0.35(0.22-0.50)	0.42(0.21-0.63)	0.52(0.37-0.68)	0.45(0.30-0.59)	0.35(0.27-0.43)	0.33(0.22-0.43)
6	Cecum	0.06(0.02-0.10)	0.11(0.02-0.21)	0.34(0.18-0.51)	0.30(0.18-0.43)	0.23(0.15-0.30)	0.18(0.12-0.23)
7	Intestine	1.75(0.90-2.60)	2.12(0.71-3.54)	3.53(1.81-5.31)	3.37(2.37-4.37)	2.73(1.80-3.65)	2.27(1.68-2.85)

continued

94. BODY MEASUREMENTS AND ORGAN WEIGHTS: MOUSE

Part II: ORGAN WEIGHTS: PIEBALD

	Structure	Measurement					
		Birth (20 subjects)	2 wk (20 subjects)	4 wk (20 subjects)	6 wk (25 subjects)	12 wk (21 subjects)	24 wk (20 subjects)
	(A)	(B)	(C)	(D)	(E)	(F)	(G)
	Males						
	Percent body weight						
8	Pancreas	0.38(0.14-0.62)	0.42(0.17-0.67)	1.06(0.63-1.49)	1.05(0.82-1.28)	0.91(0.61-1.21)	0.74(0.54-0.95)
9	Lungs	1.41(1.01-1.82)	1.20(0.93-1.47)	0.72(0.58-0.87)	0.56(0.45-0.67)	0.49(0.37-0.61)	0.41(0.35-0.47)
10	Heart	0.46(0.32-0.59)	0.60(0.37-0.83)	0.61(0.51-0.72)	0.54(0.43-0.65)	0.52(0.40-0.63)	0.44(0.37-0.52)
11	Kidney	0.40(0.25-0.55)	0.66(0.39-0.93)	0.72(0.55-0.89)	0.82(0.50-1.13)	0.88(0.62-1.14)	0.73(0.52-0.94)
12	Urinary bladder	0.214 (0.109-0.318)	0.149 (0.061-0.236)	0.074 (0.052-0.097)	0.073 (0.051-0.096)	0.056 (0.036-0.077)	0.054 (0.037-0.071)
13	Testis	0.08(0.05-0.12)[1]	0.11(0.07-0.16)	0.31(0.21-0.41)	0.38(0.26-0.50)	0.41(0.29-0.52)	0.32(0.20-0.43)
14	Vesicular gland		0.016 (0.0086-0.0240)[1]	0.017 (0.0015-0.0330)	0.16 (0.044-0.290)	0.39 (0.22-0.56)	0.39 (0.23-0.54)
15	Adrenal	0.017 (0.0072-0.0280)[1]	0.015 (0.0063-0.0240)[1]	0.012 (0.0069-0.0160)	0.0092 (0.0060-0.0120)	0.0063 (0.0038-0.0087)	0.0044 (0.0026-0.0063)
16	Liver	4.22(2.88-5.57)	3.38(1.40-5.35)	5.14(3.68-6.60)	6.49(4.68-8.30)	5.16(3.89-6.43)	4.28(2.67-5.90)
17	Spleen	0.10(0.02-0.18)	0.47(0.10-0.84)	0.50(0.20-0.79)	0.32(0.17-0.47)	0.25(0.12-0.39)	0.22(0.08-0.35)
18	Thymus	0.26(0.09-0.44)	0.65(0.39-0.90)	0.53(0.32-0.75)	0.33(0.21-0.45)	0.15(0.08-0.22)	0.09(0.03-0.14)
19	Thyroid		0.020 (0.010-0.036)[c]	0.047 (0.015-0.130)[c]	0.039 (0.013-0.140)[c]	0.058 (0.012-0.200)[c]	0.092 (0.021-0.240)[c]
20	Fat[2]	0.14 (0.07-0.22)	0.93 (0.28-1.86)[c]	1.73 (0.96-2.50)	3.46 (1.46-5.47)	6.09 (3.16-9.02)	10.56 (2.89-18.20)
21	Remainder[3]	61.6(47.1-76.1)	66.5(48.7-84.3)	61.4(48.0-74.8)	61.0(47.7-74.3)	65.2(53.7-76.7)	65.6(49.2-82.0)
	Females						
22	Tail length, mm	11.65 (10.15-13.15)	40.10 (29.54-50.66)	64.85 (57.13-72.57)	74.96 (70.78-79.14)	81.00 (72.54-89.46)	83.95 (77.41-90.49)
23	Body weight, g	1.37 (1.06-1.68)	6.07 (4.45-7.69)	12.06 (9.66-14.46)	18.29 (16.03-20.55)	23.59 (18.97-28.21)	32.29 (25.51-39.07)
	Percent body weight						
24	Brain	6.39(5.15-7.62)	5.84(5.13-6.55)	3.34(3.06-3.62)	2.36(2.13-2.61)	1.93(1.65-2.22)	1.43(1.25-1.62)
25	Eyeball	0.265 (0.180-0.350)	0.180 (0.156-0.204)	0.122 (0.109-0.135)	0.091 (0.080-0.102)	0.084 (0.075-0.093)	0.069 (0.063-0.074)
26	Stomach	0.38(0.25-0.52)	0.42(0.26-0.58)	0.53(0.40-0.67)	0.52(0.39-0.65)	0.44(0.28-0.59)	0.35(0.23-0.47)
27	Cecum	0.06(0.03-0.10)	0.12(0.02-0.21)	0.33(0.23-0.43)	0.32(0.18-0.47)	0.29(0.15-0.42)	0.18(0.09-0.28)
28	Intestine	1.96(0.84-3.10)	2.23(1.06-3.39)	3.75(2.47-5.02)	3.73(2.56-4.90)	3.40(2.35-4.46)	2.33(1.58-3.08)
29	Pancreas	0.40(0.26-0.54)	0.43(0.22-0.64)	1.06(0.67-1.42)	1.16(0.81-1.51)	1.04(0.66-1.43)	0.78(0.55-1.00)
30	Lungs	1.50(1.11-1.89)	1.24(0.94-1.54)	0.74(0.57-0.90)	0.60(0.48-0.72)	0.54(0.39-0.69)	0.40(0.34-0.46)
31	Heart	0.46(0.32-0.60)	0.62(0.43-0.82)	0.62(0.50-0.75)	0.56(0.47-0.64)	0.51(0.43-0.58)	0.40(0.30-0.49)
32	Kidney	0.39(0.23-0.54)	0.69(0.43-0.96)	0.70(0.54-0.86)	0.66(0.49-0.84)	0.60(0.46-0.74)	0.48(0.37-0.59)
33	Urinary bladder	0.211 (0.103-0.319)	0.141 (0.067-0.215)	0.073 (0.048-0.099)	0.063 (0.045-0.081)	0.053 (0.039-0.067)	0.043 (0.027-0.058)
34	Ovary	0.019 (0.0058-0.0320)[1]	0.012 (0.0026-0.0200)[1]	0.012 (0.0072-0.0170)	0.015 (0.0057-0.0250)	0.027 (0.014-0.040)	0.026 (0.0093-0.0430)
35	Uterus	0.036 (0.0088-0.0640)[1]	0.052 (0.033-0.071)	0.076 (0.033-0.290)[c]	0.17 (0.052-0.290)	0.16 (0.014-0.320)	0.15 (0.035-0.270)
36	Adrenal	0.020 (0.0066-0.0330)[1]	0.016 (0.0063-0.0250)[1]	0.016 (0.0091-0.0230)	0.018 (0.013-0.022)	0.018 (0.011-0.025)	0.016 (0.0060-0.0260)
37	Liver	4.37(3.21-5.52)	3.57(1.73-5.41)	5.47(3.67-7.26)	5.91(4.81-7.02)	5.16(3.82-6.49)	4.83(2.96-6.69)
38	Spleen	0.09(0.03-0.29)[c]	0.53(0.08-0.97)	0.54(0.16-0.92)	0.40(0.15-0.61)	0.37(0.23-0.51)	0.28(0.05-0.50)
39	Thymus	0.25(0.13-0.38)	0.64(0.39-0.89)	0.61(0.37-0.86)	0.45(0.25-0.65)	0.22(0.12-0.33)	0.12(0.06-0.18)
40	Thyroid		0.021 (0.007-0.040)[c]	0.038 (0.013-0.110)[c]	0.038 (0.013-0.200)[c]	0.066 (0.025-0.190)[c]	0.092 (0.019-0.211)[c]
41	Fat[2]	0.13 (0.05-0.21)	0.87 (0.35-1.76)[c]	1.85 (0.87-2.77)	3.47 (1.45-5.48)	7.08 (1.90-12.27)	13.91 (6.13-21.68)
42	Remainder[3]	60.6(47.4-73.7)	66.7(47.6-85.8)	61.2(46.9-75.5)	61.1(50.6-71.6)	62.1(49.7-74.5)	62.0(48.1-76.0)

/1/ Right and left members together. /2/ From abdominal cavity only. /3/ Skin, subcutaneous fat, tail bones, muscles, and submaxillary glands.

Contributor: Latyszewski, M.

Reference: Latyszewski, M. Unpublished, 1954.

95. BODY MEASUREMENTS AND ORGAN WEIGHTS: RAT

Part I: BODY WEIGHT: LONG-EVANS, WISTAR, AND SHERMAN

For additional information, consult references 1, 4, 6, 7. Values in parentheses are ranges, estimate "b" (cf. Introduction).

	Age wk	Weight, g							
		Males				Females			
		Long-Evans[1] (30-50 subjects)[2]	Wistar[3] (30-50 subjects)[2]	Sherman[3] Small[4] (27 subjects)[5]	Sherman[3] Large[4] (26 subjects)[5]	Long-Evans[1] (30-50 subjects)[2]	Wistar[3] (30-50 subjects)[2]	Sherman[3] Small[4] (39 subjects)[5]	Sherman[3] Large[4] (38 subjects)[5]
	(A)	(B)	(C)	(D)	(E)	(F)	(G)	(H)	(I)
1	Birth	6.12	5.63	5.50(4.9-6.1)	6.08(4.9-7.7)	5.75	5.30	5.52(4.8-6.2)	5.75(4.9-6.6)
2	1	....	....	13.4(10.0-16.5)	17.5(12.5-22.5)	....	....	13.1(10.5-16.0)	16.2(13.0-19.0)
3	2	....	....	25.3(20.5-30.0)	36.9(28.5-45.0)	....	....	24.9(20.0-30.0)	33.5(27.5-39.5)
4	3	40	43	40.4(32.0-48.5)	59.6(48.0-71.0)	39	41	36.8(30.5-43.0)	53(43-63)
5	4	56	52	60.7(50.5-70.5)	92.9(78.0-108.0)	52	55	55.6(48.0-63.0)	79.5(68.0-91.0)
6	5	92	84	89.6(76.0-104.0)	138(117-158)	84	79	77.5(68.0-87.0)	113(99-128)
7	6	125	110	121(106-136)	188(157-218)	105	97	100(89-111)	147(128-166)
8	7	155	141	150(124-175)	233(195-260)	123	116	116(106-127)	172(149-195)
9	8	185	170	177(149-205)	274(231-317)	140	128	130(122-137)	196(169-222)
10	10	221	200	222(191-254)	339(291-386)	167	147	154(145-163)	227(199-256)
11	12	259	225	252(213-291)	393(328-458)	178	165	169(159-179)	251(232-280)
12	15	295	251	285(241-329)	440(379-501)	198	180	185(165-205)	274(238-310)
13	20	350	280	326(278-373)	490(423-556)	223	200	202(178-225)	303(270-335)
14	30	405	322	376(335-417)	....	250	228	230(205-255)	335(298-373)
15	40	434	342	....	....	265	245	240(215-265)	358(311-404)
16	52	470	364	....	....	276	243	248(221-275)	....
	Reference	2, 3	2, 3	5	5	2, 3	2, 3	5	5

/1/ Mixed colors. /2/ Diet: 15% casein, 10% whole milk, 67.5% wheat, 5.2% butter, 0.8% NaCl, 1.5% $CaCO_3$. 5% yeast added during late pregnancy and lactation. /3/ Albino. /4/ Selectively bred for body size. /5/ Diet: 25% whole milk, 10% lactalbumen, 20% cottonseed flour, 25.5% wheat, 14% glucose, 2.5% yeast, 2.5% bone ash, 0.5% iodized NaCl. Vitamins in pure form added per 100 g diet: 2.5 mg α-tocopherol, 750 units carotene, 0.6 mg thiamine HCl, 0.6 mg pyridoxine, 1.1 mg riboflavin, 1.1 mg calcium pantothenate, 0.9 µg vitamin B_{12}.

Contributor: Zucker, Lois M.

References: [1] Dunn, M. S., E. A. Murphy, and L. B. Rockland. 1947. Physiol. Revs. 27:72. [2] Freudenberger, C. B. 1932. Am. J. Anat. 50:293. [3] Freudenberger, C. B. 1933. Anat. Record. 56:47. [4] Zucker, L. M., and T. F. Zucker. 1942. J. Gen. Physiol. 25:445. [5] Zucker, L. M., and T. F. Zucker. Unpublished. Columbia Univ., New York, 1952. [6] Zucker, T. F., et al. 1941. Growth 5:399. [7] Zucker, T. F., et al. 1941. J. Nutrition 22:123.

Part II: BODY WEIGHT AND LENGTH: WILD NORWAY

Rats were obtained from Parson's Island in the Chesapeake Bay and reared in a semi-feral state in a quarter-acre pen. Purina chow was the primary source of food. Values in parentheses are the 10th and 90th percentiles.

	Age da	Males		Females	
		Weight g	Length[1] mm	Weight g	Length[1] mm
	(A)	(B)	(C)	(D)	(E)
1	40	85(67-112)	164(146-179)	104(79-142)	155(139-172)
2	60	170(127-218)	185(168-201)	152(120-200)	179(167-191)
3	80	237(176-299)	202(185-218)	194(149-249)	197(183-205)
4	100	289(217-361)	215(199-231)	230(178-291)	208(195-217)
5	120	330(251-408)	224(209-240)	260(203-327)	212(200-226)
6	160	388(302-472)	238(223-253)	311(245-383)	222(207-240)

/1/ Tail not included.

continued

95. BODY MEASUREMENTS AND ORGAN WEIGHTS: RAT

Part II: BODY WEIGHT AND LENGTH: WILD NORWAY

	Age da	Males		Females	
		Weight g	Length[1] mm	Weight g	Length[1] mm
	(A)	(B)	(C)	(D)	(E)
7	200	424(335-509)	246(232-260)	348(276-423)	230(216-248)
8	240	446(358-531)	250(238-264)	376(300-452)	236(222-254)
9	280	460(374-545)	253(241-266)	397(319-473)	240(227-257)
10	320	468(385-551)	255(243-267)	413(333-488)	243(230-259)
11	360	474(392-556)	256(244-269)	424(344-497)	245(233-261)
12	400	477(397-558)	257(246-269)	433(352-507)	247(234-261)
13	440	480(400-560)	257(246-269)	440(358-512)	248(236-262)
14	480	482(402-561)	257(246-269)	445(363-516)	249(237-262)

/1/ Tail not included.

Contributor: Calhoun, John B.

Reference: Calhoun, J. B. Unpublished. Walter Reed Army Medical Center, Washington, D. C., 1952.

Part III: ORGAN WEIGHTS: ALBINO

Subjects were male albino rats from the Yale-Connecticut Agriculture Experiment Station strain. All rats received daily a basal diet of 35% casein, 37% cornstarch, 15% lard, 9% butterfat, and 4% salt mixture. The rapid growth group received daily, in addition to the basal diet, 0.2-0.6 g yeast and 20-30 g fresh lettuce. At each of the body weights specified, approximately 10 standard and 10 rapid growth rats were sacrificed.

	Specification	Measurements for Rats Weighing								
		60 g	90 g	120 g	150 g	185 g	240 g	300 g	360 g	420 g
	(A)	(B)	(C)	(D)	(E)	(F)	(G)	(H)	(I)	(J)
	Standard Growth Rate									
1	Age, da	35	52	64	74	89	123	159	198	271
2	Body length, mm	136	152	173	185	196	213	228	236	251
3	Tail length, mm	96	123	138	155	160	173	183	193	202
4	Eyes, g	0.158	0.181	0.192	0.214	0.221	0.265	0.280	0.293	0.333
5	Heart, g	0.262	0.299	0.438	0.478	0.574	0.647	0.800	0.902	0.968
6	Kidney, g	0.354	0.451	0.634	0.692	0.810	0.867	1.050	1.092	1.286
7	Testes, g	......	0.343	1.786	1.170	2.369	2.661	2.734	2.852	2.402
	Muscles, g									
8	Extensor digitorum	0.053	0.076	0.115	0.145	0.165	0.214	0.254	0.281	0.329
9	Tibialis anticus	0.238	0.315	0.468	0.562	0.681	0.888	1.083	1.171	1.438
10	Posterior digastricus	0.028	0.038	0.050	0.066	0.072	0.090	0.104	0.115	0.138
11	Hypophysis, g	0.0015	0.0027	0.0041	0.0037	0.0052	0.0061	0.0080	0.0074	0.0104
12	Spleen, g	0.212	0.233	0.256	0.267	0.372	0.506	0.541	0.681	0.812
13	Thymus, g	0.168	0.270	0.200	0.264	0.241	0.236	0.221	0.196	0.174
14	Thyroid, g	0.0063	0.0100	0.0099	0.0152	0.0143	0.0172	0.0163	0.0205	0.0250
	Rapid Growth Rate									
15	Age, da	23.4	31	35	46	57	73	100	108	140
16	Body length, mm	129	152	166	182	197	209	224	239	244
17	Tail length, mm	85	102	125	144	153	165	177	194	201
18	Eyes, g	0.146	0.164	0.174	0.192	0.204	0.213	0.238	0.262	0.281
19	Heart, g	0.265	0.369	0.461	0.514	0.639	0.696	0.821	0.972	1.045
20	Kidney, g	0.351	0.502	0.623	0.667	0.826	0.861	1.002	1.237	1.430
21	Testes, g	0.318	0.690	1.171	1.379	2.046	2.357	2.710	3.038	3.288
	Muscles, g									
22	Extensor digitorum	0.046	0.079	0.101	0.140	0.164	0.197	0.248	0.300	0.337
23	Tibialis anticus	0.192	0.313	0.424	0.547	0.649	0.799	1.065	1.321	1.497
24	Posterior digastricus	0.026	0.037	0.050	0.061	0.067	0.081	0.091	0.117	0.144
25	Hypophysis, g	0.0019	0.0027	0.0043	0.0043	0.0054	0.0060	0.0071	0.0087	0.0101
26	Spleen, g	0.288	0.323	0.356	0.378	0.392	0.446	0.510	0.652	0.872
27	Thymus, g	0.210	0.293	0.371	0.416	0.554	0.543	0.376	0.428	0.352
28	Thyroid, g	0.0107	0.0132	0.0135	0.0163	0.0181	0.0188	0.0202	0.0209	0.0258

continued

95. BODY MEASUREMENTS AND ORGAN WEIGHTS: RAT

Part III: ORGAN WEIGHTS: ALBINO

Contributor: Moment, Gairdner B.

References: [1] Donaldson, H. H. 1924. The rat. Ed. 2. Wistar Institute Press, Philadelphia. [2] Moment, G. B. 1933. J. Exptl. Zool. 65:359.

96. BODY WEIGHT: RABBIT

Values are for New Zealand Whites from the herd at the Rabbit Experiment Station, U.S. Department of Agriculture, Fontana, California.

Part I: BODY WEIGHT FROM BIRTH TO WEANING

Values are averages read from a graph for 103 litters (males and females). Animals were fed a selective, balanced ration.

	Age da	Weight kg
	(A)	(B)
1	Birth	0.065
2	7	0.146
3	14	0.260
4	21	0.357
5	28	0.584
6	35	0.916
7	42	1.25
8	49	1.56
9	56	1.75

Part II: BODY WEIGHT FROM WEANING TO BREEDING AGE

Daily ration consisted of two and one-half ounces of a complete ration in pelleted form and an unrestricted amount of No. 2 leafy or better grade alfalfa hay. Values in parentheses are ranges, estimate "c" (cf. Introduction).

	Age wk	Weight, kg	
		Males	Females
	(A)	(B)	(C)
1	8	1.95(1.6-2.3)	2.04(1.5-2.5)
2	10	2.32(2.0-2.6)	2.37(1.9-2.6)
3	12	2.67(2.3-3.0)	2.72(2.1-3.0)
4	14	2.98(2.5-3.3)	3.05(2.3-3.4)
5	16	3.13(2.6-3.5)	3.26(2.6-3.7)
6	18	3.30(2.8-3.7)	3.49(2.9-4.0)
7	20	3.45(2.8-3.9)	3.70(3.0-4.3)
8	22	3.53(3.0-4.0)	3.85(3.3-4.4)
9	24	3.61(3.0-4.3)	4.00(3.4-4.8)
10	26	3.73(3.0-4.4)	4.08(3.5-4.9)

Contributor: Templeton, George S.

Reference: Templeton, G. S. Unpublished. U. S. Dept. of Agriculture, Fontana, Calif., 1955.

97. BODY AND ORGAN WEIGHTS: CHICKEN

Part I: BODY WEIGHT: CORNISH, NEW HAMPSHIRE, AND WHITE LEGHORN

	Age wk	Weight, kg					
		Males			Females		
		Cornish	New Hampshire	White Leghorn	Cornish	New Hampshire	White Leghorn
	(A)	(B)	(C)	(D)	(E)	(F)	(G)
1	Birth	0.032	0.041	0.036	0.032	0.036	0.036
2	1	0.059	0.086	0.059	0.059	0.082	0.073
3	2	0.109	0.154	0.123	0.105	0.154	0.118
4	3	0.182	0.272	0.191	0.172	0.250	0.195
5	4	0.268	0.404	0.268	0.256	0.363	0.272
6	5	.....	0.563	0.354	.....	0.504	0.367
7	6	.....	0.735	0.449	.....	0.640	0.436
8	7	.....	0.934	0.603	.....	0.807	0.549
9	8	0.727	1.152	0.689	0.636	0.948	0.640
10	9	.....	1.325	0.875	.....	1.107	0.721
11	10	.....	1.628	0.944	.....	1.284	0.776
12	12	1.272	1.849	1.243	1.045	1.551	0.934
13	14	.....	2.554	.....	.....	1.828	1.107
14	16	1.727	2.994	.....	1.318	2.019	1.270

continued

97. BODY AND ORGAN WEIGHTS: CHICKEN

Part I: BODY WEIGHT: CORNISH, NEW HAMPSHIRE, AND WHITE LEGHORN

	Age wk	Weight, kg					
		Males			Females		
		Cornish	New Hampshire	White Leghorn	Cornish	New Hampshire	White Leghorn
	(A)	(B)	(C)	(D)	(E)	(F)	(G)
15	18	.....	3.293	.....	.....	2.254	1.402
16	20	2.091	3.375	.....	1.545	2.309	1.551
	Reference	1	2	2	1	2	2

Contributor: Johnson, Elton L.

References: [1] Gilbreath, J. C., Jr., and C. W. Upp. 1952. Louisiana Agr. Expt. Sta. Tech. Bull. 464. [2] Johnson, E. L. Unpublished. Iowa State College, Ames, 1953.

Part II: ORGAN WEIGHTS (AT 5-30 DAYS): WHITE LEGHORN

	Age da	No. of Subjects	Body Weight kg	Weight, g							Length Intestine cm
				Comb	Gonads	Adrenals	Thyroid	Liver	Pancreas	Intestine	
	(A)	(B)	(C)	(D)	(E)	(F)	(G)	(H)	(I)	(J)	(K)
	Males										
1	5	28	0.0491	0.0117	0.0105	0.0084	......	1.8020	0.2794	4.33	60.7
2	10	32	0.0768	0.0348	0.0195	0.0131	0.0054	2.5728	0.4500	5.90	70.5
3	15	18	0.1060	0.1155	0.0370	0.0158	0.0065	3.8266	0.6763	5.11	82.8
4	20	36	0.1752	0.2873	0.0510	0.0270	0.0093	5.0633	0.8567	4.00	90.0
5	25	29	0.1907	0.3166	0.0610	0.0309	0.0103	6.2359	0.9382	5.41	91.4
6	30	30	0.2723	1.3370	0.0860	0.0346	0.0139	8.7408	1.1246	4.11	96.5
	Females										
7	5	14	0.0478	0.0112	0.0070	0.0089	......	2.0745	0.2113	4.19	56.0
8	10	14	0.0578	0.0148	0.0133	0.0140	0.0055	2.2369	0.3930	5.87	64.9
9	15	19	0.0954	0.0267	0.0243	0.0146	0.0063	3.3199	0.6468	5.30	75.8
10	20	12	0.1352	0.0564	0.0427	0.0224	0.0103	4.8807	0.8139	3.57	76.3
11	25	12	0.2126	0.0682	0.0593	0.0264	0.0123	5.9953	0.9950	3.10	83.2
12	30	14	0.2666	0.1146	0.0704	0.0328	0.0107	7.3582	1.1117	3.64	92.1

Contributor: Venzke, Walter G.

Reference: Breneman, W. R. 1941. Endocrinology 28:946.

Part III: ORGAN WEIGHTS (AT 6-136 DAYS): LEGHORN

	Age da	Males						Females					
		No. of Subjects	Body Weight kg	Weight, g				No. of Subjects	Body Weight kg	Weight, g			
				Brain	Adrenals	Liver	Thyroid			Brain	Adrenals	Liver	Thyroid
	(A)	(B)	(C)	(D)	(E)	(F)	(G)	(H)	(I)	(J)	(K)	(L)	(M)
1	6	13	0.0464	1.0556	0.0147	1.6242	0.0036	7	0.0437	0.9971	0.0095	1.8524	0.0038
2	13	14	0.0801	1.3378	0.0185	3.1548	0.0083	6	0.0682	1.2107	0.0163	3.4482	0.0063
3	20	15	0.1197	1.5411	0.0263	4.2091	0.0089	15	0.1197	1.5001	0.0198	4.2529	0.0094
4	27	8	0.1601	1.7039	0.0254	5.0124	0.0113	12	0.1719	1.7148	0.0228	5.1676	0.0132
5	35	10	0.2273	1.9173	0.0368	6.6918	0.0143	10	0.2231	1.9261	0.0305	6.1386	0.0167
6	48	8	0.3168	2.1142	0.0441	9.0164	0.0198	12	0.2951	2.1168	0.0390	8.4172	0.0233
7	62	11	0.3918	2.3334	0.0611	13.719	0.0294	6	0.3978	2.3487	0.0498	11.843	0.0300
8	87	10	0.3532	2.4980	0.1135	12.365	0.0536	10	0.3596	2.3811	0.0864	11.032	0.0689
9	108	10	0.5007	2.8056	0.1265	15.305	0.0631	10	0.4907	2.5822	0.0989	12.761	0.1097
10	136	8	0.7331	2.9279	0.0714	16.188	0.0894	16	0.6151	2.7224	0.0973	14.498	0.0762

continued

97. BODY AND ORGAN WEIGHTS: CHICKEN

Part III: ORGAN WEIGHTS (AT 6-136 DAYS): LEGHORN

Contributor: Walker, Henry

Reference: Quiring, D. P. 1950. Functional anatomy of the vertebrates. McGraw-Hill, New York.

98. BODY WEIGHT: TURKEY

	Age wk	Weight, kg					
		Males			Females		
		Broad-Breasted Bronze	Beltsville Small White	Eastern Wild Turkey[1]	Broad-Breasted Bronze	Beltsville Small White	Eastern Wild Turkey[1]
	(A)	(B)	(C)	(D)	(E)	(F)	(G)
1	Birth	0.054	0.045	0.04	0.050	0.045	0.04
2	1	0.113	0.095	....	0.109	0.086	....
3	2	0.204	0.181	0.08	0.195	0.163	0.08
4	4	0.585	0.472	0.28	0.517	0.404	0.25
5	6	1.252	0.921	0.56	0.998	0.721	0.48
6	8	2.028	1.483	0.85	1.651	1.148	0.69
7	10	2.939	2.205	1.22	2.354	1.674	0.96
8	12	4.037	2.726	1.64	3.166	2.087	1.24
9	14	4.922	3.357	2.10	3.715	2.608	1.58
10	16	6.214	4.264	2.60	4.604	3.062	1.98
11	18	6.985	4.704	3.32	5.121	3.357	2.52
12	20	8.328	5.643	4.05	5.851	3.742	3.00
13	22	8.850	.....	4.62	6.083	.....	3.32
14	24	10.614	7.438	5.10	6.836	4.382	3.48
15	26	11.508	8.038	5.50	7.307	4.631	3.62
16	28	12.633	9.008	5.78	7.625	4.740	3.71
17	30	....	9.113	5.95	.....	5.085	3.77
18	36	14.710	.....	6.26	7.997	.....	3.91
19	40	14.814	.....	6.35	8.437	.....	3.96
	Reference	1	1	2	1	1	2

/1/ Approximately 60 gobblers and 60 hens *(Meleagris gallopavo silvestris)*, reared in captivity.

Contributors: (a) Johnson, Elton L., (b) Mosby, Henry S.

References: [1] Johnson, E. L. Unpublished. Iowa State College, Ames, 1953. [2] Mosby, H. S., and C. O. Handley. 1943. The wild turkey in Virginia: its status, life history, and management. Virginia Commission of Game and Inland Fisheries, Richmond.

99. BODY WEIGHT: GOOSE, DUCK, AND QUAIL

	Age wk	Weight, kg			
		Anser anser[1]		*Anas platyrhynchos*[2], ♂♀	*Colinus virginianus*[3], ♂♀
		♂	♀		
	(A)	(B)	(C)	(D)	(E)
1	Birth	.....	0.077	0.059	0.004
2	1	0.227	0.227	0.150	0.018
3	2	0.635	0.589	0.458	0.027
4	3	1.270	1.270	0.744	0.045
5	4	1.905	1.769	1.148	0.063
6	5	2.404	1.814	1.506	0.082
7	6	3.039	2.585	2.005	0.095
8	8	3.946	3.447	2.758	0.132
9	10	4.264	3.719	.....	.....

/1/ Pilgrim goose. /2/ White Pekin duck. /3/ Bobwhite.

continued

99. BODY WEIGHT: GOOSE, DUCK, AND QUAIL

	Age wk	Weight, kg			
		Anser anser[1]		*Anas platyrhynchos*[2], ♂♀	*Colinus virginianus*[3], ♂♀
		♂	♀		
	(A)	(B)	(C)	(D)	(E)
10	12	5.035	4.218	.....	0.159
11	16	5.352	4.672	.....	0.172
	Reference	1	1	3	2

/1/ Pilgrim goose. /2/ White Pekin duck. /3/ Bobwhite.

Contributor: Johnson, Elton L.

References: [1] Aitken, J. R. Unpublished. Central Experimental Farm, Ottawa, Canada, 1953. [2] Callenbach, E. W. Unpublished. Univ. of Pennsylvania, 1953. [3] Heuser, G. F., et al. 1951. Poultry Sci. 30:672.

100. BODY LENGTH: REPTILES

Unless otherwise specified, values are for snout-vent length for Serpentes and Sauria, and carapace length for Chelonia. Subjects (column B): GS = growing season; adult = breeding individual (animal either had given birth, contained eggs, had engaged in mating activities, or sexual maturity had been established by sperm smear). Values in parentheses are ranges, estimate "c" (cf. Introduction). Classification adapted from Schmidt and Inger, *Living Reptiles of the World,* 1957.

	Family and Species (Location)	Subjects (Age)	Length mm	Reference
	(A)	(B)	(C)	(D)
	Serpentes			
	Crotalidae			
1	*Ancistrodon*	(at birth)	220(200-299)	22
2	*contortrix*	♂ (1 yr)	354(300-409)	
3	*mokeson*	♀ (1 yr)	345(300-390)	
4	(Kansas)	♂ (2 yr)	480(410-530)	
5		♀ (2 yr)	450(391-510)	
6		♂ (3 yr)	560(531-589)	
7		♀ (3 yr)	538(511-565)	
8		♂ (4 yr)	620(590-650)	
9		♀ (4 yr)	578(566-589)	
10		♂ (5 yr)	668(651-684)	
11		♀ (5 yr)	598(590-615)	
12		♂ (6 yr)	710(685-734)	
13		♀ (6 yr)	626(616-635)	
14		♂ (7 yr)	760(735-785)	
15		♀ (7 yr)	643(636-650)	
16		♂ (8+ yr)	786+	
17		♀ (8+ yr)	651+	
18	*A. piscivorus*	9 (newborn)	338	2,
19	*piscivorus*[1]	1 (8 mo)	228	46,
20	(Florida)	1 (5 yr 8 mo)	1115	49
21		1 (8 yr 3 mo)	1282	
22		1 (9 yr 1 mo)	1308	
23		1 (10 yr 2 mo)	1320	
24		1 (11 yr 2 mo)	1371	
25		1 (12 yr 2 mo)	1397	
26		31♀ (adult)	881.6(660-1118)	
27	*Crotalus viridis*	20♂ (1 yr)	457.2(365-498)	52
28	*lutosus* (Utah)	14♀ (1 yr)	449.5(419-503)	
29		4♂ (2 yr)	556.8(492-627)	
30		2♀ (2 yr)	553.7(530-574)	
31		6♂ (3 yr)	655.3(609-711)	
32		1♀ (3 yr)	685.8	
33		2♂ (4 yr)	731.5(678-723)	
	Crotalidae			
34	*Crotalus viridis*	2♀ (4 yr)	662.9(642-681)	52
35	*lutosus* (Utah)	2♂ (5 yr)	703.6(645-762)	
36		2♂ (6 yr)	769.6(724-815)	
37		1♀ (6 yr)	665.5	
38		1♂ (8 yr)	909.3	
39		2♀ (8 yr)	713.7(711-716)	
40		1♂ (9 yr)	833.1	
41	*C. viridis ore-*	(newborn)	280	18
42	*ganus*	(6 mo)	315	
43	(California)	(8 mo)	375	
44		(10.5 mo)	435	
45		(18 mo)	500	
46		(21 mo)	565	
47		(24 mo)	630	
48		(32 mo)	680	
49		(35 mo)	720	
50		31♀ (adult)	799.3(680-885)	
51	*Sistrurus cate-*	57 (newborn)	223.8(190-264)	29,
52	*natus catena-*	(1 yr)	375	55
53	*tus*[1]	(3 yr)	541	
54	(Illinois,	10♂ (adult)	663(560-787)	
55	Wisconsin)	10♀ (adult)	610(547-670)	
	Colubridae			
56	*Cemophora*	4 (hatchling)	156(150-164)	53
57	*coccinea*[1] (Va.)	4 (3.5 mo)	162(157-170)	
58	*Drymarchon*	6 (hatchling)	457(381-508)	25,
59	*corais coupe-*	5 (hatchling)	(432-485)	30
60	*ri*[1] (Florida)	1 (1 yr)	870	
61		2♂ (adult)	2057(1828-2286)	
62		3♀ (adult)	1625(1219-1981)	
63	*Elaphe guttata*	11 (hatchling)	(302-341)	7,24
64	*guttata*[1]	4 (hatchling)	295(254-305)	
65	(Maryland,	1 (8 mo)	393	
66	Indiana)	4♀ (ca. 18 mo)	635(533-737)	
67		2♀ (adult)	1067(1054-1080)	

/1/ Total length.

continued

100. BODY LENGTH: REPTILES

	Family and Species (Location)	Subjects (Age)	Length mm	Reference
	(A)	(B)	(C)	(D)
	Serpentes			
	Colubridae			
68	*Elaphe obsole-*	15 (newborn)	306.6(267-331)	32,
69	*ta obsoleta*[1]	15 (ca. 46 da)	330	54
70	(Maryland)	15 (ca. 77 da)	356	
71		15 (ca. 108 da)	403(343-545)	
72		1 (4 mo)	545	
73		♂ (adult)	(1095-1835)	
74		♀ (adult)	(715-1800)	
75	*Masticophis*	5♂ (1 yr)	627.4(579-655)	52
76	*taeniatus*	4♀ (1 yr)	586.7(538-622)	
77	*taeniatus*	1♂ (2 yr)	789.9	
78	(Utah)	2♂ (3 yr)	863.6(807-919)	
79		1♂ (4 yr)	833.1	
80		2♀ (4 yr)	894.1(833-904)	
81		1♂ (5 yr)	858.5	
82	*Natrix sep-*	12 (newborn)	183(166-225)	50
83	*temvittata*[1]	12 (3 mo)	230.5(196-255)	
84	(Ohio)	17 (1 yr)	325.2(256-375)	
85		68♂ (>2 yr)	529(375-692)	
86		58♀ (>2 yr)	584(375-787)	
87	*Opheodrys*	♂♀ (9 mo)	152	43
88	*vernalis*	♂ (21 mo)	356	
89	*blanchardi*[1]	♀ (21 mo)	406	
90	(Illinois)	♀ (33 mo)	559	
91	*Storeria oc-*	264 (newborn)	85.9(67-98)	8
92	*cipitomacu-*	10♂ (1 yr)	174.5(141-208)	
93	*lata occipito-*	10♀ (1 yr)	187(170-204)	
94	*maculata*[1] (Michigan)	49♂ (adult, 2+ yr)	251.1(220-295)	
95		90♀ (adult, 2+ yr)	259.1(220-325)	
96	*Thamnophis*	(at birth)	200	11
97	*butleri*	♂ (1 yr)	290	
98	(Michigan)	♀ (1 yr)	300	
99		♂ (2 yr)	330	
100		♀ (2 yr)	360	
101		♂ (3 yr)	350	
102		♀ (3 yr)	400	
103		♂ (4 yr)	380	
104		♀ (4 yr)	430	
105		♂ (5 yr)	385	
106		♀ (5 yr)	445	
107		♂ (6 yr)	390	
108		♀ (6 yr)	450	
109		♂ (7 yr)	395	
110		♀ (7 yr)	455	
111		♂ (8 yr)	395	
112		♀ (8 yr)	460	
113	*T. radix radix*[1]	12 (9 mo)	254	43
114	(Illinois)	12 (21 mo)	432	
115		12 (33 mo)	584	
116		1♀ (45 mo)	665	
117	*T. sauritis*	(at birth)	200	11
118	*sauritis*	♂ (1 yr)	350	
119	(Michigan)	♀ (1 yr)	390	
120		♂ (2 yr)	400	
121		♀ (2 yr)	480	
122		♂ (3 yr)	420	
123		♀ (3 yr)	520	
124		♂ (4 yr)	450	
125		♀ (4 yr)	550	
	Colubridae			
126	*Thamnophis*	♂ (5 yr)	480	11
127	*sauritis*	♀ (5 yr)	570	
128	*sauritis*	♂ (6 yr)	490	
129	(Michigan)	♀ (6 yr)	590	
130		♂ (7 yr)	500	
131		♀ (7 yr)	600	
132		♂ (8 yr)	505	
133		♀ (8 yr)	605	
134	*T. sirtalis*	10 (at birth)	230(213-248)	42
135	*concinnus*[1]	2 (1 yr)	463(380-546)	
136	(Oregon)	1 (2 yr)	597	
137		1♀ (adult)	673+	
138	*T. sirtalis*	40♂ (newborn)	141.2(118-151)	11,33
139	*sirtalis*	38♀ (newborn)	139.5(117-151)	
140	(Michigan)	♂ (1 yr)	350	
141		♀ (1 yr)	370	
142		♂ (2 yr)	430	
143		♀ (2 yr)	480	
144		♂ (3 yr)	480	
145		♀ (3 yr)	550	
146		♂ (4 yr)	520	
147		♀ (4 yr)	590	
148		♂ (5 yr)	550	
149		♀ (5 yr)	640	
150		♂ (6 yr)	580	
151		♀ (6 yr)	670	
152		♂ (7 yr)	590	
153		♀ (7 yr)	690	
154		♂ (8 yr)	600	
155		♀ (8 yr)	700	
	Sauria			
	Anniellidae			
156	*Anniella pul-*	3 (newborn)	50.8(47.0-54.5)	34
157	*chra nigra*	(<1 yr)	(46-82)	
158	(California)	(2 yr)	(82-120)	
159		(3 yr)	(120-160)	
160		4♂ (adult)[2]	139.3(124-154)	
161		3♀ (adult)[2]	152.7(126-176)	
	Anguidae			
162	*Gerrhonotus*	27 (hatchling)	31.4(26-35)	4,44
163	*multicarina-tus webbi* (California)	(3 mo)	37(32-42)	
	Teiidae			
164	*Cnemidopho-*	(hatchling)	(32-35)	21
165	*rus sexline-*	1♀ (9 mo)	39.5	
166	*atus* (Kansas)	1♂ (10 mo)	48	
167		3♀ (10 mo)	43.6(42-46)	
168		2♂ (11 mo)	56.3(50.5-62.0)	
169		3♀ (11 mo)	57(55-61)	
170		2♂ (12 mo)	70.5(70-71)	
171		3♀ (12 mo)	66(61-69)	
172		27 (2 yr)	72.8(68-77)	
173		11 (3 yr)	75.6	
174		5 (4 yr)	78.9(77.5-81.0)	
175		4 (5 yr)	81.5(79-84)	
176		1 (6 yr)	83	
	Scincidae			
177	*Eumeces*	(hatchling)	(20-21)	26
178	*egregius*	(3 da)	22	
179	(Georgia)	(7 da)	24	

/1/ Total length. /2/ Believed capable of breeding but not subjected to tests.

continued

100. BODY LENGTH: REPTILES

	Family and Species (Location)	Subjects (Age)	Length mm	Reference
	(A)	(B)	(C)	(D)
	Sauria			
	Scincidae			
180	*Eumeces*	(20 da)	25.5	26
181	*egregius*	(ca. 2 mo)	(32-33)	
182	(Georgia)	(ca. 1 yr)	(34-36)	
183		4♀ (adult)	47.2(45-48)	
184	*E. fasciatus*	(hatchling)	(23-27)	19,
185	(Kansas)	1 (<2 wk)	27	20
186		1♂ (3 wk)	34	
187		1 (1 mo)	36	
188		1♂ (8.5 mo)	43	
189		1♂ (9 mo)	46.5	
190		3♀ (9 mo)	49.0(46.0-50.5)	
191		1♂ (10 mo)	48	
192		1♀ (10 mo)	48	
193		2♂ (11 mo)	58.7(52.5-65.0)	
194		2♀ (11 mo)	52.7(51.0-54.5)	
195		1♂ (12 mo)	61	
196		1♀ (12 mo)	59	
197		2♂ (13 mo)	60(56-64)	
198		1♀ (13 mo)	64	
199		1♂ (14 mo)	66	
200		1♂ (21 mo)	72.5	
201		4♂ (22 mo)	69.0(67-73)	
202		3♀ (22 mo)	74	
203		2♂ (24 mo)	71.0(70-72)	
204		2♀ (26 mo)	71.5(69-74)	
205		2♂ (33 mo)	76.5(73-80)	
206		2♀ (33 mo)	78	
207		1♂ (34 mo)	78	
208		2♀ (34 mo)	77(76-78)	
209		1♀ (35 mo)	73	
210		1♀ (37 mo)	79.5	
211		2♂ (45 mo)	78(74-82)	
212		2♀ (45 mo)	80	
213		1♂ (57 mo)	82	
214		1♂ (>9 yr)	80	
215	*E. skiltonian-*	(hatchling)	25.5(24.7-26.3)	41
216	*us*[3]	(4 mo)	40(37-43)	
217	(California)	(6 mo)	45(41-49)	
218		(10 mo)	45	
219		(11 mo)	50	
220		(20 mo)	62	
221		(24 mo)	65	
222		(36 mo)	68(61-75)	
223	*Neoseps reyn-*	1 (hatchling)	24	48
224	*oldsi*[4]	(ca. 1 yr)	45	
225	(Florida)	(adult)	(45-57)	
226		♂ (adult)	63[5]	
227		♀ (adult)	65[5]	
	Xantusiidae			
228	*Xantusia vigi-*	(newborn)	23(22-24)	37
229	*lis vigilis*	(1 yr)	29	
230	(California)	(2 yr)	36	
231		♂ (3 yr)	(38-39)	
232		♀ (3 yr)	(42-43)	
	Iguanidae			
233	*Anolis caro-*	(hatchling)	(22-25)	27
234	*linensis ca-*	(8 mo)	40	
235	*rolinensis*	(12 mo)	(35-45)	
236	(Louisiana)	♀ (18 mo)	(45-48)	
237		(21 mo)	(50-52)	
238		♂ (24 mo)	60	
	Iguanidae			
239	*Liolaemus*	♀ (at birth)	28	39
240	*multiformis*	♀ (6 mo)	50	
241	*multiformis*	♀ (1 yr)	60	
242	(Peru)	♀ (21+ mo)	(70-100)	
	Agamidae			
243	*Agama agama*	(hatchling)	(30-34)	13
244	*africana*	17 (6 wk-7 mo)	(50-59)	
	(Liberia)			
245		17 (subadult)	(60-69)	
246		31 (young adult)	(70-79)	
247		64♂ (adult)[2]	(80-118)	
248		65♀ (adult)[2]	(80-101)	
	Chelonia			
	Trionychidae			
249	*Trionyx ferox*	♂ (hatchling)	38	9
250	*spinifera*	♀ (hatchling)	38	
251	(Minnesota)	♂ (3 mo)	51	
252		♀ (3 mo)	51	
253		♀ (7 mo)	63	
254		♀ (2 yr)	102	
255		♀ (5 yr)	178	
256		♂ (10 yr)	159	
257		♀ (10 yr)	249	
258		♂ (15 yr)	171	
259		♀ (15 yr)	297	
260		♀ (20 yr)	333	
261		♀ (30 yr)	381	
262		♀ (53 yr)	432	
263		10 (adult)[6]	236(162-407)	12
264		1♂ (adult)[7]	165[5]	
265		1♀ (adult)[7]	367[5]	
	Testudinidae			
266	*Gopherus ag-*	13 (hatchling)	44.8(36.0-47.6)	23,
267	*assizii*	1 (1 da)	41	28,
268	(California)	1 (3 da)	38	35,
269		1 (4 da)	44	36,
270		8 (12 da)	47.6(46.3-48.5)	45,
271		8 (26 da)	49.0(47.4-49.8)	47,
272		8 (40 da)	49.4(47.3-50.4)	51
273		8 (12 wk)	51.0(48.7-51.8)	
274		8 (8 mo)	51.2(48.6-57.4)	
275		1 (8.5 mo)	44.5	
276		8 (10.5 mo)	51.3(47.5-61.3)	
277		6 (1 yr)	50.1(42.0-70.4)	
278		6 (15.5 mo)	53.9(50.0-64.3)	
279		1 (23 mo)	84	
280		2 (2 yr)	54.1(51.8-56.3)	
281		1 (34 mo)	89	
282		1♂ (3 yr)	72.3	
283		1♂ (5 yr)	83.4	
284		1♂ (6 yr)	87.3	
285		1♂ (8 yr)	115	
286		1♂ (10 yr)	123	
287		1♂ (11 yr)	138	
288		1♂ (12 yr)	150	
289		1♂ (13 yr)	164	
290		1♂ (14 yr)	174	
291		1♂ (15 yr)	187	
292		1♂ (18 yr)	205	
293		1♂ (20 yr)	232	
294		30♂ (adult)[2]	283	

/2/ Believed capable of breeding but not subjected to tests. /3/ Based on 409 specimens. /4/ Based on 142 specimens. /5/ Maximum length. /6/ Michigan. /7/ Ohio.

continued

100. BODY LENGTH: REPTILES

	Family and Species (Location)	Subjects (Age)	Length mm	Reference
	(A)	(B)	(C)	(D)
	Chelonia			
	Testudinidae			
295	*Gopherus agassizii* (California)	30♀ (adult)[2]	242.7	23, 28, 35, 36, 45, 47, 51
296		1♂ (adult)	359[5]	
297		1♀ (adult)	369[5]	
298		65♂ (adult)[2,8]	271.2(223-316)	
299		50♀ (adult)[2,8]	236.9(170-293)	
	Emydidae			
300	*Clemmys muhlenbergii* (Pennsylvania, New York)	1 (hatchling)	34	6,12
301		1♂ (2 yr)	53.2	
302		1♂ (4 yr 3 mo)	84	
303		22♂ (adult)	89.8(80-108)	
304		29♀ (adult)	87.5(80-94)	
305	*Malaclemys terrapin centrata* (North Carolina)	200 (hatchling)	30.7(27.1-32.8)	3
306		200 (1 yr)	61.9(59.5-65.5)	
307		100 (2 yr)	89.6(68.5-95.7)	
308	*M. terrapin pileata*[9] (Louisiana)	12 (hatchling)	(18.0-35.7)	10
309		12 (end 1st GS)	(30.3-61.1)	
310		12 (end 2nd GS)	(54.4-86.7)	
311		12 (end 3rd GS)	(65.4-107.3)	
312		10 (end 4th GS)	(91.1-115.5)	
313		6 (end 5th GS)	(102.5-117.5)	
314		2 (end 6th GS)	(109.9-115.0)	
315		57♂ (adult)	(98.7-123.0)	
316		2♀ (adult)	176.5(176-177)	
317	*Terrapene carolina carolina* (Eastern United States)	17 (hatchling)	31(30-33)	5, 12, 15, 17, 38
318		1 (hatchling)	29	
319		1 (8 yr 5 mo)	101	
320		1♀ (20 yr)	93	
321		1♀ (31 yr)	126.5	
322		1♀ (ca. 60 yr)	117.4[9]	
323		1♀ (64 yr)	138	
324		5 (large adult)	149.4(134-165)	
325	*T. ornata ornata*[9] (Kansas)	46♂ (1 yr)	45(27-64)	31
326		65♀ (1 yr)	43(26-62)	
327		47♂ (2 yr)	57(35-72)	
328		67♀ (2 yr)	55(34-74)	
329		48♂ (3 yr)	66(37-86)	
330		66♀ (3 yr)	65(42-80)	
	Emydidae			
331	*Terrapene ornata ornata*[9] (Kansas)	48♂ (4 yr)	75(53-96)	31
332		67♀ (4 yr)	72(56-94)	
333		46♂ (5 yr)	84(64-114)	
334		67♀ (5 yr)	80(61-102)	
335		38♂ (6 yr)	92(66-108)	
336		63♀ (6 yr)	87(67-115)	
337		32♂ (7 yr)	97(70-114)	
338		59♀ (7 yr)	94(76-117)	
339		30♂ (8 yr)	102(82-118)	
340		47♀ (8 yr)	102(81-125)	
341		22♂ (9 yr)	106(83-119)	
342		35♀ (9 yr)	107(89-129)	
343		19♂ (10 yr)	109(92-119)	
344		29♀ (10 yr)	111(94-135)	
345		15♂ (11 yr)	112(97-121)	
346		17♀ (11 yr)	114(95-129)	
347		9♂ (12 yr)	115(99-121)	
348		12♀ (12 yr)	118(111-131)	
349		7♀ (13 yr)	120(114-129)	
	Kinosternidae			
350	*Kinosternon baurii baurii* (Florida)	5 (hatchling)	23.2(20.5-25.0)	12, 16
351		4 (1 mo)	24.3(22.0-25.9)	
352		5 (3 mo)	26.9(23.8-30.2)	
353		1♀ (subadult)	71.1	
354		2♂ (adult)	79.9(75.8-84.0)	
355		5♀ (adult)	94.2(81.2-104.7)	
356	*Sternotherus odoratus* (Michigan)	4 (hatchling)[10]	22.8(22-24)	1,14, 40
357		200 (hatchling)	23(19-25)	
358		2[11,12] (hatchling)	(18.3-22.0)	
359		2[11,12] (3 da)	(18.6-22.2)	
360		2[11,12] (5 da)	(19.3-22.4)	
361		2[11,12] (7 da)	(19.5-22.7)	
362		2[11,12] (9 da)	(19.6-23.2)	
363		2[11,12] (11 da)	(19.7-23.4)	
364		2[11,12] (14 da)	(19.7-23.4)	
365		2[11,12] (30 da)	(19.9-23.7)	
366		9 (6 mo)	32.5(26-37)	
367		4 (1.5 yr)	42.5(39-45)	
368		9 (2.5 yr)	52(48-55)	
369		10 (3.5 yr)	61.5(56.5-64.0)	
370		11 (4.5 yr)	67(64-70)	
371		15 (5.5 yr)	72(69-75)	
372		12 (6.5 yr)	74.5(72-78)	
373		5 (7.5 yr)	78(74.5-80.0)	
374		(8+ yr)	>80	
375		3♀ (adult)[10]	97(80-108)	

/2/ Believed capable of breeding but not subjected to tests. /5/ Maximum length. /8/ Utah. /9/ Plastron length. /10/ Iowa. /11/ Broods. /12/ Indiana.

Contributor: Hardy, Ross

References: [1] Adler, K. K. 1960. Copeia, p. 156. [2] Allen, E. R., and D. Swindell. 1948. Herpetologica 4(suppl. 1):1. [3] Allen, J. F., and R. A. Littleford. 1955. Ibid. 11:77. [4] Atsatt, S. R. 1952. Copeia, p. 276. [5] Babcock, H. L. 1939. Ibid., p. 175. [6] Barton, A. J., and J. W. Price, Sr. 1955. Ibid., p. 159. [7] Bechtel, H. B., and E. Bechtel. 1958. Ibid., p. 148. [8] Blanchard, F. N. 1937. Ibid., p. 151. [9] Breckenridge, W. J. 1955. Ibid., p. 5. [10] Cagle, F. R. 1952. Ibid., p. 74. [11] Carpenter, C. C. 1952. Ibid., p. 237. [12] Carr, A. 1952. Handbook of turtles. Comstock, Ithaca. [13] Daniel, P. M. 1960. Copeia,

continued

p. 94. [14] Dodge, C. H. 1956. Herpetologica 12:176. [15] Edney, J. M., and W. R. Allen. 1951. Copeia, p. 312. [16] Einem, G. E. 1956. Ibid., p. 186. [17] Ewing, H. E. 1939. Ibid., p. 87. [18] Fitch, H. S. 1949. Am. Midland Naturalist 41:513. [19] Fitch, H. S. 1954. Univ. Kansas Publs. Museum Nat. Hist. 8(1):1. [20] Fitch, H. S. 1956. Herpetologica 12:328. [21] Fitch, H. S. 1958. Univ. Kansas Publs. Museum Nat. Hist. 11(2):11. [22] Fitch, H. S. 1960. Ibid. 13(4):85. [23] Grant, C. 1936. Zoologica 21(4):225. [24] Groves, F. 1957. Herpetologica 13:79. [25] Groves, F. 1960. Copeia, p. 51. [26] Hamilton, W. J., Jr., and J. A. Pollack. 1958. Herpetologica 14:25. [27] Hamlett, G. W. D. 1952. Copeia, p. 183. [28] Hardy, R., and A. R. Hardy. Unpublished. Long Beach State College, Calif., 1962. [29] Klauber, L. M. 1937. Occasional Papers San Diego Soc. Nat. Hist. 3:26. [30] LeBuff, C. R. 1953. Herpetologica 9:166. [31] Legler, J. M. 1960. Univ. Kansas Publs. Museum Nat. Hist. 11(10):529. [32] Littleford, R. A., and W. F. Keller. 1946. Copeia, p. 169. [33] Martof, B. 1954. Ibid., p. 100. [34] Miller, C. M. 1944. Ecol. Monographs 14(3):271. [35] Miller, L. 1932. Trans. San Diego Soc. Nat. Hist. 7(8):187. [36] Miller, L. 1955. Copeia, p. 113. [37] Miller, M. R. 1951. Ibid., p. 114. [38] Nichols, J. T. 1939. Ibid., p. 14. [39] Pearson, O. P. 1954. Ibid., p. 111. [40] Risley, P. L. 1932. Papers Mich. Acad. Sci. 17:685. [41] Rodgers, T. L., and V. H. Memmler. 1943. Trans. San Diego Soc. Nat. Hist. 10:61. [42] Rothman, N., and B. Rothman. 1960. Herpetologica 16:100. [43] Seibert, H. C., and C. W. Hagen, Jr. 1947. Copeia, p. 6. [44] Shaw, C. E. 1943. Ibid., p. 194. [45] Shaw, C. E. 1959. Herpetologica 15:69. [46] Stabler, R. M. 1951. Ibid. 7(2):89. [47] Stuart, G. R. 1954. Copeia, p. 61. [48] Telford, S. R., Jr. 1959. Ibid., p. 110. [49] Wharton, C. H. 1960. Herpetologica 16:125. [50] Wood, J. T., and W. E. Duellman. 1950. Am. Midland Naturalist 43:173. [51] Woodbury, A. M., and R. Hardy. 1948. Ecol. Monographs 18:145. [52] Woodbury, A. M., F. LaM. Heyrend, and A. Call. 1951. Herpetologica 7(1):28. [53] Woolcott, W. S. 1959. Copeia, p. 263. [54] Wright, A. H., and A. A. Wright. 1957. Handbook of snakes. Comstock, Ithaca. [55] Wright, B. A. 1941. Am. Midland Naturalist 25:659.

101. BODY LENGTH: AMPHIBIANS

Values are for snout-vent length, unless otherwise indicated. Subjects (column B): NM = newly metamorphosed; AT = at transformation; JT = just transformed; AJ = "August" juvenile; adult = breeding individual (animal either had given birth, contained eggs, had engaged in mating activities, or sexual maturity had been established by sperm smear). Values in parentheses are ranges, estimate "c" (cf. Introduction). Classification adapted from Cochran, *Living Amphibians of the World*, 1961.

	Family and Species (Location)	Subjects (Age)	Length mm	Reference
	(A)	(B)	(C)	(D)
	Salientia			
	Microhylidae			
1	*Gastrophryne*	27 (NM)	15.5(15-17)	4,5
2	*olivacea*	114 (2 wk)	17.2(14-20)	
3	(Kansas)	12 (3 wk)	18.7(16-20)	
4		37 (4 wk)	19.3(17.0-21.5)	
5		62 (5 wk)	20.8(17-24)	
6		49 (7 wk)	22.3(18-24)	
7		(2 mo)	(22.3-26.5)	
8		2♀ (10 mo)	24(23-25)	
9		14♀ (12 mo)	30.8(29-32)	
10		1♂ (23 mo)	32	
11		8♀ (24 mo)	36.1	
12		37♂ (3 yr)	34.2	
13		19♀ (3 yr)	38.2	
14		43♂ (4 yr)	34.4(30-38)	
15		20♀ (4 yr)	37.6(34-40)	
16		1♂ (7 yr)	33	
	Ranidae			
17	*Rana catesbei-*	(AT)	52(36-60)	9
18	*ana*[1]	(8 mo)	55(39-64)	
19	(New York)	(9 mo)	62(45-70)	
20		(10 mo)	73(46-82)	
21		(11 mo)	74(47-94)	
22		(12 mo)	86(59-106)	
23		(13 mo)	92(65-112)	
24		(15 mo)	94(68-114)	
25		♂ (adult)	>85	
26		♀ (adult)	>90	
27	*R. clamitans*	286 (AT)	32.6(28.4-36.3)	8,9
28	(Michigan,	(1 mo)	40(35-48)	
29	New York)	(2 mo)	48(42-58)	
30		(3 mo)	53(46-60)	
31		(12 mo)	57(50-64)	
32		(13 mo)	60(56-70)	
33		♂ (14 mo)	60	
34		♀ (14 mo)	65	

/1/ Total length.

continued

101. BODY LENGTH: AMPHIBIANS

	Family and Species (Location)	Subjects (Age)	Length mm	Reference
	(A)	(B)	(C)	(D)
	Salientia			
	Ranidae			
35	*Rana clamitans*	♂ (15 mo)	70	8,9
36	(Michigan,	♀ (15 mo)	(75-80)	
37	New York)	(2 yr)	83.6	
38		(3 yr)	89.1	
39		(4 yr)	92.3	
40		♂ (adult)	103[a]	
41		♀ (adult)	105[a]	
42	*R. pipiens*	(AT)	25(20.0-30.5)	9
43	(New York)	(1 mo)	33(28-39)	
44		(2 mo)	41(36-48)	
45		(3 mo)	46(40-53)	
46		♂ (15 mo)	(52-82)	
47		♀ (15 mo)	(54.0-92.5)	
	Hylidae			
48	*Hyla regilla*	1156 (JT)	13.8(12.1-15.3)	7
49	(Oregon)	5 (2 wk)	19.8(18-21)	
50		4 (3 wk)	22(19-25)	
51		6 (4 wk)	20.3(17-23)	
52		6 (5 wk)	21.9(20-24)	
53		7 (6 wk)	21.9(20-24)	
54		1 (7 wk)	23	
55		1 (8 wk)	21	
56		2♂ (9 mo)	31(29.4-32.6)	
57		38 (2+ yr)	38.6(37-40)	
	Bufonidae			
58	*Bufo valliceps*	16♂ (AJ)	20.8(12-34)	1
59	(Texas)	5♀ (AJ)	26.0(15-38)	
60		1♀ (1 mo later)	53	
61		1♂ (2 mo later)	55	
62		8♂ (8 mo later)	68.2(61-78)	
63		5♂ (9 mo later)	72.6(64-77)	
64		2♀ (10 mo later)	94(93-95)	
65		5♂ (11 mo later)	78.2(71-86)	
66		2♀ (11 mo later)	99.5(97-102)	
67		6♂ (12 mo later)	79.8(75-88)	
68		3♀ (13 mo later)	82.5(70-104)	
69	*B. woodhousei*	(NM)	10	12
70	*woodhousei*	(1 mo)	27.3	
71	(S. Dakota)	(2 mo)	31.5	
72		(1 yr)	37.5(25-50)	
	Bufonidae			
73	*Bufo wood-*	65♂ (adult)[3]	62.2(37-84)	12
74	*housei wood-*	34♀ (adult)[3]	63.6(29.2-92.8)	
75	*housei*	♂ (adult)[4]	(55.8-84.0)	
76	(S. Dakota)	♀ (adult)[4]	(67.3-92.8)	
	Caudata			
	Sirenidae			
77	*Siren interme-*	(hatchling)	10.5	2
78	*dia nettingii*	♂ (1 yr)	140	
79	(Texas)	♀ (1 yr)	110	
80		♂ (2 yr)	230	
81		♀ (2 yr)	185	
82		♂ (3 yr)	297	
	Plethodontidae			
83	*Ensatina esch-*	45 (hatchling)	22.6(20-26)	11
84	*scholtzii xan-*	(ca. 6 mo)	(23-32)	
85	*thoptica*	(1.5 yr)	(36-45)	
86	(California)	(2.5 yr)	(47-53)	
87		♂ (adult)	59.5(53.0-68.5)	
88		♀ (adult)	67.7(61-78)	
89	*Eurycea bis-*	(hatchling)	9	3
90	*lineata rivi-*	19 (1 mo)	9.2(8-11)	
91	*cola*	41 (4 mo)	15.4(12-17)	
92	(Ohio)	6 (8 mo)	16.8(15-18)	
93		6 (12 mo)	20.0(18-22)	
94		14 (16 mo)	19.2(17-22)	
95		30 (20 mo)	22.7(19-28)	
96		7 (24 mo)	26.6(23-32)	
97		2 (28 mo)	30(29-31)	
98		182♂ (adult)	35.2(24-42)	
99		180♀ (adult)	37.6(22-48)	
100	*Plethodon glu-*	10 (hatchling)	13.7(12-15)	6
101	*tinosus glu-*	14 (2 mo)	17.2(15-19)	
102	*tinosus*	36 (3 mo)	20(15-23)	
103	(Florida)	16 (5 mo)	22.3(20-25)	
104		15 (8 mo)	31.9(27-36)	
105		23 (12 mo)	39.9(32-46)	
106		12 (14 mo)	41.5(34-46)	
107		1♀ (17 mo)	43	
108		1♂ (22 mo)	50	
109		112♂ (adult, 2+ yr)	58.2(55-65)	
110		138♀ (adult, 2+ yr)	59.4(55-69)	
111	*P. jordanii* *clemsonae*	12 (hatchling-1 mo)	26.3(21-30)	10
112	(S. Carolina)	25 (2 mo)	29.4(21-35)	
113		12 (3 mo)	34.3(26-45)	
114		6 (12 mo)	56.5(51-65)	
115		34♂ (adult)	57(45-69)	
116		5♀ (adult)	63(58-66)	

/a/ Maximum length. /3/ Nonbreeding. /4/ Breeding.

Contributor: Hardy, Ross

References: [1] Blair, W. F. 1953. Copeia, p. 208. [2] Davis, W. B., and F. T. Knapp. 1953. Ibid., p. 119. [3] Duellmann, W. E., and J. T. Wood. 1954. Ibid., p. 92. [4] Fitch, H. S. 1956. Herpetologica 12:281. [5] Fitch, H. S. 1956. Univ. Kansas Publs. Museum Nat. Hist. 8(4):275. [6] Highton, R. 1956. Copeia, p. 75. [7] Jameson, D. L. 1956. Ibid., p. 25. [8] Martof, B. 1956. Am. Midland Naturalist 55(1):101. [9] Ryan, R. A. 1953. Copeia, p. 73. [10] Schwartz, A. 1957. Ibid., p. 94. [11] Stebbins, R. C. 1954. Univ. Calif. (Berkeley) Publs. Zool. 54(2):43. [12] Underhill, J. C. 1960. Herpetologica 16:237.

102. BODY LENGTH AND WEIGHT: FISHES

Length Determination (column B): F = fork length, measured from tip of snout to end of rays in center of caudal fin; T = total length, measured from tip of head (jaws closed) to tip of tail; S = standard length, measured from tip of snout (upper jaw) to end of vertebral column. Ages are given in completed years. Classification adapted from Herald, *Living Fishes of the World*, 1961.

	Family and Species	Determination	Length, cm 1 yr	2 yr	4 yr	6 yr	8 yr	10 yr	Maximum	Weight, kg 1 yr	2 yr	4 yr	6 yr	8 yr	10 yr	Maximum	Reference
	(A)	(B)	(C)	(D)	(E)	(F)	(G)	(H)	(I)	(J)	(K)	(L)	(M)	(N)	(O)	(P)	(Q)
	Percomorphi																
	Sphyraenidae																
1	*Sphyraena argentea*	F	36	51	69	80	...	...	108	0.18	0.491	1.2	1.9	.....	.....	4.4	85
	Scombridae																
2	*Neothunnus macropterus*	F	38	55	76	105	135	...	158	.....	.....	.....	.....	.....	.....	204	75,86
3	*Pneumatophorus diego*	F	27	31	35	38	39	...	57	.....	.....	.....	.....	.....	.....	1.6	27,86
4	*Thunnus germo*	F	29	38	53	71	88	...	110	.....	.....	.....	.....	.....	.....	30	34,75
5	*T. thynnus*	F	64	82	118	153	...	...	311	.....	.....	.....	.....	.....	.....	726	52,68,86
	Sciaenidae																
6	*Aplodinotus grunniens*	T	11	22	38	46	66	76	69[1]	0.036	0.135	0.6	1.18	2.04	5.1	6.972	12,13
	Percidae																
7	*Perca flavescens*	T	7	12	20	25	27	30	41.9	0.003	0.03	0.11	0.23	0.285	0.37	1.913	13,34,77
8	*Stizostedion canadense*	T	13	24	32	37	41	42	46	0.026	0.12	0.31	0.51	0.62	0.62	0.836	13,45
9	*S. lucioperca*	S	17	37	49	61	73	...	....	0.089	0.82	1.79	3.29	6.00	.....	.....	9
10	*S. vitreum*	T	13	24	39	48	56	64	103	0.03	0.13	0.57	1.15	1.7	2.27	10.093	13,34,52
	Centrarchidae																
11	*Ambloplites rupestris*	T	4	7	14	20	23	26	31	0.006	0.028	0.065	0.165	0.255	0.38	0.595	11,13
12	*Chaenobryttus coronarius*	T	4	10	18	20	...	...	23.6	0.001	0.015	0.129	0.214	.....	.....	0.284	13,50,71
13	*Lepomis cyanellus*	T	5	10	13	17	...	...	20.6[1]	0.003	0.023	0.055	0.14	.....	.....	0.184	5,12,13
14	*L. gibbosus*	T	5	10	16	20	21	...	36	0.003	0.026	0.058	0.2	0.21	.....	0.454	11,13
15	*L. humilis*	S	3	5	9	...	...	...	10.5	0.001	0.005	0.03	.....	.....	.....	0.03	6,13
16	*L. macrochirus*	T	5	9	16	20	23	23	39	0.005	0.026	0.07	0.17	0.34	0.34	1.955	13,30
17	*L. megalotis*	T	5	9	14	17	...	...	19	0.005	0.017	0.04	0.051	.....	.....	0.227	10,13, 81,84
18	*L. microlophus*	T	9	13	17	21	...	...	24.1	0.023	0.058	0.14	0.26	.....	.....	0.307	13,46
19	*Micropterus dolomieu*	T	10	19	31	36	42	42	67	0.02	0.1	0.425	0.65	0.94	1.08	2.948	13,89
20	*M. punctulatus*	T	10	25	38	42	...	...	45	0.015	0.25	0.905	1.1	.....	.....	1.358	13,80
21	*M. salmoides*	T	11	20	34	41	46	51	95	0.023	0.12	0.57	1.02	1.36	1.81	10.48	13,43
22	*Pomoxis annularis*	T	7	15	25	32	38	...	40	0.006	0.03	0.21	0.45	0.71	.....	0.865	13,40,71
23	*P. nigromaculatus*	T	7	15	25	28	32	34	43	0.006	0.045	0.255	0.37	0.57	0.68	1.352	11,13
	Serranidae																
24	*Morone americana*	T	9	14	20	24	28	30	36	0.011	0.04	0.12	0.205	0.285	0.315	0.771	13,17
25	*M. chrysops*	T	14	25	36	38	41	...	42	0.055	0.255	0.63	0.74	0.91	.....	1.985	13,87
26	*M. interrupta*	T	6	18	25	28	...	...	32	0.028	0.085	0.25	.....	.....	.....	0.51	13,70
27	*Roccus saxatilus*	F	12	24	45	61	75	84	152	.....	.....	.....	.....	.....	.....	57	14,34, 53,76
	Anacanthini																
	Gadidae																
28	*Gadus morhua*	T	16	41	64	81	...	...	142	.....	.....	.....	.....	.....	.....	25	34,72
29	*Lota lota maculosa*	T	12	25	36	41	46	51	104	.....	0.13	0.57	0.97	.....	.....	11.8	13,42
30	*Melanogrammus aeglefinus*	F	20	30	45	55	61	...	90	.....	0.29	0.9	1.53	.....	.....	.....	73,74
	Ostariophysi																
	Ictaluridae																
31	*Ameiurus melas*	T	8	14	19	25	25	...	32[1]	0.009	0.055	0.125	0.31	.....	.....	0.68	13,65
32	*A. natalis*	T	6	13	33	...	...	...	39	0.008	0.05	0.63	.....	.....	.....	0.902	13,50
33	*A. nebulosus*	T	8	14	...	...	...	...	42	0.009	0.057	.....	.....	.....	.....	1.1	13,48
34	*Ictalurus lacustris*	T	8	15	30	41	53	69	127	0.045	0.135	0.23	0.68	1.63	4.3	24.05	13,34
35	*Pilodictis olivaris*	T	18	28	38	53	76	89	104	0.014	0.057	0.34	1.5	.....	.....	20.168	7,13,44

/1/ Standard length.

continued

102. BODY LENGTH AND WEIGHT: FISHES

	Family and Species	Determination	Length, cm							Weight, kg							Reference
			1 yr	2 yr	4 yr	6 yr	8 yr	10 yr	Maximum	1 yr	2 yr	4 yr	6 yr	8 yr	10 yr	Maximum	
	(A)	(B)	(C)	(D)	(E)	(F)	(G)	(H)	(I)	(J)	(K)	(L)	(M)	(N)	(O)	(P)	(Q)
	Ostariophysi																
	Siluridae																
36	*Silurus glanis*	T	20	34	61	79	92	111	500	.....	.....	.....	.....	.....	.....	300	9
	Catostomidae																
37	*Catostomus catostomus*	F	6	11	25	32	38	38	59	.....	.....	.....	.....	.....	.....	......	60
38	*C. commersonii*	T	10	20	36	43	49	51	64	0.026	0.23	0.9	1.4	1.56	.....	3.14	13
39	*Ictiobus cyprinellus*	T	13	25	42	56	65	74	102	0.09	0.45	1.4	3.3	.....	.....	23.6	13,21,36
	Cyprinidae																
40	*Abramis brama*	S	6	12	21	29	36	42	48+	.....	.....	.....	.....	.....	.....	.....	9
41	*Aspius aspius*	S	13	24	40	...	...	...	....	0.032	0.160	0.700	.....	.....	.....	.....	9
42	*Barbus brachycephalus*	S	...	23	45	60	70	...	105	.....	.....	.....	.....	.....	.....	.....	9
43	*B. goktschaicus*	S	3	6	12	18	21	...	....	.....	.....	.....	.....	.....	.....	.....	9
44	*Carassius auratus*	T	9	14	...	...	...	...	....	.....	.....	.....	.....	.....	.....	.....	23
45	*C. carassius*	S	5	8	14	...	...	...	....	.....	.....	.....	.....	.....	.....	.....	9
46	*Cyprinus carpio*	T	18	31	48	53	58	66	127	0.09	0.45	1.8	2.5	3.2	5.1	37.88	13,28,34
47	*Leuciscus idus*	S	...	16	27	32	...	...	....	.....	0.072	0.444	0.672	.....	.....	.....	9
48	*Notemigonus crysoleucas*	T	6	14	20	22	...	...	24.9	0.008	0.02	0.04	0.1	.....	.....	0.2	13,88
49	*Notropis cornutus*	T	5	10	15	21	...	...	21.1	.....	.....	.....	.....	.....	.....	.....	62
50	*Rutilus rutilus caspicus*	S	...	15	19	23	...	...	....	.....	.....	.....	.....	.....	.....	.....	9
51	*Scardinius erythrophthalmus*	S	7	10	17	...	...	...	....	0.006	0.020	0.114	.....	.....	.....	.....	9
52	*Semotilus atromaculatus*	T	5	10	16	18	...	...	17.2[1]	0.006	0.03	0.11	.....	.....	.....	.....	13,49
	Haplomi																
	Esocidae																
53	*Esox lucius*	T	20	38	61	79	97	107	120	0.09	0.27	1.1	2.1	2.95	4.5	28	13,28
54	*E. masquinongy*	T	20	41	66	86	104	117	147	0.09	0.45	2.27	4.5	7.25	9.4	46	13
55	*E. niger*	T	19	28	41	51	...	...	76	0.03	0.1	0.45	1.08	.....	.....	4.086	13
	Isospondyli																
	Osmeridae																
56	*Osmerus mordax*	T	14	18	25	...	...	...	36	0.023	0.036	0.11	.....	.....	.....	0.141	8,13,70
	Thymallidae																
57	*Thymallus signifer*	S	11	22	31	33	38	40	46[2]	0.028	0.17	0.425	0.6	0.79	1.05	1.36	13,54
	Coregonidae																
58	*Coregonus clupeaformis*	T	15	23	42	53	58	64	71[2]	0.03	0.085	0.7	1.36	2.27	2.78	4.88	13,45,82
59	*Leucichthys artedii*	S	9	15	23	25	30	33	46[2]	0.023	0.04	0.17	0.23	0.525	0.71	1.25	13,52
60	*Stenodus leucichthys nelma*	S	22	28	42	56	71	85	100+	0.12	0.26	0.82	1.75	3.74	6.43	12.3+	9
	Salmonidae																
61	*Oncorhynchus gorbuscha*	F	31	...	...	...	...	...	68	.....	.....	......	.....	.....	.....	3.4	51
62	*O. keta*	F	30	50	77	...	...	...	92	.....	.....	.....	.....	.....	.....	.....	51
63	*O. kisutch*	F	7	41	76	...	...	...	76	.....	.....	.....	.....	.....	.....	14	34,51,67
64	*O. nerka*	F	8	20	53	66	...	...	72	.....	.....	.....	.....	.....	.....	.....	15,35
65	*O. tshawytscha*	F	13	46	81	104	...	...	120	.....	1.16	6.5	14.5	.....	.....	57	39,78
66	*Salmo clarki*	T	10.7	16	30	48	...	...	99	.....	.....	.....	.....	.....	.....	18.6	13,34, 58,64
67	*S. gairdneri*	T	8.6	23	39	51	91	...	122	0.028	0.113	0.57	1.53	5.22	.....	21.8	13,61
68	*S. salar salar*	F	4	10	76	107	...	...	120	0.011	0.033	4.54	16	.....	.....	47	13,19,34
69	*S. salar sebago*	T	5	13	46	61	...	...	91	0.011	0.057	1.02	1.7	.....	.....	16.5	3,13,34
70	*S. trutta*	T	10	20	36	56	64	...	120	0.025	0.095	0.88	1.8	4.26	.....	18.5	13,34,38
71	*Salvelinus aureolus*	T	15	25	42	...	...	...	72	0.025	0.13	0.7	.....	.....	.....	3.63	33,34
72	*S. fontinalis*	T	10	16	35	53	56	...	80	0.025	0.06	0.65	1.59	.....	.....	6.58	13,22
73	*S. malma*	F	16	21	27	34	...	...	103[3]	.....	.....	.....	.....	.....	.....	14.53	34,55
74	*S. namaycush*	T	13	23	36	51	59	69	121	0.03	0.14	0.45	1.13	1.95	3.82	36	13,34

/1/ Standard length. /2/ Fork length. /3/ Total length.

continued

102. BODY LENGTH AND WEIGHT: FISHES

	Family and Species	Determination	Length, cm 1 yr	2 yr	4 yr	6 yr	8 yr	10 yr	Maximum	Weight, kg 1 yr	2 yr	4 yr	6 yr	8 yr	10 yr	Maximum	Reference
	(A)	(B)	(C)	(D)	(E)	(F)	(G)	(H)	(I)	(J)	(K)	(L)	(M)	(N)	(O)	(P)	(Q)
	Isospondyli																
	Dorosomidae																
75	*Dorosoma cepedianum*	T	13	24	29	44	...	...	52	0.077	0.121	0.46	.....	.....	.....	2.7	13,32, 47,56
	Clupeidae																
76	*Alosa pseudoharengus*	T	8	13	16	22	...	...	33	0.006	0.017	0.04	0.07	.....	.....	0.34	13,37
77	*A. sapidissima*	T	14	25	41	53	58	...	67	.....	.....	1.82	1.94	2.5	.....	6.35	13,31,41
78	*Caspialosa caspica*	F	13	16	22	...	...	...	....	.....	.....	.....	.....	.....	.....	.....	9
79	*Clupea pallasi*	F	6	14	21	24	26	28	40	.....	.....	.....	.....	.....	.....	0.31	66
80	*Sardinops caerulea*	S	16	20	23	24	25	26	29	.....	.....	.....	.....	.....	.....	.....	25,26
	Elopidae																
81	*Tarpon atlanticus*	F	....	...	...	...	...	...	227	.....	.....	.....	.....	.....	.....	112	34
	Ginglymodi																
	Lepisosteidae																
82	*Lepisosteus osseus*	T	16	32	...	...	...	102	160	.....	.....	.....	.....	.....	.....	18	2,13,57, 63
	Chondrostei																
	Polyodontidae																
83	*Polyodon spathula*	S	25	64	84	97	102	112	188[3]	0.077	1.35	2.27	3.4	5	6.8	74	1,13,24, 29
	Acipenseridae																
84	*Acipenser fulvescens*	F	24	30	45	54	60	71	168	0.068	0.136	0.39	0.72	1	1.4	50	13,18, 41,79
85	*A. gueldenstaedtii*	T	28	42	66	84	99	112	136	.....	.....	.....	.....	.....	.....	.....	9
86	*A. nudiventris*	T	....	...	....	...	97	111	182	.....	.....	.....	.....	.....	.....	21+	9
87	*A. oxyrhynchus*	T	28	30	61	65	83	184	254	.....	0.14	1.02	1.32	3	36	91	37,69
88	*A. ruthenus*	T	....	...	32	36	43	49	77	0.049	0.082	0.150	0.275	0.375	.....	.....	9
89	*A. transmontanus*	F	35	46	56	87	99	118	....	.....	.....	.....	.....	.....	.....	907	16,20,59
	Petromyzones																
	Petromyzonidae																
90	*Petromyzon marinus*	T	3.8	7.9	43	...	...	...	84	.....	.....	.....	.....	.....	.....	1.14	4,83

/3/ Total length.

Contributors: (a) Carlander, Kenneth D., (b) Ricker, William Edwin

References: [1] Adams, L. A. 1942. Am. Midland Naturalist 28:617. [2] Allen, E. R. 1946. Fishes of Silver Springs, Florida. The Author, Silver Springs, Florida. [3] Alonso Cuenca, S. 1951. Montes (Madrid) 7:285. [4] Applegate, V. C. 1950. U. S. Fish Wildlife Service Spec. Sci. Rept. Fisheries 55. [5] Bailey, R. M., and K. F. Lagler. 1938. Papers Mich. Acad. Sci. 23:577. [6] Barney, R. L., and B. J. Anson. 1923. Ann. Rept. U. S. Comm. Fish and Fisheries, 1922, app. 15. [7] Barnickol, P. G., and W. C. Starrett. 1951. Illinois Nat. Hist. Survey Bull. 25:267. [8] Beckman, W. C. 1942. Copeia, p. 120. [9] Berg, L. S. 1948. Freshwater fishes of the U.S.S.R. and its neighboring countries. Ed. 4. Academy of Sciences of the U.S.S.R., Moscow [10] Burress, R. 1951. Missouri Conservation Comm. 12:16. [11] Carlander, K. D. 1942. Minn. Bur. Fishery Research Invest. Rept. 42. [12] Carlander, K. D. 1949. Iowa Cooperative Wildlife Research Unit. Progr. Rept. 39. [13] Carlander, K. D. 1950. Handbook of freshwater fishery biology. W. C. Brown, Dubuque, Iowa. [14] Clark, G. H. 1938. Calif. Fish and Game 24:176. [15] Clemens, W. A. 1950. Brit. Columbia Dept. Fisheries Rept., 1948, suppl. 25. [16] Clemens, W. A., and G. V. Wilby. 1946. Fisheries Research Board Can. Bull. 68. [17] Cooper, G. P. 1941. Maine Dept. Inland Fisheries and Game Fish Survey Rept. 4. [18] Cuerrier, J. P. 1949. Chasse et peche (Montreal) 1:26. [19] Dixon, B. 1934. J. conseil 9:66. [20] Donaldson, I. Unpublished, 1958. [21] Eddy, S., and K. D. Carlander. 1939. Minn. Conservationist 69:8. [22] Eddy, S., and T. Surber. 1947. Northern fishes.

continued

Univ. Minn. Press, Minneapolis. [23] Embody, G. C. 1915. Cornell Country Life Ser. 3:57. [24] Evermann, B. W., and E. L. Goldsborough. 1902. N. Y. State Fish Comm. Rept., 1901, p. 169. [25] Felin, F. E., and J. B. Phillips. 1948. Calif. Div. Fish and Game Fish Bull. 69. [26] Felin, F. E., J. B. Phillips, and A. E. Daugherty. 1951. Calif. Fish and Game 37:339. [27] Fitch, J. E. 1951. Calif. Div. Fish and Game Fish Bull. 83. [28] Flower, S. S. 1935. Proc. Zool. Soc. (London), p. 265. [29] Forbes, S. A., and R. E. Richardson. 1909. Rept. Illinois Nat. Hist. Survey, Urbana. [30] Ford, T. 1947. Alabama Conservation 19:7. [31] Fredin, R. A. Unpublished, 1952. [32] Freeman, B. D., and M. T. Huish. 1953. Report. Florida Game and Fresh Water Fish Commission, Tallahassee. [33] Fuller, J. L., and G. P. Cooper. 1946. Maine Dept. Inland Fisheries and Game Fish Survey Rept. 7. [34] Gabrielson, I. N., and F. R. La Monte, ed. The fisherman's encyclopedia. Stackpole and Heck, New York. [35] Gilbert, C. H., and W. H. Rich. 1927. U. S. Bur. Fisheries Bull 48:1. [36] Gowanloch, J. N. 1951. Louisiana Conservationist 3:10. [37] Greeley, J. R. 1937. N. Y. State Dept. Conservation Biol. Survey Lower Hudson Watershed 26th Ann. Rept., 1936, suppl. 11. [38] Haakh, T. 1929. Arch. Hydrobiol. 20:124. [39] Haig-Brown, R. L. 1947. The western angler. W. Morrow, New York. [40] Hansen, D. F. 1951. Illinois Nat. Hist. Survey Bull. 25:209. [41] Harkness, W. J. K. 1923. Univ. Toronto Biol. Ser. 24:15. [42] Hart, J. L. 1940. Fisheries Research Board Can. Progr. Repts. Pacific Coast Stas. 44:14. [43] Henshall, J. A. 1904. Book of the black bass. Steward and Kidd, New York. [44] Jordan, D. C., and B. W. Evermann. 1908. American food and game fishes. Doubleday Page, New York. [45] Kennedy, W. A. 1949. Fisheries Research Board Can. Bull. 81. [46] Krumholz, L. A. 1950. Trans. North Am. Wildlife Conf. 15:251. [47] Lagler, K. F., and V. C. Applegate. 1942. Indiana Lakes and Streams Invest. 2:99. [48] Langlois, T. H. 1936. Copeia, p. 120. [49] Leonard, A. K. 1927. Univ. Toronto Biol. Ser. 29:35. [50] Lewis, W. M. 1950. Iowa State Coll. J. Sci. 24:287. [51] Marr, J. C. 1943. Stanford Ichthyol. Bull. 2:157. [52] McClane, A. J., ed. 1951. The Wise fishermen's encyclopedia. W. H. Wise, New York. [53] Merriman, D. 1941. U. S. Fish Wildlife Service Fishery Bull. 50:1. [54] Miller, R. B. 1946. Copeia, p. 227. [55] Miller, R. B. 1949. Preliminary biological surveys of Alberta watersheds, 1947-49. Dept. Lands and Forests, Alberta, Canada. [56] Moen, T. 1956. Iowa Conservation Comm. Quart. Biol. Rept. 8:42. [57] Moody, H. L. 1957. Quart. J. Florida Acad. Sci. 20:21. [58] Oregon State Game Comm. 1952. Fishery Div. Ann. Rept., 1951. [59] Pycha, R. L. 1956. Calif. Fish and Game 42:23. [60] Rawson, D. S. 1951. J. Fisheries Research Board Can. 8:207. [61] Rayner, H. J. 1949. Oregon State Game Comm. Bull. 4:1. [62] Roach, L. S. 1948. Ohio Conserv. Bull. 12:12. [63] Roach, L. S. 1949. Ibid. 13:13. [64] Robertson, O. H. 1947. Ecology 28:87. [65] Rose, E. T., and T. Moen. 1951. Trans. Am. Fisheries Soc. 80:50. [66] Rounsefell, G. A. 1930. U. S. Bur. Fisheries Bull. 45:227. [67] Rounsefell, G. A., et al. 1938. Ibid. 49:693. [68] Schaefer, M. B., and J. C. Marr. 1948. U. S. Fish Wildlife Service Fishery Bull. 51:187. [69] Schiemenz, F. 1930. Tabulae Biologicae 6:582. [70] Schneberger, E. 1937. Trans. Am. Fisheries Soc. 66:139. [71] Schoffman, R. J. 1940. Reelfoot Lake Biol. Sta. Rept. 4:22. [72] Schroeder, W. C. 1930. U. S. Bur. Fisheries Bull. 46:1. [73] Schuck, H. A. 1951. U. S. Fish Wildlife Service Fishery Bull. 52:151. [74] Schuck, H. A., and E. L. Arnold, Jr. 1951. Ibid. 52:177. [75] Shimada, B. M., and W. G. van Campen. 1950. U. S. Fish Wildlife Service Spec. Sci. Rept. Fisheries 22. [76] Smith, H. M. 1907. N. Carolina Geol. Econ. Survey 2:271. [77] Smith, L. L., Jr., and N. L. Moe. 1944. Minn. Dept. Conservation Bull. 7. [78] Snyder, J. O. 1931. Calif. Div. Fish and Game Fish Bull. 34. [79] Speaker, E. B. 1946. Iowa Conservationist 5:60. [80] Stroud, R. H. 1948. J. Tenn. Acad. Sci. 23:31. [81] Tompkins, W. A., and B. T. Carter. 1951. Kentucky Div. Game and Fish Fishery Bull. 6. [82] Van Oosten, J., and R. Hile. 1949. Trans. Am. Fisheries Soc. 77:178. [83] Vladykov, V. D. 1951. Can. Fish Culturist 10:1. [84] Wales, J. H. 1946. Calif. Fish and Game 32:109. [85] Walford, L. A. 1932. Calif. Div. Fish and Game Fish Bull. 37. [86] Walford, L. A. 1937. Marine game fishes of the Pacific coast. Univ. California Press, Berkeley. [87] Ward, H. C. 1951. Copeia, p. 95. [88] Webster, D. A. 1942. Connecticut State Geol. Nat. Hist. Survey Bull. 63:122. [89] Williamson, L. O. 1940. Wisconsin Conservation Bull. 5:37.

IX. PLANT DEVELOPMENT AND COMPARATIVE MORPHOLOGY

103. FLOWERING, SIZE, GROWTH RATE, AND LIFE SPAN: FOREST TREES, NORTH AMERICAN

Values are approximate, as great variation exists within species.

	Species	Common Name	Age at First Flowering yr	Trunk Diameter[1] at Maturity, ft		Height at Maturity, ft		Relative Growth Rate	Life Span[2] yr
				Average	Maximum	Average	Maximum		
	(A)	(B)	(C)	(D)	(E)	(F)	(G)	(H)	(I)
	Gymnospermae								
1	*Abies amabilis*	Pacific silver fir	20	2-4	6	140-160	250	Moderate	250-300
2	*A. balsamea*	Balsam fir	15	1-1.5	3	40-60	85	Rapid	100-150
3	*A. concolor*	White fir	30-40	3-4	6	120-150	200	Moderate	150-400
4	*A. fraseri*	Fraser fir	20	1-2	2.5	30-50	65	Moderate	200-300
5	*A. grandis*	Grand fir	20-30	2-4	6	120-160	250	Moderate	200-400
6	*A. lasiocarpa*	Alpine fir	15-25	1.5-2	3	60-100	160	Moderate	150-200
7	*A. magnifica*	California red fir	.....	4-5	10	150-180	230	Moderate	250-400
8	*A. procera*	Noble fir	50	2.5-5	8	140-160	260	Rapid	300-500
9	*Chamaecyparis lawsoniana*	Port Orford cedar	8	3.5-6	16	140-180	225	Moderate	300-500
10	*C. nootkatensis*	Alaska cedar	.....	2-3	7	60-90	130	Slow	300-600
11	*C. thyoides*	Atlantic white cedar	4-10	1-2.5	5	50-80	120	Slow	100-200
12	*Cupressus arizonica*	Arizona cypress	.....	1-2.5	5	50-60	90	Slow	100-300
13	*Juniperus deppeana*	Alligator juniper	.....	1.5-3	6	30-50	60	Very slow	300-500
14	*J. occidentalis*	Western juniper	.....	1-2.5	3	20-30	40	Slow	300
15	*J. osteosperma*	Utah juniper	.....	1-1.5	2.5	15-20	30	Very slow	150-300
16	*J. scopulorum*	Rocky Mountain juniper	10-20	1-2	3	20-40	55	Slow	100-300
17	*J. virginiana*	Eastern red cedar	10-15	1-2	4	40-50	100	Slow	150-300
18	*Larix laricina*	Tamarack	20	1-2	3	40-80	100	Moderate	100-200
19	*L. occidentalis*	Western larch	20-40	3-4	8	140-180	210	Slow	300-600
20	*Libocedrus decurrens*	Incense cedar	.....	2.5-4	11	80-110	190	Slow	300-400
21	*Picea engelmannii*	Engelmann spruce	16-25	1-3	6	100-120	165	Slow	200-500
22	*P. glauca*	White spruce	10-15	1.5-2	4	60-70	120	Slow	150-350
23	*P. mariana*	Black spruce	10-18	0.5-1	3	30-40	100	Slow	150-250
24	*P. pungens*	Blue spruce	20-50	1-2	3	70-100	150	Slow	150-350
25	*P. rubens*	Red spruce	30	1-2	4	60-70	120	Slow	200-300
26	*P. sitchensis*	Sitka spruce	20	2-5	16	180-200	300	Rapid	400-750
27	*Pinus attenuata*	Knobcone pine	5	1-2	3	60-80	100	Rapid	100-150
28	*P. banksiana*	Jack pine	5	1-1.5	2	30-60	90	Rapid	80-150
29	*P. contorta*	Lodgepole pine	5-20	1-2.5	3	30-70	150	Slow	120-300
30	*P. echinata*	Shortleaf pine	8-14	2-2.5	4	80-100	150	Rapid	200-300
31	*P. edulis*	Pinyon	20-25	1-2	3	15-30	50	Very slow	150-400
32	*P. elliottii*	Slash pine	6-15	1-2	3	80-90	130	Rapid	150-250
33	*P. flexilis*	Limber pine	10-30	1.5-2.5	7	30-50	85	Slow	200-400
34	*P. glabra*	Spruce pine	10	2-2.5	4	80-90	120	Rapid	75-150
35	*P. jeffreyii*	Jeffrey pine	6-8	3-4	9	90-100	130	Moderate	300-500
36	*P. lambertiana*	Sugar pine	7	2-4	10	160-180	250	Rapid	300-600
37	*P. monophylla*	Single-leaf pinyon	.....	1-2	3	20-30	50	Very slow	150-225
38	*P. monticola*	Western white pine	10-20	2.5-3.5	8	150-180	120	Rapid	200-500
39	*P. palustris*	Longleaf pine	16-20	2-3	4	80-120	150	Rapid	300-400
40	*P. ponderosa*	Ponderosa pine	5-20	3-4	9	100-180	235	Moderate	300-500
41	*P. resinosa*	Red pine	10	2-3	5	50-80	120	Rapid	200-350
42	*P. rigida*	Pitch pine	5-10	1-2	3	50-60	100	Rapid	100-200
43	*P. sabiniana*	Digger pine	6	1-2	4	40-50	90	Moderate	80-150
44	*P. strobus*	Eastern white pine	10	2-4	6	80-120	220	Rapid	300-500
45	*P. taeda*	Loblolly pine	6-12	2-2.5	5	90-110	190	Rapid	150-250
46	*P. virginiana*	Virginia pine	5	1-1.5	3	30-40	100	Moderate	100-200
47	*Pseudotsuga menziesii*	Douglas fir	.....	4-6	15	180-250	385	Rapid	....
48	*Sequoia gigantea*	Giant sequoia	60	10-15	38	250-280	350	Rapid	2000-3000
49	*S. sempervirens*	Redwood	20	6-12	20	150-275	365	Rapid	800-1500
50	*Taxodium distichum*	Bald cypress	.....	2-5	12	80-120	150	Slow	600-1200
51	*Taxus brevifolia*	Pacific yew	.....	1-1.5	2	20-40	65	Slow	250-350

/1/ Measurements at breast height (4.5 ft). /2/ Age at natural death.

continued

103. FLOWERING, SIZE, GROWTH RATE, AND LIFE SPAN: FOREST TREES, NORTH AMERICAN

	Species	Common Name	Age at First Flowering yr	Trunk Diameter[1] at Maturity, ft		Height at Maturity, ft		Relative Growth Rate	Life Span[2] yr
				Average	Maximum	Average	Maximum		
	(A)	(B)	(C)	(D)	(E)	(F)	(G)	(H)	(I)
				Gymnospermae					
52	*Thuja occidentalis*	Northern white cedar	30	2-3	6	30-50	125	Slow	300-400
53	*T. plicata*	Western red cedar	15-25	4-8	20	150-200	250	Rapid	500-800
54	*Tsuga canadensis*	Eastern hemlock	30	2-3	6	60-80	160	Slow	300-600
55	*T. heterophylla*	Western hemlock	20-30	2-5	9	100-170	260	Moderate	300-600
56	*T. mertensiana*	Mountain hemlock	25-30	2.3-3.5	5	70-100	130	Moderate	200-500
				Angiospermae					
57	*Acer macrophyllum*	Big leaf maple	10	1-3	8	50-80	120	Rapid	150-300
58	*A. negundo*	Box elder	.....	1.5-3	6	40-50	75	Very rapid	75-100
59	*A. rubrum*	Red maple	.....	1-2.5	5	50-70	120	Rapid	80-250
60	*A. saccharinum*	Silver maple	.....	2-3	7	60-80	120	Rapid	50-125
61	*A. saccharum*	Sugar maple	.....	2-3	5	60-80	135	Slow	200-300
62	*Aesculus glabra*	Ohio buckeye	.....	1-2	2.5	30-60	90	Moderate	....
63	*A. octandra*	Yellow buckeye	.....	2-3	4	70-90	100	Rapid	60-80
64	*Alnus rubra*	Red alder	10	1-3	5	80-100	130	Rapid	60-100
65	*Arbutus menziesii*	Pacific madrone	.....	1-2	4	40-80	125	Slow	....
66	*Betula alleghaniensis*	Yellow birch	40	1-2	4	60-80	100	Rapid	150-300
67	*B. lenta*	Sweet birch	40	1-2	5	50-60	80	Moderate	150-250
68	*B. nigra*	River birch	.....	2-3	5	70-80	100	Rapid	....
69	*B. papyrifera*	Paper birch	15	1-2	5	50-70	120	Rapid	80-100
70	*B. populifolia*	Gray birch	8	0.6-1	1.5	20-30	60	Rapid	50
71	*Carya cordiformis*	Bitternut hickory	30	1-2	4	50-60	85	Slow	175
72	*C. glabra*	Pignut hickory	30	1-2	4	60-80	120	Slow	200-300
73	*C. illinoensis*	Pecan	10	2-4	6	90-120	180	Moderate	300
74	*C. laciniosa*	Shellbark hickory	40	1-2	4	60-80	120	Slow	350
75	*C. ovata*	Shagbark hickory	40	1-2	4	60-80	120	Slow	250-300
76	*C. tomentosa*	Mockernut hickory	25	1-2.5	3.5	50-70	100	Slow	200-300
77	*Castanea dentata*	American chestnut	.....	2-4	10	70-90	120	Rapid	100-300
78	*Castanopsis chrysophylla*	Golden chinkapin	.....	1-2.5	8	60-80	150	Rapid	200-400
79	*Catalpa speciosa*	Northern catalpa	10	1-3	5	30-60	120	Rapid	100
80	*Celtis laevigata*	Sugarberry	.....	1.5-2.5	5	60-80	130	Moderate	....
81	*C. occidentalis*	Hackberry	.....	1-2	5	40-80	130	Rapid	75-150
82	*Cornus florida*	Flowering dogwood	5	0.5-1	1.5	20-40	50	Slow	125
83	*C. nuttallii*	Pacific dogwood	10	0.5-1	1.5	30-50	70	Slow	125
84	*Diospyros virginiana*	Persimmon	10	1-1.5	7	30-50	130	Slow	60-80
85	*Fagus grandifolia*	American beech	40	1-3	4	70-100	120	Slow	300-400
86	*Fraxinus americana*	White ash	20	2-3	6	60-80	125	Rapid	260-300
87	*F. latifolia*	Oregon ash	.....	2-3	5	60-80	130	Moderate	150-250
88	*F. nigra*	Black ash	.....	1-2	5	40-60	90	Slow	....
89	*F. pennsylvanica*	Green ash	.....	1-2	2.5	35-50	85	Rapid	....
90	*F. quadrangulata*	Blue ash	25	1-2	4	40-50	120	Rapid	200-300
91	*Gleditsia triacanthos*	Honey locust	10	2-3	6	70-80	140	Rapid	120
92	*Ilex opaca*	American holly	5	1-2	4	40-50	140	Slow	100-150
93	*Juglans cinerea*	Butternut	20	1-2	3	40-60	110	Rapid	80
94	*J. nigra*	Black walnut	12	2-3	7	50-90	150	Rapid	150-250
95	*Liquidambar styraciflua*	Sweet gum	20-25	2-5	6	80-140	200	Rapid	200-300
96	*Liriodendron tulipifera*	Yellow poplar	15-20	2-5	12	80-120	200	Rapid	200-250
97	*Lithocarpus densiflora*	Tan oak	.....	1-3	7	70-90	150	Moderate	150-300
98	*Maclura pomifera*	Osage orange	10	1-2	5	20-50	70	Moderate	75-100
99	*Magnolia acuminata*	Cucumber tree	30	2-3	5	70-90	100	Rapid	80-250
100	*M. grandiflora*	Southern magnolia	.....	2-3	4.5	60-80	135	Moderate	80-120
101	*Morus rubra*	Red mulberry	10	0.5-1	1.5	20-40	50	Moderate	125
102	*Nyssa aquatica*	Water tupelo	5-10	3-4	5	80-100	120	Rapid	....
103	*N. sylvatica*	Black tupelo	.....	2-3	4	50-80	100	Rapid	....
104	*Ostrya virginiana*	Hop hornbeam	.....	1-1.5	1.5	30-40	55	Slow	....
105	*Platanus occidentalis*	Sycamore	25	2-5	14	80-120	175	Rapid	250-500
106	*Populus balsamifera*	Balsam poplar	.....	1-2	5	60-80	100	Rapid	100-150
107	*P. deltoides*	Eastern cottonwood	10	3-4	11	80-100	175	Very rapid	60-100
108	*P. grandidentata*	Bigtooth aspen	20	1-2	3	60-70	80	Rapid	70-100

/1/ Measurements at breast height (4.5 ft). /2/ Age at natural death.

continued

103. FLOWERING, SIZE, GROWTH RATE, AND LIFE SPAN: FOREST TREES, NORTH AMERICAN

	Species	Common Name	Age at First Flowering yr	Trunk Diameter[1] at Maturity, ft		Height at Maturity, ft		Relative Growth Rate	Life Span[2] yr
				Average	Maximum	Average	Maximum		
	(A)	(B)	(C)	(D)	(E)	(F)	(G)	(H)	(I)
	Angiospermae								
109	*Populus sargentii*	Plains cottonwood	.....	2-3	5	50-80	110	Rapid	50-90
110	*P. tremuloides*	Quaking aspen	5-20	1-2	4.5	40-60	120	Very rapid	70-100
111	*P. trichocarpa*	Black cottonwood	.....	3-4	8	80-120	225	Rapid	150-200
112	*Prunus serotina*	Black cherry	10-15	1.5-3	5	50-60	100	Rapid	100-200
113	*Quercus alba*	White oak	20	2.5-4	8	80-100	150	Slow	300-600
114	*Q. agrifolia*	California live oak	.....	1-3	6	30-60	110	Slow	150
115	*Q. bicolor*	Swamp white oak	35	2-3	7	60-70	100	Slow	300
116	*Q. chrysolepis*	Canyon live oak	.....	2-4	11	60-80	100	Slow	200-300
117	*Q. coccinea*	Scarlet oak	20	2-3	4	70-80	110	Moderate	150
118	*Q. douglasii*	Blue oak	.....	1-2	3	50-80	130	Slow	....
119	*Q. emoryii*	Emory oak	.....	1-2	3	30-50	65	Slow	....
120	*Q. falcata*	Southern red oak	25	2-3	7	60-80	110	Moderate	200-275
121	*Q. gambelii*	Gambel oak	.....	0.5-1	1.5	20-30	50	Slow	....
122	*Q. garryana*	Oregon white oak	.....	2-3	8	50-70	120	Slow	....
123	*Q. kelloggii*	California black oak	.....	1.5-2.5	11	50-80	100	Slow	175-300
124	*Q. laurifolia*	Laurel oak	.....	2-3	7	60-70	100	Moderate	....
125	*Q. lobata*	California white oak	.....	3-5	10	50-90	130	Rapid	200-300
126	*Q. lyrata*	Overcup oak	.....	1.5-2.5	4.5	40-70	110	Slow	300-400
127	*Q. macrocarpa*	Bur oak	35	2-3	7	70-80	170	Slow	200-400
128	*Q. marilandica*	Blackjack oak	.....	0.5-1.5	2	20-30	55	Slow	100
129	*Q. michauxii*	Swamp chestnut oak	.....	2-3	9	60-80	120	Slow	100-200
130	*Q. muehlenbergii*	Chinkapin oak	.....	2-3	4	60-80	160	Rapid	....
131	*Q. nigra*	Water oak	25	1.5-3	5	60-70	125	Rapid	175
132	*Q. nuttallii*	Nuttall oak	.....	1-2	3.5	50-70	120	Moderate	....
133	*Q. palustris*	Pin oak	20	2-3	5	60-80	120	Rapid	125-150
134	*Q. phellos*	Willow oak	.....	1.5-3	6	80-100	130	Moderate	....
135	*Q. prinus*	Chestnut oak	20	2-3	6	50-60	100	Moderate	300-400
136	*Q. rubra*	Northern red oak	25	2-3	11	60-70	150	Rapid	200-400
137	*Q. shumardii*	Shumard oak	.....	4-5	8	80-100	180	Rapid	....
138	*Q. stellata*	Post oak	25	1-2	4	40-50	100	Slow	250
139	*Q. velutina*	Black oak	20	2-3	7	20-30	55	Moderate	150-200
140	*Q. virginiana*	Live oak	.....	3-4	11	40-50	100	Moderate	200-300
141	*Rhamnus purshiana*	Buckthorn	5	0.5-1	3	30-40	60	Rapid	40-50
142	*Robinia pseudoacacia*	Black locust	6	1-2	5	40-60	100	Rapid	60-100
143	*Sabal palmetto*	Cabbage palmetto	.....	1-1.5	2	30-50	90	Slow	50-80
144	*Salix amygdaloides*	Peachleaf willow	.....	1-1.5	3	20-40	60	Rapid	50-100
145	*S. nigra*	Black willow	10	1-2	6	30-40	120	Rapid	50-125
146	*Sassafras albidum*	Sassafras	10	1-2.5	6	40-70	110	Rapid	100-500
147	*Swietenia mahagoni*[3]	West Indies mahogany	.....	0.5-1	1.5	30-40	60	Slow	150-200
148	*Tilia americana*	American basswood	15	2-3	5	60-80	125	Rapid	100-140
149	*T. heterophylla*	White basswood	15	1.5-2.5	3	60-80	125	Moderate	ca. 100
150	*Ulmus americana*	American elm	15	2-4	11	80-100	120	Rapid	150-300
151	*U. rubra*	Slippery elm	15	1-2	4	50-70	90	Rapid	300
152	*U. thomasii*	Rock elm	20	1-2.5	5	50-70	100	Rapid	250
153	*Umbellularia californica*	California laurel	30	1-3	6	60-100	175	Moderate	200

/1/ Measurements at breast height (4.5 ft). /2/ Age at natural death. /3/ Attains greater size in the tropics.

Contributors: (a) Little, Elbert L., Jr., (b) Harrar, E. S., (c) Josephson, Horace R., (d) Robinson, Florence B.

References: [1] Collingwood, G. H., and W. D. Bush. 1947. Knowing your trees. American Forestry Association, Washington, D. C. [2] Harlow, W. M., and E. S. Harrar. 1958. Textbook of dendrology covering the important forest trees of the United States and Canada. Ed. 4. McGraw-Hill, New York. [3] Little, E. L., Jr. Unpublished. 1953. [4] Preston, R. J., Jr. 1948. North American trees (exclusive of Mexico and tropical United States). Iowa State College Press, Ames. [5] Righter, F. I. 1937. J. Forestry 37:935. [6] Sudworth, G. B. 1908. Forest trees of the Pacific slope. U. S. Dept. of Agriculture Forest Service, Washington, D. C. [7] U. S. Dept. of Agriculture Forest Service. 1948. U. S. Dept. Agr. Misc. Publ. 654.

104. TIME PERIODS IN DEVELOPMENT:

Time periods are averages, based on observations of the growing seasons for one to several localities and years. latitude, altitude, slope, rainfall, and other conditions. Where geographical and altitudinal variations have been season.

Part I: EASTERN

	Species	Leafing	Leaf Falling	Flowering[1]
	(A)	(B)	(C)	(D)
	Gymnospermae			
1	*Abies balsamea*	May20-June10	Sept20-Oct20	May10-31
2	*Juniperus virginiana*	Mar10-May20	Oct1-31	Mar10-May20
3	*Larix laricina*	May1-31	Sept20-Oct31	Apr20-May31
4	*Picea glauca*	May10-31	....	May1-31
5	*P. mariana*	June1+	....	June1-10
6	*P. rubens*	....	....	June1-10
7	*Pinus banksiana*	May20+	Oct10+	May10-June10
8	*P. echinata*	Feb20+ (May20-July31)	Sept1-Dec31[4]	Feb20+ (May10-20)
9	*P. elliottii*	Feb20+	....	Jan20-Feb20
10	*P. palustris*	Mar1+	Sept1-Dec31[4]	Feb1-Mar31
11	*P. resinosa*	May20-Aug31	Oct1+	June1-20
12	*P. rigida*	May20-July31	....	Apr20-May20
13	*P. strobus*	May1-Aug10 (May20-Aug20)	Sept1-Oct20 (Sept10-30)	May10-June10 (June20-30)
14	*P. taeda*	Feb10+ (Mar10+)	(Sept1-Dec31[4])	Feb20-Mar10(Apr1-20)
15	*Taxodium distichum*	Mar10-Apr20	Oct20-Nov30	Mar1-Apr20
16	*Thuja occidentalis*	May10+	....	May20-31
17	*Tsuga canadensis*	May20-June20	Sept10-Oct31	May10-June10
	Angiospermae (Dicotyledoneae)			
18	*Acer negundo*	Mar20-Apr20 (Apr20-May20)	Oct1-Nov10 (Oct1-20)	Mar20-Apr20 (Apr20-May10)
19	*A. rubrum*	Mar1-Apr20 (May10-June10)	Oct20-Nov10 (Sept20-Oct10)	Jan10-31 (May1-10)
20	*A. saccharinum*	Feb20-Mar20 (Apr10-May10)	Oct20-Nov10 (Oct10-31)	Feb1-Mar1 (Mar20-Apr20)
21	*A. saccharum*	Apr20-May10 (May20-June10)	Oct1-Nov10 (Sept20-Oct10)	Apr20-May10 (May10-31)
22	*Aesculus glabra*	Mar20-May10	Oct1-31	Mar20-May20
23	*Betula alleghaniensis*	Apr20-May10 (May20-June10)	Oct10-31 (Sept20-Oct20)	Apr20-30 (May10-20)
24	*B. lenta*	Apr10-May31	Oct1-31	Apr1-May10
25	*B. papyrifera*	Apr20-May10 (May20-June10)	Oct1-31 (Sept20-Oct20)	Apr20-May10 (June1-10)
26	*B. populifolia*	Apr20-May20	Oct1-31	Apr20-May20
27	*Carya glabra*	Apr1-30 (May1-20)	Oct1-Nov10 (Oct1-31)	Apr10-May10 (May10-31)
28	*C. ovata*	Apr1-May10	Oct1-31	Apr10-May31
29	*C. tomentosa*	Apr1-30	Oct1-31	Apr10-May10
30	*Castanea dentata*	Apr20-May20	Oct10-Nov30	June20-July10
31	*Celtis occidentalis*	Apr10-May20	Oct1-31	Apr20-May20
32	*Cornus florida*	Mar20-Apr20 (May1-20)	Oct1-Nov10 (Oct1-20)	Mar20-Apr20 (May1-20)
33	*Diospyros virginiana*	Apr10-30 (May1-31)	(Oct1-31)	May1-31 (June10-20)
34	*Fagus grandifolia*	Mar1-31 (May20-June10)	Nov1-Dec20 (Oct1-31)	Apr1-20 (June1-30)
35	*Fraxinus americana*	Apr10-30 (May20-June10)	Oct1-Nov10 (Sept20-Oct10)	Apr1-May10 (May1-20)
36	*F. nigra*	May20-June30	Sept20-Oct10	May20+
37	*F. pennsylvanica*	Apr1-30 (Apr20-June10)	(Sept10-Oct10)	Apr10-30 (Apr20-May10)
38	*Gleditsia triacanthos*	Apr1-May20	Oct1-Nov10	May1-June10
39	*Ilex opaca*	Apr1-May10	Mar1-31	Apr10-June10
40	*Juglans cinerea*	Apr10-May20	Sept10-Oct20	Apr10-May20
41	*J. nigra*	Apr1-30 (May10-31)	Sept20-Oct31 (Oct1-20)	Apr1-May10 (May1-31)
42	*Liquidambar styraciflua*	Mar10-Apr30	Oct1-Nov10	Mar10-May10
43	*Liriodendron tulipifera*	Mar20-Apr20 (Apr20-May20)	Oct10-Nov10 (Sept1-Oct31)	Apr1-30 (May1-June10)
44	*Magnolia acuminata*	Apr20-May20	Oct1-31	May1-31
45	*Morus rubra*	Apr1-30	Oct1-31	Apr10-May20
46	*Nyssa sylvatica*	Apr1-30 (May1-31)	(Sept20-Nov10)	Apr10-May10 (May20-June10)
47	*Ostrya virginiana*	Apr1-20 (May20-June10)	(Sept20-Oct20)	Mar20-31 (May20-31)
48	*Platanus occidentalis*	Apr1-May10	Oct10-Nov10	Apr1-May10
49	*Populus balsamifera*	Apr20-May10 (May10-June10)	Oct20-Nov10 (Sept10-Oct10)	Apr10-20 (May1-10)
50	*P. deltoides*	Mar10-Apr10 (May1-20)	Oct10-Nov10 (Sept10-Oct20)	Mar1-20 (Apr20-May10)
51	*P. grandidentata*	Apr10-May10 (May20-June20)	Oct1-20 (Oct1-20)	Apr1-20 (Apr20-May10)
52	*Prunus serotina*	Mar20-Apr20 (May10-June10)	Oct10-Nov10 (Sept20-Oct10)	Apr1-30 (June1-10)
53	*Quercus alba*	Mar20-Apr20 (May10-June10)	Oct20-Mar10 (Oct10-31)	Apr1-20 (May10-20)
54	*Q. bicolor*	May1-20	Oct10-31	May10-20
55	*Q. coccinea*	Apr20-May20	Oct20+	Apr20-May10

/1/ Pollination dates are given for conifers. /2/ Cones are retained for 2-3 years, during which seedfall continues. the winter but in smaller quantities.

FOREST TREES, NORTH AMERICAN

Within one species there may be wide variation in the growth period of the various stages, due to differences in observed for a species, the "short" growing season is given in parentheses to distinguish it from the "long" growing

UNITED STATES

Seed Maturing	Seed Falling	Height Growth	Diameter Growth	
(E)	(F)	(G)	(H)	
		Gymnospermae		
Aug20-Sept10	Sept10-Nov30	May20-Aug20	May20-Sept10	1
Sept20-Nov20	Feb1-Mar31	....	....	2
Aug20-Sept10	Sept10-30	May20-Aug20	May20-July10	3
Aug20-Sept10	Sept10-Nov30	May10-July31	....	4
Aug20-Sept20	Sept20+[2]	June1-Aug20	....	5
To Sept10	Sept10+	June1-July31	May20-Sept10	6
Sept1-20	Sept20+[3]	May10-July10	....	7
(Oct1-20)	(Oct20-Dec31[5])	(May1-July31)	(Mar20-Aug31)	8
Sept1-20	Sept20-Nov10	....	....	9
Sept1-Oct20	Oct20-Nov30+	....	Mar1-Aug31	10
Sept10-30	Oct1-Dec31[5]	May1-Aug10	May1-Sept30	11
To Oct31	Nov1-Apr30	Apr20-July10	Apr20+	12
Aug1-Sept30 (Sept1-20)	Oct1-31 (Sept20-Oct31)	Apr20-June30 (May20-Aug10)	Apr20-Sept30 (May1-Sept30)	13
Oct1-31 (Sept20-Oct10)	Nov1-Dec31[5] (Oct10-Dec31[5])	(Mar20-Aug10)	(Mar20-Aug20)	14
Oct1-20	Oct20-Dec31[5]	....	....	15
Aug20-Sept30	Oct1-31	May10-Aug31	May20-Sept10	16
Sept1-Oct20	Oct20-Apr30	May20-Aug20	....	17
		Angiospermae (Dicotyledoneae)		
Aug31+ (Sept1-20)	Sept1-Dec31[5] (Oct1+)	(Apr10-June30)	....	18
To Mar20 (To June30)	Mar20-Apr20 (July1+)	(May10-July31)	May1-July20	19
To Mar31 (May1-20)	Apr1-30 (May20-June10)	(Apr10-July31)	(Apr20-Aug20)	20
To Sept20 (Aug10+)	Sept20-Oct31+ (Sept1+)	Apr10-May31 (May10-Aug31)	June10-Aug31 (June1-Sept10)	21
To Sept20	Sept20-Oct20	....	....	22
Aug1-10 (Aug20+)	Aug10-Oct31+ (Sept20+)	(May20-Aug10)	(June10-Aug10)	23
Aug20-Sept10	Sept10-Oct31+	....	....	24
To July31 (Sept10-30)	Aug1+ (Oct1-31)	....	....	25
Sept20-30	Oct1-Nov30+	....	May20-Aug10	26
To Oct10 (To Sept30)	Oct10-Nov10+	....	....	27
Sept10-30	Oct1-Nov10+	....	....	28
To Sept30	Oct1-31+	....	Apr1-July20	29
Sept20-Oct10	Oct10-Nov30	....	....	30
Sept20-30	Oct1-Dec31[5]	....	....	31
To Oct31 (Sept20-30)	Nov1-30 (Oct10-Nov30)	....	Apr10-July10	32
(Oct10-31)	(Nov1-Dec31[5])	....	Mar10-June30	33
To Sept20 (Sept10+)	Sept20-Nov10 (Oct10+)	....	(Apr10-July10)	34
(To Aug31)	(Sept1-Oct31)	(May20-June30)	(May10-July31)	35
July10-Aug31	July20-Oct31+	May20-July20	May20-Sept10	36
....	....	(Apr20-July20)	(Apr10-July31)	37
Sept20-Oct10	Oct10-Dec31[5]	....	....	38
Sept10-Oct20	Mar1-31	....	....	39
Sept20-30	Oct1-Nov20	....	....	40
Sept1-30 (Sept1-30)	Oct1-Nov10	....	....	41
Sept10-30	Oct1-31	....	May20-Aug20	42
Sept10-30	Oct1-Jan10	(Apr20-July31)	(May1-Aug10)	43
Sept1-10	Sept10-Oct10	....	....	44
June1-30	July1-Aug31	....	....	45
To Sept10 (To Sept20)	Sept10-Oct20 (Sept20-Oct20)	....	....	46
May1+ (To Aug31)	(Sept1+)	....	....	47
Sept20-30	Oct1-Mar1+	Apr1-July20	....	48
(May10-20)	....	(May10-June30)	....	49
Apr1-10 (May10-31)	Apr10-30 (May20-June30)	....	....	50
Apr20-30 (May10-20)	May1-20 (May20-June10)	....	....	51
To June30 (Aug20+)	July1-Aug31+ (Sept1+)	Mar20-June30	May20-Sept30	52
Sept20-Oct10 (Sept10-30)	Oct10-Nov10 (Sept20+)	....	Mar20-July31	53
To Sept30	....	....	....	54
Sept1-30	Oct1-31	....	....	55

/3/ Seedfall continues for several years. /4/ Leaf fall continues throughout the year. /5/ Seedfall continues through

continued

104. TIME PERIODS IN DEVELOPMENT:

Part I: EASTERN

	Species	Leafing	Leaf Falling	Flowering[1]
	(A)	(B)	(C)	(D)
	Angiospermae (Dicotyledoneae)			
56	*Quercus falcata*	Apr1-30	....	Apr1-May10
57	*Q. macrocarpa*	Apr1-30 (May10-31)	Oct20-Nov20 (Sept20-Oct20)	Apr20-May10 (June1-20)
58	*Q. nigra*	Mar1-Apr10	....	Feb20-Apr10
59	*Q. prinus*	Apr20-May20	Oct10+	May1-20
60	*Q. rubra*	Apr10-May10 (May20-June10)	Oct20-Nov10 (Oct1-20)	Apr20-May10 (May20-June10)
61	*Q. stellata*	Apr1-30 (May1-20)	Oct10-Nov10 (Oct10+)	Apr10-20 (May10-20)
62	*Q. velutina*	Apr20-May31	Oct20-Nov30	Apr20-May20
63	*Q. virginiana*	Mar1-Apr10	Feb10-Mar10	Mar10-Apr30
64	*Robinia pseudoacacia*	Apr1-May10	Sept20-Oct31	Apr20-May31
65	*Salix nigra*	Mar20-Apr20 (Apr20-May20)	Oct10-Nov10 (Oct1-31)	Mar10-31 (Apr20-May10)
66	*Sassafras albidum*	Apr10-30 (Apr20-May20)	(Oct10-31)	Mar20-Apr30 (Apr20-May10)
67	*Tilia americana*	Apr20-May10 (May20+)	Oct1-Nov10 (Sept20-Oct10)	June1-30 (July20-31)
68	*Ulmus alata*	Mar20-Apr20	....	Feb1-Mar10
69	*U. americana*	Mar20-Apr10 (May20-June10)	Oct1-Nov10 (Oct1-20)	Feb1-Mar1 (May10-31)
70	*U. rubra*	Mar20-Apr10 (Apr20-May20)	Oct1-31 (Sept20-Oct20)	Feb20-Mar10 (Apr10-30)
71	*U. thomasii*	Apr10-May10	Sept20-Oct20	Apr1-30

/1/ Pollination dates are given for conifers. /5/ Seedfall continues through the winter but in smaller quantities.

Contributors: (a) Little, Elbert L., Jr., (b) Delisle, Albert L.

References: [1] Baldwin, H. I. 1931. Ecology 12:665. [2] Cook, D. B. 1941. Ibid. 22:285. [3] Cook, D. B. 1941. Forests 25:1386. [6] Jackson, L. W. R. 1952. Ecology 33:336. [7] Johnston, J. P. 1941. J. Forestry 39:67. U. S. Weather Bur. Monthly Rev., Suppl. 2:3. [11] Leopold, A., and S. E. Jones. 1947. Ecol. Monographs 17:81. Univ. 1(2a):87. [14] Penfound, W. T., T. F. Hall, and A. D. Hess. 1945. Ecology 26:332. [15] Reimer, C. W. 1949. Dept. of Agriculture Forest Service. 1948. U. S. Dept. Agr. Misc. Publ. 654:416. [18] Wright, J. W. 1953. U. S.

Part II: WESTERN

	Species	Leafing	Leaf Falling	Flowering[1]
	(A)	(B)	(C)	(D)
	Gymnospermae			
1	*Abies concolor*	May10-20 (July1-10)	Sept1 (Oct1-31)	June1-10 (May1-20)
2	*A. grandis*	May1+ (June1+)	....	May1-10 (June10-20)
3	*A. lasiocarpa*	June1-10 (June20-30)	Aug10-Sept30 (Sept1-Oct31)	June1-10 (June20-July10)
4	*Juniperus occidentalis*	May10+	....	May10-20
5	*J. scopulorum*	May20-31 (June1-10)	....	May20-31 (June10-20)
6	*Larix occidentalis*	Apr10+ (May10+)	....	Apr20-30 (June1-20)
7	*Libocedrus decurrens*	May20-31	....	May20-31
8	*Picea engelmannii*	May20-31 (June20-30)	Sept1-20 (Sept1-Oct31)	May20-June10 (June20-30)
9	*P. pungens*	May20-31 (June10-20)	Sept10+ (Sept10-Oct10)	May20-31 (June20-30)
10	*P. sitchensis*	Apr20+	....	May1-10 (May20-31)
11	*Pinus contorta*	May1-31 (June20-30)	Oct1-Nov10 (Sept10-Oct31)	May10-31 (July1-20)
12	*P. edulis*	May20-June10 (June10-Aug10)	Sept20-Oct31 (May20-June20)	May10-31 (June10-30)
13	*P. flexilis*	May20-June20 (June1-20)	Sept20-Oct31 (Oct1-31)	June1-10 (June20-July10)
14	*P. jeffreyi*	June10-30	Oct10-Nov10	June10-30
15	*P. lambertiana*	July1-20	Oct10-Nov20	June10-30
16	*P. monticola*	May10+ (June1+)	....	May20-31 (June20-July10)
17	*P. ponderosa*	May20-June10 (June10-July31)	Oct1-Nov10 (Sept1-Oct10)	May20-June10 (June10-30)
18	*Pseudotsuga menziesii*	May1-20 (June20-30)	Oct10-Nov10 (Sept10-30)	Apr10-30 (July1-10)
19	*Thuja plicata*	....	(Sept1-Oct31)	Apr20-30 (May20-31)
20	*Tsuga heterophylla*	May1+ (June1+)	(Sept1-Dec31)	May1-10 (May20-31)

/1/ Pollination dates are given for conifers. /2/ Seedfall continues through the winter but in smaller quantities.

UNITED STATES

Seed Maturing	Seed Falling	Height Growth	Diameter Growth	
(E)	(F)	(G)	(H)	
Angiospermae (Dicotyledoneae)				
Sept1-30	Oct1-31	...	Apr1-July10	56
(Sept10-30)	(Oct1-31)	...	...	57
To Sept30	Oct1-31	...	...	58
Sept1-20	Sept20-Nov30	...	...	59
Sept1-20 (Sept1-10)	Sept20-Nov10 (Sept10-20)	(May20-June20)	Apr10-July31	60
Sept20-Oct10	Oct10-Nov10 (Oct1-10)	...	Apr1-July10	61
Sept1-30	Oct1-Nov10	...	...	62
Sept20-Oct10	Oct10-Nov30	...	...	63
Sept10-Oct10	Oct10-Dec31[5]	...	...	64
Apr1-20 (May10-31)	Apr20-May20 (June1-30)	...	...	65
(Aug20-Sept10)	(Sept10-Oct10)	...	...	66
Aug1-31 (Aug20-31)	Sept1-Oct20+ (Sept1-30)	Apr20-June20	June10-Sept20	67
Apr1-20	Apr20+	...	Apr20-July20	68
Mar10-31 (June20+)	Apr1-30 (July20+)	...	(May10-Aug10)	69
Apr1-10 (May10-20)	Apr10-30 (May20-June10)	...	(Apr20-Aug31)	70
May10-20	May20-July10	...	...	71

J. Forestry 39:956. [4] Friesner, R. C. 1942. Butler Univ. Botan. Studies 5:160. [5] Illick, J. S. 1919. Am. [8] Kienholz, R. 1934. Botan. Gaz. 96:73. [9] Kienholz, R. 1941. Ecology 22:249. [10] Lamb, G. N. 1915. [12] Little, S. 1941. Forest Leaves 31(4):1. [13] Lodewick, J. E. 1928. Bull. N. Y. State Coll. Forestry Syracuse Butler Univ. Botan. Studies 9:43. [16] Smith, J. W. 1915. U. S. Weather Bur. Monthly Rev., Suppl. 2:21. [17] U. S. Dept. Agr. Forest Service, Northeastern Forest Expt. Sta. Paper 60.

UNITED STATES

Seed Maturing	Seed Falling	Height Growth	Diameter Growth	
(E)	(F)	(G)	(H)	
Gymnospermae				
...	(Oct1-31)	May10+ (June20-Aug10)	(May1-Aug10)	1
(Aug1-31)	Sept10-Oct31 (Sept1-Oct31)	...	Apr20-Aug20 (May10-Sept20)	2
Sept10-20 (Aug20-Sept10)	Sept20-Oct10 (Sept10-30)	May20-July20 (June10-July31)	May20-Aug10	3
...	Sept20+	May10+	...	4
Sept20-30 (Oct1-20)	Oct1+	May1+ (May20+)	...	5
Sept1+ (Aug10+)	Oct1+ (Sept1+)	...	Apr20-July20 (May20-July20)	6
...	Oct1-Nov30	May20-Aug31	Apr10-Aug31	7
Aug1-Sept10 (Sept1-30)	Sept1-Oct10 (Sept20-Oct20)	May20+ (June20-July31)	May1-July20	8
...	...	May20+ (June1+)	...	9
(Sept10-30)	Sept20+ (Oct1-Dec31[2])	(May20-July20)	Apr20-Aug20 (May20-Sept10)	10
Sept1-20 (Aug1-31)	Sept20-Oct10[3] (Sept1-30[3])	May1-July20 (June20+)	...	11
Sept1-30 (Aug1-Sept10)	Oct1-31 (Sept20-Oct20)	May1+ (May20-July10)	(June1-Sept10)	12
Sept1-30 (Aug20-Sept10)	Oct1-31 (Sept10-Oct31)	May20-July31	...	13
...	Sept10-Oct20	May10-Aug10	Apr10-Sept20	14
...	Oct1-31	May20-July20	Apr10-Aug31	15
(Aug1-31)	Sept20+ (Sept1+)	May10+	(May1-July20)	16
Aug1-Sept30 (Aug1-31)	Sept1-Nov30 (Sept1-30)	May1-Aug10 (June1-July20)	Apr10-Sept20 (May20-Aug31)	17
Aug20-Sept20 (Aug10-20)	Sept10-Oct20 (Aug20-Sept20)	May1-July31 (June1-July31)	May1-Aug20 (May20-Aug10)	18
Sept20-30 (Aug10-Sept10)	Sept20-Dec31[2] (Sept10+)	May10-Sept10	Apr20-Oct10 (May10-Sept10)	19
Aug10-Sept10 (Sept10-30)	Sept10+ (Oct1-Dec31[2])	(May20-Aug10)	(May10-Sept10)	20

/3/ Most seeds are retained several years until cones are opened by a fire.

continued

104. TIME PERIODS IN DEVELOPMENT:

Part II: WESTERN

	Species	Leafing	Leaf Falling	Flowering[1]
	(A)	(B)	(C)	(D)
	Angiospermae (Dicotyledoneae)			
21	*Acer macrophyllum*	Mar1-Apr10 (Apr10-May10)	Oct20-Nov30 (Sept20-Oct31)	Mar10-Apr10 (Apr20-May10)
22	*Alnus rubra*	Mar20-Apr20 (Apr10-May10)	To Nov10 (To Oct20)	Mar10-Apr10 (Apr20-May10)
23	*Cornus nuttallii*	Mar20-Apr20 (Apr20-May10)	To Nov10 (To Oct31)	Apr20-May20 (May1-June10)
24	*Populus tremuloides*	Apr20-30 (June1-10)	Oct10-Nov20 (Sept1-30)	Apr1-20 (June10-20)
25	*P. trichocarpa*	Apr1-30 (Apr20-May20)	To Nov10 (Sept20-Oct10)	Apr10-30 (May10-31)
26	*Quercus agrifolia*	Mar1-Apr30	....	Apr1-30
27	*Q. chrysolepis*	Apr20-June20	....	June1-10
28	*Q. gambelii*	May20-31 (June1-10)	Sept20-Oct10 (Sept20-30)	May10-31

/1/ Pollination dates are given for conifers. /2/ Seedfall continues through the winter but in smaller quantities.

Contributors: (a) Little, Elbert L., Jr., (b) Delisle, Albert L.

References: [1] Daubenmire, R. F. 1946. Botan. Gaz. 107:462. [2] Daubenmire, R. F., and M. E. Deters. 1947. 247:143. [5] U. S. Dept. of Agriculture Forest Service. 1948. U. S. Dept. Agr. Misc. Publ. 654:416.

105. BUDDING, FLOWERING, AND HEIGHT AT

Photoperiodic Classification (column C): L = long day, I = indeterminate,

	Family and Species	Beginning of Test	Photo-periodic Classi-fication	Development at Light Exposures of: 10 hr Bd da	10 hr Fl da	10 hr Ht cm	12 hr Bd da	12 hr Fl da	12 hr Ht cm	12.5 hr Bd da	12.5 hr Fl da	12.5 hr Ht cm
	(A)	(B)	(C)	(D)	(E)	(F)	(G)	(H)	(I)	(J)	(K)	(L)
	Gramineae											
1	*Agrostis nebulosa*	May 14	L	...	...	.....	...	...	.....	...	...	.....
2	*Calamagrostis cinnoides*	Mar 30	I	...	...	.....	58	76	104.1	63	88	108.0
3	*Triodia flava*	May 20	S	29	38	66.0	39	44	63.5	39	46	94.0
4	*Tripsacum dactyloides*	Mar 31	S	63	72	162.6	65	74	142.2	68	75	114.3
	Salicaceae											
5	*Salix humilis*	Apr 10	S	68	...	.....	55	...	.....	60	88	55.9
	Amaranthaceae											
6	*Gomphrena globosa*	May 13	I	21	33	20.3	21	33	25.4	21	36	27.9
	Nyctaginaceae											
7	*Bougainvillea glabra*	May 24	S	28	45	96.5	36	57	101.6	69	88	142.2
8	*Mirabilis jalapa*	May 9	I	26	36	22.9	26	37	33.0	26	37	48.3
	Portulacaceae											
9	*Portulaca grandiflora*	May 11	I	...	11	10.2	...	11	3.8	...	...	.....
	Caryophyllaceae											
10	*Dianthus chinensis*	May 16	I	32	46	27.9	13	28	25.4	11	19	14.0
	Ranunculaceae											
11	*Aquilegia canadensis*	Mar 27	S	4	25	48.3	4	28	48.3	...	...	.....
	Capparidaceae											
12	*Cleome spinosa*	May 31	I	26	38	71.1	27	35	71.1	...	...	.....
	Cruciferae											
13	*Iberis umbellata*	May 14	I	13	37	30.5	13	30	27.9	17	37	27.9
	Crassulaceae											
14	*Bryophyllum pinnatum*	May 18	S	9	99	127.0	...	...	.....	...	...	.....
15	*Kalanchoe laxiflora*	May 8	I	...	...	.....	...	...	.....	173	239	96.5
	Leguminosae											
16	*Baptisia tinctoria*	May 27	I	56	82	35.6	56	80	50.8	56	79	45.7
17	*Phaseolus multiflorus*	May 21	I	13	55	66.0	14	22	53.3	14	21	78.7
18	*Soja max*	May 25	S	20	23	22.9	21	27	35.6	24	27	45.7
	Tropaeolaceae											
19	*Tropaeolum majus*	May 7	I	31	40	25.4	31	39	25.4	...	...	.....
	Euphorbiaceae											
20	*Euphorbia marginata*	May 13	I	27	32	12.7	33	42	17.8	...	...	.....
21	*E. pulcherrima*	May 13	S	32	65	119.4	39	44	134.6	48	180	167.6

FOREST TREES, NORTH AMERICAN

UNITED STATES

Seed Maturing	Seed Falling	Height Growth	Diameter Growth	
(E)	(F)	(G)	(H)	
Angiospermae (Dicotyledoneae)				
To Sept30 (To Aug31)	Oct1-Dec31[2]	....	May1-July31	21
Sept10+ (Oct20+)	(Nov1-Dec31[2])	....	....	22
Aug20+ (Sept10+)	....	....	....	23
May1-10 (June20-30)	May10-20 (July1-10)	Apr10+ (May20-Aug10)	(May20-Aug31)	24
May31+ (June30+)	....	....	....	25
....	Dec1-20	....	Mar20-July31	26
....	Oct1-31	Apr10-July20	Apr20-Aug31	27
....	....	May10+ (June1+)	....	28

Ibid. 109:1. [3] Fowells, H. A. 1941. J. Forestry 39:601. [4] Pearson, G. A. 1931. U. S. Dept. Agr. Tech. Bull.

VARIOUS LIGHT EXPOSURES: ANGIOSPERMS

S = short day. Columns D-AA: Bd = budding, Fl = flowering, Ht = height.

Development at Light Exposures of															
13hr			13.5 hr			14 hr			14.5 hr			24 hr			
Bd da	Fl da	Ht cm	Bd da	Fl da	Ht cm	Bd da	Fl da	Ht cm	Bd da	Fl da	Ht cm	Bd da	Fl da	Ht cm	
(M)	(N)	(O)	(P)	(Q)	(R)	(S)	(T)	(U)	(V)	(W)	(X)	(Y)	(Z)	(AA)	
49	58	25.4	48	58	33.0	37	45	27.9	35	41	40.6	34	48	27.9	1
70	98	88.9	63	84	104.1	57	84	116.8	67	91	114.3	60	84	94.0	2
42	47	76.2	43	51	114.3	50	56	63.5	69	87	129.5	92	103	106.7	3
68	75	170.2	68	76	147.3	81	89	142.2	82	89	152.4	82	89	165.1	4
61	...	.....	61	...	.....	61	76	.....	...	...	.....	...	...	.....	5
23	32	20.3	21	33	22.9	21	41	38.1	21	35	30.5	18	32	26.7	6
96	157	152.4	145	164	190.5	103	153	127.0	143	157	134.6	131	157	.....	7
26	41	38.1	26	41	53.3	26	41	48.3	30	47	68.6	26	44	30.5	8
...	10	7.6	...	10	8.9	...	10	10.2	...	10	10.2	...	10	10.2	9
29	34	35.6	28	39	35.6	12	28	17.8	14	35	22.9	11	25	15.2	10
4	36	76.2	...	...	.....	14	36	76.2	...	...	.....	4	36	76.2	11
27	36	86.4	...	...	.....	28	40	91.4	...	...	.....	28	38	165.1	12
13	30	17.8	17	41	33.0	17	30	33.0	13	30	22.9	17	30	30.5	13
...	...	.....	...	...	.....	...	...	.....	...	...	.....	...	...	.....	14
173	199	119.4	...	...	.....	173	192	129.5	173	204	127.0	173	192	129.5	15
56	82	43.2	56	83	43.2	56	83	38.1	56	83	55.9	59	86	43.2	16
14	22	78.7	14	25	116.8	14	28	167.6	20	28	116.8	14	32	142.2	17
25	31	40.6	34	37	48.3	42	48	68.6	50	60	76.2	81	90	96.5	18
31	39	30.5	35	43	35.6	44	49	30.5	32	36	38.1	35	43	27.9	19
27	32	15.2	...	...	.....	...	...	.....	...	...	.....	27	30	15.2	20
107	179	193.0	162	191	188.0	163	193	193.0	163	195	231.1	158	197	177.8	21

continued

	Family and Species	Beginning of Test	Photo-periodic Classi-fication	Development at Light Exposures of 10 hr Bd da	10 hr Fl da	10 hr Ht cm	12 hr Bd da	12 hr Fl da	12 hr Ht cm	12.5 hr Bd da	12.5 hr Fl da	12.5 hr Ht cm
	(A)	(B)	(C)	(D)	(E)	(F)	(G)	(H)	(I)	(J)	(K)	(L)
	Balsaminaceae											
22	*Impatiens balsamina*	June 23	I	20	28	35.6	20	28	45.7	...	...	.....
	Malvaceae											
23	*Hibiscus syriacus*	Mar 27	L	...	...	.....	...	...	.....	95	117	77.5
24	*Malvaviscus conzatti*	May 9	I	29	54	78.7	32	63	94.0	32	63	106.7
	Oenotheraceae											
25	*Oenothera missouriensis*	May 21	L	...	...	.....	...	...	.....	...	...	.....
26	*O. speciosa*	Apr 16	I	15	37	.....	13	35	.....	13	36	14.0
	Umbelliferae											
27	*Trachymene coerulea*	May 14	I	17	38	33.0	27	45	50.8	28	46	40.6
	Primulaceae											
28	*Anagallis linifolia*	May 14	I	25	30	22.9	25	31	22.9	23	27	22.9
29	*Steironema ciliatum*	Apr 15	L	...	...	.....	...	...	.....	56	65	53.3
	Plumbaginaceae											
30	*Statice armeria laucheana*	Apr 22	I	30	41	12.7	24	29	15.2	30	37	12.7
	Apocynaceae											
31	*Vinca minor*	June 7	I	18	26	40.6	18	23	30.5	...	...	.....
	Convolvulaceae											
32	*Convolvulus sepium*	May 19	L	...	...	.....	...	...	.....	...	...	.....
	Polemoniaceae											
33	*Cobaea scandens*	May 26	S	24	53	116.8	36	91	104.1	...	...	.....
	Verbenaceae											
34	*Caryopteris incana*	June 5	S	26	38	33.0	26	38	40.6	...	...	.....
35	*Clerodendron thomsonae*	May 24	I	24	52	48.3	24	52	48.3	28	52	45.7
36	*Verbena hybrida*	May 29	I	19	34	15.2	13	26	17.8	...	...	.....
	Labiatae											
37	*Koellia incana*	Apr 20	I	...	...	.....	60	78	61.0	60	74	63.5
38	*Perilla frutescens*	May 17	S	25	39	55.9	37	47	68.6	39	58	76.2
39	*Salvia sclarea*	Mar 27	L	...	...	.....	...	...	.....	...	...	.....
	Solanaceae											
40	*Nicotiana tabacum*[1]	May 14	I	18	30	101.6	19	30	114.3	...	...	.....
41	*N. tabacum*[2]	June 7	S	...	16	129.5	...	73	162.6	...	...	.....
	Scrophulariaceae											
42	*Antirrhinum majus*	May 31	I	28	45	40.6	24	35	30.5	...	...	.....
	Cucurbitaceae											
43	*Lagenaria leucantha*	May 27	I	4	18	68.6	4	18	53.3	...	...	.....
	Compositae											
44	*Calendula officinalis*	May 9	I	26	42	22.9	26	41	33.0	26	41	38.1
45	*Chrysanthemum* sp.[3]	....	I	21	54	40.6	24	54	33.0	24	54	40.6
46	*Cosmos bipinnatus*[4]	May 7	I	10	17	48.3	10	24	91.4	10	17	48.3
47	*C. bipinnatus*[5]	May 7	S	10	19	50.8	10	26	78.7	10	25	68.6
48	*Gaillardia aristata*	Apr 28	I	15	39	14.0	27	49	33.0	23	45	20.3
49	*Silphium trifoliatum*	Apr 18	L	89	107	96.5	89	110	142.2	68	90	142.2
50	*Solidago ulmifolia*	Apr 23	S	31	73	63.5	45	73	55.9	69	88	35.6

/1/ Extra early. /2/ Maryland mammoth variety. /3/ Yellow Normandie variety. /4/ Extra early express pink.

Contributor: Williams, Bert C.

Reference: Garner, W. W., and H. A. Allard. 1940. U. S. Dept. Agr. Tech. Bull. 727.

VARIOUS LIGHT EXPOSURES: ANGIOSPERMS

Development at Light Exposures of															
13 hr			13.5 hr			14 hr			14.5 hr			24 hr			
Bd da	Fl da	Ht cm	Bd da	Fl da	Ht cm	Bd da	Fl da	Ht cm	Bd da	Fl da	Ht cm	Bd da	Fl da	Ht cm	
(M)	(N)	(O)	(P)	(Q)	(R)	(S)	(T)	(U)	(V)	(W)	(X)	(Y)	(Z)	(AA)	
20	29	48.3	20	28	43.2	...	...	.....	...	...	.....	30	38	53.3	22
96	123	120.7	95	126	115.6	103	136	111.8	106	144	132.1	103	130	111.8	23
32	63	111.8	32	63	106.7	37	63	119.4	37	66	111.8	50	63	139.7	24
...	...	.....	...	...	.....	22	35	17.8	22	38	22.9	21	36	17.8	25
15	50	25.4	15	10	22.9	15	37	22.9	15	40	22.9	15	41	22.9	26
29	49	55.9	25	45	45.7	29	49	63.5	30	53	55.9	17	41	33.0	27
28	37	27.9	25	27	17.8	27	31	27.9	31	34	27.9	27	29	25.4	28
87	93	61.0	49	61	48.3	48	65	63.5	49	68	58.4	49	68	50.8	29
26	27	15.2	26	40	15.2	25	29	15.2	37	47	15.2	25	33	12.7	30
...	...	.....	...	...	.....	...	...	.....	...	...	.....	18	23	30.5	31
...	...	.....	44	59	101.6	...	...	.....	...	...	.....	35	49	114.3	32
55	91	116.8	...	...	.....	60	92	152.4	...	...	.....	64	97	152.4	33
24	35	40.6	...	...	.....	54	71	72.4	...	...	.....	59	71	71.1	34
29	52	53.3	28	52	.....	32	52	55.9	28	38	55.9	28	57	45.7	35
28	41	20.3	...	...	.....	27	44	20.3	...	...	.....	20	40	20.3	36
...	...	.....	54	74	76.2	61	78	73.7	...	...	.....	56	78	53.3	37
39	50	63.5	49	70	96.5	53	83	104.1	62	96	119.4	93	114	127.0	38
...	...	.....	...	...	.....	67	83	48.3	...	...	.....	63	72	73.7	39
18	30	114.3	...	...	.....	18	30	111.8	...	...	.....	18	32	106.7	40
...	73	154.9	...	...	.....	...	88	167.6	...	...	.....	...	90	149.9	41
20	33	35.6	...	...	.....	20	35	40.6	...	...	.....	20	33	33.0	42
4	22	53.3	...	...	.....	...	...	.....	...	...	.....	4	22	45.7	43
26	41	38.1	26	47	50.8	26	41	45.7	26	44	50.8	26	41	43.2	44
25	59	35.6	24	56	50.8	38	73	48.3	38	78	50.8	46	71	45.7	45
10	19	50.8	10	15	.....	10	21	48.3	10	24	66.0	10	19	43.2	46
10	21	53.3	14	28	81.3	28	46	144.8	19	31	88.9	26	40	121.9	47
25	51	35.6	18	36	35.6	27	49	55.9	22	39	38.1	21	46	58.4	48
68	89	177.8	65	89	210.8	65	89	193.0	54	79	137.2	54	78	144.8	49
49	77	48.3	58	82	81.3	57	88	91.4	85	108	76.2	67	114	91.4	50

/5/ Extra early crimson.

106. MAXIMUM GROWTH RATES: PLANTS AND PLANT ORGANS

The growth curve of a plant or organ is often described as sigmoid with (1) an acceleration phase, (2) a short, or sometimes prolonged, linear phase, and (3) a final phase of deceleration. Growth Rate (column D): A = absolute, maximum, instantaneous rate of growth in phase 2, calculated from dX/dt, where X is the dimension measured and t is time; R = relative maximum rate of growth, calculated from (1/X)(dX/dt); E = relative elemental rate of growth of an organ--the relative rate of growth of an infinitesimal portion or element growing most rapidly in length (dX), area (dA), or other dimension. For increase in a linear dimension, the relative elemental rate may be stated as d(dX/dt)/dX, and for increase in area as $\partial(\partial X/\partial t)/\partial X + \partial(\partial Y/\partial t)/\partial Y$.

	Species	Material	Dimension	Growth: Rate	Growth: Time and Specification	Maximum Size	Environmental Conditions: Location	Environmental Conditions: Special Factor	Reference
	(A)	(B)	(C)	(D)	(E)	(F)	(G)	(H)	(I)
	Charophyta								
1	*Nitella* sp.	Internodal cell	Length	A 1.7 mm/da	0-1 da (after reaching length of 0.4 mm)	13 mm at 10 da (after reaching length of 0.4 mm)	Laboratory	Mineral nutrient at 23-26°C, fluorescent light	8
2				E 1.1/da[1]					
	Fungi								
3	*Phycomyces blakesleeanus*	Sporangiophore	Length	A 3.0 mm/hr	Stage 4[2]		Laboratory	Moist chamber at 22-25°C	3,4
4				R 1.8/hr	Stage 4[2]; 0.8 mm from tip				
5	*Daedalea quercina*	Mycelial pellets	Dry wt	A 45 mg/da	0-8 da	482 mg at 14 da	Laboratory	70 ml shake culture, optimal synthetic medium at 28°C; 0.03 mg inoculum	11
6	*Fomes geotropus*	Mycelial pellets	Dry wt	A 193 mg/da	0-7 da	1350 mg at 7 da			
7	*F. subroseus*	Mycelial pellets	Dry wt	A 30 mg/da	1-8 da	298 mg at 14 da			
8	*Lentinus tigrinus*	Mycelial pellets	Dry wt	A 140 mg/da	1-7 da	924 mg at 7 da			
9	*L. trabea*	Mycelial pellets	Dry wt	A 93 mg/da	0-7 da	652 mg at 7 da			
10	*Polyporus palustris*	Mycelial pellets	Dry wt	A 60 mg/da	0-6 da	402 mg at 14 da	Laboratory	70 ml shake culture, optimal synthetic medium at 28°C; 0.03 mg inoculum	11
11	*P. tulipiferus*	Mycelial pellets	Dry wt	A 75 mg/da	1-6 da	552 mg at 14 da			
12	*Trametes serialis*	Mycelial pellets	Dry wt	A 112 mg/da	0-7 da	789 mg at 7 da			
	Angiospermae								
13	*Hordeum sativum*	Kernel	Length	A 1.8 mm/da	3 da after pollination	9 mm at 20 da after pollination	Field	Mean temperature of 26°C	9
14				R 0.35/da	2 da after pollination				
15			Fresh wt	A 4.8 mg/da	6 da after pollination	57 mg at 24 da after pollination			
16				R 0.5/da	2 da after pollination				
17			Dry wt	A 2.2 mg/da	12 da after pollination	32 mg at 24 da after pollination			
18				R 0.58/da	2 da after pollination				
19	*Zea mays*	Plant	Dry wt	A 19.8 g/wk	13 wk after planting	122 g at 16 wk after planting	Field		2
20				R 1.37/wk	5 wk after planting				
21		Primary root	Length	A 2.0 mm/hr	2 da after soaking seed		Laboratory	On moist filter paper at 25°C in dark	7
22				E 0.4/hr	2 da; 4 mm from tip				
23	*Dendrocalamus* sp.	Stem	Length	A 26.7 cm/da	1-2 mo after bud opening	14 m at 2.5 mo after bud opening	Field	Daily fluctuating temperature of 23-32°C; daily rain	12
24	*Sinocalamus oldhami*	Stem	Length	A 31.4 cm/da[3]	18 da after buds appeared above ground[4]	Not reached at end of observations	Field; Cuba	Sept 27-Oct 15, 1953	10

/1/ Growth is uniform over length of internodal cell, hence relative rate of elongation of cell as a whole equals relative elemental rate for each point. /2/ Stage of growth following formation of the sporangium. /3/ Average rate = 24.9 cm/da; night average = 0.97 cm/hr, and day average = 0.71 cm/hr. /4/ Height of 7 shoots of 1 plant = 3.2-7.7 m.

continued

106. MAXIMUM GROWTH RATES: PLANTS AND PLANT ORGANS

	Species	Material	Dimension	Growth: Rate	Growth: Time and Specification	Maximum Size	Environmental Conditions: Location	Environmental Conditions: Special Factor	Reference
	(A)	(B)	(C)	(D)	(E)	(F)	(G)	(H)	(I)
	Angiospermae								
25	*Lilium longiflorum floridii*	Flower bud	Length	A 11.5mm/da	2 da before anthesis	155 mm at anthesis	Greenhouse	Daily fluctuating temperature between means of 16-27°C	5,6
26				R 0.077/da	2-30 da before anthesis				
27		Anther	Length	R 0.088/da	20-30 da before anthesis	29 mm at anthesis			
28			Fresh wt	R 0.18/da	20-30 da before anthesis	160 mg at anthesis			
29			Dry wt	R 0.18/da	20-30 da before anthesis	35 mg at 9 da before anthesis			
30	*Lycopersicon esculentum*	Stem	Length	A 29.3 mm/da	6 wk after planting		Laboratory	Daily alternation: 8 hr light at 26.5°C and 16 hr dark at 17°C	14
31	*Nicotiana tabacum*	Leaf	Area	E 0.85/da[5]	Leaf 8.6 cm long, 3 cm from base, 0.5 cm from midrib				1,13

/5/ Assuming that drawings of leaf were made at weekly intervals [1].

Contributors: (a) Erickson, Ralph O., (b) Jennison, Marshall W., (c) Wetmore, Ralph H.

References: [1] Avery, G. S. 1933. Am. J. Botany 20:565. [2] Briggs, G. E., F. Kidd, and C. West. 1920. Ann. Appl. Biol. 7:103. [3] Castle, E. S. 1937. J. Cellular Comp. Physiol. 9:477. [4] Castle, E. S. 1942. Am. J. Botany 29:664. [5] Erickson, R. O. 1947. Nature 159:275. [6] Erickson, R. O. 1948. Am. J. Botany 35:729. [7] Erickson, R. O., and D. R. Goddard. 1951. Growth, Suppl. 10:89. [8] Green, P. 1954. Am. J. Botany 41:403. [9] Harlan, H. V. 1920. J. Agr. Research 19:393. [10] Hay, J. Unpublished, 1953. [11] Jennison, M. W., M. D. Newcomb, and R. Henderson. 1955. Mycologia 47:275. [12] Kraus, G. 1895. Ann. Jard. Botan. Buitenzorg 12:196. [13] Richards, O. W., and A. J. Kavanagh. 1943. Am. Naturalist 77:385. [14] Went, F. W. 1944. Am. J. Botany 31:135.

107. ROOT SYSTEMS: PLANTS

Part I: NUMBER AND SIZE

Root categories: I = main roots (seminal or adventitious, arising directly from base of plant), II = secondary roots (arising directly from main roots), III = tertiary roots (arising directly from secondary roots), IV = quaternary roots (arising directly from tertiary roots).

	Family and Species	Roots: Number I	Number II	Number III	Number IV	Total Length, cm I	Total Length II	Total Length III	Total Length IV	Root Hairs: Diameter, μ I	Diameter II	Diameter III	Length, μ I	Length II	Length III	Reference
	(A)	(B)	(C)	(D)	(E)	(F)	(G)	(H)	(I)	(J)	(K)	(L)	(M)	(N)	(O)	(P)
	Pteridophyta															
	Equisetaceae															
1	*Equisetum arvense*	...	......	......	......	....	......	....	....	15	15	...	1200	1200	...	3
2	*E. kansanum*	...	......	......	......	....	......	....	....	13	13	...	1500	1500	...	3
	Gymnospermae															
	Cupressaceae															
3	*Juniperus monosperma*[1, 2]	1	3.4	2.0	......	4.8	6.4	0.8	....	15	15	14	70	84	56	5

/1/ Data applicable to seedlings 6 months old. /2/ Total surface area of roots = 1830 sq mm, total surface area of root hairs = 27 sq mm.

continued

107. ROOT SYSTEMS: PLANTS

Part I: NUMBER AND SIZE

	Family and Species	Roots								Root Hairs						Reference
		Number				Total Length, cm				Diameter, μ			Length, μ			
		I	II	III	IV	I	II	III	IV	I	II	III	I	II	III	
	(A)	(B)	(C)	(D)	(E)	(F)	(G)	(H)	(I)	(J)	(K)	(L)	(M)	(N)	(O)	(P)
	Gymnospermae															
	Pinaceae															
4	*Picea engelmannii*[1,3]	1	12	43	4.7	75	140	70	0.5	18	18	18	140	125	110	5
5	*Pinus ponderosa*[1,4]	1	15	70	12	100	505	465	23	24	26	22	140	155	240	5
6	*Pseudotsuga menziesii*[1,5]	1	6.3	5.0	0.3	10.1	11.5	1.9	0.03	22	23	22	240	125	155	5
	Angiospermae (Monocotyledoneae)															
	Typhaceae															
7	*Typha latifolia*	...	25[6]	......	......	....	......	....	....	...	12	...	....	1200	...	3
	Gramineae															
8	*Agropyron elongatum*	...	......	......	......	....	......	....	....	12	12	12	800	750	750	3
9	*A. palustris*	...	......	......	......	....	......	....	....	11	11	10	900	800	800	3
10	*Agrostis astoriana*	...	......	......	......	....	......	....	....	13	12	12	600	600	50	3
11	*A. tenuis*	...	......	......	......	....	......	....	....	10	10	10	400	400	300	3
12	*Avena sativa*[7]	110	2190	2400	......	915	2440	1220	....	14	13	13	1400	1100	860	1
13	*Cynodon dactylon*	4	660	22	......	60	1980	9	....	12	8	8	770	270	260	6
14	*Eragrostis curvula*	...	......	......	......	....	......	....	....	8	8	8	270	270	200	6
15	*Festuca commutata*	...	......	......	......	....	......	....	....	13	13	12	400	400	350	7
16	*Poa pratensis*[8]	900	39,700	43,900	......	5490	26,520	6100	....	11	9	7	1120	935	510	1
17	*Secale cereale*[9]	130	3670	2600	......	1220	3960	1220	....	15	12	12	1720	940	590	1
18	*Setaria viridis*	12	3360	......	......	170	405	....	....	8	8	...	100	100	...	7
19	*Triticum aestivum*[10]	...	......	......	......	2000	1230	....	....	...	...	...	....	....	...	4
	Angiospermae (Dicotyledoneae)															
	Ulmaceae															
20	*Celtis occidentalis*	...	......	......	......	....	......	....	....	...	8	8	....	170	170	2,3
21	*Ulmus pumila*	1	55	1100	88,000	55	2200	8800	176,000	...	10	...	....	....	200	2,3
	Chenopodiaceae															
22	*Salsola pestifer*	1	105	3150	630	35	1050	630	63	...	8	7	....	160	140	2,3
	Amaranthaceae															
23	*Amaranthus torreyii*	1	40	325	255	8	730	280	25	...	9	9	....	230	220	2,3
	Caryophyllaceae															
24	*Cerastium arvense*	1	14	105	......	7	35	16	....	12	12	10	750	600	600	2,3
	Capparidaceae															
25	*Cleome serrulata*	...	......	......	......	....	......	....	....	...	...	6	....	....	150	2,3
	Cruciferae															
26	*Descurainia pinnata*	1	10	520	1560	5	130	1040	470	7	7	6	350	300	210	2,3
	Leguminosae															
27	*Gleditsia triacanthos*	...	......	......	......	....	......	....	....	...	13	13	....	200	180	2,3
28	*Glycine soja*	1	51	470	260	11	255	375	105	17	17	14	240	80	80	2,3
29	*Parosela dalea*	1	52	1560	1560	13	520	1560	310	15	15	150	110	110	90	2,3
30	*Pueraria hirsuta*	1	54	755	......	9	380	225	....	12	12	11	150	140	140	2,3
31	*Trifolium repens*	35	980	135	......	245	685	27	....	8	8	7	250	250	200	2,3
	Zygophyllaceae															
32	*Tribulus terrestris*	1	200	160	......	25	160	32	....	...	7	7	....	140	130	2,3
	Euphorbiaceae															
33	*Euphorbia albomarginata*	1	22	220	......	11	220	155	....	9	8	8	300	240	240	2,3
	Umbelliferae															
34	*Sium suave*	...	......	......	......	....	......	....	....	8	8	...	150	150	...	2,3
	Oleaceae															
35	*Fraxinus lanceolata*	...	......	......	......	....	......	....	....	...	5	5	....	370	370	2,3
	Convolvulaceae															
36	*Convolvulus arvensis*	1	28	170	......	14	335	32	....	...	14	14	....	80	80	2,3

/1/ Data applicable to seedlings 6 months old. /3/ Total surface area of roots = 260 sq mm, total surface area of root hairs = 110 sq mm. /4/ Total surface area of roots = 1350 sq mm, total surface area of root hairs = 180 sq mm. /5/ Total surface area of roots = 300 sq mm, total surface area of root hairs = 54 sq mm. /6/ Per centimeter of main roots. /7/ Total surface area of roots = 320 sq cm, total volume = 2610 cu mm. Total surface area of root hairs = 3440 sq cm; number of root hairs in a core of soil 3 inches in diameter and 6 inches deep = 6.3 million. /8/ Total surface area of roots = 2140 sq cm, total volume = 13,900 cu mm. Total surface area of root hairs = 15,780 sq cm; number of root hairs in a core of soil 3 inches in diameter and 6 inches deep = 51.5 million. /9/ Total surface area of roots = 505 sq cm, total volume = 4580 cu mm. Total surface area of root hairs = 7680 sq cm; number of root hairs in a core of soil 3 inches in diameter and 6 inches deep = 12.5 million. /10/ Total surface area of roots = 310 sq cm.

continued

107. ROOT SYSTEMS: PLANTS

Part I: NUMBER AND SIZE

	Family and Species	Roots								Root Hairs						Reference
		Number				Total Length, cm				Diameter, µ			Length, µ			
		I	II	III	IV	I	II	III	IV	I	II	III	I	II	III	
	(A)	(B)	(C)	(D)	(E)	(F)	(G)	(H)	(I)	(J)	(K)	(L)	(M)	(N)	(O)	(P)
	Angiospermae (Dicotyledoneae)															
	Labiatae															
37	*Nepeta cataria*	1	100	1200	200	10	300	600	20	8	8	8	410	390	340	2,3
	Solanaceae															
38	*Solanum elaeagnifolium*	1	130	650	......	65	650	325	....	...	7	7	....	120	110	2,3
	Bignoniaceae															
39	*Catalpa bignonioides*	...	......	......	......	....	......	....	....	...	10	10	....	250	250	3
	Plantaginaceae															
40	*Plantago major*	26	635	1450	......	275	1150	435	....	12	10	10	220	210	200	3
	Compositae															
41	*Tagetes patula*	1	72	430	......	12	110	130	....	14	14	14	180	160	140	3
42	*Taraxacum officinale*	1	180	900	......	30	720	360	....	...	7	7	....	130	130	3

Contributor: Dittmer, Howard J.

References: [1] Dittmer, H. J. 1938. Am. J. Botany 25:654. [2] Dittmer, H. J. 1948. Botan. Gaz. 109:354. [3] Dittmer, H. J. 1949. Am. J. Botany 36:152. [4] Pavlychenko, T. K. 1937. Ecology 18:62. [5] Reinhart, J. 1948. Thesis. Univ. New Mexico, Albuquerque. [6] Weaver, J. E., and W. J. Himmell. 1930. Plant Physiol. 5:69. [7] Weaver, J. E., and E. Zink. 1945. Ibid. 20:359.

Part II: PENETRATION

	Family	Species	Location	Soil Type	Age	Growth Stage	Root Penetration		Reference
							Depth cm	Spread cm	
	(A)	(B)	(C)	(D)	(E)	(F)	(G)	(H)	(I)
1	Pinaceae	*Pinus rigida*	New York	Sandy soil	30 yr	....	>275	915-1068	4
2	Gramineae	*Avena sativa*	Nebraska	Silt loam over loess	3 mo	Maturing grain	207	40	7
3		*Triticum aestivum*	Nebraska	Silt loam over loess	3 mo	Mature grain	204	40	7
4		*Zea mays*	Nebraska	Silt loam over loess	4 mo	Mature	250	122	7
5	Liliaceae	*Asparagus officinalis*	Nebraska	Silt loam over clay	6 yr	....	305	122	6
6	Juglandaceae	*Carya illinoensis*	Georgia	Sandy soil over clay	6 yr	....	183	732	9
7	Fagaceae	*Quercus macrocarpa*	Nebraska	Silt loam	65 yr	Height, 37.5 ft	>305	>1829	8
8	Chenopodiaceae	*Beta vulgaris*	Nebraska	Silt loam over clay	3.5 mo	Edible roots	305	122	6
9	Cruciferae	*Brassica oleracea*	Nebraska	Silt loam over clay	4 mo	Mature heads	238	107	6
10	Rosaceae	*Prunus armeniaca*	Oklahoma	Silt loam over clay	....	Seedling	244	975	2
11		*P. persica*	Georgia	Sandy soil over clay	2 yr	....	91	183	3
12		*Pyrus malus*	Nebraska	Porous loess	3 yr	....	427-488	214-305	8
13			Nebraska	Porous loess	17 yr	....	915-1068	>458	8
14			New York	Heavy clay	25 yr	....	>152	>396	1
15	Leguminosae	*Medicago sativa*	Nebraska	Alluvial silt loam	2 yr	....	366	<30	5
16		*Phaseolus vulgaris*	Nebraska	Silt loam over clay	2.5 mo	Mature pods	137	61	6
17	Solanaceae	*Lycopersicon esculentum*	Nebraska	Silt loam over clay	4 mo	Fruiting	137	168	6
18		*Solanum tuberosum*	Nebraska	Silt loam over loess	3 mo	Mature tubers	143	64	7
19	Cucurbitaceae	*Cucurbita maxima*	Nebraska	Silt loam over clay	2.6 mo	Fruiting	183	579	6
20	Compositae	*Lactuca sativa*	Nebraska	Silt loam over clay	3 mo	Flowering	183	46	6

Contributor: Kramer, Paul J.

References: [1] Boynton, D., and E. F. Savage. 1936. Proc. Am. Soc. Hort. Sci. 34:164. [2] Bunger, M. T., and H. J. Thomson. 1938. J. Forestry 36:790. [3] Cowart, F. F. 1938. Proc. Am. Soc. Hort. Sci. 36:145.

continued

107. ROOT SYSTEMS: PLANTS

Part II: PENETRATION

[4] McQuilkin, W. E. 1935. J. Agr. Research 51:983. [5] Weaver, J. E. 1920. Carnegie Inst. Wash. Publ. 292. [6] Weaver, J. E., and W. Bruner. 1927. Root development of vegetable crops. McGraw-Hill, New York. [7] Weaver, J. E., C. J. Frank, and J. W. Crist. 1922. Carnegie Inst. Wash. Publ. 316. [8] Weaver, J. E., and J. Kramer. 1932. Botan. Gaz. 94:51. [9] Woodroof, J. G., and N. C. Woodroof. 1934. J. Agr. Research 49:511.

108. INTERCELLULAR SPACE IN LEAVES: ANGIOSPERMS

Between the upper and lower surface of a leaf are numerous intercellular spaces or air chambers, constituting a connected system throughout the leaf. Values are volume of intercellular space expressed as percent of total volume of leaf. Values for leaves in shade are enclosed in parentheses. Method (column D): T = measurement made by infiltrating intercellular space with turpentine, W = measurement made by infiltrating intercellular space with water, C = measurement made on camera lucida drawings of leaf sections.

	Family and Species	Location	Specification	Method	Volume, %	Reference
	(A)	(B)	(C)	(D)	(E)	(F)
	Monocotyledoneae					
	Liliaceae					
1	*Allium ursinum*	Germany	Field	T	66	1
2			Greenhouse; well-lighted, well-watered	T	52	
3			Greenhouse; leaf dried 30 min	T	20	
4	*Colchicum autumnale*	Germany	Field	T	60	1
5			Greenhouse; well-lighted, well-watered	T	48	
6			Greenhouse; leaf dried 30 min	T	19	
7	*Tulipa* spp.	Germany; greenhouse	Well-lighted, well-watered	T	40	1
8			Leaf dried 30 min	T	20	
	Musaceae					
9	*Musa sapientum*	Germany	Entire leaf	W	24.8	7
10			Petiole of leaf only	W	48	
	Dicotyledoneae					
	Juglandaceae					
11	*Juglans regia*	Northern Germany; botanical garden	Inner leaf	T	(25)	2
12			Peripheral leaf	T	18(21)	
	Betulaceae					
13	*Corylus tubulosa*	Northern Germany; botanical garden	Mature leaf	T	17(33)	2
14			Immature leaf	T	7(11)	
	Fagaceae					
15	*Fagus sylvatica*	Northern Germany; botanical garden	Mature leaf	T	22(28)	2
16			Immature leaf	T	5(6)	
17			Inner leaf	T	(32)	
18			Peripheral leaf	T	(29)	
19	*Quercus coccinea*	Northern Germany; botanical garden	Mature leaf	T	24(33)	2
20			Immature leaf	T	8(8)	
	Moraceae					
21	*Cecropia peltata*	Germany	Entire leaf	W	30.9	7
22			Petiole of leaf only	W	25.3	
	Proteaceae					
23	*Gevuina avellana*	Germany; greenhouse	Well-lighted, well-watered	T	50	1
24			Leaf dried 30 min	T	45	
	Cercidiphyllaceae					
25	*Cercidiphyllum japonicum*	Northern Germany; botanical garden	Mature leaf	T	18(26)	2
26			Immature leaf	T	6(6)	
	Magnoliaceae					
27	*Drimys* spp.	Germany; greenhouse	Well-lighted, well-watered	T	25	1
28			Leaf dried 30 min	T	19	
	Saxifragaceae					
29	*Bergenia cordifolia*	Germany; greenhouse	Well-lighted, well-watered	T	26	1
30			Leaf dried 30 min	T	26	

continued

108. INTERCELLULAR SPACE IN LEAVES: ANGIOSPERMS

	Family and Species	Location	Specification	Method	Volume, %	Reference
	(A)	(B)	(C)	(D)	(E)	(F)
			Dicotyledoneae			
	Platanaceae					
31	*Platanus occidentalis*	Northern Germany; botanical garden	Inner leaf	T	(27)	2
32			Peripheral leaf	T	(33)	
	Rosaceae					
33	*Photinia glabra*	Japan	Young leaf	W	24.18(27.32)	3
34			Old leaf	W	21.59(26.34)	
35	*Pyrus communis*	Northern Germany; botanical garden	Mature leaf	T	13(22)	2
36			Immature leaf	T	9(9)	
37			Inner leaf	T	(22)	
38			Peripheral leaf	T	(16)	
	Leguminosae					
39	*Medicago sativa*	Utah, U.S.; field	Early primary leaf	C	29.4	5
40			Late primary leaf	C	26.5	
41			Secondary leaf	C	26.1	
42			Tertiary leaf	C	22.5	
43			Quaternary leaf	C	18.6	
44	*Phaseolus* spp.	Northern Germany; greenhouse	Moist habitat	T	27	2
45			Dry habitat	T	19	
	Tropaeolaceae					
46	*Tropaeolum* spp.	Northern Germany; botanical garden	Moist habitat	W	35	2
47			Dry habitat	W	17	
	Corynocarpaceae					
48	*Corynocarpus laevigata*	Germany; greenhouse	Well-lighted, well-watered	T	18	1
49			Leaf dried 30 min	T	15	
	Celastraceae					
50	*Cassine maurocenia*	Germany; greenhouse	Well-lighted, well-watered	T	17	1
51			Leaf dried 30 min	T	17	
	Hippocastanaceae					
52	*Aesculus rubicunda*	Northern Germany; botanical garden	Mature leaf	T	26(33)	2
53			Immature leaf	T	6(6)	
54			Inner leaf	T	(38)	
55			Peripheral leaf	T	(33)	
	Balsaminaceae					
56	*Impatiens* spp.	Northern Germany; greenhouse	Moist habitat	T	49	2
57			Dry habitat	T	34	
	Tiliaceae					
58	*Tilia glabra*	Northern Germany; botanical garden	Inner leaf	T	(28)	2
59			Peripheral leaf	T	(19)	
60	*T. parvifolia*	Northern Germany; botanical garden	Mature leaf	T	20(26)	2
61			Immature leaf	T	3.5(4)	
	Cornaceae					
62	*Cornus sanguinea*	Northern Germany; botanical garden	Mature leaf	T	21(29)	2
63			Immature leaf	T	9(12)	
	Theophrastaceae					
64	*Theophrasti minor*	Germany; greenhouse	Well-lighted, well-watered	T	38	1
65			Leaf dried 30 min	T	33	
	Primulaceae					
66	*Lysimachia ciliata*	Germany	Field	T	59	1
67			Greenhouse; well-lighted, well-watered	T	31	
68			Greenhouse; leaf dried 30 min	T	24	
	Oleaceae					
69	*Fraxinus excelsior*	Northern Germany; botanical garden	Inner leaf	T	(28)	2
70			Peripheral leaf	T	19(21)	
71	*Syringa vulgaris*	Iowa, U.S.	Mature leaf	C	20.6-25.1(23.7)	4,6
72			Immature leaf	C	28.9	6
73		Northern Germany; botanical garden	Mature leaf	T	20(28)	2
74			Immature leaf	T	9(10)	
	Apocynaceae					
75	*Nerium oleander*	Iowa, U.S.; artificial light	175 ft-candles; top leaf	C	30.3	6
76			175 ft-candles; bottom, leaf	C	34.5	
77			76.8 ft-candles; top leaf	C	26.7	
78			76.8 ft-candles; bottom leaf	C	41.8	

continued

108. INTERCELLULAR SPACE IN LEAVES: ANGIOSPERMS

	Family and Species	Location	Specification	Method	Volume, %	Reference
	(A)	(B)	(C)	(D)	(E)	(F)
	Dicotyledoneae					
	Apocynaceae					
79	*Vinca rosea*	Iowa, U.S.; artificial light	175 ft-candles; top leaf	C	25.2	6
80			175 ft-candles; bottom leaf	C	41.2	
81			76.8 ft-candles; top leaf	C	27.5	
82			76.8 ft-candles; bottom leaf	C	35.9	
	Bignoniaceae					
83	*Catalpa speciosa*	Iowa, U.S.; open lawn	Small leaf	C	(30.7)	6
84			Medium leaf	C	43.2	
85			Large leaf	C	31.9	
	Compositae					
86	*Doronicum* spp.	Germany	Field	T	71	1
87			Greenhouse; well-lighted, well-watered	T	59	
88			Greenhouse; leaf dried 30 min	T	22	

Contributor: Turrell, Franklin M.

References: [1] Nius, E. 1931. Jahrb. wiss. Botan. 74:3. [2] Schröder, J. 1937. Beitr. Biol. Pflanz. 25:75. [3] Takenouchi, M. 1933. Bul. Sci. Fak. Terkult. Kjusu Imp. Univ. Fukuoka 5:254. [4] Turrell, F. M. 1936. Am. J. Botany 23:255. [5] Turrell, F. M. 1942. Ibid. 29:400. [6] Turrell, F. M. Unpublished. Univ. California Citrus Expt. Sta., Riverside, 1936. [7] Unger, F. 1854. Sitzber. Akad. Wiss. Wien Math.-naturw. Kl., I, 12:367.

109. SURFACE AREA OF LEAVES: SPERMATOPHYTES

Values are for total (upper and lower) leaf surface. Specification (column C): ft-c = foot-candles.

	Family and Species	Location	Specification	Surface Area: sq cm per leaf	Surface Area: sq cm per plant	Reference
	(A)	(B)	(C)	(D)	(E)	(F)
	Gymnospermae					
	Pinaceae					
1	*Abies lasiocarpa*	Southern Wyoming	Mesic; 10,000 ft altitude	0.812		15
2			Xeric; 6000-7000 ft altitude	0.553		
3	*Picea engelmannii*	Southern Wyoming	Mesic; 10,000 ft altitude	0.692		15
4			Xeric; 6000-7000 ft altitude	0.441		
	Pinus banksiana	Minnesota, Cloquet Experimental Forest	34-yr-old tree			8
5			Unthinned forest	0.524		
6			Heavily-thinned forest	0.516		
7			Moderately-thinned forest	0.497		
8	*P. contorta*	Southern Wyoming	Mesic; 10,000 ft altitude	2.32		15
9			Xeric; 6000-7000 ft altitude	1.28		
	P. resinosa	Burlington, Vt.; experimental forest	27-yr-old tree			2
10			2 x 2 ft spacing; 19,439 needles/tree	4.01	77,872	
11			4 x 4 ft spacing; 51,060 needles/tree		204,546	
	P. strobus	Burlington, Vt.; experimental forest	27-yr-old tree			2
12			2 x 2 ft spacing; 121,805 needles/tree	1.22	148,968	
13			4 x 4 ft spacing; 186,644 needles/tree		228,265	
	Angiospermae (Monocotyledoneae)					
	Gramineae					
14	*Triticum aestivum*	Palo Alto, Calif.; sand culture	23- to 53-da-old tree; artificial light, 600 ft-c; 5 leaves/plant		92.4-130.4	20
15			1st leaf	10.6		
16			3rd leaf	25.8		
17			5th leaf	30.8		
18	*Zea mays*	Midwest, U.S.; field		1200-2632	12,836-16,847	12

continued

109. SURFACE AREA OF LEAVES: SPERMATOPHYTES

	Family and Species	Location	Specification	Surface Area sq cm per leaf	Surface Area sq cm per plant	Reference
	(A)	(B)	(C)	(D)	(E)	(F)
	Angiospermae (Monocotyledoneae)					
	Palmae					
19	*Phoenix dactylifera*		12-yr-old tree	87,496	5,250,000	11
	Araceae					
20	*Colocasia antiquorum*	Northern Kentucky; yard	In shade; 10 leaves/plant	18,143[1]	181,460	24
	Angiospermae (Dicotyledoneae)					
	Chenopodiaceae					
21	*Atriplex canescens*	White Sands, N. M.		2.08[1]	93,094	13
	Saxifragaceae					
22	*Ribes glandulosum*	North Hudson, N.Y.; cultivated field	Leaf 2.54 cm wide	8.23		3
23			Leaf 8.89 cm wide	88.62		
24	*R. rotundifolium*	Lansing, Mich.; cultivated field	Leaf 1.52 cm wide	4.00		3
25			Leaf 5.08 cm wide	33.02		
	Rosaceae					
26	*Fragaria chiloensis*	Glendale, Md.; cultivated field	With runners		2,292-24,826	5
27			Without runners		1532-6884	
28	*Pyrus malus*	Ithaca, N.Y.; orchard	2-yr-old tree, 5 ft high		22,420	4
29			5-yr-old tree		326,344-673,793	
30			9-yr-old tree		519,844-3,364,359	
31		Kent, England; orchard	9-yr-old tree; 10,435-20,000 leaves/plant	25.6-35.4	234,016-636,464	22
32	*Rubus occidentalis*	Lansing, Mich.; cultivated field	Shoots		26,242	10
33			Fruiting cane		32,633	
	Leguminosae					
34	*Medicago sativa*	Salt Lake City, Ut.; experimental plot	88 leaves/mature stem		32,736	9
			3 leaflets/compound leaf			17
35			Early primary leaves	3.96		
36			Late primary leaves	4.10		
37			Secondary leaves	2.30		
38			Tertiary leaves	1.30		
39			Quaternary leaves	0.72		
40	*Phaseolus vulgaris*	England; greenhouse	15-da-old tree; 2 leaves/plant	98.12	196.24	21
	Rutaceae					
41	*Citrus sinensis*	Riverside, Calif.; grove	3-yr-old tree; 16,419 leaves/tree	5.40-259	688,838	19
42			6-yr-old tree; 37,257 leaves/tree	4.52-120	1,179,556	
43			12-yr-old tree; 92,708 leaves/tree	0.12-131	2,921,756	
44			29-yr-old tree; 172,613 leaves/tree	4.24-97	4,057,220	
	Anacardiaceae					
45	*Rhus trilobata*	White Sands, N.M.		42.2[1]	126,480	13
	Vitaceae					
46	*Vitis vinifera*	Davis, Calif.; vineyard	9-yr-old vines; 26-32 leaves/single shoot	176-304	4576-9740	23
	Frankeniaceae					
47	*Frankenia jamesii*	White Sands, N.M.		0.46[1]	4364	13
	Apocynaceae					
	Nerium oleander		Artificial light			18
48			300.7 ft-c; 23 leaves/plant	21.0	482.2	
49			85.9 ft-c; 24 leaves/plant	22.4	536.2	
	Vinca rosea		Artificial light			18
50			300.7 ft-c; 257 leaves/plant	9.0	2307.2	
51			85.9 ft-c; 163 leaves/plant	7.8	1265.4	
	Asclepiadaceae					
52	*Asclepias arenaria*	White Sands, N.M.	36 leaves/plant	96.0[1]	3412	13
	Convolvulaceae					
53	*Ipomoea purpurea*	Manchester, England; greenhouse	9 nodes		1497	1
54			Leaf at 1st node	67.2		
55			Leaf at 3rd node	108.2		
56			Leaf at 5th node	166.0		
57			Leaf at 7th node	202.8		
58			Leaf at 9th (and last) node	184.6		

/1/ Largest leaf on plant.

continued

109. SURFACE AREA OF LEAVES: SPERMATOPHYTES

	Family and Species	Location	Specification	Surface Area sq cm per leaf	Surface Area sq cm per plant	Reference
	(A)	(B)	(C)	(D)	(E)	(F)
	Angiospermae (Dicotyledoneae)					
	Boraginaceae					
59	*Coldenia hispidissima*	White Sands, N.M.		0.42[1]	4624	13
	Solanaceae					
60	*Solanum tuberosum*	Vermont; greenhouse	Single shoot or branch	88-208	544	14
61			5-7 leaflets/compound leaf	8-30		
	Bignoniaceae					
62	*Catalpa speciosa*	Iowa; open lawn	26,024 leaves/plant		3,804,770	16
63			Very small leaves	58.76		
64			Small leaves	141.36		
65			Medium leaves	274.40		
66			Large leaves	484.82		
67			Very large leaves	756.68		
	Cucurbitaceae					
68	*Cucumis sativus*	Cheshunt, England; greenhouse	25°C, artificial light[2]		220.0-292.6	7
69			Cotyledons	30.44		
70			1st leaf	36.6-49.6		
71			2nd leaf	57.4-68.2		
72			3rd leaf	65.6-84.6		
73			4th leaf	27.2-55.0		
74			5th leaf	2.8-4.8		
75			35°C, artificial light[2]		32.48-35.28	6
76			35°C, in sunlight		366-3370	6
77			32.4°C, in sunlight 16 da		24.8	7
78			29°C, in sunlight 19 da		103.4	7
79			21.5°C, in sunlight 19 da		119.2	7
80			17.3°C, in sunlight 19 da		70.4	7
81	*Cucurbita foetidissima*	White Sands, N.M.		1128[1]	1,823,952	13
	Compositae					
82	*Helianthus annuus*	White Sands, N.M.		76[1]	4512	13
83	*Verbesina enceli-oides*	White Sands, N.M.		24[1]	1118	13

/1/ Largest leaf on plant. /2/ Lower limit of range (in column D or E) at artificial light intensity of 135 ft-candles, upper limit at 270 ft-candles.

Contributor: Turrell, Franklin M.

References: [1] Ashby, E., and E. Wangermann. 1950. New Phytologist 49:23. [2] Burns, G. P., and E. S. Erwin. 1942. Vermont Agr. Expt. Sta. Bull. 499. [3] Caruthers, R. S. 1929. Phytopathology 19:399. [4] Chandler, W. H. 1923. Cornell Univ. Agr. Expt. Sta. Bull. 415. [5] Darrow, G. M. 1930. J. Agr. Research 41:307. [6] Gregory, F. G. 1921. Ann. Botany (London) 35:93. [7] Gregory, F. G. 1928. Ibid. 42:469. [8] Hansen, T. S. 1937. Minn. Agr. Expt. Sta. Tech. Bull. 124. [9] Hill, G. R., Jr., and M. D. Thomas. 1933. Plant Physiol. 8:223. [10] Marshall, R. E. 1933. J. Agr. Research 47:437. [11] Mathez, F., and D. E. Bliss. 1942. Rept. Ann. Date Growers' Inst. Coachella (Calif.) 19:3. [12] Montgomery, E. G. 1911. Univ. Nebraska Agr. Expt. Sta. 24th Ann. Rept., p. 108. [13] Shields, L. M. 1951. Am. J. Botany 38:175. [14] Stone, W. E. 1933. J. Agr. Research 46:565. [15] Stover, E. L. 1944. Botan. Gaz. 106:12. [16] Turrell, F. M. 1934. Proc. Iowa Acad. Sci. 41:79. [17] Turrell, F. M. 1942. Am. J. Botany 29:400. [18] Turrell, F. M. 1944. Botan. Gaz. 105:413. [19] Turrell, F. M. 1961. Ibid. 122:284. [20] Van de Sande Bakhuyzen, H. L. 1937. Studies on wheat grown under constant conditions. Stanford Univ. Food Research Institute, Palo Alto. [21] Vyvyan, M. C. 1924. Ann. Botany (London) 38:60. [22] Vyvyan, M. C., and H. Evans. 1932. J. Pomol. Hort. Sci. 10:228. [23] Winkler, A. J. 1930. Proc. Am. Soc. Hort. Sci. 27:158. [24] Yarbrough, J. A. 1934. Proc. Iowa Acad. Sci. 41:71.

X. COMPARATIVE ANIMAL MORPHOLOGY

110. SENSE ORGANS: VERTEBRATES

Part I: EYEBALL DIMENSIONS

For extensive nontabular data, consult references 9 and 12.

	Species	Dimensions, mm Hori-zontal	Ver-tical	Sag-ittal
	(A)	(B)	(C)	(D)
1	*Homo sapiens*	24	23.5	24.0
2	*Gorilla gorilla*	22.5	22.5	22.5
3	*Sus scrofa*	26.9	26.0	24.8
4	*Equus caballus*	50.5	50.5	45.5
5	*Elephas indicus*	41.0	40.0	35.1
6	*Canis vulpes*	16.0	16.0	15.4
7	*Panthera leo*	35.0	...	35.7
8	*Balaenoptera musculus*	145	129	107
9	*Talpa europaea*	ca. 1	ca. 1	ca. 1
10	*Anser domesticus*	....	12	10
11	*Iguana* sp.	16.6	13.7	14.6
12	*Alligator* sp.	20.0	20.0	....
13	*Rana temporaria*	5.8	5.6	5.3
14	*Amia calva*	12.5	12.0	10.0
15	*Clupea harengus*	11.5	11.5	7.5
16	*Petromyzon fluviatilis*	4.9	4.5	4.0

Contributor: Low, Frank N.

References: [1] Best, C. H., and N. B. Taylor. 1961. The physiological basis of medical practice. Ed. 7. Williams and Wilkins, Baltimore. [2] Duke-Elder, S. 1944. Textbook of ophthalmology. C. V. Mosby, St. Louis. v. 1, p. 937. [3] Hartline, H. K. 1941-42. Harvey Lectures 37:39. [4] Hecht, S. 1937. Physiol. Revs. 17:239. [5] Hecht, S., S. Shlaer, and M. H. Pirenne. 1942. J. Gen. Physiol. 25:819. [6] Low, F. N. 1951. Arch. Ophthalmol. (Chicago) 45:80. [7] Lythgoe, R. J. 1926. Med. Research Council (Brit.) Spec. Rept. Ser. 104. [8] Østerberg, G. 1935. Acta Ophthalmol. 13(suppl. 6):64. [9] Rochon-Duvigneaud, A. 1943. Les yeux et la vision des vertébrés. G. Masson, Paris. [10] Shlaer, S., E. L. Smith, and A. M. Chase. 1942. J. Gen. Physiol. 25:553. [11] Steindorff, K., et al. 1947. Tabulae Biologicae 22(1). [12] Walls, G. L. 1942. Cranbrook Inst. Sci. Bull. 19.

Part II: EYEBALL VOLUMES

For extensive nontabular data, consult references 9 and 12, Part I. Values in parentheses are ranges, estimate "c" (cf. Introduction).

	Volume	*Homo sapiens*	*Bos taurus* (ox)	*Ovis aries*	*Sus scrofa*	*Equus caballus*	*Felis catus*	*Canis familiaris*	*Oryctolagus cuniculus*
	(A)	(B)	(C)	(D)	(E)	(F)	(G)	(H)	(I)
1	Total eyeball, ml	5.37	32(28-44)	12.2(8-14)	7.22(3-9)	45(40-47)	3.93(4-9)	4.46(1-5)	3.0
2	Lens, ml	0.25	2.2	0.9	0.8	2.8	0.5	0.5	0.25
3	Anterior chamber, ml	0.35	1.7	0.8	0.3	2.4	0.6	0.4	0.27
4	Posterior chamber, ml	0.16	1.52	0.5	0.3	1.56	0.32	0.17	0.06
5	Vitreous humor, ml	3.9	20.9	7.0	5.7	28.8	2.8	3.2	2.0

Contributor: Low, Frank N.

References: See Part I.

continued

110. SENSE ORGANS: VERTEBRATES

Part III: OPTICAL CONSTANTS

	Eye Area	Constant	*Homo sapiens*	*Bos taurus* (ox)	*Ovis aries*	*Sus scrofa*	*Equus caballus*	*Felis catus*	*Canis familiaris*
	(A)	(B)	(C)	(D)	(E)	(F)	(G)	(H)	(I)
1	Cornea	Refractive index	1.376	1.3757	1.3755	1.3755	1.3786	1.3784	1.3768
2		Curvature, radius, mm	7.7	16.8	12.75	11.0	18.75	9.5	8.68
3		Distance, mm[1]	0.5	1.5-2.0	0.8-1.2	1.0-1.2	1.0-1.5	0.8-1.0	0.48
	Lens								
4	Capsule	Refractive index	1.386[2]	1.3805	1.3659	1.3659	1.3796	1.3778	1.3714
5	Center	Refractive index	1.406	1.4655	1.4575	1.4400	1.4512	1.4589	1.4447
6	Outer cortex	Refractive index	.....	1.3853	1.3780	1.3780	1.3917	1.3868	......
7	Anterior cortex	Refractive index	.....	1.3851	1.3851	......	1.3912	......	1.3841
8	Posterior cortex	Refractive index	.....	1.3855	1.3855	......	1.3921	......	1.3843
9	Anterior surface	Curvature, radius, mm	10.0	11.3	8.9	7.2	14.0	6.7	6.54
10		Distance from cornea, mm	3.6	4.4	3.0	2.8	5.5	4.5	4.83
11	Posterior surface	Curvature, radius, mm	6.0	9.7	7.9	6.3	10.1	7.4	5.51
12		Distance from cornea, mm	7.2	16.2	13.4	10.7	18.1	12.3	12.18
13	Aqueous humor	Refractive index	1.336	1.3363	1.3362	1.3352	1.3362	1.3355	1.3361
14	Vitreous humor	Refractive index	1.336	1.3359	1.3357	1.3349	1.3356	1.3350	1.3358
15	Retina	Distance from cornea, mm	24	36.1	27.7	24.6	42.4	21.3	21.85
	Reference		1, 2	4, 6	3, 4	3, 4	3, 4	3, 4	5

/1/ Posterior to anterior surface. /2/ Refractive index of lens capsule plus cortex.

Contributor: Motokawa, K.

References: [1] Bethe, A. 1929. Handbuch der normalen und pathologischen Physiologie. J. Springer, Berlin. v. 12, pt. 1. [2] Gulstrand, A. 1909. In H. L. F. von Helmholtz, ed. Handbuch der physiologischen Optik. Ed. 3. L. Voss, Hamburg. v. 1. [3] Klingberg, A. 1889. Dioptrik der Augen eineger Hausthiere. Güstrow. [4] Koschel, O. 1883. Z. vergl. Augenheilk. 2:53. [5] Meyer, W. 1897. Dissertation. Univ. Rostock, Germany. [6] Moennich, P. 1883. Z. vergl. Augenheilk. 2:1.

Part IV: EAR MEASUREMENTS

	Animal	Structure and Measurement	Value	Reference
	(A)	(B)	(C)	(D)
	Outer and Middle Ear			
	Man	Tympanic membrane		
1		Diameter, mm	8-10	11
2		Thickness, mm	0.1	8
3		Area, sq mm	55.8-85.0	9,15-17,20
4		Malleus weight, mg	23-27	16,20
5		Incus weight, mg	25-32	16,20
6		Stapes weight, mg	2.05-4.35	1
		Stapes footplate		
7		Length, mm	2.64-3.36	1
8		Width, mm	1.08-1.66	1
9		Area, sq mm	2.65-3.75	9
10		Oval window area, mm	2.0 x 3.7	20
11		Round window area, sq mm	2	9
	Cat	Tympanic membrane		
12		Diameter, mm	5.5-8.6	10
13		Thickness, mm	0.03	10
	Cat	Tympanic membrane		
14		Area, sq mm	32.3-47.6	12,21
15		Malleus weight, mg	10.0-11.4	10
16		Incus weight, mg	3.0-4.5	10
17		Stapes weight, mg	0.2-0.9	10
		Stapes footplate		
18		Length, mm	1.6	10
19		Width, mm	1	10
20		Area, sq mm	1.07-1.33	21
21		Oval window area, sq mm	1.12-1.27[1]	21
22		Round window area, sq mm	2.78-3.29	21
23	Guinea pig	Tympanic membrane area, sq mm	23.5-28.0	22
24		Stapes footplate area, sq mm	0.79-0.95	22
25		Oval window area, sq mm	1.41	2
26		Round window area, sq mm	1.02	2

/1/ The oval window may appear to be slightly smaller than the stapes footplate, since the footplate is inserted in a groove on the external rim of the aperture.

continued

110. SENSE ORGANS: VERTEBRATES

Part IV: EAR MEASUREMENTS

	Animal	Structure and Measurement	Value	Reference
	(A)	(B)	(C)	(D)
		Inner Ear		
	Man	Cochlea		
27		Turns, no.	2.17-2.90	6
28		1st whorl diameter, mm	8.25	4
29		2nd whorl diameter, mm	4.62	4
		Scala vestibuli		
30		Area at base, sq mm	5-7	19
31		Area at apex, sq mm	1	19
32		Vestibule maximum diameter, mm	3.5	4
		Scala tympani		
33		Area at base, sq mm	0.5-2.4	19
34		Area at apex, sq mm	0.8	19
		Scala media		
35		Area at base, sq mm	0.2	19
36		Area at apex, sq mm	0.2	19
37		Length, mm	35	13
38		Shortest fluid pathway, mm	20	23
39		Outer wall, height at apex, mm	0.35-0.40	13
		Basilar membrane		
40		Length, mm	25.3-35.5	6
41		Width at base, mm	0.08	18
42		Width near apex, mm	0.423-0.651	18
43		Thickness, mm	<0.003	9
44		Radial fibers, no.	24,000	13
		Organ of Corti		
45		Area, cross section, sq mm	0.0053-0.0223[2]	19
		Tectorial membrane,[3] mm		
46		Radial breadth	0.112	7
47		At middle	0.208	7
48		At apex	0.208	7
49		Maximum depth	0.204	7
50		At middle	0.048	7
51		At apex	0.064	7
		Inner hair cells		
52		No.	3500	13
53		Height, mm	0.34	7
		Outer hair cells		
54		No.	12,000[4]	13
55		Height at base, mm	0.028	7
56		Height at middle, mm	0.044	7
57		Height at apex, mm	0.066	7
	Man	Organ of Corti		
58		Inner pillar cells, no.	5600	13
59		Outer pillar cells, no.	3850	13
	Cat	Cochlea		
60		Turns, no.	3+	4
61		1st whorl diameter, mm	6	4
62		2nd whorl diameter, mm	3.5	4
63		Scala vestibuli, maximum diameter, mm	2.75	4
		Scala media		
64		Length, mm	25	13
65		Shortest fluid pathway, mm	16.3	20
66		Outer wall, height at apex, mm	0.33	13
		Basilar membrane		
67		Length, mm	19.4-25.4	3
68		Width near apex, mm	0.35[5]	13
69		Radial fibers, no.	15,700	13
		Organ of Corti		
70		Area, cross section, sq mm	0.0055-0.0201[5]	3
		Tectorial membrane,[3] mm		
71		Radial breadth	0.2	13
72		At middle	0.29	13
73		At apex	0.3	13
74		Maximum depth at middle	0.045	13
		Inner hair cells		
75		No.	2600	13
76		Height, mm	0.03	13
		Outer hair cells		
77		No.	9900[6]	13
78		Height at middle, mm	0.033	13
79		Inner pillar cells, no.	4700	13
80		Outer pillar cells, no.	3300	13
	Dog	Cochlea		
81		Turns, no.	3.25	4
82		1st whorl diameter, mm	6.25	4
83		2nd whorl diameter, mm	3.5	4
84		Scala vestibuli, maximum diameter, mm	3	4
85		Scala media, length, mm	16-17	13
		Basilar membrane		
86		Length, mm	14.5-16	13
87		Width at base, mm	0.3	13

/2/ From base to apex. /3/ Values may reflect the fact that the tectorial membrane is easily affected by histological procedures. /4/ 4 rows. /5/ At midpoint of long axis of basilar membrane. /6/ 3 rows.

continued

110. SENSE ORGANS: VERTEBRATES

Part IV: EAR MEASUREMENTS

	Animal	Structure and Measurement	Value	Reference
	(A)	(B)	(C)	(D)
		Inner Ear		
	Dog	Basilar membrane		
88		Width near apex, mm	0.41	13
89		Radial fibers, no.	10,500[7]	13
		Organ of Corti		
		Tectorial membrane,[3] mm		
90		Radial breadth	0.13	7
91		At middle	0.15	7
92		At apex	0.14	7
93		Maximum depth	0.027	13
94		At middle	0.027	13
95		At apex	0.027	13
		Inner hair cells		
96		No.	1600	13
97		Height, mm	0.03	13
		Outer hair cells		
98		No.	6100-6200[4]	13
99		Height at base, mm	0.03	13
100		Height at middle, mm	0.039	13
101		Height at apex, mm	0.036	13
102		Inner pillar cells, no.	2800	13
103		Outer pillar cells, no.	1940	13
104	Guinea pig	Cochlear turns, no.	4	5
		Scala vestibuli		
105		Area at base, sq mm	3.2	2
106		Area at apex, sq mm	0.22	2
		Scala tympani		
107		Area at base, sq mm	1.4	2
108		Area at apex, sq mm	0.1	2
		Scala media		
109		Area at base, sq mm	0.1	2
110		Area at apex, sq mm	0.1	2
111		Length, mm	18.8	2
		Basilar membrane		
112		Length, mm	18.8	2
113		Width at base, mm	0.06	5
114		Width near apex, mm	0.194-0.228	5
	Guinea pig	Basilar membrane		
115		Thickness, mm	0.0074-0.0134[2]	2
		Organ of Corti		
116		Area, cross section, sq mm	0.012-0.017[8]	2
	Rat	Cochlea		
117		Turns, no.	2.25	4
118		1st whorl diameter, mm	2.5	4
119		2nd whorl diameter, mm	1.75	4
120		Scala vestibuli, maximum diameter, mm	2	4
	Rabbit	Cochlea		
121		Turns, no.	2.5	4
122		1st whorl diameter, mm	3	4
123		2nd whorl diameter, mm	2	4
124		Scala vestibuli, maximum diameter, mm	2.75	4
	Chicken	Basilar membrane		
125		Length, mm	2.7	7
126		Width at base, mm	0.066	7
127		Width near apex, mm	0.4[9]	7
		Organ of Corti		
		Outer hair cells, height, mm		
128		At base	0.006-0.010[10]	7
129		At middle	0.020[9]	7
130		At apex	0.012[11]	7
	Parrot	Organ of Corti		
		Outer hair cells, height, mm		
131		At base	0.008-0.009	14
132		At middle	0.01-0.012	14
133		At apex	0.007-0.008	14
	Pigeon	Organ of Corti		
		Outer hair cells, height, mm		
134		At base	0.006-0.008	14
135		At middle	0.012-0.133	14
136		At apex	0.006-0.008	14
	Starling	Organ of Corti		
		Outer hair cells, height, mm		
137		At base	0.008-0.01	14
138		At middle	0.012	14
139		At apex	0.005-0.006	14

/2/ From base to apex. /3/ Values may reflect the fact that the tectorial membrane is easily affected by histological procedures. /4/ 4 rows. /7/ In tympanic layer. /8/ Maximum for point near apex; at extreme apex, area diminishes to 0.015 sq mm. /9/ At the columella. /10/ In the region of the vestibule. /11/ At the point where the scala tympani ends in a blind pocket.

Contributor: Lawrence, Merle

References: [1] Bast, T. H., and B. J. Anson. 1949. The temporal bone and the ear. C. C. Thomas, Springfield, Ill. [2] Fernández, C. 1952. J. Acoust. Soc. Amer. 24:519. [3] Freedman, R. 1947. Thesis. Princeton Univ., Princeton. [4] Gray, A. A. 1907. The labyrinth of animals. J. and A. Churchill, London. [5] Guild, S. R. 1927.

continued

Science 65:67. [6] Hardy, M. 1938. Am. J. Anat. 62:291. [7] Held, H. 1926. In A. Bethe, ed. Handbuch der normalen und pathologischen Physiologie. Receptionsorgane I. J. Springer, Berlin. pp. 467-534. [8] Helmholtz, H. L. F. 1863. Die Lehre von den Tonempfindungen als physiologische Grundlage für die Theorie des Musik. Ed. 1. F. Vieweg und Sohn, Braunschweig. [9] Keith, A. 1918. In T. Wrightson and A. Keith, ed. An enquiry into the analytical mechanism of the internal ear. Macmillan, London. [10] Lawrence, M. Unpublished. Univ. Michigan, Ann Arbor, 1953. [11] Lewis, W. N., ed. 1918. Gray's Anatomy of the human body. Ed. 20. Longmans, Green; London. [12] Payne, M. C., and F. J. Githler. 1951. Arch. Otolaryngol. 54:666. [13] Retzius, G. 1884. Das Gehörorgan der Wirbelthiere. Samson and Wallin, Stockholm. v. 2. [14] Satoh, N. 1917. Der histologische Bau der Vogelschnecke und ihre Schädigung durch akustische Reize und durch Detonation. B. Schwabe, Basel. [15] Schwalbe, G. 1887. Lehrbuch der Anatomie der Sinnesorgan. E. Besold, Erlangen. [16] Stuhlman, O., Jr. 1937. J. Acoust. Soc. Amer. 9:119. [17] Von Békésy, G. 1941. Akust. Z. 6:1. [18] Wever, E. G. 1938. Ann. Otol. Rhinol. Laryngol. 47:37. [19] Wever, E. G. 1949. Theory of hearing. J. Wiley and Sons, New York. [20] Wever, E. G., and M. Lawrence. 1954. Physiological acoustics. Princeton Univ. Press, Princeton. [21] Wever, E. G., M. Lawrence, and K. R. Smith. 1948. Arch. Otolaryngol. 48:19. [22] Whittle, G. T. 1946. Thesis. Princeton Univ., Princeton. [23] Wilkinson, G., and A. A. Gray. 1924. The mechanism of the cochlea. Macmillan, London.

111. TOOTH ERUPTION: VERTEBRATES

Part I: PRIMATES

Deciduous-tooth eruption measured in days, permanent-tooth in years. Site (column B): MX = maxilla, MD = mandible. Values in parentheses are ranges, estimate "b" (columns C, D, G, H) or "c" (columns E, F) (cf. Introduction).

	Tooth	Site	*Homo sapiens*[1]		*Pan troglodytes*		*Macaca mulatta*	
			Male	Female	Male	Female	Male	Female
	(A)	(B)	(C)	(D)	(E)	(F)	(G)	(H)
	Deciduous							
	Incisors							
1	1st	MX	277(187-367)	292(172-412)	111(77-161)	76(40-108)	19.1(-0.7[2] to 38.8)	19.5(0.3-38.7)
2		MD	222(126-318)	237(112-362)	95(55-126)	70(53-83)	15.2(-3.6[2] to 34.1)	16(-0.7[2] to 32.7)
3	2nd	MX	316(173-459)	362(201-523)	122(83-177)	94(74-112)	39(15-63)	38(14-62)
4		MD	395(228-562)	420(206-634)	124(68-188)	88(65-112)	23(0-46)	23(4-42)
5	Canines	MX	575(414-736)	611(421-801)	355(266-411)	327(226-445)	68(39-96)	71(44-99)
6		MD	587(415-759)	614(412-816)	376(293-459)	351(265-492)	71(42-99)	73(41-105)
	Molars							
7	1st	MX	486(349-623)	477(340-614)	126(77-180)	111(74-152)	73(49-97)	68(41-95)
8		MD	492(378-606)	474(343-605)	150(79-210)	135(106-176)	78(53-103)	73(47-99)
9	2nd	MX	839(576-1102)	863(606-1120)	308(226-446)	290(243-379)	164(117-212)	155(109-201)
10		MD	787(560-1014)	824(573-1075)	247(183-338)	225(154-291)	152(114-190)	139(101-178)
	Reference		7		5		3	
	Permanent							
	Incisors							
11	1st	MX	7.47(5.88-9.06)	7.20(5.61-8.79)	5.6(4.9-6.5)	5.6(4.5-6.7)	2.51(2.05-2.97)	2.51(2.13-2.89)
12		MD	6.54(5.01-8.07)	6.26(4.73-7.79)	5.6(5.2-6.4)	5.8(5.0-7.0)	2.42(1.98-2.86)	2.46(2.04-2.88)
13	2nd	MX	8.67(6.75-10.59)	8.20(6.28-10.12)	6.7(5.8-7.7)	6.8(5.8-8.2)	2.76(2.28-3.24)	2.75(2.27-3.23)
14		MD	7.70(5.98-9.42)	7.34(5.62-9.06)	6.2(5.6-6.9)	6.0(5.0-7.3)	2.54(2.10-2.98)	2.59(2.07-3.11)
15	Canines	MX	11.69(9.00-14.38)	10.98(8.29-13.67)	9.0(8.0-9.8)	9.0(7.6-10.0)	4.06(3.30-4.82)	3.54(2.76-4.32)
16		MD	10.79(8.30-13.28)	9.86(7.37-12.35)	9.2(8.0-10.0)	8.6(7.9-9.1)	3.87(3.19-4.55)	3.17(2.51-3.83)
	Premolars							
17	1st	MX	10.40(7.52-13.28)	10.03(7.15-12.91)	6.9(6.0-8.1)	6.9(6.0-8.0)	3.58(2.92-4.24)	3.41(2.83-3.99)
18		MD	10.82(7.94-13.70)	10.18(7.30-13.06)	7.4(6.3-8.2)	7.3(6.3-8.0)	3.74(3.06-4.42)	3.40(2.78-4.02)

/1/ White. /2/ Prenatal eruption.

continued

111. TOOTH ERUPTION: VERTEBRATES

Part I: PRIMATES

	Tooth	Site	*Homo sapiens*[1]		*Pan troglodytes*		*Macaca mulatta*	
			Male	Female	Male	Female	Male	Female
	(A)	(B)	(C)	(D)	(E)	(F)	(G)	(H)
	Permanent							
	Premo-lars							
19	2nd	MX	11.18(8.10-14.26)	10.88(7.80-13.96)	7.2(6.3-8.3)	7.4(6.2-8.3)	3.68(2.96-4.40)	3.72(2.86-4.58)
20		MD	11.47(8.18-14.76)	10.89(7.60-14.18)	7.4(6.3-8.2)	7.6(6.0-9.1)	3.68(3.04-4.32)	3.55(2.79-4.31)
	Molars							
21	1st	MX	6.40(4.83-7.97)	6.22(4.65-7.79)	3.3(3.0-3.8)	3.3(2.7-3.8)	1.49(1.17-1.81)	1.44(1.20-1.68)
22		MD	6.21(4.64-7.78)	5.94(4.37-7.51)	3.3(3.0-3.6)	3.2(2.7-3.8)	1.37(1.05-1.69)	1.32(1.12-1.52)
23	2nd	MX	12.68(9.99-15.37)	12.27(9.58-14.96)	6.8(5.7-7.8)	6.8(5.9-7.6)	3.28(2.78-3.78)	3.36(2.84-3.88)
24		MD	12.12(9.45-14.79)	11.66(8.99-14.33)	6.5(5.6-7.0)	6.4(5.9-7.3)	3.15(2.65-3.65)	3.15(2.69-3.61)
25	3rd	MX	20.5(16-27)	20.5(16-27)	11.4(10.0-13.6)	11.3(9.7-13.1)	5.6(4.9-6.3)	6.43(4.45-7.41)
26		MD	20.5(16-27)	20.5(16-27)	10.3(9.0-11.1)	10.7(9.0-13.1)	5.4(4.8-6.0)	5.81(4.67-6.95)
	Reference		1,2		6		4	

/1/ White.

Contributors: (a) Riesen, Austin H., (b) Hurme, V. O., (c) Schultz, Adolph H.

References: [1] Hurme, V. O. 1948. Child Develop. 19:181. [2] Hurme, V. O. 1949. J. Dent. Children 16:11. [3] Hurme, V. O., and G. van Wagenen. 1953. Proc. Am. Phil. Soc. 97:291. [4] Hurme, V. O., and G. van Wagenen. 1961. Ibid. 105:105. [5] Nissen, H. W., and A. H. Riesen. 1945. Growth 9:265. [6] Nissen, H. W., and A. H. Riesen. Unpublished. Univ. Chicago, Chicago, 1962. [7] Robinow, M., T. W. Richards, and M. Anderson. 1942. Growth 6:127.

Part II: ARTIODACTYLS, PERISSODACTYLS, AND CARNIVORES

Deciduous-tooth eruption measured in days, permanent-tooth in years. Site (column B): MX = maxilla, MD = mandible. PN (columns C, E-G) = prenatal.

	Tooth	Site	*Bos taurus*	*Capra hircus*	*Ovis aries*	*Sus scrofa*	*Equus caballus*	*Canis familiaris*
	(A)	(B)	(C)	(D)	(E)	(F)	(G)	(H)
	Deciduous							
	Incisors							
1	1st	MX	....	....	....	14-28	PN-14	21-42
2		MD	PN-7	4	PN-7	14-28	PN-14	21-42
3	2nd	MX	....	....	....	60-90	14-42	21-42
4		MD	PN-14	5	7-14	45-90	14-42	21-42
5	3rd	MX	....	....	....	PN	150-270	28-42
6		MD	PN-21	7	14-21	PN	150-270	28-42
7	4th	MD	14-42	30	21-28	....	....	....
8	Canines	MX	....	....	....	PN	Vestigial[1]	21-28
9		MD	....	....	....	PN	Vestigial[1]	21-28
	Molars							
10	1st	MX	PN-14	7	14-42	35-49	PN-14	28-35
11		MD	PN-14	7	14-42	35-49	PN-14	28-35
12	2nd	MX	PN-10	7	14-42	4-8	PN-14	21-35
13		MD	PN-10	7	14-42	14-28	PN-14	21-35
14	3rd	MX	PN-10	7	14-42	4-8	PN-14	21-28
15		MD	PN-10	7	14-42	14-28	PN-14	21-28
	Reference		4, 5	3	4	1	2, 4	2, 4

/1/ Does not erupt.

continued

111. TOOTH ERUPTION: VERTEBRATES

Part II: ARTIODACTYLS, PERISSODACTYLS, AND CARNIVORES

	Tooth	Site	*Bos taurus*	*Capra hircus*	*Ovis aries*	*Sus scrofa*	*Equus caballus*	*Canis familiaris*
	(A)	(B)	(C)	(D)	(E)	(F)	(G)	(H)
	Permanent							
	Incisors							
16	1st	MX	....	....	....	1.0	2.2-3.0	0.2-0.4
17		MD	1.5-2.0	1.0-1.3	1.0-1.5	1.0	2.2-3.0	0.2-0.4
18	2nd	MX	....	....	....	1.3-1.7	3.5-4.0	0.2-0.4
19		MD	2.0-2.5	1.7-1.8	1.5-2.0	1.3-1.7	3.5-4.0	0.2-0.4
20	3rd	MX	....	....	....	0.7-0.8	4.2-5.0	0.2-0.4
21		MD	2.8-3.3	2.7-3.0	2.5-3.0	0.7-0.8	4.2-5.0	0.3-0.4
22	4th	MD	3.5-4.0	3.5-4.0	3.5-4.0	....	....	....
23	Canines	MX	....	....	....	0.7-0.8	3.5-5.0[2]	0.3-0.5
24		MD	....	....	....	0.7-0.8	3.5-5.0	0.3-0.5
	Premolars							
25	1st	MX	2.0-2.5	1.0-1.3	1.5-2.0	0.4	0.4-0.5	0.3-0.5
26		MD	2.0-2.5	1.0-1.3	1.5-2.0	0.4	0.4-0.5[3]	0.3-0.5
27	2nd	MX	1.5-2.5	1.0-1.3	1.5-2.0	1.0-1.3	2.0-2.5	0.4-0.5
28		MD	1.5-2.5	1.0-1.3	1.5-2.0	1.0-1.3	2.0-2.5	0.4-0.5
29	3rd	MX	2.5-3.0	1.7-1.8	1.5-2.0	1.0-1.3	3.0-3.5	0.4-0.5
30		MD	2.5-3.0	1.7-1.8	1.5-2.0	1.0-1.3	2.5-3.0	0.4-0.5
31	4th	MX	....	....	....	1.0-1.3	4.0-4.5	0.4-0.5
32		MD	....	....	....	1.0-1.3	3.5-4.0	0.4-0.5
	Molars							
33	1st	MX	0.4-0.7	20 da	0.4	0.3-0.5	0.5-1.0	0.3-0.5
34		MD	0.4-0.7	20 da	0.3	0.3-0.5	0.5-1.0	0.3-0.5
35	2nd	MX	1.0-1.5	45 da	0.7-1.0	0.7-1.0	1.5-2.2	0.4-0.5
36		MD	1.0-1.5	45 da	0.7-1.0	0.7-1.0	1.5-2.2	0.3-0.4
37	3rd	MX	2.0-2.5	0.8-0.9	1.5-2.0	1.5-1.7	3.5-4.5	....
38		MD	2.0-2.5	0.8-0.9	1.5-2.0	1.5-1.7	3.5-4.5	0.5-0.6
	Reference		4	3	4	1, 4	4	4

/2/ Usually absent in mares. /3/ Rarely erupts.

Contributors: (a) Hurme, V. O., (b) Riesen, Austin H.

References: [1] Avery, J. K. 1952. Ph. D. Thesis. Univ. Rochester, N. Y. [2] Ellenberger, W., and H. Baum. 1915. Handbuch der vergleichenden Anatomie der Haustiere. Ed. 14. A. Hirschwald, Berlin. [3] Paul, D. L. 1946. Indian Farming 7:133. [4] Sisson, S., and J. D. Grossman. 1938. The anatomy of the domestic animals. W. B. Saunders, Philadelphia. [5] Youatt, W. 1834. Cattle. Baldwin and Dradock, London.

Part III: RODENTS

Tooth eruption measured in days. Site (column B): MX = maxilla, MD = mandible. PN (column F) = prenatal.

	Tooth	Site	*Mesocricetus auratus*	*Mus musculus* (albino)	*Rattus norvegicus* (albino)	*Sigmodon hispidus hispidus*
	(A)	(B)	(C)	(D)	(E)	(F)
1	Incisors	MX	0-2	10	8-10	PN-1
2		MD	0-2	10	8-10	PN
	Molars					
3	1st	MX	7-9	15	20	5-7
4		MD	7-8	15	19	4-7
5	2nd	MX	13-14	15-20	22-23	9-13
6		MD	12-13	15-20	21-22	7-12
7	3rd	MX	32-36	28	31-36	28-33
8		MD	29-32	28	29-35	26-30
	Reference		3, 5	1	2, 4	6

continued

111. TOOTH ERUPTION: VERTEBRATES

Part III: RODENTS

Contributors: (a) Hurme, V. O., (b) Riesen, Austin H.

References: [1] Bhaskar, S. N., J. P. Weinmann, and I. Schour. 1948. J. Dental Research 27:755. [2] Hoffman, M. M., and I. Schour. 1940. Anat. Record 78:233. [3] Keyes, P. H., and P. P. Dale. 1944. J. Dental Research 23:427. [4] Mellanby, H. 1939. Brit. Dental J. 66:76. [5] Orland, F. J. 1946. J. Dental Research 25:445. [6] Shaw, J. H., N. M. Shaffer, and L. W. Soldan, Jr. 1950. Ibid. 29:197.

112. DIGESTIVE SYSTEM: VERTEBRATES

Part I: ORGAN MEASUREMENTS

Meat-eating animals have a simple, short digestive tract. Grass- and grain-eating animals usually have a more complicated system with a long bowel and several large pouches.

	Order and Species	Organ	Measurement	Value	Reference
	(A)	(B)	(C)	(D)	(E)
	Primates				
1	*Homo sapiens*	Small intestine	Length, cm	300	1
2		Colon	Length, cm	125	2
	Artiodactyla				
	Bos taurus (ox)	Salivary glands			
3		Parotid	Weight, g	115	4
4		Mandibular	Weight, g	140	4
5		Esophagus	Length, cm	90-105	4
6			Diameter, cm	5	4
7		Stomach	Capacity, L	252.5	3
8		Duodenum	Length, cm	100	4
9		Pancreas	Weight, g	350	4
10		Small intestine	Length, cm	4600	3
11			Capacity, L	66.0	3
12		Cecum	Length, cm	75	4
13			Diameter, cm	12	4
14			Capacity, L	9.9	3
15		Colon	Length, cm	1080	4
16			Diameter, cm	5-12	4
17		Colon + rectum	Capacity, L	28.0	3
18	*Capra hircus*	Small intestine	Length, cm	2620	3
19			Capacity, L	9.0	3
20		Cecum	Length, cm	36	3
21			Capacity, L	1.0	3
22		Colon	Length, cm	617	3
23		Colon + rectum	Capacity, L	4.6	3
24	*Ovis aries*	Esophagus	Diameter, cm	2.5	4
25		Small intestine	Length, cm	2620	3
26			Diameter, cm	2-3	4
27			Capacity, L	9.0	3
28		Cecum	Length, cm	25	4
29			Width, cm	5	4
30			Capacity, L	1.0	3
31		Colon	Length, cm	400-500	4
32			Width, cm	5	4
33		Colon + rectum	Capacity, L	4.6	3
34	*Sus scrofa*	Sublingual gland	Length, cm	5	4
35			Width, cm	1.3	4
36		Esophagus	Diameter, cm	5.6	4
	Artiodactyla				
37	*Sus scrofa*	Stomach	Capacity, L	8.0	3
38		Small intestine	Length, cm	1829	3
39			Capacity, L	9.2	3
40		Cecum	Length, cm	20-30	4
41			Width, cm	8-10	4
42			Capacity, L	1.55	3
43		Colon	Length, cm	499	3
44		Colon + rectum	Capacity, L	8.7	3
	Perissodactyla				
	Equus caballus	Salivary glands			
45		Parotid	Weight, g	200-225	4
46			Length, cm	20-25	4
47			Width, cm	2	4
48		Mandibular	Weight, g	45-60	4
49			Length, cm	20-25	4
50			Width, cm	2.5-3.0	4
51		Sublingual	Weight, g	15-16	4
52			Length, cm	12-15	4
53		Esophagus	Length, cm	125-130	4
54		Stomach	Capacity, L	17.96	3
55		Duodenum	Length, cm	100	4
56		Pancreas	Weight, g	350	4
57		Small intestine	Length, cm	2244	3
58			Capacity, L	63.82	3
59		Cecum	Length, cm	100	3
60			Capacity, L	33.54	3
61		Large colon	Length, cm	300-370	4
62			Diameter, cm	20-25	4
63			Capacity, L	81.25	3
64		Small colon	Length, cm	350	4
65			Diameter, cm	7.5-10.0	4
66		Rectum	Length, cm	30	4
67		Small colon + rectum	Capacity, L	14.77	3
68		Anus	Length, cm	500	4
	Carnivora				
69	*Felis catus*	Stomach	Capacity, L	0.341	3
70		Small intestine	Length, cm	172	3
71			Capacity, L	0.114	3
72		Large intestine	Length, cm	35	3
73			Capacity, L	0.124	3

continued

112. DIGESTIVE SYSTEM: VERTEBRATES

Part I: ORGAN MEASUREMENTS

	Order and Species	Organ	Measurement	Value	Reference
	(A)	(B)	(C)	(D)	(E)
	Carnivora				
74	*Canis familiaris*	Stomach	Capacity, L	4.33	3
75		Small intestine	Length, cm	414	3
76			Capacity, L	1.62	3
77		Cecum	Length, cm	8	3
78			Capacity, L	0.09	3
79		Colon	Length, cm	60	3
80		Colon + rectum	Capacity, L	0.91	3
	Lagomorpha				
81	*Oryctolagus cuniculus*	Small intestine	Length, cm	356	3
82		Cecum	Length, cm	61	3
83		Colon	Length, cm	165	3

Contributors: (a) Wadsworth, James R., (b) Alvarez, Walter C.

References: [1] Alvarez, W. C. 1948. An introduction to gastroenterology. Ed. 4. P. B. Hoeber, New York. [2] Alvarez, W. C. Unpublished. Univ. Minnesota, Minneapolis, 1953. [3] Dukes, H. H. 1955. The physiology of domestic animals. Ed. 7. Comstock, Ithaca. [4] Sisson, S., and J. D. Grossman. 1953. The anatomy of domestic animals. Ed. 4. W. B. Saunders, Philadelphia,

Part II: ENZYMES

Tissue or Secretion (column D): T = tissue, S = secretion. Symbols (columns E-S): + = present, - = absent, ± = doubtful.

	Order	Animal	Organ	Tissue or Secretion	Enzyme: Amylase (Diastase)	Carbonic Anhydrase	Elastase	Enterokinase	Erepsin, Peptidase	Invertase (Saccharase)	Lipase, Esterases	Maltase	Pepsin	Phosphatase	Ribonuclease	Rennin (Chymosin)	Trypsin, Other Non-acid Proteases	Urease	β-D-Galactosidase	Reference
	(A)	(B)	(C)	(D)	(E)	(F)	(G)	(H)	(I)	(J)	(K)	(L)	(M)	(N)	(O)	(P)	(Q)	(R)	(S)	(T)
1	Primates	Man	Salivary gland	T							+									27
2				S	+				+		+			+						15
3			Esophagus	T							+									27
4			Stomach	T							+		+	+				+		K,27;M,N,15;R,9
5				S							+		+			-[1]				K,22;M,15;P,28
6			Pancreas	T					+		+			+						I,K,22;N,21
7				S	+				+		+	+					+			E,L,Q,4;I,K,22
8			Small intestine	T	+				+					+						E,15;I,22;N,24
9				S	±			+	+	+	±									E,22;H-K,31
10			Cecum & colon	T										+						24
11		Monkey	Salivary gland	S	+				+											E,15;I,3
12			Stomach	S									+							26
13			Small intestine	S				+												15
14	Artiodactyla	Cattle (cow)	Salivary gland	T							+			+					+	7
15				S	+						+									E,7;K,15
16			Esophagus	T									-							22
17			Stomach	T	+						+					+[2]		+		E,R,24;K,15;P,27
18				S									+			±[2]				M,4;P,15

/1/ In adult. /2/ Only in young.

continued

112. DIGESTIVE SYSTEM: VERTEBRATES

Part II: ENZYMES

	Order	Animal	Organ	Tissue or Secretion	Amylase (Diastase)	Carbonic Anhydrase	Elastase	Enterokinase	Erepsin, Peptidase	Invertase (Saccharase)	Lipase, Esterases	Maltase	Pepsin	Phosphatase	Ribonuclease	Rennin (Chymosin)	Trypsin, Other Non-acid Proteases	Urease	β-D-Galactosidase	Reference
	(A)	(B)	(C)	(D)	(E)	(F)	(G)	(H)	(I)	(J)	(K)	(L)	(M)	(N)	(O)	(P)	(Q)	(R)	(S)	(T)
19	Artio-	Cattle	Pancreas	T	+						+				+		+			E,22;K,15;O,Q,27
20	dactyla	(cow)		S	+												+			22
21			Small intes-	T									-	+						M,22;N,13
22			tine	S				+												15
23		Goat	Salivary gland	S	-															22
24			Stomach	T														-		24
25				S												+[2]				24
26			Small intestine	S	±			+	-	±	±						-			E,I-K,Q,31;H,15
27		Sheep	Salivary gland	T							+			+					+	7
28				S	-						+									15
29			Esophagus	T									-							22
30			Stomach	T							+		+			+[2]		+		K,15;M,R,24;P,28
31			Pancreas	T	+						+				+		+			E,K,15;O,2;Q,24
32				S	+												+			E,15;Q,24
33			Small intestine	S				+												15
34			Cecum & colon	T							-									22
35		Swine	Salivary gland	T							+			+					+	7
36				S	+															15
37			Esophagus	T									-							22
38			Stomach	T					+		±		+					+		I,M,15;K,11;R,9
39				S	-								+			+[2]				E,M,10;P,15
40			Pancreas	T	+		+		+		+			+	+		+			E,I,K,Q,15;G,18;K,12;N,16;O,23
41				S	+		+										+			E,Q,22;G,18
42			Small intestine	T				+	-		+		±	+						H,23;I,31;K,15;M,22;N,24
43				S	+			+		±	±						-			E,J,K,Q,31;H,15
44	Perisso-	Horse	Salivary gland	S	±						+									E,22;K,24
45	dactyla		Stomach	T							+									15
46			Small intes-	T									-							22
47			tine	S[3]	+			+		+	-	+					+			E,J-L,Q,1;H,15
48			Cecum & colon	T	+															29
49	Carniv-	Cat	Salivary gland	T										+						24
50	ora			S	-															15
51			Stomach	T		+					+			+				+		F,4;K,15;N,24;R,9
52				S									+							4
53			Pancreas	T		+			+			+		+						F,L,4;I,15;N,21
54				S	+						+									4
55			Small intestine	T		+		+	±					+			+			F,4;H,I,Q,15;N,24
56				S	+			+	±	±	-						-			E,I,J,Q,31;H,15;K,24
57			Cecum & colon	T							+			+						K,19;N,24
58			Colon	S							-									19
59		Dog	Salivary gland	T		+					+			+					+	F,5;K,N,S,7
60				S	+						+									E,7;K,15
61			Esophagus	T									-							22

/2/ Only in young. /3/ Lactase also present [1].

continued

112. DIGESTIVE SYSTEM: VERTEBRATES

Part II: ENZYMES

	Order	Animal	Organ	Tissue or Secretion	Enzyme: Amylase (Diastase)	Carbonic Anhydrase	Elastase	Enterokinase	Erepsin, Peptidase	Invertase (Saccharase)	Lipase, Esterases	Maltase	Pepsin	Phosphatase	Ribonuclease	Rennin (Chymosin)	Trypsin, Other Non-acid Proteases	Urease	β-D-Galactosidase	Reference
	(A)	(B)	(C)	(D)	(E)	(F)	(G)	(H)	(I)	(J)	(K)	(L)	(M)	(N)	(O)	(P)	(Q)	(R)	(S)	(T)
62	Carnivora	Dog	Stomach	T		+					+							+		F,4;K,22;R,9
63				S	±						+		+			±[2]				E,K,22;M,P,3
64			Pancreas	T	+		+		+		+				+		+			E,I,K,Q,4;G,6;O,23
65				S	+				+		+	+					+			4
66			Small intestine	T				+	+		+			+						H,4;I,K,22;N,24
67				S	+			+	+	±	±						±			E,J,K,Q,31;H,I,4
68			Cecum & colon	S	±			-	±		+									E,K,22;H,I,17
69	Rodentia	Guinea pig	Salivary gland	S	+															15
70			Stomach	T		+					+									F,16;K,15
71			Pancreas	T		+	+		+					+						F,16;G,8;I,15;N,21
72				S							+									22
73			Small intestine	T					+											15
74		Mouse	Stomach	T		+														16
75			Pancreas	T		+								+						F,16;N,21
76		Rat	Salivary gland	T							+			+					+	7
77				S	+															25
78			Stomach	T	+	+					+		+					+		E,20;F,4;K,15;M,24;R,9
79				S									+							14
80			Pancreas	T	+	+	+				+			+			+			E,F,K,Q,4;G,8;N,21
81				S	+															4
82			Small intestine	T	+	+		+	+			+		+						E,I,L,30;F,4;H,N,24
83			Colon	T	+															20
84	Lagomorpha	Rabbit	Salivary gland	T							+			+					+	7
85				S	+															7
86			Stomach	T		+					+		+	+				+		F,4;K,15;M,22;N,24;R,9
87				S							+									22
88			Pancreas	T		+			+											F,4;I,15
89				S	+						+						+			4
90			Small intestine	T		+			+				-	+						F,4;I,M,22;N,24
91				S	+			+	-		±						-			E,I,K,Q,31;H,15
92			Cecum & colon	T									+							24
93	Galliformes	Chicken	Salivary gland	S	+															15
94			Stomach	T							+		+							K,15;M,27
95			Pancreas	T	+									+						E,15;N,21
96			Small intestine	T	+															15
97	Salientia	Frog	Salivary gland	S	+															15
98			Esophagus	T									+							22
99			Stomach	T									+					+		M,15;R,9
100				S									+							15
101			Pancreas	T					+			+					+			I,15;L,Q,24
102			Small intestine	T					+			-								I,15;L,24

/2/ Only in young.

continued

112. DIGESTIVE SYSTEM: VERTEBRATES

Part II: ENZYMES

Contributor: Hollander, Franklin

References: [1] Alexander, F., and A. K. Chowdhury. 1958. Nature 181:190. [2] Aqvist, S. E. G., and C. B. Anfinsen. 1959. J. Biol. Chem. 234:1112. [3] Babkin, B. P. 1929. Die äussere Sekretion der Verdauungsdrüsen. Ed. 2. J. Springer, Berlin. [4] Babkin, B. P. 1950. Secretory mechanism of the digestive glands. Ed. 2. P. B. Hoeber, New York. [5] Brusilow, S. W., and C. L. Diaz. 1962. Am. J. Physiol. 202:158. [6] Carter, A. E. 1956. Science 123:669. [7] Chauncey, H. H., and G. Quintarelli. 1961. Am. J. Anat. 108:263. [8] Cohen, H., H. Megel, and W. Kleinberg. 1958. Proc. Soc. Exptl. Biol. Med. 97:8. [9] Conway, E. J. 1953. The biochemistry of gastric acid secretion. C. C. Thomas, Springfield, Ill. [10] Dukes, H. H. 1955. The physiology of domestic animals. Ed. 7. Comstock, Ithaca. [11] Evans, R. A., and D. A. Stansfield. 1961. Nature 190:1110. [12] Gjessing, E., and J. C. Hartnett. 1960. Federation Proc. 19:49. [13] Harris, E. S., et al. 1952. Proc. Soc. Exptl. Biol. Med. 81:593. [14] Hirschowitz, B. I., and W. G. Underhill. 1959. Am. J. Physiol. 196:837. [15] Koningsberger, V. J., E. J. Slijper, and H. J. Vonk, ed. 1946. Tabulae Biologicae 21(1). [16] Kurata, Y. 1953. Stain Technol. 28:231. [17] Kuvaeva, I. B. 1957. Fiziol. Zhur. S.S.S.R. 43:311. [18] Lewis, U. J., D. E. Williams, and N. G. Brink. 1956. J. Biol. Chem. 222:705. [19] Martin, B. F. 1959. Nature 183:1464. [20] McGeachin, R. L., and K. F. Norwood, Jr. 1959. Am. J. Physiol. 196:972. [21] Moog, F. 1962. Federation Proc. 21:51. [22] Oppenheimer, C. 1925-26. Die Fermente und ihre Wirkungen. Ed. 5. G. Thieme, Leipzig. v. 1, 2. [23] Oppenheimer, C., and L. Pincussen, ed. 1929. Ibid. G. Thieme, Leipzig. v. 3. [24] Oppenheimer, C. 1935-39. Ibid. W. Junk, Haag. suppl. [25] Schneyer, L. H., and C. A. Schneyer. 1956. Federation Proc. 15:164. [26] Smith, G. P., and F. P. Brooks. 1959. Ibid. 18:147. [27] Sumner, J. B., and K. Myrbäck. 1951. The enzymes: chemistry and mechanism of action. Academic Press, New York. v. 1. [28] Sumner, J. B., and K. Myrbäck. 1951. Ibid. Academic Press, New York. v. 2. [29] Sym, E. A., W. Stankiewicz, and F. Zielinski. 1939. Enzymologia 6:113. [30] Van Genderen, H., and C. Engel. 1938. Ibid. 5:71. [31] Wright, R. D., et al. 1940. Quart. J. Exptl. Physiol. 30:73.

113. KIDNEY MEASUREMENTS: VERTEBRATES

	Order	Animal	Body Weight kg	Kidney Weight[1] g	Glomerulus Radius μ	Glomerulus Thousands/ Kidney[2]	Glomerulus Vol/Kidney cu mm	Glomerulus Vol/g Kidney cu mm	Reference
	(A)	(B)	(C)	(D)	(E)	(F)	(G)	(H)	(I)
1	Primates	Man	70	156	100	1095	4599	29	3
2		Monkey	3.9	9	83	187	447	50	1
3	Artiodactyla	Cattle (ox)	410	640	122	3992	29,860	47	1
4		Swine	47	77	83	1193	2859	37	1
5	Proboscidea	Elephant	4545	3650	169	7510	151,900	42	2
6	Carnivora	Cat	2.8	8	66	184	227	28	1
7		Dog	9.1	31	90	408	1247	40	1
8	Rodentia	Groundhog	1.2	1.8	70	96	135	75	1
9		Guinea pig	0.56	1.9	63	76	79	42	1
10		Mouse	0.02	0.12	37	12.4	2.6	22	2
		Rat							
11		Albino	0.24	0.75	61	31	30	40	2
12		Kangaroo	0.07	0.30	48	18.8	8.9	30	2
13	Lagomorpha	Rabbit[3]	1.9	6.5	71	199	300	46	1
14	Marsupialia	Opossum	2	5.2	88	91	256	49	1

/1/ Weight of one kidney. /2/ Number of glomeruli decreases after maturity and as animal approaches senility. /3/ Values recalculated by Rytand.

Contributors: (a) Smith, Homer W., (b) Rytand, D. A.

continued

113. KIDNEY MEASUREMENTS: VERTEBRATES

References: [1] Kunkel, P. A., Jr. 1930. Bull. Johns Hopkins Hosp. 47:285. [2] Rytand, D. A. 1937-38. Am. J. Anat. 62:507. [3] Smith, H. W. 1951. The kidney. Oxford Univ. Press, New York.

114. REPRODUCTIVE ORGAN MEASUREMENTS: MAMMALS

Part I: MALE

Abbreviations (columns B, E-G): *L* = length, *W* = width, *T* = Thickness, *Wt* = weight. Values are averages of ranges reported in the literature.

	Order and Species	Testis	Epididymis, Length m	Ductus Deferens, Length cm	Seminal Vesicles	Prostate Gland	Bulbourethral Gland	Penis Length,[1] cm
	(A)	(B)	(C)	(D)	(E)	(F)	(G)	(H)
	Primates							
1	*Homo sapiens*	*L* 4.2 cm, *W* 3.8 cm, *T* 2.5 cm, *Wt* (20-35) g	8[2]	(38-61)	*L* 4.3 cm, *W* 1.7 cm, *T* 0.9 cm	*L* 4 cm, *W* 2.8 cm, *T* 1.9 cm, *Wt* 16.6 g		13
	Artiodactyla							
2	*Bos taurus*	*L* 12.7 cm, *W* 7.1 cm, *T* (6-7) cm, *Wt* 351 g		(25-38)	*L* 13.1 cm, *W* 3.2 cm, *Wt* 75.4 g	*L* 3.8 cm, *W* 1.3 cm, *T* 1.3 cm	*L* 3.4 cm, *W* 2.1 cm, *T* 1.6 cm, *Wt* 6.4 g	98
3	*Capra hircus*	*L* 10 cm, *Wt* (255-284) g	(40-60)			Disseminate		40
4	*Ovis aries*	*L* 10 cm, *Wt* (255-284) g	(40-60)		*L* 5.7 cm, *W* 2.5 cm	Disseminate		40
5	*Sus scrofa*	*L* 6 cm, *W* (3.8-4.5) cm, *Wt* (150-367) g	(62-64)[2]	(25-30)	*L* (12-15) cm, *W* 4.4 cm, *Wt* (200-250) g	*W* 2.5 cm, *Wt* (15-26) g	*L* 12 cm, *W* 3 cm, *Wt* (146-209) g	(46-51)
	Perissodactyla							
6	*Equus caballus*	*L* 11 cm, *W* 5 cm, *T* 7 cm, *Wt* (225-300) g	(72-86)	(15-20)	*L* 17.5 cm, *W* 5 cm	*W* 7 cm[3]	*L* 5 cm, *W* 2.5 cm	51
	Carnivora							
7	*Canis familiaris*	*L* (3-4) cm, *Wt* (3-29) g			Absent		Absent	10
8	*Felis catus*	*L* 1.5 cm, *W* 1 cm, *Wt* 2.016 g				*W* 1 cm	*Wt* (0.4-0.5) g	
	Rodentia							
9	*Cavia porcellus*	*L* (0.12-0.13) cm, *W* (0.10-0.12) cm, *T* 0.8 cm, *Wt* (2.5-4.0) g			*L* 10 cm, *W* 0.6 cm, *Wt* (1-10) g			(0.45-0.50)
10	*Mus musculus*					3 pairs		
11	*Rattus rattus*	*L* 2 cm, *Wt* 1 g?				2 pairs: *L* (1.4-1.8) cm, *W* (0.3-0.6) cm		
	Lagomorpha							
12	*Oryctolagus cuniculus*	*L* 3 cm, *W* 0.8 cm, *Wt* 2.6 g			Single, unpaired: *L* 2.5 cm	2-lobed, with isthmus	Paired	4

/1/ Nonerect. /2/ Extended. /3/ Diameter at isthmus.

Contributors: (a) Winters, L. M., (b) Chang, M. C., (c) Almquist, J. O.

References: [1] Almquist, J. O., and R. P. Amann. 1961. J. Dairy Sci. 44:1668. [2] Asdell, S. A. 1946. Patterns of mammalian reproduction. Comstock, Ithaca. [3] Eisendrath, D. N., and H. C. Rolnick. 1938. Urology. J. B. Lippincott, Philadelphia. [4] Eckstein, P., and S. Zuckerman. 1956. In A. S. Parkes, ed. Marshall's Physiology of reproduction. Ed. 3. Longmans, Green; London. v. 1, p. 43. [5] Hotchkiss, R. S. 1944. Fertility in men. J. B. Lippincott, Philadelphia. [6] Lesbouyries, G. 1949. Reproduction des mammifères

continued

114. REPRODUCTIVE ORGAN MEASUREMENTS: MAMMALS

Part I: MALE

domestiques. Sexualité. Vigot Frères, Paris. [7] Lewis, W. H., ed. 1942. Gray's Anatomy of the human body. Ed. 24. Lea and Febiger, Philadelphia. [8] Rice, V. A., and F. N. Andrews. 1951. Breeding and improvement of farm animals. McGraw-Hill, New York. [9] Saphir, O. 1951. Autopsy diagnosis and technic. Ed. 3. P. B. Hoeber, New York. [10] Schonfeld, W. A., and G. W. Beebe. 1942. J. Urol. 48:759. [11] Sisson, S., and J. D. Grossman. 1953. The anatomy of domestic animals. Ed. 4. W. B. Saunders, Philadelphia. [12] Stromsten, F. A., ed. 1952. Davison's Mammalian anatomy. Ed. 7. Blakiston, Philadelphia. [13] Wells, L. J. 1943. Surgery 14:436. [14] Winters, L. M. 1948. Animal breeding. J. Wiley and Sons, New York.

Part II: FEMALE

Size and weight of the ovaries depend on the stage of the ovarian cycle and the number and size of corpora lutea and follicles. Weight of the uterus also depends on the ovarian cycle, as well as on the age of the animal, size of breed, and virgin or parous condition of the uterus. Abbreviations (columns B, E, F): *L* = length, *W* = width, *T* = thickness, *Wt* = weight. Values in parentheses are averages of ranges reported in the literature.

	Order and Species	Ovaries	Uterine Tubes, Length cm	Uterine Horns, Length cm	Body of Uterus	Cervix	Vagina, Length cm	Vulva, Length cm
	(A)	(B)	(C)	(D)	(E)	(F)	(G)	(H)
	Primates							
1	*Homo sapiens*	*L* 3.5 cm, *W* 1.8 cm, *T* 1.2 cm, *Wt* 7 g[1]	(7-14)		*L* 8 cm, *Wt* (33-41) g[2,3]	*L* (2.9-3.4) cm[2]	9[4], 7[5]	
	Artiodactyla							
2	*Bos taurus*	*L* 3.8 cm, *W* 2.5 cm, *Wt* 19 g	(20-23)	38	*L* 3.8 cm	*L* 10 cm, *W* 2.5 cm	(25-30)	10
3	*Capra hircus*	*W* 1.5 cm	(10-15)	(10-12)	*L* 2 cm	*L* 4 cm	(10-12)	(2.5-3.0)
4	*Ovis aries*	*L* 1.5 cm, *T* 1 cm, *Wt* 4.8 g[6]	(10-15)	(10-12)	*L* 2.5 cm	*L* 3.8 cm	(7.5-10.0)	(2.5-3.0)
5	*Sus scrofa*	*Wt* (3.5-10.0) g	(15-30)	(120-150)	*L* 5 cm	*L* 10 cm	(10-13)	7.5
	Perissodactyla							
6	*Equus caballus*	*L* 7.5 cm, *T* 3.5 cm, *Wt* (70-80) g	(20-30)	25	*L* (18-20) cm, *W* 10 cm	*L* (5-8) cm, *W* 3.8 cm	(15-20)	(10-30)
	Carnivora							
7	*Canis familiaris*	*W* 2 cm	(5.0-7.6)	(11-15)	*L* (2-3) cm	*L* 1 cm	(7.5-15.0)	
8	*Felis catus*	*L* 1 cm, *Wt* 0.22 g	5	10	*L* 2 cm		2	2
9	*Mustela putorius*				*Wt* 0.4[7], 1[8], 5 g[9]			
	Rodentia							
10	*Cavia porcellus*	*L* (0.3-0.6) cm	(5-6)	(3.0-4.6)			(2.5-4.0)	
11	*Rattus rattus*	*L* 0.5 cm, *W* 0.3 cm	(2.5-3.0)	(4-6)			2.5	
	Lagomorpha							
12	*Oryctolagus cuniculus*	*L* 1.5 cm, *W* 0.7 cm, *T* 0.6 cm, *Wt* 0.55 g	(7-17)	(7-17)[10]		*L* 0.7 cm, *W* 0.7 cm[10]	(7-11)	4[11]

/1/ After pregnancy. /2/ Virgin uterus. /3/ Parous uterus approximately 35 g heavier. /4/ Posterior wall. /5/ Anterior wall. /6/ In breeding season, otherwise smaller. /7/ Anestrus. /8/ Estrus. /9/ Pseudopregnant. /10/ Duplex uterus, with 2 cervixes opening into vagina. /11/ At vestibule.

Contributors: (a) Winters, L. M., (b) Chang, M. C.

References: [1] Curtis, A. H. 1949. A textbook of gynecology. W. B. Saunders, Philadelphia. [2] Dukes, H. H. 1955. The physiology of domestic animals. Ed. 7. Comstock, Ithaca. [3] Eckstein, P., and S. Zuckerman. 1956. In A. S. Parkes, ed. Marshall's Physiology of reproduction. Ed. 3. Longmans, Green; London. v. 1, p. 43. [4] Francis, C. C. 1952. The human pelvis. C. V. Mosby, St. Louis. [5] Hammond, J. 1925. Reproduction in the rabbit. Oliver and Boyd, Edinburgh. [6] Hammond, J., and F. H. A. Marshall. 1930. Proc. Roy. Soc. (London), B, 105:607. [7] Lesbouyries, G. 1949. Reproduction des mammifères domestiques. Sexualité. Vigot

continued

Frères, Paris. [8] Saphir, O. 1951. Autopsy diagnosis and technic. Ed. 3. P. B. Hoeber, New York. [9] Sisson, S., and J. D. Grossman. 1953. The anatomy of domestic animals. Ed. 4. W. B. Saunders, Philadelphia. [10] Winters, L. M. 1948. Animal breeding. J. Wiley and Sons, New York.

115. SKELETAL WEIGHTS: MAMMALS AND BIRDS

For further information on various species, consult the following references: man [2, 3, 7, 21-23, 25-28, 32], orangutan [32], swine [24], dog [9], rat [4, 5, 29], birds [1, 6, 10, 12, 13, 30, 31]. Values are for single bones, unless otherwise specified in column C. Values in parentheses (column D) are ranges, estimate "b" for Mammalia, and estimate "c" for Aves (cf. Introduction).

	Species	Specification	Bone	Weight g	Reference
	(A)	(B)	(C)	(D)	(E)
			Mammalia		
1	*Homo sapiens*	100♂; age 19-78 yr; bones macerated, cleaned, and dried, but not degreased	Entire skeleton[1]	4957(3517-6397)	11
2			Skull[1]	642.6(415.6-871.6)	
3			Mandible[1]	81.98(49.0-114.9)	
			Vertebrae		
4			Cervical (7)	73.1(47.8-98.4)	
5			Thoracic (12)	217.3(140.1-294.5)	
6			Lumbar (5)	173.1(102.1-244.1)	
7			Sacrum	111.5(49.1-173.9)	
8			Sternum	32.5(14.7-50.3)	
9			Ribs (24)	330.2(201.3-459.1)	
			Right extremity		
10			Clavicle	26.99(16.39-37.59)	
11			Scapula	77.66(51.7-103.6)	
12			Humerus	180.3(122.7-237.9)	
13			Radius	54.02(36.72-71.32)	
14			Ulna	67.19(45.17-89.21)	
15			Carpus (8)	15.28(8.96-21.60)	
16			Metacarpus (5)	28.34(18.26-38.42)	
17			Phalanges (14)[2]	25.05(16.27-33.83)	
18			Innominate	223.7(132.1-315.3)	
19			Pelvis and coccyx	564.0(327.8-800.2)	
20			Femur	458.9(306.1-611.7)	
21			Patella	16.11(8.43-23.79)	
22			Tibia	268.3(171.3-365.3)	
23			Fibula	57.58(33.82-81.34)	
24			Tarsus (7)	105.1(59.7-150.5)	
25			Metatarsus (5)	37.01(22.29-51.73)	
26			Phalanges (14)[3]	11.7(6.6-16.8)	
27	*Mephitis mesomelas avia*	74♂; bones room-dried	Skull	13.755(9.37-18.14)	15
28			Mandible	5.391(3.515-8.267)	
29			Scapula	3.095(1.867-4.223)	
30			Humerus (2)	6.211(3.577-8.845)	
31			Radius (2)	1.887(1.183-2.591)	
32			Ulna (2)	2.627(1.523-3.731)	
33			Tibia (2)	5.557(3.333-7.781)	
34			Fibula (2)	0.996(0.626-1.366)	
35		69♀; bones room-dried	Skull	11.169(8.03-14.31)	
36			Mandible	4.200(3.042-5.358)	
37			Scapula	2.253(1.371-3.135)	
38			Humerus (2)	4.524(2.982-6.066)	
39			Radius (2)	1.417(0.971-1.933)	
40			Ulna (2)	1.948(1.230-2.666)	

/1/ Without teeth. /2/ Hand. /3/ Foot.

continued

115. SKELETAL WEIGHTS: MAMMALS AND BIRDS

	Species	Specification	Bone	Weight g	Reference
	(A)	(B)	(C)	(D)	(E)
			Mammalia		
41	*Mephitis mesome-*	69♀; bones room-dried	Tibia (2)	4.272(2.750-5.794)	15
42	*las avia*		Fibula (2)	0.760(0.496-1.020)	
43	*Cavia porcellus*	85♂; left extremity; bones air-	Scapula	0.646(0.436-0.856)	8
44		dried	Humerus	0.947(0.745-1.149)	
45			Radius, ulna	0.746(0.570-0.922)	
46			Femur	1.568(1.218-1.918)	
47			Tibia, fibula	1.262(1.004-1.520)	
48		25♀; left extremity; bones air-	Scapula	0.580(0.472-0.688)	
49		dried	Humerus	0.885(0.737-1.033)	
50			Radius, ulna	0.687(0.563-0.811)	
51			Femur	1.471(1.173-1.769)	
52			Tibia, fibula	1.164(0.980-1.348)	
53	*Ondatra zibethica*	125 specimens; bones room-	Skull	9.309	18
54	*cinnamominus*	dried	Mandible	5.10	
55			Humerus (2)	2.183	
56			Radius (2), ulna (2)	1.998	
57			Femur (2)	4.452	
58			Tibia (2)	4.590	
			Aves		
59	*Zenaidura macro-*	26♂, 14♀; length 280.73	Skull, mandible	0.345	17
60	*ura carolinensis*	(275.818-284.182) mm; wing-	Humerus (2)	0.527	
61		spread 148.45(144.11-152.79)	Radius (2)	0.165	
62		mm	Ulna (2)	0.399	
63			Femur (2)	0.240	
64			Tibia (2), fibula (2)	0.323	
65			Tarsometatarsus	0.138	
66	*Gallus domesticus*	97♂♀, single-comb White Leg-	Radius (2)	1.98	14
67		horns; age 300 da; bones	Ulna (2)	5.21	
68		oven-dried	Femur (2)	14.98	
69			Humerus (2), ♂	9.06	
70			Tibia (2), ♂	18.81	
71			Tarsometatarsus (2), ♂	10.9	
72			Humerus (2), ♀	7.00	
73			Tibia (2), ♀	14.26	
74			Tarsometatarsus (2), ♀	5.94	
75	*Meleagris gallo-*	12♀; age 5-7 mo; moist, liga-	Humerus (2)	25.4(22.1-29.3)	19
76	*pavo*	mentous skeletons	Radius (2)	6.30(5.2-7.3)	
77			Ulna (2)	22.1(17.4-39.5)	
78			Femur (2)	40.3(29.7-49.6)	
79			Tibia (2), fibula (2)	51.7(39.9-60.1)	
80			Tarsometatarsus	23.5(19.4-27.4)	
81	*Buteo borealis*	24♂; length 552.2(538.48-565.92)	Skull	5.195	16
82	*borealis*	mm; wingspread 376.8	Mandible	1.049	
83		(365.7-387.9) mm	Humerus (2)	7.635	
84			Radius (2)	2.307	
85			Ulna (2)	6.556	
86			Femur (2)	5.353	
87			Tibia (2), fibula (2)	8.017	
88			Tarsometatarsus	5.627	
89		27♀; length 562.3(556.04-568.56)	Skull	6.070	
90		mm; wingspread 411.3	Mandible	1.250	
91		(392.72-429.88) mm	Humerus (2)	9.518	
92			Radius (2)	3.099	
93			Ulna (2)	9.201	
94			Femur (2)	6.551	
95			Tibia (2), fibula (2)	10.139	
96			Tarsometatarsus	7.331	
97	*Anas platyrhynchos*	32♂; bones room-dried	Skull	4.722	20
98	*platyrhynchos*		Mandible	2.118	
99			Humerus (2)	7.792	
100			Radius (2)	1.709	

continued

	Species	Specification	Bone	Weight g	Reference
	(A)	(B)	(C)	(D)	(E)
	Aves				
101	*Anas platyrhynchos platyrhynchos*	32♂; bones room-dried	Ulna (2)	4.093	20
102			Femur (2)	2.125	
103			Tibia (2), fibula (2)	3.477	
104			Tarsometatarsus	1.699	
105		26♀; bones room-dried	Skull	4.080	
106			Mandible	1.810	
107			Humerus (2)	6.695	
108			Radius (2)	1.536	
109			Ulna (2)	3.684	
110			Femur (2)	1.771	
111			Tibia (2), fibula (2)	3.020	
112			Tarsometatarsus	1.517	

Contributors: (a) Strong, R. M., (b) Latimer, Homer B., (c) Eaton, Orson N.

References: [1] Balducci, E. 1903. Arch. zool. ital. 1:375. [2] Bischoff, E. 1863. Z. rat. Med. 20:75. [3] Daffner, F. 1899. In A. Eulenburg, ed. Real-Encyclopädie ges. Heilk. 22:456. [4] Donaldson, H. H. 1912. Anat. Record 6:53. [5] Donaldson, H. H. 1919. Am. J. Anat. 26:237. [6] Dosse, O. 1937. Zool. Jahrb., Abt. 2, 63:299. [7] Dursy, E. 1863. Lehrbuch der systematischer Anatomie. M. Schauenburg, Lahr. [8] Eaton, O. N. 1939. Am. J. Anat. 64:485. [9] Falck, C. F. 1854. Arch. pathol. Anat. u. Physiol. 7:37. [10] Hiller, E. 1885. Landwirtsch. Vers.-Sta. 31:319. [11] Ingalls, N. W. 1931. Am. J. Anat. 48:45. [12] Latimer, H. B. 1924. J. Agr. Research 29:363. [13] Latimer, H. B. 1927. Anat. Record 35:365. [14] Latimer, H. B. 1927. Am. J. Anat. 40:1. [15] Latimer, H. B. 1937. J. Morphol. 60:379. [16] Latimer, H. B. 1938. Kansas Univ. Sci. Bull. 25:199. [17] Latimer, H. B., and C. W. Asling. 1938. Ibid. 25:137. [18] Latimer, H. B., and R. D. Riley. 1934. J. Morphol. 56:203. [19] Latimer, H. B., and J. A. Rosenbaum. 1926. Anat. Record 34:15. [20] Latimer, H. B., and H. P. Wager. 1941. Kansas Univ. Sci. Bull. 27:5. [21] Lowrance, E. W. 1957. Anat. Record 128:69. [22] Lowrance, E. W., and H. B. Latimer. 1957. Am. J. Anat. 101:445. [23] Lowrance, E. W., and H. B. Latimer. 1958. Ibid. 102:455. [24] McMeekan, C. P. 1940. J. Agr. Sci. 30:276. [25] Mühlmann, M. 1927. Ergeb. Anat. u. Entwicklungsgeschichte 27:1. [26] Trotter, M. 1954. Am. J. Phys. Anthropol. 12:537. [27] Trotter, M. 1956. Human Biol. 28:146. [28] Trotter, M., and R. R. Peterson. 1955. Anat. Record 123:341. [29] Weikel, J. H., J. F. Bonner, and W. F. Neuman. 1955. Proc. Soc. Exptl. Biol. Med. 88:122. [30] Weiske, H. 1889. Landwirtsch. Vers.-Sta. 36:81. [31] Wetcker, H., and A. Brandt. 1903. Arch. Anthropol. Braunschweig 28:1. [32] Wetzel, G. 1910. Arch. Entwicklungsmech. Organ. 30:507.

Values are fresh weight unless otherwise specified. Classification adapted from

	Order and Family	Species	No. of Subjects	Body Weight kg	Brain g	Eyes g
	(A)	(B)	(C)	(D)	(E)	(F)
	Primates					
	Hominidae	*Homo sapiens*				
1		Chinese (Australia)	1♂	57.2	1248	......
2		Dane	5♂	60.4	1458	......
3			7♀	49.3	1218	......
4		Filipino (Hawaii)	2♂	41.96	1311	......
5		Negro (U.S.A.)	4♂	73	1365	......
6		White (U.S.A.)	14♂	67.78	1319	......
7	Pongidae	*Pan troglodytes*	1♂	52.16	440	......
8			1♀	43.99	325	......
9	Cercopithecidae	*Cercopithecus aethiops centralis*	2♂	4.185	57.75	8.82
10		*C. mitis kibonotensis*	1♂	2.9	61.46	9.94
11			1♀	1.22	50.3	......
12		*Macaca mulatta*	4♂	3.292	91.7	......
13			7♀	3.627	93.1	......
14		*Papio cynocephalus*	1♂	19.51	175	13.18
15	Callithricidae	*Leontocebus geoffroyi*	8♂♀	0.793	19.9	......
16	Cebidae	*Alouatta palliata inconsonons*	28♂♀	6.174	50.34	......
17		*Ateles geoffroyi*	63♂♀	7.63	107	......
18		*Cebus capucinus*	14♂♀	3.101	72.18	......
19		*Lagothrix humboldti*	1♀	5.26	86.2	......
20		*Saimiri orstedii*	60♂♀	0.607	19.9	......
21	Lorisidae	*Galago senegalensis*	1♀	0.2	5	3.7
22	Lemuridae	*Lemur catta*	1♀	1.725	21.8	......
	Artiodactyla					
23	Bovidae	*Aepyceros melampus*	2♂	37.86	149	44
24		*Alcelaphus cokei*	1♂	134	275	56.36
25		*Bison bison*	1♂	54.88	334	42.68
		Bos taurus				
26		Aberdeen Angus	1♀	710	......	......
27		Ayrshire	44♀	510	408	......
28		Guernsey	62♀	472	425	......
29		Hereford	7♀	375	375	......
30		Holstein	5♂	916	458	......
31			198♀	604	423	......
32		Jersey	10♂	621	438	......
33			218♀	436	393	......
34		*Capra hircus*	1♂	27.66	115	29.55
35		*Gazella thomsoni*	2♂	24.37	91.8	26.6
36		*Ovis aries*	6♂	51	90	......
37			7♀	52.1	106.5	30.49
38		*Raphicerus campestris*	2♂	8.62	49.5	14.87
39		*Redunca redunca*	2♂	31.7	109	33.4
40		*Rhynchotragus kirki*	1♂	4.57	37	......
41		*Syncerus caffer*	1♂	759	560	55
42		*Tragelaphus scriptus*	1♂	53.07	190	......
43			1♀	35.38	140	40.53
44	Giraffidae	*Giraffa camelopardalis*	1♂	1220	700	127
45	Cervidae	*Cervus canadensis*	1♂	13.61	194.2	......
46		*Odocoileus virginianus*	1♂	65.22	210	......
47		*O. virginianus chiriquensis*	1♀	13.93	......	......
48		*Rangifer arcticus*	2♂	128.47	306	41.66
49			1♀	71.87	278	33.35
50	Camelidae	*Camelus dromedarius*	7♂	443	......	......
51			5♀	346	......	......
52	Hippopotamidae	*Hippopotamus amphibius*	1♀	1351	723	42.7
53	Tayassuidae	*Pecari angulatus*	2	13.83	......	......
54	Suidae	*Phacochoerus aethiopicus*	1♂	65.32	125	17.91
55		*Sus scrofa*	53♂	102.06	......	......

/1/ For 3 subjects. /2/ For 5 subjects. /3/ For 1 subject. /4/ For 13 subjects. /5/ For 11 subjects. /6/ For

VERTEBRATES

MAMMALS

Simpson, *The Principles of Classification and a Classification of Mammals*, 1945.

Stomach-Intestines g	Liver g	Lungs g	Heart g	Kidneys g	Thyroid g	Adrenals g	Spleen g	Reference	
(G)	(H)	(I)	(J)	(K)	(L)	(M)	(N)	(O)	
....	....	....	....	....	21.54	10.1	......	12	1
....	....	....	396	....	30.6	17[1]	......		2
....	....	....	324	....	15.85	14.8[2]	......		3
....	....	....	200[3]	....	20.95	9.3[3]	......		4
....	....	....	389	259	31.77	12.69	......		5
....	1568[4]	....	318[4]	286[5]	28.5	13.71	142.2[6]		6
6200	1210	600	250	210	4.85	8.93	......	12	7
....	....	....	219	....	4.55	8.4	......		8
....	94.4	17.01	19.98	15.89	0.175	0.735	......	12	9
350	50	14.39	7.59	8.71	0.39	0.41	......		10
250	29.65	9.98	6.56	7.84	0.172	0.22	......		11
....	69	....	12.7	....	0.611	0.75	......		12
....	....	68.5	12.2	....	0.578	0.996	......		13
....	367	175	79.94	70.92	1.8	2.05	......		14
....	25.41	8.48	3.91	4.24	......	0.63	1.65	12	15
....	201	38.68	20.67	35.95	......	1.16	45.68	12	16
....	213	51.38	32.5	31.2	......	1.75	40.8		17
....	....	34.07	18.6	14.3	......	1.06	11.3		18
....	....	63.5	48	....	0.45	1.2	......		19
....	25.6	7.2	3.68	3.99	......	0.63	0.9		20
17.6	6.03	1.44	1.38	1.54	0.015	0.125	......	12	21
....	....	24.7	8.2	....	0.27	0.232	......	12	22
5800	605	510	270.05	162.5	5.67	3.82	210	12	23
14,540	1525	1850	875	387	1.83	9.61	625	12	24
....	695	1190	361	256	5.47	6.64	146	12	25
21,655	6674	2627	1917	1775	56.8	56.8	852	16	26
25,143	6018	3315	1887	1122	35.7	30.6	816	17	27
23,553	6089	3162	1746	991	33.04	28.32	849	17	28
20,738	3825	2288	1162	675	15	18.75	5.63	16	29
28,762	8427	6220	3389	1832	91.6	45.8	1474	17	30
29,173	7248	4349	2235	1450	36.24	36.24	966	17	31
24,467	7017	3664	2174	1180	80.73	24.84	1180	17	32
22,236	5755	3052	1613	1003	26.16	26.16	785	17	33
1466	525	....	....	....	......	....	......	12	34
....	525	280	245	105	1.83	2	......	12	35
....	816	613	244	84	......	....	81	15	36
....	957	704.8	276.7	159.8	10.2	8.3	119.6	12	37
550	175	150	72.2	38.51	1.22	1.35	......	12	38
....	523	462	242	102	1.34	2.11	......	12	39
....	93.2	44.4	36.8	21.4	0.73	0.56	......	12	40
150,000	7712	8110	3628	1825	38.05	50.4	......	12	41
6700	1100	540	350	225	5.08	5.09	......	12	42
....	625	915	325	131	6.76	4.43	92.75	12	43
130,000	19,050	12,060	4990	2268	64.7	78.12	2266	12	44
....	374	319	131.1	73.4	6.14	2.38	......	12	45
....	1025	1318	632	....	5.1	12.25	......		46
....	516	520	15.9	55	......	3	35		47
25,400	2445	2450	1086	151	8.37	5.99	310		48
....	466	1275	710	82.77	3.99	2.29	131		49
....	....	....	....	2196	......	....	......	13	50
....	....	....	....	1947	......	....	......		51
374,000	23,580	11,340	4536	3160	119	61.1	3175	12	52
....	371	120	70.5	51.5	......	4.5	91	12	53
9550	1500	550	325	300	3.6	8.24	......	12	54
1817	1488.3	....	303.5	237.83	6.88	4.99	117.74	12	55

6 subjects.

continued

116. ORGAN WEIGHTS:

Part I:

	Order and Family	Species	No. of Subjects	Body Weight kg	Brain g	Eyes g
	(A)	(B)	(C)	(D)	(E)	(F)
	Artiodactyla					
56	Suidae	*Sus scrofa*	36♀	102.06	......	......
57			3♀	90.2	68	......
	Perissodactyla					
58	Rhinocerotidae	*Rhinoceros bicornis*	1♂	764	655	22.56
59	Tapiridae	*Tapirus bairdii*	1♀	58.06	159.4	14.88
60	Equidae	*Equus asinus*	4♂♀	279.2	......	......
		E. caballus				
61		Thoroughbred	5♂[7]	485.31	706.7	106.34
62			10♀	443.36	637.7	105
63		Percheron	1♂[7]	635.04	662	136.7
64			1♀	771.4	650	137.4
65		*E. quagga granti*	2♂	254.99	541	94
	Sirenia					
66	Trichechidae	*Trichechus manatus*	1♂	424	351	58
67			1♀	557.92	......	59.9
	Hyracoidea					
68	Procaviidae	*Heterohyrax brucei*	1♂	0.75	12.27	......
	Proboscidea					
69	Elephantidae	*Loxodonta africana*	1♂	6554	5712	116.15
	Carnivora					
70	Phocidae	*Erignathus barbatus*	1♀	281	460	63.06
71		*Phoca hispida*	3♂	39.76	251	73.34
72			2♀	39.68	255	70.2
73		*P. richardi geronimensis*	1♂	107.3	442	60.72
74	Odobenidae	*Odobenus rosmarus*	1♂	667	1126	26.63
75	Felidae	*Felis capensis*	1♂	9.555	66.74	18.02
76			2♀	5.819	53.16	10.23
77		*F. catus*	52♂	2.822	27.56	......
78			53♀	2.445	26.54	......
79		*F. ocreata*	1♀	2.7	28.48	6.41
80		*F. oregonensis*	1♂	28.79	106.7	9.2
81		*Panthera leo*	2♂	190.38	258	59.23
82		*P. onca*	1♂	34.47	147	17.28
83		*P. tigris*	1♂	209	302	......
84	Hyaenidae	*Crocuta crocuta*	2	62.37	175	40.42
85	Viverridae	*Genetta tigrina*	2♂	1.302	15.89	3.72
86			1♀	1.525	15.35	3.44
87		*Ichneumia albicauda*	1♂	4.4	28.3	4
88	Mustelidae	*Mephitis mephitis*	1♂	1.7	10.3	......
89			2♀	2.26	10	......
90		*Mustela arctica*	3♂	0.1693	5.64	0.153
91			1♀	0.121	3.47	0.11
92	Procyonidae	*Nasua narica panamaensis*	1♂	6.25	44.17	2.33
93		*Potos flavus aztecus*	1♀	2.62	31.05	1.9
94		*Procyon lotor pumilis*	1♀	2.226	33.55	3.32
95	Ursidae	*Thalarctos maritimus*	1♀	317.5	507	......
96		*Ursus horribilis*	1♀	142.88	233.9	......
97	Canidae	*Canis familiaris*	169♂[8]	10.08	......	......
98			177♀[8]	8.86	......	......
99		Greyhound	1♂	24.49	105.9	12.36
100		Husky	2♂	31.75	130.7	10.88
101		Mongrel	2♂	11.26	87.6	16.85
102			2♀	14.75	66.53	9.73
103		*C. latrans*	1♀	8.51	84.24	11.11
104		*C. lupus nubilus*	1♀	29.94	152	16.84
105		*Otocyon megalotis*	1♀	3.335	26.09	4.65
106		*Urocyon cinereoargenteus*	1♂	3.759	37.28	4.02
107		*Vulpes fulva*	1♀	4.625	53.3	4.18
108		*V. lagopus*	1♂	3.385	44.5	5.8

/3/ For 1 subject. /7/ Stallion. /8/ Mostly mongrels.

VERTEBRATES

MAMMALS

Stomach-Intestines g	Liver g	Lungs g	Heart g	Kidneys g	Thyroid g	Adrenals g	Spleen g	Reference	
(G)	(H)	(I)	(J)	(K)	(L)	(M)	(N)	(O)	
1988.07	1547.3	....	324.39	264.09	7.52	4.99	138.64	12	56
....	1490	677	260	128	......	....	97	14	57
129,270	14,310	7350	4800	3000	53.05	168.66	2720	12	58
....	815	2068	540	482	7.44	11.02	......	12	59
13,396	3594	4026	2048	513	......	42.53	766	12	60
....	5685	7154	4688	1971.7	32.15	33.03	3474		61
....	6176	4758	3663	1667	29.76	43.5	3856		62
....	8520	5710	5600	1700	40.84	39.22	3430		63
....	6725	5400	4700	1750	56.55	37.4	1550		64
....	4037	2025	1925	850	20.08	23.08	1170		65
....	5500	3050	1250	....	57.51	....	......	12	66
....	6236	3741	1247	1361	78.87	14.36	......		67
255	31.53	5.532	3.63	6.45	0.081	0.161	......	12	68
924,000	107,670	138,790	26,080	18,180	860	940	......	12	69
26,330	5454	4536	1245	1320	22.83	22.04	......	12	70
2992	1244	738	281	273	3.49	2.49	110		71
....	930	730	302	236	3.44	3.41	150		72
....	4485	1880	1435	894	10.02	6.27	520		73
29,484	19,504	9072	4536	4536	70.04	27.07	......	12	74
400	225	125	37.3	100	0.42	1.03	......	12	75
350	86.18	50.72	28.45	40.34	0.33	0.4	......	12	76
....	101.5	....	11.12	21.118	0.235	0.389	7.57	3-9	77
....	88.61	....	9.777	16.89	0.218	0.359	5.67	3-9	78
78	32.75	9	5.86	10.07	0.1	0.19	......	12	79
....	1255	326	184	131.7	2.2	9.6	......	12	80
....	5725	2300	1017.5	1610[3]	20.57	32.73	540	12	81
....	894	576	186	164.5	1.72	7.46	62.12	12	82
....	....	1888	698	....	50.5	20.8	......	12	83
6804	3194	6809	447	400	6.68	15.08	......	12	84
....	49.68	12.99	7.51	8.93	0.29	0.49	......	12	85
97	58.54	22.55	8.46	14.05	0.04	0.19	......		86
275	61	58	28.3	34.96	0.21	0.61	......		87
....	45.7	27.1	9.82	10.1	0.274	0.468	......	12	88
....	....	....	....	7.86	0.055	0.305	......		89
....	9.67	3.85	2.83	1.8	0.108	0.015	0.713		90
....	5.5	3.6	1.95	1.81	0.015	0.03	......		91
....	150	43	37.97	....	1.54	0.54	5.5	12	92
....	98.6	78.5	14.3	....	0.56	0.19	......		93
225	140	19.41	19.73	35.85	0.19	1.55	......		94
....	4126	2580	1220	730	21.5	29.8	......	12	95
....	....	....	1132.5	547.8	53.6	65.5	304		96
....	....	....	78.02	....	1.341	1.2398	23.39	18	97
....	....	....	66.98	....	1.1429	1.24	21.18	18	98
....	1067	363.5	308.8	105.9	2.34	3.36	175	12	99
1944	1438	431	297	248	2.85	3.16	......	12	100
....	465.2	138.4	126.3	....	3.36	1.54	......	12	101
712	300	108.1	95.4	44.65	1.11	1.09	......	12	102
....	292.5	61.28	72.71	80.07	0.69	1.049	14.21	12	103
....	925	379	315	223	3.49	3.37	44.3	12	104
660	125	35.05	24.65	31.91	0.49	0.49	......	12	105
425	50.8	19.12	21.97	17.43	0.154	0.39	......	12	106
....	....	....	41.75	0.1469	0.5285	....	......	12	107
....	....	....	....	....	0.736	0.353	......	12	108

continued

	Order and Family	Species	No. of Subjects	Body Weight kg	Brain g	Eyes g
	(A)	(B)	(C)	(D)	(E)	(F)
	Cetacea					
109	Balaenopteridae	*Balaenoptera musculus*	1	58,059	6800	......
110		*Megaptera nodosa*	3♂	39,311	6439	980[3]
111	Phocaenidae	*Phocaena phocaena*	1♂	142.43	1735	57.19
112	Monodontidae	*Delphinapterus leucas*	4♂	447.03	2349	31.71
113			2♀	303.23	2354	22.01
114	Physeteridae	*Physeter catodon*	1♂	39,009	4023	290
	Rodentia					
115	Dasyproctidae	*Cuniculus paca*	3♂♀	3.627	21.85	......
116		*Dasyprocta punctata*	2♂♀	3.172	18.34	......
117	Hydrochoeridae	*Hydrochoerus isthimius*	2♂♀	27.67	52.21	......
118	Caviidae	*Cavia cutleri*	46♂	0.2146	3.28	......
119			56♀	0.2149	3.32	......
120	Erethizontidae	*Erethizon dorsatum*	1♂	3.41	19.15	......
121			1♀	2.8	30.77	2.8
122	Zapodidae	*Zapus hudsonicus*	1♂[10]	0.0152	0.522	0.025
123			3♀[10]	0.0193	0.6961	0.028
124	Gliridae	*Claviglis saturatus*	1♂	0.0177	0.551	0.052
125	Muridae	*Mastomys coucha microdon*	1♂	0.218	0.7132	0.075
126		*Mus musculus* (piebald)	20♂	0.0331	0.4402	0.0251
127			20♀	0.0324	0.4632	0.0223
128		*Rattus norvegicus*	2♂	0.278	2.3	0.296
129		*R. norvegicus* (albino)	10♂	0.185	......	0.221
130			21♂	0.1469	......	......
131			20♀	0.1469	......	......
132			100♂	0.1895	......	......
133			158♀	0.1695	......	......
134			64♀	0.1445	......	......
135	Cricetidae	*Cricetus cricetus*	2♂	0.1075	1.012	0.212
136			2♀	0.1287	1.062	0.226
137		*Dicrostonyx rubricatus*	4♂	0.0521	0.8983	0.1451
138		*Lemmus trimucronatus*	1♂	0.048	1.312	0.0242
139			4♀	0.0292	1.126	0.023
140		*Microtus drummondi*	67♂[10]	0.0237	0.6606	0.0239
141			42♀[10]	0.0229	0.6464	0.0236
142		*M. pennsylvanicus*	53♂[10]	0.0279	0.7394	0.0254
143			42♀[10]	0.0252	0.7166	0.0269
144		*Ondatra zibethica*	1♂	0.9	5.33	1.88
145		*Peromyscus* sp.	14♂[10]	0.0122	0.407	0.235
146	Castoridae	*Castor canadensis*	1♂	4.18	25.48	......
147			1♀	5.83	29.52	1.5
148	Sciuridae	*Citellus parryii*	5♂	0.878	5.63	1.77
149			3♀	0.958	5.74	1.73
150		*Sciurus hudsonicus*	4♂	0.183	4.71	0.497
151			4♀	0.248	5.02	0.534
152		*Tamias striatus*	2♂	0.075	2.22	0.556
	Lagomorpha					
153	Leporidae	*Lepus* sp.	2♂	3.68	10.59	......
154			22♀	2.587	10.14	......
155		*L. arcticus*	2♂	2.64	13.9	4.75
156			2♀	1.901	14.36	4.59
157		*Sylvilagus gabbi*	2	0.439	4.5	......
	Edentata					
158	Dasypodidae	*Dasypus novemcinctus*	10♂♀	3.401	7.5	......
159	Myrmecophagidae	*Tamandua tetradactyla*	2♂♀	3.692	25	......
	Chiroptera					
160	Desmontidae	*Desmodus rotundus*	5♂♀	0.028	0.936	......
	Insectivora					
161	Talpidae	*Scalopus aquaticus*	1♂	0.0396	1.16	......
162	Soricidae	*Blarina brevicauda*	29♂	0.0188	0.352	0.0018
163			39♀	0.0163	0.3443	0.0011

/3/ For 1 subject. /9/ For 2 subjects. /10/ Preserved weights. /11/ For 21 subjects. /12/ For 79 subjects.

VERTEBRATES

MAMMALS

Stomach-Intestines g	Liver g	Lungs g	Heart g	Kidneys g	Thyroid g	Adrenals g	Spleen g	Reference	
(G)	(H)	(I)	(J)	(K)	(L)	(M)	(N)	(O)	
....	....	....	....	....	3450	1385	......	12	109
....	491,333	....	196,000	192,000[3]	3049[9]	1210[3]	6045[3]		110
13,255	2962	5250	738	....	18.29	10.41	53.02	12	111
12,075	6807	12,093	2454	2214	111.04	29.2	200	12	112
9296	4825	7936	1722	1857	65.94	29.23	153		113
....	420,000	....	126,000	....	800	350	......	12	114
....	187	23.5	16.10	22.7	......	1.6	12.07	12	115
....	85	16	17.54	15.39	......	0.98	6.04		116
....	577	227	84.13	69.75	......	5.2	50.58	12	117
....	11.73	2.563	1.291	2.821	0.035	0.135	......	12	118
....	12.06	2.934	1.29	2.829	0.036	0.18	......		119
....	108	27.1	15.5	38	0.341	0.355	......	12	120
....	112	29.88	19.75	26.97	0.72	0.62	......		121
....	0.743	0.243	0.133	0.266	0.003	0.005	......	12	122
....	1.124	0.246	0.1557	0.218	0.001	0.008	0.0261		123
0.75	0.308	0.272	0.116	0.091	0.006	0.0042	......	12	124
2.63	0.944	0.2408	0.122	0.265	0.001	0.0095	......	12	125
....	1.4167	0.1357	0.1456	0.2416	0.0305	0.0015	0.0728	10	126
....	1.5644	0.1296	0.1296	0.1555	0.0298	0.0052	0.0907	10	127
7.02	9.31	2.29	1.61	3.03	0.032	0.149	0.82	12	128
....	....	....	0.574	0.81	0.0143	....	0.372	11	129
....	8.17	....	....	1.43	......	....	0.65	19	130
....	7.14	....	....	1.33	......	....	0.54	19	131
....	7.75[11]	....	0.65	1.317	......	0.0277[12]	......	1, 2	132
....	....	....	0.589	1.131	......	....	......	1	133
....	6.491[13]	....	....	....	......	0.0446	......	2	134
....	5.43	0.51	0.543	0.996	0.0088	0.0302	......	12	135
....	6.76	0.583	0.6	1.27	0.0074	0.0118	......		136
....	2.63	0.827	0.311	0.774	0.0042	0.0138	0.21		137
....	3.8	0.74	0.6	0.525	0.0046	0.0251	......		138
....	2.33	0.804	0.434	44.04	0.0058	0.0167	......		139
....	1.082	0.4036	0.1612	0.3634	0.0032	0.0085	......		140
....	1.129	0.393	0.1609	0.3814	0.0031	0.016	......		141
....	1.312	0.3984	0.1937	0.3126	0.0042	0.0071	......		142
....	1.349	0.3916	0.1973	0.313	0.0046	0.0164	......		143
176	21.95	4.35	3.23	7.45	0.0133	0.143	......		144
....	0.65	0.22	0.0983	0.1477	0.0014	0.0037	......		145
....	99.82	63.47	16.57	35.86	0.207	0.228	......	12	146
....	203	33.3	27	72.6	0.644	0.752	4.75		147
....	36.27	9.87	5.85	7.16	0.105	0.228	2.12	12	148
....	44.83	10.57	5.92	7.12	0.116	0.208	1.14		149
....	3.99	2.66	1.57	1.14	0.023	0.049	......		150
....	6.64	3.17	1.82	1.32	0.029	0.075	......		151
4.65	5.55	0.719	0.597	0.756	0.03	0.07	0.222		152
....	97.9	....	10.57	22.35	0.685	0.503	......	12	153
....	82.63	13.72	9.23	18.3	0.403	0.662	......		154
....	65.22	44.04	28.87	25.44	0.099	0.191	......		155
....	66.11	43.79	28.45	19.29	0.16	0.24	......		156
....	19.5	4.5	2	3.5	......	0.75	0.75		157
....	106	24	9	16.3	......	1.2	7.4	12	158
....	76.5	27	18	21	......	0.75	7	12	159
....	....	....	....	....	0.028	0.012	......	12	160
....	1.548	0.737	0.272	0.629	0.0095	0.0175	......	12	161
....	1.092	0.4214	0.1922	0.24	0.0026	0.0048	......	12	162
....	0.8896	0.3575	0.1723	0.2041	0.0021	0.0037	......		163

/13/ For 29 subjects.

continued

Part I:

	Order and Family	Species	No. of Subjects	Body Weight kg	Brain g	Eyes g
	(A)	(B)	(C)	(D)	(E)	(F)
	Marsupialia					
164	Didelphidae	*Didelphis marsupialis*	4♂♀	1.147	4.8	......
165		*Philander laniger*	1	0.222	......	......

Contributors: (a) Quiring, Daniel P., (b) Swett, Walter W., (c) Latimer, Homer B., (d) Latyszewski, M., (e) Webster,

References: [1] Addis, T., and H. Gray. 1950. Growth 14:49. [2] Addis, T., and H. Gray. 1950. Ibid. 14:81. H. B. 1937. J. Comp. Neurol. 68:395. [6] Latimer, H. B. 1939. Growth 3:89. [7] Latimer, H. B. 1939. Ibid. Unpublished, 1954. [11] Moment, G. B. 1932. J. Exptl. Zool. 65:359. [12] Quiring, D. P. 1950. Functional N. C., 1961. [14] Smith, A. H., et al. 1951. J. Animal Sci. 10:893. [15] Smith, A. H., et al. 1952. Ibid. 11:638. 1937. J. Agr. Research 55:239. [18] Van Liere, E. J., and D. W. Northrup. Unpublished. West Virginia Univ.,

Part II:

Values are fresh weights. Classification adapted from Wetmore, *A*

	Order and Family	Species	No. of Subjects	Body Weight kg	Brain g	Eyes g
	(A)	(B)	(C)	(D)	(E)	(F)
	Passeriformes					
1	Fringillidae	*Melospiza melodia*	1♀	0.021	1.1	......
2		*Serinus canarius*	1♂	0.0171	0.966	0.336
3			1♀	0.0153	0.564	0.23
4	Icteridae	*Molothrus ater*	1♀	0.066	2.693	......
5		*Quiscalus quiscalus aeneus*	1♂	0.082	2.92	1.917
6	Ploceidae	*Passer domesticus*	75♂	0.02357	1.0278	0.4591
7			44♀[1]	0.02341	0.998	0.507
8	Sturnidae	*Sturnus vulgaris*	15♂	0.05736	1.8701	0.8384
9			10♀	0.05835	1.8248	1.056
10	Turdidae	*Sialia sialis*	1♂	0.029	1.392	......
11			1♀	0.034	1.281	......
12		*Turdus migratorius*	2♂	0.0693	2.09	......
13	Mimidae	*Dumetella carolinensis*	1♀	0.033	1.412	......
14	Corvidae	*Corvus brachyrhynchos*	1♂	0.337	9.3	......
15	Hirundinidae	*Hirundo erythrogastra*	1♂	0.215	0.904	......
16			2♀	0.021	0.879	......
17	Tyrannidae	*Sayornis phoebe*	1♂	0.0181	0.793	......
18			1♀	0.0175	0.75	......
	Coraciiformes					
19	Bucerotidae	*Bucorvus caffer*	1♂	3.25	26.25	35.45
	Apodiformes					
20	Trochilidae	*Amazilia tzacatl*	1♀	0.0048	0.1998	0.1201
	Strigiformes					
21	Strigidae	*Bubo virginianus*	1♂	1.177	13.7	......
	Columbiformes					
22	Columbidae	*Columba livia*	3♂	0.282	2.694	......
23			1♀	0.247	2.285	......
	Charadriiformes					
24	Alcidae	*Alle alle*	1♂	0.104	1.92	2
25			1♀	0.102	1.93	1.94
26	Laridae	*Larus argentatus*	2♀	0.535	5.08	7.74
27		*L. delawarensis*	1♀	0.72	8.73	8.74
28		*L. philadelphia*	1♂	0.205	2.49	3.14

/1/ Data from reference 2.

VERTEBRATES

MAMMALS

Stomach-Intestines g	Liver g	Lungs g	Heart g	Kidneys g	Thyroid g	Adrenals g	Spleen g	Reference	
(G)	(H)	(I)	(J)	(K)	(L)	(M)	(N)	(O)	
....	67	9.5	5	7.5	......	1	......	12	164
....	9	3	3	4	......	1	1.5		165

Stewart H., (f) Moment, Gairdner B., (g) Smith, Arthur H., (h) Van Liere, Edward J., (i) Schmidt-Nielsen, Knut

[3] Latimer, H. B. 1936. Am. J. Anat. 58:329. [4] Latimer, H. B. 1937. Anat. Record 68:469. [5] Latimer, 3:435. [8] Latimer, H. B. 1940. Ibid. 4:259. [9] Latimer, H. B. 1942. Ibid. 6:341. [10] Latyszewski, M. anatomy of the vertebrates. McGraw-Hill, New York. [13] Schmidt-Nielsen, K. Unpublished. Duke Univ., Durham, [16] Swett, W. W., et al. 1937. U. S. Dept. Agr. Bur. Dairy Ind. BDIM-589(revised). [17] Swett, W. W., et al. Morgantown. 1952. [19] Webster, S. H., E. J. Liljegren, and D. J. Zimmer. 1947. Am. J. Anat. 81:477.

BIRDS

Classification for the Birds of the World, Smithsonian Institution, 1960.

Stomach-Intestines g	Liver g	Lungs g	Heart g	Kidneys g	Thyroid g	Adrenals g	Spleen g	
(G)	(H)	(I)	(J)	(K)	(L)	(M)	(N)	
......	......	......	0.235	......	0.0145	0.005	......	1
2.296	1.01	0.2516	0.2854	0.2673	0.0193	0.0059	0.0184	2
1.74	0.738	......	0.133	......	0.009	0.007	......	3
......	......	......	1.06	......	0.014	0.017	......	4
6.38	2.63	1.743	1.159	1.299	0.0116	0.0133	0.051	5
2.698	1.2062	0.3674	0.4077	0.345	0.0042	0.0063	0.0426	6
2.637	1.048	0.393	0.376	0.348	0.0038	0.0058	0.042	7
5.2473	1.9874	1.0736	0.9293	0.9829	0.0063	0.0147	0.0665	8
5.6575	2.1952	1.089	0.8688	1.08	0.0063	0.0113	0.0411	9
......	......	......	0.493	......	0.0093	0.013	......	10
......	......	......	0.383	......	0.006	0.022	......	11
......	......	1.677	1.018	......	0.0105	0.0213	......	12
......	......	0.607	0.327	......	0.004	0.004	......	13
......	......	9.97	3.2	......	0.038	0.077	......	14
......	......	......	0.302	......	0.006	0.007	......	15
......	......	......	0.283	......	0.0083	0.0085	......	16
......	0.207	......	......	......	0.006	0.005	......	17
......	......	......	0.165	......	0.0025	0.0055	......	18
260	57.78	52.27	56.61	23.3	0.23	0.25	......	19
......	0.2511	0.0951	0.1138	0.0391	0.00045	0.00035	......	20
......	......	10.7	8.6	......	0.085	0.165	......	21
......	......	5.07	4.836	......	0.028	0.0421	......	22
......	......	4.09	4.651	......	0.031	0.046	......	23
6.74	4.34	1.91	1.24	2.31	0.009	0.037	......	24
6.6	2.51	1.41	1.24	1.88	0.008	0.015	......	25
......	27.33	......	5.24	......	0.04	0.133	......	26
1.54	23.51	9.13	7.35	7.45	0.051	0.12	......	27
21.56	9.12	7.12	3.44	3.2	0.0216	0.0529	......	28

continued

116. ORGAN WEIGHTS:

Part II:

	Order and Family	Species	No. of Subjects	Body Weight kg	Brain g	Eyes g
	(A)	(B)	(C)	(D)	(E)	(F)
	Gruiformes					
29	Otididae	*Choriotis kori*	1♂	10	15.63	52.45
30			1♀	5.54	12.94	40.25
31	Gruidae	*Balearica pavonina*	1♂	4.825	12.85	11.2
32			1♀	4.071	13.54	12
33		*Grus canadensis*	1♂	1.651	8.58	10.97
	Galliformes					
34	Numididae	*Numida meleagris*	1♂	1.62	4.2	......
35	Phasianidae	*Francolinus sephaena*	1♂	0.208	1.5	......
36		*Gallus domesticus*	8♂	0.7331	2.9279	4.25
37			16♀	0.6151	2.7224	3.58
38		*Phasianus colchicus*	1♂	0.625	3.289	5.32
39	Tetraonidae	*Lagopus lagopus*	3♂	0.542	2.377	2.316
40			1♀	0.54	2.8	3.022
	Falconiformes					
41	Falconidae	*Falco sparverius*	1♂	0.112	2.51	3.3
42	Accipitridae	*Accipiter velox*	1♀	0.52	5.7	......
43		*Aquila rapax*	2♂	2.438	13.91	30.96
44			2♀	2.625	14.09	32.84
45		*Buteo vulpinus*	1♂	0.56	7.9	......
46		*Haliaeetus vocifer*	1♀	3.5	12.93	22.28
47	Cathartidae	*Cathartes aura*	1♂	0.495	9.32	7.95
	Anseriformes					
48	Anatidae	*Dafila acuta tzitzihoa*	1♀	0.67	4.95	1.7
49		*Mergus serrator*	1♀	0.77	5.289	2.76
50		*Nettion carolinensis*	1♀	0.305	3.116	1.16
51		*Nyroca affinis*	1♂	1.041	....	2.9
52		*N. marila*	1♀	0.787	4.7859	1.76
	Ciconiiformes					
53	Phoenicopteridae	*Phoeniconaias minor*	2♂	1.598	8.05	3.82
54			3♀	1.483	6.99	2.97
55	Ciconiidae	*Ciconia ciconia*	1♂	3.35	16.24	18.3
56			2♀	3.35	15.78	16.5
57		*Leptoptilus crumeniferus*	2♂	7.13	30.14	27.89
58	Scopidae	*Scopus umbretta*	1♂	0.3175	3.93	......
59	Ardeidae	*Casmerodius albus*	1♀	1.03	6.12	......
	Pelecaniformes					
60	Fregatidae	*Fregata aquila*	1♂	1.405	9.45	12.99
61	Pelecanidae	*Pelecanus occidentalis*	2♀	3.29	17.95	12.73
	Procellariiformes					
62	Procellariidae	*Puffinus griseus*	1♀	0.268	3.01	3.27
	Gaviiformes					
63	Gaviidae	*Gavia stellata*	2♂	1.568	6.38	4.89
64			1♀	1.53	6.12	5.47
	Struthioniformes					
65	Struthionidae	*Struthio camelus*	1♂	123	42.11	95.26

Contributor: Quiring, Daniel P.

References: [1] Quiring, D. P. 1950. Functional anatomy of the vertebrates. McGraw-Hill, New York. [2] Quiring,

Stomach-Intestines g	Liver g	Lungs g	Heart g	Kidneys g	Thyroid g	Adrenals g	Spleen g	
(G)	(H)	(I)	(J)	(K)	(L)	(M)	(N)	
655	200	100	97	66.42	0.91	0.87	......	29
490	98.61	70.48	60.25	22.09	0.44	0.33	......	30
......	86.1	42.05	32.37	21.62	0.265	0.3	......	31
......	125	46.21	41.21	30.34	0.34	0.38	......	32
78.59	29.34	15.33	19.01	11.71	0.14	0.248	0.67	33
......	28.6	29.08	14.22	7.34	0.293	0.36	......	34
......	8.65	......	1.46	2.7	0.02	0.053	......	35
......	16.188	4.41	4.19	4.54	0.0894	0.0714	0.97	36
......	14.498	3.78	3.91	4.17	0.0762	0.0973	0.95	37
56.5	9.115	......	5.61	4.82	0.051	0.12	......	38
......	12.99	9.61	7.863	3.87	0.0255	0.0273	......	39
......	13.405	10.74	9.46	4.87	0.017	0.036	......	40
7.43	2.52	1.52	1.12	1.11	0.016	0.028	......	41
......	......	7.7	3.7	......	0.042	0.11	......	42
......	37.55	23.18	14.17	13.57	0.31	0.5	......	43
......	48.45	......	18.54	14.16	0.19	0.45	......	44
......	10.87	4.64	4.58	3.36	0.18	0.26	......	45
150	46.28	47.33	32.23	18.43	0.28	0.4	......	46
170	20.99	14.73	10.24	10.11	0.115	0.156	......	47
99.43	30.33	17.13	8.34	8.14	0.559	0.0818	0.89	48
46.3	19.77	18.16	11.01	9.67	0.0657	0.01033	0.22	49
33.84	8.17	9.218	2.88	3.105	0.0281	0.043	0.42	50
......	58.3	17.6	13.4	18.1	0.133	0.152	......	51
99.15	23	18.01	8	9.11	0.0855	0.185	......	52
......	40.91	23.32	13.53	19	0.57	0.59	......	53
248	40.27	21.35	14.68	17.02	0.27	0.34	......	54
......	71.4	27.2	28.75	26.24	0.43	0.49	......	55
......	61.06	42.26	32.12	19.84	0.4	0.44	......	56
692	110	72.23	55.24	42.94	0.64	2.06	......	57
......	......	8.16	7.22	......	0.037	0.061	......	58
135	33.02	33.1	9.25	8.16	0.13	0.21	......	59
......	35.88	......	16.59	......	0.089	0.175	......	60
255	73.15	29.83	22.12	......	0.183	0.993	......	61
18.21	10.03	2.45	2.46	3.23	0.031	0.049	......	62
106.27	74.02	22.31	22.24	27.61	0.21	0.219	......	63
97.42	60.87	22.62	22.72	22.71	1.33	0.223	......	64
23,133	2050	2900	1205	920	17.33	23.01	......	65

D. P., and P. H. Bade. 1943. Growth 7:299.

continued

116. ORGAN WEIGHTS:

Part III: REPTILES AND

Values are fresh weights unless otherwise specified. Classification for

	Order and Family	Species	No. of Subjects	Body Weight kg	Brain g	Eyes g
	(A)	(B)	(C)	(D)	(E)	(F)
			Reptilia			
	Serpentes					
1	Crotalidae	*Ancistrodon piscivorus*	1♀	0.728	0.64	0.61
2	Colubridae	*Coluber constrictor*	1♂	0.286	0.303	0.219
3			2♀	0.5035	0.285	0.165[1]
4		*Tropidonotus natrix*	20♂♀	0.07	0.1	......
5		*Zamenis viridis*	6♂♀	0.22	0.209	......
6	Pythonidae	*Python molurus*	1♂	6.14	1.123	1.12
7	Boidae	*Boa imperator*	1♀	1.829	0.44	0.55
	Sauria					
8	Helodermatidae	*Heloderma suspectum*	1♂	0.514	0.729	......
9	Lacertidae	*Lacerta viridis*	15♂♀	0.05	0.121	......
10	Iguanidae	*Amblyrhynchus cristatus*	1♀[2]	4.19	1.44	1.06
11		*Iguana iguana*	1♀	1.34	......	......
12		*Phrynosoma cornutum*	2♂	0.025	0.1383	0.3927
13			3♀	0.0249	0.1269	0.2761
	Crocodylia					
14	Alligatoridae	*Alligator mississipiensis*	2♂	189	12.64	28.2
15			1♀	52.4	7.23	15.96
16	Crocodylidae	*Crocodylus acutus*	1♂	134	15.6	......
	Chelonia					
17	Trionychidae	*Amyda ferox*	1♀	3.253	2.5	......
18	Chelonidae	*Chelonia mydas*	1♂	114.3	8.6	66.2
19			1♀	68.04	5.81	21.08
20	Testudinidae	*Testudo graeca*	30♂♀	0.32	0.3	......
21	Emydidae	*Chrysemys elegans*	21♂[3]	0.8339	......	......
22			1♀[3]	0.8653	......	......
23		*Clemmys guttata*	1♂	2.163	1.36	1.35
24		*Emys europea*	30♂♀	0.25	0.25	......
25		*Malacoclemmys lesueurii*	1♂[3]	0.2543	......	......
26	Chelydridae	*Aromochelys tristata*	1♂[3]	0.116	......	......
27			2♀[3]	0.0883	......	......
28		*Chelydra serpentina*	1♀	5.125	0.98	0.72
29		*Macrochelys lacertina*	1♂	1.848	1.01	1.21
			Amphibia			
	Salientia					
30	Ranidae	*Rana catesbeiana*	6♂	0.5199	0.4625	2.57
31		*R. pipiens*	10♂[3]	0.0361	......	......
32			19♀[3]	0.0381	......	......

/1/ For 1 subject. /2/ Preserved weights. /3/ Data from reference 1. /4/ Weight of esophagus included.

Contributors: (a) Quiring, Daniel P., (b) Latimer, Homer B.

References: [1] Latimer, H. B. 1920. Anat. Record 18:35. [2] Quiring, D. P. 1950. Functional anatomy of the

reptiles adapted from Schmidt and Inger, *Living Reptiles of the World,* 1957.

Stomach-Intestines g	Liver g	Lungs g	Heart g	Kidneys g	Thyroid g	Adrenals g	Spleen g	
(G)	(H)	(I)	(J)	(K)	(L)	(M)	(N)	
				Reptilia				
300	64.45	22.62	4.77	13.47	0.5	1.06	5.57	1
12.02	2.57	3.45	0.96	2.58	0.056	0.056	0.78	2
......	......	4.13[1]	......	......	0.1225	0.1425	......	3
......	2.8	......	......	0.88	0.01	0.035	0.12	4
......	4.82	......	......	1.93	0.045	0.08	0.125	5
......	......	......	18.5	......	1.33	2.68	......	6
......	30.37	14	5.64	9.57	0.15	0.15	......	7
......	35	6.45	4.17	......	0.152	0.056	......	8
......	2.5	......	......	0.58	0.008	0.02	0.08	9
610	60.4	64.4	21.51	11.6	0.04	0.09	......	10
42.6	33.35	......	2.6	3.7	0.117	0.215	......	11
......	0.5705	0.5705	0.1264	0.6397	0.0044	0.0093	0.0311	12
......	0.8857	0.6174	0.1	0.2257	0.007	0.0087	0.0105	13
4900	711	1014	286.5	......	11.075	8.68	135[1]	14
......	708	393	137	......	4.28	6.62	......	15
......	1145	1125	134	......	5.2	4.3	......	16
......	90	......	16	15	0.51	0.44	......	17
8750	775	2650	435	840	24.55	3.84	250	18
......	540	......	180	......	3.46	3.27	62.57	19
......	8.5	......	......	1.55	0.036	0.031	0.18	20
6.231[4]	5.434	1.073	0.317	0.317	......	......	0.216	21
7.318[4]	5.924	0.84	0.307	0.359	......	......	0.47	22
108.5	53.5	31.95	7.05	8.45	0.125	0.413	2.25	23
......	7.3	......	......	1.38	0.025	0.028	0.16	24
3.119[4]	3.76	1.141	0.248	0.243	......	......	0.19	25
3.166[4]	2.555	0.863	0.35	0.505	......	......	0.029	26
3.54	2.331	0.954	0.258	0.159	......	......	0.035	27
......	160	85	13.43	24.5	0.48	0.62	......	28
......	184	34.9	12.88	15.9	0.59	0.51	16.41	29
				Amphibia				
24.56	14.77	2.76	1.65	1.421	0.3336	0.1342	0.373	30
3.503[4]	2.806	0.855	0.435	0.435	......	......	0.185	31
3.773[4]	2.884	0.765	0.479	0.473	......	......	0.169	32

vertebrates. McGraw-Hill, New York.

continued

116. ORGAN WEIGHTS: VERTEBRATES

Part IV: FISHES

Values are fresh weights. Classification adapted from Herald, *Living Fishes of the World*, 1961.

	Order and Family	Species	No. of Subjects	Body Weight kg	Brain g	Eyes g	Stomach-Intestines g	Liver g	Heart g	Kidneys g	Thyroid g	Spleen g
	(A)	(B)	(C)	(D)	(E)	(F)	(G)	(H)	(I)	(J)	(K)	(L)
						Pisces						
	Plectognathi											
1	Balistidae	*Balistes carolinensis*	1♂	0.295	0.872	3.36	5.54	12.86	0.364	.....	0.005	0.09
	Percomorphi											
2	Sphyraenidae	*Sphyraena barracuda*	3♂	8.823	4.687	40	409[1]	62.7[1]	30.61	.....	0.11[1]	......
3			3♀	8.723	2.757	38.32	430[1]	59.62[2]	11.81	.....	0.1563	13.37[1]
4	Istiophoridae	*Istiophorus americanus*	1♀	25.2	2.74	116.32	.....	......	49.15	.....	......	......
5		*Makaira albida*	1♀	24.94	3.41	171.02	.....	......	47.6	225	0.45	......
6	Scombridae	*Gymnosarda alleterata*	1♂	6.291	3.57	33.8	351	128	29.43	.....	0.051	20.4
7		*Scomberomorus maculatus*	2♀	1.457	1.61	7.91	.....	6.21	2.93	.....	0.03	1.7
8		*S. regalis*	1♂	2.43	2.18	......	.....	......	5.33	.....	0.037	......
9		*Thunnus secundodorsalis*	1♂	5.21	3.09	85.81	216	139	31.22	.....	0.056	......
10	Labridae	*Lachnolaimus maximus*	1♂	0.48	0.91	4.97	5.02	3.7	0.452	.....	0.014	0.35
11	Sciaenidae	*Aplodinotus grunniens*	1♀	0.937	0.891	6.88	.....	......	1.71	.....	0.012	......
12	Pomadasyidae	*Haemulon plumieri*	1♂	0.3	0.81	4.47	5.19	3.55	0.31	.....	0.01	0.18
13	Lutianidae	*Lutjanus analis*	1♀	2.49	2.09	19.15	.....	14.26	5.12	.....	0.048	1.17
14		*Ocyurus chrysurus*	1♀	0.255	0.94	4.2	7.72	2.41	0.37	1.45	0.007	0.3
15		*Rhomboplites aurorubens*	1♂	0.202	0.65	2.54	3.11	1.76	0.33	.....	0.006	......
16	Coryphaenidae	*Coryphaena hippurus*	1♂	19.04	9.76	64	.....	......	28.37	98.7	0.36	......
17	Carangidae	*Caranx bartholomaei*	1♂	4.812	4.72	20.22	182	65.13	13.96	.....	0.058	8.7
18			1♀	4.274	7.56	9.52	.....	......	11.62	.....	0.043	......
19		*C. hippos*	1♂	2.305	2.97	33.25	.....	18.7	4.87	.....	0.031	2.66
20		*Trachinotus glaucus*	1♀	8.504	3.08	79.13	302	86.25	24.83	.....	0.11	7.42
21	Percidae	*Perca flavescens*	6♂	0.167	0.254	0.93	4.85	1.476	0.3087	0.459	0.0035	0.149
22			1♀	0.192	0.337	1.4	7.92	2.96	0.44	.....	0.002	......
23	Serranidae	*Mycteroperca bonaci*	1♂	2.712	2.001	13.19	55.47	11.66	2.08	.....	0.032	......
24		*Promicrops itaiara*	1♂	32.89	2.31	33.6	1200	350	49.23	56.8	0.32	17
	Anacanthini											
25	Gadidae	*Gadus callarius*	3♂	2.518	1.9792	26.73	179.2	96.2	3.9	11.4	0.0476	2.15
26			3♀	2.625	2.218	26.91	159.7	97.1	4.09	9.4	0.0257	2.01
27		*Melanogrammus aeglefinus*	6♀	3.275	2.0502	26.16	291.5	132.6	5.71	11.08	0.0692	2.64
	Apodes											
28	Muraenidae	*Gymnothorax funebris*	1	3.51	0.51	1.39	325	101.5	4.62	.....	0.054	4.28
	Ostariophysi											
29	Cyprinidae	*Carassius auratus*	1♂	0.00554	0.069	......	.....	......	0.014	.....	0.009	......
30			1♀	0.00952	0.097	0.14	0.98	......	0.026	.....	0.004	......
31		*Cyprinus carpio*	4♂	1.0421	1.2833	2.865	96.44	......	1.617	6.779	0.0089	2.544
32			2♀	1.061	1.191	3.142	70.1	......	1.554	4.88	0.008	2.32
	Haplomi											
33	Esocidae	*Esox lucius*	4♂	0.3523	0.464	4.88	21.67	3.55	0.66	1.777	0.0047	0.421
34			2♀	0.3738	0.535	4.915	20.8	3.78	0.56	1.555	0.0118	0.42
	Isospondyli											
35	Osmeridae	*Osmerus mordax*	1	0.04766	1.09	......	.....	......	1.29	......	0.006	......
36	Coregonidae	*Coregonus clupeaformis*	3♂	0.7465	0.503	2.34	42.88	8.84	0.892	7.98	0.0153	0.75
37			3♀	0.7986	0.593	2.69	38.67	10.61	0.973	8.2	0.0091	0.6

/1/ For 1 subject. /2/ For 2 subjects.

continued

116. ORGAN WEIGHTS: VERTEBRATES

Part IV: FISHES

	Order and Family	Species	No. of Subjects	Body Weight kg	Brain g	Eyes g	Stomach-Intestines g	Liver g	Heart g	Kidneys g	Thyroid g	Spleen g
	(A)	(B)	(C)	(D)	(E)	(F)	(G)	(H)	(I)	(J)	(K)	(L)
						Pisces						
	Isospondyli											
38	Salmonidae	*Salmo gairdneri*	2♂	2.75	0.818	4.35	89.38	40.74	6.22	20.64	0.0163	2.86
39		*S. salar*	2♂	4.922	1.029	7.84	216.8	69.46	15.22	36.2	0.01	11
40			4♀	5.361	1.143	8.014	230.9	96.56	10.72	39.59	0.017	11.71
41		*S. trutta*	1♂	0.292	0.57	2.29	20.1	3.885	0.385	1.25	0.007	1.205
42		*Salvelinus fontinalis*	1♂	0.2301	0.466	1.94	28.24	3.75	1.15	3.32	......	0.17
43			1♀	0.255	0.439	2.02	16.01	5.86	0.99	.....	......	0.22
44		*S. namaycush*	1♂	2.5	1.233	7.26	154.7	36	4.34	20.92	0.0095	2.16
45			5♀	3.24	1.323	9.33	220.3	52.43	5.17	27.97	0.0134	1.77
46	Clupeidae	*Alosa ohiensis*	1♀	0.615	0.527	1.91	.....	......	2.21	4.25	0.01	......
						Chondrichthyes						
	Batoidei											
47	Dasyatidae	*Dasyatis sabina*	2♂	17.58	76.52	30.67	410	815	47.58	107.2	1.76	......
48	Torpedinidae	*Torpedo torpedo*	1♂	0.345	0.78	1.3	.....	6.9	0.22	12.9	0.029	......
	Selachii											
49	Carcharhinidae	*Galeocerdo tigrinis*	1♀	200	107.5	88.43	.....	40,370	291.5	.....	12.73	......
50	Carcharidae	*Carcharias littoralis*	1♂	35.83	50.03	52.21	750	2925	40.14	.....	2.57	150
51			1♀	35.38	48.8	44.24	1375	2875	41.6	96.4	1.81	98.82

Contributor: Quiring, Daniel P.

Reference: Quiring, D. P. 1950. Functional anatomy of the vertebrates. McGraw-Hill, New York.

117. BODY WEIGHT: INSECTS

Larval stage (column B) is for last instar, unless otherwise specified. Values in parentheses are ranges, estimate "c" (cf. Introduction). Classification adapted from Borrer and DeLong, *An Introduction to the Study of Insects*, 1954.

	Order and Species	Stage	Fresh Weight mg	Reference
	(A)	(B)	(C)	(D)
	Hymenoptera			
1	*Apis mellifera*	Egg	ca. 0.1	13
2		Larva, worker	137	25
3		Larva, queen	262	25
4		Pupa	150(147-176)	42
5		Adult, worker	120(87-134)	11, 12
6	*Camponotus gigas*	Adult	(75-347)	18
7	*Caraphractus cinctus*	Egg	ca. 0.0002	35
8		Adult	ca. 0.005	35
9	*Cimbex 4-maculatus*	Adult	903	2
10	*Polistes variatus*	Adult, queen	148.5	15
	Diptera			
11	*Aedes aegypti*	Adult, ♀ (unfed)	0.1	1
12		Adult, ♀ (fed)	0.19	1
	Diptera			
13	*Anopheles quadrimaculatus*	Larva	1.91	5
14		Pupa, ♂	2.99	5
15		Pupa, ♀	3.45	5
16		Adult, ♂	1.37	5
17		Adult, ♀ (unfed)	1.66	5
18	*Calliphora erythrocephala*	Adult, ♂	(50-69)	24
19		Adult, ♀	(60-77)	24
20	*Culex quinquefasciatus*	Larva	2.2[1]; 2.3[2]	17
21	*C. tarsalis*	Pupa	2.2	16
22	*Drosophila melanogaster*	Pupa	1	4
23	*Glossina palpalis*	Adult, ♀, 1-3 da (unfed)	25.4	1
24	*Lucilia sericata*	Egg	0.007	28
25		Larva, 1 hr	0.05	28

/1/ DDT-resistant. /2/ DDT-susceptible.

continued

117. BODY WEIGHT: INSECTS

	Order and Species	Stage	Fresh Weight mg	Reference
	(A)	(B)	(C)	(D)
	Diptera			
26	*Lucilia sericata*	Larva, 24 hr	1.5(1-2)	28
27		Larva, 48 hr	17.8(16-20)	28
28		Larva, 72 hr	52(45-57)	28
29		Larva, 96 hr	52(43-56)	28
30		Larva, 144 hr	42(39-44)	28
31		Pupa	28.3(24-35)	28
32		Adult, ♂	27	24
33		Adult, ♀	40	24
34	*Musca domestica*	Pupa	(22-27)	46
35		Adult	(15-30)	27
36	*Phormia regina*	Larva	44(22-63)	45
37		Adult, ♂	(38-40)	24
38		Adult, ♀	(42-50)	24
39	*Rhagoletis pomonella*	Adult, ♂	4.6(2.5-7.5)	29
40		Adult, ♀	6.9(1.7-11.0)	29
41	*Sarcophaga securifera*	Larva, 48 hr	238	37
42	*Tipula abdominalis*	Larva	1200(800-1600)	35
	Lepidoptera			
43	*Ascia rapae*	Larva	156(110-165)	10
44	*Bombyx mori*	Larva[3]	1770	30
45		Pupa	1170	30
46	*Calleria mellonella*	Larva	175(85-310)	45
47	*Carpocapsa pomonella*	Larva	47(42-63)	10
48	*Datana ministra*	Larva	523(340-900)	3
49	*Deilephila euphorbiae*	Larva	4038	14
50		Pupa	2609	14
51		Adult	1263	14
52	*Ephestia kuehniella*	Pupa	26.0[4]	41
53	*Heliothis virescens*	Larva	(400-440)	9
54	*H. zea*	Larva	(700-790)	9
55	*Loxostege sticticalis*	Larva	72.6	32
56		Pupa	60.3	32
57		Adult, ♂	11.9	32
58		Adult, ♀	19.8	32
59	*Malacosoma americanum*	Larva	510(260-860)	3
60	*Prodenia eridania*	Larva	(700-790)	9
61	*Protoparce 5-maculatus*	Larva	8,300(6,200-10,500)	10
62	*P. sexta*	Larva	(800-890)	9
63	*Tineola biselliella*	Larva	(4.9-9.2)[5]	44
64		Pupa	(3.0-5.5)[5]	44
65		Adult, ♂	(2.1-4.3)[5]	44
66		Adult, ♀	(4.1-9.4)[5]	44
	Coleoptera			
67	*Bruchus obtectus*	Adult, ♂	(2.9-6.8)	26
68		Adult, ♀	(2.8-8.3)	26
69	*Ceratomegilla fuscilabrus*	Adult	13.1	15
70	*Dytiscus marginalis*	Larva	1366(1305-1498)	20
71		Pupa	1950	20
72		Adult	1356(1186-1466)	20
73	*Goliathus goliathus*	Adult	ca. (40,000-100,000)	35
74	*Hippodamia convergens*	Adult	21.3	15
75	*Leptinotarsa decemlineata*	Larva	98(83-110)	10
76		Adult	160(146-176)	10
77	*Phyllophaga fusca*	Adult	581.2	15
78	*Popillia japonica*	Larva	(196-276)	21-23
79		Pupa	(176-222)	21-23
80		Adult, ♂	114	21-23
81		Adult, ♀	146	21-23
82	*Tenebrio molitor*	Larva	(83-180)	26
83	*Tribolium confusum*	Larva	2.0(1.5-2.4)	45
84		Adult, 1 da	1.75(1.5-2.0)	45
85		Adult, older	2.1(1.4-3.5)	35
	Homoptera			
86	*Toxoptera graminum*	Adult	16	2
	Hemiptera			
87	*Leptocoris trivittatus*	Adult	(32.2-39.1)	15
88	*Oncopeltus fasciatus*	Adult, ♂	47.4(31-75)	48
89		Adult, ♀	65.9(40-95)	48
90	*Rhodnius prolixus*	Adult	ca. 80	47
	Anoplura			
91	*Enderleinellus zonatus*	Adult, ♂	ca. 0.005	35
	Orthoptera			
92	*Blatta orientalis*	Adult, ♂, 5 da	400(323-515)	45
93		Adult, ♀, 5 da	750(540-870)	45
94		Adult, ♀, 60-70 da	1036(833-1165)	45
95		Adult, ♀, 120 da	914(781-1200)	45
96	*Blatella germanica*	Adult, ♂	48	17
97		Adult, ♀	107	17
98	*Dixippus morosus*	Adult	1050(900-1100)	8,43
99	*Locusta migratoria migratorioides*	Larva, 1st instar	14.3	7
100		Larva, 2nd instar	(33.2-37.6)	7
101		Larva, 3rd instar	(66.4-77.4)	7
102		Larva, 4th instar	(164-221)	7
103		Larva, 5th instar	(372-578)	7
104		Adult, ♀, 1 da	(960-1900)	31
105		Adult, ♂[6]	1350(1200-1400)	31
106		Adult, ♀[6]	2500(2250-2900)	33
107	*Macropanesthia rhinocerus*	Adult	19,300(18,400-19,500)	6
108	*Melanoplus differentialis*	Adult, ♂	854(436-1232)	36
109		Adult, ♀	1428(812-2607)	36
110	*M. femurrubrum*	Adult, ♂	283(160-384)	36
111		Adult, ♀	369(184-593)	36
112	*M. mexicanus*	Egg	5.5(3.8-7.8)	38
113		Adult, ♂	(153-161)	40

/3/ Italian strain, 4100 mg; Japanese strain, 8417 mg. [2] /4/ 12.9 mg when reared in dry air. /5/ Lower limit from specimens reared at 30°C, upper limit from specimens reared at 20°C. /6/ At maximum growth.

continued

117. BODY WEIGHT: INSECTS

	Order and Species	Stage	Fresh Weight mg	Reference
	(A)	(B)	(C)	(D)
	Orthoptera			
114	*Melanoplus mexicanus*	Adult, ♀	(156-165)	40
115	*Nyctobora noctivaga*	Adult	(1290-2190)	19
116	*Periplaneta americana*	Adult, ♂	789	17
117		Adult, ♀	975	17
	Orthoptera			
118	*Sphodromantis bioculata*	Adult	2079	34
	Odonata			
119	*Anax junius*	Larva	(1200-1500)	39
120		Adult	(500-900)	39

Contributors: (a) Richards, A. Glenn, (b) Hoskins, W. M.

References: [1] Barlow, F., and A. B. Hadaway. 1952. Bull. Entomol. Research 42:769. [2] Bodenheimer, F. S. 1933. Quart. Rev. Biol. 8:92. [3] Campbell, F. L. 1926. J. Agr. Research 32:359. [4] Chiang, H. C., and A. C. Hodson. 1950. Ecol. Monographs 20:173. [5] Cutkomp, L. K. Unpublished. Univ. Minnesota, St. Paul, 1952. [6] Day, M. F. 1950. Australian J. Sci. Research, B, 3:61. [7] Duarte, A. J. 1938. Bull. Entomol. Research 29:425. [8] Eidmann, H. 1924. Z. Morphol. Ökol. Tiere 2:567. [9] Gast, R. T. 1959. J. Econ. Entomol. 57:1115. [10] Hansberry, R., W. W. Middlekauff, and L. B. Norton. 1940. Ibid. 33:511. [11] Haydak, M. H. 1934. J. Agr. Research 49:21. [12] Haydak, M. H. 1936. J. Econ. Entomol. 29:870. [13] Haydak, M. H. Unpublished, 1952. [14] Heller, J. 1926. Biochem. Z. 172:59. [15] Hodson, A. C. 1937. Ecol. Monographs 7:271. [16] Hoskins, W. M. 1932. J. Econ. Entomol. 25:1212. [17] Hoskins, W. M. Unpublished. Univ. California, Berkeley, 1961. [18] Huxley, J. S. 1932. Problems in relative growth. Dial Press, New York. [19] Kitchel, R. L., and W. M. Hoskins. Unpublished. Univ. California, Berkeley, 1953. [20] Korschelt, E. 1923-24. Bearbeitung einheimischer Tiere. Der Gelbrand *Dytiscus marginalis* L. W. Engelmann, Leipzig. v. 1, 2. [21] Ludwig, D. 1931. J. Exptl. Zool. 60:309. [22] Ludwig, D. 1946. Ann. Entomol. Soc. Amer. 39:496. [23] Ludwig, D. 1949. Physiol. Zool. 22:308. [24] McIndoo, N. E. 1937. J. Agr. Research 55:909. [25] Melampy, R. M., E. R. Willis, and S. E. McGregor. 1940. Physiol. Zool. 13:283. [26] Menusan, H. 1936. Ann. Entomol. Soc. Amer. 29:279. [27] Metcalf, C. L., W. P. Flint, and R. L. Metcalf. 1951. Destructive and useful insects. Ed. 3. McGraw-Hill, New York. [28] Michelbacher, A. E., and W. M. Hoskins. Unpublished. Univ. California, Berkeley, 1953. [29] Middlekauff, W. W. 1941. J. Econ. Entomol. 34:621. [30] Needham, D. M. 1929. Biol. Revs. Biol. Proc. Cambridge Phil. Soc. 4:307. [31] Norris, M. J. 1950. Brit. Museum Nat. Hist. Anti-Locust Bull. 6. [32] Pepper, J. H., and E. Hastings. 1943. Montana Agr. Expt. Sta. Bull. 413. [33] Phipps, J. 1950. Bull. Entomol. Research 40:539. [34] Przibram, H., and F. Megusar. 1912. Arch. Entwicklungsmech. Organ. 34:680. [35] Richards, A. G. Unpublished. Univ. Minnesota, St. Paul, 1952. [36] Richardson, C. H., and L. E. Haas. 1932. J. Econ. Entomol. 25:1078. [37] Ricks, M., and W. M. Hoskins. Unpublished. Univ. California, Berkeley, 1953. [38] Salt, R. W. 1949. Can. J. Research, D, 27:236. [39] Shafer, G. D. 1923. Stanford Univ. Publs. Univ. Ser. Biol. Sci. 3:307. [40] Smith, D. S., and F. E. Northcott. 1951. Can. J. Zool. 29:297. [41] Speicher, B. R. 1931. Proc. Penna. Acad. Sci. 5:79. [42] Strauss, J. 1911. Z. Biol. 56:347. [43] Teissier, G. 1931. Trav. sta. biol. Roscoff 9:29. [44] Titschack, E. 1925. Z. wiss. Zool. 124:213. [45] Tsao, C.-H., and A. G. Richards. 1952. Ann. Entomol. Soc. Amer. 45:585. [46] Vladimerova, M. S., and E. S. Smirnov. 1936. Med. Parazitol. Parazitar. Bolezni 7:755. [47] Wigglesworth, V. B. 1948. Proc. Roy. Soc. (London), B, 135:430. [48] Worthley, H. N. 1943. Publ. Am. Assoc. Advance. Sci. 20.

XI. SEX RATIOS AND LIFE SPANS

118. SEX RATIOS AT BIRTH: MAMMALS AND BIRDS

Values are percentage of males in a sample of newborn animals. Values in parentheses are ranges, estimate "b" (cf. Introduction).

	Order and Species	Breed or Common Name	No. of Subjects	Sex Ratio % males	Reference
	(A)	(B)	(C)	(D)	(E)
	Mammalia				
	Primates				
1	*Homo sapiens*[1]	White, U.S.A.	....	51.32	71
2		Non-white, U.S.A.	....	50.59	71
	Artiodactyla				
3	*Bos indicus*	Indian	8770	50.9	14
4		Sindhi	497	50.5(46.0-55.0)	17
5		Zebu	20,424	51.1(50.4-51.8)	81
6	*B. taurus*	Alpine Brown	2163	49.7(47.5-51.9)	10
7		Ayrshire	680	49.0(45.2-52.8)	64
8		Danish	2393	50.4(48.4-52.4)	62
9		Finnish Ayrshire	56,333	51.4(51.0-51.8)	38
10		Finnish Landrace, East-	18,029	50.5(49.8-51.2)	38
11		Finnish Landrace, West-	8042	52.6(51.5-53.7)	38
12		Guernsey	782	44.4(40.8-48.0)	64
13		Hereford	2878	50.5(48.6-52.4)	64
14		Holstein-Friesian	3250	48.6(46.8-50.4)	64
15		Jersey	606	51.5(47.4-55.6)	64
16		Lowland, Black Pied	4956	51.8(50.4-53.2)	2
17		Norwegian	1217	50.7(47.8-53.6)	46
18		Østland, Red Polled	3286	50.3(48.6-52.0)	4
19		Schwyz	1287	53.8(51.0-56.6)	51
20		Shorthorn, dairy	2087	49.3(47.1-51.5)	63
21		Swedish Landrace	3683	51.9(50.3-53.5)	38
22		Swedish Lowland	11,441	51.6(50.7-52.5)	38
23		Swedish Red and White	52,709	51.5(51.1-51.9)	38
24		Swiss Brown	20,579	49.9(49.2-50.6)	25
25		Welsh Black	2825	50.2(48.3-52.1)	63
26		Various breeds	3442	53.1(51.4-54.8)	35
27	*Capra hircus*	Angora	3165	50.1(48.3-51.9)	52
28		British Saanen	350	55.1(49.8-60.4)	58
29		Saanen	415	51.3(46.4-56.2)	23
30		Toggenburg	566	50.5(46.3-54.7)	23
31		Crossbreds	988	50.8(47.6-54.0)	23
32	*Cervus canadensis*	American elk	....	51(46-56)	56
33	*Ovis aries*	Blackface	9549	48.3(47.3-49.3)	33
34		Cheviot	10,512	49.0(48.0-50.0)	33
35		East Friesian Milch	5806	49.9(48.6-51.2)	15
36		Karakul	448	51.8(47.1-56.5)	27
37		Leicester	8965	44.1(43.1-45.1)	33
38		Merino	1372	46.8(44.1-49.5)	42
39		Navajo	3521	48.5(46.8-50.2)	9
40		Southdown	5014	51.0(49.6-52.4)	33
41		Swedish	82,262	49.6(49.3-49.9)	40
42		Welsh Mountain	17,566	48.5(47.7-49.3)	78
43	*Sus scrofa*	Berkshire	2607	51.4(49.4-53.4)	37
44		Chester White	24,004	48.5(47.9-49.1)	55
45		Croatian Bagun	2367	51.0(48.9-53.1)	66
46		Duroc-Jersey	16,233	48.8(48.0-49.6)	59
47		German Improved	22,557	50.5(49.8-51.2)	44
48		German Land	12,401	50.4(49.5-51.3)	44
49		German Large White	9401	50.4(49.4-51.4)	45
50		German Pasture	2561	54.4(52.4-56.4)	19
51		Mangalitsas	3068	50.0(48.2-51.8)	65
52		Inbred, non-inbred, and linecross	20,971	52.1(51.4-52.8)	75
53		Various breeds	5657	51.9(50.6-53.2)	13

/1/ Values for man are based on a 50% sample of live births registered in 1959.

continued

118. SEX RATIOS AT BIRTH: MAMMALS AND BIRDS

	Order and Species	Breed or Common Name	No. of Subjects	Sex Ratio % males	Reference
	(A)	(B)	(C)	(D)	(E)
		Mammalia			
	Perissodactyla				
54	*Equus asinus*	Ass	35	48.6(31.7-65.5)	7
55	*E. caballus*	German	861,640	49.6(49.5-49.7)	20-22
56		Mura mares x Ardenner	170	50.6(42.9-58.3)	76
57		Østland	1198	50.6(47.7-53.5)	5,6
58		Thoroughbred	45,998	49.9(49.4-50.4)	82
59		Various breeds	25,560	49.9(49.3-50.5)	48
60	*E. mulus*	Mule	1416	44.3(41.7-46.9)	14
	Carnivora				
61	*Canis familiaris*	Bull terrier	1303	55.9(53.1-58.7)	11
62		Cocker spaniel	3858	51.6(50.0-53.2)	50
63		French bulldog	3350	50.4(48.7-52.1)	18
64		German sheep dog	324,323	52.8(52.6-53.0)	18
65		German shepherd	1440	55.4(52.8-58.0)	79
66		Greyhound	6878	52.4(51.2-53.6)	48
67		Schnauzer	608	50.5(46.4-54.6)	18
68		Bull, Irish, and fox terriers	4202	52.7(51.2-54.2)	31
69		Collie, St. Bernard, spaniel	9330	54.0(53.0-55.0)	31
70	*Mustela vison*	Pastel	1702	49.9(47.5-52.3)	73
71		Standard	3717	50.5(48.9-52.1)	73
72		Various hybrids	2682	51.0(49.1-52.9)	73
73	*Vulpes fulva*	Red fox	117	48.7(39.5-57.9)	69
74		Silver fox	2479	52.9(50.9-54.9)	39
	Rodentia				
75	*Cavia porcellus*	Guinea pig	2418	51.9(49.9-53.9)	61
76	*Mus musculus*	Mouse	2525	50.3(48.3-52.3)	53
77		Albino mouse	34,835	49.7(49.2-50.2)	8
78		Japanese mouse, waltzing mouse	479	50.5(45.9-55.1)	77
79	*Neotoma* sp.	Wood rat	83	50.6(39.6-61.6)	26
80	*Ondatra zibethica*	Muskrat	820	53.4(47.8-59.0)	3
81	*Peromyscus* sp.	Deer mouse	7547	50.7(49.5-51.9)	41
82	*Rattus norvegicus*	Albino	2034	48.6(46.4-50.8)	57
83		Gray	14,829	49.8(49.0-50.6)	43
84		Hybrid and piebald	12,641	51.0(50.1-51.9)	43
85		Wild brown	1044	51.3(48.2-54.4)	68
	Lagomorpha				
86	*Oryctolagus cuniculus*	Blue Vienna	104	51.9(42.1-61.7)	74
87		Flemish giant	79	57.0(45.9-68.1)	74
88		Polish	331	50.5(45.0-56.0)	72
89		Wild	142	47.9(39.5-56.3)	70
90		Various breeds	17,058	49.5(48.7-50.3)	67
		Aves			
	Passeriformes				
91	*Serinus* sp.	Lizard canary	200	43.5(36.5-50.5)	32
	Columbiformes				
92	*Columba* sp.	Pigeon	2630	50(48-52)	49
93	*Zenaidura macroura*	Mourning dove	3491	51.8(50.1-53.5)	60
	Galliformes				
94	*Bonasa umbellus*	Ruffed grouse	464	52(47-56)	16
95	*Gallus domesticus*	Legbar	5632	56.4(55.1-57.7)	24
96		New Hampshire	985	48.7(45.5-51.9)	80
97		Rhode Island Red	755	50.0(46.4-53.6)	29
98		White Leghorn	8355	49.8(48.7-50.9)	30
99		Various breeds	96,008	49.2(48.9-49.5)	12
100	*Meleagris gallopavo*	Turkey	12,064	49.2(48.3-50.1)	1
101	*Perdix perdix*	European gray partridge	331	43(38-48)	54
102	*Phasianus colchicus*	Ring-neck pheasant	129	42	47
	Anseriformes				
103	*Anas* sp.	Duck	7338	50.4(49.2-51.6)	28
104	*A. acuta*	Pintail	....	53(49-57)	34
105	*A. platyrhynchos*	Mallard	....	53(49-57)	34
106	*Aythya americana*	Redhead	....	53(48-58)	36
107	*A. valisineria*	Canvasback	....	51(47-55)	36

continued

118. SEX RATIOS AT BIRTH: MAMMALS AND BIRDS

Contributors: (a) Venge, Ole, (b) Craft, W. A., (c) Hickey, Joseph J., (d) Schachter, Joseph

References: [1] Asmundson, V. S. 1942. Am. Naturalist 75:389. [2] Bauer, K. 1940. Z. Tierzücht. Züchtungsbiol. 47:243. [3] Beer, J. R., and W. Truax. 1950. J. Wildlife Management 14:323. [4] Berge, S. 1942. Z. Tierzücht. Züchtungsbiol. 52:127. [5] Berge, S. 1944. Tidsskr. Landbr. 11-12. [6] Berge, S. 1945. Ibid. 1-2. [7] Berliner, V. R. 1943. Mississippi Farm Research 6:7. [8] Bluhm, A. 1941. Wilhelm Roux' Arch. Entwicklungsmech. Organ. 141:15. [9] Blum, C. T. 1943. J. Heredity 34:141. [10] Bonadonna, T., and L. Valerani. 1946. Zootec. e Vet. 1:129. [11] Briggs, L. C., and N. Kaliss. 1942. J. Heredity 33:222. [12] Byerly, T. C., and M. A. Jull. 1935. Poultry Sci. 14:217. [13] Carmichael, W. J., and J. B. Rice. 1920. Illinois Agr. Expt. Sta. Bull. 226:67. [14] Craft, W. A. 1938. Quart. Rev. Biol. 13:19. [15] Cremer, E. 1935. Z. Schafz. 24:122. [16] Darrow, R. W. 1947. In G. Bump, et al., ed. The ruffed grouse. N. Y. State Conservation Dept., Albany. [17] Dave, C. N. 1941. Poona Agr. Coll. Mag. 33:24. [18] Druckseis, H. 1935. Dissertation. Univ. München. [19] Dschaparidse, D. 1935. J. Landwirtsch. 83:161. [20] Düsing, C. 1887. Landwirtsch. Jahrb. 16:699. [21] Düsing, C. 1888. Ibid. 17:373. [22] Düsing, C. 1892. Ibid. 21:277. [23] Eaton, O. N. 1945. Genetics 30:51. [24] Ebbell, H. 1949. World's Poultry Sci. J. 5:164. [25] Engeler, W. 1933. Arb. schweiz. Stammb. Braunvieh (Luzern), p. 137. [26] Feldman, H. W. 1935. J. Mammal. 16:300. [27] Frölich, G. 1936. Z. Schafz. 25:40. [28] Frouda, F. M., and P. B. H. Infante. 1948. Philippine Agr. 32:165. [29] Hays, F. A. 1952. Poultry Sci. 31:1094. [30] Hazel, L. N., and W. F. Lamoreux. 1946. J. Heredity 37:333. [31] Heape, W. 1906-08. Proc. Cambridge Phil. Soc. 14:121. [32] Heape, W. 1906-08. Ibid. 14:201. [33] Henning, W. L. 1939. J. Agr. Research 58:565. [34] Hickey, J. J. Unpublished. Univ. Wisconsin, Madison, 1955. [35] Hilder, R. A., M. H. Fohrman, and R. R. Graves. 1944. J. Dairy Sci. 27:981. [36] Hochbaum, H. A. 1944. The canvasback on a prairie marsh. Am. Wildlife Institute, Washington, D. C. [37] Ilancic, D. 1941. Vet. Arh. 11:425. [38] Johansson, I. 1932. Z. Tierzücht. Züchtungsbiol. 24:183. [39] Johansson, I. 1938. Lantbruks-Högskol. Ann. 5:179. [40] Johansson, I., and A. Hansson. 1943. Ibid. 11:145. [41] Karol, J. J. 1928. Biol. Bull. 55:151. [42] Kennedy, J. F., and R. A. Bettenay. 1950. Australian J. Agr. Research 1:76. [43] King, H. D. 1927. Wilhelm Roux' Arch. Entwicklungsmech. Organ. 112:61. [44] Krallinger, H. 1930. Züchtungskunde 5:490. [45] Krizenecky, J. 1935. Sbornik Ceske Akad. Zemedelske 10:51. [46] Landmark, L. 1924. Norsk. Landmbl. 43:166. [47] Latham, R. M. 1942. Penna. Game News 13:6. [48] Lawrence, P. S. 1941. Quart. Rev. Biol. 16:35. [49] Levi, W. M. 1941. The pigeon. R. L. Bryan, Columbia, S. Carolina. [50] Little, C. C. 1948. J. Heredity 39:181. [51] Ljutikov, K. M. 1935. Problemy Zhivotnovodstva 2:49. [52] Lush, J. L., J. M. Jones, and W. H. Dameron. 1930. Texas Agr. Expt. Sta. Bull. 407. [53] MacDowell, E. C., and E. M. Lord. 1925. Proc. Soc. Exptl. Biol. Med. 22:389. [54] McCabe, R. A., and A. S. Hawkins. 1946. Am. Midland Naturalist 36:1. [55] McPhee, H. C. 1927. J. Agr. Research 34:715. [56] Murie, O. J. 1951. The elk of North America. Wildlife Management Institute, Washington, D. C. [57] Murray, G. N. 1941. Onderstepoort J. Vet. Sci. Animal Ind. 16:331. [58] Paget, R. F. 1943. Brit. Goat Soc. Monthly J. 36:57. [59] Parkes, A. S. 1923. Biometrika 15:373. [60] Pearson, A. M., and G. C. Moore. 1941. Alabama Conservation 1:8. [61] Pictet, A. 1941. Verhandl. schweiz. naturforsch. Ges. 121:161. [62] Riemann, A. T. 1948. Mdrskr. Dyrl. 59:248. [63] Roberts, E. J. 1930. J. Agr. Sci. 20:359. [64] Roberts, E., and W. W. Yapp. 1927-28. Illinois Agr. Expt. Sta. Rept. 175. [65] Romic, S. 1943. Vet. Arh. 13:199. [66] Romic, S. 1947. Ibid. 17:1. [67] Sawin, P. B., and D. S. Gadbois. 1947. Genetics 32:286. [68] Schein, M. N. 1950. Am. Naturalist 84:489. [69] Sheldon, W. G. 1949. J. Mammal. 30:236. [70] Southern, H. N. 1940. Ann. Appl. Biol. 27:509. [71] U. S. National Office of Vital Statistics. 1961. Vital statistics of the United States, 1959. U. S. Dept. of Health, Education, and Welfare, Washington, D. C. [72] Venge, O. 1950. Acta Zool. (Stockholm) 31:1. [73] Venge, O. 1953. Ibid. 34:293. [74] Venge, O. Unpublished. Royal Agricultural College of Sweden, Uppsala, 1953. [75] Vernon, E. H. 1948. J. Animal Sci. 7:516. [76] Vladescu, D. 1937. Rev. vet. militaire 8:157. [77] Weldon, W. F. R. 1906. Biometrika 5:436. [78] White, R. G., and J. A. F. Roberts. 1927. Welsh J. Agr. 3:70. [79] Whitney, L. F. 1939. J. Heredity 30:388. [80] Williams, C., G. F. Godfrey, and R. B. Thompson. 1951. Poultry Sci. 30:599. [81] Wilson, S. G. 1946. J. Agr. Sci. 36:246. [82] Wriedt, C. 1930. Nord. Jordbrugsforskn. 411.

119. ADULT SEX RATIOS: MAMMALS AND BIRDS

Sex ratios vary widely with geographical area, time of year, and population conditions. Values in parentheses are ranges, estimate "b" (cf. Introduction).

	Order	Species	No. of Subjects	Sex Ratio % males	Reference
	(A)	(B)	(C)	(D)	(E)
		Mammalia			
1	Carnivora	*Felis concolor*	1958	48.0	32
2		*Martes americana*	1183	61.6	30
3		*M. martes*	462	50.2	16
4		*Meles meles*	24	54.2(33.9-74.5)	25
5		*Mustela erminea*	84	57.1(46.3-67.9)	25
6		*M. nivalis*	80	72.5(62.6-82.4)	25
7		*M. vison*	248	51.2	26
8		*Phoca groenlandica*	1414	51.0(48.3-53.7)	9
9		*Procyon lotor*	256	52.0(45.8-58.2)	29
10		*Urocyon cinereoargenteus*	256	60.9	26
11		*Vulpes fulva*	100	52.0	26
12	Rodentia	*Castor canadensis*	207	52.2(45.3-59.1)	5
13		*Microtus* sp.	1036	57.2(54.1-60.3)	6
14		*Ondatra zibethica*	9304	56.0(55.0-57.0)	10
15		*Rattus norvegicus*	3937	42.7(41.1-44.3)	28
16		*R. rattus*	139,528	38.4(38.1-38.7)	7
17		*Sciurus niger*	1104	50.5	2
18	Lagomorpha	*Lepus americanus*	1625	54.0(51.5-56.5)	1
19		*Sylvilagus floridanus*	13,431	51.6	27
20	Chiroptera	*Myotis lucifugus*	3703	72.5(71.0-74.0)	15
21		*M. sodalis*	2289	51.4(49.3-53.5)	15
22		*Pipistrellus subflavus*	214	73.5(67.5-79.5)	15
		Aves			
23	Passeriformes	*Agelaius* sp.	420	76.9(72.7-81.1)	17
24		*Corvus brachyrhynchos*	401	53.4	11
25		*Melospiza melodia*	465	51.2	24
26		*Quiscalus* sp.	412	30.3(25.8-34.8)	19
27		*Sturnus* sp.	2522	68.0	19
28		*Zonotrichia leucophrys*	492	61.2	13
29	Galliformes	*Bonasa umbellus*	2266	42.5[1]	8
30		*Centrocercus urophasianus*	1881	50.2(48-52)	14
31		*Colinus virginianus*	7521	59.0	4
32		*Lophortyx californica*	511	58	12
33		*Pedioecetes phasianellus*	103	63(54-72)	3
34		*Perdix perdix*	388	60(58-62)	21,22
35		*Phasianus colchicus*	606	26	20
36		*Tympanuchus pallidicinctus*	432	47	18
37	Anseriformes	*Anas acuta*	2254	34	23
38		*A. platyrhynchos*	8805	52	31

/1/ Based on identification of birds flushed.

Contributors: (a) Venge, Ole, (b) Hickey, Joseph J., (c) Emlen, John T., Jr.

References: [1] Aldous, C. M. 1937. J. Mammal. 18:46. [2] Allen, D. L. 1943. Mich. Dept. Conservation Game Div. Publ. 100:134. [3] Ammann, G. A. 1947. Summary of sharptail population data for Drummond Island, Michigan. Michigan Dept. of Conservation, Lansing. [4] Bennitt, R. 1951. Missouri Conservation Comm. Tech. Bull. 2. [5] Bradt, G. W. 1938. J. Mammal. 19:139. [6] Brambell, F. W. R., and I. W. Rowlands. 1936. Trans. Roy. Soc. (London), B, 226:71. [7] Buxton, P. A. 1936. J. Animal Ecol. 5:53. [8] Darrow, R. W. 1947. In G. Bump, et al., ed. The ruffed grouse. N. Y. State Conservation Dept., Albany. [9] Dorofejev, S. V. 1936. Compt. rend. acad. sci. U.R.S.S. 11:47. [10] Dozier, H. L., and R. W. Allen. 1942. J. Wildlife Management 6:294. [11] Emlen, J. T., Jr. 1936. Bird-Banding 7(2):83. [12] Emlen, J. T., Jr. 1940. J. Wildlife Management 4:92. [13] Emlen, J. T., Jr. 1943. Condor 45(5):196. [14] Girard, G. L. 1937. Univ. Wyoming Publs. 3(1):1. [15] Griffin, D. R. 1940. J. Mammal. 21:181. [16] Lampio, T. 1951. Finnish Foundation Game Preservation

continued

119. ADULT SEX RATIOS: MAMMALS AND BIRDS

Papers Game Research Inst. (Helsinki) 7:3. [17] Lawrence, P. S. 1941. Quart. Rev. Biol. 16:35. [18] Lee, L. 1950. J. Wildlife Management 14:475. [19] Mayr, E. 1939. Am. Naturalist 73:156. [20] McCabe, R. A. 1949. Univ. Wisconsin Summaries Doctoral Dissertations 10:231. [21] McCabe, R. A., and A. S. Hawkins. 1946. Am. Midland Naturalist 36:1. [22] Middleton, A. D. 1935. J. Animal Ecol. 4:137. [23] Munro, J. A. 1944. Can. J. Research 22:60. [24] Nice, M. M. 1937. Trans. Linnaean Soc. N. Y. 4:173. [25] Pelseneer, P. 1925. Acad. roy. Belg. Classe sci. Mém. 8:1. [26] Petrides, G. A. 1950. Am. Midland Naturalist 43:355. [27] Petrides, G. A. 1951. Ibid. 46:312. [28] Schein, M. N. 1950. Am. Naturalist 84:489. [29] Stuewer, F. W. 1943. J. Wildlife Management 7:60. [30] Yeager, L. E. 1950. Trans. North Am. Wildlife Conf. 15:319. [31] Yocum, C. F. 1949. Condor 51:222. [32] Young, S. P. 1946. The puma, mysterious American cat. American Wildlife Institute, Washington, D. C. p. 109.

120. HYBRID SEX RATIOS: MAMMALS, BIRDS, AND INSECTS

	Order	Parental Species		Hybrid Progeny			Reference
		Male	Female	No. of Males	No. of Females	Sex Ratio % males	
	(A)	(B)	(C)	(D)	(E)	(F)	(G)
			Mammalia				
1	Artiodactyla	*Bison bison*	*Bos taurus*	17	91	15.7	1,3,4,9
2		*Bos grunniens*	*B. taurus*	13	23	36.1	3,4
3		*B. taurus*	*Bison bison*	45	100	31.0	1,3,4
4	Perissodactyla	*Equus asinus*	*E. caballus*	607	761	44.4	1
5	Rodentia	*Cavia rufescens*	*C. porcellus*	14	23	37.8	5
6		*C. porcellus*	F_1 hybrid[1]	31	52	37.3	5
7		*Mus bactrianus*	*M. musculus*	104	101	50.7	7,8
8		*M. musculus*	*M. bactrianus*	29	31	48.3	7,8
			Aves				
9	Columbiformes	*Columba guinea*	*C. livia*	8	14	36.4	17
10		*C. livia*	*Streptopelia risoria*	353	10	97.2	10,17,18
11		*S. chinensis*	*S. risoria*	26	19	57.8	17
12		*S. humilis*	*S. risoria*	15	18	45.4	17,18
13		*S. orientalis*	*S. turtur*	15	5	75	17,18
14		*S. risoria*	*S. humilis*	18	18	50	18
15		*S. risoria*	*S. orientalis*	68	49	58.1	17,18
16		*S. senegalensis*	*S. risoria*	24	24	50	17,18
17		*S. turtur*	*S. orientalis*	7	14	33.3	18
18		*S. turtur*	*S. risoria*	41	43	48.8	18
19		*Zenaidura carolinensis*	*S. risoria*	28	0	100	17,18
20	Galliformes	*Chrysolophus amherstiae*	*C. pictus*	29	37	43.9	16
21		*C. pictus*	*C. amherstiae*	13	11	54.2	16
22		*Gallus domesticus*	*Phasianus torquatus*	66	69	49	14
23		*Gennaeus swinhoii*	*G. nycthemerus*	8	14	36.4	16
24		*P. colchicus*	*Gallus domesticus*	100	1	99.1	9,14
25		*P. torquatus*	*G. domesticus*	23	6	79.3	14
26		*P. torquatus*	*P. reevesi*	188	17	91.7	13,16
27		*Tetrao tetrix*	*T. urgallus*	40	8	83.3	9
28	Anseriformes	*Anas fulvigula*	*A. platyrhynchos*	17	14	54.8	13
29		*A. platyrhynchos*	*Cairina moschata*	106	88	54.6	2,17
30		*C. moschata*	*A. platyrhynchos*	160	125	56.1	2,17
			Insecta				
31	Diptera	*Drosophila arizonensis*	*D. aldrichi*	0	...	0	11
32		*D. arizonensis*	*D. mulleri*	...	0	100	11
33		*D. montana*	*D. texana*	172	168	50.5	12
34		*D. montana*	*D. virilis*	884	891	49.8	12
35		*D. occidentalis*	*D. munda*	110	88	55.5	15

/1/ Offspring of *C. rufescens* and *C. porcellus*.

continued

120. HYBRID SEX RATIOS: MAMMALS, BIRDS, AND INSECTS

	Order	Parental Species		Hybrid Progeny			Reference
		Male	Female	No. of Males	No. of Females	Sex Ratio % males	
	(A)	(B)	(C)	(D)	(E)	(F)	(G)
			Insecta				
36	Diptera	*Drosophila persimilis*	*D. miranda*	...	...	50	11
37		*D. persimilis*	*D. pseudoobscura*	786	845	48.2	6
38		*D. pseudoobscura*	*D. miranda*	...	...	50	11
39		*D. simulans*	*D. melanogaster*	0	...	0	11
40		*D. subquinaria*	*D. munda*	169	172	49.6	15
41		*D. texana*	*D. montana*	531	53	90.9	12
42	Lepidoptera	*Calasymbolus astylus*	*Smerinthus ocellata*	25	0	100	1
43		*Chaerocampa elpenor*	*Deilephila galii*	>20	8	>71	1
44		*Clostera anachoreta*	*C. curtula*	21	2	91.3	1
45		*Lycia hirtaria*	*Nyssia graecaria*	65	0	100	1
46		*L. hirtaria*	*N. zonaria*	208	0	100	1
47		*L. hirtaria*	*Poecilopsis isabellae*	38	32	54.3	1
48		*L. hirtaria*	*P. pomonaria*	98	92	51.5	1
49		*N. zonaria*	*L. hirtaria*	181	279	39.3	1
50		*N. zonaria*	*P. pomonaria*	44	102	30.1	1
51		*Oporabia dilutata*	*O. autumnata*	52	47	52.5	1
52		*P. lapponaria*	*N. zonaria*	155	3	98.1	1
53		*P. pomonaria*	*L. hirtaria*	276	89	75.6	1
54		*P. pomonaria*	*N. zonaria*	161	7	95.8	1
55		*P. pomonaria*	*P. lapponaria*	38	39	49.3	1
56		*Saturnia pavonia*	*S. pyri*	106	100	51.4	1
57		*S. pavonia*	*S. spini*	113	100	53	1
58		*Smerinthus atlanticus*	*Amorpha austauti*	45	5	90	1
59		*S. ocellata*	*A. austauti*	93	7	93	1
60		*S. ocellata*	*A. populi*	490	10	98	1
61		*Tephrosia bistortata*	*T. crepuscularia*	313	327	48.9	1
62		*T. crepuscularia*	*T. bistortata*	378	12	96.9	1

Contributor: Irwin, M. R.

References: [1] Craft, W. A. 1938. Quart. Rev. Biol. 13:19. [2] Crew, F. A. E., and P. C. Koller. 1935-36. Proc. Roy. Soc. Edinburgh, B, 56:210. [3] Deakin, A., G. W. Muir, and A. G. Smith. 1935. Can. Dept. Agr. Publ. 479, Tech. Bull. 2. [4] Deakin, A., et al. 1941. Progress report of Wainwright experiment. Canada Dept. of Agriculture, Ottawa. [5] Detlefson, J. A. 1914. Carnegie Inst. Wash. Publ. 2. [6] Dobzhansky, T. 1941. Genetics and the origin of species. Ed. 2. Columbia Univ. Press, New York. [7] Green, C. V. 1930. Am. Naturalist 64:540. [8] Green, C. V. 1935. Ibid. 69:19. [9] Haldane, J. B. S. 1922. J. Genet. 12:101. [10] Painter, T. S., and L. J. Cole. 1943. J. Morphol. 72:411. [11] Patterson, J. T. 1942. Univ. Texas Publ. 4228:7. [12] Patterson, J. T., and A. B. Griffin. 1944. Ibid. 4445:212. [13] Phillips, J. C. 1921. Genetics 6:366. [14] Sandness, G. C., and W. Landauer. 1938. Am. Naturalist 72:180. [15] Sears, J. W. 1947. Univ. Texas Publ. 4720:137. [16] Thomas, R. H., and J. S. Huxley. 1927. J. Genet. 18:233. [17] University of Wisconsin Department of Genetics and Department of Poultry Husbandry. Unpublished, 1952. [18] Whitman, C. O. 1919. Carnegie Inst. Wash. Publ. 257(2).

121. SEX RATIOS: AQUATIC ANIMALS

Values are percentage of females in a natural population.

	Category	Species	Identity	Sex Ratio % females	Remarks	Reference
	(A)	(B)	(C)	(D)	(E)	(F)
				Sex Ratio Highly Variable		
1	Sex ratio varies with locality	*Mirounga angustirostris*	Marine mammal	11-71	Sex ratio high in breeding populations, low in outlying populations due to belligerence among adult males	3
2		*Trichoniscus biformatus*	Hygrophilic isopod	ca. 50-100	Dioecious in favorable habitats; parthenogenetic and tetraploid in unfavorable habitats	49
3		*Cyprinotus incongruens*	Freshwater ostracod	ca. 50-100	In Germany, hermaphroditic as well as parthenogenetic populations known; males frequently present in Hungary and Bohemia; males almost as abundant as females in North Africa	30
4		*Triops longicaudatus*	Freshwater notostracan	?-100	Bisexual over most of range; parthenogenetic or hermaphroditic in California and islands of Pacific	33
5		*Artemia salina*	Salt lake anostracan	?-100	Dioecious as well as (presumed) parthenogenetic populations known	55
6		*Eubranchipus vernalis*	Freshwater anostracan	33-60	Males predominate in some populations; females predominate in others	13
7		*Ostrea virginica*	Estuarine pelecypod	3-33	Populations contain males, females, hermaphrodites, and "undetermined" individuals; sexual inversion related to physiological and environmental factors	6, 8
8		*Craspedacusta sowerbii*	Freshwater hydromedusa	0-100	Most populations one sex or the other; only a few mixed populations reported	42
9	Sexes occupy different habitats	*Micropogon undulatus*	Estuarine teleost	43-78	Male spawning migration from estuaries precedes female spawning migration	53
10		*Gibbonsia elegans*	Marine teleost	49-92	Adult females more abundant in shallow waters than adult males	56
11		*Morone chrysops*	Freshwater teleost	ca. 0-ca. 100	Males and females migrate in unisexual schools to spawning grounds	44
12		*Osmerus mordax*	Freshwater teleost	0-66	Males predominate in streams immediately preceding and following spawning runs	22
13		*Perca flavescens*[1]	Freshwater teleost	0-100	Male schools appear to inhabit deeper water than do female schools	14
14		*Callinectes sapidus*[1]	Estuarine brachyuran	4-85	Females tend to inhabit more saline waters than do males, especially during colder weather	7, 17
15	Sex ratio seasonally variable	*Gambusia affinis*	Freshwater teleost	73-89	Apparent sex ratio (as determined by secondary sexual characters) increases during summer months	2
16		*Scyliorhinus caniculus*	Marine elasmobranch	40-80	Sex ratio low in winter, high in summer with local variations	19
17		*Callinectes sapidus*[1]	Estuarine brachyuran	18-50	Sex ratio in estuary declines during spring and summer spawning seasons when adult females apparently migrate to more saline waters	12
18		*Cambarus propinquus*	Freshwater astacuran	23-48	Females disappear from "active" population during period of oviposition	51
19		*Penaeus setiferus*	Estuarine penaeid	ca. 43-83	Sex ratio increases in inside (brackish) waters during spawning season	54
20		*Gammarus deubeni*	Brackish water amphipod	45-74	Temperature-controlled sex determination: spring young are males, summer young are females	28
21		*Urosalpinx cinerea*	Marine gastropod	47-95	Sex ratio increases during breeding season	9
22		*Lacuna pallidula*	Marine gastropod	39-ca. 100	Sex ratio lowest in August and September, increases regularly during year due to greater mortality of males	15
23		*Ostrea edulis*	Estuarine pelecypod	1-56	Sex ratio highest during early summer, decreases thereafter due primarily to sex change of individuals	41

/1/ Species included in several categories.

continued

121. SEX RATIOS: AQUATIC ANIMALS

	Category	Species	Identity	Sex Ratio % females	Remarks	Reference
	(A)	(B)	(C)	(D)	(E)	(F)
				Sex Ratio Relatively Constant		
24	Sex ratio changes gradually during lifetime	*Neothunnus macropterus*	Marine teleost	28-41	Males predominate in upper size groups (females apparently have higher mortality rate in upper size groups)	39
25		*Amphigonopterus aurora*	Tide-pool teleost	46-66	Sex ratio increases during most of life (females appear to outlive males)	23
26		*Gambusia holbrooki*	Freshwater teleost	49-ca. 90	Sex ratio increases during life (males less viable than females)	16
27		*Leucichthys artedii*	Freshwater teleost	42-100	Sex ratio increases throughout life due to greater viability of females	20
28		*Lepibema chrysops*	Freshwater teleost	0-69	Sex ratio decreases in upper age groups (males appear to outlive females)	45
29		*Perca flavescens*[1]	Freshwater teleost	17-100	Sex ratio increases with age due to differential destruction of males (by fishery)	27
30		*Eubranchipus oregonus*	Freshwater anostracan	43-100	Females predominate in upper age groups (outlive males)	10
31		*Patella vulgata*	Marine gastropod	6-65	Sex ratio increases throughout life due to sex reversal (protandry)	40
32		*Lioplax subcarinata*	Freshwater gastropod	63-81	Sex ratio increases during winter due to differential mortality of sexes (males live 1 year, females 2 years)	48
33	Males predominate	*Parathunnus sibi*	Marine teleost	ca. 40	Weighted (size) modes indicate constant sex ratio throughout size range studied	26
34		*Lepomis* spp. (hybrids)[2]	Freshwater teleosts	3-11	Males predominate in populations of *L. cyanellus*, *L. gibbosus*, and *L. macrochirus*, and females are almost absent from the three types of interspecific hybrids	1
35		*Perca flavescens*[1]	Freshwater teleost	27-43	Excess of males may be due to differential mortality, not due to biased sampling or differential fishing pressure	14
36		*Lampetra planeri*	Freshwater cyclostome	35-47	Males predominate in spawning populations with local and annual variation	18
37		*Panulirus guttatus*	Marine palinuran	ca. 10	Predominance of males may be due to differential mortality or utilization of different habitat by females	47
38		*Atya scabra*	Freshwater caridean	21-39	Adult males appear to predominate in primary habitat, with females mainly inhabiting marginal areas	11
39	Sexes in approximately equal numbers	*Ondatra zibethica*	Freshwater mammal	46-51	At low population densities, males more numerous; at high population densities, sexes subequal or females predominate	4
40		*Acipenser fulvescens*	Freshwater chondrostean	56-93	Sex ratio nearly equal up to 59 inches (29 years); beyond this, sex ratio increases due to greater longevity of female	43
41		*Cancer magister*	Marine brachyuran	ca. 50	Sex ratio nearly equal in larval, postlarval, and adult populations, although some segregation of sexes is indicated in commercial catches	34
42		*Panulirus interruptus*	Marine palinuran	21-71	Sex ratio varies somewhat with each catching procedure, but overall data give nearly equal ratio	32
43		*Mysis relicta*	Freshwater schizopod	51-93	Sex ratio nearly equal during most of life, although females may outlive males	31
44		*Pseudocalanus minutus*	Marine copepod	ca. 50	Sex ratio nearly equal through copepodite stages; increases abruptly thereafter (presumably due to death of males)	35
45		*Streptocephalus sealii*	Freshwater anostracan	33-60	Either sex may predominate slightly (especially females in winter)	38
46		*Asterias rubens*	Marine echinoderm	47-57	Sex ratio increases slightly during spring months; may be due to differential mortality	52

/1/ Species included in several categories. /2/ Apparently an exception to "Haldane's rule," i.e., in cases of interspecific hybridization, when one sex in the offspring is absent, rare, or sterile, that sex is the heterogametic one [55].

continued

121. SEX RATIOS: AQUATIC ANIMALS

	Category	Species	Identity	Sex Ratio % females	Remarks	Reference
	(A)	(B)	(C)	(D)	(E)	(F)
				Sex Ratio Relatively Constant		
47	Males rare	*Lebistes reticulatus*	Freshwater teleost	ca. 67	Irrespective of original sex composition, artificial populations always stabilize at same sex ratio	5
48		*Carcharhinus milberti*	Marine elasmobranch	95	Males rare in catches and presumed rare in breeding populations	46
49		*Potamocypris smaragdina*	Freshwater ostracod	ca. 50-100	Males normally absent (females parthenogenetic, occasionally up to 50%)	21
50		*Oithona similis*	Marine copepod	87-98	Males never abundant, almost absent in late winter	35
51		*Pleuroxus hammulatus*	Freshwater cladoceran	ca. 99	Males almost unknown	29
52		*Pomatiopsis cincinnatiensis*	Semi-aquatic gastropod	61-87	Sex ratio discrepancy apparently not due to differential longevity	50
53	Males unknown	*Mollienisia formosa*	Freshwater teleost	100	Females inseminated by males of other congeneric species	24
54		*Stygobromus spinosus*	Subterranean amphipod	100	Females presumably parthenogenetic	25
55		*Candona caudata*	Freshwater ostracod	100	Females presumably parthenogenetic	21
56		*Caenestheriella gynecia*	Freshwater conchostracan	100	Females presumably parthenogenetic	37
57		*Campeloma rufum*	Freshwater gastropod	100	Females parthenogenetic	36
58		Bdelloidea species	Freshwater rotifers	100	Females parthenogenetic	42
59		Gastrotricha species	Freshwater gastrotrichans	100	Females parthenogenetic	42

Contributor: Darnell, Rezneat M.

References: [1] Bailey, R. M., and K. F. Lagler. 1938. Papers Mich. Acad. Sci. 23:577. [2] Barney, R. L., and B. J. Anson. 1921. Ecology 2(2):53. [3] Bartholomew, G. A. 1952. Univ. Calif. (Berkeley) Publs. Zool. 47(15):369. [4] Beer, J. R., and W. Truax. 1950. J. Wildlife Management 14(3):324. [5] Breder, C. M., and C. W. Coates. 1932. Copeia, p. 147. [6] Burkenroad, M. D. 1937. J. Marine Research (Sears Foundation) 1:75. [7] Churchill, E. P., Jr. 1919. U. S. Bur. Fisheries Bull. 36:95. [8] Coe, W. R. 1938. Biol. Bull. 74:64. [9] Cole, H. A. 1941. Nature 147:116. [10] Coopey, R. W. 1950. Trans. Am. Microscop. Soc. 69:125. [11] Darnell, R. M. 1956. Am. Midland Naturalist 55:131. [12] Darnell, R. M. 1959. Trans. Am. Fisheries Soc. 88:294. [13] Dexter, R. W., and C. Kuehnle. 1951. Ohio J. Sci. 51:73. [14] Eschmeyer, R. W. 1938. Papers Mich. Acad. Sci. 23:611. [15] Gallien, L., and M. de Larambergue. 1938. Trav. sta. zool. Wimereux 13:293. [16] Geiser, S. W. 1924. Biol. Bull. 47(3):175. [17] Gunter, G. 1950. Univ. Texas Inst. Marine Sci. Publ. 1(2):7. [18] Hardisty, M. W. 1954. Nature 173:874. [19] Harris, J. E. 1952. J. Marine Biol. Assoc. United Kingdom 31(2):269. [20] Hile, R. 1936. U. S. Bur. Fisheries Bull. 48(19):211. [21] Hoff, C. C. 1942. Illinois Biol. Monographs 19(1-2):1. [22] Hoover, E. E. 1936. Copeia (2):85. [23] Hubbs, C. L. 1921. Biol. Bull. 40(4):181. [24] Hubbs, C. L., and L. C. Hubbs. 1946. Genetics 31:218. [25] Hubrecht, L. 1943. Am. Midland Naturalist 29:683. [26] Iverson, E. S. 1955. U. S. Fish Wildlife Service Spec. Sci. Rept. Fisheries 162:1. [27] Jobes, F. W. 1952. U. S. Fish Wildlife Service Fishery Bull. 70:205. [28] Kinne, O. 1959. Veröffentl. Inst. Meeresforsch. Bremerhaven 6:177. [29] Kiser, R. W. 1950. Trans. Am. Microscop. Soc. 69:243. [30] Klie, W. 1926. Biologie der Tiere Deutschlands. Gebrüder Bornträger, Berlin. v. 22, pt. 16. [31] Larkin, P. A. 1948. Fisheries Research Board Can. Bull. 78:1. [32] Lindberg, R. G. 1955. Univ. Calif. (Berkeley) Publs. Zool. 59(6):157. [33] Longhurst, A. R. 1954. Bull. Brit. Museum Zool. 3:1. [34] MacKay, D. C. G. 1942. Fisheries Research Board Can. Bull. 62:1. [35] Marshall, S. M. 1949. J. Marine Biol. Assoc. United Kingdom 28:45. [36] Mattox, N. T. 1938. J. Morphol. 62:243.

continued

121. SEX RATIOS: AQUATIC ANIMALS

[37] Mattox, N. T. 1950. Trans. Am. Microscop. Soc. 69:50. [38] Moore, W. G. 1955. Ecology 36(2):176. [39] Murphy, G. L., and R. S. Shomura. 1955. U. S. Fish Wildlife Service Spec. Sci. Rept. Fisheries 137:1. [40] Orton, J. H. 1928. J. Marine Biol. Assoc. United Kingdom, n.s. 15:851. [41] Orton, J. H. 1936. Mém. musée hist. nat. Belg., Ser. 2, 3:997. [42] Pennak, R. W. 1953. Freshwater invertebrates of the United States. Ronald Press, New York. [43] Probst, R. T., and E. L. Cooper. 1954. Trans. Am. Fisheries Soc. 84:207. [44] Riggs, C. D. 1955. Indiana Lakes and Streams Invest. 4(3):87. [45] Sigler, W. F. 1949. Iowa State Coll. Agr. Expt. Sta. Research Bull. 366:203. [46] Springer, S. 1940. Copeia (3):188. [47] Sutcliffe, W. H., Jr. 1953. Ecology 34(4):794. [48] Van Cleave, H. J., and R. Chambers. 1935. Am. Midland Naturalist 16:913. [49] Vandel, A. 1940. Bull. biol. France et Belg. 74:94. [50] Van der Schalie, H., and D. S. Dundee. 1955. Trans. Am. Fisheries Soc. 74(2):119. [51] Van Devanter, W. C. 1937. Illinois Biol. Monographs 15(3):1. [52] Vevers, H. G. 1952. J. Marine Biol. Assoc. United Kingdom 31:35. [53] Wallace, D. H. 1940-41. Trans Am. Fisheries Soc. 70:475. [54] Weymouth, F. W., M. J. Lindner, and W. W. Anderson. 1933. U. S. Bur. Fisheries Bull. 14:1. [55] White, M. J. D. 1948. Animal cytology and evolution. Cambridge Univ. Press, London. [56] Williams, G. C. 1954. Copeia (4):267.

122. EXPECTATION OF LIFE AT VARIOUS AGES: MAN, UNITED STATES

For the years 1900-1902 and 1909-1911, data were derived from death registrations in 10 states and the District of Columbia; for 1919-1921, from death registrations in 34 states and the District of Columbia; for 1929-1931, 1939-1941, 1949-1951, 1953, and 1959, for death registrations in the entire continental United States.

	Age yr	Average Remaining Lifetime, yr							
		1900-1902	1909-1911	1919-1921	1929-1931	1939-1941	1949-1951	1953	1959
	(A)	(B)	(C)	(D)	(E)	(F)	(G)	(H)	(I)
	White Male								
1	Birth[1]	48.2	50.2	56.3	59.1	62.8	66.3	66.8	67.3
2	1	54.6	56.3	60.2	62.2	65.0	67.4	67.7	68.2
3	5	54.5	55.4	58.3	59.4	61.7	63.8	64.0	64.4
4	10	50.6	51.3	54.2	55.0	57.0	59.0	59.2	59.6
5	15	46.3	46.9	49.7	50.4	52.3	54.2	54.4	54.7
6	20	42.2	42.7	45.6	46.0	47.8	49.5	49.8	50.1
7	25	38.5	38.8	41.6	41.8	43.3	44.9	45.2	45.5
8	30	34.9	34.9	37.7	37.5	38.8	40.3	40.6	40.8
9	35	31.3	31.1	33.7	33.3	34.4	35.7	35.9	36.1
10	40	27.7	27.4	29.9	29.2	30.0	31.2	31.4	31.5
11	45	24.2	23.9	26.0	25.3	25.9	26.9	27.0	27.2
12	50	20.8	20.4	22.2	21.5	22.0	22.8	23.0	23.0
13	55	17.4	17.0	18.6	18.0	18.3	19.1	19.2	19.2
14	60	14.4	14.0	15.3	14.7	15.1	15.8	15.8	15.8
15	65	11.5	11.3	12.2	11.8	12.1	12.8	12.9	12.7
16	70	9.0	8.8	9.5	9.2	9.4	10.1	10.3	10.1
17	75	6.8	6.8	7.3	7.0	7.2	7.8	7.9	7.9
18	80	5.1	5.1	5.5	5.3	5.4	5.9	6.1	5.9
19	85	3.8	3.9	4.1	4.0	4.0	4.4	4.7	4.5
20	90	2.9	3.0	3.2	3.0	3.1	3.3	...	...
	White Female								
21	Birth[1]	51.1	53.6	58.5	62.7	67.3	72.0	72.9	73.9
22	1	56.3	58.7	61.5	64.9	68.9	72.8	73.6	74.4
23	5	56.0	57.7	59.4	62.2	65.6	69.1	69.8	70.7
24	10	52.2	53.6	55.2	57.7	60.9	64.3	65.0	65.8
25	15	47.8	49.1	50.7	53.0	56.1	59.4	60.1	60.9
26	20	43.8	44.9	46.5	48.5	51.4	54.6	55.3	56.0
27	25	40.1	40.9	42.6	44.3	46.8	49.8	50.5	51.2
28	30	36.4	37.0	38.7	40.0	42.2	45.0	45.7	46.4

/1/ Increase in average remaining lifetime mainly due to decreased infant mortality.

continued

122. EXPECTATION OF LIFE AT VARIOUS AGES: MAN, UNITED STATES

	Age yr	Average Remaining Lifetime, yr							
		1900-1902	1909-1911	1919-1921	1929-1931	1939-1941	1949-1951	1953	1959
	(A)	(B)	(C)	(D)	(E)	(F)	(G)	(H)	(I)
		White Female							
29	35	32.8	33.1	34.9	35.7	37.7	40.3	40.9	41.6
30	40	29.2	29.3	30.9	31.5	33.3	35.6	36.2	36.9
31	45	25.5	25.5	27.0	27.4	28.9	31.1	31.7	32.3
32	50	21.9	21.7	23.1	23.4	24.7	26.8	27.3	27.8
33	55	18.4	18.2	19.4	19.6	20.7	22.6	23.0	23.5
34	60	15.3	14.9	15.9	16.1	17.0	18.6	19.0	19.4
35	65	12.2	12.0	12.8	12.8	13.6	15.0	15.3	15.6
36	70	9.6	9.4	9.9	10.0	10.5	11.7	12.0	12.1
37	75	7.3	7.2	7.6	7.6	7.9	8.9	9.1	9.2
38	80	5.5	5.4	5.7	5.6	5.9	6.6	6.7	6.5
39	85	4.1	4.1	4.2	4.2	4.3	4.8	5.1	4.4
40	90	3.0	3.0	3.2	3.2	3.2	3.5	...	...
		Nonwhite Male							
41	Birth[1]	32.5	34.1	47.1	47.6	52.3	58.9	59.7	60.9
42	1	42.5	42.5	51.6	51.1	55.9	61.1	61.7	63.0
43	5	45.0	44.3	50.2	48.7	53.0	57.7	58.3	59.5
44	10	41.9	40.7	46.0	44.3	48.3	53.0	53.5	54.7
45	15	38.3	36.8	41.8	39.8	43.7	48.2	48.8	49.9
46	20	35.1	33.5	38.4	36.0	39.5	43.7	44.2	45.3
47	25	32.2	30.4	35.5	32.7	35.7	39.5	39.9	40.9
48	30	29.3	27.3	32.5	29.5	32.1	35.3	35.7	36.5
49	35	26.2	24.4	29.5	26.4	28.5	31.2	31.6	32.3
50	40	23.1	21.6	26.5	23.4	25.1	27.3	27.6	28.3
51	45	20.1	18.9	23.6	20.6	21.9	23.6	23.8	24.5
52	50	17.3	16.2	20.5	17.9	19.1	20.3	20.4	20.9
53	55	14.7	13.8	17.5	15.5	16.6	17.4	17.5	17.6
54	60	12.6	11.7	14.7	13.2	14.4	14.9	14.9	14.9
55	65	10.4	9.7	12.1	10.9	12.2	12.8	12.7	12.5
56	70	8.3	8.0	9.6	8.8	10.1	10.7	11.2	11.2
57	75	6.6	6.6	7.6	7.0	8.2	8.8	9.5	10.4
58	80	5.1	5.5	5.8	5.4	6.6	7.1	8.0	9.4
59	85	4.0	4.5	4.5	4.3	5.3	5.4	6.9	8.3
60	90	3.2	4.0	3.6	3.4	4.2	3.8	...	...
		Nonwhite Female							
61	Birth[1]	35.0	37.7	46.9	49.5	55.6	62.7	64.4	66.2
62	1	43.5	45.2	50.4	52.3	58.5	64.4	66.1	68.0
63	5	46.0	46.4	48.7	49.8	55.4	60.9	62.6	64.4
64	10	43.0	42.8	44.5	45.3	50.8	56.2	57.8	59.6
65	15	39.8	39.2	40.4	40.9	46.1	51.4	53.0	54.7
66	20	36.9	36.1	37.2	37.2	42.0	46.8	48.3	50.0
67	25	33.9	33.0	34.4	33.9	38.2	42.4	43.7	45.3
68	30	30.7	29.6	31.5	30.7	34.4	38.0	39.3	40.7
69	35	27.5	26.4	28.6	27.5	30.7	33.8	35.0	36.3
70	40	24.4	23.3	25.6	24.3	27.2	29.8	30.9	32.1
71	45	21.4	20.4	22.6	21.4	23.9	26.1	26.9	28.1
72	50	18.7	17.7	19.8	18.6	21.0	22.7	23.4	24.3
73	55	15.9	15.0	17.1	16.3	18.4	19.6	20.3	20.8
74	60	13.6	12.8	14.7	14.2	16.1	17.0	17.4	17.8
75	65	11.4	10.8	12.4	12.2	13.9	14.5	14.7	15.2
76	70	9.6	9.2	10.3	10.4	11.8	12.3	12.9	13.3
77	75	7.9	7.6	8.4	8.6	9.8	10.2	10.8	12.0
78	80	6.5	6.1	6.6	6.9	8.0	8.2	9.1	10.2
79	85	5.1	5.1	5.2	5.5	6.4	6.2	7.6	8.6
80	90	4.0	4.5	4.1	4.2	5.0	4.1	...	...
		Total Population							
81	Birth[1]	49.2	51.5	56.4	59.2	63.6	68.1	68.8	69.7
82	1	55.2	57.1	59.9	61.9	65.8	69.2	69.8	70.5
83	5	55.0	56.2	58.0	59.3	62.5	65.5	66.1	66.8
84	10	51.1	52.2	53.8	54.8	57.8	60.7	61.3	62.0

/1/ Increase in average remaining lifetime mainly due to decreased infant mortality.

continued

122. EXPECTATION OF LIFE AT VARIOUS AGES: MAN, UNITED STATES

	Age yr	Average Remaining Lifetime, yr 1900-1902	1909-1911	1919-1921	1929-1931	1939-1941	1949-1951	1953	1959
	(A)	(B)	(C)	(D)	(E)	(F)	(G)	(H)	(I)
		Total Population							
85	15	46.8	47.7	49.4	50.3	53.1	55.9	56.5	57.1
86	20	42.8	43.5	45.3	45.9	48.5	51.2	51.7	52.4
87	25	39.1	39.6	41.5	41.9	44.1	46.6	47.1	47.7
88	30	35.5	35.7	37.7	37.8	39.7	41.9	42.4	43.0
89	35	31.9	31.9	33.9	33.7	35.3	37.3	37.8	38.3
90	40	28.3	28.2	30.1	29.7	31.0	32.8	33.2	33.7
91	45	24.8	24.5	26.3	25.8	26.9	28.5	28.9	29.3
92	50	21.3	21.0	22.5	22.1	23.0	24.4	24.7	25.1
93	55	17.9	17.6	18.9	18.5	19.3	20.6	20.9	21.1
94	60	14.8	14.4	15.5	15.2	15.9	17.0	17.3	17.5
95	65	11.9	11.6	12.5	12.2	12.8	13.8	14.0	14.1
96	70	9.3	9.1	9.7	9.6	10.0	10.9	11.2	11.2
97	75	7.1	7.0	7.5	7.3	7.6	8.4	8.6	8.7
98	80	5.3	5.3	5.6	5.5	5.7	6.3	6.5	6.4
99	85	4.0	4.0	4.2	4.2	4.3	4.7	5.1	4.7

Contributor: Grove, Robert D.

References: [1] Sirken, M. G., and G. A. Carlson. 1954. U. S. Public Health Service Vital Statistics Spec. Repts. 41(1):30. [2] U. S. National Office of Vital Statistics. 1961. Vital Statistics of the United States, 1959. U. S. Dept. of Health, Education, and Welfare, Washington, D. C.

123. EXPECTATION OF LIFE AT BIRTH: MAN, VARIOUS NATIONS AND REGIONS

	Region	Period	Expectation of Life, yr Male	Female
	(A)	(B)	(C)	(D)
	North America			
1	Barbados	1945-47	49.17	52.94
2	British Honduras	1944-48	44.99	48.97
3	Canada	1955-57	67.61	72.92
4	Costa Rica	1949-51	54.65	57.05
5	El Salvador	1949-51	49.94	52.40
6	Greenland	1946-51	32.17	37.49
7	Grenada	1945-47	47.22	52.46
8	Guadeloupe and Martinique	1951-55	55.4	59.2
9	Guatemala	1949-51	43.82	43.52
10	Haiti	1950	32.61	32.61
11	Hawaii	1949-51	67.76	71.29
12	Jamaica	1950-52	55.73	58.89
13	Mexico	1950	46.67	49.85
14	Panama	1952-54	60.41	63.09
15	Puerto Rico	1939-41	45.12	46.92
16	Trinidad and Tobago	1954-56	59.81	63.13
	United States			
17	Total	1959	66.5	73.0
18	Whites	1959	67.3	73.9
19	Nonwhites	1959	60.9	66.2
	South America			
20	Argentina	1947	56.9	61.4
21	Bolivia	1949-51	49.71	49.71
	Brazil			
22	Native-born	1940-50	39.3	45.5
23	Federal District	1949-51	49.80	55.96
24	British Guiana (excluding Amerindians)	1945-47	49.32	52.05
25	Chile	1952	49.84	53.89
26	Ecuador (Quito)	1949-51	50.37	53.70
27	Peru (Lima)	1940-43	46.10	46.10
28	Venezuela	1950-51	56.34	58.76
	Europe			
29	Austria	1949-51	61.91	66.97
30	Belgium	1946-49	62.04	67.26
31	Bulgaria (excluding southern Dobruja)	1925-28	45.92	46.64
32	Czechoslovakia	1958	67.23	72.30
33	Denmark (excluding Greenland and Faeroes Islands)	1951-55	69.87	72.60
34	Finland	1951-55	63.4	69.8
35	France	1959	67.0	73.6
	Germany			
36	Federal Republic[1]	1958-59	66.67	71.72
37	Soviet Zone	1956-57	66.34	71.03
38	Greece (excluding Dodecanese Islands)	1926-30	49.09	50.89
39	Hungary[1]	1958	65.12	69.36

/1/ Provisional.

continued

123. EXPECTATION OF LIFE AT BIRTH: MAN, VARIOUS NATIONS AND REGIONS

	Region	Period	Expectation of Life, yr	
			Male	Female
	(A)	(B)	(C)	(D)
	Europe			
40	Iceland	1941-50	66.1	70.3
41	Ireland	1950-52	64.53	67.08
42	Italy	1954-57	65.75	70.02
43	Luxemburg	1946-48	61.69	65.75
44	Malta and Gozo	1957	65.7	68.9
45	Netherlands	1953-55	71.0	73.9
46	Norway	1951-55	71.11	74.70
47	Poland	1958	62.8	68.9
48	Portugal	1957-58	59.8	65.0
49	Spain	1950	58.76	63.50
50	Sweden	1959	71.69	75.24
51	Switzerland	1948-53	66.36	70.85
	United Kingdom			
52	England and Wales	1959	68.1	73.8
53	Northern Ireland	1957-59	67.44	71.82
54	Scotland	1959	66.0	71.44
55	Union of Soviet Socialist Republics	1957-58	64	71
56	Yugoslavia	1952-54	56.92	59.33
	Africa			
57	Congo (Africans)	1950-52	37.64	40.00
58	Egypt	1936-38	36.65	41.48
	Guinea			
59	Rural	1954-55	30.5	30.5
60	Urban	1954-55	35.8	35.8
61	Ivory Coast (indigenes)	1956-58	35	35
62	Kenya (Europeans)	1946-49	63.8	69.3
63	Mauritius (excluding island dependencies)	1951-53	49.79	52.29
64	Reunion	1951-53	47.50	53.40
	Rhodesia and Nyasaland			
65	Europeans	1935-37	58.52	62.57
66	Indigenes	1953-55	48	49
	Union of South Africa			
67	Asians	1945-47	50.70	49.75
68	Colored[2]	1945-47	41.70	44.00
69	Whites	1945-47	63.78	68.31
	Asia			
70	Cambodia	1958-59	44.2	43.3
71	Ceylon	1954	60.3	59.4
72	Cyprus	1948-50	63.6	68.8
73	India	1941-50	32.45	31.66
74	Israel (Jews)	1959	70.23	72.26
75	Japan	1959	65.21	69.88
76	Korea	1938	47.20	50.59
77	Philippines	1946-49	48.81	53.36
78	Ryukyu Islands	1955-57	65.8	72.0
79	Taiwan	1936-40	41.08	45.73
80	Thailand	1947-48	48.69	51.90
	Oceania			
81	Australia (whites)	1953-55	67.14	72.75
	New Zealand			
82	Europeans	1950-52	68.29	72.43
83	Maoris	1950-52	54.05	55.88

/2/ Refers to persons of mixed racial descent.

Contributors: (a) Spiegelman, Mortimer, (b) Grove, Robert D.

References: [1] United Nations Statistical Office. 1961. Demographic yearbook, 1960. United Nations, New York. table 23. (Also in Population Index 27:377, 1961.) [2] U. S. National Office of Vital Statistics. 1961. Vital statistics of the United States, 1959. U. S. Dept. of Health, Education, and Welfare, Washington, D. C.

124. LIFE SPANS: MAMMALS

Life spans are for animals in captivity, unless otherwise indicated. When no symbol (♂, ♀) precedes age, sex of animal was unspecified. Classification adapted from Simpson, *The Principles of Classification and a Classification of Mammals*, 1945.

	Family and Species	Recorded Life Span		Reference
		Average	Maximum	
	(A)	(B)	(C)	(D)
	Primates			
	Hominidae			
1	*Homo sapiens*	♂66.5 yr, ♀73 yr	....	30
	Pongidae			
2	*Gorilla gorilla*	....	26 yr	24
3	*Hylobates lar*	....	>23 yr	8
4	*Pan troglodytes*	15-20 yr	37 yr	13
5	*Pongo pygmaeus*	>8 yr	28 yr	8,11
	Pongidae			
6	*Symphalangus syndactylus*	....	♀>5 yr 7 mo	8
	Cercopithecidae			
7	*Cercocebus* spp.	10 yr	14 yr	8
8	*C. fuliginosus*	....	>11 yr	8
9	*Cercopithecus diana*	....	19 yr	26
10	*Colobus polykomos*	....	♂18 yr[1]	25
11	*Cynopithecus niger*[2]	2 yr	18 yr	8,13
12	*Erythrocebus patas*	....	>20 yr[1]	8

/1/ Still alive at time of report. /2/ Not in captivity.

continued

124. LIFE SPANS: MAMMALS

	Family and Species	Recorded Life Span		Reference
		Average	Maximum	
	(A)	(B)	(C)	(D)
	Primates			
	Cercopithecidae			
13	*Macaca fuscata*	15 yr	♀>19 yr	8
14	*M. mulatta*	15 yr	29 yr	6,8
15	*M. sylvana*	....	♀>27 yr	8
16	*Mandrillus leucophaeus*	<10 yr	♂>16 yr	8
17	*M. sphinx*	10 yr	26 yr 5 mo	8
18	*Nasalis lervatus*	....	♂>4 yr	25
19	*Papio cynocephalus*	10-13 yr	25 yr	8
20	*P. doguera*	....	30 yr	26
21	*P. hamadryas*	15 yr	♀24 yr	8
22	*P. porcarius*	....	45 yr	8
23	*Pithecia pithecia*	....	♂11 yr 11 mo[1]	25
24	*Presbytis entellus*	....	22 yr	26
	Callithricidae			
25	*Hapale jacchus*	>11 yr	16 yr	8
26	*Leontideus rosalia*	....	10 yr 4 mo	4
	Cebidae			
27	*Ateles ater*	....	♀6 yr 4 mo[1]	8
28	*A. geoffroyi*	....	18 yr	26
29	*Cebus fatuellus*	9-11 yr	♂31 yr[1]	8,25
30	*Lagothrix humboldti*	....	♂5 yr 11 mo	8
	Tarsiidae			
31	*Tarsius syrichta*	....	♀>12 yr	29
	Lorisidae			
32	*Galago crassicaudatus*	....	12 yr 8 mo	19
33	*G. senegalensis*	....	♂>9 yr 9 mo	8
34	*Nycticebus coucang*	....	♀8 yr 2 mo[1]	19
	Daubentoniidae			
35	*Daubentonia madagascariensis*	5 yr	♂>8 yr 10 mo	8
	Lemuridae			
36	*Hapalemur griseus*	>10 yr	>12 yr 1 mo	8
37	*Lemur fulvus*	10.5 yr	♂>25 yr	8
38	*L. macaco*	10.5 yr	♂21 yr	8
39	*Microcebus coquereli*	6.8 yr	15 yr 3 mo	8,22
	Tupaiidae			
40	*Tupaia tana*	....	>2 yr 3 mo	8
	Artiodactyla			
	Bovidae			
41	*Addax masomaculatus*	....	>18 yr 3 mo	8
42	*Aegoryx algazel*	....	18 yr	8
43	*Alcelaphus buselaphus*	....	>18 yr 11 mo	8
44	*Ammotragus lervia*	8 yr	♀>15 yr 5 mo	8
45	*Anoa depressicornis*	5.3 yr	♀>28 yr 5 mo	19,22
46	*Antidorcas marsupialis*	....	♂9 yr 11 mo	8
47	*Antilope cervicapra*	7 yr	♂15 yr 1 mo[1]	8
48	*Bibos frontalis*	....	♀>15 yr 8 mo	8
49	*Bison bison*	>10 yr	♀>22 yr	8
50	*Bos grunniens*	....	♂>22 yr 3 mo	8
51	*B. indicus*	10-14 yr	21-25 yr	8
52	*B. taurus*	20-25 yr	30 yr	8
53	*Boselaphus tragocamelus*	....	♀21 yr	8
54	*Bubalus bubalis*	....	30 yr	8
55	*Budorcas taxicolor*	....	♂8 yr	8
56	*Capra caucasica*	....	19 yr 4 mo	8
57	*C. hircus*	8-10 yr	18 yr	8,13
58	*C. ibex*	....	17 yr	8
59	*Cephalophus maxwelli*	....	♀9 yr	8
60	*C. sylvicultor*	....	♂8 yr	8
	Bovidae			
61	*Connochaetes taurinus*	....	16 yr	8
62	*Demaliscus albifrons*	....	17 yr[1]	8
63	*Gazella rufifrons*	....	♂11 yr	8
64	*G. soemmerringi*	>9 yr	♂>13 yr	8
65	*Gorgon albojubatus*	....	20 yr	26
66	*Hemitragus jemlaicus*	8-10 yr	♀16 yr	8
67	*Hippotragus equinus*	....	>14 yr	8
68	*H. niger*	....	16 yr 8 mo[1]	8
69	*Kobus defassa*	9 yr	>16 yr 8 mo	8
70	*K. kob*	....	17 yr	26
71	*Limnotragus selousi*	....	♀14 yr	8
72	*Naemorhedus goral*	....	>17 yr 7 mo	8
73	*Onotragus leche*	9 yr	♂15 yr	8
74	*Oreamnos americanus*	....	>9 yr 7 mo	8
75	*Oryx beisa*	6.9 yr	18 yr 6 mo	8,22
76	*Ourebia montana*	....	>13 yr 8 mo	8
77	*O. nigricaudata*	....	♂>8 yr 10 mo	8
78	*Ovibos moschatus*	....	♀>10 yr 2 mo	8
79	*Ovis aries*	10-15 yr	20 yr	13,22
80	*O. musimon*	>8 yr	♀19 yr	8
81	*Pseudois nahoor*	>8 yr	♀>16 yr	8,13
82	*Redunca arundinum*	....	♂>9 yr	8
83	*Rupicapra rupicapra*	....	>16 yr 10 mo	8
84	*Strepsiceros strepsiceros*	....	23 yr	26
85	*Sylvicapra grimmia*	....	♂8 yr	8
86	*Syncerus caffer*	10 yr	>15 yr 5 mo	8
87	*Taurotragus oryx*	9.2 yr	25 yr	8
88	*Tetracerus quadricornis*	....	10 yr	8
89	*Tragelaphus scriptus*	....	>9 yr	8
	Antilocapridae			
90	*Antilocapra americana*	8 yr	15 yr	8
	Giraffidae			
91	*Giraffa camelopardalis*	14 yr	>28 yr	8
92	*Okapia johnstoni*	....	♂>15 yr 1 mo	19
	Cervidae			
93	*Alces alces*	15-20 yr	25 yr	8
94	*Axis axis*	10.1 yr	18 yr 7 mo	8
95	*Cervus canadensis*	14 yr	22 yr	8
96	*C. elaphus*	....	19 yr	8
97	*C. unicolor*	....	♀>26 yr 5 mo	19
98	*Dama dama*	10.8 yr	♀15 yr 6 mo[1]	8
99	*Hydropotes inermis*	....	10 yr 9 mo	22
100	*Hyelaphus porcinus*	10 yr	18 yr 6 mo	8
101	*Moschus moschiferus*	15 yr	....	13
102	*Muntiacus reevesi*	>6 yr	>11 yr	8
103	*Odocoileus hemionus*	8 yr	15 yr	8
104	*O. peruvianus*	8 yr	13 yr	8
105	*Rangifer tarandus*	....	12 yr	8
106	*Rucervus duvauceli*	12 yr	>23 yr	8
107	*Rusa unicolor*	....	17 yr 4 mo	8
108	*Sika mantchuricus*	....	♀>14 yr 2 mo	8
109	*S. nippon*	6 yr	♀18 yr 5 mo	8
	Camelidae			
110	*Camelus bactrianus*	....	>25 yr 5 mo	8
111	*C. dromedarius*	....	>24 yr 9 mo	8
112	*Lama glama*	15 yr	♂>21 yr 4 mo	13,19
113	*L. guanacus*	12 yr	>19 yr	8
114	*L. pacos*	12 yr	20 yr	8,26
115	*L. vicugna*	12 yr	16 yr 10 mo[1]	8

/1/ Still alive at time of report.

continued

124. LIFE SPANS: MAMMALS

	Family and Species	Recorded Life Span		Reference
		Average	Maximum	
	(A)	(B)	(C)	(D)
	Artiodactyla			
	Hippopotamidae			
116	*Hippopotamus amphibius*	40 yr	♂>49 yr 6 mo	8,19
	Tayassuidae			
117	*Choeropsis liberiensis*	....	♂>39 yr 7 mo	19
118	*Pecari tajucu*	....	15 yr 9 mo	8
119	*Tayassu pecari*	....	♂>9 yr 4 mo	8
	Suidae			
120	*Babirussa alfurus*	....	21 yr	26
121	*B. babirussa*	....	>12 yr	8
122	*Phacochoerus aethiopicus*	....	♀>15 yr 2 mo	19
123	*Potamochoerus porcus*	....	14 yr 7 mo	8
124	*Sus andamanensis*	....	♂>12 yr 3 mo	8
125	*S. leucomystax*	....	♀>13 yr 1 mo	
126	*S. scrofa*	16 yr	27 yr	13
	Perissodactyla			
	Rhinocerotidae			
127	*Diceros bicornis*	....	>22 yr 7 mo	8
128	*Rhinoceros sandaicus*	....	>14 yr	8
129	*R. samatraensis*	....	♂35 yr	8
130	*R. unicornis*	40-45 yr	47 yr	8,13
	Tapiridae			
131	*Tapirus indicus*	....	♀>11 yr 2 mo	8
132	*T. terrestris*	<6 yr	30 yr 5 mo	1,8
	Equidae			
133	*Equus asinus*	50 yr	....	13
134	*E. asinus africanus*	....	♀22 yr 2 mo	8
135	*E. burchelli*	>12 yr	♂>27 yr 10 mo	8,19
136	*E. caballus*	20-30 yr	50 yr	8
137	*E. grevyi*	....	>15 yr	8
138	*E. hemippus*	....	♂>22 yr 10 mo	8
139	*E. indicus*	....	♂>15 yr 7 mo	8
140	*E. kiang*	....	24 yr 11 mo	8
141	*E. mulus*	....	36 yr 9 mo	8
142	*E. onager*	....	♂24 yr 5 mo	8
143	*E. przewalski*	11-16 yr	♂28 yr	8
144	*E. quagga*	....	>21 yr 4 mo	8
145	*E. taeniopus*	14.6 yr	19 yr 4 mo	8
146	*E. zebra*	22 yr	>25 yr 7 mo	8,13
	Hyracoidea			
	Procaviidae			
147	*Procavia capensis*	....	♂>6 yr 2 mo	8
148	*P. syriaca*	>4 yr	7 yr 4 mo	8
	Proboscidea			
	Elephantidae			
149	*Elephas maximus*	40 yr	57 yr	9
150	*Loxodonta africana*	24.3 yr	>35 yr 4 mo	8
	Tubulidentata			
	Orycteropodidae			
151	*Orycteropus afer*	....	>9 yr 8 mo	8
152	*O. capensis*	....	9 yr 9 mo	22

	Family and Species	Recorded Life Span		Reference
		Average	Maximum	
	(A)	(B)	(C)	(D)
	Carnivora			
	Phocidae			
153	*Halichoerus grypus*	....	18 yr	8
154	*Mirounga angustirostris*	....	♀5 yr[1]	25
155	*Phoca vitulina*	....	19 yr	1
	Odobenidae			
156	*Odobenus rosmarus*	....	11 yr	3
	Otariidae			
157	*Arctocephalus doriferus*	....	>16 yr	8
158	*A. pusillus*	13 yr	♀>20 yr	8
159	*Callorhinus alascanus*	....	>9 yr	8
160	*C. ursinus*	....	25 yr	23
161	*Eumetopias jubata*	13 yr	♀19 yr	8
162	*Otaria byronia*	....	♀19 yr 6 mo	8
163	*Zalophus californianus*	>13 yr	23 yr	8
	Felidae			
164	*Acinonyx jubatus*	6 yr	>15 yr 7 mo	8
165	*Felis bengalensis*	....	>12 yr	8
166	*F. catus*	13-17 yr	21 yr	28
167	*F. chaus*	....	>9 yr 9 mo	8
168	*F. concolor*	9 yr	16 yr	8
169	*F. pardalis*	....	12 yr 8 mo	22
170	*F. sylvestris*	....	♀16 yr	8
171	*F. viverrina*	....	>10 yr	8
172	*Herpailurus eyra*	....	9 yr	8
173	*Lynx canadensis*	6.1 yr	>11 yr 7 mo	8,22
174	*L. caracal*	5.3 yr	>16 yr 10 mo	8,22
175	*L. lynx*	....	>16 yr 1 mo	8
176	*L. rufa*	....	15 yr	8
177	*Panthera leo*	20-25 yr	29 yr	8
178	*P. nebulosa*	....	♀8 yr	8
179	*P. onca*	14 yr	>22 yr 4 mo	8
180	*P. pardus*	14 yr	23 yr	8
181	*P. tigris*	11 yr	♀>19 yr 6 mo	8,19
182	*P. uncia*	....	♂>8 yr 8 mo	19
	Hyaenidae			
183	*Crocuta crocuta*	12 yr	♀25 yr	8
184	*Hyaena hyaena*	12 yr	24 yr	8
185	*Proteles cristatus*	4.4 yr	12 yr 11 mo	8,22
	Viverridae			
186	*Arctictis binturong*	....	18 yr	8
187	*Arctogalidia leucotis*	....	>10 yr	8
188	*Bdeogale puisa*	....	♂10 yr	8
189	*Civettictis civetta*	....	♂>13 yr	8
190	*Cryptoprocta ferox*	....	17 yr	8
191	*Cynictis penicillata*	....	>12 yr 10 mo	8
192	*Galerella pulverulenta*	....	>8 yr	8
193	*Genetta pardena*	>7 yr	12 yr 6 mo	8
194	*Herpestes vitticollis*	....	13 yr	8
195	*Ichneumia albicauda*	....	10 yr	8
196	*Mungos mungo*	5 yr	♀>8 yr	8
197	*Nandinia binotata*	....	10 yr	8
198	*Paradoxurus larvatus*	8 yr	>15 yr	8
199	*Suricata suricata*	....	>6 yr 2 mo	8
200	*Viverra zibetha*	....	16 yr	8
201	*Viverricula malaccensis*	....	♂>7 yr	8
	Mustelidae			
202	*Enhydra lutris*	....	8 yr	23

/1/ Still alive at time of report.

continued

124. LIFE SPANS: MAMMALS

	Family and Species	Recorded Life Span		Reference
		Average	Maximum	
	(A)	(B)	(C)	(D)
	Carnivora			
	Mustelidae			
203	*Grison furax*	....	7 yr 3 mo	8
204	*Ictonyx libyca*	....	4 yr 7 mo	8
205	*Lutra canadensis*	....	19 yr	23
206	*L. lutra*	....	>12 yr	8
207	*Martes americana*	....	>10 yr[1]	8
208	*M. martes*	10 yr	>13 yr 6 mo	8
209	*Meles anakuma*	>10.7 yr	14 yr 9 mo	8
210	*M. meles*	....	14 yr[1]	8
211	*Mellivora indica*	....	12 yr 8 mo	8
212	*M. ratel*	....	>23 yr 6 mo	8
213	*Mephitis mephitis*	....	6 yr 1 mo	8
214	*Mustela nivalis*	....	>7 yr 9 mo	8
215	*M. vison*	....	10 yr	23
216	*Putorius putorius*	....	13 yr[1]	8
217	*Taxidea taxus*	11 yr	13 yr 10 mo	8
218	*Tayra barbara*	7 yr	17 yr 6 mo	8
	Procyonidae			
219	*Ailuropoda melanoleuca*	....	15 yr	26
220	*Bassariscus astutus*	....	8 yr	8
221	*Nasua* spp.	....	10 yr 1 mo	8
222	*Potos flavus*	....	♂19 yr 5 mo[1]	19
223	*Procyon cancrivorus*	5.7 yr	>15 yr 10 mo	8,22
224	*P. lotor*	4.2 yr	>13 yr 9 mo	8,22
	Ursidae			
225	*Melursus ursinus*	....	21 yr 6 mo	8
226	*Thalarctos maritimus*	16 yr	33 yr 4 mo	8
227	*Tremarctos ornatus*	....	♀21 yr 4 mo	25
228	*Ursus americanus*	....	♀25 yr 11 mo	8
229	*U. americanus cinnamomum*	14 yr	21 yr 7 mo	8
230	*U. arctos*	19 yr	34 yr[1]	8
231	*U. horribilis*	20 yr	31 yr 5 mo	8
232	*U. japonicus*	....	♀10 yr 3 mo	8
233	*U. malayanus*	11 yr	20 yr 6 mo	8,22
234	*U. piscator*	....	25 yr 9 mo	22
235	*U. syriacus*	>8.9 yr	21 yr 7 mo	22
236	*U. tibetanus*	15.7 yr	....	8
	Canidae			
237	*Alopex lagopus*	8.8 yr	14 yr	8
238	*Canis aureus*	1-2 yr	10 yr 2 mo	22
239	*C. dingo*	3.6 yr	♀12 yr 1 mo	22
240	*C. familiaris*	13-17 yr	34 yr	14,28
241	*C. latrans*	9 yr	♂15 yr	8,18
242	*C. lupaster*	>9 yr	>16 yr	8
243	*C. lupus*	12 yr	14 yr	8,13
244	*C. lupus nubilus*	9 yr	>16 yr 3 mo	8
245	*Chrysocyon brachyurus*	....	<5 yr	8
246	*Cuon dukhunensis*	....	♀>9 yr	8
247	*Dusicyon australis*	....	>5 yr 3 mo	8
248	*Lycaon pictus*	6-7 yr	♀10 yr 1 mo	8
249	*Nyctereutes procyonides*	....	♀>5 yr	8
250	*Otocyon megalotis*	....	>5 yr	8
251	*Urocyon cinereoargenteus*	....	>8 yr 5 mo	8
252	*Vulpes fulva*	....	>12 yr	8
253	*V. vulpes*	....	♂>9 yr 9 mo	8
	Cetacea			
	Balaenidae			
254	*Balaena mysticetus*	24 yr	....	8
255	*Eubalaena gracialis*	....	40 yr	15
	Valaenopteridae			
256	*Balaenoptera physalus*	....	36 yr	15
	Delphinidae			
257	*Delphinus delphis*	25-30 yr	....	13
	Rodentia			
	Thryonomyidae			
258	*Thryonomys swinderianus*	....	4 yr 2 mo	26
	Octodontidae			
259	*Octodon degus*	>4 yr	>5 yr 2 mo	8
	Capromyidae			
260	*Capromys pilorides*	....	>9 yr 8 mo	8
261	*Myocastor coypus*	>4 yr	10 yr	8,22
	Chinchillidae			
262	*Chinchilla laniger*	4 yr	7 yr	22
263	*Lagidium peruanum*	....	8 yr	26
264	*L. viscacia*	5 yr	>6 yr 8 mo	8
	Dasyproctidae			
265	*Cuniculus paca*	....	>12 yr 8 mo	8
266	*Dasyprocta aguti*	6 yr	>10 yr	8
267	*D. mexicana*	6 yr	13 yr	8
	Hydrochoeridae			
268	*Hydrochoerus hydrochoerus*	....	11 yr 6 mo	22
	Caviidae			
269	*Cavia porcellus*	>2 yr	>6 yr	8
270	*Dolichotis australis*	5 yr	>13 yr	8
	Erethizontidae			
271	*Coendou villosus*	3.3 yr	>8 yr 11 mo	8,22
	Hystricidae			
272	*Atherurus africanus*	....	>8 yr	8
273	*A. macrourus*	....	>8 yr	8
274	*Hystrix cristata*	8-12 yr	>20 yr 4 mo	8
275	*H. europaeus*	15-20 yr	....	13
	Dipodidae			
276	*Jaculus jaculus*	>3 yr	7 yr	8,26
277	*J. orientalis*	>1 yr	>4 yr	8
	Gliridae			
278	*Eliomys quercinus*	2-3 yr	>5 yr 6 mo	8
279	*Glis glis*	2-3 yr	>4 yr 1 mo	8
280	*Muscardinus avellanarius*	....	2 yr 11 mo	8
	Muridae			
281	*Acomys hunteri*	>3.5 yr	>4 yr 5 mo	8
282	*Arvicanthis niloticus*	>3.7 yr	>6 yr 8 mo	8
283	*Cricetomys gambianus*	....	>4 yr 5 mo[1]	8
284	*Hydromys chrysogaster*	....	1 yr 5 mo	22
285	*Micromys minutus*	2 yr	2 yr 6 mo	8
286	*Mus musculus*	1-2 yr	>3 yr	11,27
287	*Phloemys cumingi*	....	♂9 yr 6 mo[1]	19
288	*Rattus norvegicus*	2.5 yr	>3 yr 1 mo	8,13
289	*R. norvegicus albus*	3 yr	>3 yr 4 mo	6,10
290	*R. rattus*	2-3 yr	4 yr	8
	Rhizomyidae			
291	*Rhizomys badius*	....	>3 yr 4 mo	8

/1/ Still alive at time of report.

continued

	Family and Species	Recorded Life Span		Reference
		Average	Maximum	
	(A)	(B)	(C)	(D)
	Rodentia			
	Cricetidae			
292	*Arvicola amphibius*	....	1 yr 4 mo	22
293	*Clethrionomys glareolus*	....	>4 yr 11 mo	8
294	*Cricetus cricetus*	2 yr	2 yr 6 mo	8
295	*Gerbillus gerbillus*	....	>5 yr	8
296	*Meriones calurus*	....	♀>5 yr 7 mo	8
297	*Mesocricetus auratus*	1 yr	1 yr 9 mo	6
298	*Microtus pennsylvanicus*	....	1 yr 4 mo	7
299	*Neotoma lepida*	....	5 yr 7 mo	26
300	*Ondatra zibethica*	....	6 yr 3 mo	22
301	*Onychomys leucogaster*	....	>2 yr	8
302	*Oryzomys longicaudatus*	....	>2 yr 10 mo	8
303	*Peromyscus maniculatus*	>4 yr	♀8 yr 4 mo	5,8
304	*P. polionotus*	....	5 yr 3 mo	26
305	*Reithrodon typicus*	....	>3 yr 5 mo	8
	Pedetidae			
306	*Pedetes cafer*	....	>7 yr 7 mo	8
	Castoridae			
307	*Castor canadensis*	....	♀19 yr	8
308	*C. fiber*	20-25 yr	....	13
	Heteromyidae			
309	*Dipodomys agilis*	....	6 yr 3 mo	26
310	*D. deserti*	....	5 yr 5 mo	2
311	*D. merriami*	....	5 yr 6 mo	12
312	*Perognathus flavus*	....	4 yr 11 mo	8
	Sciuridae			
313	*Atlantoxerus getulus*	....	5 yr	8
314	*Callosciurus finlaysoni*	....	♂>11 yr	8
315	*Citellus grammurus*	....	>9 yr 10 mo	8
316	*C. mugosaricus*	....	>7 yr 1 mo	8
317	*Cynomys gunnisoni*	....	♂>10 yr	31
318	*C. ludovicianus*	4.9 yr	♀8 yr 6 mo	8,31
319	*Eutamias quadrimaculatus*	....	>8 yr	8
320	*Funambulus palmarum*	....	>5 yr 6 mo	8
321	*Glaucomys volans*	>5.1 yr	>6 yr	8
322	*Marmota marmota*	7 yr	>13 yr 8 mo	8,22
323	*M. monax*	....	>9 yr 8 mo	8
324	*Petaurista alborufus*	....	>13 yr 6 mo	8
325	*P. inornatus*	....	>11 yr	8
326	*P. leucogenys*	....	8 yr 5 mo	8
327	*Ratufa bicolor*	....	♂17 yr	25
328	*Sciurus carolinensis*	9 yr	14-15 yr	8
329	*S. griseus griseus*	....	11 yr[1]	8
330	*S. niger*	....	♀>9 yr 11 mo	8
331	*Tamias striatus*	2.4 yr	7 yr 6 mo	22
332	*Tamiasciurus hudsonicus*	....	>8 yr	8
333	*Xerus rutilus*	....	♂>6 yr 1 mo	8
	Lagomorpha			
	Leporidae			
334	*Oryctolagus cuniculus*	5-6 yr	>13 yr	8
335	*Sylvilagus bachmani*	....	6 yr[1]	16
336	*S. floridanus*	....	9 yr 9 mo[1]	16
	Pholidota			
	Manidae			
337	*Manis* spp.	....	<2 yr	8
	Edentata			
	Dasypodidae			
338	*Euphractus villosus*	10 yr	18 yr	8
339	*Tolypeutes tricinctus*	....	11 yr	8
	Bradypodidae			
340	*Choloepus didactylus*	....	>11 yr	8
	Myrmecophagidae			
341	*Myrmecophaga tridactyla*	....	>14 yr 4 mo	8
342	*Tamandua tetradactyla*	....	♀>4 yr 11 mo	8
	Chiroptera			
	Vespertilionidae			
343	*Antrozous pallidus*[2]	....	6 yr 5 mo	21
344	*Eptesicus fuscus*[2]	....	18 yr 2 mo	21
345	*Myotis lucifugus*[2]	....	22 yr 10 mo	21
346	*M. sodalis*[2]	....	10 yr	21
347	*M. subulatus*[2]	....	11 yr 11 mo	21
348	*Nyctalus noctula*	....	>4 mo	8
349	*Pipistrellus subflavus*[2]	....	10 yr 9 mo	21
350	*Plecotus townsendi*[2]	....	10 yr	21
	Rhinolophidae			
351	*Rhinolophus rouxi*	....	4-5 yr	8
	Pteropodidae			
352	*Cynonycteris collaris*	1.5 yr	9 yr	8,22
353	*Pteropus formosus*	....	♀>7 yr 9 mo	8
354	*P. giganteus*	....	♀>17 yr 1 mo	8
355	*P. poliocephalus*	....	>6 yr 11 mo	8
356	*Rousettus aegyptiacus*	>6.7 yr	♀>12 yr 7 mo	8
357	*R. leachi*	....	♀>19 yr 9 mo	8
	Insectivora			
	Soricidae			
358	*Crocidura olivieri*	>1 yr	>1 yr 3 mo	8
359	*Sorex palustris*	....	1 yr 6 mo	23
	Macroscelididae			
360	*Elephantulus rozeti*	....	>3 yr 4 mo	8
	Erinaceidae			
361	*Erinaceus europaeus*	....	♀>3 yr 11 mo	19
362	*Hemiechinus auritus*	....	3 yr	8
	Tenrecidae			
363	*Tenrec ecaudatus*	0.9 yr	♂>2 yr	8
	Marsupialia			
	Macropodidae			
364	*Bettongia gaimardi*	....	>9 yr 6 mo	8
365	*B. penicillata*	....	>8 yr	8
366	*Macropus giganteus*	....	14 yr	8
367	*M. rufus*	....	16 yr 4 mo	8
368	*Potorous tridactylus*	....	6-7 yr	8
369	*Protemnodon bicolor*	....	2 yr 6 mo	17
	Phalangeridae			
370	*Acrobates pygmaeus*	....	>3 yr 11 mo	8
371	*Petaurus* spp.	>6.5 yr	10-11 yr	8
372	*Phascolomis mitchelli*	>11 yr	>26 yr	8
373	*Pseudocheirus peregrinus*	....	>5 yr 8 mo	8
374	*Trichosurus caninus*	....	>8 yr 11 mo	8

/1/ Still alive at time of report. /2/ Not in captivity.

continued

124. LIFE SPANS: MAMMALS

	Family and Species	Recorded Life Span: Average	Recorded Life Span: Maximum	Reference
	(A)	(B)	(C)	(D)
	Marsupialia			
	Phalangeridae			
375	*Trichosurus vulpecula*	<6 yr	>9 yr 8 mo	8
	Peramelidae			
376	*Macrotis lagotis*	....	>7 yr 1 mo	8
	Dasyuridae			
377	*Dasyurus viverrinus*	....	>6 yr 10 mo	8
378	*Sarcophilus harrisi*	....	♀>5 yr 9 mo	8
379	*Thylacinus cynocephalus*	....	♀>8 yr 4 mo	8
	Didelphidae			
380	*Didelphis virginiana*	>3 yr	>7 yr	8
	Didelphidae			
381	*Metachirops fuscogriseus*	3.5 yr	....	8
	Monotremata			
	Ornithorhynchidae			
382	*Ornithorhynchus anatinus*	....	14 yr;♂>10 yr 4 mo	20
	Tachyglossidae			
383	*Tachyglossus aculeatus*	....	50 yr[1]	24
384	*Zaglossus bruijni*	....	>19 yr 3 mo	8

/1/ Still alive at time of report.

Contributors: (a) Rockstein, Morris, (b) Cole, LaMont C., (c) Manville, Richard H., (d) Crandall, Lee S.

References: [1] Bourlière, F. 1954. The natural history of mammals. Knopf, New York. [2] Brattstrom, B. H. 1960. J. Mammal. 41:404. [3] Copenhagen Zoo. Unpublished, 1956. [4] Crandall, L. S. Unpublished. New York Zoological Society, N. Y., 1952. [5] Dice, L. R. 1933. J. Mammal. 14:147. [6] Farris, E. J. 1950. The care and breeding of laboratory animals. J. Wiley and Sons, New York. [7] Fisher, H. J. 1945. J. Mammal. 26:435. [8] Flower, S. S. 1931. Proc. Zool. Soc. (London), p. 145. [9] Flower, S. S. 1947. Ibid. 117:680. [10] Griffith, J. Q., and E. J. Farris. 1942. The rat in laboratory investigation. J. B. Lippincott, Philadelphia. [11] Gruneberg, H. 1943. Genetics of the mouse. Cambridge Univ. Press, London. [12] Hooper, E. T. 1956. J. Mammal. 37:124. [13] Korschelt, E. 1922. Lebensdauer Altern und Tod. G. Fischer, Jena. [14] Lankester, E. R. 1870. On comparative longevity in man and the lower animals. Macmillan, London. [15] Laws, R. M. 1955. Zoo Life 10:41. [16] Lord, R. D., Jr. 1961. J. Mammal. 42:99. [17] Mann, W. M. 1930. Wild animals in and out of the zoo. Smithsonian Institution, New York. [18] Manville, R. H. 1953. J. Mammal. 34:390. [19] Manville, R. H. 1957. Ibid. 38:279. [20] Manville, R. H. 1958. Ibid. 39:582. [21] Manville, R. H. Unpublished. Fish and Wildlife Service, U. S. Natl. Museum, Washington, D. C., 1961. [22] Mitchell, P. C. 1911. Proc. Zool. Soc. (London), p. 425. [23] Palmer, R. S. 1954. The mammal guide. Doubleday, Garden City, N. Y. [24] Philadelphia Zoological Gardens. Unpublished, 1952. [25] Pournelle, G. H. 1960. J. Mammal. 41:114. [26] Rabb, G. B. 1960. Ibid. 41:113. [27] Snell, G. D. 1941. Biology of the laboratory mouse. Blakiston, Philadelphia. [28] Todd, T. W. 1939. In E. V. Cowdry, ed. Problems of ageing. Williams and Wilkins, Baltimore. p. 71. [29] Ulmer, F. A., Jr. 1960. J. Mammal. 41:512. [30] U. S. National Office of Vital Statistics. 1961. Vital statistics of the United States, 1959. U. S. Dept. of Health, Education, and Welfare, Washington, D. C. [31] Young, S. P. 1944. J. Mammal. 25:317.

125. LIFE SPANS: BIRDS

Classification adapted from Wetmore, *A Classification for the Birds of the World*, Smithsonian Institution, 1960.

Part I: IN CAPTIVITY

	Family and Species	Recorded Maximum Life Span	Reference
	(A)	(B)	(C)
	Passeriformes		
	Fringillidae		
1	*Carduelis carduelis*	27 yr	3
2	*Chloris chloris*	19 yr 6 mo	3
3	*Emberiza luteola*	13 yr 9 mo	5
4	*Paroaria cucullata*	30 yr	3
5	*Pheucticus ludovicianus*	23 yr	6
6	*Richmondena cardinalis*	22 yr	3
7	*Serinus canarius domesticus*	24 yr	4
	Thraupidae		
8	*Rhamphocelus brasilius*	7 yr 4 mo	5
	Icteridae		
9	*Molothrus badius*	12 yr 1 mo	5
	Ploceidae		
10	*Amadina castanotis*	8 yr 1 mo	5
11	*Estrilda amandava*	10 yr 2 mo	5
12	*Passer italiae*	20 yr	5
	Sturnidae		
13	*Sturnus vulgaris*	>15 yr 10 mo	5
	Bombycillidae		
14	*Bombycilla garrulus*	3 yr 3 mo	5
	Turdidae		
15	*Hylocichla mustelina*	2 yr 5 mo	5
16	*Luscinia luscinia*	3 yr 9 mo	5
17	*Sialia sialis*	4 yr 6 mo	5
18	*Turdus merula*	18 yr	4
19	*T. migratorius*	12 yr 10 mo	5
20	*T. musicus*	11 yr 5 mo	5
	Mimidae		
21	*Mimus polyglottos*	6 yr 7 mo	5
	Timaliidae		
22	*Garrulax* spp.	8 yr 11 mo	5
	Sittidae		
23	*Sitta carolinensis*	8 yr 6 mo	3
	Paridae		
24	*Parus atricapillus*	7 yr 6 mo	3
25	*P. major*	9 yr	5
	Paradisaeidae		
26	*Paradisaea apoda*	>12 yr 1 mo	3
27	*Seleucides ignotus*	>20 yr 10 mo	1
	Corvidae		
28	*Corvultur crassirostris*	10 yr	3
29	*Corvus corax*	69 yr	5
30	*C. frugilegus*	>14 yr	3
31	*Cyanocitta cristata*	4 yr 6 mo	5
32	*C. yucatanica*	7 yr 10 mo	5
33	*Garrulus glandarius*	>17 yr	3
34	*Nucifraga caryocatactes*	>14 yr 6 mo	3
35	*Pica pica*	12 yr 2 mo	5
	Hirundinidae		
36	*Hirundo rustica*	<1 yr	2
	Alaudidae		
37	*Alauda arvensis*	24 yr	5
	Menuridae		
38	*Menura superba*	8 yr 11 mo	5
	Coraciiformes		
	Alcedinidae		
39	*Dacelo novaguineae*	>13 yr 9 mo	3
	Alcedinidae		
40	*Halcyon* spp.	11 yr	5
	Bucerotidae		
41	*Buceros bicornis*	>33 yr 5 mo	3
	Strigiformes		
	Strigidae		
42	*Bubo bubo*	68 yr	2,5
43	*Ketupa ceylonensis*	39 yr	2
44	*Nyctea nyctea*	24 yr 5 mo	3
	Tytonidae		
45	*Tyto alba*	>13 yr	3
	Psittaciformes		
	Psittacidae		
46	*Agapornis cana*	8 yr 1 mo	5
47	*Amazona amazonica*	30 yr	2
48	*A. levaillanti*	39 yr	2
49	*Ara ararauna*	43 yr	3
50	*A. macao*	64 yr	5
51	*A. militaris*	31 yr	2
52	*Coracopsis nigra*	34 yr	2
53	*C. vasa*	54 yr	2
54	*Kakatoe galerita*	51 yr	2
55	*K. gymnopis*	39 yr	2
56	*K. sulphurea*	34 yr	2
57	*Licmetis pastinator*	40 yr	2
58	*Pionus maximiliani*	>9 yr 3 mo	5
59	*Platycercus pallidiceps*	32 yr	2
60	*Psittacula torquatus*	20 yr 10 mo	5
61	*Psittacus erithacus*	41 yr	2
	Columbiformes		
	Columbidae		
62	*Columba livia domestica*	35 yr	2
63	*Streptopelia risoria*	35 yr	2
64	*Turtur risorius*	30-40 yr	5
	Charadriiformes		
	Alcidae		
65	*Fratercula arctica*	8 yr[1]	3
	Laridae		
66	*Larus argentatus*	>44 yr	2,5
67	*L. fuscus*	31 yr	2
	Charadriidae		
68	*Pluvialis apricaria*	1 yr 11 mo	5
	Gruiformes		
	Rallidae		
69	*Fulica ardesiaca*	3 yr	5
	Gruidae		
70	*Grus communis*	42 yr 10 mo	5
71	*Megalornis grus*	43 yr	2
72	*Sarcogeranus leucogeranus*	30 yr	2
	Galliformes		
	Meleagrididae		
73	*Meleagris gallopavo*	12 yr 4 mo	3
	Phasianidae		
74	*Coturnix coturnix*	10 yr	3

/1/ Still alive at time of report.

continued

125. LIFE SPANS: BIRDS

Part I: IN CAPTIVITY

	Family and Species	Recorded Maximum Life Span	Reference
	(A)	(B)	(C)
	Galliformes		
	Phasianidae		
75	*Excalfactoria chinensis*	>3 yr 4 mo	5
76	*Gallus domesticus*	30 yr	5
77	*Perdix perdix*	>5 yr	3
78	*Phasianus colchicus*	27 yr	2
	Numididae		
79	*Numida meleagris*	3 yr 4 mo	5
	Falconiformes		
	Accipitridae		
80	*Aegypius monachus*	32 yr	2
81	*Aquila adalberti*	44 yr 6 mo	3
82	*Buteo desertorum*	18 yr 9 mo	5
83	*Geranoaetus melanoleucus*	>42 yr	5
84	*Gyps fulvus*	>41 yr 5 mo	1
85	*Haliaeetus* spp.	28 yr	5
86	*H. albicilla*	42 yr	2
87	*Harpia harpyja*	>16 yr 10 mo	2
88	*Ibycter australis*	33 yr	2
89	*Milvus milvus*	38 yr	2
90	*Polyborus brasiliensis*	41 yr	2
91	*Terathopius ecaudatus*	55 yr	2
92	*Uroaetus audax*	33 yr	2
	Cathartidae		
93	*Gymnogyps californianus*	36 yr 6 mo[1]	3
94	*Vultur gryphus*	52 yr	2,5
	Anseriformes		
	Anatidae		
95	*Aix sponsa*	28 yr 1 mo[1]	3
96	*Anas platyrhynchos*	19 yr[1]	3
97	*Anser domesticus*	31 yr	2
98	*A. erythropus*	24 yr	5
99	*Branta canadensis*	33 yr	2
100	*B. leucopis*	32 yr	2
101	*Cereopsis novaehollandiae*	33 yr	2
102	*Cygnus buccinator*	>29 yr 5 mo	3
103	*Nyroca* spp.	19 yr[1]	2
104	*Plectropterus gambensis*	>25 yr	3

	Family and Species	Recorded Maximum Life Span	Reference
	(A)	(B)	(C)
	Ciconiiformes		
	Phoenicopteridae		
105	*Phoenicopterus roseus*	22 yr 9 mo	5
	Threskiornithidae		
106	*Threskiornis strictipennis*	33 yr	2
	Ciconiidae		
107	*Ciconia nigra*	30 yr	2,5
108	*Leptoptilus dubius*	30 yr	2
109	*Mycteria americana*	36 yr	2
	Ardeidae		
110	*Ardea cinerea*	>24 yr	5
111	*Leucophoyx thula*	16 yr 10 mo	3
	Pelecaniformes		
	Phalacrocoracidae		
112	*Phalacrocorax carbo*	23 yr	5
	Pelecanidae		
113	*Pelecanus conspicillatus*	32 yr	2
114	*P. crispus*	35 yr	2
115	*P. onocrotalus*	52 yr	2
	Sphenisciformes		
	Spheniscidae		
116	*Aptenodytes patagonica*	26 yr	3
	Apterygiformes		
	Apterygidae		
117	*Apteryx australis*	20 yr[1]	3
	Casuariiformes		
	Casuariidae		
118	*Casuarius papuanus*	26 yr	5
	Rheiformes		
	Rheidae		
119	*Rhea americana*	>26 yr	3
	Struthioniformes		
	Struthionidae		
120	*Struthio australis*	40 yr	2
121	*S. camelus*	50 yr	4

/1/ Still alive at time of report.

Contributors: (a) Rockstein, Morris, (b) Cole, LaMont C.

References: [1] Crandall, L. S. Unpublished. New York Zoological Society, N. Y., 1952. [2] Flower, S. S. 1925. Proc. Zool. Soc. (London), p. 1365. [3] Flower, S. S. 1938. Ibid., A, 108:195. [4] Korschelt, E. 1922. Lebensdauer Altern und Tod. G. Fischer, Jena. [5] Mitchell, P. C. 1911. Proc. Zool. Soc. (London), p. 425. [6] Ross, J. H. 1952. Bull. Mass. Audubon Soc. 36:261.

continued

125. LIFE SPANS: BIRDS

Part II: IN NATURAL HABITAT

	Family and Species	Recorded Maximum Life Span
	(A)	(B)
	Passeriformes	
	Fringillidae	
1	*Richmondena cardinalis*	10 yr
2	*Spinus tristis*	7 yr 6 mo
	Icteridae	
3	*Agelaius phoeniceus*	14 yr 6 mo
4	*Quiscalus quiscalus*	11 yr
	Sturnidae	
5	*Sturnus vulgaris*	8 yr
	Bombycillidae	
6	*Bombycilla cedrorum*	8 yr
	Turdidae	
7	*Hylocichla mustelina*	6 yr
8	*Sialia sialis*	7 yr
9	*Turdus migratorius*	12 yr 6 mo
	Sittidae	
10	*Sitta carolinensis*	8 yr
	Paridae	
11	*Penthestes atricapillus*	9 yr
	Corvidae	
12	*Corvus brachyrhynchos*	13 yr 9 mo
13	*Cyanocitta cristata*	14 yr[1]
	Hirundinidae	
14	*Progne subis*	14 yr
	Piciformes	
	Picidae	
15	*Ceophloeus pileatus*	9 yr 8 mo
	Strigiformes	
	Tytonidae	
16	*Tyto alba*	11 yr 6 mo
	Columbiformes	
	Columbidae	
17	*Columba leucocephala*	8 yr 3 mo
18	*Melopelia asiatica*	12 yr 2 mo
	Charadriiformes	
	Alcidae	
19	*Cepphus grylle*	8 yr
20	*Fratercula arctica*	8 yr[1]
21	*Uria aalge*	11 yr[1]
	Laridae	
22	*Hydropogne tschegrava*	26 yr 1 mo
23	*Larus argentatus*	19 yr
24	*L. delawarensis*	21 yr
25	*L. glaucescens*	20 yr 8 mo
26	*Sterna antillarum*	21 yr
27	*S. fuscata*	18 yr
28	*S. hirundo*	20 yr[1]
29	*S. paradisea*	22 yr 1 mo
	Scolopacidae	
30	*Philohela minor*	8 yr
	Gruiformes	
	Rallidae	
31	*Fulica americana*	13 yr 6 mo
	Falconiformes	
	Pandionidae	
32	*Pandion haliaetus*	21 yr
	Accipitridae	
33	*Buteo borealis*	12 yr 4 mo
34	*B. regalis*	16 yr
35	*B. swainsoni*	13 yr
	Cathartidae	
36	*Coragyps atratus*	12 yr[1]
	Anseriformes	
	Anatidae	
37	*Anas acuta tzitzihoa*	20 yr 6 mo
38	*A. discors*	14 yr
39	*A. platyrhynchos*	20 yr 6 mo
40	*A. rubripes*	18 yr 6 mo
41	*Branta canadensis*	14 yr 6 mo
42	*Chen caerulescens*	13 yr 3 mo
43	*Mareca americana*	15 yr 6 mo
44	*Mergus merganser*	12 yr
	Ciconiiformes	
	Ciconiidae	
45	*Mycteria americana*	11 yr 6 mo
	Ardeidae	
46	*Ardea herodias*	15 yr 4 mo
47	*Casmerodius albus egretta*	16 yr
	Pelecaniformes	
	Anhingidae	
48	*Anhinga anhinga*	12 yr
	Phalacrocoracidae	
49	*Phalacrocorax auritus*	14 yr
	Sulidae	
50	*Morus bassanus*	16 yr 8 mo
	Pelecanidae	
51	*Pelecanus erythrorhynchos*	10 yr 6 mo
52	*P. occidentalis*	14 yr 6 mo
	Podicipediformes	
	Podicipedidae	
53	*Colymbus grisegena holboelli*	5 yr
	Gaviiformes	
	Gaviidae	
54	*Gavia immer*	8 yr

/1/ Still alive at time of report.

Contributor: Low, Seth H.

Reference: Low, S. H. Unpublished. U. S. Fish and Wildlife Service, Patuxent Research Refuge Records, 1952.

126. LIFE SPANS: REPTILES

Life spans are for animals in captivity. Classification adapted from Schmidt and Inger, *Living Reptiles of the World*, 1957.

	Family and Species	Recorded Maximum Life Span	Reference
	(A)	(B)	(C)
	Serpentes		
	Crotalidae		
1	*Ancistrodon contortrix mokeson*	18 yr 6 mo[1]	9
2	*A. piscivorus*	21 yr	3,4
3	*Bothrops lanceolatus*	3 yr[1]	6
4	*Crotalus adamanteus*	15 yr 1 mo[1]	13
5	*C. atrox*	22 yr 2 mo[1]	13
6	*C. cerastes laterorepens*	12 yr 8 mo	9
7	*C. durissus*	>13 yr	3
8	*C. horridus*	15 yr 7 mo	9
9	*C. ruber ruber*	14 yr 6 mo	11
10	*C. tortugensis*	18 yr 4 mo	10
11	*C. unicolor*	13 yr 6 mo	9
12	*C. viridis helleri*	19 yr 5 mo	11
13	*Sistrurus catenatus*	14 yr	8
14	*Trimeresurus purpureomaculatus*	5 yr 9 mo	1
	Viperidae		
15	*Bitis arietans*	>13 yr 11 mo	4
16	*Causus rhombeatus*	>6 yr 7 mo	3
17	*Vipera aspis*	>3 yr	3
18	*V. berus*	>2 yr 1 mo	3
	Elapidae		
19	*Bungarus candidus*	5 yr 4 mo	4
20	*Dendroaspis angusticeps*	>5 yr 3 mo	6
21	*D. viridis*	11 yr 3 mo	6
22	*Micrurus lemniscatus*	10 yr	4
23	*Naja hannah*	12 yr 6 mo	3
24	*N. melanoleuca*	26 yr 3 mo[1]	9
25	*N. naja*	12 yr 4 mo	1
26	*N. nigricollis*	19 yr 2 mo[1]	8
27	*N. nivea*	15 yr 3 mo	8
28	*Pseudechis porphyriacus*	9 yr 2 mo	1
	Colubridae		
29	*Alsophis portoricensis*	2 yr 1 mo	1
30	*Boiga dendrophila*	11 yr 9 mo	8
31	*Clelia clelia*	6 yr	1
32	*Coluber constrictor*	5 yr 4 mo[1]	6
33	*Drymarchon corais couperi*	25 yr 11 mo	13
34	*Elaphe guttata guttata*	21 yr 9 mo	8
35	*E. obsoleta quadrivittata*	17 yr 11 mo	10
36	*E. situla*	23 yr	4
37	*Farancia abacura abacura*	3 yr 2 mo	1
38	*Helicops schistosus*	12 yr 3 mo	1
39	*Heterodon contortrix*	6 yr	6
40	*Lampropeltis doliata amaura*	20 yr 7 mo	12
41	*L. getulus holbrooki*	16 yr	14
42	*L. triangulum triangulum*	8 yr 9 mo	1
43	*Leptodeira annulata*	4 yr 11 mo	3
44	*Lioheterodon madagascariensis*	12 yr 6 mo	4
45	*Masticophis flagellum testaceus*	13 yr 5 mo	8
46	*Natrix erythrogaster erythrogaster*	8 yr 10 mo	6
47	*N. fasciata*	>9 yr 5 mo	3
48	*N. piscator*	9 yr	3,4
49	*N. sipedon sipedon*	7 yr	4
50	*Opheodrys aestivus*	2 yr 5 mo	6
51	*O. vernalis*	2 yr 6 mo	6,8
52	*Pituophis catenifer annectens*	17 yr 7 mo	12
53	*P. melanoleucus melanoleucus*	18 yr 5 mo[1]	14
	Colubridae		
54	*Rhinocheilus lecontei lecontei*	17 yr 1 mo[1]	13
55	*Storeria occipitomaculata occipitomaculata*	2 yr 2 mo	1
56	*Thalerophis mexicanus*	6 yr 4 mo	1
57	*Thamnophis ordinata*	11 yr	3
58	*T. sauritus sauritus*	6 yr 7 mo	3
59	*T. sirtalis*	6 yr	6
	Pythonidae		
60	*Loxocemus bicolor*	16 yr[1]	13
61	*Morelia argus*	13 yr 4 mo	4
62	*Python curtus curtus*	25 yr 9 mo[1]	14
63	*P. molurus bivittatus*	25 yr 8 mo[1]	14
64	*P. reticulatus*	>21 yr 4 mo	3
65	*P. sebae*	20 yr 4 mo[1]	14
	Boidae		
66	*Acrantophis madagascariensis*	19 yr 5 mo	3
67	*Boa annulata*	12 yr 4 mo	1
68	*B. canina*	3 yr 6 mo	1
69	*B. enydris cooki*	14 yr 3 mo	8
70	*Charina bottae bottae*	4 yr 4 mo	16
71	*Constrictor constrictor*	>23 yr	3,4
72	*Epicrates angulifer*	22 yr 7 mo	14
73	*E. cenchria maurus*	27 yr 4 mo	8
74	*E. striatus*	16 yr	1
75	*Eunectes barbouri*	13 yr 11 mo	1,8
76	*E. deschauenseei*	13 yr 10 mo	1,8
77	*E. murinus*	28 yr	4
78	*Lichanura roseofusca roseofusca*	12 yr	8
79	*Tropidophis melanurus*	2 yr 5 mo	1
80	*Ungaliophis continentalis*	17 yr 8 mo	8
	Sauria		
	Varanidae		
81	*Varanus* spp.[2]	15 yr	4
82	*V. bengalensis*	5 yr 6 mo	1
83	*V. gouldi*	6 yr 1 mo	6
84	*V. salvator*	10 yr 9 mo	6
	Helodermatidae		
85	*Heloderma horridum*	9 yr	1
86	*H. suspectum*	24 yr 7 mo	2
	Anguidae		
87	*Anguis fragilis*	32 yr	4
88	*Ophisaurus apodus*	24 yr	7
89	*O. apus*	>17 yr 2 mo	3
90	*O. ventralis*	3 yr 9 mo	1
	Lacertidae		
91	*Lacerta lepida*	14 yr	4
92	*Latastia longicaudata*	2 yr 4 mo[1]	4
	Teiidae		
93	*Callopistes flavipunctatus*	>4 yr 4 mo	4
94	*Dracaena guianensis*	8 yr 6 mo	1
95	*Tupinambis nigropunctatus*	11 yr 11 mo	1
96	*T. teguixin*	12 yr 11 mo	3
	Gerrhosauridae		
97	*Gerrhosaurus flavigularis*	>11 yr 3 mo	4
	Cordylidae		
98	*Cordylus giganteus*	5 yr 3 mo	1
	Scincidae		
99	*Chalcides ocellatus*	9 yr 6 mo	4

/1/ Still alive at time of report. /2/ Species: *niloticus, varius*.

continued

126. LIFE SPANS: REPTILES

	Family and Species	Recorded Maximum Life Span	Reference
	(A)	(B)	(C)
	Sauria		
	Scincidae		
100	*Egernia cunninghami*	>19 yr 11 mo	3,4
101	*E. major*	>7 yr 4 mo	4
102	*Lygosoma casuarinae*	5 yr 4 mo	1
103	*L. quoyii*	>5 yr 2 mo[1]	4
104	*Tiliqua gigas*	>8 yr 8 mo	4
105	*T. scincoides*	>17 yr	3
106	*Trachysaurus rugosus*	7 yr 11 mo	1
	Iguanidae		
107	*Anolis equestris*	3 yr 5 mo	1
108	*A. luteogularis*	2 yr 11 mo	1
109	*Basiliscus vittatus*	5 yr 11 mo	1
110	*Conolophus subcristatus*	17 yr	14
111	*Corythophanes cristatus*	> 2 yr 5 mo	4
112	*Crotaphytus collaris baileyi*	2 yr	6
113	*Cyclura cornuta*	7 yr	4
114	*C. macleayi*	3 yr 5 mo	1
115	*C. stejnegeri*	2 yr 4 mo	6
116	*Dipsosaurus dorsalis dorsalis*	12 yr 3 mo	14
117	*Iguana iguana*	5 yr 2 mo	14
118	*Leiocephalus carinatus*	3 yr 9 mo	1
119	*Sceloporus graciosus*	8 yr	15
120	*S. undulatus*	4 yr 1 mo	6
	Chamaeleonidae		
121	*Chamaeleon* spp.	>3 yr 6 mo	3
122	*C. dilepis*	3 yr 4 mo	8
	Agamidae		
123	*Amphibolurus barbatus*	3 yr 3 mo	1
124	*Physignathus lesueuri*	>6 yr	4
125	*Uromastix aegyptius*	15 yr	4
	Gekkonidae		
126	*Eublepharis macularis*	>11 yr	4
127	*Gekko vittatus*	4 yr 3 mo	4
128	*Hoplodactylus pacificus*	11 yr 6 mo	4
129	*Tarentola mauritanica*	7 yr 5 mo	3
	Crocodylia		
	Gavialidae		
130	*Gavialis gangeticus*	25 yr	4
	Alligatoridae		
131	*Alligator mississipiensis*	>56 yr[1]	4
132	*A. sinensis*	>50 yr[1]	4
133	*Caiman latirostris*	22 yr 1 mo	1
134	*C. niger*	>28 yr	4
135	*C. sclerops*	16 yr 7 mo	1
136	*Paleosuchus palpebrosus*	5 yr 9 mo	3
	Crocodylidae		
137	*Crocodylus acutus*	13 yr 6 mo	1
138	*C. cataphractus*	>20 yr[1]	4
139	*C. intermedius*	>22 yr 4 mo[1]	4
140	*C. niloticus*	40 yr	5
141	*C. palustris*	30 yr 11 mo	3
142	*C. porosus*	15 yr 7 mo	4
143	*C. siamensis*	>16 yr 3 mo[1]	4
144	*Osteolaemus tetraspis*	33 yr 5 mo	1
145	*Tomistoma schlegeli*	23 yr	4
	Chelonia		
	Chelidae		
146	*Chelodina longicollis*	36 yr 9 mo	4
147	*Chelys fimbriata*	10 yr 4 mo	1
148	*Emydura novaeguineae*	14 yr	4
149	*Hydraspis hilari*	20 yr 9 mo	1
150	*Hydromedusa tectifera*	8 yr 10 mo	1
151	*Phrynops geoffroyana*	5 yr	4
152	*Platemys spixi*	>21 yr 4 mo[1]	4
	Pelomedusidae		
153	*Pelomedusa subrufa*	10 yr 2 mo	1
154	*Pelusios subniger*	40 yr 8 mo[1]	4
	Trionychidae		
155	*Trionyx ferox*	25 yr	4
156	*T. triunguis*	25 yr 6 mo	4
	Chelonidae		
157	*Caretta caretta*	33 yr	1
158	*Chelonia mydas*	12 yr 1 mo[1]	4
159	*Eretmochelys imbricata*	16 yr	4
	Testudinidae		
160	*Gopherus polyphemus*	8 yr 6 mo	1
161	*Kinixys belliana*	9 yr 9 mo	1
162	*Malacochersus tornieri*	7 yr 4 mo	1
163	*Testudo elephantopus*	100-150 yr	4
164	*T. gigantea*	68 yr	4
165	*T. graeca*	33 yr	4
166	*T. sumeirei*	152 yr	4
167	*T. vicina*	30 yr 4 mo[1]	6
	Emydidae		
168	*Chrysemys picta*	11 yr	4
169	*Clemmys bealei*	27 yr 4 mo	1
170	*C. guttata*	42 yr	4
171	*C. insculpta*	13 yr 5 mo[1]	8
172	*Cyclemys amboinensis*	19 yr 11 mo	1
173	*Emys orbicularis*	66 yr	4
174	*Geoclemys reevesi*	24 yr 3 mo	1
175	*Geoemyda punctularia*	6 yr 8 mo[1]	6
176	*G. spengleri*	3 yr 5 mo[1]	6
177	*Graptemys pseudogeographica*	21 yr 6 mo[1]	1
178	*Malaclemys terrapin centrata*	>21 yr[1]	4
179	*Orlitia borneenis*	>8 yr 6 mo	4
180	*Pseudemys floridana mobilensis*	12 yr 6 mo	1
181	*P. ornata*	5 yr 8 mo[1]	6
182	*P. scripta*	7 yr 1 mo	6
183	*Terrapene carolina*	83-88 yr	4
	Kinosternidae		
184	*Kinosternon baurii*	>20 yr[1]	4
185	*K. sonoriense*	21 yr 9 mo	1
186	*K. subrubrum*	>38 yr[1]	4
187	*Sternotherus odoratus*	53 yr 3 mo[1]	1
	Chelydridae		
188	*Chelydra serpentina*	20 yr	4
189	*Macrochelys temmincki*	58 yr 8 mo[1]	1
	Rhynchocephalia		
	Rhynchoecephalidae		
190	*Sphenodon punctatus*	>28 yr[1]	3

/1/ Still alive at time of report.

Contributors: (a) Tanner, Vasco M., (b) Rockstein, Morris, (c) Cole, LaMont C., (d) Shaw, Charles E.

continued

126. LIFE SPANS: REPTILES

References: [1] Conant, R., and R. J. Hudson. 1949. Herpetologica 5:1. [2] Crossman, A. M. 1956. Copeia (1):54. [3] Flower, S. S. 1925. Proc. Zool. Soc. (London), p. 911. [4] Flower, S. S. 1937. Ibid., p. 1. [5] Korschelt, E. 1922. Lebensdauer Altern und Tod. G. Fischer, Jena. [6] Mann, W. M. 1934. Wild animals in and out of the zoo. Smithsonian Institution, New York. p. 338. [7] Perkins, C. B. 1947. Copeia (2):144. [8] Perkins, C. B. 1954. Ibid. (3):229. [9] Perkins, C. B. 1955. Ibid. (3):262. [10] Shaw, C. E. 1957. Ibid. (1):50. [11] Shaw, C. E. 1957. Ibid. (4):310. [12] Shaw, C. E. 1958. Ibid. (3):221. [13] Shaw, C. E. 1959. Ibid. (4):336. [14] Shaw, C. E. Unpublished. San Diego Zoological Gardens, California, 1961. [15] Stebbins, R. C. 1948. Copeia (1):20. [16] Tanner, V. M. Unpublished. Brigham Young Univ., Provo, Utah. 1952.

127. LIFE SPANS: AMPHIBIANS

Life spans are for animals in captivity. Classification adapted from Cochran, *Living Amphibians of the World*, 1961.

	Family and Species	Recorded Maximum Life Span	Reference
	(A)	(B)	(C)
	Gymnophiona		
	Caeciliidae		
1	*Siphonops annulatus*	>9 yr 6 mo	2,3
	Salientia		
	Microhylidae		
2	*Kaloula pulchra*	>6 yr 1 mo	3
3	*Microhyla carolinensis*	6 yr 1 mo	1
	Rhacophoridae		
4	*Rhacophorus buergeri*	>3 yr 2 mo	3
	Ranidae		
5	*Rana catesbeiana*	>15 yr 8 mo	3
6	*R. clamitans*	>10 yr 2 mo	3
7	*R. esculenta*	>5 yr 2 mo	3
8	*R. mascareniensis*	>4 yr 4 mo	3
9	*R. occipitalis*	>4 yr 3 mo	3
10	*R. oxyrhyncha*	>5 yr 5 mo	3
11	*R. pipiens*	>5 yr 11 mo	3
12	*R. temporaria*	>4 yr 4 mo	2,3
13	*R. tigrina*	>6 yr 7 mo	2,3
	Hylidae		
14	*Hyla arborea*	>14 yr 1 mo	2,3
15	*H. aurea*	>7 yr 3 mo	2
16	*H. caerulea*	>15 yr	3
17	*H. cinerea*	6 yr 3 mo	1
18	*H. gratiosa*	5 yr 11 mo	1
19	*H. raddiana*	>2 yr 4 mo	2
20	*H. regilla*	>3 yr 9 mo	3
21	*H. septentrionalis*	6 yr 9 mo	1
22	*H. versicolor*	6 yr 9 mo	3
	Bufonidae		
23	*Bufo alvarius*	2 yr	1
24	*B. americanus*	10-15 yr	2
25	*B. arenarum*	>7 yr 5 mo	2
26	*B. boreas*	6 yr	1
27	*B. calamita*	16 yr	2
28	*B. compactilis*	4 yr 3 mo	1
29	*B. dodsoni*	>3 yr 8 mo	2
30	*B. marinus*	15 yr	4
31	*B. mauritanicus*	>4 yr	2
32	*B. melanosticus*	>4 yr 4 mo	2
	Bufonidae		
33	*Bufo peltacephalus*	13 yr 2 mo	1
34	*B. pentoni*	>1 yr 7 mo	2
35	*B. regularis*	>6 yr 8 mo	2
36	*B. viridis*	>8 yr 10 mo	2
37	*B. vittatus*	>2 yr 5 mo	2
	Leptodactylidae		
38	*Calyptocephalus gayi*	>3 yr 2 mo	2
39	*Ceratophrys ornata*	>13 yr	3
40	*Leptodactylus mystacinus*	>7 yr	2
41	*L. ocellatus*	>5 yr 4 mo	2
42	*L. pentadactylus*	15 yr 9 mo	1
43	*Limnodynastes tasmaniensis*	>4 yr	3
	Pelobatidae		
44	*Megalophrys* spp.	>2 yr 10 mo	2
45	*Pelobates fuscus*	11 yr	3
46	*Scaphiopus couchi*	3 yr 4 mo	1
	Discoglossidae		
47	*Alytes obstetricans*	>5 yr	2
48	*Bombina bombina*	20 yr	3
49	*B. variegata pachypus*	>6 yr 11 mo	2
50	*Discoglossus pictus*	>6 yr 11 mo	2
	Pipidae		
51	*Pipa pipa*	7 yr 10 mo[1]	3
52	*Xenopus gilli*	>9 yr[1]	3
53	*X. laevis*	15 yr	3
54	*X. muelleri*	>8 yr 9 mo[1]	3
	Caudata		
	Sirenidae		
55	*Siren lacertina*	>24 yr 6 mo	2
	Proteidae		
56	*Necturus maculosus*	>8 yr 10 mo	3
57	*Proteus anguinus*	14 yr 6 mo	3
	Plethodontidae		
58	*Eurycea lucifuga*	>1 yr	3
59	*Typhlomolge rathbuni*	>1 yr	3
	Amphiumidae		
60	*Amphiuma means*	>26 yr 9 mo	2,3
	Salamandridae		
61	*Pleurodeles waltl*	>19 yr 6 mo	3
62	*Salamandra atra*	>3 yr 1 mo	2

/1/ Still alive at time of report.

continued

127. LIFE SPANS: AMPHIBIANS

	Family and Species	Recorded Maximum Life Span	Reference
	(A)	(B)	(C)
	Caudata		
	Salamandridae		
63	*Salamandra maculosa*	>24 yr	3
64	*Salamandrina terdigitata*	>1 yr 6 mo	3
65	*Triturus alpestris*	15 yr	3
66	*T. cristatus*	>4 yr 1 mo	2
67	*T. cristatus* (hybrid)	17 yr	2
68	*T. helvetica*	>12 yr	3
69	*T. macrosoma*	>3 yr 9 mo	2
70	*T. marmorata*	>5 yr 1 mo	2
71	*T. poireti*	14 yr	3
	Salamandridae		
72	*Triturus pyrrhogaster*	25 yr	3
73	*T. torosus*	21 yr	3
74	*T. viridescens*	>2 yr 11 mo	2
75	*T. vulgaris*	18 yr	3
76	*Tylototriton verrucosus*	>4 yr 11 mo	2
	Ambystomidae		
77	*Ambystoma maculatum*	>24 yr	3
78	*A. tigrinum*	11 yr	3
	Cryptobranchidae		
79	*Cryptobranchus alleganiensis*	>28 yr 7 mo	3
80	*Megalobatrachus maximus*	52 yr	3

Contributors: (a) Rockstein, Morris, (b) Cole, LaMont C., (c) Tanner, Vasco M.

References: [1] Conant, R., and R. G. Hudson. 1949. Herpetologica 5:1. [2] Flower, S. S. 1925. Proc. Zool. Soc. (London), p. 269. [3] Flower, S. S. 1936. Ibid. (2):369. [4] Perkins, C. B. 1947. Copeia (2):144.

128. LIFE SPANS: FISHES

Classification adapted from Herald, *Living Fishes of the World,* 1961.

Part I: IN CAPTIVITY

	Family and Species	Recorded Maximum Life Span	Reference
	(A)	(B)	(C)
	Dipneusti		
	Protopteridae		
1	*Protopterus annectans*	18 yr	1,2
	Lepidosirenidae		
2	*Lepidosiren paradoxa*	>8 yr 3 mo	2
	Ceratodontidae		
3	*Ceratodus forsteri*	>19 yr 8 mo	1,2
	Cladista		
	Polypteridae		
4	*Polypterus senegalus*	34 yr	2
	Plectognathi		
	Tetraodontidae		
5	*Tetraodon fahaka*	>5 yr 11 mo	1
6	*T. solandri*	7 yr	2
	Thoracostei		
	Gasterosteidae		
7	*Gasterosteus aculeatus*	2 yr 5 mo	2
	Scleroparei		
	Cottidae		
8	*Cottus burbalis*	3 yr 5 mo	2
	Triglidae		
9	*Trigla hirundo*	6 yr 9 mo	1,2
	Percomorphi		
	Mugilidae		
10	*Mugil cephalus*	11 yr	2
	Anabantidae		
11	*Anabas kingsleyeae*	8 yr 8 mo	1
12	*A. testudineus*	11 yr	2
13	*Macropodus opercularis*	>8 yr	1
	Pholidae		
14	*Pholis gunnellus*	1 yr 2 mo	1,2
	Blenniidae		
15	*Blennius gattorugine*	5 yr	1,2
	Gobiidae		
16	*Gobius minutus*	<2 yr	1
17	*G. paganellus*	1 yr	1
18	*Latrunculus pellucidus*	1 yr	1
19	*Periophthalmus barbarus*	2 yr 2 mo	3
	Eleotridae		
20	*Eleotris* spp.	>5 yr 7 mo[1]	1
	Scombridae		
21	*Scomber scombrus*	3-4 yr	1
	Labridae		
22	*Tautoga onitis*	>8 yr	1
	Cichlidae		
23	*Acara tetramerus*	>7 yr	1
24	*Herichthys cyanoguttatus*	5 yr	2
25	*Tilapia* spp.	>7 yr	1
	Sparidae		
26	*Archosargus probatocephalus*	>6 yr	1
27	*Spondyliosoma cantharus*	>15 yr	1
	Sciaenidae		
28	*Pogonias cromis*	6 yr 6 mo	1
29	*Sciaenops ocellata*	>7 yr	1
	Pomadasyidae		
30	*Anisotremus davidsoni*	7 yr 3 mo	3

/1/ Still alive at time of report.

continued

128. LIFE SPANS: FISHES

Part I: IN CAPTIVITY

	Family and Species	Recorded Maximum Life Span	Reference
	(A)	(B)	(C)
	Percomorphi		
	Lutianidae		
31	*Lutjanus griseus*	>7 yr	1
32	*L. peru*	7 yr 2 mo	3
33	*L. synagris*	>7 yr	1
	Centropomidae		
34	*Lates niloticus*	7 yr 9 mo	1
	Carangidae		
35	*Seriola dorsalis*	7 yr 3 mo	3
	Percidae		
36	*Hadropterus maculatus*	>7 yr[1]	1
37	*Perca flavescens*	12 yr	2
38	*P. fluviatilis*	>10 yr 8 mo	2
	Centrarchidae		
39	*Ambloplites rupestris*	12 yr	1,2
40	*Lepomis auritus*	>8 yr[1]	1
41	*L. cyanellus*	>7 yr 6 mo[1]	1
42	*L. gibbosus*	13 yr	2
43	*L. megalotis*	12 yr	2
44	*Micropterus salmoides*	>11 yr[1]	1
45	*Pomoxis nigromaculatus*	12 yr	2
46	*P. sparoides*	>7 yr 6 mo[1]	1
	Serranidae		
47	*Epinephelus gigas*	24 yr	1,2
48	*Morone labrax*	>10 yr 1 mo	2
49	*Roccus saxatilus*	24 yr	2
	Solenichthys		
	Syngnathidae		
50	*Hippocampus guttulatus*	>6 yr	1
51	*H. hippocampus*	>1 yr 3 mo	1
52	*H. hudsonius*	>4 yr 7 mo	1
	Apodes		
	Congridae		
53	*Conger conger*	9 yr[1]	1
	Anguillidae		
54	*Anguilla anguilla*	55 yr	2
55	*A. rostrata*	50 yr	1
	Ostariophysi		
	Mochocidae		
56	*Synodontis schall*	31 yr	1,2
	Ictaluridae		
57	*Ictalurus catus*	>8 yr 1 mo	1
	Pimelodidae		
58	*Pimelodus* spp.	>7 yr[1]	1
	Siluridae		
59	*Saccobranchus fossilis*	>17 yr 6 mo	1
	Claridae		
60	*Clarias lazera*	>16 yr 2 mo	1
	Ariidae		
61	*Galeichthys felis*	>7 yr[1]	1
	Callichthyidae		
62	*Callichthys punctatus*	>8 yr 10 mo	1
	Cobitidae		
63	*Misgurnus anguillicaudatus*	>10 yr 2 mo	2
64	*M. fossilis*	>21 yr 8 mo[1]	1
	Cyprinidae		
65	*Abramis brama*	17 yr	2
66	*Barbus bynni*	>16 yr 3 mo[1]	1
67	*Carassius auratus*	30 yr	1,2
	Cyprinidae		
68	*Cyprinus carpio*	47 yr	2
69	*Leuciscus cephalus*	11 yr	2
70	*L. idus*	29 yr 9 mo	1,2
71	*L. leuciscus*	8 yr	1
72	*Notemigonus crysoleucas*	>7 yr[1]	1
73	*Phoxinus phoxinus*	13 yr	2
74	*Scardinius erythrophthalmus*	10 yr[1]	1
	Gymnotidae		
75	*Electrophorus electricus*	>11 yr 6 mo	1
	Characidae		
76	*Alestes* spp.	>8 yr 4 mo	1
77	*Hydrocyon* spp.	>7 yr 11 mo	1
	Haplomi		
	Esocidae		
78	*Esox lucius*	10 yr	1
79	*E. masquinongy*	10 yr	1
	Isospondyli		
	Mormyridae		
80	*Hyperopisus bebe*	>10 yr 1 mo	1
81	*Marcusenius isidori*	>28 yr	2
	Notopteridae		
82	*Xenomystis nigri*	>11 yr 5 mo[1]	1
	Coregonidae		
83	*Coregonus clupeaformis*	12 yr	2
	Salmonidae		
84	*Salmo gairdneri*	>3 yr 11 mo	1
85	*S. trutta*	10 yr	2
86	*Salvelinus malma*	20 yr	2
87	*S. namaycush*	12 yr	2
	Ginglymodi		
	Lepisosteidae		
88	*Lepisosteus osseus*	24 yr	2
89	*L. platostomus*	>20 yr[1]	1
	Protospondyli		
	Amiidae		
90	*Amia calva*	24 yr	2
	Chondrostei		
	Acipenseridae		
91	*Acipenser ruthenus*	>46 yr 1 mo	2
92	*A. sturio*	>6 yr 10 mo	1,2
	Batoidei		
	Dasyatidae		
93	*Dasyatis pastinaca*	>21 yr	2
	Rajidae		
94	*Raja maculata*	>5 yr 10 mo	2
	Selachii		
	Scyliorhinidae		
95	*Scyliorhinus stellaris*	18 yr	2
	Orectolobidae		
96	*Ginglymostoma* spp.	9 yr	2
	Petromyzones		
	Petromyzonidae		
97	*Lampetra fluviatilis*	<1 yr	1

/1/ Still alive at time of report.

continued

128. LIFE SPANS: FISHES

Part I: IN CAPTIVITY

Contributors: (a) Rockstein, Morris, (b) Cole, LaMont C., (c) Carlander, Kenneth D., (d) Prescott, John H.

References: [1] Flower, S. S. 1925. Proc. Zool. Soc. (London), p. 247. [2] Flower, S. S. 1935. Ibid., p. 265. [3] Prescott, J. H. Unpublished. Marineland of the Pacific, California, 1961.

Part II: IN NATURAL HABITAT

	Family and Species	Recorded Maximum Life Span	Reference
	(A)	(B)	(C)
	Heterosomata		
	Soleidae		
1	*Solea solea*	9 yr	17
	Pleuronectidae		
2	*Eopsetta jordani*	18 yr	20
3	*Glyptocephalus cynoglossus*	14 yr	11
4	*Hippoglossoides platessoides*	6 yr	4
5	*Hippoglossus hippoglossus*	40 yr	34
6	*H. stenolepis*	40 yr	3
7	*Hypsopsetta guttulata*	9 yr	9
8	*Lepidopsetta bilineata*	15 yr	76
9	*Limanda aspera*	15 yr	76
10	*Microstomus pacificus*	15 yr	44
11	*Platichthys stellatus*	13 yr	76
12	*Pleuronectes platessa*	<30 yr	34
	Bothidae		
13	*Citharichthys sordidus*	9 yr	31
14	*Lophopsetta aquosa*	7 yr	74
15	*Paralichthys californicus*	15 yr	31
16	*Pseudorhombus cinnamoneus*	5 yr	64
17	*Rhombus maximus*	12 yr	77
	Thoracostei		
	Gasterosteidae		
18	*Gasterosteus aculeatus*	3 yr	42
	Scleroparei		
	Platycephalidae		
19	*Neoplatycephalus macrodon*	6 yr	24
	Anoplopomatidae		
20	*Anoplopoma fimbria*	20 yr	31
	Ophiodontidae		
21	*Ophiodon elongatus*	16 yr	31
	Cottidae		
22	*Myoxocephalus octodecemspinosus*	11 yr	75
23	*Scorpaenichthys marmoratus*	>13 yr	81
	Scorpaenidae		
24	*Medialuna californiensis*	8 yr	9
25	*Pontinus clemensi*	8 yr	30
26	*Sebastes marinus*	>50 yr	36, 54
27	*Sebastodes alutus*	>20 yr	1
	Percomorphi		
	Atherinidae		
28	*Atherinopsis californiensis*	11 yr	9
29	*Leuresthes tenuis*	4 yr	18
	Sphyraenidae		
30	*Sphyraena argentea*	11 yr	119
	Zoarcidae		
31	*Macrozoarces americanus*	17 yr	82
	Pholidae		
32	*Centronotus gunnellus*	5 yr	88
	Callionymidae		
33	*Callionymus lyra*	7 yr	16
	Scombridae		
34	*Germo alalunga*	9 yr	105
35	*Neothunnus macropterus*	9 yr	105
36	*Pneumatophorus diego*	11 yr	29
37	*Scomber scombrus*	15 yr	80
38	*Scomberomorus maculatus*	5 yr	55
39	*Thunnus thynnus*	7 yr	100
	Trichiuridae		
40	*Trichiurus lepturus*	6 yr	72
	Labridae		
41	*Pimelometopon pulchrum*	53 yr	32
	Embiotocidae		
42	*Amphistichus argenteus*	9 yr	15
43	*Cymatogaster aggregata*	3 yr	9
44	*Embiotoca lateralis*	9 yr	108
45	*Hyperprosopon argenteum*	6 yr	9
46	*Taeniotoca lateralis*	9 yr	108
	Sciaenidae		
47	*Aplodinotus grunniens*	13 yr	28
48	*Cheilotrema saturnum*	20 yr	62
49	*Cynoscion nobilis*	>20 yr	31
50	*Menticirrhus undulatus*	8 yr	9
51	*Roncador stearnsi*	15 yr	9
	Centropomidae		
52	*Centropomus undecimalis*	7 yr	118
	Carangidae		
53	*Seriola dorsalis*	12 yr	10
54	*Trachurus symmetricus*	>30 yr	31
	Malacanthidae		
55	*Caulolatilus princeps*	13 yr	31
	Percidae		
56	*Boleosoma longinamum*	4 yr	90
57	*Etheostoma blennoides*	4 yr	59
58	*Lucioperca lucioperca*	14 yr	34
59	*Perca fluviatilis*	10 yr	103
60	*Percina caprodes*	3 yr	14
61	*Poecilichthys zonalis*	3 yr	59
62	*Stizostedion canadense*	13 yr	47
63	*S. vitreum*	18 yr	52
	Centrarchidae		
64	*Ambloplites rupestris*	18 yr	13
65	*Centrarchus macropterus*	6 yr	97
66	*Chaenobryttus coronarius*	7 yr	14
67	*Lepomis cyanellus*	9 yr	5

continued

128. LIFE SPANS: FISHES

Part II: IN NATURAL HABITAT

	Family and Species	Recorded Maximum Life Span	Reference
	(A)	(B)	(C)
	Percomorphi		
	Centrarchidae		
68	*Lepomis humilis*	4 yr	7
69	*L. macrochirus*	10 yr	53
70	*L. microlophus*	8 yr	94
71	*Micropterus coosae*	10 yr	85
72	*M. dolomieu*	14 yr	34
73	*M. punctulatus*	7 yr	111
74	*M. salmoides*	16 yr	50
75	*Pomoxis annularis*	9 yr	70
	Serranidae		
76	*Lepibema chrysops*	9 yr	106
77	*Morone americana*	16 yr	23
78	*M. interrupta*	7 yr	61
79	*Paralabrax clathratus*	>20 yr	31
80	*Stereolepis gigas*	72-75 yr	31
	Zeomorphi		
	Zeidae		
81	*Zeus faker*	9 yr	25
	Anacanthini		
	Gadidae		
82	*Brosme brosme*	14 yr	51
83	*Eleginus navaga*	12 yr	87
84	*Gadus morhua*	16 yr	33
85	*G. virens*	23 yr	101
86	*Lota lota*	16 yr	92
87	*Melanogrammus aeglefinus*	15 yr	34
88	*Merlangius merlangus*	9-10 yr	68
89	*Merluccius merluccius*	12 yr	34
90	*Molva molva*	14 yr	51
91	*Phycis blennoides*	10 yr	49
92	*Theragra chalcogramma*	15 yr	76
	Microcyprini		
	Poeciliidae		
93	*Gambusia affinis*	1 yr 6 mo	56
	Synentognathi		
	Scomberesocidae		
94	*Cololabis saira*	4 yr	73
	Hemirhamphidae		
95	*Reporhamphus melanochir*	7 yr	63
	Apodes		
	Congridae		
96	*Conger myriaster*	8 yr	114
97	*Muraenesox cinereus*	15 yr	84
	Anguillidae		
98	*Anguilla vulgaris*	15 yr	43
	Ostariophysi		
	Ictaluridae		
99	*Ameiurus melas*	9 yr	96
100	*A. natalis*	4 yr	60
101	*A. nebulosis*	3 yr	60
102	*Ictalurus lacustris*	13 yr	60
103	*Pilodictis olivaris*	15 yr	8
	Catostomidae		
104	*Carpiodes carpio*	6 yr	115
105	*Catostomus catostomus*	13 yr	92
	Catostomidae		
106	*Catostomus commersonii*	12 yr	92
107	*Erimyzon sucetta*	8 yr	116
108	*Ictiobus bubalus*	12 yr	102
109	*I. cyprinellus*	14 yr	39
110	*Moxostoma aureolum*	9 yr	28
111	*Thoburnia rhothoeca*	7 yr	91
	Cyprinidae		
112	*Abramis brama*	10 yr	103
113	*Couesius plumbeus*	4 yr	93
114	*Hybognathus nuchalis*	2 yr	89
115	*Hyborhynchus notatus*	3 yr	14
116	*Idus melanotus*	6 yr	103
117	*Lavinia exilicauda*	6 yr	78
118	*Leuciscus rutilus*	8 yr	103
119	*Notemigonus crysoleucas*	9 yr	22
120	*Notropis cornutus*	6 yr	95
121	*Orthodon microlepidotus*	5 yr	79
122	*Ptychocheilus grandis*	9 yr	113
123	*P. oregonensis*	11 yr	21
124	*Rhinichthys cataractae*	5 yr	57
125	*Rutilus rutilus*	12 yr	34
126	*Semotilus corporalis*	6 yr	120
	Iniomi		
	Myctophidae		
127	*Lampanyctus leucopsaurus*	6 yr	58
	Haplomi		
	Esocidae		
128	*Esox lucius*	24 yr	71
129	*E. masquinongy*	19 yr	14
130	*E. niger*	8 yr	67
	Isospondyli		
	Hiodontidae		
131	*Amphiodon alosoides*	10 yr	70
132	*Hiodon tergisus*	7 yr	6
	Osmeridae		
133	*Mallotus villosus*	7 yr	46
134	*Osmerus mordax*	6 yr	66
135	*Thaleichthys pacificus*	4 yr	109
	Thymallidae		
136	*Thymallus signifer*	11 yr	69
	Coregonidae		
137	*Coregonus clupeaformis*	26 yr	48
138	*Leucichthys artedii*	13 yr	48
139	*L. nigripinnis*	11 yr	53
140	*L. zenithicus*	10 yr	117
141	*Prosopium cylindraceum*	14 yr	92
142	*P. williamsoni*	17 yr	65
143	*Stenodus leucichthys*	16 yr	27
	Salmonidae		
144	*Oncorhynchus gorbuscha*	1 yr 9 mo	99
145	*O. keta*	5 yr	45
146	*O. kisutch*	4 yr	99
147	*O. nerka*	8 yr	12
148	*O. tshawytscha*	7 yr	99
149	*Salmo clarki*	10 yr	83
150	*S. gairdneri*	9 yr	112
151	*S. salar salar*	13 yr	34
152	*S. salar sebago*	8 yr	14
153	*Salvelinus alpinus*	22 yr	110

continued

128. LIFE SPANS: FISHES

Part II: IN NATURAL HABITAT

	Family and Species	Recorded Maximum Life Span	Reference
	(A)	(B)	(C)
	Isospondyli		
	Salmonidae		
154	*Salvelinus aureolus*	5 yr	38
155	*S. fontinalis*	8 yr	37
156	*S. namaycush*	41 yr	110
	Engraulidae		
157	*Engraulis mordax*	7 yr	19
	Dorosomidae		
158	*Dorosoma cepedianum*	10 yr	86
	Clupeidae		
159	*Alosa pseudoharengus*	9 yr	40
160	*A. sapidissima*	13 yr	35
161	*Clupea harengus*	19 yr	34
162	*C. pallasi*	19 yr	98
163	*Sardinops caerulea*	13 yr	107
	Ginglymodi		
	Lepisosteidae		
164	*Lepisosteus osseus*	30 yr	13
	Protospondyli		
	Amiidae		
165	*Amia calva*	30 yr	13
	Chondrostei		
	Polyodontidae		
166	*Polyodon spathula*	24 yr	104
	Acipenseridae		
167	*Acipenser brevirostris*	14 yr	41
168	*A. fulvescens*	152 yr	2
169	*A. oxyrhynchus*	12 yr	41
170	*A. transmontanus*	82 yr	26
	Petromyzones		
	Petromyzonidae		
171	*Ichthyomyzon fossor*	6 yr	14
172	*Petromyzon marinus*	7 yr	121

Contributors: (a) Carlander, Kenneth D., (b) Fitch, John E.

References: [1] Alverson, D., and S. Westrheim. 1961. Rappts. procès-verbaux réunions Conseil permanent intern. exploration mer 150:12. [2] Anderson, A. W., ed. 1954. Com. Fisheries Rev. 16(9):28. [3] Babcock, J. 1929. Can. Fisherman 16(1):39. [4] Bagenal, T. 1955. J. Marine Biol. Assoc. United Kingdom 34(2):297. [5] Bailey, R. M., and K. F. Lagler. 1938. Papers Mich. Acad. Sci. 23:577. [6] Bajkov, A. 1930. Trans. Am. Fisheries Soc. 60:215. [7] Barney, R. L., and B. J. Anson. 1923. U. S. Fish Comm. Rept. 1922, appendix 15. [8] Barnickol, P. G., and W. C. Starrett. 1951. Illinois Nat. Hist. Survey Bull. 25:267. [9] Baxter, J. L. 1960. Inshore fishes of California. California Dept. of Fish and Game, Sacramento. [10] Baxter, J. L., et al. 1960. Calif. Dept. Fish and Game Fish Bull. 110:29. [11] Bowers, A. B. 1960. J. conseil permanent intern. exploration mer 25(2). [12] Bransby, J. T. 1944. U. S. Fish Wildlife Service Fishery Bull. 50:237. [13] Breder, C. M., Jr. 1936. Bull. N. Y. Zool. Soc. 39:116. [14] Carlander, K. D. 1950. Handbook of freshwater fishery biology. W. C. Brown, Dubuque, Iowa. [15] Carlisle, J. G., Jr., et al. 1960. Calif. Dept. Fish and Game Fish Bull. 109:36. [16] Chang, H. 1951. J. Marine Biol. Assoc. United Kingdom 30(2):281. [17] Christensen, J. 1960. Danmarks Fisk.-Havundersokelser Medd. 3(2):19. [18] Clark, F. N. 1938. Calif. Fish and Game 24:52. [19] Clark, F. N., and J. B. Phillips. 1952. Ibid. 38:198. [20] Cleaver, F. 1949. Wash. Dept. Fisheries Biol. Rept. 48A:3. [21] Clemens, W. A. 1939. Fisheries Research Board Can. Bull. 56:27. [22] Cooper, G. P. 1936. Papers Mich. Acad. Sci. 22:587. [23] Cooper, G. P. 1941. Maine Dept. Inland Fisheries and Game Fish Survey Rept. 4. [24] Dakin, W. 1939. Records Australian Museum 20(4):282. [25] Desbrosses, P. 1939. Rappts. procès-verbaux réunions Conseil permanent intern. exploration mer 111:84. [26] Donaldson, I. Unpublished, 1959. [27] Dymond, J. R. 1943. Trans. Roy. Soc. Can., V, 24:172. [28] Eddy, S., and K. D. Carlander. 1942. Minn. Dept. Conservation Fisheries Research Unit Invest. Rept. 28. [29] Fitch, J. E. 1951. Calif. Div. Fish and Game Fish Bull. 83:27. [30] Fitch, J. E. 1955. J. Wash. Acad. Sci. 45:61. [31] Fitch, J. E. 1960. Offshore fishes of California. California Dept. of Fish and Game, Sacramento. [32] Fitch, J. E. 1960. Outdoor Calif. 21(7):2. [33] Fleming, A. M. 1960. J. Fisheries Research Board Can. 17:775. [34] Flower, S. S. 1935. Proc. Zool. Soc. (London), p. 265. [35] Fredin, R. A. Unpublished. U. S. Fish and Wildlife Service, Beaufort, N. Carolina, 1952. [36] Fridriksson, A. 1961. Rappts. procès-verbaux réunions Conseil permanent intern. exploration mer 150:163. [37] Fry, H. D., Jr. 1936. Calif. Fish and Game 22:65. [38] Fuller, J. L., and G. P. Cooper. 1946. Maine Dept.

continued

Inland Fisheries and Game Fish Survey Rept. 7. [39] Gowanloch, J. N. 1951. Louisiana Conservationist 3:10. [40] Graham, J. J. 1956. Univ. Toronto Studies Biol. Ser. 62. [41] Greeley, J. R. 1937. N. Y. State Conservation Dept. Biol. Survey 11(suppl. 25th Ann. Rept.). [42] Greenbank, J., and P. R. Nelson. 1959. U. S. Fish Wildlife Service Fishery Bull. 153:537. [43] Haempel, A., and E. Neresheimer. 1914. Z. Fischerei 14(4):265. [44] Hagerman, F. B. 1952. Calif. Div. Fish and Game Fish Bull. 85:31. [45] Hammett, F. S., and D. W. Hammett. 1939. Growth 3:197. [46] Hansen, P. 1943. Ann. biol. conseil permanent intern. exploration mer 1:121. [47] Hart, J. L. 1928. Univ. Toronto Studies Biol. Ser. 31:45. [48] Hart, J. L. 1931. Contribs. Can. Biol. and Fisheries 6:429. [49] Hart, T. 1950. J. conseil permanent intern. exploration mer 16(3):335. [50] Hile, R. 1931. Indiana Lakes and Streams Invest. 2:9. [51] Joenoes, G. 1961. Ber. deut. wiss. Komm. Meeresforsch. 16(2):129. [52] Juday, C., and C. L. Schloemer. 1938. Limnol. Lab. Wisconsin Geol. Nat. Hist. Survey 5. [53] Keleher, J. J. 1952. J. Fisheries Research Board Can. 8:469. [54] Kelly, G. F., and R. S. Wolf. 1959. U. S. Fish Wildlife Service Fishery Bull. 156:1. [55] Klima, E. F. 1959. Florida Board Conservation Tech. Ser. 27:1. [56] Krumholz, L. A. 1948. Ecol. Monographs 18:1. [57] Kuehn, J. H. 1949. Proc. Minn. Acad. Sci. 17:81. [58] Kulikova, E. B. 1953. In B. N. Nikitin, ed. Marine biology. American Institute of Biological Sciences, Washington, D. C. p. 284. [59] Lachner, E. A., E. F. Westlake, and P. S. Handwerk. 1950. Am. Midland Naturalist 43:92. [60] Lewis, W. M. 1950. Iowa State Coll. J. Sci. 24:287. [61] Lewis, W. M., and K. D. Carlander. 1948. Ibid. 22:185. [62] Limbaugh, C. 1961. Calif. Fish and Game 47(2):163. [63] Ling, J. K. 1958. Australian J. Marine and Freshwater Research 9:60. [64] Matsuura, S. 1961. Record Oceanog. Works Japan Spec. Rept. 5:103. [65] McHugh, J. L. 1941. J. Fisheries Research Board Can. 5:337. [66] McKenzie, R. A. 1958. Ibid. 15:1313. [67] Meehean, O. L. 1935. Proc. Louisiana Acad. Sci. 2:139. [68] Messtorff, J. 1959. Ber. deut. wiss. Komm. Meeresforsch., n.F. 15(4):277. [69] Miller, R. B. 1946. Copeia, p. 227. [70] Miller, R. B. 1949. Preliminary biological surveys of Alberta watersheds, 1947-49. Alberta Dept. of Lands and Forests, Edmonton. [71] Miller, R. B., and W. A. Kennedy. 1948. J. Fisheries Research Board Can. 7:176. [72] Misu, H. 1958. Bull. Seikai Regional Fisheries Research Lab. 15:1. [73] Miyauti, T. 1936. Bull. Japan. Soc. Sci. Fisheries 5(6):272. [74] Moore, E. 1947. Bull. Bingham Oceanog. Collection 11:1. [75] Morrow, J. 1951. Ibid. 13(2):1. [76] Mosher, K. 1954. J. conseil permanent intern. exploration mer 19(3):337. [77] Mulicki, Z. 1959. Rappts. procès-verbaux réunions Conseil permanent intern. exploration mer 147:45. [78] Murphy, G. I. 1948. Calif. Fish and Game 34:101. [79] Murphy, G. I. 1950. Ibid. 36:119. [80] Nedelec, C. 1958. Rev. trav. inst. pech. marit. 22(2):121. [81] O'Connell, C. P. 1953. Calif. Div. Fish and Game Fish Bull. 93:60. [82] Olsen, Y. H., and D. Merriman. 1946. Bull. Bingham Oceanog. Collection 9:1. [83] Oregon State Game Commission. 1951. Ann. Rept. Fishery Div., p. 238. [84] Otaki, H. 1961. Bull. Seikai Regional Fisheries Research Lab. 21:47. [85] Parsons, J. W. 1952. Southeastern Assoc. Game and Fish Comm. 6th Ann. Cong. [86] Patriarche, M. H. 1953. Trans. Am. Fisheries Soc. 82:242. [87] Pokrovskaya, T. N. 1957. In B. N. Nikitin, ed. Marine biology. American Institute of Biological Sciences, Washington, D. C. pp. 284-290. [88] Qasim, S. 1957. J. Animal Ecol. 26(2):389. [89] Raney, E. C. 1942. Trans. Am. Fisheries Soc. 71:215. [90] Raney, E. C., and E. A. Lachner. 1942. Am. Midland Naturalist 29:229. [91] Raney, E. C., and E. A. Lachner. 1946. Ibid. 36:675. [92] Rawson, D. S. 1951. J. Fisheries Research Board Can. 8:207. [93] Rawson, D. S., and C. A. Elsey. 1950. Trans. Am. Fisheries Soc. 78:31. [94] Reighard, J. 1915. U. S. Fish Comm. Bull. 33:215. [95] Roach, L. S. 1948. Ohio Conservation Bull. 12:12. [96] Rose, E. T., and T. Moen. 1951. Trans. Am. Fisheries Soc. 80:50. [97] Roseberry, D. A., and R. R. Bowers. 1952. Virginia Wildlife 13:21. [98] Rounsefell, G. A. 1930. U. S. Bur. Fisheries Bull. 45:227. [99] Rounsefell, G. A., and G. B. Kelez. 1938. Ibid. 49:693. [100] Schaefer, M. B., and J. C. Marr. 1948. Ibid. 51:187. [101] Schmidt, U. 1955. Ber. deut. wiss. Komm. Meeresforsch., n.F. 14(1):46. [102] Schoffman, R. J. 1944. J. Tenn. Acad. Sci. 19:3. [103] Seemann, W. 1961. Z. Fischerie, n.F. 9(7-10):603. [104] Shields, J. T. 1958. S. Dakota Dept. Game, Fish and Parks Mimeo. Rept. D.-J. F-1-R-7. [105] Shimada, B. M., and W. G. van Campen. 1950. U. S. Fish Wildlife Service Spec. Sci. Rept. Fisheries 22.

continued

128. LIFE SPANS: FISHES

Part II: IN NATURAL HABITAT

[106] Sigler, W. F. 1949. Iowa Agr. Expt. Sta. Research Bull. 366:203. [107] Silliman, R. P. 1950. U. S. Fish Wildlife Service Spec. Sci. Rept. Fisheries 15. [108] Sivalingam, S. 1956. Ceylon J. Sci., C, 7(2):135. [109] Smith, W. E., and R. W. Saalfeld. 1955. Wash. Dept. Fisheries Research Papers 1(3):3. [110] Sprules, W. M. 1952. J. Fisheries Research Board Can. 9:1. [111] Stroud, R. H. 1948. J. Tenn. Acad. Sci. 23:31. [112] Summer, F. H. 1948. Trans. Am. Fisheries Soc. 75:77. [113] Taft, A. C., and G. I. Murphy. 1950. Calif. Fish and Game 36:163. [114] Takai, T. 1959. J. Shimonoseki Coll. Fisheries 8(3):209. [115] Thompson, W. 1950. Oklahoma Game and Fish Dept. Biennial Rept. 18:1. [116] Underhill, A. H. 1941. Trans. North Am. Wildlife Conf. (5):251. [117] Van Oosten, J. 1937. Papers Mich. Acad. Sci. 22:691. [118] Volpe, A. V. 1959. Florida Board Conservation Tech. Ser. 31:1. [119] Walford, L. A. 1932. Calif. Div. Fish and Game Fish Bull. 37:1. [120] Webster, D. A. 1942. Connecticut State Geol. and Nat. Hist. Survey Bull. 63:122. [121] Wigley, R. L. 1959. U. S. Fish Wildlife Service Fishery Bull. 59:561.

129. LIFE SPANS: INVERTEBRATES

Life spans are for animals in captivity, unless otherwise indicated. Classification adapted from Lord Rothschild, *A Classification of Living Animals*, 1961.

	Class and Species	Recorded Maximum Life Span	Reference
	(A)	(B)	(C)
	Chordata		
	Cephalochordata[1]		
1	*Branchiostoma lanceolatum*	7 mo	7
	Ascidiacea		
2	*Botryllus aurolineatus*	3 mo	18
3	*Ciona intestinalis*	5 mo	18
4	*Clavelina bittoana*	2-3 mo	18
	Echinodermata		
	Asteroidea		
5	*Asterias rubens*	>5 yr	18
	Holothuroidea		
6	*Cucumaria planci*	>10 yr	18
	Arthropoda		
	Arachnida		
7	*Atypus* spp.	10 yr	24
8	*A. piceus*	7 yr[2]	18
9	*Avicularia avicularis*	15 yr	18
10	*Dermacentor andersoni*	3-4 yr	8
11	*Latrodectus mactans*	♂100 da, ♀360 da	9,33
12	*Mygale hentzi*	♂9 yr, ♀20 yr	9
13	*Tegenaria civilis*	4 yr	24
	Crustacea		
14	*Astacus fluviatilis*	30 yr	18
15	*Callinectes sapidus*[3]	♀3 yr	4
16	*Cyclops viridis*[3]	♀10 mo	37
17	*Cyprinotus incongruens*	3-4 mo	18
18	*Daphnia* spp. (winter eggs)	7 yr	1
19	*D. longispina*	67 da	1
20	*D. magna*	108 da	22
	Crustacea		
21	*Herpetocypris strigata*	1 yr 2 mo	18
22	*Homarus gammarus*	33 yr	15
23	*Orconectes immunis*[3]	♂23 mo, ♀37 mo	36
	Insecta		
24	*Acrididae*[4]	<1 yr	8
25	*Aedes geniculatus*	1 yr 6 mo	3
26	*Akis lustianica*	7 yr	18
27	*Aphis evonymi*	31 da	38
28	*Apis mellifera* (queen)	5 yr	18
29	*A. mellifera* (drone)	6 mo	18
30	*A. mellifera* (worker)	11 mo	18
31	*Blaps mortisaga*	6 yr	18
32	*Blattella germanica*	1 yr 5 mo	14
33	*Buprestis splendens*	30 yr	38
34	*Calosoma sycophania*	3 yr	8
35	*Carabus auratus*	7-11 yr	18
36	*Cerambycidae*[4]	45 yr[2]	18
37	*Cerambyx* spp. (larva)	45 yr[2]	21
38	*Cetonia aurata*	6 yr	20
39	*Cimex lectularius* (unfed)	♀6 mo	38
40	*Cybister roeselii*	8 yr	24
41	*Drosophila melanogaster* (normal)	46 da	31
42	*D. melanogaster* (vestigial)	20 da	31
43	*Eristalis tenax*	35 da	38
44	*Forficula auricularia*	5 yr	15,19
45	*Formica fusca* (queen)	13 yr	18
46	*F. sanguinea* (worker)	5 yr	18
47	*Grylloblatta* spp.	3-4 yr	8
48	*Gryllotalpa* spp.	1 yr	38
49	*Hesperophanes mixtus*	9-10 yr	18
50	*Hylotrupes bajulus*	9 yr[2]	19
51	*Lasius* spp.	10-15 yr	18

/1/ Subphylum. /2/ Including developmental period. /3/ In natural habitat. /4/ Family.

continued

129. LIFE SPANS: INVERTEBRATES

	Class and Species	Recorded Maximum Life Span	Reference
	(A)	(B)	(C)
	Arthropoda		
	Insecta		
52	*Lepisma saccharina*	2 yr	8
53	*Liposcelis* spp.	1 yr	3
54	*Lucanus cervus*	8 yr 6 mo	18
55	*L. cervus* (larva)	6 mo	19
56	*Magicicada septendecim*	17 yr[2]	18
57	*Mantis religiosa*	8 yr	20
58	*Melanoplus differentialis*	3 mo	8
59	*Melolontha vulgaris* (larva)	4-5 yr	18
60	*Musca domestica*	76 da	15,19
61	*Nannothemis bella*	2 yr 10 mo	3
62	*Periplaneta americana*	4 yr 7 mo	14
63	*Rhagoletis pomonella*	103 da	8
64	*Stromatium fulvum*	11 yr	21
65	*Timarcha* spp.	5 yr	18
66	*Tribolium* spp.	3 yr	8
	Symphyla		
67	*Scutigerella immaculata*	11-12 mo	8
	Chilopoda		
68	*Lithobius forficatus*	3 yr	18
	Annelida		
	Hirudinea		
69	*Hirudo medicinalis*	27 yr	15,18
	Oligochaeta		
70	*Allolobophora longa*	5.5-10 yr	35
71	*Eisenia foetida*	3-4.5 yr	35
72	*Lumbricus terrestris*	6 yr	35
	Polychaeta		
73	*Lagis koreni*	1 yr	28,29
74	*Nereis irrorata*	2 yr	6
75	*N. procera*	10 mo	10
76	*Ophryotrocha puerilis*	6-12 mo	12
77	*Pectinaria belgica*	3 yr	16
78	*Perinereis cultrifera*	3 yr	6
79	*Platynereis agassizi*	9 mo	10
80	*P. dumerilio*	6 mo	16
81	*Spirorbis borealis*	1 yr	28,29
	Echiuroidea		
	Echiurida		
82	*Urechis* spp.	25 yr	23
	Mollusca		
	Cephalopoda		
83	*Loligo pealeii*[3]	3-4 yr	5
84	*L. subulata*[3]	1 yr 6 mo	5
85	*Octopus* spp.	10-12 yr	32
	Bivalvia		
86	*Aequipecten irradians*[3]	2 yr 6 mo	11
87	*Anodonta* spp.	20-30 yr	32
88	*Arca* spp.	>2 yr	32
89	*Cardium corbis*[3]	>16 yr	5
90	*Cumingia tellinoides*[3]	4 yr	5
91	*Margaritana margaritifera*	70-80 yr	5,32
92	*Mya arenaria*[3]	>8 yr	5
93	*Mytilus edulis*	8-10 yr	5,32
94	*Nucula turgida*[3]	10-11 yr	5
95	*Ostrea edulis*	7-12 yr	32
96	*Pecten maximus*[3]	22 yr	5
97	*Siliqua patula*[3]	19-25 yr	5
98	*Tellina tenuis*	5 yr	5,32
	Bivalvia		
99	*Teredo navalis*[3]	2 yr	5
100	*Tivela stultorum*	20 yr	5,32
101	*Unio crassus*[3]	15 yr	5
102	*Venus mercenaria*[3]	25-40 yr	5
	Scaphopoda		
103	*Dentalium tarentinum*	1-2 yr	32
	Gastropoda		
104	*Acmaea dorsuosa*[3]	15 yr	5
105	*Ancylus* spp.	4-5 yr	18
106	*Aplysia punctata*[3]	1 yr	5
107	*Bithynia tentaculata*[3]	>2 yr	5
108	*Campylaea cingulata*	4-5 yr	18
109	*Doris* spp.	1 yr	18
110	*Eolis amoena*[3]	2 mo	5
111	*Haliotis rufescens*[3]	>13 yr	5
112	*Helix pomatia*	18 yr[5]	18
113	*Limapontia capitata*	2 yr	5
114	*Limax cinereo-niger*	5 yr	5
115	*Littorina littorea*	20 yr	5,15
116	*Lunatia heros*	30 yr	18
117	*Lymnaea* spp.	4-5 yr	18
118	*Nassa obsoleta*[3]	3 yr	5
119	*Nerita japonica*[3]	2-3 yr	5
120	*Neritina fluviatilis*[3]	5 yr	5
121	*Patella vulgata*[3]	15 yr	5
122	*Planorbis corneus*	6 yr	5
123	*Testacella* spp.	5-6 yr	5
124	*Trochus niloticus*[3]	>12 yr	5
125	*Viviparus malleatus*	♂4 yr, ♀7 yr	30
	Polyplacophora		
126	*Chaetopleura apiculata*	4 yr	5,32
127	*Chiton tuberculatus*	8-12 yr	32
128	*Ischnochiton magdalenensis*[3]	3-4 yr	5
	Acanthocephala		
	Metacanthocephala		
129	*Macracanthorhynchus hirudinaceus*	1 yr	17
	Aschelminthes		
	Nematoda		
130	*Ancylostoma caninum* (in dog)	2 yr	34
131	*A. duodenale*	7 yr	34
132	*Anguina tritici*[6]	27 yr	17
133	*Cephalobus dubias*	5 mo	17
134	*Dioctophyme renale* (in dog)	2 yr	34
135	*Diplogaster robustus*	16 da	17
136	*Dirofilaria immitis* (in dog)	7 yr	34
137	*Ditylenchus dipsaci*[6]	9 yr	17
138	*Enterobius vermicularis*	2 mo	17
139	*Filaroides osleri* (in dog)	5 mo	34
140	*Haemonchus contortus*	1 yr	17
141	*Heterakis spumosa*	10 mo	34
142	*Loa loa*	15 yr	34
143	*Necator americanus*	12 yr	34
144	*Pratylenchus pratensis*[7]	11 yr	17
145	*Pristionchus aerivora*	54 da	17
146	*Rhabditis elegans*	12 da	17
147	*Trichinella spiralis*[8]	5 wk	34
148	*T. spiralis* (cysts)	30 yr	15
149	*Trichostrongylus* spp.	8 yr 6 mo	34
150	*Tylenchus polyhypnus*	39 yr	17

/2/ Including developmental period. /3/ In natural habitat. /5/ Still alive at time of report. /6/ Desiccated in dry wheat gall. /7/ Desiccated in fig roots. /8/ Adults in guinea pigs.

continued

129. LIFE SPANS: INVERTEBRATES

	Class and Species	Recorded Maximum Life Span	Reference
	(A)	(B)	(C)
	Aschelminthes		
	Nematoda		
151	*Wuchereria bancrofti*	17 yr	34
	Gastrotricha		
152	*Lepidodermella squamatum*	21 da	17
	Rotifera		
153	*Adineta vaga*	22 da	17
154	*Asplanchna sieboldi*	3 wk	17
155	*Brachionus calyciflorus*	19 da	17
156	*Cupelopagis vorax*	40 da	17
157	*Epiphanes brachionus*	17 da	17
158	*Euchlanis dilatata*	23 da	17
159	*Floscularia conifera*	18 da	17
160	*Habrotrocha constricta*	34 da	17
161	*Keratella quadrata*	29 da	17
162	*Lecane inermis*	14 da	17
163	*Macrotrachela quadricornifera*	2 mo	17
164	*Mniobia russeola*	30 da	17
165	*Philodina citrina*	21 da	17
166	*Proales decipiens*	12 da	17
167	*Rotaria macrura*	58 da	17
	Platyhelminthes		
	Cestoda		
168	*Diphyllobothrium latum* (in man)	29 yr	34
169	*Moniezia expansa*	70 da	34
170	*Taenia saginata* (in man)	35 yr	34
	Turbellaria		
171	*Planaria torva*	1 yr 2 mo	15,18
172	*Yungia aurantiaca*	1 yr	18
	Cnidaria		
	Anthozoa		
173	*Actinia equina*	15 yr	15
	Anthozoa		
174	*Actinia mesembryanthemum*	67 yr	17
175	*Cerianthus membranaceus*	40 yr	17
176	*Favites* spp.	>22-28 yr	18
177	*Flabellum* spp.	24 yr	18
178	*Goniastrea* spp.	>22-28 yr	18
179	*Heliactis bellis*	20 yr	18
180	*Monastrea* spp.	>22-28 yr	18
181	*Pocillopora* spp.	>22-28 yr	18
	Scyphozoa		
182	*Cotylorhiza tuberculata*	6-7 mo	18
	Hydrozoa		
183	*Corymorpha palma*	6 mo	23
184	*Hydra grisea*	1-2 yr	18
185	*Syncoryne decipiens*	4 yr	19
	Porifera		
	Demospongiae		
186	*Axinella* spp.	4 yr	18
187	*Hippospongia* spp.	50 yr	17
	Calcarea		
188	*Grantia capillosa*	3 mo	18
	Protozoa		
	Ciliata		
189	*Didinium nasutum* (cysts)	10 yr	2
	Rhizopoda		
190	*Discorbis patelliformis*	14 da[9]	26
191	*Elphidium crispum*	2-4 yr[10]	27
192	*Mastigamoeba* spp. (cysts)	20 yr	13
193	*Spirillina vivipara*	4 da[11]	25
	Mastigophora		
194	*Oikomonas* spp. (cysts)	20 yr	13

/9/ Sexually produced; asexually produced, 45 da. /10/ Life cycle, including sexual and asexual phases. /11/ Sexually produced; asexually produced, 12 da.

Contributors: (a) Cole, LaMont C., (b) Rockstein, Morris, (c) Rehder, Harald A., (d) Hartman, Olga, (e) Goodnight, Clarence J., (f) Bookhout, C. G., (g) Myers, Earl H.

References: [1] Banta, A. M. 1939. Carnegie Inst. Wash. Publ. 513, Genetics 40. [2] Brown, F. A., Jr. 1950. Selected invertebrate types. J. Wiley and Sons, New York. [3] Calvert, P. P. 1929. Proc. Am. Phil. Soc. 68:227. [4] Churchill, E. P. 1919. U. S. Bur. Fisheries Bull. 36:93. [5] Comfort, A. 1957. Proc. Malacol. Soc. (London) 32:219. [6] Durchon, M. 1948. Compt. rend. 227:157. [7] Flower, S. S. 1925. Proc. Zool. Soc. (London), p. 247. [8] Galtsoff, P. S. 1937. Culture methods for invertebrate animals. Comstock, Ithaca. [9] Gertsch, W. J. 1949. American spiders. Van Nostrand, New York. [10] Guberlet, J. E. 1933. Proc. 5th Pan-Pacific Sci. Congr., p. 4218. [11] Gutsell, J. S. 1930. U. S. Bur. Fisheries Bull. 46:569. [12] Hartmann, M., and W. Huth. 1936. Zool. Jahrb. 56:389. [13] Hausman, L. A. 1934. Am. Naturalist 68:456. [14] Haydak, M. H. Unpublished, 1952. [15] Heilbrunn, L. V. 1952. An outline of general physiology. W. B. Saunders, Philadelphia. [16] Hemplemann, F. 1931. In T. Krumbach, ed. Handbuch der Zoologie. W. de Gruyter, Berlin. v. 2, p. 116. [17] Hyman, L. H. 1940. The invertebrates. McGraw-Hill, New York. [18] Korschelt, E. 1922. Lebensdauer Altern und Tod. G. Fischer, Jena. [19] Korschelt, E. 1927. Tabulae Biologicae 4:346. [20] Lankester, E. K. 1870. On comparative longevity in man and the lower animals. Macmillan, London. [21] Linsley, E. G. 1938. Pan-Pacific Entomologist 14:97. [22] MacArthur, J. W., and W. H. T. Baillie. 1929. J. Exptl. Zool. 53:221. [23] MacGinitie, G. E., and N. MacGinitie. 1949. Natural history of marine animals. McGraw-Hill, New York. [24] McCook, H. C.

continued

129. LIFE SPANS: INVERTEBRATES

1887. Proc. Acad. Nat. Sci. Phila. 39:369. [25] Myers, E. H. 1936. J. Roy. Microscop. Soc. 56:132. [26] Myers, E. H. 1940. J. Marine Biol. Assoc. United Kingdom 24:221. [27] Myers, E. H. 1942. Proc. Am. Phil. Soc. 85:332. [28] Nilsson, D. 1925. Arkiv Zool., A, 17:13. [29] Nilsson, D. 1925. Ibid., A, 17:34. [30] Niwa, N. 1950. Bull. Japan. Soc. Sci. Fisheries 16:108. [31] Pearl, R. 1928. Quart. Rev. Biol. 3:391. [32] Pelseneer, P. 1935. Acad. roy. Belg. Classe sci. Publs. fondation Agathon de Potter 1:617. [33] Rehder, H. A. Unpublished. Smithsonian Institution, Washington, D. C., 1961. [34] Sandground, J. H. 1936. J. Parasitol. 22:464. [35] Stephenson, J. 1930. The oligochaeta. Oxford Univ. Press, New York. [36] Tack, P. I. 1941. Am. Midland Naturalist 25:420. [37] Walter, E. 1922. Zool. Jahrb. Abt. system. Okol. Geog. Tiere 44:375. [38] Weismann, A. 1882. Über die Dauer des Lebens. G. Fischer, Jena.

130. LIFE SPANS: FUNGI

Life span indicates survival at end of test period and does not necessarily represent maximum longevity. Reproductive bodies were kept in air-dry storage, unless otherwise specified. Reproductive Body (column B): S = spores, A = ascospores, T = teliospores, U = urediospores.

	Family and Species	Reproductive Body	Life Span	Reference
	(A)	(B)	(C)	(D)
	Mycetozoa			
	Physaraceae			
1	*Badhamia panicea*	S	23 yr	6
2	*B. utricularis*	S	20 yr	6
3	*Fuligo septica*	S	30 yr	6
4	*Physarum cinereum*	S	29 yr	6
5	*P. flavicomum*	S	60 yr	2
6	*P. straminipes*	S	26 yr	6
	Didymiaceae			
7	*Didymium squamulosum*	S	30 yr	6
8	*Lepidoderma tigrinum*	S	26 yr	6
	Stemonitaceae			
9	*Diachaea leucopoda*	S	30 yr	6
10	*Stemonitis axifera*	S	50 yr	2
11	*S. ferruginea*	S	32 yr	6
12	*S. flavogenita*	S	5 yr	6
	Lamprodermaceae			
13	*Lamproderma violaceum*	S	13 yr	6
	Cribrariaceae			
14	*Cribraria intricata*	S	52 yr	2
15	*Lindbladia effusa*	S	36 yr	2
	Reticulariaceae			
16	*Dictydiaethalium plumbeum*	S	22 yr	6
17	*Enteridium olivaceum*	S	17 yr	6
18	*E. rozeanum*	S	53 yr	2
19	*Reticularia lycoperdon*	S	10 yr	6
	Trichiaceae			
20	*Hemitrichia clavata*	S	32 yr	6
21	*Trichia botrytis*	S	26 yr	6
22	*T. favoginea*	S	16 yr	6
23	*T. lateritia*	S	28 yr	6
24	*T. scabra*	S	27 yr	6
	Ascomycetes			
	Aspergillaceae			
25	*Penicillium glaucum*	A	2 yr	1
	Basidiomycetes			
	Melampsoraceae			
26	*Cronartium ribicola*	T	87 da	7
27		U	59 da	7
28	*Melampsora lini*	U	7 wk[1]	3
	Pucciniaceae			
29	*Puccinia coronata*	U	300 da[2]	4
30	*P. glumarum*	U	21 da[3]	5
31	*P. tritici*	U	114 da[4]	5
	Ustilaginaceae			
32	*Ustilago carbo*	S	7.5 yr[5]	1
	Tilletiaceae			
33	*Tilletia caries*	S	8.5 yr[5]	1
34	*Urocystis cepulae*	S	5 yr[6]	8
	Agaricaceae			
35	*Coprinus stercorarius*	S	1 yr	1

/1/ At 7°C and 20-80% relative humidity; 2-week life span at 20°C and 20-80% relative humidity. /2/ At 10°C and 25% relative humidity; 100-day life span at 10°C and 75-90% relative humidity. /3/ At 30°C and 76% relative humidity. /4/ At 13°C and 25% relative humidity; 62-day life span at 13°C and 1.5% relative humidity; 5-day life span at 13°C and 100% relative humidity. /5/ Storage conditions unspecified. /6/ Buried in soil.

Contributor: Steinbauer, George P.

References: [1] De Bary, A. 1887. Comparative morphology of the fungi, mycetozoa and bacteria. Clarendon Press, Oxford. ch. 6. [2] Elliott, E. W. 1949. Mycologia 41:141. [3] Hart, H. 1926. Phytopathology 16:185. [4] Hoerner, G. R. 1921. Botan. Gaz. 72:173. [5] Raeder, J. M., and W. M. Bever. 1931. Phytopathology 21:767. [6] Smith, E. C. 1929. Mycologia 21:321. [7] Spaulding, P., and A. Rathbun. 1925. Gravatt J. Agr. Research 31:901. [8] Wolf, F. A., and F. T. Wolf. 1947. The fungi. J. Wiley and Sons, London. v. 2, p. 210.

131. LIFE SPANS: POLLEN

Temp. (column C): "17.5; 21" indicates that tests were conducted at temperatures averaging 17.5°C during the winter and 21°C during the summer; Ly = lyophylized. Relative Humidity (column D): 0 indicates lack of humidity due to storage over concentrated sulfuric acid in desiccator, unless otherwise specified; A = air; A-D = air-dry; Un = uncontrolled; Ly = lyophylized (freeze-drying followed by storage in nitrogen in otherwise uncontrolled environment). Life Span (column E): values in parentheses are percent viability based on germination tests made on artificial media at age noted for life span. Classification adapted from Engler and Diels, *Syllabus der Pflanzenfamilien*, 1936.

	Family	Species	Storage Conditions		Life Span da (% Viability)	Reference
			Temp. °C	Relative Humidity %		
	(A)	(B)	(C)	(D)	(E)	(F)
	Gymnospermae					
1	Ginkgoaceae	*Ginkgo biloba*	7	0[1]	730 (35-45)	45
2	Pinaceae	*Picea abies*	2	10-75	365 (48)	16
3		*P. canadensis*	2	10-75	365 (57)	16
4		*P. excelsa*	2	10	365 (63)	16
5		*Pinus laricio*	24	A-D	60	24
6		*P. montana*	17.5; 21	0	272	33
7		*P. pinaster*	17.5; 21	0	275	33
8		*P. resinosa*	0-4	50[2]	413 (92)	7
9		*P. strobus*	0-4	50[2]	413 (91)	7
10		*P. sylvestris*	17.5; 21	0	279	33
11		*P. taeda*	Ly	Ly	379 (32)	20
12		*Tsuga canadensis*	1-16	10-50	365 (70-90)	38
	Angiospermae (Monocotyledoneae)					
13	Typhaceae	*Typha angustifolia*	24	A-D	24	36
14		*T. latifolia*	17-22	0[1]	>336 (56)	14
15	Pandanaceae	*Pandanus furcatus*	17.5; 21	0-30	92	33
16	Sparganiaceae	*Sparganium erectum*	17.5; 21	0	63	33
17	Scheuchzeriaceae	*Triglochin maritima*	17.5; 21	30	21	33
18	Alismataceae	*Alisma plantago*	17.5; 21	Un	1	33
19	Gramineae	*Alopecurus pratensis*	17.5; 21	0-90	2	33
20		*Buchloe dactyloides*	4	90	7-8[3]	17
21		*Dactylis glomerata*	17.5; 21	30	3	33
22		*Hordeum vulgare*	2.2[4]	....	19-26 (9.5-40.5)[3]	35
23		*Lolium perenne*	17.5; 21	0-90	1	33
24		*Poa compressa*	17.5; 21	0-90	1	33
25		*Saccharum officinarum*	Ly	Ly	140 (89)[5]	20
26		*S. spontaneum*	4	90-100	8 (70-90)[3]	39
27		*Secale cereale*	17.5; 21	Un	0.5	33
28		*Triticum vulgare*	16-18	Humid	0.5	10
29		*Zea mays*	5-10	50-80	3 (70)[3]	22
30	Cyperaceae	*Carex paludosa*	17.5; 21	30	13	33
31	Palmae	*Phoenix dactylifera*	-13[6]	....	365 (60-70)[3]	5
32	Commelinaceae	*Tradescantia virginiana*	17.5; 21	0	40	33
33	Juncaceae	*Juncus effusus*	17.5; 21	0	8	33
34		*Luzula angustifolia*	17.5; 21	30	16	33
35		*L. campestris*	24	A-D	3	23
36	Liliaceae	*Allium cepa*	Ly	Ly	191 (22)	20
37		*Aloe longearistata*	17.5; 21	0	78	33
38		*Brodiaea capitata*	17-22	0-27.2	38	14
39		*B. grandiflora*	17-22	27.2	111	14
40		*Colchicum autumnale*	17.5; 21	30	229	33
41		*Disporum hookeri*	17-22	0-27.2	69	14
42		*Fritillaria imperialis*	24	A-D	40	24
43		*F. lanceolata floribunda*	17.5; 21	0	96 (1)	14
44		*Hemerocallis flava*	17.5; 21	0	29	33
45		*H. fulva rosea*	3	10	90 (12)[3]	15
46		*Lilium* spp.	10	35-50	426 (>45)	28,29
47		*L. auratum*	-5[7]	50	210 (38)	28,29
48		*L. bulbiferum*	17.5; 21	0-30	142	33

/1/ Storage over calcium chloride in desiccator. /2/ Humidified at 75% relative humidity and 4°C for 12 hours after storage. /3/ Data recorded on basis of seed or fruit set. /4/ Flower spike or flower cut in early morning and kept under refrigeration. /5/ Peroxidase test for viability. /6/ Pollen mixed with diluent and then stored in sealed or stoppered vials. /7/ Pollen stored under reduced pressure in vacuumized tubes.

continued

131. LIFE SPANS: POLLEN

	Family	Species	Storage Conditions		Life Span da (% Viability)	Reference
			Temp. °C	Relative Humidity %		
	(A)	(B)	(C)	(D)	(E)	(F)
	Angiospermae (Monocotyledoneae)					
49	Liliaceae	*Lilium candidum*	24	A-D	67	24
50		*L. regale*	-20	A-D	161 (65)	32
51		*Polygonatum vulgare*	24	A-D	30	23
52		*Scilla nutans*	24	A-D	70	23
53		*Smilacina amplexicaulis*	24	27.2	76	14
54		*Trillium sessile giganteum*	17-22	27.2	102	14
55		*Tulipa gesneriana*	17.5; 21	30	108	33
56		*Zygadenus fremonti*	17-22	0-27.2	95	14
57	Amaryllidaceae	*Agave densiflora*	17.5; 21	0-30	133	33
58		*Amaryllis* spp. (hybrids)	10	50	150 (67)	28
59		*Galanthus nivalis*	17.5; 21	30	76	33
60		*Haemanthus puniceus*	24	A-D	30	24
61		*Lycoris aurea*	24	0	75	43
62		*L. radiata*	24	0	62	43
63		*Narcissus poeticus*	24	A-D	72	24
64		*N. pseudonarcissus*	24	A-D	80	23
65	Iridaceae	*Gladiolus hybrida*	10	50	102 (30)[8]	30
66		*Iris graminea*	17.5; 21	0	57	33
67		*I. pseudacorus*	17.5; 21	0-30	29	33
68	Orchidaceae	*Epipactis latifolia*	24	A-D	23	24
69		*Gymnadenia conopsea*	24	A-D	20	24
70		*Listera ovata*	17.5; 21	0	164	33
	Angiospermae (Dicotyledoneae)					
71	Salicaceae	*Populus laurifolia*	-3 to +3	A-D	15	2
72		*P. suaveolens*	-3 to +3	A-D	45	2
73		*Salix caprea*	17.5; 21	0	70	33
74		*S. gracistyla*	10	A-D	105 (1)	26
75	Juglandaceae	*Carya illinoensis*	5	Moist	4 (40)	49
76		*Juglans sieboldiana*	0	40-60	253 (12)	3
77	Betulaceae	*Alnus glutinosa*	17.5; 21	0	53	33
78		*Betula lutea*	Room	25	30 (3)	16
79		*B. verrucosa*	24	Moist	16 (20)	2
80		*Corylus americana*	0	40	242 (8)	3
81		*C. avellana*	0-4	40-50	253 (8.5-9.0)	3
82		*C. rostrata californica*	17-22	0-27.2	>40	14
83	Fagaceae	*Fagus sylvatica*	24	A-D	41	23
84		*Quercus coccinea*	2	25-35	365 (46)	16
85		*Q. robur*	0	60	66 (41)	34
86	Moraceae	*Cannabis sativa*	17.5; 21	0	8	33
87		*Ficus carica*	Ly	Ly	354 (22)	20
88	Urticaceae	*Urtica dioica*	17.5; 21	0-30	4	33
89	Loranthaceae	*Viscum album*	17.5; 21	30	89	33
90	Polygonaceae	*Polygonum bistorta*	17.5; 21	0-60	8	33
91		*Rumex acetosella*	17.5; 21	0	14	33
92	Chenopodiaceae	*Chenopodium bonus-henricus*	17.5; 21	0-30	8	33
93	Nymphaeaceae	*Nuphar advena*	17.5; 21	0	32	33
94		*Nymphaea alba*	17.5; 21	0-30	30-35	33
95	Ranunculaceae	*Aquilegia truncata*	17-22	27.2	76	14
96		*Caltha palustris*	17.5; 21	30	64	33
97		*Clematis integrifolia*	17.5; 21	0	103	33
98		*Delphinium hesperium*	17-22	0-91.6	5	14
99		*Nigella sativa*	17.5; 21	0	21	33
100		*Paeonia albiflora*	17.5; 21	0-30	157	33
101		*Ranunculus acris*	17.5; 21	0	49	33
102		*R. aquatilis*	17.5; 21	0	51	33
103		*R. californicus*	17-22	A; 91.6	2	14
104		*Thalictrum flavum*	17.5; 21	0	98	33
105		*Trollius europaeus*	17.5; 21	0-30	102-124	33
106	Lauraceae	*Persea americana*[9]	15	0[1]	153	40

/1/ Storage over calcium chloride in desiccator. /8/ Data recorded on basis of seed set per capsule. /9/ Horticultural varieties.

continued

131. LIFE SPANS: POLLEN

	Family	Species	Storage Conditions Temp. °C	Storage Conditions Relative Humidity %	Life Span da (% Viability)	Reference
	(A)	(B)	(C)	(D)	(E)	(F)
	Angiospermae (Dicotyledoneae)					
107	Papaveraceae	*Eschscholtzia californica*	17-22	0[1]	19	14
108		*Papaver bracteatum*	24	A-D	16	36
109		*P. hybridum*	17.5; 21	0-30	49	33
110		*P. rhoeos*	17.5; 21	0	97	33
111	Cruciferae	*Arabis albida*	17.5; 21	0	36	33
112		*A. virginica*	17-22	0	62	14
113		*Matthiola* spp.	5-10	0	64 (20)	37
114	Crassulaceae	*Sedum acre*	17.5; 21	0-30	143	33
115		*S. boloniense*	17.5; 21	30	140	33
116		*Sempervivum tectorum*	17.5; 21	30	194	33
117	Saxifragaceae	*Deutzia scabra*	24	A-D	20-24	24,36
118		*Philadelphus floribundus*	24	A-D	32	36
119		*Ribes sanguineum glutinosum*	17-22	0-27.2	117	14
120	Rosaceae	*Chaenomeles lagenaria*	2.2	0	550 (37.6)	21
121		*Cydonia oblonga*	2.2	25	550 (54)	21
122		*Fragaria* spp.	24	A-D	>16	4
123		*Gillenia trifoliata*	24	A-D	48	36
124		*Potentilla arguta*	17.5; 21	0	44	33
125		*Prunus amygdalus*	-18	....	1130 (24)	11
126		*P. armeniaca*	2-8	50	913 (30)	25
127		*P. avium*	-18	....	743 (26)	11
128		*P. cerasus*	2-8	50	1460 (20)	25
129		*P. domestica*	2-8	50	1278 (20)	25
130		*P. padus*	17.5; 21	0-30	181	33
131		*P. persica*	2-8	50	1095 (1-20)	25
132		*P. persica nectarina*	2.2	25	550 (63)	21
133		*P. salicina*	-17	Un	439 (35)	11
134		*P. spinosa*	17.5; 21	0	154	33
135		*Pyrus communis*	2-8	50	1278 (20)	25
136		*P. malus*	2-8	50	1460 (20)	25
137		*P. phaeocarpa*	....	....	550 (46)	21
138		*Rubus parviflorus*	17-22	0	74 (59.4)	14
139		*Spiraea filipendula*	17.5; 21	0	71	33
140	Leguminosae	*Astragalus cicer*	24	A-D	12	24
141		*Colutea arborescens*	24	A-D	12	24
142		*Cytisus laburnum*	17.5; 21	30	261	33
143		*Lathyrus latifolius*	5-10	A-D	45 (Very good)	37
144		*L. odoratus*	24	A	23[3]	4
145		*Lupinus cytisoides*	17-22	0[1]	145	14
146		*L. latifolius*	17-22	27.2	118	14
147		*L. perennis*	17.5; 21	30	260	33
148		*L. polyphyllus*	-190	A-D	93 (78)	9
149		*Medicago sativa*	Room	0[1]	180[3]	1
150		*Melilotus alba*	17.5; 21	30	96	33
151		*Pisum sativum*	-5	35	450	48
152		*Robinia pseudoacacia*	24	A-D	30	24
153		*Trifolium hybridum*	24	A-D	12	24
154		*Vicia faba*	17.5; 21	0	21	33
155	Tropaeolaceae	*Tropaeolum majus*	17.5; 21	0	88	33
156	Rutaceae	*Citrus* sp.	2	25	550 (63)	21
157		*C. medica*	0	0[1]	21 (60)	41
158		*C. paradisi*	10[7]	....	42 (50)	18
159		*Poncirus trifoliata*	4	0[1]	36-61[3]	41
160	Euphorbiaceae	*Aleurites fordi*	5[4]	....	24 (>40)	8
161		*Hevea* sp.	6	67-80	19	6
162		*Ricinus communis*	17-22	0[1]	4	14
163	Anacardiaceae	*Pistacia* sp.	-1	10.5-21.5	365-730 (5-55)[3]	42
164		*P. atlantica*	2.2	25	550 (30.2)	21
165	Aceraceae	*Acer* sp.	17-22	A-D	18	14

/1/ Storage over calcium chloride in desiccator. /3/ Data recorded on basis of seed or fruit set. /4/ Flower spike or flower cut in early morning and kept under refrigeration. /7/ Pollen stored under reduced pressure in vacuumized tubes.

continued

131. LIFE SPANS: POLLEN

	Family	Species	Storage Conditions: Temp. °C	Storage Conditions: Relative Humidity %	Life Span da (% Viability)	Reference
	(A)	(B)	(C)	(D)	(E)	(F)
		Angiospermae (Dicotyledoneae)				
166	Hippocastanaceae	*Aesculus hippocastanum*	24	0-30	72	33
167	Vitaceae	*Ampelopsis quinquefolia*	17.5; 21	30	23	33
168		*Vitis* spp.[9]	-12	28	1460 (21)	27
169	Tiliaceae	*Tilia platyphyllos*	17.5; 21	0	16	33
170	Malvaceae	*Abutilon darwini*	17.5; 21	A-D	14	33
171		*Gossypium pima*	4.4-10.0	....	4 (64)[3]	13
172	Theaceae	*Camellia japonica*	24	A-D	60	36
173	Guttiferae	*Hypericum perforatum*	17.5; 21	0	81	33
174	Violaceae	*Viola odorata*	17.5; 21	0	235	33
175		*V. pedunculata*	17-22	0	111 (10)	14
176		*V. tricolor*	24	A-D	26	36
177	Caricaceae	*Carica papaya*[9]	1.1	10	150 (45)	44
178		*C. quercifolia*	1.1	10	150 (80)	44
179	Cactaceae	*Cereus flagelliformis*	17.5; 21	30	13	33
180		*C. grandiflorus*	17.5; 21	0-30	17	33
181		*Echinopsis eyriesi*	17.5; 21	A; 30	8	33
182		*E. zuccariniana*	17.5; 21	A; 30-60	6	33
183	Thymelaeceae	*Daphne mezereum*	17.5; 21	0-30	76	33
184	Lythraceae	*Lythrum salicaria*	17.5; 21	30	43	33
185	Oenotheraceae	*Oenothera biennis*	17.5; 21	A; 30	8	33
186	Hippuridaceae	*Hippuris vulgaris*	17.5; 21	A; 60-90	5	33
187	Cornaceae	*Cornus mas*	17.5; 21	30	74	33
188		*C. pubescens californica*	17-22	27.2	30	14
189	Ericaceae	*Rhododendron* spp.	-190	....	730-1095	47
190		*R. arboreum*	24	A-D	35	24
191		*R. molle*	17.5; 21	0-30	178	33
192	Primulaceae	*Cyclamen persicum*	17-22	0[1]	185	14
193		*Dodecatheon patulum*	17-22	0-27.2	89	14
194		*Hottonia palustris*	17.5; 21	0	41	33
195		*Primula elatior*	17.5; 21	0	179	33
196		*P. officinalis*	17.5; 21	0	158	33
197	Oleaceae	*Olea europa*	-18	....	379 (36)	11
198	Apocynaceae	*Vinca major*	24	A-D	43	36
199		*V. minor*	24	A-D	55	23
200	Asclepiadaceae	*Asclepias cornuti*	24	A-D	11	36
201	Convolvulaceae	*Ipomoea batatas*	Ly	Ly	354 (76)[5]	20
202	Boraginaceae	*Pulmonaria obscura*	17.5; 21	0-30	71-73	33
203	Labiatae	*Ajuga reptans*	24	A-D	32	36
204		*Lamium album*	24	A-D	6	23
205		*L. galeobdolon*	24	A-D	31	23
206		*Stachys bullata*	17-22	27.2	49	14
207	Solanaceae	*Atropa belladonna*	24	A-D	34	23
208		*Lycopersicon esculentum*	-190	....	1095	47
209		*Nicotiana glauca*	17-22	0[1]	147 (50)	14
210		*N. sylvestris*	17-22	....	205[10]	14
211		*Solandra grandiflora*	17-22	0[1]	27	14
212		*Solanum dulcamara*	17.5; 21	0-30	41	33
213		*S. melongena*	18-20	39	11 (21)[3]	46
214		*S. tuberosum*	-30 to -20	Un	365[3]	19
215		*S. umbelliferum*	17-22	27.2	41	14
216	Scrophulariaceae	*Antirrhinum majus*	10-22	....	670 (Poor)	22
217		*Castilleja parviflora*	17-22	27.2	91	14
218		*Digitalis ambigua*	24	A-D	21	24
219		*D. purpurea*	0-4	0	172	33
220		*Linaria vulgaris*	24	A-D	21	24
221		*Mimulus* spp.	5-10	A; 0	64 (Poor)	37
222		*Orthocarpus purpurascens*	17-22	0	34	14
223		*Penstemon cordifolius*	17-22	0[1]	116	14
224		*Scrophularia californica*	17-22	0-63	18	14

/1/ Storage over calcium chloride in desiccator. /3/ Data recorded on basis of seed or fruit set. /5/ Peroxidase test for viability. /9/ Horticultural varieties. /10/ Pollen sealed in ampules with CO_2 and stored under reduced pressure.

continued

131. LIFE SPANS: POLLEN

	Family	Species	Storage Conditions: Temp. °C	Storage Conditions: Relative Humidity %	Life Span da (% Viability)	Reference
	(A)	(B)	(C)	(D)	(E)	(F)
	Angiospermae (Dicotyledoneae)					
225	Scrophulariaceae	*Veronica buxbaumi*	17.5; 21	30	6	33
226		*V. chamaedrys*	17.5; 21	30	21	33
227	Gesneriaceae	*Achimenes* spp.	5-10	0	64 (Poor)	37
228		*Sinningia* spp.	5-10	0	64 (Good)	37
229		*Streptocarpus* spp.	5-10	0	94 (Poor)	37
230	Plantaginaceae	*Plantago lanceolata*	17.5; 21	0-30	32-35	33
231		*P. major*	24	A-D	12	23
232		*P. media*	17.5; 21	0	68	33
233	Rubiaceae	*Cinchona hybrida*	10	38	142 (23)	31
234		*C. ledgeriana*	10	35-50	365 (5-10)	31
235		*Coffea* spp.	Room	0->60	21-28[3]	9
236	Caprifoliaceae	*Sambucus glauca*	17-22	0-27.2	94	14
237		*Viburnum opulus*	17.5; 21	0	164	33
238	Cucurbitaceae	*Cucumis melo*	-18	....	30 (98)	11
239		*Cucurbita moschata*	-17	Un	30 (98)[3]	12
240	Campanulaceae	*Campanula medium*	17.5; 21	0-30	69-74	33
241		*C. persicifolia*	24	A-D	21	24
242		*C. trachelium*	24	A-D	30	24
243	Compositae	*Onopordon illyricum*	17.5; 21	30	8	33

/3/ Data recorded on basis of seed or fruit set.

Contributors: (a) Pfeiffer, Norma E., (b) Hesse, Claron O.

References: [1] Anonymous. 1960. Crops and Soils 13(1):19. [2] Bogdanov, P. L. 1935. Sovet. Botan. 1:98. [3] Cox, L. G. 1943. Northern Nut Growers Assoc. Ann. Rept. 34:58. [4] Crandall, C. S. 1912. Proc. Am. Soc. Hort. Sci. 9:121. [5] Crawford, C. L. 1937. Ibid. 35:91. [6] Dijkman, M. J. 1951. Hevea. Univ. Miami Press, Coral Gables. [7] Duffield, J. W., and A. G. Snow, Jr. 1941. Am. J. Botany 28:175. [8] Fernholz, D. L., and L. Hines. 1942. Proc. Am. Soc. Hort. Sci. 40:251. [9] Ferwerda, F. P. 1937. Arch. Koffiecult. Indonesie 11:135. [10] Firbas, H. 1922. Z. Pflanzenzücht. 8:70. [11] Griggs, W. H., G. H. Vansell, and B. T. Iwakiri. 1953. Calif. Agr. 7:12. [12] Griggs, W. H., G. H. Vansell, and J. F. Reinhardt. 1950. J. Econ. Entomol. 43:549. [13] Harrison, G. J., and H. J. Fulton. 1934. J. Agr. Research 49:891. [14] Holman, R. M., and F. Brubaker. 1926. Univ. Calif. (Berkeley) Publs. Botany 13:179. [15] Johnson, B. L., and A. Griffiths, Jr. 1950. Proc. Am. Soc. Hort. Sci. 55:507. [16] Johnson, L. P. V. 1943. Can. J. Research, C, 21:332. [17] Jones, M. D., and L. C. Newell. 1948. J. Amer. Soc. Agron. 40:195. [18] Kellerman, M. 1915. Science 42:375. [19] King, J. R. 1955. Am. Potato J. 32:460. [20] King, J. R. 1961. Econ. Botany 15(1):91. [21] King, J. R., and C. O. Hesse. 1938. Proc. Am. Soc. Hort. Sci. 36:310. [22] Knowlton, H. E. 1922. Cornell Univ. Agr. Expt. Sta. Mem. 52:747. [23] Mangin, L. 1886. Bull. soc. botan. France 33:337. [24] Molisch, H. 1893. Sitzber. Akad. Wiss. Wien Math.-naturw. Kl., I, 102:423. [25] Nebel, B. R. 1939. Proc. Am. Soc. Hort. Sci. 37:130. [26] Nohara, S. 1922. Japan. J. Botany 2(1):1. [27] Olmo, H. P. 1942. Proc. Am. Soc. Hort. Sci. 41:219. [28] Pfeiffer, N. E. 1936. Contribs. Boyce Thompson Inst. 8:141. [29] Pfeiffer, N. E. 1938. Ibid. 9:199. [30] Pfeiffer, N. E. 1939. Ibid. 10:429. [31] Pfeiffer, N. E. 1944. Ibid. 13:281. [32] Pfeiffer, N. E. 1955. Ibid. 18:153. [33] Pfundt, M. 1909. Jahrb. wiss. Botan. 47:1. [34] Piatnitskii, S. S. 1947. Doklady Vsesoyuz. Akad. Sel'sko-Khoz. Nauk im. V. I. Lenina 12:32. [35] Pope, M. M. 1939. J. Agr. Research 59:453. [36] Rittinghaus, P. 1886. Verhandl. naturhist. Ver. preuss. Rheinland 43:123. [37] Roemer, T. 1914. Z. Pflanzenzücht. 2:83. [38] Santamour, F. S., Jr., and H. Nienstaedt. 1956. J. Forestry 54:269. [39] Sartoris, P. B. 1942. Am. J. Botany 29:395. [40] Schroeder, C. A. 1942. Proc. Am. Soc. Hort. Sci. 41:181. [41] Soost, R. K., and J. W. Cameron. 1954. Ibid. 63:234. [42] Stone, C. L., L. E. Jones, and W. E. Whitehouse. 1943. Ibid. 42:305. [43] Tokugawa, Y. 1914. J. Coll. Sci. Imp. Univ. Tokyo 35:1. [44] Traub, H. P., and C. T. O'Rork, Jr. 1936. Proc. Am. Soc. Hort. Sci. 34:18.

continued

131. LIFE SPANS: POLLEN

[45] Tulecke, W. R. 1954. Bull. Torrey Botan. Club 81:509. [46] Vasil, I. K. 1958. Science and Culture 24(5):233. [47] Visser, T. 1955. Mededel. Landbouwhogeschool Wageningen 55:1. [48] Warnock, S. J., and D. J. Hagedorn. 1956. Agron. J. 48:347. [49] Woodroof, J. G. 1930. J. Agr. Research 40:1059.

132. LIFE SPANS: SEEDS

For life spans of forest trees, see table 103, page 379. Classification adapted from Engler and Diels, *Syllabus der Pflanzenfamilien,* 1936.

Part I: IN AIR-DRY STORAGE

	Family	Species	Storage Conditions	Viability % Initial	Viability % Final	Life Span	Reference
	(A)	(B)	(C)	(D)	(E)	(F)	(G)
			Gymnospermae				
1	Pinaceae	*Abies nobilis*	-5°C	...	18	5 yr	18
2		*Pinus caribaea*	5°C	78	49	7 yr	3
3		*P. echinata*	5°C	84	50	7 yr	3
4		*P. palustris*	5°C; 35% relative humidity	96	58	232 da	7
5		*P. taeda*	5°C	84	66	7 yr	3
			Angiospermae (Monocotyledoneae)				
6	Gramineae	*Avena sativa*	20-30°C	98	91	13 yr	14
7		*Festuca rubra*	20°C; 10% moisture content	95	97	15 mo	20
8		*Holcus sorghum*	...	100	98	6 yr	22
9		*Hordeum vulgare*	...	100	76	10 yr	22
10		*Pennisetum ciliare*	23°C; 15% relative humidity	46	26	6.5 yr	1
11		*Phleum pratense*	20-30°C	97	56	10 yr	14
12		*Secale cereale*	...	100	52	9 yr	22
13		*Triticum aestivum*	...	100	91	10 yr	22
14		*Zea mays*	...	92	79	9 yr	22
15	Liliaceae	*Allium cepa*	5-10°C; 6.4% moisture content; sealed	94	89	13 yr	11
16		*Lilium regale*	5°C; 4.5% moisture content; sealed	90	94	6 yr	6
17	Orchidaceae	*Cattleya* sp.	5°C	...	...	5 yr	2
18		*Cymbidium* sp.	5°C	...	...	3 yr	2
19		*Cypripedium* sp.	5°C	...	...	3 yr	2
20		*Phalaenopsis* sp.	5°C	...	...	3 yr	2
21		*Vanda* sp.	5°C	...	...	3 yr	2
			Angiospermae (Dicotyledoneae)				
22	Salicaceae	*Populus tremuloides*	20-30°C	100	45	8 wk	21
23	Ulmaceae	*Ulmus americana*	5°C; 7% moisture content; sealed	82	88	16 mo	5
24			20°C; 5% relative humidity	70	28	10 mo	24
25	Nymphaeaceae	*Nelumbo* sp.	...	...	...	150 yr	27
26	Ranunculaceae	*Delphinium* sp.	10°C; sealed	72	54	19 yr	9
27	Cruciferae	*Brassica oleracea*	20-30°C; dried over CaO; sealed	84	60	4 yr	6
28	Rosaceae	*Prunus americana*	...	100	48	46 mo	16
29	Leguminosae	*Albizzia julibrissin*	...	...	...	147 yr	27
30		*Anthyllis vulneraria*	...	...	...	90 yr	26
31		*Arachis hypogaea*	5°C; 35-76% relative humidity	96	100	232 da	7
32		*Astragalus marsiliensis*	...	...	...	86 yr	10
33		*Cassia bicapsularis*	...	...	...	115 yr	10
34		*C. multijuga*	...	...	...	158 yr	10
35		*Cytisus scoparius*	...	...	...	81 yr	26
36		*Dioclea pauciflora*	...	...	...	93 yr	10
37		*Lathyrus odoratus*	5°C; 10.9% moisture content; sealed	76	71	2.5 yr	6
38		*Leucaena leucocephala*	...	...	...	99 yr	10
39		*Lotus uliginosus*	...	...	1	100 yr	27
40		*Medicago orbicularis*	...	...	...	78 yr	26
41		*M. sativa*	23°C; 15% relative humidity	100	98	6.5 yr	1
42		*Melilotus alba*	...	...	...	81 yr	26
43		*Phaseolus vulgaris*	23°C; 15% relative humidity	92	23	6 yr	1
44		*Soja max*	...	100	48	8 yr	22

continued

132. LIFE SPANS: SEEDS

Part I: IN AIR-DRY STORAGE

	Family	Species	Storage Conditions	Viability % Initial	Viability % Final	Life Span	Reference
	(A)	(B)	(C)	(D)	(E)	(F)	(G)
			Angiospermae (Dicotyledoneae)				
45	Leguminosae	*Trifolium hybridum*	20-30°C	98	45	10 yr	14
46		*T. pratense*	....	...	1	100 yr	27
47		*T. striatum*	....	...	...	90 yr	26
48	Linaceae	*Linum usitatissimum*	5°C; 35% relative humidity	97	98	1 yr	7
49	Aceraceae	*Acer saccharinum*	10°C; over water	...	95	6 mo	19
50	Malvaceae	*Gossypium* spp.	7% moisture content; sealed	95	80	1 yr	15
51	Violaceae	*Viola tricolor*	5°C; 5.2% moisture content	68	63	2.5 yr	6
52	Umbelliferae	*Daucus carota*	20-30°C; 10.7% moisture content	67	52	6 yr	4
53	Oleaceae	*Fraxinus excelsior*	5°C; 10.8% moisture content; sealed	53	35	7 yr	8
54		*F. nigra*	5°C; 7.5% moisture content; sealed	...	40	1 yr	25
55		*F. pennsylvanica*	5°C; 7.6% moisture content; sealed	68	39	8 yr	8
56	Convolvulaceae	*Convolvulus arvensis*	....	...	62	50 yr	12
57	Verbenaceae	*Verbena teucrioides*	5°C; 4.2% moisture content	53	39	3 yr	6
58	Solanaceae	*Capsicum frutescens*	5°C; 10.4% moisture content	73	74	6 yr	4
59		*Lycopersicon esculentum*	0°C; over $CaCl_2$	75	61	312 da	23
60		*Solanum melongena*	20-30°C; 10.4% moisture content	87	74	6 yr	4
61		*S. tuberosum*	0°C; sealed	45	87	12 yr	13
62	Compositae	*Callistephus chinensis*	5°C; 4.6-7.9% moisture content; sealed	78	83	3 yr	6
63		*Lactuca sativa*	28°C; sealed over $CaCl_2$	78	67	312 da	23
64			0°C; 50% relative humidity	98	99	8 mo	17
65		*Taraxacum officinale*	5°C; 7.9% moisture content; sealed	95	88	3 yr	6

Contributor: Steinbauer, George P.

References: [1] Akamine, E. K. 1943. Hawaii Agr. Expt. Sta. Bull. 90. [2] Anonymous. 1934. Orchid Rev., p. 321. [3] Barton, L. V. 1935. Contribs. Boyce Thompson Inst. 7:379. [4] Barton, L. V. 1939. Ibid. 10:205. [5] Barton, L. V. 1939. Ibid. 10:221. [6] Barton, L. V. 1939. Ibid. 10:399. [7] Barton, L. V. 1941. Ibid. 12:85. [8] Barton, L. V. 1945. Ibid. 13:427. [9] Barton, L. V. 1946. Am. Delphinium Soc. Yearbook 11:27. [10] Becquerel, P. 1907. Ann. sci. nat. Botan. et biol. végétale, Ser. 9, 5:193. [11] Brown, E. 1939. Science 89:292. [12] Brown, E. O., and R. H. Porter. 1942. Iowa Agr. Expt. Sta. Research Bull. 294. [13] Clark, C. F. 1940. Am. Potato J. 17:147. [14] Eastham, A. 1914. Agr. Gaz. Can. 1:634. [15] Flores, F. B. 1938. Philippine J. Agr. 9:347. [16] Giersbach, J., and W. Crocker. 1932. Contribs. Boyce Thompson Inst. 4:39. [17] Griffiths, A. E. 1942. Cornell Univ. Agr. Expt. Sta. Mem. 245. [18] Isaac, L. A. 1934. Ecology 15:216. [19] Jones, H. A. 1920. Botan. Gaz. 69:127. [20] Kearns, V., and E. H. Toole. 1939. U. S. Dept. Agr. Tech. Bull. 670. [21] Moss, E. H. 1938. Botan. Gaz. 99:529. [22] Robertson, D. W., and A. M. Lute. 1933. J. Agr. Research 46:455. [23] San Pedro, A. V. 1936. Philippine Agr. 24:649. [24] Steinbauer, C. E., and G. P. Steinbauer. 1931. Proc. Am. Soc. Hort. Sci. 28:441. [25] Steinbauer, G. P. 1937. Plant Physiol. 12:813. [26] Turner, J. H. 1933. Kew Bull. Roy. Botan. Gardens, p. 257. [27] Youngman, B. J. 1951. Ibid., p. 423.

continued

132. LIFE SPANS: SEEDS

Part II: UNDISTURBED IN SOIL

For additional information on life spans of seeds buried in soil, consult reference 1. Seeds buried at 8 inches, unless otherwise indicated.

	Family and Species	Viability % Initial	Viability % Final	Life Span yr	Reference
	(A)	(B)	(C)	(D)	(E)
	Angiospermae (Monocotyledoneae)				
	Gramineae				
1	*Agropyron repens*	80	21	1	3,6
2	*Avena fatua*	70	9	1	3,6
3	*Bromus racemosus*[1]	100	12	6	3,6
4	*B. secalinus*	...	...	<5	2
5	*Phalaris arundinacea*	69	5	21	3,6
6	*Phleum pratense*	...	1	21	3,6
7	*Poa pratensis*	91	1	30	3,6
8	*Setaria lutescens*[2]	56	4	10	2,3,6
	Cyperaceae				
9	*Cyperus esculentus*	...	9	21	3,6
	Angiospermae (Dicotyledoneae)				
	Urticaceae				
10	*Boehmeria nivea*	...	14	30	3,6
	Polygonaceae				
11	*Polygonum hydropiper*[1]	...	...	50	2
12	*P. persicaria*	...	3	30	3,6
13	*Rumex crispus*[2]	81	6	39	2,3,6
	Chenopodiaceae				
14	*Beta vulgaris*[3]	153	1	10	3,6
15	*Chenopodium album*	67	30	16	3,6
	Amaranthaceae				
16	*Amaranthus retroflexus*[2]	95	11	10	2,3,6
	Portulacaceae				
17	*Portulaca oleracea*[2]	83	1	30	2,3,6
	Caryophyllaceae				
18	*Agrostemma githago*[1]	...	...	<5	2
19	*Stellaria media*[2]	97	6	10	2,3,6
	Nymphaeaceae				
20	*Nelumbo nucifera*[4]	...	...	1040	4,5
	Cruciferae				
21	*Brassica nigra*[2]	1	2	10	2,3,6
22	*Capsella bursa-pastoris*[2]	...	2	10	2,3,6
23	*Lepidium virginicum*[1]	...	...	40	2
24	*Sisymbrium altissimum*	88	79	6	3,6
	Leguminosae				
25	*Medicago sativa*	85	1	6	3,6
26	*Trifolium hybridum*	90	1	21	3,6
27	*T. pratense*	90	1	30	3,6
28	*T. repens*[2]	85	1	30	2,3,6
	Euphorbiaceae				
29	*Chamaesyce maculata*[1]	...	...	<5	2
	Malvaceae				
30	*Abutilon theophrasti*	...	13	30	3,6
31	*Malva rotundifolia*[1]	...	...	20	2
	Oenotheraceae				
32	*Oenothera biennis*[2]	...	32	30	2,3,6
	Oleaceae				
33	*Fraxinus americana*	50	4	6	3,6
	Convolvulaceae				
34	*Cuscuta epilinum*	...	16	1	3,6
	Verbenaceae				
35	*Verbena urticifolia*	2	83	21	3,6
	Solanaceae				
36	*Nicotiana tabacum*	89	13	30	3,6
37	*Solanum nigrum*	98	82	30	3,6
	Scrophulariaceae				
38	*Verbascum blattaria*[1]	...	...	70	2
39	*V. thapsus*	83	21	30	3,6
	Plantaginaceae				
40	*Plantago lanceolata*	83	4	10	3,6
41	*P. major*[2]	24	6	21	2,3,6
	Compositae				
42	*Ambrosia artemisiifolia*[2]	59	21	30	2
43	*Anthemis cotula*[1]	...	...	25	2
44	*Arctium lappa*	100	11	16	2
45	*Chrysanthemum leucanthemum*	96	4	30	2
46	*Cirsium arvense*	57	1	21	2
47	*Erechtites heiracifolia*[1]	...	...	<5	2
48	*Helianthus annuus*	100	44	1	2
49	*Taraxacum laevigatum*	86	7	6	3,6
50	*Xanthium pensylvanicum*	50	15	16	2

/1/ Seeds buried at 18 inches. /2/ For additional data on seeds of this species buried for 70 years, consult reference 2. /3/ Seed balls rather than seeds, which accounts for the 153% initial viability. /4/ In peat bed.

Contributor: Steinbauer, George P.

References: [1] Crocker, W. 1938. Botan. Rev. 4:235. [2] Darlington, H. T. 1951. Am. J. Botany 38:379. [3] Duvel, J. W. T. 1905. U. S. Dept. Agr. Bur. Plant Ind. Bull. 83. [4] Libby, W. F. 1951. Science 114:291. [5] Ohga, I. 1926. Am. J. Botany 13:754. [6] Toole, E. H., and E. Brown. 1946. J. Agr. Research 72:201.

continued

132. LIFE SPANS: SEEDS

Part III: AT VARIOUS TEMPERATURES

Seeds were stored in sealed containers. Median life span is number of years for 50% seed survival; maximum life span is for a single seed.

	Family	Species	Moisture Content[1] %	Life Span (Years) at 24°C Medi-an	Life Span (Years) at 24°C Maxi-mum	Life Span (Years) at 5°C Medi-an	Life Span (Years) at 5°C Maxi-mum	Life Span (Years) at -4°C Medi-an	Life Span (Years) at -4°C Maxi-mum	Refer-ence
	(A)	(B)	(C)	(D)	(E)	(F)	(G)	(H)	(I)	(J)
1	Pinaceae	*Abies grandis*	11	<1	<1	1	>10	...	>16	10
2		*A. procera*	11	<1	1	1	>10	...	>16	10
3		*Picea abies*	5	...	...	...	...	17	>17	2,10
4		*Pinus caribaea*	Air-dry	4	8	8	>8	>10	>10	2,10
5		*P. echinata*	Air-dry	1	2	11	>11	>12	>12	2,10
6		*P. palustris*	Air-dry	<1	<1	1	5	4	>6	2,10
7		*P. taeda*	Air-dry	1	2	10	>11	>12	>12	2,10
8	Liliaceae	*Allium cepa*	6	11	14	...	...	>20	>28	1,3,10,12
9		*Lilium regale*	5	8	11	13	14	>17	>17	9,10
10	Iridaceae	*Gladiolus* spp.	8	6	10	7	8	>10	>20	10,12
11	Ulmaceae	*Ulmus americana*	7	2	4	8	10	15	>15	4,10
	Ranunculaceae	*Delphinium* spp.								
12		Annual	Air-dry	5	9	16	19	>18	>18	5,10
13		Perennial	Air-dry	2	3	7	13	>18	>18	5,10
14		*Paeonia suffruticosa*	Air-dry	<1	<1	3	8	5	7	10
15	Cruciferae	*Brassica oleracea botrytis*	Air-dry	>3	8	...	...	...	...	1
16	Leguminosae	*Lathyrus* spp.	10	2	4	>3	>3	...	...	5
17	Rutaceae	*Citrus limon*	56	<1	<1	>1	>1	<1	<1	6
18		*C. paradisi*	60	<1	1	1	>1	<1	<1	6
19	Malvaceae	*Gossypium* spp.	5	1	8	>13	>13	>13	>13	10
20	Violaceae	*Viola* spp.	4	2	>3	3	4	>2	>2	5
21	Umbelliferae	*Daucus carota*	5	16	>20	...	...	>20	>28	1,3,10,12
22	Oleaceae	*Fraxinus excelsior*	7	1	<2	7	<8	...	...	7
23		*F. pennsylvanica*	7	2	5	8	<9	...	...	7
24	Verbenaceae	*Verbena teucrioides*	6	3	6	9	13	>15	>15	5,10
25	Solanaceae	*Capsicum frutescens*	5	8	12	...	...	>20	>28	1,3,10,12
26		*Lycopersicon esculentum*	5	17	>20	...	...	>20	>28	1,3,10,12
27		*Solanum melongena*	5	18	>20	...	...	>20	>28	1,3,10,12
28	Rubiaceae	*Cinchona ledgeriana*	6	2	4	7	8	>9	>17	8,12
29	Campanulaceae	*Lobelia cardinalis*	5	<1	1	16	>25	20	>25	11
30	Compositae	*Callistephus chinensis*	7	2	3	10	12	>15	>15	5,10
31		*Lactuca sativa*	4	13	15	...	...	>20	>28	1,3,10,12
32		*Taraxacum officinale*	6	6	>11	>14	>14	>14	>14	5,10
33		*Venidium* spp.	5	>4	>4	>4	>4	>4	>4	5

/1/ At time of storage.

Contributor: Barton, Lela V.

References: [1] Barton, L. V. 1935. Contribs. Boyce Thompson Inst. 7:323. [2] Barton, L. V. 1935. Ibid. 7:379. [3] Barton, L. V. 1939. Ibid. 10:205. [4] Barton, L. V. 1939. Ibid. 10:221. [5] Barton, L. V. 1939. Ibid. 10:399. [6] Barton, L. V. 1943. Ibid. 13:47. [7] Barton, L. V. 1945. Ibid. 13:427. [8] Barton, L. V. 1947. Ibid. 15:1. [9] Barton, L. V. 1948. Boyce Thompson Inst. Plant Research Professional Paper 2(6):45. [10] Barton, L. V. 1953. Contribs. Boyce Thompson Inst. 17:87. [11] Barton, L. V. 1960. Ibid. 20:395. [12] Barton, L. V. Unpublished. Boyce Thompson Institute, Yonkers, N. Y., 1961.

XII. ENVIRONMENTAL FACTORS AND GROWTH

133. EFFECT OF TEMPERATURE ON GROWTH: VERTEBRATES

Part I: MOUSE

Subjects were male albino mice. Values in parentheses are ranges, estimate "b" (cf. Introduction).

	Age wk	20°C		24°C		33°C	
		No. of Subjects	Body Weight g	No. of Subjects	Body Weight g	No. of Subjects	Body Weight g
	(A)	(B)	(C)	(D)	(E)	(F)	(G)
1	3	24	8.35(7.37-9.33)	50	8.16(7.34-8.98)	48	8.64(8.02-9.26)
2	4	24	11.10(9.96-12.24)	50	12.44(11.58-13.30)	48	12.46(11.60-13.32)
3	5	24	14.67(12.79-16.55)	50	17.10(16.20-18.00)	48	14.41(13.53-15.29)
4	6	24	18.60(16.86-20.34)	50	19.56(18.66-20.46)	48	15.78(15.46-16.10)
5	7	24	19.37(17.83-20.91)	50	21.06(20.00-22.12)	45	16.45(15.47-17.43)
6	8	24	21.39(20.43-22.35)	50	22.22(20.96-23.48)	45	16.88(15.92-17.84)
7	12	24	25.10(23.58-26.62)	43	25.27(24.19-26.35)	32	19.75(18.39-21.11)
8	16	20	26.90(24.84-28.96)	42	27.19(25.69-28.69)	19	20.51(19.07-21.95)
9	20	16	27.62(26.18-29.06)	42	27.81(26.39-29.23)	12	20.79(19.15-22.43)

Contributor: Mills, Clarence A.

Reference: Ogle, C. 1934. Am. J. Physiol. 107:635.

Part II: RAT

Subjects were male albino rats. Weight Specification (column B): Relative = mg organ weight per g body weight.

	Structure	Weight Specification	Weight at 120 Days of Age			Weight at 210 Days of Age		
			18.3°C	28.3°C	35°C	18.3°C	28.3°C	35°C
	(A)	(B)	(C)	(D)	(E)	(F)	(G)	(H)
1	Body	Absolute, g	145	155	150	217	204	184
2	Heart	Absolute, g	0.483	0.512	0.456	0.751	0.719	0.649
3		Relative	3.26	3.30	3.04	3.46	3.52	3.48
4	Testes	Absolute, g	1.96	2.12	1.60	2.19	2.26	1.77
5		Relative	13.23	13.65	10.70	10.10	11.10	9.59
6	Prostate and	Absolute, g	0.87	1.06	1.01	2.19	1.64	1.86
7	seminal vesicles	Relative	5.87	6.84	6.75	10.10	8.05	10.08
8	Adrenals	Absolute, g	21.22	24.72	22.20	24.52	23.32	16.84
9		Relative	0.143	0.159	0.148	0.113	0.114	0.091
10	Liver	Absolute, g	7.79	7.52	6.55	9.98	9.30	8.45
11		Relative	52.60	48.42	43.80	46.03	45.66	45.80
12	Pituitary	Absolute, g	5.72	6.65	6.48	8.42	5.68	7.00
13		Relative	0.034	0.043	0.043	0.039	0.028	0.038

Contributor: Herrington, L. P.

Reference: Herrington, L. P., and J. H. Nelbach. 1942. Endocrinology 30:375.

continued

133. EFFECT OF TEMPERATURE ON GROWTH: VERTEBRATES

Part III: CHICK

Values are wet weights for Single-Comb White Leghorn embryos, incubated at the specified temperatures.

	Age da	Body Weight at 35°C	35.56°C	37.22°C	38.77°C	40.56°C	41.67°C
	(A)	(B)	(C)	(D)	(E)	(F)	(G)
1	4	.....	....	......	0.0656	0.225	0.0961
2	5	.....	....	0.059	0.203	0.434	....
3	6	.....	....	0.189	0.4417	0.909	0.6529
4	7	.....	....	0.377	0.7602	1.376	....
5	8	0.311	0.3134	0.639	1.3477	2.032	1.6091
6	9	0.583	0.5246	1.234	1.8470	3.046	....
7	10	0.939	0.8693	1.591	2.6708	4.113	2.9898
8	11	1.323	....	2.133	3.7303	6.259	....
9	12	1.730	1.5623	3.081	5.5533	8.457	6.6143
10	13	2.226	....	4.292	7.1474	10.426	....
11	14	.....	2.5816	6.162	8.8553	13.485	10.2785
12	15	3.525	....	8.758	13.3434	15.314	....
13	16	.....	5.1552	10.989	16.6058	18.505	15.6434
14	17	5.150	....	12.685	20.8031	20.427	....
15	18	.....	7.6114	15.895	22.5553	......	15.1821
16	19	8.322	....	17.529	28.8203	......	....
17	20	.....	11.6309	21.708	28.6532	......	....
18	21	11.49	....	27.133	....	......	....

Contributor: Henderson, Earl W.

Reference: Henderson, E. W. 1930. Univ. Missouri Agr. Expt. Sta. Research Bull. 149.

134. EFFECT OF TEMPERATURE ON HATCHING TIME: AMPHIBIANS AND BONY FISHES

Hatching time = average number of days from fertilization to emergence of larva from egg membrane. Classification for fishes adapted from Herald, *Living Fishes of the World,* 1961.

	Family and Species	Temp. °C	Hatching Time da	Reference
	(A)	(B)	(C)	(D)
	Amphibia			
	Ranidae			
1	*Rana clamitans*	15	7-8	31
2		19.8	3-4	
3		25.3	2	
4		33.4	1.3	
5	*R. palustris*	15.5	6-7	31
6		18.6	4-5	
7		19.9	3.5	
8		25.7	2	
9		30.4	2	
10	*R. pipiens*	12	14-18	1,31, 40
11		15	7-8	
12		18	5-6	
13		19.8	4.0-4.5	
14		25	2.5-3.0	
15		26	2.5	
16		30	1.5-2.0	
17	*R. sylvatica*	10	11-14	31,35
18		15.4	5-6	
19		18.5	4	
20		19.9	3-4	
21		23.7	2	
	Hylidae			
22	*Pseudacris clarki*	25	4.0-4.5	9
	Pipidae			
23	*Xenopus laevis*	18	3	45
	Salamandridae			
24	*Triturus vulgaris*	15-16	16-18	11
	Pisces			
	Soleidae			
25	*Achirus fasciatus*	23.3-24.4	1.5	18
	Pleuronectidae			
26	*Pseudopleuronectes americanus*	20.6	15	3
	Gasterosteidae			
27	*Apeltes quadracus*	22	6	27
28	*Gasterosteus aculeatus*	8.3	27.9	28
29		11	15.1	
30		14	10.7	
31		16	8.1	
32		18	6.4	
33		20.5	5.4	
34		24	4.8	
35		27	4.3	
	Triglidae			
36	*Prionotus carolinus*	22	2.5	27
	Atherinidae			
37	*Menidia beryllina*	26-28	8-10	16
38	*M. menidia notata*	22	8-9	27
	Blenniidae			
39	*Chasmodes besquianus*	24.5-27.0	11	18
40	*Hypleurochilus geminatus*	26-28	6-8	18
41	*Hypsoblennius hentz*	24.5-27.0	10-12	18
	Gobiidae			
42	*Gobionellus boleosoma*	20	0.75	18
43	*Gobiosoma bosci*	26-28	4	18
	Scombridae			
44	*Scomber scombrus*	12	6	48
45		14	4.5	
46		15	4	
47		18	3	
48		21	2	
	Scaridae			
49	*Calotomus japonicus*	15.6	2.4	39
50		18.6	2.0	
51		20.0	1.9	
52		21.4	1.7	
53		22.6	1.4	
54		24.4	1.3	
55		25.8	1.1	

continued

	Family and Species	Temp. °C	Hatching Time da	Reference
	(A)	(B)	(C)	(D)
	Pisces			
	Scaridae			
56	*Calotomus japonicus*	27.6	1.0	39
57		29.5	0.9	
	Labridae			
58	*Tautoga onitis*	22	1.7	27
59	*Tautogolabrus adspersus*	22	1.7	27
	Cichlidae			
60	*Hemichromis bimaculatus*	26.7	2	42
	Ephippidae			
61	*Chaetodipterus faber*	26.7	1	38
	Sparidae			
62	*Archosargus probatocephalus*	24.7	1.7	37
63	*Pagrosomus major*	11.8	4.7	19
64		13.9	3.5	
65		16.0	2.7	
66		18.0	2.1	
67		19.4	1.8	
68		20.8	1.6	
69		21.8	1.4	
70	*Stenotomus chrysops*	22	1.7	27
	Sciaenidae			
71	*Bairdiella chrysura*	18.9-21.1	2	46
72		27.2-27.8	0.75	26
73	*Cynoscion regalis*	20.0-21.1	1.5-1.7	46
74	*Menticirrhus saxatilis*	20.0-21.1	2	46
	Serranidae			
75	*Roccus saxatilus*	17.9	2	34
	Gadidae			
76	*Gadus* sp.	6	17.2	2
77		8	11.9	
78		10	9.0	
79		12	8.5	
80	*G. callarias*	-0.56	50	4
81		0	40	
82		1.11	31	
83		2.2	25	
84		4.4	17	
85		6.1	14	
86		8.3	10	
87	*G. merlangus*	5	15.3	8
88		6	13.5	
89		8	10.3	
90		10	8.0	
91		12	6.5	
92		14	5.8	
93	*G. morhua*	-1	42.0	8
94		3	23.0	
95		4	20.5	
96		5	17.5	
97		6	15.5	
98		8	13.0	
99		10	10.5	
100		12	9.7	
101		14	8.5	
102	*Melanogrammus aeglefinus*	-1	42.0	8
103		3	23.0	
104		4	20.5	
105		5	17.8	
106		6	15.5	
107		8	13.0	
108		10	10.8	
	Gadidae			
109	*Melanogrammus aeglefinus*	12	9.7	8
110		14	8.8	
111	*Merluccius bilinearis*	22	2	27
112	*Urophycis chuss*	15.6	4	18
	Cyprinodontidae			
113	*Fundulus heteroclitus*	25	12	41
	Anguillidae			
114	*Anguilla rostrata*	24-28	7	10
	Ictaluridae			
115	*Ictalurus* sp.	27	7-9	29
	Catostomidae			
116	*Catostomus commersonii*	11.7	12	5
117		11.6	7	
118		18.3	5	
119		21.1	4	
	Cyprinidae			
120	*Brachydanio rerio*	27	3	7
121	*Carassius auratus*	9.4	23.8	22
122		11.0	18.0	
123		12.0	14.8	
124		13.3	12.7	
125		14.3	11.4	
126		15.8	9.0	
127		16.2	7.7	
128		17.4	7.0	
129	*Leuciscus hakuensis*	6.6	16.6	22
130		9.2	12.6	
131		10.7	7.8	
132		12.7	6.6	
133		14.4	4.8	
134		15.4	4.2	
135		16.9	3.7	
136		18.1	3.9	
137		19.0	3.3	
138		20.3	2.8	
139	*Notropis bifrenatus*	24	2-3	13
140	*Richardsonius balteatus*	21-23	3-7	44
	Characidae			
141	*Aphiocharax rubripinnis*	25.0-25.6	1.0-1.5	43
	Esocidae			
142	*Esox lucius*	6.1	14-15	6
143		7.9	14	
144		11.1	7	
145		12.6	6-11	
	Osmeridae			
146	*Hypomesus olidus*	7.0	38	15,32
147		10.0	24	
148		13.5	13	
149		14.5	12	
150		15.3	10.6	
151		16.7	9.4	
152		17.5	8.5	
153		18.5	8.7	
154	*Osmerus mordax*	5.8	19	25
155		13.9	13	
	Coregonidae			
156	*Coregonus clupeaformis*	0.5	141	36
157		2	119	
158		4	82.9	
159		6	57.8	
160		8	41.2	
161		10	29.3	
	Salmonidae			
162	*Oncorhynchus masou*	6.1	87	20

continued

134. EFFECT OF TEMPERATURE ON HATCHING TIME: AMPHIBIANS AND BONY FISHES

	Family and Species	Temp. °C	Hatching Time da	Reference
	(A)	(B)	(C)	(D)
	Pisces			
	Salmonidae			
163	*Oncorhynchus masou*	7.6	70	20
164		8.8	58	
165		10.4	48	
166		11.8	46	
167		13.0	38	
168		14.3	36	
169		16.1	29	
170	*Plecoglossus altivelis*	6.9	44	33
171		8.9	37	
172		9.8	31	
173		11.0	27	
174		12.2	22.8	
175		13.0	20	
176		13.9	18.6	
177		15.0	19	
178		16.9	14.3	
179		18.2	12.5	
180		24.0	8.5	
181	*Salmo clarki*	6.4	53-57	30
182		8.3	37-45	
183		11.3	24-29	
184	*S. fario*	2.8	165	12
185		3.6	135	
186		4.5	109	
187		5.7	96	
188		6.6	81	
189		7.3	73	
	Salmonidae			
190	*Salmo fario*	8.0	65	12
191		9.0	56	
192		10.0	47	
193		11.1	38	
194		12.2	32	
195	*S. irideus*	3.1	102	21,23
196		4.5	73	
197		6.5	58-74	
198		7.8	47-51	
199		9.0	38-40	
200		10.6	32-33	
201		12.0	28	
202		13.0	24	
203		15.0	21	
204	*S. salar*	10	50	14
205	*Salvelinus fontinalis*	3	125	24
206		10	50	
	Engraulidae			
207	*Anchoviella epsetus*	19-21	2	17
208	*A. mitchilli*	27.2-27.8	1	26
	Clupeidae			
209	*Clupea harengus*	1.8	46-51	47
210		2.1	46-56	
211		2.3	41-53	
212		2.6	37-52	
213		3.2	28-41	
214		4.0	29-35	
215		5.5	20-34	
216	*Pomolobus aestivalis*	22	2	27

Contributors: (a) Atlas, Meyer, (b) Clark, Clarence F.

References: [1] Atlas, M. Unpublished. Yeshiva Univ., New York, 1953. [2] Bonnet, D. D. 1939. Biol. Bull. 76:440. [3] Breder, C. M. 1921-22. U. S. Bur. Fisheries Bull. 38:314. [4] Brice, J. J. 1887. U. S. Fish Comm. Rept., appendix. [5] Carbine, W. F. 1943. Copeia, p. 48. [6] Clark, C. F. Unpublished. Ohio Dept. of Natural Resources, Division of Wildlife, Columbus, 1962. [7] Creaser, C. W. 1934. Copeia, p. 159. [8] Dannevig, H. 1894. Fisheries Board Scot. 13th Ann. Rept. (3):147. [9] Eaton, T. H., and R. M. Imagawa. 1948. Copeia, p. 263. [10] Fish, M. 1927. Zoologica 8:292. [11] Glaesner, L. 1915. In F. Keibel, ed. Normentafeln zur Entwicklungsgeschichte der Wirbeltiere. G. Fischer, Jena. Heft 14. [12] Gray, J. 1928. Brit. J. Exptl. Biol. 6:126. [13] Harrington, R. W. 1949. Copeia, p. 252. [14] Hayes, F. R., I. R. Wilmot, and D. A. Livingstone. 1951. J. Exptl. Zool. 116:380. [15] Higurashi, T. 1925. J. Imp. Fisheries Inst. Japan 21:5. [16] Hildebrand, S. F. 1921-22. U. S. Bur. Fisheries Bull. 38:38. [17] Hildebrand, S. F., and L. E. Cable. 1930. Ibid. 46:383. [18] Hildebrand, S. F., and L. E. Cable. 1938. Ibid. 48:505. [19] Kajiyama, E. 1929. J. Imp. Fisheries Inst. Japan. 24:110. [20] Kawajiri, M. 1927. Ibid. 23:18. [21] Kawajiri, M. 1927. Ibid. 23:59. [22] Kawajiri, M. 1928. Ibid. 23:66. [23] Kawajiri, M. 1928. Ibid. 24:2. [24] Kendall, W. C. 1915-16. U. S. Bur. Fisheries Bull. 35:549. [25] Kendall, W. C. 1926. Ibid. 42:340. [26] Kuntz, A. 1913. Ibid. 33:3. [27] Kuntz, A., and L. Radcliffe. 1915-16. Ibid. 35:3. [28] Leiner, M. 1932. Z. vergleich. Physiol. 16:590. [29] Lenz, G. 1947. Progressive Fish Culturist 9:222. [30] Merriman, D. 1935. J. Exptl. Biol. 12:297. [31] Moore, J. A. 1939. Ecology 20:459. [32] Nakai, N. 1928. J. Imp. Fisheries Inst. Japan 23:124. [33] Nakai, N. 1928. Ibid. 24:35. [34] Pearson, J. S. 1938. U. S. Bur. Fisheries Bull. 49:831. [35] Pollister, A. W., and J. A. Moore. 1937. Anat. Record 68:492. [36] Price, J. W. 1940. J. Gen. Physiol. 23:449. [37] Rathbun, R. 1888-89. U. S. Fish Comm. Rept., p. 59. [38] Ryder, J. A. 1887. Ibid., p. 489. [39] Seno, H., K. Ebina, and T. Okada. 1926.

continued

134. EFFECT OF TEMPERATURE ON HATCHING TIME: AMPHIBIANS AND BONY FISHES

J. Imp. Fisheries Inst. Japan 21:44. [40] Shumway, W. 1940. Anat. Record 78:145. [41] Solberg, A. 1938. J. Exptl. Zool. 78:445. [42] Solberg, A., and F. J. Brinley. 1931. Aquarium J. 1:257. [43] Stroop, W. 1932. Ibid. 1:147. [44] Weisel, G. F., and H. W. Newman. 1951. Copeia, p. 187. [45] Weisz, P. 1945. Anat. Record 93:167. [46] Welsh, W. W., and C. M. Breder. 1923-24. U. S. Bur. Fisheries Bull. 39:141. [47] Williamson, H. C. 1908. Fisheries Board Scot. 27th Ann. Rept., p. 100. [48] Worley, L. G. 1933. J. Gen. Physiol. 16:841.

135. EFFECT OF TEMPERATURE ON HATCHING TIME: INSECTS AND TICKS

Hatching time = average number of hours or days from oviposition to emergence of larva from egg membrane. Classification for insects adapted from Borrer and DeLong, *An Introduction to the Study of Insects*, 1954.

	Order and Species	Temp. °C	Hatching Time	Reference
	(A)	(B)	(C)	(D)
	Insecta			
	Hymenoptera			
1	*Iridomyrmex humilis*	21.1	27 da	23
2		23.3	23 da	
3		27.2	19-22 da	
4		28.1	12 da	
	Diptera			
5	*Anopheles minimus*	16	7 da	30
6		20	3.5 da	
7		25	2.5 da	
8		30	2 da	
9		35	2 da	
10	*A. quadrimaculatus*	10.0	20.5 da	13
11		14.5	8.0 da	
12		18.3	4.5 da	
13		22.0	2.9 da	
14		25.4	1.9 da	
15		28.6	1.6 da	
16		34.8	1.4 da	
17	*Cochliomyia americana*	23.3	25.2 hr	7
18		37.2	9.2 hr	
19	*C. macellaria*	17.8	33.0 hr	20
20		20.6	22.0 hr	
21		23.3	16.0 hr	
22		26.1	12.1 hr	
23		28.9	9.7 hr	
24		31.7	8.2 hr	
25		34.4	7.3 hr	
26		37.2	6.7 hr	
27		40.0	6.7 hr	
28	*Drosophila melanogaster*	15.0	67.9 hr	24
29		16.2	57.0 hr	
30		18.2	41.4 hr	
31		20.1	33.4 hr	
32		22.1	26.5 hr	
33		24.1	22.5 hr	
34		27.0	18.8 hr	
35		29.0	17.1 hr	
36		30.8	16.9 hr	
37	*Haematobia irritans*	26.1	17.1 hr	20
38		28.9	14.0 hr	
39		31.7	12.3 hr	
40		34.4	11.3 hr	
41	*Lucilia cuprina*	23.3	15.1 hr	20
42		26.1	12.0 hr	
43		28.9	9.8 hr	
44		31.7	8.5 hr	
45		34.4	7.8 hr	
	Diptera			
46	*Lucilia cuprina*	37.2	7.7 hr	20
47		40.0	8.9 hr	
48	*L. nuicolor*	23.3	14.0 hr	20
49		26.1	11.4 hr	
50		28.9	9.3 hr	
51		31.7	8.3 hr	
52		34.4	7.8 hr	
53		37.2	8.1 hr	
54	*L. sericata*	17.8	42.4 hr	20
55		20.6	29.4 hr	
56		23.3	20.9 hr	
57		26.1	15.8 hr	
58		28.9	12.6 hr	
59		31.7	10.3 hr	
60		34.4	8.8 hr	
61		37.2	8.1 hr	
62		40.0	8.1 hr	
63	*Musca domestica*	15.0	51.5 hr	20
64		17.8	33.3 hr	
65		20.6	23.1 hr	
66		23.3	17.2 hr	
67		26.1	13.5 hr	
68		28.9	10.7 hr	
69		31.7	9.0 hr	
70		34.4	8.1 hr	
71		37.2	7.6 hr	
72		40.0	8.1 hr	
73	*Phormia regina*	15.0	52.0 hr	20
74		17.8	34.4 hr	
75		20.6	24.1 hr	
76		23.3	18.1 hr	
77		26.1	14.3 hr	
78		28.9	11.4 hr	
79		31.7	9.5 hr	
80		34.4	8.6 hr	
81		37.2	8.1 hr	
82		40.0	8.7 hr	
83	*Sciara coprophila*	22-24	5-6 da	7
84	*Simulium ornatum*	16	5-6 da	7
	Lepidoptera			
85	*Carpocapsa pomonella*	20	10-11 da	26
86		21	10-12 da	
87		22	9 da	
88		28	9 da	
89		32	5 da	
90	*Ephestia kuhniella*	13.0	21 da	31
91		16.0	13.3 da	
92		21.0	6.1 da	

continued

135. EFFECT OF TEMPERATURE ON HATCHING TIME: INSECTS AND TICKS

	Order and Species	Temp. °C	Hatching Time	Reference
	(A)	(B)	(C)	(D)
	Insecta			
	Lepidoptera			
93	*Ephestia kuhniella*	25.5	4.1 da	31
94		27.0	3.8 da	
95		29	3.5 da	
96		30	3.3 da	
97		32	3.1 da	
98		33	3.7 da	
99	*Euproctis chrysor-*	16	30 da	25
100	*rhoea*	20	23 da	
101		25	17.5 da	
102		27	15 da	
103	*Galleria mellonella*	22.2	17 da	6
104		27.8	11 da	
105		30.6-32.8	9 da	
106	*Prodenia littoralis*	29	2 da	17
107	*Samia cecropia*	16	24 da	25
108		20	13-16 da	
109		25	10 da	
110		32	7-11 da	
111	*Sitotroga cerealella*	26.7	5 da	7
	Coleoptera			
112	*Anthonomus grandis*	16.7	11 da	14
113		21.1	5.1 da	
114		22.6	3.5-4.0 da	
115		27.2	2.5-3.0 da	
116	*Bruchus obtectus*	17.6	19.5 da	21
117		21.0	10.7 da	
118		24.2	7.3 da	
119		27.1	5.7 da	
120		30.1	4.9 da	
121		34.0	5 da	
122	*Colandra oryzae*	15.2	18.4 da	2
123		18.2	10.4 da	
124		26.4	4.3 da	
125		29.1	3.6 da	
126		32.3	3.3 da	
127	*Hypera postica*	17.4	19.8 da	29
128		22.0	9.4 da	
129		27.0	6.9 da	
130		32.0	5.5 da	
131	*Hyperaspid vincigurrae*	30	5 da	9
132	*Leptinotarsa decemli-*	11.0	14 da	25
133	*neata*	18.5	6.5 da	
134		25.0	4.5-5.5 da	
135		29.5	3-5 da	
136	*Popillia japonica*	15.0	61 da	19
137		22.5	15 da	
138		30.0	8 da	
139	*Rhizopertha dominica*	22.0	15.2 da	2
140		26.0	9.0 da	
141		30.0	6.0 da	
142		34.0	4.8 da	
143		36.0	4.5 da	
144		38.2	4.9 da	
145	*Sitona lineata*	7.0	50 da	1
146		14.3	21 da	
147		16.6	16 da	
148		18.0	14 da	
149		18.7	12.7 da	
150		19.2	11.5 da	
151		24.0	7.5 da	
152		28.0	7.1-8.5 da	
	Coleoptera			
153	*Tenebrio molitor*	12	55 da	25
154		15	40 da	
155		20	14 da	
156		25	9 da	
157		32	6 da	
158	*Tomicus typographus*	14[1]	16 da	10
159		14[2]	18 da	
160		17[1]	11.5 da	
161		17[2]	12.5 da	
162		20[1]	8.5 da	
163		20[2]	8.5 da	
164		24[1]	5.5 da	
165		24[2]	6.5 da	
166	*Tribolium confusum*	17	38.8 da	4,28
167		22	14.1 da	
168		27	6.0 da	
169		32	4.4 da	
	Hemiptera			
170	*Blissus leucopterus*	24.5	15 da	16
171		34.5	7 da	
172	*Pentatoma lignata*	23.5	6.0 da	22
173		24.3	6.8 da	
174		26.3	5.4 da	
175		28.2	3.6 da	
	Anoplura			
176	*Haematopinus suis*	35	13-15 da	7
177	*Pediculus humanus*	24	17-21 da	18
178		26	13-19 da	
179		29	9-11 da	
180		32	7-9 da	
181		35	5-7 da	
	Mallophaga			
182	*Lipeurus heterogra-phus*	33-34	5-7 da	32
	Orthoptera			
183	*Arphia xanthoptera*	36	17 da	3
184	*Chortophaga australior*	23	39 da	3
185	*C. viridifasciata*	23	53 da	3
186		36	19 da	
187	*Dicromorpha viridis*	23	86 da	3
188	*Encotolophus sordidus*	23	73 da	3
189	*Melanoplus differenti-*	5	438 da	3
190	*alis*	10	281 da	
191		15	184 da	
192		20	106 da	
193		23	89 da	
194		26	69.6 da	
195		30	48 da	
196		36	28 da	
197	*M. femur-rubrum*	5	226 da	3
198		10	145 da	
199		15	92 da	
200		20	59 da	
201		23	45 da	
202		26	34.3 da	
203		30	24 da	
204		36	14 da	
205	*Periplaneta americana*	21	54-60 da	8
206		28	32-34 da	
207		30	29-30 da	
208		33	31-33 da	
209		36	32-34 da	
210	*Romalea microptera*	23	150 da	3

/1/ Humidity = 55-56%. /2/ Humidity = 95-98%.

continued

135. EFFECT OF TEMPERATURE ON HATCHING TIME: INSECTS AND TICKS

	Order and Species	Temp. °C	Hatching Time	Reference
	(A)	(B)	(C)	(D)
	Insecta			
	Collembola			
211	*Sminthurus viridis*	8.7	48 da	5
212		15.0	16-19 da	
213		20.0	10-11 da	
214		25.2	8 da	
	Arachnida			
	Acari			
215	*Amblyomma americanum*	13	117 da	12
216		26	28-29 da	
217		27	26-27 da	
218	*A. cajenense*	23	51-56 da	12
219		27	37 da	
220	*A. dissimile*	24	40 da	12
221		29	27 da	
222	*A. maculatum*	15	102 da	12
223		21	52 da	
224		27	21 da	
225	*A. tuberculatum*	21	91 da	12
226	*Argas miniatus*	15.6	107 da	12
227		20.6	29 da	
228		27.2	13 da	
229		32.2	9 da	
230	*Dermacentor nitens*	23	39 da	12
231		29	24 da	
232	*D. occidentalis*	25	38 da	12
233		32	16 da	
	Acari			
234	*Dermacentor parumapertus*	29-32	20-24 da	12
235	*D. variabilis*	24	31 da	12
236		27	24 da	
237		29	20 da	
238	*D. venustus*	22	32 da	12
239		27	16 da	
240	*Hemaphysalis leporis*	27.8	23 da	12
241	*Ixodes kingi*	24	52 da	12
242		27	40 da	
243		31	32 da	
244	*Margaropus annulatus*	12	137 da	15
245		22	47 da	
246		27	23 da	
247	*M. annulatus australis*	26	24 da	12
248		30	19-23 da	
249		35	15-18 da	
250	*Ornithodorus coriaceus*	26.7	15-21 da	11,27
251		28.6	13 da	
252		29.7	11 da	
253		30.0	10 da	
254	*O. megnini*	20.0	21 da	12
255		24.4	13-15 da	
256		26.1	12 da	
257		30.0	10 da	
258	*Rhipicephalus sanguineus*	16.1	142 da	12
259		21.0	41 da	
260		29.0	19 da	

Contributors: (a) Atlas, Meyer, (b) Ludwig, Daniel

References: [1] Anderson, K. T. 1930. Z. Morphol. Okol. Tiere 17:649. [2] Birch, L. C. 1945. Australian J. Exptl. Biol. Med. Sci. 23:29. [3] Bodine, J. H. 1925. J. Exptl. Zool. 42:95. [4] Chapman, R. N., and L. Baird. 1934. Ibid. 68:293. [5] Davidson, J. 1931. Australian J. Exptl. Biol. Med. Sci. 8:143. [6] El-Sawaf, S. K. 1950. Bull. soc. Fouad Ier entomol. 34:252. [7] Florence, L. 1937. Culture methods for invertebrate animals. Comstock, Ithaca. [8] Gier, H. T. 1947. Ann. Entomol. Soc. Amer. 11:305. [9] Hafez, M., and S. El-Ziady. 1952. Bull. soc. Fouad Ier entomol. 36:220. [10] Hennings, C. 1907. Biol. Zentr. 27:324. [11] Herms, W. B. 1916. J. Parasitol. 2:137. [12] Hooker, W. A., F. C. Bishopp, and H. P. Wood. 1912. U. S. Dept. Agr. Bur. Entomol. Bull. 106. [13] Huffaker, C. B. 1944. Ann. Entomol. Soc. Amer. 37:10. [14] Hunter, W. D., and W. E. Hinds. 1905. U. S. Dept. Agr. Bur. Entomol. Bull. 51. [15] Hunter, W. D., and W. A. Hooker. 1907. Ibid. 72. [16] Janes, M. J. 1935. Ann. Entomol. Soc. Amer. 28:111. [17] Janisch, E. 1932. Trans. Entomol. Soc. London 80:151. [18] Leeson, H. S. 1941. Parasitology 33:244. [19] Ludwig, D. 1928. Physiol. Zool. 1:358. [20] Melvin, R. 1934. Ann. Entomol. Soc. Amer. 27:406. [21] Menusen, H. 1934. Ibid. 27:515. [22] Merrill, A. W. 1910. U. S. Dept. Agr. Bur. Entomol. Bull. 86. [23] Newell, W., and T. C. Barber. 1912. Ibid. 122. [24] Powsner, L. 1935. Physiol. Zool. 8:474. [25] Sanderson, E. D. 1910. J. Econ. Entomol. 3:113. [26] Simpson, C. B. 1903. U. S. Dept. Agr. Bur. Entomol. Bull. 41. [27] Smith, C. N. 1944. Ann. Entomol. Soc. Amer. 37:326. [28] Stanley, J. 1939. Ibid. 32:564. [29] Sweetman, H. L., and J. Wedemeyer. 1933. Ecology 14:46. [30] Thomson, R. C. M. 1940. J. Malaria Inst. India 3:323. [31] Voute, A. D. 1936. Z. angew. Entomol. 22:1. [32] Wilson, F. H. 1934. J. Parasitol. 11:305.

136. OPTIMUM TEMPERATURE AND HUMIDITY FOR DEVELOPMENT: INSECTS AND TICKS

Stage (column B): E = egg, L = larva, N = nymph, P = pupa.

	Order and Species	Stage	Temp. °C	Humidity %	Reference
	(A)	(B)	(C)	(D)	(E)
	Diptera				
1	*Cochliomyia macellaria*	E	37.2	100	21
2	*Drosophila melanogaster*	P	29-31	100	16
3	*Haematobia irritans*	E	34.5	100	21
4	*Hypoderma lineatum*	P	20-25	0-76	26
5	*Lucilia australis*	E	34.5	100	21
6	*L. cuprina*	E	34.5-37.2	100	21
7	*L. sericata*	E	34.5-37.2	100	21
8	*L. unicolor*	E	34.5	100	21
9	*Musca domestica*	E	37.2	100	21
10	*Phaenicia sericata*	E	10-37	100	2,36
11	*Phormia regina*	E	34.5	100	21
12	*Winthemia quadripustulata*	P	27	73.4	9
	Lepidoptera				
13	*Agrostis segetum*	P	17-21	65-85	13
14	*Bombyx mori*	P[1]	25	7-100	14
15	*Hofmannophila pseudospretella*	E	15-25	90	37
16	*Protoparce quinquemaculata*	P	27	0-73.4	9
17	*Tineola bisselliella*	L	23.9	75	5,6
	Coleoptera				
18	*Acanthoscelides ob-*	E	25.2	90	22
19	*tectus*	L	25.2	90-98	22
20	*Anomala orientalis*	E	25.5	100	35
21		P	27	100	35
22	*Callosobruchus chinensis*	L	30.4	76	34
23	*C. maculatus*	E	30	63	29
24	*Colandra oryzae*	E, L, P	29.1	14[2]	1
25	*Dermestes maculatus*	E	32	80	30
	Coleoptera				
26	*Epilachna corrupta*	E	27	81-100	28
27	*Eurostus hilleri*	E	20	90	12
28	*Hylotrupes bajulus*	E[3]	27	90-95	31
29	*Hypera postica*	E	27	93	33
30		L	32	32	33
31		P	32	32-92	33
32	*Lasioderma serricorne*	E	32	75	27
33	*Ptinus tectus*	E	25	70	3
34		L	24.7	70	3
35		P	27	90	3
36	*Rhizopertha domi-*	E	36	14[2]	1
37	*nica*	L	34	14[2]	1
38		P	34-38.2	14[2]	1
39	*Tenebrio molitor*	L	27	75	15
40		P	35	60	25
41	*Tribolium castane-*	E	37.5	>10	11
42	*um*	L	35	High	11
43		P	37.5	>10	11
44	*T. destructor*	L	27-28	70-80	19,20, 23
45		P	27-29	77	10
	Hemiptera				
46	*Cimex lectularius*	N	18	44-77	4
47	*C. rotunda*	N	18	77-93	4
	Orthoptera				
48	*Camnula pellucida*	E	27	60-90	24
49	*Locusta migratoria migratorioides*	N	32.2-37.8	60-70	7,8
50	*Schistocerca gregaria*	N	37.8	60-70	7,8
	Thysanura				
51	*Thermobia domestica*	N	37	84	32
	Acari				
52	*Ixodes ricinus*	N	25-30	90-100	17,18

/1/ Including prepupal stage. /2/ Moisture content of grain. /3/ Optimum development occurs also at 19.3°C, 70-80% humidity, and at 16.6°C, 50-60% humidity.

Contributor: Ludwig, Daniel

References: [1] Birch, L. C. 1945. Australian J. Exptl. Biol. Med. Sci. 23:29. [2] Evans, A. C. 1934. Parasitology 26:366. [3] Ewer, D. W., and R. F. Ewer. 1942. J. Exptl. Biol. 18:290. [4] Geisthardt, G. 1937. Z. Parasitenk. 9:151. [5] Griswold, G. H. 1944. Cornell Univ. Agr. Expt. Sta. Mem. 262:1. [6] Griswold, G. H., and M. F. Crowell. 1936. Ecology 17:241. [7] Hamilton, A. G. 1936. Trans. Roy. Entomol. Soc. London 85:1. [8] Hamilton, A. G. 1950. Ibid. 101:1. [9] Hefley, H. M. 1928. J. Econ. Entomol. 21:213. [10] Havelka, J., and J. Winkler. 1951. Entomol. Listy 13:121. [11] Howe, R. W. 1953. Ann. Appl. Biol. 44:356. [12] Howe, R. W., and H. D. Burges. 1952. Bull. Entomol. Research 43:153. [13] Kozhantchikov, I. 1936. Bull. Plant Protection Lenin Acad. Agr. Sci., Ser. 1, 19:1. [14] Leclercq, J. 1946. Experientia 2:1. [15] Leclercq, J. 1950. Physiol. Comparata et Oecol. 2:161. [16] Ludwig, D., and R. M. Cable. 1933. Physiol. Zool. 6:493. [17] MacLeod, J. 1934. Parasitology 26:282. [18] MacLeod, J. 1935. Ibid. 27:123. [19] Magis, N. 1954. Bull. soc. roy. sci. Liège 11:420. [20] Mathlein, R. 1943. Statens Växtskyddsanstalt Medd. 41:5. [21] Melvin, R. 1934. Ann. Entomol. Soc. Amer. 27:406. [22] Menusan, H. 1934. Ibid. 27:515. [23] Naton, E. 1960. Z. angew.

continued

136. OPTIMUM TEMPERATURE AND HUMIDITY FOR DEVELOPMENT: INSECTS AND TICKS

Entomol. 46:233. [24] Parker, J. R. 1930. Univ. Montana Agr. Expt. Sta. Bull. 233. [25] Payne, N. M. 1932. Entomol. News 43:6. [26] Pfadt, R. E. 1947. J. Econ. Entomol. 40:293. [27] Powell, T. E. 1931. Ecol. Monographs 1:333. [28] Pyenson, L., and H. L. Sweetman. 1931. Bull. Brooklyn Entomol. Soc. 26:221. [29] Schoof, H. F. 1941. Ecology 22:297. [30] Scoggen, J. K., and O. E. Tauber. 1949. Iowa State Coll. J. Sci. 23:363. [31] Steiner, P. 1937. Z. angew. Entomol. 23:531. [32] Sweetman, H. L. 1938. Ecol. Monographs 8:285. [33] Sweetman, H. L., and J. Wedemeyer. 1933. Ecology 14:46. [34] Utida, S. 1941. Mem. Coll. Agr. Kyoto Imp. Univ. 49:1. [35] Van Zwaluwenburg, R. H. 1937. Hawaiian Planters Record 41:25. [36] Wardle, R. A. 1930. Ann. Appl. Biol. 17:554. [37] Woodroffe, G. E. 1951. Bull. Entomol. Research 41:529.

137. DIAPAUSE: INSECTS AND MITES

Diapause in insects and mites may be facultative (influenced by the environment and not present in each generation) or obligate (occurring in virtually every individual and in each generation without respect to environment). Species experiencing facultative diapause generally complete two or more generations annually (bivoltine or multivoltine cycles), whereas those with obligate diapause produce one generation (univoltine cycle). Dormant Stage (column B): I = instar, FI = final instar, FD = fully developed, S = small, HG = half-grown.

	Order and Species	Dormant Stage	Diapause		Reference
			Type	Duration	
	(A)	(B)	(C)	(D)	(E)
	Hymenoptera				
1	*Acantholyda erythrocephala*	Prepupa	Obligate	1-3 yr	66
2	*Apanteles glomeratus*	Prepupa	Facultative	....	33
3	*Cephus cinctus*	Prepupa	Obligate	6-8 mo	60
4	*Exeristes roborator*	Larva (FI)	Obligate	80 da	5
5	*Gilpinia polytoma*	Prepupa	Obligate	1-4 yr	57
6	*Hebracon brevicornis*	Adult	Facultative	Up to 102 da	69
7	*Melittobia chalybii*	Larva (FI)	Facultative	Several mo	63
8	*Mormoniella vitripennis*	Larva (FI)	Facultative	10 wk	65
9	*Sceliphron cementarium*	Larva (FI)	Obligate	....	14
10	*Spalangia drosophilae*	Larva (FI)	Facultative	Several mo	68
11	*Trichogramma cacaeciae*	Larva (FI)	Facultative	6-8 mo	48
	Siphonaptera				
12	*Ceratophyllus fasciatus*	Larva (FI)	Obligate	2-12 mo	3
	Diptera				
13	*Aedes hexodontus*	Embryo (FD)	Obligate	Throughout winter	9
14	*A. tristeriatus*	Embryo (FD)	Facultative	Up to 6 mo	4
15	*Drosophila deflexa*	Larva (FI)	Facultative	Several mo	8
16	*Epistrophe balteata*	Adult	Facultative	Few da	44,64
17	*E. bifasciata*	Larva (FI)	Obligate	Up to 9 mo	44,64
18	*Leptonylemyia coarctata*	Embryo (FD)	Obligate	2 mo	79
19	*Lipara lucens*	Larva (FI)	Obligate	Throughout winter	77
20	*Lucilia sericata*	Larva (FI)	Facultative	Several wk to many mo	23,53
21	*Sitodiplosis mosellana*	Larva (FI)	Obligate	Up to 12 yr	6,7
	Lepidoptera				
22	*Abraxas miranda*	Pupa	Obligate and facultative	2-14 wk	52
23	*Acronicta rumicis*	Pupa	Facultative	<1 yr	40
24	*Alsophila pometaria*	Egg	Obligate	ca. 6 mo	31
25	*Antheraea pernyi*	Pupa	Facultative	ca. 6 mo	84
26	*Aporia crataegi*	Larva (2nd or 3rd I)	Obligate	....	85
27	*Araschnia levana*	Pupa	Facultative	....	72
28	*Barathra brassica*	Pupa	Facultative	Several mo	76
29	*Bombyx mori*	Embryo (S or HG)	Facultative[1] or obligate[2]	5-9 mo	38
30	*Chilo suppressalis*	Larva (FI)	Facultative	2-3 mo	32
31	*Cydia pomonella*	Larva (FI)	Facultative	4-9 mo	73
32	*Dendrolimus pini*	Larva	Facultative	Up to 9 mo	25
33	*Diataraxia oleracea*	Pupa	Facultative	Up to 100 da	80
34	*Diatraea lineolata*	Larva (FI)	Facultative	Several wk to several mo	37
35	*Ephestia elutella*	Larva	Facultative	8-9 mo	78
36	*Epiblema strenuana*	Larva (FI)	Facultative	6-9 mo	59

/1/ Bivoltine strains. /2/ Univoltine strains.

continued

137. DIAPAUSE: INSECTS AND MITES

	Order and Species	Dormant Stage	Diapause Type	Diapause Duration	Reference
	(A)	(B)	(C)	(D)	(E)
	Lepidoptera				
37	*Euproctis chrysorrhoea*[3]	Larva (2nd or 3rd I)	Facultative	6 mo	34
38	*Fumea crassiorella*	Larva (HG)	Obligate and facultative	Up to 5 mo	50
39	*Grapholitha molesta*	Larva (FI)	Facultative	6-9 mo	27
40	*Harrisina brillians*	Pupa	Facultative	....	70
41	*Laspeyresia molesta*	Larva (FI)	Facultative	6-9 mo	27
42	*Loxostege sticticalis*	Larva (FI)	Facultative	6-9 mo	55
43	*Lymantria dispar*	Embryo (FD)	Obligate	6-9 mo	75
44	*Malacosoma disstria*	Embryo (FD)	Obligate	6-9 mo	35
45	*Mamestra brassicae*	Pupa	Facultative	....	35
46	*Operophtera brumata*	Pupa	Obligate	120-145 da	41
47	*Philosamia cynthia*	Pupa	Facultative	....	24
48	*Pieris brassicae*	Pupa	Facultative	....	47
49	*P. rapae*	Pupa	Facultative	6-52 wk	51
50	*Platyedra gossypiella*	Larva (FI)	Facultative	Several wk to several mo	71
51	*Platysamia cecropia*	Pupa	Obligate	6 wk to 5 mo	81-83
52	*Plodia interpunctella*	Larva (FI)	Facultative	....	74
53	*Polychrosis botrana*	Pupa	Facultative	....	39
54	*Pyrausta nubilalis*	Larva (FI)	Facultative[1] or obligate[2]	6-9 mo	2
55	*Telea polyphemus*	Pupa	Facultative[4] or obligate[5]	....	26
	Coleoptera				
56	*Anatolica eremita*	Adult	....	6 mo	29
57	*Anthrenus verbasci*	Larva (S-FI)	Obligate	Many mo	11
58	*Collaphellus sophiae*	Adult	Obligate	3-3½ mo	62
59	*Dytiscus marginalis*	Adult	Obligate[6]	....	36
60	*Epilachna corrupta*	Adult	Facultative	Throughout winter	28
61	*Haltica ampelophaga*	Adult	Facultative	ca. 6 mo	56
62	*Leptinotarsa decemlineata*	Adult	Facultative[6]	Many mo	17,20
63	*Popillia japonica*	Larva (3rd I)	Facultative	50 da	45,46
64	*Trogoderma granarium*	Larva (FI)	Facultative	Up to 4 yr	19
	Hemiptera				
65	*Eurydema ornatum*	Adult	Facultative	....	16
66	*Eurygaster integriceps*	Adult	Obligate	....	30
67	*Reduvius personatus*	Larva	Obligate	Few wk to several mo	58
	Orthoptera				
68	*Austroicetes cruciata*	Egg	Obligate	ca. 7 mo	1
69	*Camnula pellucida*	Egg	Obligate	6 mo	54
70	*Dociostaurus maroccanus*	Egg	Obligate	....	12
71	*Gryllulus commodus*	Egg	Obligate	Several wk	18
72	*Gryllus campestris*	Larva (FI)	....	....	67
73	*Locusta migratoria gallica*	Egg	Obligate	14-156 da	42
74	*Locustana pardalina*	Egg	Obligate	Few wk to several mo	49
75	*Melanoplus bivittatus*	Embryo (FD)	Obligate	Few wk to many mo	61
76	*M. differentialis*	Egg	Obligate	Few wk to many mo	13,15
	Odonata				
77	*Anax imperator*	Larva (FI)	Facultative	2-3 mo	21
78	*Lestes sponsa*	Egg	Obligate	15 wk	22
	Acari				
79	*Metatetranychus ulmi*	Egg	Facultative	....	10,43
80	*Tetranychus telarius*	Adult	Facultative	....	43

/1/ Bivoltine strains. /2/ Univoltine strains. /3/ Also known as *E. phaeorrhoea.* /4/ Predominant in southern climate. /5/ Predominant in northern climate. /6/ Reproductive diapause involving corpus allatum.

Contributors: (a) Andrewartha, H. G., (b) Lees, A. D., (c) Wilkes, A.

References: [1] Andrewartha, H. G. 1943. Bull. Entomol. Research 34:1. [2] Arbuthnott, K. D. 1949. U. S. Dept. Agr. Tech. Bull. 869. [3] Bacot, A. 1914. J. Hyg., Plague suppl. 3:447. [4] Baker, F. C. 1935. Can. Entomologist 67:149. [5] Baker, W. A., and L. G. Jones. 1934. U. S. Dept. Agr. Tech. Bull. 460. [6] Barnes, H. F. 1943. J. Animal Ecol. 12:137. [7] Barnes, H. F. 1952. Ann. Appl. Biol. 39:370. [8] Basden, E. B. 1954. Proc. Roy. Entomol. Soc. London, A, 29:114. [9] Beckel, W. E. 1958. Can. J. Zool. 36:541. [10] Blair, C. A.,

continued

and J. R. Groves. 1952. J. Hort. Sci. 27:14. [11] Blake, G. M. 1958. Bull. Entomol. Research 49:751. [12] Bodenheimer, F. S., and A. Shulov. 1951. Bull. Research Council Israel 1:59. [13] Bodine, J. H. 1929. Physiol. Zool. 2:459. [14] Bodine, J. H., and T. C. Evans. 1932. Biol. Bull. 63:235. [15] Bodine, J. H., et al. 1939. J. Cellular Comp. Physiol. 14:173. [16] Bonnemaison, L. 1948. Compt. rend. 227:985. [17] Breitenbrecher, J. K. 1918. Carnegie Inst. Wash. Publ. 263:341. [18] Browning, T. O. 1952. Australian J. Sci. Research, B, 5:112. [19] Burges, H. D. 1959. Ann. Appl. Biol. 47:445. [20] Busnel, R. A., and A. Drilhon. 1937. Compt. rend. 124:916. [21] Corbet, P. S. 1954. Ph. D. Thesis. Cambridge University, England. [22] Corbet, P. S. 1956. Proc. Roy. Entomol. Soc. London, A, 31:45. [23] Cragg, J. B., and P. Cole. 1952. J. Exptl. Biol. 29:600. [24] Danilyevsky, A. S. 1939. Zool. Zhur. 1926. [25] Danilyevsky, A. S., and K. F. Gayspitz. 1948. Compt. rend. acad. sci. U.R.S.S. 59(2):337. [26] Dawson, R. W. 1931. J. Exptl. Zool. 59:87. [27] Dickson, R. C. 1949. Ann. Entomol. Soc. Amer. 42:511. [28] Douglass, J. R. 1928. J. Econ. Entomol. 21:203. [29] Edelman, I. M. 1951. Entomol. Obozrenie 31:374. [30] Fedotov, D. M. 1944. Compt. rend. acad. sci. U.R.S.S. 42(9):408. [31] Flemion, F., and A. Harzell. 1936. Contribs. Boyce Thompson Inst. 8:167. [32] Fukaya, M., and J. Mitsuhashi. 1957. Japan. J. Appl. Entomol. and Zool. 1:145. [33] Gayspitz, K. F., and I. I. Kyao. 1953. Entomol. Obozrenie 33:32. [34] Grison, P. 1947. Compt. rend. 225:1089. [35] Hodson, A. C., and C. J. Weinman. 1945. Univ. Minn. Agr. Expt. Sta. Tech. Bull. 170. [36] Joly, P. 1945. Arch. zool. exptl. et gén. 84:49. [37] Kevan, D. K. McE. 1944. Bull. Entomol. Research 35:23. [38] Kogure, M. 1933. J. Dept. Agr. Kyushu Imp. Univ. 4:1. [39] Komarova, O. S. 1949. Compt. rend. acad. sci. U.R.S.S. 68(4):789. [40] Kozhantschikov, I. W. 1938. Bull. Entomol. Research 29:253. [41] Kozhantschikov, I. V. 1950. Entomol. Obozrenie 31:178. [42] LeBerre, J. R. 1951. Rev. zool. agr. appl. 10-12:1. [43] Lees, A. D. 1953. Ann. Appl. Biol. 40:449. [44] Lees, A. D. 1955. The physiology of diapause in arthropods. Cambridge Univ. Press, London. [45] Ludwig, D. 1932. Physiol. Zool. 5:431. [46] Ludwig, D. 1953. J. Gen. Physiol. 36:751. [47] Maercks, H. 1934. Z. Morphol. Ökol. Tiere 28:692. [48] Marchal, P. 1936. Ann. épiphyt. et phytogénét. 2:447. [49] Matthée, J. J. 1951. Union S. Africa Dept. Agr. Sci. Bull. 316. [50] Matthes, E. 1953. Mem. e estud. museo zool. univ. Coimbra 220. [51] Mazaki, S. 1955. Japan. J. Appl. Zool. 20:98. [52] Mazaki, S. 1958. Japan. J. Appl. Entomol. and Zool. 2:285. [53] Melanby, K. 1938. Parasitology 30:392. [54] Moore, H. W. 1948. Can. Entomologist 80:83. [55] Pepper, J. H., and E. Hastings. 1943. Montana Agr. Expt. Sta. Tech. Bull. 413. [56] Picard, F. 1926. Ann. épiphyt. et phytogénét. 12:177. [57] Prebble, M. L. 1941. Can. J. Research, D, 19:295. [58] Readio, P. A. 1931. Ann. Entomol. Soc. Amer. 24:19. [59] Rice, P. L. 1937. J. Econ. Entomol. 30:108. [60] Salt, R. W. 1947. Can. J. Research, D, 25:66. [61] Salt, R. W. 1949. Ibid., D, 27:236. [62] Saringer, G. 1960. Acta Biol. Acad. Sci. Hung. 11:109. [63] Schmieder, R. G. 1933. Biol. Bull. 65:338. [64] Schneider, F. 1948. Mitt. schweiz. entomol. Ges. 21:249. [65] Schneiderman, H., and J. Horwitz. 1958. J. Exptl. Biol. 35:520. [66] Schwerdtfeger, F. 1944. Z. angew. Entomol. 30:364. [67] Sellier, R. 1949. Compt. rend. 228:2055. [68] Simmonds, F. J. 1948. Trans. Roy. Soc. (London), B, 233:385. [69] Skoblo, I. S. 1941. Compt. rend. acad. sci. U.R.S.S. 33:424. [70] Smith, O. J., and R. L. Langston. 1953. J. Econ. Entomol. 46:477. [71] Squire, F. A. 1940. Bull. Entomol. Research 31:1. [72] Süffert, F. 1924. Biol. Zentr. 44:173. [73] Theron, P. P. A. 1943. J. Entomol. Soc. S. Africa 6:114. [74] Tsuji, H. 1958. Japan. J. Appl. Entomol. and Zool. 2:17. [75] Tuleschkov, K. 1935. Z. angew. Entomol. 22:97. [76] Uchida, T. and S. Mazaki. 1953. Oyo Kontyu 8:129. [77] Varley, G. C., and C. G. Butler. 1933. Parasitology 25:263. [78] Waloff, N. 1949. Trans. Roy. Entomol. Soc. London 100:147. [79] Way, M. J. 1959. Ibid. 111:351. [80] Way, M. J., and B. A. Hopkins. 1950. J. Exptl. Biol. 27:365. [81] Williams, C. M. 1947. Biol. Bull. 93:89. [82] Williams, C.M. 1949. Sci. American 182:24. [83] Williams, C. M. 1951. Federation Proc. 10:546. [84] Zolotarev, E. K. 1938. Zool. Zhur. 17:622. [85] Zolotarev, E. K. 1950. Ibid. 29:152.

138. EFFECT OF TEMPERATURE ON DEVELOPMENT: HELMINTHS

Data are for in vitro development of eggs and larvae.

	Class and Species	Stage	Medium	Temp. °C	Effect of Temperature	Reference
	(A)	(B)	(C)	(D)	(E)	(F)
			Aschelminthes			
	Nematoda					
1	*Ancylostoma caninum*	Egg	Bacteriological agar + *Bacillus coli*	12-40	Range for hatching with optimum temp. at $30^{\circ}C$	14
2		Larva	Bacteriological agar + *Bacillus coli*	15-37	Range for development with optimum temp. at $30^{\circ}C$	
3	*Ascaridia galli*	Egg	Water	19-34	Developed in 32 da at $19^{\circ}C$ and in 5 da at $34^{\circ}C$	23
4	*Ascaris lumbricoides suis*	Egg	Tyrode's solution	38-40	Hatched	19
5		Larva	Distilled water	Room	Matured in 5 wk	
6	*Dirofilaria immitis*	Egg	Cow and horse sera + synthetic ingredients	37	Developed from 4-cell stage to microfilaria	4
7		Larva	Dextrose dog serum	37	Little development; survived 3-8 da	36
8				12	Increased 2.5 times in size; survived 2 wk in ice chest	
9	*Eustrongylides ignotus*	Larva	Bacto-proteose-peptone, 1.0%; NaCl, 0.85%; glucose, 0.5%	20	Survived 30 mo; infectivity not established	31
10	*Haemonchus contortus*	Egg-larva	Rabbit kidney + liver extract agar + ground yeast	22-27	Eggs hatched in 14 da, infective larvae within 28 da	8
11	*Necator americanus*	Egg-larva	"Most favorable conditions"	8-40	Range for development with optimum temp. at $25\text{-}30^{\circ}C$	27
12		Larva	Chick embryo extract + killed *Escherichia coli*	Room?	Developed to filariform stage	32
13	*Nematospiroides dubius*	Egg	Chick embryo homogenate + liver concentrate	Room?	Egg to infective filariform larvae	12
14	*Neoaplectana glaseri*	Egg-larva	Veal infusion broth + raw liver extract	21-26	Cycle completed; survived 44 mo	28
15	*Nippostrongylus muris*	Egg	Water	22-30	Hatched within 24 hr	13
16		1st larval stage	Chick embryo extract + supplements	37.5	Developed to sexual maturity	33
17	*Rhabditis briggsae*	Larva	Nutrient agar + *Bacterium coli*	18	Developed to adult	3
18	*R. elegans*	Larva	Nutrient agar + *Bacterium coli*	18	Maintained 1.5 yr	3
19	*R. pellio*	Larva	Nutrient agar + *Bacterium coli*	18	Maintained 3.5 yr	3
20	*Strongyloides ratti*	Egg	Bacterial cultures (charcoal)	Room?	Infective larva developed	34
21	*Trichinella spiralis*	Larva	Simm's solution + chicken plasma + chick embryo extract	37	Several molts completed; few survived 9 da	35
22	*Trichuris trichiura*	Egg	Water	-12 to 54	Range for development with optimum temp. at $30^{\circ}C$	18
			Platyhelminthes			
	Cestoda					
23	*Crepidobothrium lönnbergi*	Immature worm	Hottinger's broth (modified)	Room	Increased length; survived 32 da	29
24	*Diphyllobothrium latum*	Egg	Washed feces and tap water	-10	Nonviable after 48 hr	5
25				15	Viable 8 mo	
26		Plerocercoid	Nutrient agar + hog serum	37.5	Increased size	9
27	*Echinococcus granulosus*	Scolex	Hydatid fluid + horse or ox serum	37-39	Volume of bladder increased; survived 31 da	2
28	*E. multilocularis*	Larval tissue	Human ascitic fluid + HeLa strain human epithelial cells	35	Larval proliferation including scolices	22
29	*Hymenolepis diminuta*	Cysticercoid	Tyrode's solution with human serum + organic materials	37± 0.5	Developed into mature worms in 15 da	1
30	*Ligula intestinalis*	Plerocercoid	Peptone broth	Room	Little activity; did not mature	26
31				40	Matured sexually in 7 da; survived 7 da	

continued

138. EFFECT OF TEMPERATURE ON DEVELOPMENT: HELMINTHS

	Class and Species	Stage	Medium	Temp. °C	Effect of Temperature	Reference
	(A)	(B)	(C)	(D)	(E)	(F)
			Platyhelminthes			
	Cestoda					
32	*Schistocephalus solidus*	Plerocercoid	Peptone broth	16-19	Active; normal appearance for 300 da; no eggs	25
33				40	Matured sexually within 48-60 hr; survived 4-6 da	
34	*Spirometra mansonoides*	Egg	Tap water	25-27	Hatched within 10 da	16,
35		Plerocercoid	Calf serum + chick embryo extract	37	Grew from 0.1 mm to 10.0 mm in 28 da; infective	17
36	*Taenia crassicollis*	Blastocyst	Locke's solution + chick embryo extract + horse serum	37.5	Developed to invagination of scolex; survived 35 da	15
37	*T. saginata*	Egg	Sodium hypochlorite or pepsin-pancreatin	39	Hatched in 4.5 hr	20
38			Physiological saline	2-5	Viable for 13.5 wk	
	Trematoda					
39	*Clonorchis sinensis*	Metacercaria	Tyrode's solution + rabbit serum	37	Survived 2 wk; no development	10
40	*Diplostomum flexicaudum*	Metacercaria	Tyrode's solution + lenses from eyes of vertebrates	Room	Survived and active 52 da; no growth	7
41	*Fasciola hepatica*	Egg	Water	25	Hatched in 14 da	24
42	*Gynaecotyla adunca*	Metacercaria	1% sea water	40	Matured sexually in 80 hr; survived 8 da	11
43	*Microphallus opacus*	Metacercaria	Ringer's solution and normal saline	37	Eggs in uterus within 12 hr; survived 4-5 da	21
44				12	Developed much more slowly	
45	*Posthodiplostomum minimum*	Metacercaria	Dilute Tyrode's solution + chick serum + yeast	39	Matured, but eggs infertile	6
46				5-7	Survived 1 mo; no growth	
47	*Schistosoma japonicum*	Egg	Water	2-37	Range for hatching with optimum temp. at 10-30°C	30
48	*Zygocotyle lunata*	Metacercaria	Water	-13 to 7	Withstood freezing and thawing 15 hr-10 da	37

Contributor: Patten, John A.

References: [1] Berntzen, A. K. 1961. J. Parasitol. 47:351. [2] Coutelen, F. 1927. Ann. parasitol. humaine et comparée 5:1. [3] Dougherty, E. C. 1953. J. Parasitol., Suppl. 4:32. [4] Earl, P. R. 1959. Ann. N. Y. Acad. Sci. 77:163. [5] Essex, H. E., and T. B. Magath. 1931. Am. J. Hyg. 14:698. [6] Ferguson, M. S. 1940. J. Parasitol. 26:359. [7] Ferguson, M. S. 1943. Ibid. 29:319. [8] Glaser, R. W., and N. R. Stoll. 1938. Parasitology 30:324. [9] Green, N. K., and R. A. Wardle. 1941. Can. J. Research, D, 19:240. [10] Hoeppli, R., L. C. Feng, and H. J. Chu. 1938. Chinese Med. J., Suppl. 2:343. [11] Hunter, W. S., and D. C. Chait. 1952. J. Parasitol. 38:87. [12] Jones, M. F., and P. P. Weinstein. 1957. Ibid., Suppl. 5:46. [13] Luttermoser, G. 1937. Ibid. 23:539. [14] McCoy, O. R. 1930. Am. J. Hyg. 11:413. [15] Mendelsohn, W. 1935. J. Parasitol. 21:417. [16] Mueller, J. F. 1959. Ibid. 45:353. [17] Mueller, J. F. 1959. Ibid. 45:561. [18] Nolf, L. O. 1932. Am. J. Hyg. 16:288. [19] O'Connor, G. R. 1951. J. Parasitol. 37:179. [20] Penfold, W. J., H. B. Penfold, and M. Phillips. 1937. Med. J. Australia 2:1039. [21] Rausch, R. 1947. Trans. Am. Microscop. Soc. 66:59. [22] Rausch, R., and V. L. Jentoft. 1957. J. Parasitol. 43:1. [23] Reid, W. M. 1960. Ibid. 46:63. [24] Roberts, E. W. 1950. Ann. Trop. Med. Parasitol. 44:187. [25] Smyth, J. D. 1946. J. Exptl. Biol. 23:47. [26] Smyth, J. D. 1947. Parasitology 38:173. [27] Stiles, C. W. 1921. J. Parasitol. 7:192. [28] Stoll, N. R. 1953. Ibid. 39:422. [29] Stunkard, H. W. 1932. Ibid. 19:163. [30] Sugiura, S., et al. 1954. Ibid. 40:381. [31] Von Brand, T., and W. F. Simpson. 1944. Ibid. 30:121. [32] Weinstein, P. P., and M. F. Jones. 1954. Ibid., Suppl. 5:14. [33] Weinstein, P. P., and M. F. Jones. 1956. Ibid. 42:215. [34] Weinstein, P. P., and M. F. Jones. 1957. Ibid., Suppl. 5:45. [35] Weller, T. H. 1943. Am. J. Pathol. 19:503. [36] Wellman, C., and F. M. Johns. 1912. J. Am. Med. Assoc. 59:1531. [37] Willey, C. H. 1941. Zoologica 26:65.

139. OPTIMUM TEMPERATURE FOR GROWTH: BACTERIA AND RICKETTSIA

Values are for data obtained under diverse conditions by many investigators. Data may differ for various species within the same genus, and even for various cultures of the same species. Values in parentheses are for minimum and maximum temperatures at which growth can occur. Classification adapted from Bergey's *Manual of Determinative Bacteriology*, 1957.

	Family and Species	Temp. °C	Reference
	(A)	(B)	(C)
	Pseudomonadales		
	Athiorhodaceae		
1	*Rhodopseudomonas palustris*	37	2
2	*Rhodospirillum rubrum*	30-37	2
	Nitrobacteraceae		
3	*Nitrobacter agilis*	25-30	2
4	*N. winogradskyi*	25-30	2
5	*Nitrosococcus nitrosus*	20-25	2
6	*Nitrosomonas monocella*	28	2
	Methanomonadaceae		
7	*Hydrogenomonas pantotropha*	28-30	2
	Thiobacteriaceae		
8	*Thiobacillus thiooxidans*	28-30 (18-37)	2
	Pseudomonadaceae		
9	*Acetobacter aceti*	30 (10-42)	2
10	*A. oxydans*	20-25	14
11	*A. pasteurianum*	30 (5-42)	2
12	*A. roseum*	30-35 (10-41)	2
13	*A. suboxydans*	30-35	14
14	*Mycoplana dimorpha*	<30	2
15	*Protaminobacter alboflavum*	30	2
16	*Pseudomonas aeruginosa*	37 (5-42)	16
17	*P. delphinii*	25 (1-30)	2,6
18	*P. fluorescens*	20-25 (min. 0-5)	2,13
19	*P. geniculata*	5	17
20	*P. putrefaciens*	21 (3-30)	2,7
21	*P. tomato*	20-25 (5-33)	6
22	*Xanthomonas campestris*	30-32 (5-39)	6
23	*X. hyacinthi*	28-30 (4-35)	2,6
	Spirillaceae		
24	*Cellfalcicula viridis*	20	2
25	*Cellvibrio ochraceus*	20	2
26	*Desulfovibrio desulfuricans*	25-30 (max. 35-40)	2
27	*Methanobacterium omelianskii*	37-40 (max. 46-48)	2
28	*Spirillum undula*	25	2
29	*Vibrio comma*	37 (14-42)	2
	Eubacteriales		
	Azotobacteraceae		
30	*Azotobacter chroococcum*	25-28	2
31	*A. indicum*	30	2
	Rhizobiaceae		
32	*Agrobacterium radiobacter*	28 (1-45)	2
33	*A. rubi*	27-28 (8-36)	2,6
34	*A. tumefaciens*	25-30 (0-37)	6
35	*Chromobacterium violaceum*	25-30 (min. 2-4)	2
36	*Rhizobium leguminosarum*	25	2,10,12
	Achromobacteraceae		
37	*Achromobacter ichthyodermis*	25-30 (18-37)	2
38	*A. liquefaciens*	20-25	2
39	*Alcaligenes faecalis*	25-37	2
	Achromobacteraceae		
40	*Alcaligenes viscosus*	20 (10-37)	7
41	*Flavobacterium aquatile*	10-30	2
42	*F. marinum*	20-25	2
	Enterobacteriaceae		
43	*Aerobacter aerogenes*	30-37 (2.5-45)	2,4,5,7
44	*Erwinia amylovora*	25-30 (3-44)	4,6
45	*E. carotovora*	25-30 (4-39)	6,12
46	*Escherichia coli*	30-37 (10-45)	2
47	*Klebsiella pneumoniae*	35 (12-43)	16
48	*Proteus vulgaris*	30-37	3
49	*Salmonella enteritidis*	37 (10-42)	5
50	*S. paratyphi*	37 (10-42)	5
51	*S. pullorum*	37 (10-42)	5
52	*S. schottmuelleri*	37 (10-42)	5
53	*S. typhimurium*	37 (10-42)	5
54	*S. typhosa*	37 (4-40)	15
55	*Serratia marcescens*	25-30	2
56	*Shigella alkalescens*	37 (10-45)	16
57	*S. dysenteriae*	37 (10-40)	16
	Brucellaceae		
58	*Actinobacillus lignieresi*	37 (min. 20)	3,16
59	*A. mallei*	37 (20-44)	2
60	*Brucella melitensis*	37	3,16
61	*Hemophilus ducreyi*	35-37	16
62	*H. influenzae*	37	16
63	*H. pertussis*	37	3,16
64	*Moraxella lacunata*	37	2
65	*M. liquefaciens*	20-37	2
66	*Noguchia cuniculi*	28-30	2
67	*N. granulosis*	15-30 (max. 37)	2,16
68	*Pasteurella multocida*	37	12
69	*P. pestis*	25-30 (0-43)	3,16
70	*P. pseudotuberculosis*	30 (5-43)	2
71	*P. tularensis*	37 (24-39)	16
	Bacteroidaceae		
72	*Bacteroides fragilis*	37	3
73	*Dialister pneumosintes*	37	2
74	*Fusobacterium fusiforme*	37	3
75	*F. polymorphum*	37 (31-43)	2
76	*F. praeacutum*	22-37	2
77	*Sphaerophorus necrophorus*	30-40	2
78	*Streptobacillus moniliformis*	35-38 (min. 22)	2
	Micrococcaceae		
79	*Gaffkya homari*	30-35 (6-44)	2
80	*G. tetragena*	37	2
81	*Methanococcus mazei*	30-37	2
82	*Micrococcus agilis*	25	2
83	*M. denitrificans*	25-30 (5-37)	2
84	*M. luteus*	25 (22-37)	2,7
85	*M. varians*	25 (min. 22)	2,7
86	*Sarcina aurantiaca*	30	2
87	*S. lutea*	25	2,16
88	*S. ventriculi*	30 (10-45)	2
89	*Staphylococcus aureus*	37 (10-45)	2
	Neisseriaceae		
90	*Neisseria catarralis*	37 (min. 22)	2
91	*N. gonorrhoeae*	37 (25-40)	12

continued

139. OPTIMUM TEMPERATURE FOR GROWTH: BACTERIA AND RICKETTSIA

	Family and Species	Temp. °C	Reference
	(A)	(B)	(C)
	Eubacteriales		
	Neisseriaceae		
92	*Neisseria meningitidis*	37 (25-42)	3
93	*Veillonella parvula*	37 (min. 22)	2
	Brevibacteriaceae		
94	*Brevibacterium erythrogenes*	28-35	2
95	*B. linens*	21 (8-37)	2,7
	Lactobacillaceae		
96	*Diplococcus pneumoniae*	37 (25-42)	3
97	*Lactobacillus acidophilus*	37 (max. 43-48)	2,7
98	*L. bulgaricus*	45-50 (min. 22)	2,14
99	*L. casei*	30 (10-40)	2,7
100	*L. caucasicus*	40-44 (25-45)	2
101	*L. lactis*	40 (18-50)	2
102	*L. leichmannii*	36 (max. 40-46)	2
103	*L. thermophilus*	50-62.8 (30-65)	2
104	*Leuconostoc citrovorum*	25-30 (min. 8)	7
105	*L. mesenteroides*	21-25	2
106	*Pediococcus acidilactici*	40	9
107	*P. cerevisiae*	25-30 (7-45)	2
108	*P. damnosus*	22	9
109	*P. halophilus*	30 (10-40)	9
110	*Streptococcus agalactiae*	37	2,3
111	*S. faecalis*	37 (min. 5-8)	8
112	*S. lactis*	30 (10-40)	7
113	*S. pyogenes*	37.5 (15-40)	16
114	*S. thermophilus*	40-45 (20-50)	2,7
	Propionibacteriaceae		
115	*Butyribacterium rettgeri*	37 (15-45)	2
116	*Propionibacterium freudenreichii*	30 (15-45)	7
	Corynebacteriaceae		
117	*Cellulomonas biazotea*	28-33	2
118	*Corynebacterium diphtheriae*	34-36 (15-40)	2,3,16
119	*C. michiganense*	25-27 (1-33)	2
120	*C. sepedonicum*	20-23 (4-31)	2
121	*C. xerosis*	37 (min. 18-25)	2
122	*Erysipelothrix insidiosa*	30-37 (15-44)	16
123	*Listeria monocytogenes*	37	2,5,16
124	*Microbacterium lacticum*	30 (15-35)	7,8
	Bacillaceae		
125	*Bacillus anthracis*	37 (12-45)	12,16
126	*B. brevis*	28-40 (max. 45-55)	2,12
127	*B. cereus mycoides*	30 (15-50)	7
128	*B. circulans*	30 (max. 40-45)	2
129	*B. coagulans*	45 (28-60)	7,12
130	*B. megatherium*	28-35 (max. 40-45)	2
131	*B. polymyxa*	28-35 (max. 40)	2
132	*B. popilliae*	30 (max. 36)	2
133	*B. stearothermophilus*	50-60 (33-70)	12
134	*B. subtilis*	28-40 (max. 50-55)	2
135	*Clostridium acetobutylicum*	37 (20-47)	12
136	*C. botulinum*	25 (20-35)	12
137	*C. butyricum*	30-37	2
138	*C. chauvei*	37 (max. 50)	3
139	*C. novyi*	37 (24-43)	2
140	*C. pasteurianum*	25	2
141	*C. perfringens*	35-37	7
142	*C. sporogenes*	37 (max. 50)	3
143	*C. tetani*	37 (14-43)	3
	Bacillaceae		
144	*Clostridium thermocellum*	60 (30-68)	10
145	*C. thermo-saccharolyticum*	55-62	2
	Actinomycetales		
	Mycobacteriaceae		
146	*Mycobacterium avium*	40 (30-44)	2
147	*M. balnei*	33 (max. 35)	5
148	*M. bovis*	37	2,12
149	*M. lacticola smegmatis*	28-45 (max. 50)	2
150	*M. marinum*	18-20	2
151	*M. paratuberculosis*	37.5	16
152	*M. phlei*	28-52 (15-55)	2
153	*M. tuberculosis* (human)	37 (30-42)	3,12
154	*M. ulcerans*	25-35	5,11
	Actinomycetaceae		
155	*Actinomyces bovis*	37	3,16
156	*A. israeli*	37	2
157	*A. thermophilus*	50 (28-60)	2
158	*Nocardia asteroides*	37	2,5
159	*N. gardneri*	25 (max. 37)	2
	Streptomycetaceae		
160	*Micromonospora chalcea*	30-35	2
161	*Streptomyces acidophilus*	25	2
162	*S. aureus*	25	2
163	*S. californicus*	37	2
164	*S. casei*	40-60	2
165	*S. cellulosae*	30-35	2
166	*S. coelicolor*	35	1
167	*S. griseus*	30	1
168	*S. olivaceus*	25	14
169	*S. scabies*	37	2
170	*S. thermophilus*	50 (28-60)	2
	Myxobacterales		
	Cytophagaceae		
171	*Cytophage fermentans*	28-37	18
172	*C. hutchinsonii*	30	2
	Myxococcaceae		
173	*Sporocytophaga myxococcoides*	30	2
	Spirochaetales		
	Spirochaetaceae		
174	*Spirochaeta daxensis*	44-52	2
175	*S. plicatilis*	20-25	2
	Treponemataceae		
176	*Leptospira icterohaemorrhagiae*	28-30 (25-37)	2,5
	Rickettsiales		
	Rickettsiaceae		
177	*Rickettsia australis*	32-35	2
178	*R. prowazekii*	32	2,11,16
179	*R. rickettsii*	32-35	2
180	*R. tsutsugamushi*	32 (max. 40)	11
181	*R. typhi*	35	2
	Chlamydiaceae		
182	*Miyagawanella lymphogranulomatis*	35-37	2
	Bartonellaceae		
183	*Bartonella bacilliformis*	28 (max. 37)	5,11
184	*Haemobartonella microtii*	23	2
185	*H. tyzzeri*	28	2

continued

139. OPTIMUM TEMPERATURE FOR GROWTH: BACTERIA AND RICKETTSIA

Contributors: (a) Dupre, Margaret V., (b) Johnstone, Donald B., (c) Eichbaum, Francisco W., (d) Bruner, D. W.

References: [1] Bradley, S. G. 1959. Appl. Microbiol. 8:89. [2] Breed, R. S., E. G. D. Murray, and N. R. Smith, ed. 1957. Bergey's Manual of determinative bacteriology. Ed. 7. Williams and Wilkins, Baltimore. [3] Burrows, W. 1959. Textbook of microbiology. Ed. 17. W. B. Saunders, Philadelphia. [4] Dowson, W. J. 1957. Plant diseases due to bacteria. Ed. 2. Cambridge Univ. Press, London. [5] Dubos, R. J., ed. 1958. Bacterial and mycotic infections of man. Ed. 3. J. B. Lippincott, Philadelphia. [6] Elliott, C. 1951. Manual of bacterial plant pathogens. Ed. 2. Chronica Botanica, Waltham, Mass. [7] Foster, E. M., et al. 1957. Dairy microbiology. Prentice-Hall, Englewood, N. J. [8] Frazier, W. C. 1958. Food microbiology. McGraw-Hill, New York. [9] Gunther, H. L., and H. R. White. 1961. J. Gen. Microbiol. 26:185. [10] Hawker, L. E., et al. 1960. An introduction to the biology of micro-organisms. W. Clowes and Sons, London. [11] Jawetz, E., J. L. Melnick, and E. A. Adelberg. 1960. Review of medical microbiology. Ed. 4. Lange, Los Altos, Calif. [12] Pelczar, M. J., Jr., and R. D. Reid. 1958. Microbiology. McGraw-Hill, New York. [13] Peterson, A. C., and M. F. Gunderson. 1960. Food Technol. 14:413. [14] Prescott, S. C., and C. G. Dunn. 1959. Industrial microbiology. Ed. 3. McGraw-Hill, New York. [15] Smith, A. L., ed. 1960. Carter's Microbiology and pathology. Ed. 7. C. V. Mosby, St. Louis. [16] Smith, D. T., and N. F. Conant, ed. 1957. Zinsser's Bacteriology. Ed. 11. Appleton-Century-Crofts, New York. [17] Sultzer, B. M. 1961. J. Bacteriol. 82:492. [18] Veldkamp, H. 1961. J. Gen. Microbiol. 26:331.

140. MAXIMUM TEMPERATURE FOR GROWTH: ALGAE

Most values were based on observations of algae growing in their natural habitat. Since it is difficult to determine true temperature under such conditions, and since light absorption may raise the temperature of an algal mass above that of its surroundings, the data should be interpreted with caution. A value given for a class does not necessarily hold for all species in that class.

	Class and Species (A)	Temp. °C (B)	Reference (C)
	Cyanophyta		
	Cyanophyceae		
1	*Anabaena variabilis*	35[1]	3
2	*Anacystis nidulans*	41[1]	3
3	*A. thermalis*	42	2
4	*Aphanocapsa botryoides*	54	2
5	*Bacillosiphon induratus*	70	2
6	*Chroococcus minutis fuscus*	46	2
7	*C. yellowstonensis*	41	2
8	*Cylindrospermum stagnale*	41	2
9	*Gleocapsa stegophalia*	38	2
10	*Mastigocladus laminosus*	62	2
11	*Nostoc muscorum*	33[1]	3
12	*N. sphaericum*	30	2
13	*Oscillatoria filiformis*	85	2
14	*O. geminata*	45	2
15	*Phormidium bijahensis*	85	2
16	*P. valderianum*	47	2
17	*Rivularia globiceps*	26	2
18	*Synechocystis thermalis*	62	2
	Pyrrophyta		
19	Cryptophyceae	40	2
	Chrysophyta		
20	Xanthophyceae	33	2
21	Chrysophyceae	40	2
22	Baccilariophyceae	51	2
23	*Nitzschia putrida*	30	5
	Chlorophyta		
	Chlorophyceae		
24	*Chlorella pyrenoidosa* (Emerson)	29[2]	6
25	*C. pyrenoidosa* (7-11-05)	42[3]	6
26	*Dunaliella viridis*	50	1
27	*Protococcus botryoides*	80	2
28	*Ulothrix* sp.	17	5
	Phaeophyta		
	Cyclosporeae		
29	*Fucus vesiculosus*	30	4

/1/ Maximum growth rate. /2/ Optimum growth rate at 25-26°C. /3/ Optimum growth rate at 38-39°C.

Contributors: (a) Allen, M. B., (b) Kratz, William A., (c) Sorokin, Constantine

continued

140. MAXIMUM TEMPERATURE FOR GROWTH: ALGAE

References: [1] Baas-Becking, L. G. M. 1930. Contributions to marine biology. Stanford Univ. Press, Palo Alto. [2] Copeland, J. J. 1936. Ann. N. Y. Acad. Sci. 36:1. [3] Kratz, W. A., and J. Myers. 1955. Am. J. Botany 42:282. [4] Kylin, H. 1910. Arkiv Botan. 10(1):1. [5] Oltmans, F. 1923. Morphologie und Biologie der Algen. G. Fischer, Jena. v. 3. [6] Sorokin, C. 1959. Nature 184:613.

141. MINIMUM HUMIDITY FOR GERMINATION OF SPORES: FUNGI

Data are included for spores of fungi capable of germination on a dry substratum at various ranges of relative humidity. The spores in a number of species will not germinate unless they are in contact with water. It may be noted that the powdery mildews are capable of germination under conditions of extremely low relative humidities. All figures show the lowest relative humidity for germination. In most cases the percent of germination increases as the relative humidity approaches 100 percent. Classification adapted from Bessey, *Morphology and Taxonomy of Fungi*, 1950.

	Family and Species	Structure	Substratum	Temp. °C	Relative Humidity, %	Reference
	(A)	(B)	(C)	(D)	(E)	(F)
	Phycomycetes					
	Mucoraceae					
1	*Mucor* sp.	Sporangiospores	Gelatin sheet with beerwort	25	93	21
2	*Rhizopus* sp.	Sporangiospores	Viscose sheet with wort	25	90	8
3	*R. nigricans*	Sporangiospores	Gelatin sheet with beerwort	25	93	21
	Entomophthoraceae					
4	*Entomophthora muscae*	Conidia[1]	Adult flies of *Kellymyia kellyi*	24	50	1
5	*E. sphaerosperma*	Conidia	Glass slides	21	70-100	17,18
	Ascomycetes					
	Sclerotiniaceae					
6	*Monilinia fructicola*	Conidia	Glass	22-24	95	23
	Pleosporaceae					
7	*Venturia inaequalis*	Conidia	Glass	.....	99	6
	Erysiphaceae					
8	*Erysiphe cichoracheanum*	Conidia	Dry slides	25	0.1	19,25
9	*E. graminis*	Conidia	Dry slides	22	0[2]	4,5,16
10	*E. polygoni*	Conidia	Dry slides	22	0[2]	5,25
11	*Microsphaera alni*	Conidia	Dry slides	22	0[2]	4
12	*Podosphaera leucotricha*	Conidia	Dry slides	19-22	100	2
13	*Sphaerotheca fuliginea*	Conidia	Dry slides	.....	99	12
14	*S. pannosa rosae*	Conidia	Dry slides	21	95[2]	15
	Basidiomycetes					
	Melampsoraceae					
15	*Cronartium ribicola*	Basidiospores	*Ribes* leaves	.....	96-100	14
16		Urediospores	Cellophane	.....	97-99	14
	Pucciniaceae					
17	*Puccinia coronata*	Urediospores	Glass slides, paraffin	20	99-100	7
18	*P. coronifera*	Urediospores	Glass slides	20	99	22
19	*P. dispersa*	Urediospores	Glass slides	20	99	22
20	*P. glumarum*	Urediospores	Glass slides	.....	95-99	13
21	*P. graminis*	Urediospores	Glass slides	20	99	7,22
22	*P. sorghi*	Urediospores	Glass slides	25	97.5	20
23	*P. triticina*	Urediospores	Glass slides	.....	95-99	13
	Ustilaginaceae					
24	*Ustilago hordei*	Teliospores	Glass or paraffin	20	95	7
25	*U. nuda*	Teliospores	Glass or paraffin	20	95	7
	Fungi Imperfecti					
	Sphaeropsidaceae					
26	*Phyllosticta cajani*	Conidia	Viscose sheet + 1% glucose	25	93.9	6
	Melanconiaceae					
27	*Colletotrichum falcatum*	Conidia	Viscose sheet + 1% glucose	25	95	6
28	*C. lindemuthianum*	Conidia	Viscose sheet + 1% glucose	25	95	6
29	*Gloeosporium tabernaemontanae*	Conidia	Viscose sheet + 1% glucose	25	93.9	6,26

/1/ Disease active. /2/ Approximately.

continued

141. MINIMUM HUMIDITY FOR GERMINATION OF SPORES: FUNGI

	Family and Species	Structure	Substratum	Temp. °C	Relative Humidity, %	Reference
	(A)	(B)	(C)	(D)	(E)	(F)
	Fungi Imperfecti					
	Moniliaceae					
30	*Aspergillus amstelodami*	Conidia	Gelatin sheet with beerwort	25	75	21
31	*A. candidus*	Conidia	Gelatin sheet with beerwort	25	75	21
32	*A. chevalieri*	Conidia	Viscose sheet with wort	25	80	8
33			Gelatin sheet with beerwort	25	73	21
34	*A. echinulatus*	Conidia	Gelatin sheet with beerwort	25	71	21
35	*A. flavus*	Conidia	Viscose sheet with wort	25	85	8
36	*A. fumigatus*	Conidia	Viscose sheet with wort	25	85	8
37	*A. nidulans*	Conidia	Viscose sheet with wort	25	85	8
38			Gelatin sheet with beerwort	25	82	21
39	*A. niger*	Conidia	Gelatin sheet with beerwort	25	84	21
40			Cellophane	30-40	70-78	3
41	*A. ochraceus*	Conidia	Viscose sheet with wort	25	85	8
42	*A. oryzae*	Conidia	Viscose sheet with wort	25	85-90	8
43	*A. repens*	Conidia	Viscose sheet with wort	25	80	8
44			Gelatin sheet with beerwort	25	71	21
45	*A. restrictus*	Conidia	Gelatin sheet with beerwort	25	75	21
46	*A. ruber*	Conidia	Viscose sheet with wort	25	80	8
47			Gelatin sheet with beerwort	25	70	21
48	*A. sydowi*	Conidia	Viscose sheet with wort	25	80	8
49	*A. tamari*	Conidia	Viscose sheet with wort	25	85	8
50	*A. terreus*	Conidia	Viscose sheet with wort	25	85	8
51	*A. versicolor*	Conidia	Viscose sheet with wort	25	80	8
52			Gelatin sheet with beerwort	25	78	21
53	*Beauveria bassiana*	Conidia	Glass slides	28	94-100	11
54	*Botrytis cinerea*	Conidia	Gelatin sheet with beerwort	25	93	21
55	*Penicillium chrysogenum*	Conidia	Glass	25	81	9
56			Book binding	25	73	9
57	*P. citrinum*	Conidia	Viscose with wort	25	80	8
58	*P. cyclopium*	Conidia	Gelatin sheet with beerwort	25	84	21
59	*P. duclauxi*	Conidia	Viscose with wort	25	85	8
60	*P. expansum*	Conidia	Viscose with wort	25	85	8
61	*P. fellutanum*	Conidia	Gelatin sheet with beerwort	25	80	21
62	*P. rugulosum*	Conidia	Gelatin sheet with beerwort	25	86	21
63	*P. spinulosum*	Conidia	Viscose sheet with wort	25	85	8
64	*P. wortmanni*	Conidia	Gelatin sheet with beerwort	25	82	21
65	*Ramularia* sp.	Conidia	Glass slides	22-24	95	23
66	*Scopulariopsis brevicaulis*	Conidia	Viscose sheet with wort	25	90	8
67	*Trichoderma* sp.	Conidia	Viscose sheet with wort	25	85-90	8
68	*Trichothecium roseum*	Conidia	Gelatin sheet with beerwort	25	90	21
	Dematiaceae					
69	*Alternaria brassicae*	Conidia	Viscose sheet + 1% glucose	25	90	6
70	*A. lignorum*	Conidia	Glass, shellac	30	90.9	24
71	*Cladosporium cucumerinum*	Conidia	Glass slides	22-24	98	23
72	*C. fulvum*	Conidia	Dry glass	.....	95	10
73	*C. herbarum*	Conidia	Gelatin sheet with beerwort	25	88	21
74	*Helminthosporium frumentacei*	Conidia	Viscose sheet + 1% glucose	25	91	6
75	*Stachybotrys* sp.	Conidia	Viscose sheet with wort	25	90	8
76	*Thielaviopsis* sp.	Conidia	Viscose sheet with wort	25	95	8
	Tuberculariaceae					
77	*Fusarium* sp.	Conidia	Viscose sheet with wort	25	90	8

Contributors: (a) Beneke, E. S., (b) Cooke, William B., (c) MacLeod, Donald M.

References: [1] Baird, R. B. 1957. Can. Entomologist 89:432. [2] Berwith, C. E. 1936. Phytopathology 26:1071. [3] Bonner, J. T. 1948. Mycologia 40:728. [4] Brodie, H. J. 1945. Can. J. Research 23:198. [5] Brodie, H. J., and C. C. Newfeld. 1942. Ibid. 20:41. [6] Chowdhury, S. 1937. Indian J. Agr. Sci. 7:653. [7] Clayton, C. N. 1942. Phytopathology 32:921. [8] Galloway, L. D. 1935. J. Textile Inst. 26:T123. [9] Groom, P., and T. Panissett. 1933. Ann. Appl. Biol. 20:633. [10] Guba, F. E. 1938. Mass. Agr. Expt. Sta. Bull. 350. [11] Hart, M. P., and D. M. MacLeod. 1955. Can. J. Botany 33:289. [12] Hashioka, Y. 1937. Trans. Nat. Hist. Soc. Formosa 27:129. [13] Hemmi, T., and T. Abe. 1933. Forsch. Gebiete Pflanzenkrankh. (Tokyo) 2:1. [14] Hirt, R. R.

continued

141. MINIMUM HUMIDITY FOR GERMINATION OF SPORES: FUNGI

1935. Bull. N. Y. State Coll. Forestry Syracuse Univ. 46. [15] Longree, K. 1939. Cornell Univ. Agr. Expt. Sta. Mem. 223. [16] Nair, S. K. R., and A. H. Ellingboe. 1962. Phytopathology 52:26. [17] Sawyer, W. H. 1929. Am. J. Botany 16:87. [18] Sawyer, W. H. 1931. Mycologia 23:411. [19] Schnathorst, W. C. 1960. Phytopathology 50:304. [20] Smith, M. A. 1926. Ibid. 16:69. [21] Snow, D. 1949. Ann. Appl. Biol. 36:1. [22] Stock, F. 1931. Phytopathol. Z. 3:231. [23] Thanos, A. Unpublished. Thesis. Michigan State College, East Lansing, 1952. [24] Tomkins, R. G. 1929. Proc. Roy. Soc. (London), B, 105:375. [25] Yarwood, C. E. 1936. Phytopathology 26:845. [26] Zachos, D. G., and S. A. Makris. 1959. Ann. Inst. Phytopathol. Benaki 2:24.

142. OPTIMUM TEMPERATURE FOR GROWTH: FUNGI

Values in parentheses are for minimum and maximum temperatures at which growth can occur. Classification adapted from Ainsworth and Bisby, *Dictionary of the Fungi*, 1961, and from Bessey, *Morphology and Taxonomy of Fungi*, 1950.

Part I: ANIMAL PATHOGENS AND RELATED SAPROBES

Data are for artificial culture, under humidity conditions favoring growth.

	Family	Species	Temperature, °C		Reference
			Optimum	Desirable	
	(A)	(B)	(C)	(D)	(E)
		Phycomycetes			
1	Coelomomycetaceae	*Coelomomyces* spp.	28	....	57
2	Mucoraceae	*Absidia corymbifera*	37	28-40 (20-46)	75
3		*A. ramosa*	37	28-40 (20-46)	75
4		*Coccidioides immitis*	30-37	25-37 (max. <42.5)	19,58,61
5		*Lichtheimia truchisi*	51-52	(10-53)	20
6		*Mucor cornealis*	37	(15-51)	14
7		*M. paronychius*	Room to 37	....	82
8		*M. pusillus*	45	(>24-<50)	14
9		*Rhizopus arrhizus*	32.5-35.5	(6-ca. 43)	78
10		*R. equinus*	37-39	(min. >5)	20
11		*R. oryzae*	31-34	(7.5-45.5)	78
12	Mortierellaceae	*Haplosporangium parvum*	....	Room (max. >37)	21,23
13	Entomophthoraceae	*Entomophthora aphidis*	18-30	(min. 2-10)	50,60
14		*E. coronata*	27-33	6-36	32,33
15		*E. exitialis*	24	6-30	32,33
16		*E. ignobilis*	24	1-27	32,33
17		*E. obscura*	24	6-27	32,33
18		*E. sphaerosperma*	18-21	<8-34	63,64
19		*E. virulenta*	30	6-36	32,33
		Ascomycetes			
20	Endomycetaceae	*Debaryomyces kloeckerii*	30-35	(3-37)	14
21		*Hanseniaspora valbyensis*	Room to 37	....	20
22		*Hansenula anomala*	(0.5-38.0)	....	14
23	Eurotiaceae	*Allescheria boydii*	30	25-30 (15-45)	68,84
		Basidiomycetes			
24	Septobasidiaceae	*Septobasidium* spp.	25	18-35	12,13
25	Agaricaceae	*Schizophyllum commune*	ca. 30	(<16->40)	10
		Fungi Imperfecti			
26	Zythiaceae	*Aschersonia aleyrodis*	Room to 37	....	3
27	Cryptococcaceae	*Candida albicans*	30-37	24-40 (<20->40)	41,47,54,79-81
28		*C. guilliermondi*	30-37	25-37	47
29		*C. krusei*	30-37	25-37	47
30		*C. stellatoidea*	37	25-37	47
31		*C. tropicalis*	30-37	25-37	41,47
32		*Cryptococcus neoformans*	25-30	25-37 (<17-40)	42,43,45,47
33		*Pityrosporum orbiculare*	ca. 37	30-37 (25-40)	30,31

continued

142. OPTIMUM TEMPERATURE FOR GROWTH: FUNGI

Part I: ANIMAL PATHOGENS AND RELATED SAPROBES

	Family	Species	Temperature, °C		Reference
			Optimum	Desirable	
	(A)	(B)	(C)	(D)	(E)
		Fungi Imperfecti			
34	Cryptococcaceae	*Pityrosporum ovale*	37	30-37 (min. <22)	2,31,52
35		*Torulopsis famata*	25-37	....	20
36	Moniliaceae	*Acladium castellani*	20	....	14
37		*Aspergillus flavus*	ca. 35	25-37	20,31
38		*A. fumigatus*	40	25-45 (max. >50)	67,72
39		*A. nidulans*	36-38	25-37	20,31
40		*A. niger*	37	25-37 (max. <60)	83
41		*Beauveria bassiana*	28	(10-38)	35
42		*Blastomyces dermatitidis*	31	25-33 (8-40)	29,44,56,68
43			35[1]	35-37[1]	44,68
44		*Cephalosporium falciforme*	....	Room	48
45		*C. granulomatis*	....	Room to 37	77
46		*C. recifei*	25-30	Room	16
47		*Epidermophyton floccosum*	ca. 27	25-30 (min. <18)	6,39
48		*Geotrichum candidum*	....	25-37	68
49		*Histoplasma capsulatum*	25-30	22-30 (10-40)	34,37,56,68
50			ca. 37[1]	34-37 (<34->43)[1]	17,62
51		*H. farciminosum*	37	25-37 (15-40)[2]	7,20
52		*Metarrhizium anisopliae*	25-30	10 (max. 32-34)	1
53		*Microsporum audouini*	25-30	25-30 (max. 38)	28,68
54		*M. canis*	30-32	25-32 (max. 40)	6,28
55		*M. gypseum*	25-30	25-30 (max. 38)	28,68
56		*Paracoccidoides brasiliensis*	25-30	25-30[2]	24,68
57		*Scopulariopsis brevicaulis*	20-25	Room (<6-37)	38
58		*Sorosporella uvella*	18-22	(18-40)	69
59		*Sporotrichum cracoviense*	18-37	(35-37)	20
60		*S. schenckii*	30-37	Room to 37[2]	11,20,31,36
61		*Trichoderma viride*	....	25-30	76
62		*Trichophyton concentricum*	ca. 37	25-37	15
63		*T. ferrugineum*	....	25	31,40
64		*T. gallinae*	....	25-30	20
65		*T. megnini*	....	25	6
66		*T. mentagrophytes*	30	25-30 (8-40)	6,25,40,70
67		*T. quinckeanum*	....	25-35	20
68		*T. rubrum*	....	25-30	31
69		*T. schoenleini*	33	25-37 (min. <15)	20,40,74
70		*T. soudanense*	....	Room	20
71		*T. tonsurans*	30	25-37	71
72		*T. verrucosum*	37	25-37	27
73		*T. violaceum*	25-30	25-37	20,53
74	Dematiaceae	*Cladosporium carrionii*	....	25	73
75		*C. gougerotii*	....	25-37	85
76		*C. mansoni*	30-32	25-35	20,66
77		*C. sphaerospermum*	....	Room (min. <18)	18
78		*C. trichoides*	ca. 30	Room to 30	5,46
79		*C. wernecki*	18-25	Room	66
80		*Fonsecaea compactum*	37	25-37	8,9,65
81		*F. dermatitidis*	20-30	Room to 30 (max. <43)	9
82		*F. pedrosoi*	30	25-35 (10-40)	8,9,65
83		*Madurella grisea*	30	Room to 37	49
84		*M. mycetomi*	37	Room to 37	26,49
85		*M. tabarkae*	22	(max. 35)	20
86		*Phialophora jeanselmei*	30	Room to 37	4,22,47,55
87		*P. verrucosa*	37	25-37	8,9,55
88		*Torula poikilospora*	37	....	59
89	Stilbaceae	*Hirsutella gigantea*	23	(10-30)	51

/1/ Yeast phase. /2/ Yeast phase, 37°C.

Contributors: (a) Gordon, Morris A., (b) MacLeod, Donald M., (c) Eichbaum, Francisco W., (d) Beneke, E. S.

References: [1] Balfour-Browne, F. L. 1960. Proc. Roy. Entomol. Soc. London, A, 35:65. [2] Benham, R. W.

continued

1939. J. Invest. Dermatol. 2:187. [3] Berger, E. W. 1910. Univ. Florida Agr. Expt. Sta. Bull. 103:1. [4] Berger, L., and M. Langeran. 1949. Ann. parasitol. humaine et comparée 24:574. [5] Binford, C. H., et al. 1952. Am. J. Clin. Pathol. 22:535. [6] Bonar, L., and A. D. Dreyer. 1932. Am. J. Public Health 22:909. [7] Bullen, J. J. 1949. J. Pathol. Bacteriol. 61:117. [8] Carrión, A. L. 1950. Ann. N. Y. Acad. Sci. 50:1255. [9] Carrión, A. L., and M. Silva. 1947. In W. J. Nickerson, ed. Biology of pathogenic fungi. Chronica Botanica, Waltham, Mass. ch. 3. [10] Cartwright, K. St. G., and W. P. K. Findlay. 1934. Ann. Botany (London) 48:481. [11] Conant, N. F., et al. 1954. Manual of clinical mycology. Ed. 2. W. B. Saunders, Philadelphia. [12] Couch, J. N. 1938. The genus *Septobasidium*. Univ. North Carolina Press, Chapel Hill. [13] Couch, J. N. Unpublished, 1956. [14] Da Fonseca, O. 1943. Parasitologia Médica. Ed. Guanabara, Rio de Janeiro. v. 1. [15] De Area Leao, A. E., and M. Geoto. 1950. Hospital, O (Rio de Janeiro) 37:225. [16] De Area Leao, A. E., and J. Lobo. 1934. Compt. rend. soc. biol. (Rio de Janeiro) 117:203. [17] De Monbreun, W. A. 1934. Am. J. Trop. Med. Hyg. 14:93. [18] De Vries, G. A. 1952. Contribution to the knowledge of the genus *Cladosporium* Link. Uitgeverif and Drukkerij Hollandia, Baarn. [19] Dickson, E. C. 1937. Arch. Internal Med. 59:1029. [20] Dodge, C. W. 1935. Medical mycology. C. V. Mosby, St. Louis. [21] Dowding, E. S. 1947. Can. J. Research 25:195. [22] Emmons, C. W. 1945. Arch. Pathol. 39:364. [23] Emmons, C. W., and L. L. Ashburn. 1942. Public Health Repts. (U. S.) 57:1715. [24] Furtado, T. A., J. W. Wilson, and O. A. Plunkett. 1954. Arch. Dermatol. and Syphilol. 70:166. [25] Gabrielsen, E. K. 1943. Acta Dermato-Venereol. 23:405. [26] Gammel, J. A. 1927. Arch. Dermatol. and Syphilol. 15:241. [27] Georg, L. K. 1950. Mycologia 42:683. [28] Giblett, E. R., and B. S. Henry. 1950. J. Invest. Dermatol. 14:377. [29] Gilchrist, J. C., and W. R. Stokes. 1898. J. Exptl. Med. 3:53. [30] Gordon, M. A. 1951. Mycologia 43:524. [31] Gordon, M. A. Unpublished, 1956. [32] Hall, I. M., and J. V. Bell. 1960. J. Insect Pathol. 2:247. [33] Hall, I. M., and J. V. Bell. 1961. Ibid. 3:289. [34] Hansmann, G. H., and J. R. Schenken. 1934. Am. J. Pathol. 10:731. [35] Hart, M. P., and D. M. MacLeod. 1955. Can. J. Botany 32:289. [36] Hektoen, L., and C. F. Perkins. 1900. J. Exptl. Med. 5:77. [37] Howell, A., Jr. 1940. Mycologia 32:671. [38] Janke, D. 1953. Z. Haut.- u. Geschlechtskrankh. 14:35. [39] Kadisch, E. 1929. Dermatol. Wochschr. 89:1423. [40] Kadisch, E. 1930. Dermatol. Z. 57:412. [41] Kadisch, E. 1930. Ibid. 60:48. [42] Kligman, A. M., and F. D. Weidman. 1949. Arch. Dermatol. and Syphilol. 60:726. [43] Kuhn, L. R. 1939. Proc. Soc. Exptl. Biol. Med. 41:573. [44] Levine, S., and Z. J. Ordal. 1946. J. Bacteriol. 52:687. [45] Lodder, J., and J. J. W. Kreger-van Bij. 1952. The yeasts: a taxonomic study. Interscience, New York. [46] Lucasse, C., et al. 1954. Ann. soc. belge méd. trop. 34:475. [47] MacKinnon, J. E. 1946. El siglo ilustrado. Zimologia Medica, Montevideo. [48] MacKinnon, J. E. 1951. Anales fac. med. Montevideo 36:153. [49] MacKinnon, J. E., L. V. Ferrada, and L. Montemayor. 1949. Ibid. 34:231. [50] MacLeod, D. M. 1955. Can. Entomologist 87:503. [51] MacLeod, D. M. 1959. Can. J. Botany 37:695. [52] Martin-Scott, I. 1952. Brit. J. Dermatol. 64:257. [53] Matilla, V., and J. Peña Yanez. 1951. Med. colonial (Madrid) 17:197. [54] McClary, D. O. 1952. Ann. Missouri Botan. Garden 39:137. [55] Montemayor, L. 1948. An. univ. inst. hig. Montevideo 2:32. [56] Moore, M. 1933. Ann. Missouri Botan. Garden 20:471. [57] Muspratt, J. 1946. Ann. Trop. Med. Parasitol. 40:10. [58] Negroni, P. 1949. Rev. inst. bacteriol. "Carlos G. Malbran" 14:136. [59] Nickerson, W. J. 1947. Biology of pathogenic fungi. Chronica Botanica, Waltham, Mass. p. 236. [60] Rockwood, L. P. 1950. J. Econ. Entomol. 43:704. [61] Roessler, W. G., et al. 1946. J. Infectious Diseases 79:12. [62] Salvin, S. B. 1947. J. Bacteriol. 54:655. [63] Sawyer, W. H. 1929. Am. J. Botany 16:87. [64] Sawyer, W. H. 1931. Mycologia 23:411. [65] Silva, M. 1958. Trans. N. Y. Acad. Sci., II, 21:46. [66] Simons, R. D. G., ed. 1954. Medical mycology. Elsevier, Amsterdam. [67] Skinner, C. E., C. W. Emmons, and H. M. Tsuchiya, ed. 1947. Henrici's Molds, yeasts and actinomycetes. Ed. 2. J. Wiley and Sons, New York. [68] Smith, D. T., and D. S. Martin, ed. 1948. Zinsser's Textbook of bacteriology. Ed. 9. Appleton-Century-Crofts, New York. [69] Speare, A. T. 1920. J. Agr. Research 18:399. [70] Stockdale, P. M. 1953. J. Gen. Microbiol. 8:434. [71] Swartz, H. E., and L. K.

continued

142. OPTIMUM TEMPERATURE FOR GROWTH: FUNGI

Part I: ANIMAL PATHOGENS AND RELATED SAPROBES

Georg. 1955. Mycologia 47:475. [72] Thom, C., and K. B. Raper. 1945. A manual of the aspergilli. Williams and Wilkins, Baltimore. [73] Trejos, A. 1954. Rev. biol. trop. (Costa Rica) 2:75. [74] Verujsky, D. 1887. Ann. inst. Pasteur 1:369. [75] Vogt, R. 1946. Mitt. naturforsch. Ges. Bern 3:53. [76] Ward, E. W. B., and A. W. Henry. 1961. Can. J. Botany 39:65. [77] Weidman, F. D., and A. M. Kligman. 1945. J. Bacteriol. 50:491. [78] Weimer, L., and L. L. Harter. 1923. J. Agr. Research 24:1. [79] Wickerham, L. J., and L. F. Rettger. 1939. J. Trop. Med. Hyg. 42:174. [80] Wickerham, L. J., and L. F. Rettger. 1939. Ibid. 42:187. [81] Wickerham, L. J., and L. F. Rettger. 1939. Ibid. 42:204. [82] Wilson, J. W., and O. A. Plunkett. 1949. Arch. Dermatol. and Syphilol. 59:414. [83] Wolf, F. A., and F. T. Wolf. 1947. The fungi. J. Wiley and Sons, New York. v. 2. [84] Wolf, F. T., R. R. Bryden, and J. A. MacLaren. 1950. Mycologia 42:233. [85] Young, J. M., and E. Ulrich. 1953. Arch. Dermatol. and Syphilol. 67:44.

Part II: PLANT PATHOGENS AND RELATED SOIL FUNGI

Spore Germination (column C): C = conidia; P = pycnidia, pycnospores; M = mycelium; U = urediospores; T = teliospores; E = aeciospores; B = basidiospores; L = sclerotia; A = ascospores; O = oospores; G = sporangia; Z = zoospores.

	Family	Species	Temperature, °C	
			Spore Germination	Development in Culture
	(A)	(B)	(C)	(D)
		Mycetozoa		
1	Physaraceae	*Fuligo septica*	....	25[1]
2	Plasmodiophoraceae	*Plasmodiophora brassicae*	25-30 (min. 6)	....
		Phycomycetes		
3	Synchytriaceae	*Synchytrium endobioticum*	12-20 (5-30)	....
4	Physodermataceae	*Physoderma zeae-maydis*	28-29 (23-30)	....
5	Saprolegniaceae	*Aphanomyces euteiches*	....	15-34 (9-37)
6	Pythiaceae	*Phytophthora cactorum*	C: 25-27	20-36 (5-38)
7		*P. cinnamoni*[2]	....	20-30 (5-33)
8		*P. citrophthora*[2]	28-30, then 15-18	25-38 (min. 5)
9		*P. infestans*[3]	4-20 (1-30)	15-25 (2-35)
10		*P. parasitica*[3]	25-27	20-35 (5-44)
11		*Pythium debaryanum*[3]	....	24-33 (5-40)
12		*P. ultimum*	....	25-35 (2-42)
13	Albuginaceae	*Albugo candida*[2]	C: 14-20 (0-25)	10-13 (0-25)
14	Peronosporaceae	*Peronoplasmopara cubensis*[2]	C: 15-22 (1-32)	....
15		*P. humuli*	C: 17-20 O: 20-22	....
16		*Peronospora effusa*	8-10 (3-30)	....
17		*P. parasitica*	C: 8-12 (max. <29)	8-12 (max. 29)
18		*P. tabacina*	15-23 (1-29)	(max. 20)
19		*Plasmopara viticola*[2]	C: 25-35 (5-35)[4] O: 23-35 (min. 11)	....
20		*Pythiacystis citrophthora*	....	25-27 (9-32)
21		*Sclerospora graminicola*	C: 18-30 (5-35) O: 20-34 (10-38) G: 14-18 Z: 25-27 (8-30)	....
22	Mucoraceae	*Rhizopus nigricans*[2]	19-41 (2-41)	20-36 (2-40)
		Ascomycetes		
23	Taphrinaceae	*Taphrina deformans*	....	<20-20 (10-30)
24	Erysiphaceae	*Erysiphe graminis*	A: 18 C: 12-21 (<5-29)	10 (0-25)
25		*Podosphaera leucotricha*	19-20 (10-28)	....
26	Ophiostomataceae	*Ceratostomella fimbriata*	....	23-29 (9-36)

/1/ Data from reference 2. /2/ Fungus exhibits variability among different strains or in different hosts. /3/ Fungus exhibits extreme variability among different strains or in different hosts. /4/ Also 10-16 (2-27).

continued

142. OPTIMUM TEMPERATURE FOR GROWTH: FUNGI

Part II: PLANT PATHOGENS AND RELATED SOIL FUNGI

	Family	Species	Temperature, °C	
			Spore Germination	Development in Culture
	(A)	(B)	(C)	(D)
		Ascomycetes		
27	Ophiostomataceae	*Ceratostomella ips*	....	27-29 (6-35)
28		*C. ulmi*	....	19-28 (5-40)
29	Pseudosphaeriaceae	*Ophiobolus graminis*[2]	....	20-25 (3-35)[5]
30		*O. miyabeanus*[2]	A: 25 C: 25-30 (2-41)	24-32 (5-40)
31		*O. sativus*[2]	C: 22-32 (6-39)	25-33 (1-37)
32		*Pyrenophora graminea*	....	18-30 (3-35)
33		*P. teres*	A: 20 C: 20-25	23-30 (3-33)
34	Pleosporaceae	*Venturia inaequalis*	A: 13-22 (0-35) C: 14-25 (2-31)	20 (<4-<32)
35	Mycosphaerellaceae	*Mycosphaerella rubi*	A: 23 (2-32) P: 23 (2-32)	20-23 (2-32)
36	Botryosphaeriaceae	*Botryosphaeria ribis*[2]	....	28-30 (10-35)
37	Nectriaceae	*Calonectria graminicola*[2]	....	20-22 (0-33)
38		*Gibberella zeae*[3]	A: 30 (5-32) C: 24-28 (4-32)	20-30 (3-37)
39		*Nectria cinnabarina*	A: 17-20 (5-30) C: 20-25 (>0-35)	21 (3-33)
40	Sphaeriaceae	*Guignardia bidwellii*	....	20-30
41	Gnomoniaceae	*Glomerella gossypii*	....	25-29 (10-38)
42		*G. rufomaculans*	19-36 (min. 3)	33-38 (9-38)
43	Diaporthaceae	*Endothia parasitica*[2]	A: 21 P: 15-32	18-30 (4-40)
44	Clavicipitaceae	*Claviceps purpurea*	L: 18-22	22-30
45	Dermeaceae	*Neofabraea malicorticis*	15-25 (0-30)	20 (0-<30)
46		*Pseudopeziza ribis*	A: 12 C: 20	20 (<4-32)
47	Phacidiaceae	*Coccomyces hiemalis*	....	20-24 (4-28)
48	Helotiaceae	*Dasyscypha willkommii*	15-27 (<13-31)	18-23
49	Sclerotiniaceae	*Monilinia fructicola*	....	24-27 (0-32)
50		*Sclerotinia americana*	C: 23	24-27 (3-33)
51		*S. fructigena*	C: 21-25 (min. 10)	18-25 (0-33)
52		*S. libertiana*	(3-31) A: (max. 30)	22-25 (0-33)
53		*S. sclerotiorum*[2]	A: 25 (3-30)	22-25 (0-33)
		Basidiomycetes		
54	Melampsoraceae	*Cronartium ribicola*	E: 12 (5-19) B: 10-18 (0-21) T: 12-18 (0-21) U: 14 (8-25)	....
55	Pucciniaceae	*Gymnosporangium juniperi-virginianae*[2]	E: 24 (6-32) B: 16 (8-28) T: 22-25 (4-32)	....
56		*Puccinia antirrhini*	10 (5-30)	....
57		*P. coronata*[2]	12-22 (0-35)	....
58		*P. glumarum*[2]	U: 10-20 (2-29)	....
59		*P. graminis*[3]	E: 5-20 (<5->30) B: 15-20 T: 12-20 (5-30) U: 5-25 (2-35)	....
60		*P. helianthi*	T: 18 (6-28) U: 18 (<6->28)	....
61		*P. sorghi*	U: 15-18 (4-32)	....
62		*P. triticina*[2]	U: 10-26 (2-32)	....
63		*Uromyces cariophyllinus*	14 (4-29)	....

/2/ Fungus exhibits variability among different strains or in different hosts. /3/ Fungus exhibits extreme variability among different strains or in different hosts. /5/ Data from references 1 and 5.

continued

142. OPTIMUM TEMPERATURE FOR GROWTH: FUNGI

Part II: PLANT PATHOGENS AND RELATED SOIL FUNGI

	Family	Species	Temperature, °C	
			Spore Germination	Development in Culture
	(A)	(B)	(C)	(D)
		Basidiomycetes		
64	Pucciniaceae	*Uromyces trifolii*	E: 15-20 (6-30) T: 17 (7-<30) U: 9-25 (<3->33)	....
65	Ustilaginaceae	*Ustilago avenae*	U: 15-30 (4-35) T: 15-28 (0-35)	18-26 (6-34)
66		*U. hordei*[2]	10-30 (0-35)	16-26 (<1-<35)
67		*U. nuda*[2]	20-29 (0-34)	20-25 (<10-35)
68		*U. tritici*[2]	22-30 (0-35)	24-30 (6->35)
69		*U. zeae*	T: 25-34 (5-40) U: 20-26 (max. 40)	18-26 (10-34)
70	Tilletiaceae	*Tilletia caries*	15-20 (4-29)	(1-25)
71		*T. laevis*	16-20 (4-36)	20
72		*T. tritici*	15-20 (0-36)	20 (>1-<25)
73		*Urocystis cepulae*	15-20 (9->32) M: 15 (4-28)	>18 (>9-28)
74	Hypochnaceae	*Hypochnus centrifugus*[2]	....	28-35 (8-41)
75	Thelephoraceae	*Corticium vagum*[3]	L: 20-32 (8-36)	20-33 (0-44)
76	Meruliaceae	*Merulius lacrymans*[2]	22-25	20-26 (4-32)
77	Polyporaceae	*Fomes applanatus*[2]	....	27-30 (15-35)
78		*F. igniarius*	....	30-32 (max. 42)
79		*Polystictus versicolor*[2]	....	25-32[6]
80		*Trametes pini*	....	20-25 (10-40)
81	Agaricaceae	*Armillaria mellea*[2]	....	25 (15-30)
82		*Lentinus lepideus*	....	27-28 (<9-40)
		Fungi Imperfecti		
83	Sphaeropsidaceae	*Ascophyta pisi*	20 (10-35)	20-28 (0-35)
84		*Coniothyrium wernsdorffiae*	16-17 (0-27)	20-21 (-1 to 26)
85		*Deuterophoma tracheiphila*	18-20 (min. 15)	(10-28)
86		*Diplodia zeae*	P: 30	24-32 (10-36)
87		*Macrophomina phaseoli*[2]	....	31 (8-42)
88		*Phomopsis citri*	20-27 (16-33)	24-38 (4-<40)
89		*Phyllosticta solitaria*	25-30 (5-39)	25-30 (5-35)
90		*Septoria apii*	....	16-27 (10-27)
91		*S. apii graveolentis*	....	22-24 (14-25)
92		*S. lycopersici*	....	25 (2-34)
93		*S. tritici*	2-32	20-24 (3-32)
94	Melanconiaceae	*Collectotrichum circinans*	20-26 (4-32)	26 (2-32)
95		*C. lagenarium*	22-32 (min. 4)	22-23 (6-35)
96		*C. lindemuthianum*[2]	20-32 (0-42)	18-30 (0-42)
97		*Gloeosporium venetum*	22-26 (11-32)	20-26 (11-31)
98	Moniliaceae	*Aspergillus niger*[2]	....	30-39 (7-46)
99		*Botrytis allii*[2]	19-27 (3-27)	20-25 (3-33)
100		*B. cinerea*[3]	17-25 (1-35)	15-25 (0-35)
101		*Cercosporella herpotrichoides*	....	20-23 (-5 to 30)
102		*Mycogone perniciosa*	....	21-28 (8-32)
103		*Penicillium expansum*	....	25-27 (0-30)
104		*Phymatotrichum omnivorum*	....	29 (18-36)
105		*Piricularia oryzae*	C: 25-30 (16-35)	25-30 (8-40)
106		*Verticillium albo-atrum*	....	16-31 (4-37)
107	Dematiaceae	*Alternaria brassicae*	33-35 (1-46)	25-27 (2-36)
108		*A. citri*[2]	....	25
109		*A. solani*[2]	26-28 (1-45)	26-28 (1-45)
110		*Basisporium gallarum*[2]	20-35 (9-35)	25-35 (10-40)
111		*Cephalothecium rosae*[2]	19-33 (9-35)	20-25 (5-35)
112		*Cercospora beticola*	26-33 (2-35)	24-30 (5-40)
113		*Cladosporium carpophilum*	....	19-28 (2-33)
114		*C. cucumerinum*	....	20-21 (0-32)

/2/ Fungus exhibits variability among different strains or in different hosts. /3/ Fungus exhibits extreme variability among different strains or in different hosts. /6/ Also 15 (0-40).

continued

142. OPTIMUM TEMPERATURE FOR GROWTH: FUNGI

Part II: PLANT PATHOGENS AND RELATED SOIL FUNGI

	Family	Species	Temperature, °C	
			Spore Germination	Development in Culture
	(A)	(B)	(C)	(D)
		Fungi Imperfecti		
115	Dematiaceae	*Cladosporium fulvum*[2]	18-26 (0-33)	16-26 (0-34)
116		*C. malorum*	....	25
117		*Helminthosporium gramineum*	....	15-20
118		*H. turcicum*	....	28-30 (7-35)
119		*Nigrospora oryzae*	30 (10-47)	30 (10-35)
120		*Thielaviopsis basicola*	....	23-32 (7-37)
121	Tuberculariaceae	*Fusarium conglutinans*	....	20-30 (5-35)
122		*F. lini*[2]	12-30 (7-35)	18-30 (5-37)
123		*F. lycopersici*[2]	....	24-30 (5-38)
124		*F. oxysporum*[3]	....	15-32 (4-40)
125		*F. solani martii*[2]	13-25 (5-37)	18-34 (5-39)
126		*F. vasinfectum*[2]	....	25-35 (5-40)
127	Mycelia Sterilia[7]	*Rhizoctonia solani*	....	31 (8-40)
128		*Sclerotium cepivorum*	....	20-24 (5-29)

/2/ Fungus exhibits variability among different strains or in different hosts. /3/ Fungus exhibits extreme variability among different strains or in different hosts. /7/ Class.

Contributors: (a) Chester, K. Starr, (b) Rossetti, Victoria, (c) Beneke, E. S.

References: [1] Bessey, E. A. 1950. Morphology and taxonomy of the fungi. Blakiston, Toronto. [2] Lazo, W. R. 1961. J. Protozool. 8:97. [3] Saccardo, P. A. 1888-1930. Sylloge fungorum. The author, Patavii. [4] Togashi, K. 1949. Biological characters of plant pathogens. Temperature relations. Meibundo, Tokyo. [5] Ward, E. W. B., and A. W. Henry. 1961. Can. J. Botany 39:65. [6] Yearbook Committee. 1953. Plant diseases. U. S. Dept. of Agriculture, Washington, D. C.

143. PHOTOPERIOD, WITH TEMPERATURE INTERACTIONS, FOR FLOWERING: ANGIOSPERMS

Where more than one photoperiodic classification (due to varietal differences) is given in column B, the most common is entered first. Classification is followed in parentheses by light period for flowering (>12 hr should be interpreted as 12 hours or more, <12 hr as up to 12 hours). Temperature Interactions (column C): Th = photoperiodic response occurring at relatively high temperatures (plant may also flower at other day lengths at lower temperatures), or reproductive development promoted by high temperatures during photoperiodic induction; Tl = photoperiodic response occurring at relatively low temperatures (plant may also flower at other day lengths at higher temperatures), or reproductive development promoted by low temperatures during photoperiodic induction; Tp = thermoperiodic (i.e., development affected by alternation of temperature between day and night periods); Tq = quantitative effect of temperature on critical day length (i.e., an increase in temperature lowers the minimum limits for long-day plants and raises the maximum limits for short-day plants) or on the degree of photoperiodic response; Ve = vernalization essential for complete reproductive development (or other low-temperature preconditioning of embryo plants, seedlings, buds, or plants), prior to photoperiodic induction; Va = vernalization not essential but promotes reproductive development; Vo = vernalization not effective. For additional information, consult references 25, 57, 66, 83, and 99. Classification adapted from Engler and Diels, *Syllabus der Pflanzenfamilien,* 1936.

	Family and Species	Photoperiodic Class and Light Period	Temperature Interactions	Reference
	(A)	(B)	(C)	(D)
		Monocotyledoneae		
	Gramineae			
1	*Agropyron smithii*	Long day required (>10 hr)	....	11
2	*Agrostis nebulosa*	Long day required (>13 hr)	....	5
3	*A. palustris*	Long day required (>16 hr)	....	4

continued

143. PHOTOPERIOD, WITH TEMPERATURE INTERACTIONS, FOR FLOWERING: ANGIOSPERMS

	Family and Species	Photoperiodic Class and Light Period	Temperature Interactions	Reference
	(A)	(B)	(C)	(D)
		Monocotyledoneae		
	Gramineae			
4	*Alopecurus pratensis*	Long day required (>9 hr)	...	96
5	*Andropogon gerardi*	Short day required (<18 hr)	...	11
6	*A. virginicus*	Short day favorable (12-14.5 hr)	...	5
7	*Avena sativa*	Long day required (>9 hr)	Tl; Va (for winter varieties); Vo (for spring varieties)	38
8	*Bouteloua curtipendula*	Short day required; intermediate or long day required (<16 hr)	...	68,69
9	*Bromus inermis*	Long day required (>12.5 hr)	Va	4,34,36,89
10	*Dactylis glomerata*	Long day required (>12 hr)	Vo; Va	4,18,19,89, 96,102
11	*Elymus junceus*	Long day required	Ve	84
12	*Festuca arundinacea*	Long day required	Va	91
13	*F. elatior*	Long day required	...	89
14	*Holcus sudanensis*	Short day favorable	Th; Tl (day neutral)	78
15	*Hordeum vulgare* (spring)	Long day favorable	Vo	74,78
16	*H. vulgare* (winter)	Long day required (>12 hr)	Va (7-9°C)	16,38
17	*Lolium multiflorum italicum*	Long day required (>11 hr)	Va	21,24
18	*L. perenne* (early perennial)	Long day required (>9 hr)	Ve	22,23
19	*L. perenne* (late perennial)	Long day required (>13 hr)	Ve	22,23
20	*L. temulentum*	Long day required (>9 hr)	Vo; Va	24,32
21	*Oryza sativa* (summer)	Day neutral	Th	87,88
22	*O. sativa* (winter)	Short day required (<12 hr)	Th	87,88
23	*Phalaris arundinacea*	Long day required (>12.5 hr)	...	4
24	*P. tuberosa*	Long day required	Va; Ve	51
25	*Phleum nodosum*	Long day required (>14.5 hr)	...	4,89,96
26	*P. pratense*	Long day required (>12 hr)	...	4,96
27	*Poa annua*	Day neutral	Vo	26
28	*P. bulbosa*	Long day required	Ve; Th (for normal flowers); Tl (for proliferation)	103
29	*P. pratensis*	Long day favorable	Th; Tl (day neutral or short day favorable); Ve	4,71,80,89
30	*Saccharum officinarum*	Short day favorable[1]	...	3,104
31	*S. officinarum* 28NG292	Intermediate (12-14 hr)	...	3
32	*Secale cereale* (spring)	Long day favorable	Tl; Vo	38,75,100
33	*S. cereale* (winter)	Long day favorable	Va	38,75
34	*Sorghum vulgare*	Short day favorable	...	76
35	*Triticum aestivum* (spring)	Long day favorable	Vo	38,63,64,101
36	*T. aestivum* (winter)	Long day required (>12 hr)[1]	Va	38,63,64,101
37	*Zea mays*	Day neutral; short day required	...	41,62
	Lemnaceae			
38	*Lemna perpusilla*	Short day favorable	...	48
	Liliaceae			
39	*Allium cepa*	Long day favorable; short day favorable; day neutral	Tl	38,60,85
	Orchidaceae			
40	*Cattleya trianae*	Short day required	...	49
		Dicotyledoneae		
	Polygonaceae			
41	*Fagopyrum esculentum*	Day neutral	...	7,38
	Chenopodiaceae			
42	*Beta vulgaris* (garden)	Long day favorable	Th; Tl (long day required)	78
43	*B. vulgaris* (sugar)	Long day required	Tl (7-9°C); Ve	35
44	*Chenopodium amaranticolor*	Short day required	...	92
45	*Spinacia oleracea*	Long day required (>13 hr)	Ve (for some varieties)	37,52
	Caryophyllaceae			
46	*Dianthus caryophyllus*	Long day favorable	Ve (after juvenile phase)	13,14
	Amaranthaceae			
47	*Amaranthus graecizans*	Short day favorable	Th	78
	Ranunculaceae			
48	*Delphinium cultorum*	Long day required	Tl; Th (day neutral)	78

/1/ Data applicable to most varieties.

continued

143. PHOTOPERIOD, WITH TEMPERATURE INTERACTIONS, FOR FLOWERING: ANGIOSPERMS

	Family and Species	Photoperiodic Class and Light Period	Temperature Interactions	Reference
	(A)	(B)	(C)	(D)
		Dicotyledoneae		
	Cruciferae			
49	*Brassica oleracea gemmifera*	Day neutral	Ve (after juvenile phase)	90
50	*B. pekinensis*	Long day favorable	Th; Tl (long day required)	78
51	*B. rapa*	Long day favorable	...	78
52	*Lunaria biennis*	Day neutral	Ve (after juvenile phase)	97
53	*Matthiola incana*	Long day favorable	Th; Tl (day neutral)	80
54	*Raphanus sativus*	Long day required	...	37,72
	Crassulaceae			
55	*Bryophyllum pinnatum*	Short day required (<12 hr)	...	5
56	*Kalanchoe blossfeldiana*	Short day required (<12 hr)	...	46
57	*Sedum spectabile*	Long day required (>13 hr)	...	39
	Saxifragaceae			
58	*Hydrangea macrophylla*	Day neutral (?)	Ve	86
	Rosaceae			
59	*Fragaria chiloensis*	Short day required (<10 hr)[1]	Tq	28,47
60	*F. chiloensis* (everbearing)	Long day favorable; day neutral	...	28
	Leguminosae			
61	*Glycine soja*	Short day required to short day favorable	Th; Tq	15,37,70
62	*Lespedeza stipulacea*	Short day required (<13.5 hr)	...	67
63	*Medicago sativa*	Long day favorable	Th; Tl (day neutral)[2]	80
64	*Melilotus alba*	Long day required	...	78
65	*Phaseolus lunatus*	Day neutral; short day required	...	6,37
66	*P. vulgaris*	Day neutral; short day required[3]	...	6,37,62
67	*Pisum sativum*	Day neutral; long day favorable	...	10,80
68	*Tephrosia candida*	Intermediate (>10-<13.2 hr)	...	61
69	*Trifolium* spp.[4]	Long day required	...	80
70	*Trifolium* spp.[5]	Long day favorable	Tl	78,80
71	*T. pratense*[6]	Long day required (>12 hr)	...	96
72	*Vicia faba*	Day neutral	Va	33
73	*V. sativa*	Long day favorable	Th; Tl (day neutral)	80
	Geraniaceae			
74	*Pelargonium hortorum*	Day neutral	Tl	78
	Euphorbiaceae			
75	*Euphorbia pulcherrima*	Short day required (<12.5 hr)	Tl[7]	37,77
	Aquifoliaceae			
76	*Ilex aquifolium*	Day neutral	...	81
	Balsaminaceae			
77	*Impatiens balsamina*	Day neutral	...	78
	Malvaceae			
78	*Gossypium hirsutum*	Day neutral; short day favorable	Tq	12,53
79	*Hibiscus syriacus*	Long day required (>12 hr)	...	2
80	*Malva verticillata*	Short day favorable	Th (23°C); 18°C (day neutral)	80
	Violaceae			
81	*Viola papilionacea*	Short day required (<11 hr)[8]	Th; Tq	37,38
82	*V. tricolor*	Day neutral	Tl	78
	Begoniaceae			
83	*Begonia semperflorens*	Day neutral	Tl; Th (long day favorable)	80
	Cactaceae			
84	*Zygocactus truncatus*	Short day favorable	Tl (18°C); 13°C (day neutral)	80
	Oenotheraceae			
85	*Fuchsia hybrida*	Day neutral	Th	78
86	*Oenothera biennis*	Long day favorable	Tl	80
	Umbelliferae			
87	*Anethum graveolens*	Long day required (>11 hr)	...	45
88	*Apium graveolens*	Day neutral	Ve (4-10°C)	93

/1/ Data applicable to most varieties. /2/ Vegetative in warm nights. /3/ Photoperiod influences fruit development, but floral initiation is not affected. /4/ Species include *incarnatum* and *repens*. /5/ Species include *pratense* and *repens*. /6/ Variety, English Montgomery; for American medium, long day favorable (>9 hr). /7/ Night temperature, <21°C; at 13-14°C, long day required. /8/ Production of blue petaliferous flowers; long day required for formation of fertile, cleistogamous flowers.

continued

143. PHOTOPERIOD, WITH TEMPERATURE INTERACTIONS, FOR FLOWERING: ANGIOSPERMS

	Family and Species	Photoperiodic Class and Light Period	Temperature Interactions	Reference
	(A)	(B)	(C)	(D)
		Dicotyledoneae		
	Umbelliferae			
89	*Daucus carota*	Day neutral	Ve (4-10°C)	82
	Ericaceae			
90	*Rhododendron* sp.	Day neutral	...	81
	Convolvulaceae			
91	*Ipomoea batatas*	Short day required; short day favorable	...	62
92	*I. hederacea*	Short day required	...	38,43
93	*I. purpurea*	Short day required[9]	...	43,78
	Polemoniaceae			
94	*Phlox paniculata*	Long day required	Th	78
	Labiatae			
95	*Salvia splendens*	Short day favorable	Th; Tl (day neutral)	78
	Solanaceae			
96	*Capsicum annuum*	Day neutral; short day favorable	Tp	20,29,31
97	*Datura stramonium*	Short day favorable[10]	...	78,80
98	*Hyoscyamus niger* (annual)	Long day required (>10 hr)	Tq	54
99	*H. niger* (biennial)	Long day required	Tq; Ve	54
100	*Lycopersicon esculentum*	Day neutral; long day favorable; short day favorable	Tp	1,98
101	*Nicotiana tabacum*	Day neutral[1]	...	37
102	*N. tabacum* (Havana)	Long day favorable	...	78
103	*N. tabacum* (Maryland mammoth)	Short day required (<14 hr)	Th; <13°C (day neutral)	37,80
104	*Petunia hybrida*	Long day favorable	Th; Tl (day neutral)	80
105	*Solanum nigrum*	Day neutral	Tl; Th (long day favorable)	81
106	*S. tuberosum*	Long day favorable; short day favorable; day neutral	...	3,38,50
	Scrophulariaceae			
107	*Antirrhinum majus*	Long day favorable	Th; Tl (day neutral)	55,73
108	*Digitalis purpurea*	Long day favorable	Ve	9
	Rubiaceae			
109	*Gardenia jasminoides fortuniana*	Day neutral	...	81
	Cucurbitaceae			
110	*Cucumis sativus*	Day neutral	...	27,95
	Compositae			
111	*Ambrosia artemisiifolia*	Short day required	...	37
112	*Anthemis cotula*	Long day favorable	Th; Tl (day neutral)	80
113	*Callistephus chinensis*	Long day favorable	Th	58
114	*Centaurea cyanus*	Long day favorable	Th; Tl (day neutral)	80
115	*Chrysanthemum frutescens*	Long day required	...	56
116	*C. indicum*	Short day required (<15 hr)	Tq	56
117	*C. maximum*	Long day required	...	78
118	*Cichorium intybus*	Long day required	Th; Tl (day neutral)	78
119	*Cosmos bipinnatus*	Short day favorable[1]	...	37,42
120	*C. sulphureus* (Klondyke)	Short day required (<14 hr)	Th; Tl	42,79
121	*C. sulphureus* (Orange flare)	Day neutral	Th; Tl (short day required)	79
122	*Helianthus annuus*	Short day favorable; day neutral	...	30
123	*H. tuberosus*	Short day favorable; day neutral	...	38
124	*Lactuca sativa*	Long day favorable	Th; Tl (day neutral)	8,17,94
125	*Rudbeckia bicolor*	Long day required (>10 hr)	Th	40,65
126	*R. hirta*	Long day required (>12 hr)	...	5,42
127	*Senecio cruentus*	Short day favorable	...	81
128	*Solidago* spp.[11]	Short day required	...	81
129	*Sonchus oleraceus*	Long day favorable	...	78
130	*Xanthium pensylvanicum*	Short day required (<15.5 hr)	Tq	38,44,59

/1/ Data applicable to most varieties. /9/ Night temperature, 22°C; at 18°C, day neutral; at 13°C, long day required. /10/ Becomes day neutral with aging of plant. /11/ Species include *altissima, fistulosa, juncea;* long day required for *S. cutleri.*

Contributors: (a) Greulach, Victor A., (b) Cooper, J. P., and Calder, D. M., (c) Garner, W. W., (d) Roberts, R. H., and Struckmeyer, Burdean E., (e) Hagen, Charles W., Jr.

continued

143. PHOTOPERIOD, WITH TEMPERATURE INTERACTIONS, FOR FLOWERING: ANGIOSPERMS

References: [1] Adams, J. 1924. Am. J. Botany 11:229. [2] Allard, H. A. 1935. J. Agr. Research 51:27. [3] Allard, H. A. 1938. Ibid. 57:775. [4] Allard, H. A., and M. W. Evans. 1941. Ibid. 62:193. [5] Allard, H. A., and W. W. Garner. 1940. U. S. Dept. Agr. Tech. Bull. 727. [6] Allard, H. A., and W. J. Zaumeyer. 1944. Ibid. 867. [7] Arthur, J. M., and J. D. Guthrie. 1927. Mem. Hort. Soc. N. Y. 3:73. [8] Arthur, J. M., J. D. Guthrie, and J. M. Newell. 1930. Am. J. Botany 16:338. [9] Arthur, J. M., and E. K. Harvill. 1941. Contribs. Boyce Thompson Inst. 12:111. [10] Aso, K., and U. Muari. 1924. J. Sci. Agr. Soc. (Japan) 254:31. [11] Benedict, H. M. 1940. J. Agr. Research 61:661. [12] Berkeley, E. E. 1931. Ann. Missouri Botan. Garden 18:573. [13] Blake, J. 1955. Rept. 14th Intern. Hort. Congr., p. 331. [14] Blake, J., and G. P. Harris. 1960. Ann. Botany (London), n.s. 24:247. [15] Borthwick, H. A., and M. W. Parker. 1939. Botan. Gaz. 101:341. [16] Borthwick, H. A., M. W. Parker, and P. H. Heinze. 1941. Ibid. 103:326. [17] Bremer, A. H. 1931. Gartenbauwiss. 4:469. [18] Calder, D. M. 1960. Ann. Rept. Welsh Plant Breeding Sta., p. 16. [19] Calder, D. M. Unpublished. Univ. College of Wales, Aberystwyth, 1962. [20] Cochran, H. L. 1936. Cornell Univ. Agr. Expt. Sta. Mem. 190. [21] Cooper, J. P. 1951. J. Ecol. 39:229. [22] Cooper, J. P. 1952. Ibid. 40:352. [23] Cooper, J. P. 1954. Ibid. 42:521. [24] Cooper, J. P. 1960. Ann. Botany (London), n.s. 24:232. [25] Cooper, J. P. 1960. Herbage Abstr. 30:71. [26] Cooper, J. P. Unpublished, 1955. [27] Danielson, L. L. 1944. Plant Physiol. 19:638. [28] Darrow, G. M., and G. F. Waldo. 1934. U. S. Dept. Agr. Tech. Bull. 453. [29] Dorland, R. E., and F. W. Went. 1947. Am. J. Botany 34:393. [30] Dyer, H. J., J. Skok, and N. J. Scully. 1959. Botan. Gaz. 121:50. [31] Eguchi, T. 1937. Proc. Imp. Acad. (Tokyo) 13:332. [32] Evans, L. T. 1958. Nature 182:197. [33] Evans, L. T. 1959. Ann. Botany (London), n.s. 23:251. [34] Evans, M., and C. P. Willsie. 1946. J. Am. Soc. Agron. 38:923. [35] Fife, J. M., and C. Price. 1953. Plant Physiol. 28:475. [36] Gall, H. J. F. 1947. Botan. Gaz. 109:59. [37] Garner, W. W., and H. A. Allard. 1920. J. Agr. Research 18:553. [38] Garner, W. W., and H. A. Allard. 1923. Ibid. 23:871. [39] Garner, W. W., and H. A. Allard. 1931. Ibid. 43:439. [40] Garner, W. W., C. W. Bacon, and H. A. Allard. 1924. Ibid. 27:119. [41] Gerhard, E. 1940. J. Landwirtsch. 87:161. [42] Greulach, V. A. 1942. Botan. Gaz. 103:698. [43] Greulach, V. A. 1943. Ohio J. Sci. 43:65. [44] Hamner, K. C., and J. Bonner. 1938. Botan. Gaz. 100:388. [45] Hamner, K. C., and A. W. Naylor. 1939. Ibid. 100:853. [46] Harder, R., and H. von Witsch. 1940. Gartenbauwiss. 15:226. [47] Hartman, H. T. 1947. Plant Physiol. 22:407. [48] Hillman, W. S. 1959. Am. J. Botany 46:466. [49] Holdson, J., and A. Laurie. 1951. Proc. Am. Soc. Hort. Sci. 57:379. [50] Jones, H. A., and H. A. Borthwick. 1938. Am. Potato J. 15:331. [51] Ketellapper, H. J. 1960. Ecology 41:298. [52] Knott, J. E. 1939. Cornell Univ. Agr. Expt. Sta. Mem. 218. [53] Konstantinov, P. N. 1938. U. S. Dept. Agr. Office Expt. Sta. Records 78:170. [54] Lang, A., and G. Melchers. 1943. Planta 33:653. [55] Laurie, A. 1930. Proc. Am. Soc. Hort. Sci. 27:319. [56] Laurie, A., and G. H. Poesch. 1932. Ohio Agr. Expt. Sta. Bull. 512. [57] Leopold, A. C. 1951. Quart. Rev. Biol. 26:247. [58] Lin, L. C., and D. P. Watson. 1950. Proc. Am. Soc. Hort. Sci. 55:441. [59] Long, E. M., 1939. Botan. Gaz. 101:168. [60] Magruder, R., and H. A. Allard. 1937. J. Agr. Research 54:719. [61] McClelland, T. B. 1924. Ibid. 28:445. [62] McClelland, T. B. 1928. Ibid. 37:603. [63] McKinney, H. H., and W. J. Sandow. 1933. J. Heredity 24:169. [64] McKinney, H. H., and W. J. Sandow. 1935. J. Agr. Research 51:621. [65] Murneek, A. E. 1940. Botan. Gaz. 102:269. [66] Murneek, A. E., and R. O. Whyte, ed. 1948. Vernalization and photoperiodism. Chronica Botanica, Waltham, Mass. [67] Nakata, S. 1952. Plant Physiol. 27:644. [68] Olmsted, C. E. 1943. Botan. Gaz. 105:165. [69] Olmsted, C. E. 1944. Ibid. 106:46. [70] Parker, M. W., and H. A. Borthwick. 1943. Ibid. 104:612. [71] Peterson, M. L., and W. E. Loomis. 1949. Plant Physiol. 24:31. [72] Plitt, T. M. 1932. Ibid. 7:337. [73] Post, K., and C. L. Weddle. 1940. Proc. Am. Soc. Hort. Sci. 37:1037. [74] Purvis, O. N. 1934. Ann. Botany (London) 48:919. [75] Purvis, O. N., and F. G. Gregory. 1937. Ibid., n.s. 1:569. [76] Quinby, J. R., and R. E. Karper. 1945. J. Am. Soc. Agron. 37:916. [77] Roberts, R. H., and B. E. Struckmeyer. 1937. Science 85:290. [78] Roberts, R. H., and B. E. Struckmeyer. 1938. J. Agr. Research 56:633. [79] Roberts, R. H., and B. E. Struckmeyer. 1938. J. Heredity 29:95. [80] Roberts, R. H., and B. E. Struckmeyer. 1939. J. Agr. Research 59:699. [81] Roberts, R. H. Unpublished.

continued

143. PHOTOPERIOD, WITH TEMPERATURE INTERACTIONS, FOR FLOWERING: ANGIOSPERMS

Univ. of Wisconsin, Madison, 1953. [82] Sakr, E. S., and H. C. Thompson. 1942. Proc. Am. Soc. Hort. Sci. 41:343. [83] Samygin, G. A. 1946. Trudy Inst. Fiziol. Rastenii im. K. A. Timiryazeva Akad. Nauk. S. S. S. R. 3:129. [84] Schaaf, H. M. 1961. Agron. J. 53:353. [85] Scully, N. J., H. A. Borthwick, and M. W. Parker. 1945. Botan. Gaz. 107:52. [86] Shanks, J. B., and C. B. Link. 1951. Proc. Am. Soc. Hort. Sci. 58:357. [87] Sircar, S. M. 1946. Proc. Natl. Inst. Sci. India 12:191. [88] Sircar, S. M., and B. Pariji. 1945. Nature 155:395. [89] Sprague, V. G. 1948. J. Am. Soc. Agron. 40:144. [90] Stokes, P., and K. Verkerk. 1951. Mededel. Landbouwhogeschool Wageningen 50:141. [91] Templeton, W. C. 1960. Dissertation Abstr. 21:20. [92] Thomas, R. G. 1961. Ann. Botany (London), n.s. 25:138. [93] Thompson, H. C. 1940. Proc. Am. Soc. Hort. Sci. 37:672. [94] Thompson, H. C., and J. E. Knott. 1933. Ibid. 30:507. [95] Tiedjens, V. A. 1928. J. Agr. Research 36:721. [96] Tincker, M. A. H. 1925. Ann. Botany (London) 39:721. [97] Wellensiek, S. J. 1958. Koninkl. Ned. Akad. Wetenschap. Proc., C, 61:561. [98] Went, F. W. 1945. Am. J. Botany 32:469. [99] Withrow, R. B., ed. 1959. Publ. Am. Assoc. Advance. Sci. 55. [100] Wort, D. J. 1939. Botan. Gaz. 101:457. [101] Wort, D. J. 1941. Ibid. 102:725. [102] Wycherley, P. R. 1952. Mededel. Landbouwhogeschool Wageningen 52:75. [103] Youngner, V. B. 1960. Am. J. Botany 47:753. [104] Yusuff, N. D., and N. L. Dutt. 1945. Current Sci. (India) 14:304.

144. EFFECT OF LIGHT WAVELENGTHS ON GROWTH: PLANTS

Data present the effectiveness of brief dark-period interruption for control of flowering and certain vegetative expressions. Plants, growing under radiation from carbon arc and incandescent filament lamps for a daily period of about 12 hours, were subjected at the midpoint of the dark-period to radiation of known energy and wavelength.

	Effect and Species	Relative Energy Normalized to Maximum Response at Wavelength (in Å) of											Conversion Factor[1]	Reference
		4400	4800	5000	5200	5400	5600	5800	6200	6600	6800	7000		
	(A)	(B)	(C)	(D)	(E)	(F)	(G)	(H)	(I)	(J)	(K)	(L)	(M)	(N)
	Inhibition of flowering													
1	*Glycine soja*	18	27	17	6	3.7	2	1.3	1	1.3	1.6	3.5	30	8,9
2	*Xanthium pensylvanicum*	125	173	92	40	8	5.4	2.6	1[2]	1.5	3.1	7	40	3,8
	Promotion of flowering													
3	*Hordeum vulgare*	218	185	85	35	4	1.8	1.3	1[2]	1.5	4	7	35	1,5,6
4	*Hyoscyamus niger*	...	...	...	...	4	1.8	1.3	1[2]	1.5	4	7	300	5-7
	Promotion of germination													
5	*Lactuca sativa*	...	...	...	...	...	18	10	3[2]	1	1.2	50	2	4
	Promotion of leaf elongation													
6	*Pisum sativum*	100	190	200	95	24	10	6.5	1	1	1	1.3	0.16	9
	Inhibition of stem elongation													
7	*Hordeum vulgare*	250	...	200	40	20	5	2	1.3[2]	1	2	6	100	2,5,6
	Production of pigmentation													
8	*Lycopersicon esculentum*	30	30	30	30	20	10	3	1[2]	1	1.2	7	200	10

/1/ Relative energy (columns B-L) may be converted to kiloergs per sq cm by multiplying by the appropriate factor (column M). /2/ 7200-7600 Å reverses the response caused by red (6200-6600 Å).

Contributor: Downs, R. J.

References: [1] Borthwick, H. A., S. B. Hendricks, and M. W. Parker. 1948. Botan. Gaz. 110:103. [2] Borthwick, H. A., S. B. Hendricks, and M. W. Parker. 1951. Ibid. 113:95. [3] Borthwick, H. A., S. B. Hendricks, and M. W. Parker. 1952. Proc. Natl. Acad. Sci. U. S. 38(11):929. [4] Borthwick, H. A., et al. 1952. Ibid. 38(8):662. [5] Downs, R. J. 1955. Plant Physiol. 30:468. [6] Downs, R. J. 1956. Ibid. 31:279. [7] Parker, M. W., S. B. Hendricks, and H. A. Borthwick. 1950. Botan. Gaz. 111:242. [8] Parker, M. W., et al. 1945. Science 102:152. [9] Parker, M. W., et al. 1946. Botan. Gaz. 108:1. [10] Piringer, A. A., and P. H. Heinze. 1954. Plant Physiol. 29:467.

145. EFFECT OF LIGHT INTENSITY ON GROWTH: PLANTS

	Family	Species	Location	Duration of Experiment	Light Intensity ft-candles or % of full sunlight	Growth dry weight, g or height, cm	Reference
	(A)	(B)	(C)	(D)	(E)	(F)	(G)
1	Pinaceae	*Pinus banksiana*	Cass Lake, Minnesota; nursery bed in open	4 yr	98%	280.0 g	5
2					46%	374.0 g	
3					20%	113.0 g	
4					11%	26.0 g	
5		*P. resinosa*	Cass Lake, Minnesota; nursery bed in open	4 yr	98%	121.0 g	5
6					46%	108.0 g	
7					20%	36.0 g	
8					11%	26.0 g	
9		*P. strobus*	Southern New York; nursery bed in open	100 da	100%	12.36 g; 3.15 cm	2
10					74%	11.41 g; 3.89 cm	
11					53%	10.71 g; 3.98 cm	
12					29%	8.95 g; 4.30 cm	
13	Taxodiaceae	*Sequoia sempervirens*	Yonkers, New York; pots outdoors	16 wk	100%	3.6 g	4
14					74%	3.9 g	
15					47%	4.1 g	
16					20%	2.3 g	
17	Polygonaceae	*Fagopyrum esculentum*	Yonkers, New York; pots outdoors	9 wk	100%	1.9 g	4
18					74%	1.8 g	
19					47%	2.2 g	
20					20%	1.6 g	
21	Leguminosae	*Glycine soja*	Chicago, Illinois; pots in greenhouse	7 wk	4285 ft-c	50.6 cm	3
22					1536 ft-c	55.4 cm	
23					560 ft-c	91.5 cm	
24					390 ft-c	75.3 cm	
25					250 ft-c	64.9 cm	
26					26 ft-c	Dead	
27	Solanaceae	*Nicotiana tabacum*	Yonkers, New York; pots outdoors	10 wk	100%	21.0 g	4
28					74%	17.5 g	
29					47%	15.0 g	
30					20%	18.0 g	
31	Compositae	*Helianthus annuus*	Santa Barbara, California; pots outdoors	2 mo	100%	41.2 g	1
32					32%	13.7 g	
33					16%	3.8 g	
34					8%	1.8 g	

Contributor: Kramer, Paul J.

References: [1] Clements, F. E., and F. L. Long. 1934. Plant Physiol. 9:767. [2] Mitchell, H. L. 1936. Black Rock Forest Papers 1(6):29. [3] Popp, H. W. 1926. Botan. Gaz. 82:306. [4] Shirley, H. L. 1929. Am. J. Botany 16:354. [5] Shirley, H. L. 1945. Am. Midland Naturalist 33:537.

146. EFFECT OF RADIATION ON GROWTH PROCESSES: ANIMALS AND PLANTS

Radiation exposure levels are approximations. Susceptibility to radiation varies with species, age, metabolic state, and with environmental temperature and oxygen pressure. Exposure Level (column D): r = roentgens, kr = kiloroentgens, rep = roentgen equivalents physical.

	Organism	Structure Irradiated	Radiation		Test Period[1]	Effect Observed	Reference
			Type	Exposure Level			
	(A)	(B)	(C)	(D)	(E)	(F)	(G)
1	*Mus*	Whole organism	X rays	200-300 r	2 da	Decreased synthesis of DNA in regenerating hair follicle	6
2		Whole organism	X rays	800 r	4 mo	Temporary sterility	16
3		Testis	X or γ rays	20-600 r	1-28 da	Damage to germinal cells	36
4		Sperm	X rays	400 r	....	1.1% mutation per 100 r	7

/1/ Time after irradiation when effect was observed.

continued

146. EFFECT OF RADIATION ON GROWTH PROCESSES: ANIMALS AND PLANTS

	Organism	Structure Irradiated	Radiation		Test Period[1]	Effect Observed	Reference
			Type	Exposure Level			
	(A)	(B)	(C)	(D)	(E)	(F)	(G)
5	*Mus*	Skin	X rays	35-325 r	2 hr-4 da	Decreased % of cells in mitosis	33
6		Embryonic lung (organ culture)	γ rays	818 r	4 da	Inhibition of growth and differentiation	2
7		Sarcoma 180	X rays	5-60 kr	10 da	Inhibition of growth in transplants	17
8	*Rattus*	Retina	X or γ rays	36-540 r	1.5-48 hr	Inhibition of mitosis	49
9	*Gallus*	Embryo, 5 da old	X rays	1000 r	7 da	Irradiated lens smaller than control lens	10
10		Fibroblast culture	X rays	34 r	80 min	Reduced rate of mitosis	47,48
11		Fibroblast culture	X rays	100 r	24 hr	Death of cells at next division	34,47
12	*Columba*	Squab, <15 da old	X rays	1000-2000 r	1 yr	Growth of wing bones inhibited	8
13	*Rana*	Sperm	X rays	40 kr	5 hr	Complete inactivation	25
14		Sperm	X rays	15-500 r	10 da	Abnormal development, 5-100%	25
15		Eggs, fertilized	X rays	100-1000 r	7 da	Inhibition or abnormality of development	41
16	*Siredon*	Hind limb (regenerating)	X rays	4-6 kr	45-100 da	Decreased size of regenerating hind limb	3
17	*Fundulus*	Eggs, gametes, embryos	X rays	2000 r	1 wk +	Abnormal development of embryo	46
18	*Arbacia*	Eggs	X rays	30 kr	2 hr	Delay of cleavage	24
19	*Drosophila*	Whole organism	γ rays	375-3600 r	2 wk	Increased recessive mutation rate	32
20		Adult	X rays	350 r	ca. 2 wk	1% increase in sex-linked mutations	47
21		Eggs	X rays	190 r	48 hr	Failure to hatch, 50%	37-39, 47
22		Eggs	γ rays	240 r	48 hr	Failure to hatch, 50%	51
23		Eggs	Neutrons	85 rep	48 hr	Failure to hatch, 50%	18,51
24		Eggs	β rays	275 rep	48 hr	Failure to hatch, 50%	51
25	*Melanoplus*	Neuroblast	X rays	8 r	24 hr	Reduced rate of mitosis	4
26		Eggs, 6 da old	X rays	50 r	21 da	Abnormal development, 50%	12
27	*Spisula*	Gametes	X rays	3-250 kr	48 hr	Delay of cleavage and inhibition of trocophore	42
28	*Hydra*	Whole organism	X rays	4500 r	1-3 da	Inhibition of buds	40
29	*Pandorina*	Whole organism	X rays	3-300 kr	8 da	Death at subsequent cell division	22
30	*Escherichia coli*	Whole organism	X rays	10-15 kr	ca. 30 hr	Mutation from sensitive to resistant to phage T_1	11
31	*Chaetomium globosum*	Spores	X rays	9.4-329.0 kr	3 wk	Lethal mutants in 50%	14
32	*Neurospora*	Ascospores	X rays	3-50 kr	2 wk	Production of biochemical mutants	1
33	*Penicillium*	Spores	X rays	180 kr	30 hr	50% less germination than control	23
34	*Rhizopus nigricans*	Spores	X rays	50 kr	24 hr	50% less germination than control	35
35	*Saccharomycetaceae*	Cells	X rays	10 kr	6 hr	Death at subsequent division	28
36	*Hordeum*	Seedlings	Neutrons, X, γ rays	5-40 kr	6 da	Seedling height reduced	9
37	*Lemna minor*	Whole organism	X rays	1000 r	3 wk	50% decrease in growth rate of fronds	30
38	*Lilium*	Pollen grains	X rays	210 kr	18 hr	50% less germination than control	23
39	*Tradescantia*	Dry pollen	X rays	200 r	24 hr	Chromosome breaks, 2.3%	50
40		Microspores	X rays	320 r	5 da	Chromosome breaks, 17.3%	43-45
41		Microspores	Neutrons	25 rep	5 da	Chromosome aberrations, 2.6%	5,15
42		Seedling	γ rays	50 r/da for 3 mo	3 mo +	Multiple growth centers induced, growth arrested	20,21
43	*Triticum*	Seedlings (root, 18 hr old)	X rays	500 r	100 hr	50% decrease in growth rate (longitudinal)	27
44		Seedlings (primary leaf)	X rays	1100 r	70 hr	50% decrease in growth rate (longitudinal)	13
45	*Lactuca*	Shoot just germinated	X rays	1000-2000 r	100 hr	Inhibition of linear growth	26
46	*Lycopersicon*	Shoot just germinated	X rays	1000-2000 r	100 hr	Inhibition of linear growth	27
47	*Nicotiana*	Callus (tissue culture)	X rays	10-120 kr	3-10 da	Inhibition of growth	31

/1/ Time after irradiation when effect was observed.

continued

146. EFFECT OF RADIATION ON GROWTH PROCESSES: ANIMALS AND PLANTS

	Organism	Structure Irradiated	Radiation		Test Period[1]	Effect Observed	Reference
			Type	Exposure Level			
	(A)	(B)	(C)	(D)	(E)	(F)	(G)
48	*Salpiglossis*	Whole organism	X rays	2500 r	100 da	50% decrease in growth rate; repression of flowering	29
49	*Vicia faba*	Root	X rays	140 r	1-14 da	Inhibition of cell division	18,19
50		Root	γ rays	250 r	1-14 da	Inhibition of cell division	
51		Root	α rays	36 rep	1-14 da	Inhibition of cell division	

/1/ Time after irradiation when effect was observed.

Contributors: Evans, Titus C., and Riley, Edgar F.

References: [1] Beadle, G. W., and E. L. Tatum. 1945. Am. J. Botany 32:678. [2] Borghese, E. 1961. Ann. N. Y. Acad. Sci. 95:866. [3] Brunst, V. V. 1960. Radiation Research 12:642. [4] Carlson, J. G. 1942. J. Morphol. 71:449. [5] Catcheside, D. G., and D. E. Lea. 1943. J. Genet. 45:186. [6] Cattaneo, S. M., H. Quastler, and F. G. Sherman. 1960. Radiation Research 12:587. [7] Charles, D. R. 1950. Radiology 55:579. [8] Cole, L. J. 1945. J. Exptl. Zool. 100:487. [9] Curtis, H. J., et al. 1958. Radiation Research 8:526. [10] Daisley, K. W. 1959. Ibid. 11:271. [11] Demerec, M. 1946. Proc. Natl. Acad. Sci. U. S. 32:36. [12] Evans, T. C. 1936. Physiol. Zool. 9:443. [13] Failla, G., and P. S. Henshaw. 1931. Radiology 17:1. [14] Ford, J. M., and D. P. Kirwan. 1949. J. Gen. Physiol. 32:647. [15] Giles, N. 1940. Proc. Natl. Acad. Sci. U. S. 26:567. [16] Glucksman, A. 1947. Brit. J. Radiol., Suppl. 1:101. [17] Goldfeder, A. 1945. Radiology 45:49. [18] Gray, L. H. 1946. Brit. Med. Bull. 4:11. [19] Gray, L. H., and M. E. Scholes. 1951. Brit. J. Radiol. 24:285. [20] Gunckel, J. E. 1957. Quart. Rev. Biol. 32:46. [21] Gunckel, J. E. and A. H. Sparrow. 1954. Brookhaven Symposia in Biol. 6:252. [22] Halberstaedter, L., and A. Back. 1942. Brit. J. Radiol. 15:124. [23] Haskins, C. P., and C. N. Moore. 1934. Radiology 23:710. [24] Henshaw, P. S. 1940. Am. J. Roentgenol. Radium Therapy 43:899. [25] Henshaw, P. S. 1943. J. Natl. Cancer Inst. 3:409. [26] Henshaw, P. S., and D. S. Francis. 1936. Radiology 27:293. [27] Henshaw, P. S., and D. S. Francis. 1938. Am. J. Roentgenol. Radium Therapy 40:906. [28] Holweck, F., and A. Lacassagne. 1930. Compt. rend. soc. biol. 103:60. [29] Johnson, E. L. 1936. Plant Physiol. 11:319. [30] Johnson, E. L. 1941. Univ. Colorado Studies, D, 1:165. [31] King, G. 1949. Am. J. Botany 36:265. [32] King, R. C. 1954. Radiation Research 1:369. [33] Knowlton, N. P., et al. 1948. Science 107:625. [34] Lasnitzke, I. 1943. Brit. J. Radiol. 16:61. [35] Luyet, B. J. 1932. Radiology 18:1019. [36] Oakberg, E. F. 1955. Radiation Research 2:369. [37] Packard, C. 1935. Radiology 25:223. [38] Packard, C. 1937. Ibid. 29:12. [39] Packard, C. 1945. Ibid. 45:522. [40] Park, H. D. 1958. Physiol. Zool. 31:188. [41] Rollason, G. S. 1949. Biol. Bull. 97:169. [42] Rugh, R. 1953. Ibid. 104:197. [43] Sax, K. 1939. Proc. Natl. Acad. Sci. U. S. 25:225. [44] Sax, K. 1940. Genetics 25:41. [45] Sax, K. 1941. Cold Spring Harbor Symposia Quant. Biol. 9:93. [46] Solberg, A. N. 1938. J. Exptl. Zool. 78:441. [47] Spear, F. G. 1946. Brit. Med. Bull. 4:2. [48] Spear, F. G., and L. G. Grimmett. 1933. Brit. J. Radiol. 6:387. [49] Spear, F. G., and K. Tansley. 1944. Ibid. 17:374. [50] Swanson, C. P. 1940. Proc. Natl. Acad. Sci. U. S. 26:366. [51] Zirkle, R. E. 1950. Am. J. Roentgenol. Radium Therapy 63:170.

Part I: IRRADIATION AT 39

Subjects were Sprague-Dawley rats of both sexes. Experimental animals and controls were kept in

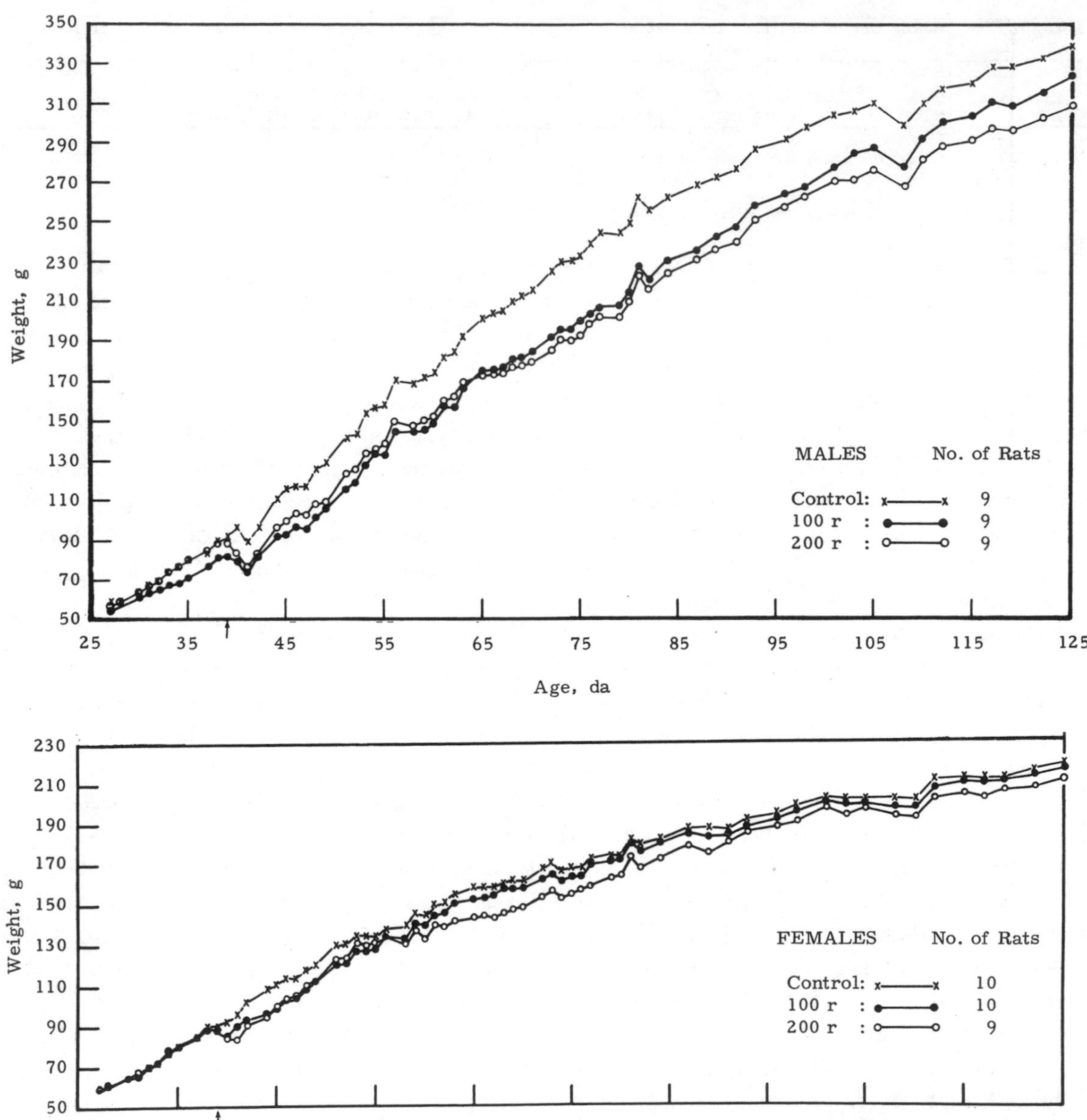

Rats Irradiated at 39 Days of Age

Contributor: Sacher, George A.

References: [1] Brues, A. M., and G. A. Sacher. 1952. In J. J. Nickson, ed. Symposium on radiobiology. Zirkle, ed. TID-5220. U. S. Dept. of Commerce, Office of Technical Services, Washington, D. C. pp. 217-224. shorter term biological hazards of a fallout field. U.S. Atomic Energy Commission, Washington, D.C. pp. 101-112.

ON GROWTH: RAT

AND 53 DAYS OF AGE

three cages, with all groups represented in each cage. For further information, consult references 1-4.

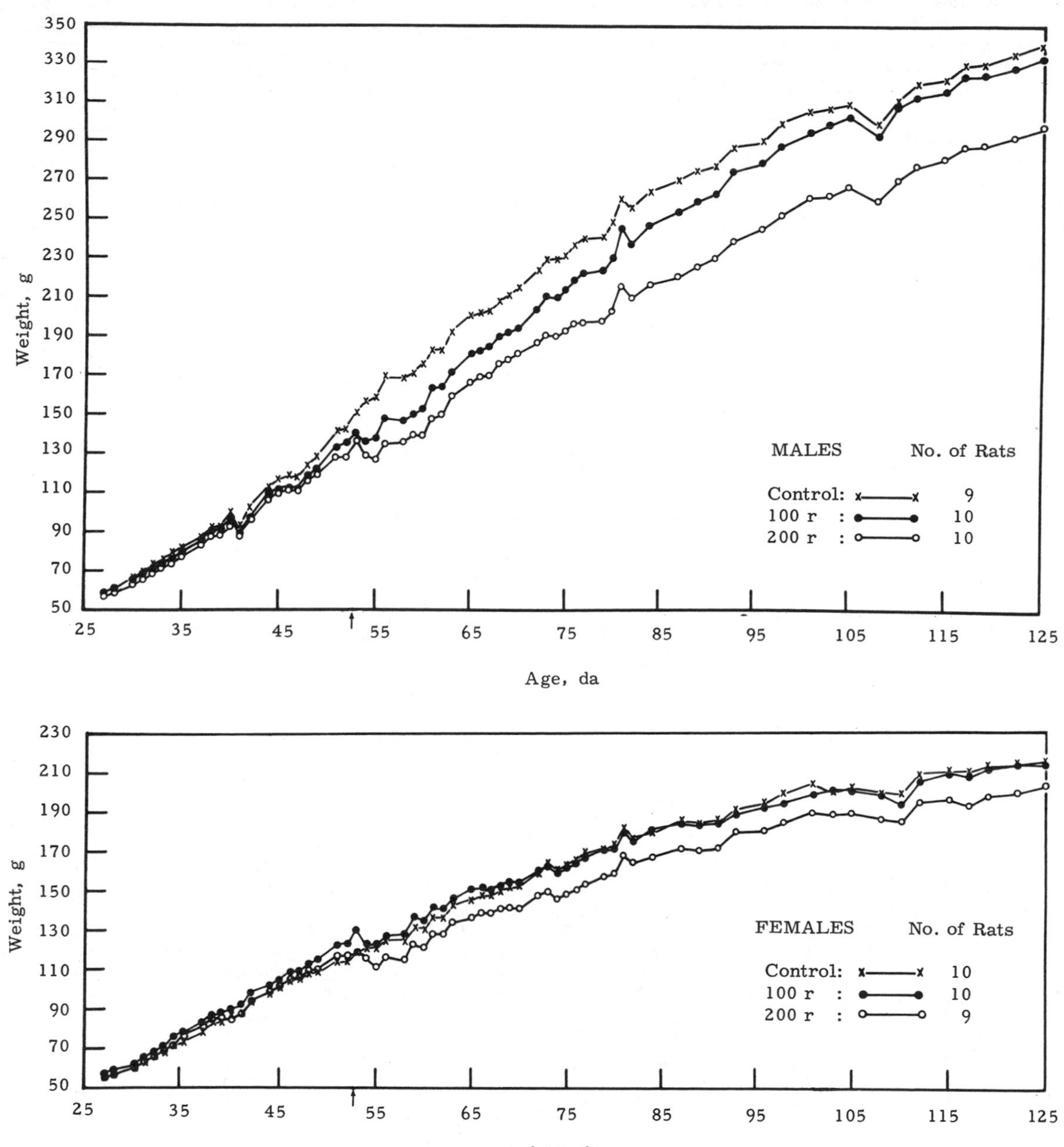

Rats Irradiated at 53 Days of Age

J. Wiley and Sons, New York. pp. 441-465. [2] Brues, A. M., G. A. Sacher, and H. O. France. 1956. In R. E. [3] Sacher, G. A. 1956. Ibid. pp. 300-314. [4] Sacher, G. A. 1958. In G. M. Dunning and J. A. Hilcken, ed. The

continued

147. EFFECT OF RADIATION ON GROWTH: RAT

Part II: IRRADIATION DAILY AFTER 52 DAYS OF AGE

Subjects were 72 male Sprague-Dawley rats, divided equally into three experimental and three control groups. Each experimental group and its controls were housed in the same cage; the three cages were kept side by side. Weighing commenced when the animals were 24 days old, and X-ray exposure when they were 52 days old [2]. Daily doses of 4, 8, and 16 roentgens were administered six days a week immediately after weighing (average exposures were 3.43, 6.85, and 13.7 r/da, respectively). After 107 days of exposure (at 159 days of age) six of the 16 r/da group and six of the cage controls were sacrificed for organ weight determinations [1].

	Age da	Body Weight, g					
		4 r/da		8 r/da		16 r/da	
		Control	Experimental	Control	Experimental	Control	Experimental
	(A)	(B)	(C)	(D)	(E)	(F)	(G)
1	24	44.3	44.5	44.7	45.6	45.2	45.2
2	27	52.9	52.8	53.1	53.9	52.7	53.5
3	29	59.5	60.3	59.7	61.3	60.0	60.7
4	30	61.5	61.4	61.8	63.8	62.6	63.6
5	31	65.6	66.1	65.9	67.5	65.7	65.6
6	32	71.5	71.8	70.7	73.4	70.5	70.2
7	33	76.7	77.5	75.3	78.7	75.6	75.6
8	34	80.2	81.2	79.3	82.3	79.5	79.4
9	36	86.7	88.5	87.2	90.4	88.4	89.3
10	37	91.7	93.8	91.9	96.3	93.8	94.3
11	38	95.7	97.1	96.6	99.7	97.6	97.1
12	40	107.2	108.4	105.6	109.7	107.7	106.4
13	41	110.7	111.0	108.2	113.4	112.7	109.9
14	43	117.3	119.4	117.6	121.5	117.7	114.4
15	44	120.8	124.5	121.3	125.8	122.3	120.7
16	45	118.8	119.4	123.9	129.4	125.7	125.0
17	46	131.3	133.0	129.4	135.4	128.7	128.3
18	47	130.7	133.5	131.0	136.6	130.5	131.3
19	48	139.6	142.3	135.5	141.6	132.7	132.7
20	50	151.2	152.3	139.5	145.6	142.6	143.0
21	51	157.5	161.2	148.5	154.4	146.2	148.0
22	52	161.1	164.5	152.9	157.9	152.6	155.3
23	53	162.3	165.3	151.4	157.7	150.7	152.7
24	54	168.6	169.7	158.0	162.6	152.6	151.2
25	55	174.4	174.8	162.1	166.1	156.0	150.4
26	57	182.3	182.3	170.3	174.6	162.8	156.9
27	58	185.7	184.5	176.6	179.3	168.2	158.1
28	59	189.3	187.6	180.2	180.4	169.0	157.1
29	60	186.2	182.2	180.7	181.8	170.5	156.4
30	61	166.9	164.9	168.4	167.9	173.7	158.8
31	62	189.3	184.3	186.6	184.5	175.6	160.3
32	64	185.3	187.3	189.5	187.6	176.1	156.9
33	65	205.3	202.0	197.1	194.5	186.8	168.9
34	66	204.6	200.0	199.9	196.7	190.7	172.1
35	67	199.4	195.1	177.3	175.2	192.3	172.4
36	68	211.5	207.2	200.0	197.5	197.9	177.0
37	69	210.9	207.6	199.9	198.1	199.8	181.9
38	71	218.9	215.4	210.5	210.5	208.3	192.3
39	72	216.8	215.2	208.7	206.3	206.0	187.0
40	73	223.8	224.6	217.6	215.7	213.3	193.1
41	74	226.0	223.8	220.6	219.2	215.7	195.4
42	75	227.2	224.1	220.3	216.4	215.8	191.3
43	76	231.5	229.0	222.4	221.7	219.5	197.3
44	78	240.2	237.1	229.7	230.3	229.0	205.1
45	79	243.3	241.3	233.6	233.6	232.3	208.2
46	80	244.7	242.1	235.7	232.2	231.8	206.7
47	81	236.5	234.1	213.3	212.7	207.7	184.9
48	82	246.1	244.6	232.7	229.1	230.4	203.3
49	83	240.4	237.0	232.0	227.4	230.3	203.5
50	85	237.4	235.4	224.7	220.3	220.2	194.1
51	86	250.2	246.6	235.9	231.6	232.2	204.0
52	87	249.1	250.1	239.4	232.9	236.7	208.7
53	88	253.0	252.9	245.0	238.2	240.5	211.4
54	89	259.4	257.0	249.7	240.1	245.1	213.3
55	90	260.2	258.7	253.9	242.1	248.0	217.3
56	92	270.6	266.8	254.2	248.4	257.7	223.4
57	93	271.2	270.7	259.1	251.8	257.6	222.1
58	94	270.5	270.5	265.9	256.5	261.8	223.3
59	95	275.9	272.2	264.1	255.0	264.3	227.1
60	96	274.7	279.9	270.5	260.4	271.4	226.7
61	97	275.9	278.3	267.1	259.8	264.5	226.1
62	99	288.7	285.9	273.5	266.8	270.0	235.1
63	100	283.2	279.7	269.3	259.7	274.2	235.7
64	101	283.9	278.7	272.8	260.9	270.9	227.3
65	102	286.2	281.5	271.1	260.7	272.5	230.3
66	103	286.2	283.5	272.7	261.8	273.4	232.4
67	104	287.2	280.2	275.7	261.1	277.4	237.1
68	106	289.2	284.6	278.1	265.2	281.1	239.6
69	107	293.4	286.8	280.9	267.8	284.4	241.1
70	108	290.9	283.6	279.0	263.6	280.5	239.3
71	109	291.9	287.0	274.4	257.5	277.1	233.7
72	110	294.7	287.7	285.9	267.7	289.3	243.3
73	111	298.0	289.3	285.7	270.0	290.2	246.0
74	113	293.3	285.7	286.0	271.7	291.1	249.2
75	114	301.6	295.1	290.0	271.9	290.1	248.0
76	115	300.2	296.5	292.2	277.5	295.1	250.8
77	116	299.0	293.4	293.8	275.2	287.8	244.8
78	117	290.5	282.7	292.8	273.2	298.2	253.2
79	118	304.2	298.4	295.9	278.6	299.5	255.7
80	120	286.9	284.2	284.8	267.9	289.3	248.0
81	121	301.9	296.3	292.4	273.1	295.2	254.8
82	122	303.3	296.5	293.2	273.3	297.1	254.8
83	123	309.6	303.3	300.6	278.5	302.4	258.0
84	124	311.2	304.1	304.1	280.8	304.9	260.8
85	125	309.7	303.2	302.6	279.5	302.1	258.0
86	127	315.9	311.3	308.3	286.7	307.1	262.8
87	128	316.5	310.8	307.2	286.3	310.2	264.6
88	129	317.6	311.8	307.6	285.3	308.2	263.8
89	130	320.7	312.8	309.0	287.2	309.9	263.1
90	131	321.2	312.9	310.8	290.8	310.2	265.0
91	132	320.4	311.8	312.2	289.2	312.8	266.9
92	134	320.2	314.0	308.6	285.3	315.8	268.1
93	135	320.8	315.3	312.4	292.3	315.5	269.8
94	136	322.2	317.3	317.0	292.6	319.3	271.5
95	137	321.9	318.5	314.4	291.7	318.3	271.8
96	138	323.1	318.7	316.0	294.3	321.0	274.1
97	139	324.3	320.6	314.9	291.8	315.0	266.3
98	141	326.7	321.5	320.6	295.8	326.4	279.4
99	142	329.0	323.0	323.4	297.8	326.8	274.5
100	143	328.3	321.4	320.9	296.2	323.8	275.0
101	144	334.7	330.7	326.8	300.5	326.9	278.7
102	145	338.9[1]	326.9	327.5[1]	298.7	325.6[2]	279.3
103	146	337.8	326.4	329.1	301.9	326.8	283.0
104	148	339.3	331.2	334.5	308.8	328.4	285.9
105	149	344.4	334.3	335.5	310.6	330.3	290.1
106	150	344.8	330.0	336.0	310.0	328.5	285.6
107	151	340.7	329.3	329.5	305.7	326.9	283.7
108	152	344.5	334.3	330.9	310.3	327.3	285.5

/1/ 2 rats removed. /2/ 1 rat removed.

continued

147. EFFECT OF RADIATION ON GROWTH: RAT

Part II: IRRADIATION DAILY AFTER 52 DAYS OF AGE

	Age da	Body Weight, g					
		4 r/da		8 r/da		16 r/da	
		Control	Experimental	Control	Experimental	Control	Experimental
	(A)	(B)	(C)	(D)	(E)	(F)	(G)
109	153	344.9	333.6	332.4	311.2	330.1	287.5
110	155	344.0	330.3	327.2	302.3	326.4	285.6
111	156	345.2	333.8	332.9	308.0	327.2	287.3
112	157	345.3	333.0	331.3	310.9	324.6	290.8
113	158	344.0	335.8	336.4	312.5	.....	.....
114	159	347.0	334.8	333.3	310.9	322.0[3]	296.2[3]
115	160	347.9	334.6	333.5	308.3	326.0	294.0
116	162	338.2	326.6	333.5	307.5	323.5	292.4
117	163	344.5	333.0	333.1	308.0	323.7	294.2
118	164	347.5	336.8	333.1	308.4	325.3	291.8
119	165	346.5	338.1	331.8	304.1	322.8	291.4
120	166	342.8	331.8	329.0	301.3	319.0	285.6
121	167	341.1	329.9	329.5	298.5	319.3	286.0
122	169	346.2	335.8	328.2	295.4	320.8	289.4
123	170	344.8	333.8	331.7	299.7	323.2	291.6
124	171	346.3	332.0	325.0	296.4	320.7	287.8
125	172	345.2	332.9	330.8	300.0	319.7	291.4
126	173	345.1	335.3	329.4	298.9	325.8	289.4
127	174	343.5	332.1	324.0	297.6	318.8	285.6
128	176	335.9	325.6	325.6	298.3	325.2	290.2
129	177	341.3	328.8	324.7	297.4	323.0	290.0
130	178	334.2	322.5	321.2	293.3	320.0	286.8
131	179	343.6	330.8	323.3	296.2	322.8	289.0
132	180	344.7	332.5	327.5	298.4	324.3	290.4
133	181	343.3	330.3	328.6	299.7	327.5	294.0
134	183	343.8	334.2	329.8	304.5	332.2	298.0
135	184	342.8	330.2	324.1	299.9	330.3	294.2
136	185	344.2	334.0	333.1	303.8	327.2	287.0
137	186	345.0	336.6[2]	332.3	306.7	334.7	296.4
138	187	341.9	332.5	328.0	301.0	331.2	294.2
139	188	341.2	331.1	330.6	304.2	334.2	291.6
140	190	342.8	331.3	330.2	305.5	335.7	296.0
141	191	344.7	333.0	332.9	305.7	335.0	296.0
142	192	343.2	332.5	334.5	307.4	338.5	299.6
143	193	347.5	337.6	334.1	310.2	340.0	300.2
144	194	342.5	333.2	332.5	309.3	339.8	298.6
145	195	343.4	333.4	332.0	307.7	338.5	297.8
146	197	346.5	336.1	335.2	311.5	340.0	300.8
147	198	343.7	333.1	334.5	310.5	337.0	300.2
148	199	347.2	334.6	331.8	308.4	337.3	298.4
149	200	343.8	331.5	329.3	305.8	333.2	295.6
150	201	346.8	333.6	333.5	310.9	339.2	301.8

/2/ 1 rat removed. /3/ 6 rats removed for organ weight determinations [1].

Contributor: Sacher, George A.

References: [1] Brues, A. M., G. A. Sacher, and H. O. France. 1956. In R. E. Zirkle, ed. TID-5220. U.S. Dept. of Commerce, Office of Technical Services, Washington, D. C. pp. 217-224. [2] Sacher, G. A. 1956. Ibid. pp. 300-314.

148. OPTIMUM pH FOR GROWTH: MICROORGANISMS

Values in parentheses are for minimum and maximum pH at which growth can occur.

Part I: PROTOZOA

Species and strain designations for *Tetrahymena* according to Corliss [2]. For additional information, consult reference 8.

	Species	Medium	Temp., °C	pH	Reference
	(A)	(B)	(C)	(D)	(E)
	Ciliata				
1	*Amphileptus* sp.	....	......	7.1-7.3 (6.8-7.5)	22
2	*Colpidium campylum*	Brewers yeast-Harris + peptone	......	5.4	14
3	*Colpoda cucullus*	....	......	6.5 & 7.5 (5.5-9.5)	22
4	*Didinium* sp.	Spring water + paramecia	......	6.4-8.4 (5.2-9.4)	1
5	*Gastrostyla* sp.	....	......	(6.0-8.5)	22
6	*Glaucoma scintillans*	Brewers yeast-Harris + peptone	......	5.6-6.8	14
7	*Holophrya* sp.	....	......	(6.5-7.4)	22
8	*Paramecium aurelia*	Hay + flour	25	7.0 (5.7-7.8)	3
9		Hay tea	......	7.0-7.2 (6.2-7.3)	28
10		With bacteria	26-28	5.9-7.7 (5.9-8.2)	21
11	*P. bursaria*	Mineral salts + peptone	19-26	6.7-6.8 (4.9-8.0)	17
12		Lettuce tea	......	7.1-7.3 (5.0-7.4)	28
13	*P. calkinsi*	Lettuce + sea water	......	7.1-7.4 (6.5-7.8)	28

continued

148. OPTIMUM pH FOR GROWTH: MICROORGANISMS

Part I: PROTOZOA

	Species	Medium	Temp., °C	pH	Reference
	(A)	(B)	(C)	(D)	(E)
	Ciliata				
14	*Paramecium caudatum*	Hay + flour	25	7.0 (5.3-8.1)	3
15		Hay tea	......	6.9-7.1 (6.2-7.2)	28
16	*P. multimicronucleatum*	Hay tea	27	7.0 (4.8-8.3)	13
17	*P. polycaryum*	Lettuce tea	......	6.9-7.3 (5.0-7.5)	28
18	*P. trichium*	Hay tea	......	6.7-7.1 (6.2-7.1)	28
19	*P. woodruffi*	Lettuce + sea water	......	7.0-7.5 (6.5-7.5)	28
20	*Plagiopyla* sp.	....	......	(6.9-7.5)	22
21	*Spirostomum ambiguum*	....	......	7.4 (6.8-7.5)	23
22	*Stentor coeruleus*	Modified Peters' + ciliates	18-20	7.7-8.0	9
23	*Stylonychia pustulata*	Hay tea	25	6.7 & 8.0 (6.0-8.0)	3
24	*Tetrahymena pyriformis* E	Tryptone	25	5.5 & 7.4 (4.5-8.5)	5
25	*T. pyriformis* Gf-J	Tryptone and others	28	5.1-6.0 (4.9-9.5)	12
26	*T. pyriformis* GL	Peptone	......	(4.5-10.2)	15
27	*T. pyriformis* GP	Tryptone and others	28	4.8-5.3 (4.0-8.9)	12
28	*T. pyriformis* H	Tryptone	25	5.5 & 7.4 (4.5-8.5)	6
29		Yeast extract + peptone	24-25	7.0	10
30	*T. pyriformis* T-P	Phelps'	24	7.0 & 9.0	29
31	*T. pyriformis* W	Peptone	......	5.6-8.0	14
32	*T. vorax* D	Peptone	......	6.2-7.6	14
	Mastigophora				
33	*Astasia klebsii*	Peptone	25	4.2-6.0 (3.2-8.2)	26
34	*A. longa*	Tryptophane	25	6.0 (3.3-9.6)	24
35		Tryptophane + acetate	25	6.5-7.0 (3.0-9.4)	24
36		Mineral salts	25	6.5-7.0 (4.6-7.0)	24
37	*Chilomonas paramecium*	Peptone	28	6.8-7.1 (4.1-8.4)	16
38		Peptone + acetate	28	7.0 (5.8-8.4)	16
39		Mineral salts + acetate	24.4	6.8 (4.8-8.0)	20
40	*Chlorogonium elongatum*	Peptone	28	7.8 (4.9-8.7)	16
41	*C. euchlorum*	Peptone	28	7.4 (4.8-8.7)	16
42	*C. tetragonium*	Tryptone + mineral salts	28	8.6 (4.2-8.8)	18
43	*Euglena anabaena*	Peptone	29.5	6.9 (4.5-8.3)	7
44	*E. deses*	Peptone	29.5	7.0 (5.3-8.0)	7
45	*E. gracilis*	Peptone	28.3	6.6 (3.9-9.9)	11
46	*E. klebsii*	Peptone	......	6.5 (5.5-7.5)	4
47	*E. mutabilis*	Peptone	......	3.4-5.4 (2.1-7.7)	27
48	*E. pisciformis*	Peptone	......	(6.0-8.0)	4
49	*E. stellata*	Peptone	......	5.5 (4.5-8.0)	4
50	*E. viridis*	Mineral salts	......	(4.0-7.2)	25
51	*Polytomella caeca*	Peptone	......	(2.2-9.2)	19

Contributors: (a) Corliss, John O., (b) Richards, Oscar W., (c) Wichterman, Ralph

References: [1] Beers, C. D. 1927. J. Morphol. and Physiol. 44:21. [2] Corliss, J. O. 1953. Parasitology 43:49. [3] Darby, H. H. 1929. Arch. Protistenk. 65:1. [4] Dusi, H. 1933. Ann. inst. Pasteur 50:840. [5] Elliott, A. M. 1933. Biol. Bull. 65:45. [6] Elliott, A. M. 1935. Arch. Protistenk. 84:156. [7] Hall, R. P. 1933. Ibid. 79:239. [8] Hall, R. P. 1953. Protozoology. Prentice-Hall, New York. p. 428. [9] Hetherington, A. 1932. Arch. Protistenk. 76:118. [10] Hetherington, A. 1936. Biol. Bull. 70:426. [11] John, T. L. 1931. Ibid. 61:387. [12] Johnson, D. F. 1935. Arch. Protistenk. 86:263. [13] Jones, E. P. 1930. Biol. Bull. 59:274. [14] Kidder, G. W. 1941. Ibid. 80:50. [15] Lengerova-Kucerova, A. 1951. Mem. soc. zool. tchecoslov. 14:207. [16] Loefer, J. B. 1935. Arch. Protistenk. 85:209. [17] Loefer, J. B. 1938. Ibid. 90:185. [18] Loefer, J. B. 1938. Anat. Record 72(suppl.):129. [19] Lwoff, A. 1941. Ann. inst. Pasteur 66:407. [20] Mast, S. O., and D. M. Pace. 1938. J. Exptl. Zool. 79:429. [21] Phelps, A. 1934. Arch. Protistenk. 82:134. [22] Pruthi, H. S. 1926. J. Exptl. Biol. 4:292. [23] Saunders, J. T. 1924. Biol. Revs. Biol. Proc. Cambridge Phil. Soc. 1:249. [24] Schoenborn, H. W. 1949. J. Exptl. Zool. 111:437. [25] Schoenborn, H. W. 1950. Trans. Am. Microscop. Soc. 69:217. [26] Von Dach, H.

continued

148. OPTIMUM pH FOR GROWTH: MICROORGANISMS

Part I: PROTOZOA

1940. Ohio J. Sci. 40:37. [27] Von Dach, H. 1943. Ibid. 43:47. [28] Wichterman, R. 1948. Biol. Bull. 95:272. [29] Wingo, W. J., and N. L. Anderson. 1951. J. Exptl. Zool. 116:571.

Part II: BACTERIA

Classification adapted from Bergey's *Manual of Determinative Bacteriology*, 1957.

	Family and Species	pH	Reference
	(A)	(B)	(C)
	Pseudomonadales		
	Athiorhodaceae		
1	*Rhodopseudomonas palustris*	(6.0-8.5)	1
2	*Rhodospirillum rubrum*	(6.0-8.5)	1
	Nitrobacteraceae		
3	*Nitrobacter agilis*	7.6-8.6 (6.6-10.0)	1
4	*Nitrosomonas* spp.	8.5-8.8 (7.6-9.4)	3
5	*Nitrosospira* spp.	7.0-7.2	1
	Thiobacteriaceae		
6	*Thiobacillus denitrificans*	7.0-9.0 (5.0-10.7)	3
7	*T. thiooxidans*	3.0-5.0 (1.0-9.8)	3
	Pseudomonadaceae		
8	*Photobacterium pierantonii*	9.0	1
9	*Pseudomonas delphinii*	6.7-7.1 (5.6-8.6)	1
10	*P. matthiolae*	(4.4-9.5)	1
11	*P. nigrifaciens*	6.8-8.4	1
12	*P. pyocyanea*	6.6-7.0 (4.4-8.0)	3
13	*P. solanacearum*	6.0 (4.0-8.0)	2
14	*Xanthomonas corylina*	6.0-8.0 (5.2-10.5)	1
15	*X. cucurbitae*	6.5-7.0 (5.8-9.0)	1
16	*X. holcicola*	7.0-7.5 (5.5-9.0)	1
17	*X. juglandis*	6.0-8.0 (5.2-10.5)	1
18	*X. panici*	6.1-6.3 (5.4-10.0)	1
	Spirillaceae		
19	*Desulfovibrio desulfuricans*	6.0-7.5 (5.0-9.0)	1
20	*Methanobacterium omelianskii*	(6.5-8.1)	1
21	*Selenomonas sputigena*	5.5-8.6 (4.5-8.6)	1
22	*Vibrio comma*	7.0-7.4 (5.6-9.6)	3
	Eubacteriales		
	Azotobacteraceae		
23	*Azotobacter chroococcum*	7.4-7.6 (min. 5.8)	3
	Rhizobiaceae		
24	*Agrobacterium tumefaciens*	(5.7-9.2)	3
25	*Rhizobium leguminosarum*	(3.2-11.0)	3
	Achromobacteraceae		
26	*Agarbacterium pastinator*	(5.9-9.0)	1
27	*Alcaligenes faecalis*	8.5 (4.6-9.7)	3
28	*Flavobacterium aquatile*	7.2-7.4 (6.5-7.8)	1
29	*F. ferrugineum*	7.0-7.5 (6.5-9.0)	1
	Enterobacteriaceae		
30	*Aerobacter aerogenes*	6.0 (4.4-9.0)	3
31	*Erwinia amylovora*	6.8 (4.0-8.8)	1
32	*E. carotovora*	(4.6-9.3)	3
33	*Escherichia coli*	6.0-7.0 (4.3-9.5)	3
34	*Proteus vulgaris*	6.5 (4.4-9.2)	3
	Enterobacteriaceae		
35	*Salmonella paratyphi*	6.2-7.2 (4.0-9.6)	3
36	*S. typhosa*	6.8-7.2 (4.0-9.6)	3
37	*Serratia marcescens*	6.0-7.0 (4.6-8.0)	3
38	*Shigella dysenteriae*	ca. 7.0 (4.5-9.6)	3
	Brucellaceae		
39	*Brucella abortus*	7.0-7.2	1
40	*B. melitensis*	6.6-8.2 (6.3-8.4)	3
41	*Noguchia granulosis*	7.8	1
42	*Pasteurella pestis*	6.2-7.0 (5.0-8.2)	3
	Bacteroidaceae		
43	*Bacteroides halosmophilus*	7.4-7.6 (5.5-8.5)	1
44	*Dialister pneumosintes*	7.4-7.8	1
45	*Sphaerophorus necrophorus*	7.5-7.8	1
46	*Streptobacillus moniliformis*	7.0-8.0	1
	Micrococcaceae		
47	*Methanococcus vannielii*	8.0 (7.4-9.2)	1
48	*Micrococcus cryophilus*	6.8-7.2 (5.5-9.5)	1
49	*Sarcina ureae*	ca. 8.8 (6.4-9.4)	1
50	*S. ventriculi*	1.5-5.0 (0.9-9.8)	1
	Neisseriaceae		
51	*Neisseria gonorrhoeae*	7.3 (5.8-8.3)	3
52	*N. meningitidis*	7.4 (6.1-7.8)	3
53	*Veillonella alcalescens*	6.0-8.0	1
54	*V. parvula*	6.5-8.0	1
55	*V. reniformis*	7.0 (6.0-8.0)	1
	Brevibacteriaceae		
56	*Brevibacterium ammoniagenes*	7.0-8.5	1
57	*B. linens*	(6.0-9.8)	1
	Lactobacillaceae		
58	*Diplococcus pneumoniae*	7.8 (7.0-8.3)	3
59	*Lactobacillus pastorianus*	8.0 (max. 9.0)	1
60	*Ramibacterium ramosum*	7.0-8.0	1
61	*Streptococcus faecalis*	6.0-7.0 (max. 11.1)	3
62	*S. liquefaciens*	6.2-7.0 (5.5-8.0)	3
63	*S. pyogenes*	7.8 (4.5-9.2)	3
64	*S. viridans*	6.8-7.8 (4.5-8.0)	3
	Corynebacteriaceae		
65	*Corynebacterium diphtheriae*	7.3-7.5 (6.0-8.3)	3
66	*C. nephridii*	6.2-7.2	1
67	*Erysipelothrix insidiosa*	7.4-7.8	1
	Bacillaceae		
68	*Bacillus anthracis*	7.0-7.4 (6.0-8.5)	3
69	*B. subtilis*	6.0-7.5 (4.5-8.5)	3
70	*Clostridium omelianskii*	(6.0-8.4)	1
71	*C. propionicum*	7.0-7.4 (5.8-8.6)	1
72	*C. sporogenes*	6.5-7.5 (5.0-9.0)	3

continued

148. OPTIMUM pH FOR GROWTH: MICROORGANISMS

Part II: BACTERIA

	Family and Species	pH	Reference
	(A)	(B)	(C)
	Eubacteriales		
	Bacillaceae		
73	*Clostridium tetani*	7.0-7.6 (5.5-8.3)	3
	Actinomycetales		
	Mycobacteriaceae		
74	*Mycobacterium avium*	6.8-7.3	1
75	*M. bovis*	5.8-6.9	1
76	*M. phlei*	6.0 (5.5-8.8)	1
	Mycobacteriaceae		
77	*Mycobacterium tuberculosis*	6.8-7.7 (5.0-8.4)	3
	Actinomycetaceae		
78	*Actinomyces chromogenus*	7.2-7.5 (4.7-9.1)	2
79	*Nocardia corallina*	6.8-8.0	1
80	*N. rubropertincta*	6.8-7.2	1
	Streptomycetaceae		
81	*Streptomyces mirabilis*	6.0-6.6	1
82	*S. scabies*	8.5 (5.4-9.0)	3

Contributors: (a) Thimann, Kenneth V., (b) Stephen, R. C.

References: [1] Breed, R. S., E. G. D. Murray, and N. R. Smith. 1957. Bergey's Manual of determinative bacteriology. Williams and Wilkins, Baltimore. [2] Small, J. 1954. Modern aspects of pH. Baillière, Tindall, and Cox; London. p. 214. [3] Thimann, K. V. 1955. The life of bacteria. Macmillan, New York. p. 144.

Part III: FUNGI

Classification adapted from Ainsworth and Bisby, *Dictionary of the Fungi*, 1961, and from Bessey, *Morphology and Taxonomy of Fungi*, 1950.

	Family and Species	pH	Reference
	(A)	(B)	(C)
	Mycetozoa		
	Plasmodiophoraceae		
1	*Plasmodiophora brassicae*	6.5 (max. 10.0)	4
	Phycomycetes		
	Synchytriaceae		
2	*Synchytrium endobioticum*	5.0-5.1 (3.9-8.5)	4
	Rhizidiaceae		
3	*Chytridium* sp.	5.2-7.5	1
	Entophlyctaceae		
4	*Phlyctorhiza variabilis*	7.2-7.6	1
	Blastocladiaceae		
5	*Blastocladia simplex*	(min. 5.3)	3
	Saprolegniaceae		
6	*Aphanomyces euteiches*	4.5-6.5	1
	Pythiaceae		
7	*Pythiogeton* sp.	6.5	1
8	*Pythium* sp.	(2.5-8.5)	6
9	*P. de baryanum*	5.0-6.0	4
	Mucoraceae		
10	*Mucor glomerula*	(3.2-9.2)	2,5,6
11	*Phycomyces blakesleeanus*	3.6-4.1 (3.0-7.5)	5
	Ascomycetes		
	Sclerotiniaceae		
12	*Sclerotinia sclerotiorum*	3.2	4
	Melanosporaceae		
13	*Melanospora destruens*	(4.8-7.6)	2
14	*Neurospora crassa*	4.3-6.5	1
	Gnomoniaceae		
15	*Glomerella gossypii*	6.0	4
	Diaporthaceae		
16	*Diaporthe sojae*	4.0-5.4 (min. 2.2)	4
17	*Endothia parasitica*	5.7	4
	Nectriaceae		
18	*Gibberella saubinetti*	4.0-4.5 and 7.0 (3.0-8.5)	4
	Pseudosphaeriaceae		
19	*Ophiobolus graminis*	4.9-7.4	1
	Mycosphaerellaceae		
20	*Septoria pepli*	4.8-6.8	1
	Pleosporaceae		
21	*Physalospora baccae*	4.2-7.4 (3.0->10.0)	4
	Aspergillaceae		
22	*Aspergillus flavus*	5.5-8.4	1
23	*A. niger*	4.4-7.5 (2.8-8.8)	1,2,6
24	*A. oryzae*	(1.6-9.3)	2,5,6
25	*A. terricola*	(1.6-9.3)	2,5,6
26	*Penicillium cyclopium*	(<2.8-9.6)	2,6
27	*P. expansum*	4.4-7.5	1
28	*P. glaucum*	5.0-6.5	1
29	*P. italicum*	3.0-6.0 (1.9-9.3)	2,4-6
30	*P. variabile*	(1.6-11.1)	2,3,5,6
	Saccharomycetaceae		
31	*Saccharomyces cerevisiae*	4.0-5.0 (min. 2.4)	5

continued

148. OPTIMUM pH FOR GROWTH: MICROORGANISMS

Part III: FUNGI

	Family and Species	pH	Reference
	(A)	(B)	(C)
	Basidiomycetes		
	Pucciniaceae		
32	*Puccinia graminis*	4.0 and 6.0 (2.5-8.0)	4
	Ustilaginaceae		
33	*Ustilago cruenta*	7.2 (5.0-7.6)	4
34	*U. hordei*	5.0 (5.0-7.5)	4
35	*U. laevis*	7.4 (4.6-8.6)	4
36	*U. sorghi*	6.2 (5.4-8.4)	4
	Thelephoraceae		
37	*Coniophora cerebella*	3.0 (min. 1.9)	3,6
38	*Corticium solani*	2.8-3.9 or 6.2 (2.0-10.4)	4
39	*Stereum gausapatum*	(2.0-8.2)	6
	Meruliaceae		
40	*Merulius confluens*	4.0	1
41	*M. lacrymans*	3.0 (min. 1.0)	3,6
	Polyporaceae		
42	*Daedalea anfragosa*	3.5-6.5 (2.8-7.5)	4
43	*D. confragosa*	(3.5-7.2)	6
44	*Fomes annosus*	4.6-4.9	1
45	*F. fraxineus*	6.0-7.0	1
46	*F. roseus*	3.0 (min. 1.9)	3,6
47	*Lenzites saepiaria*	3.0 (1.9-7.4)	2,3,6
48	*Polyporus adustus*	3.7-6.3 (2.0-8.0)	4,6
49	*Polystictus versicolor*	4.0-5.5 (2.5-7.6)	4,6
	Boletaceae		
50	*Boletus variegatus*	5.0	1
	Agaricaceae		
51	*Armillaria mellea*	3.9 (2.0-7.8)	4,6
52	*Coprinus* sp.	4.8-6.9	1
53	*Marasmius foetidus*	3.1 (2.0-6.8)	5
54	*M. graminum*	5.7-6.4 (3.5-9.0)	1,5
55	*Pholiota adiposa*	4.0-6.0 (2.8-7.5)	4,6
56	*Pleurotus ostreatus*	5.2-6.8 (3.0-8.5)	4,6
57	*Schizophyllum commune*	5.6-6.0 (2.8-8.5)	4,6
58	*Tricholoma nudum*	5.0-6.0	1
	Fungi Imperfecti		
	Melanconiaceae		
59	*Colletotrichum circinans*	(2.6-8.0)	4
60	*Colletotrichum hibisci*	3.5-8.0	1
61	*Gloeosporium lindemuthianium*	4.5 (3.8-7.4)	4
	Moniliaceae		
62	*Botrytis cinerea*	5.0-6.0 (<2.8-10.0)	2,4
63	*Geotrichum* sp.	3.0	1
64	*Mycogone perniciosa*	6.7	1
65	*Trichophyton persicolor*	6.5-7.0	1
66	*Trichosporon cutaneum*	4.0-9.0	1
67	*Verticillium malthousii*	5.3	1
68	*V. psalliotae*	6.7-7.0	1
	Dematiaceae		
69	*Cercospora kikuchii*	4.1	1
70	*Chalara quercina*	4.5	1
71	*Helminthosporium leptochloe*	7.4-9.1 (2.6-11.6)	4
72	*H. monoceras*	6.8 (2.75-9.83)	4
73	*H. oryzae*	8.6-8.8 or 6.6-7.4 (2.5-10.0)	4
	Tuberculariaceae		
74	*Fusarium aquaeductum*	4.0-9.0	1
75	*F. aurantiacum*	6.3-7.0	1
76	*F. bullatum*	(2.0-11.2)	2,5,6
77	*F. culmorum*	4.7 and 6.4 (3.0-10.0)	4
78	*F. lycopersici*	4.5-5.3 and 5.8-6.8 (2.2-8.4)	3,4,6
79	*F. minimum*	5.5 (3.0->9.0)	4
80	*F. oxysporum*	(1.8-11.1)	2,5
81	*F. redolens*	5.0 (3.0-10.0)	4
82	*F. rostratum*	4.5 and 7.0	4
83	*F. solani*	6.0 (3.0-10.0)	4
84	*F. viticola*	4.8 (3.0-10.0)	4
	Mycelia Sterilia[1]		
85	*Rhizoctonia crocorum*	4.2	4
86	*R. solani*	2.8-3.9 (2.5-8.5)	2,4,6
87	*Sclerotium rolfsii*	4.0-10.0 (1.5-10.0)	4

/1/ Class.

Contributors: (a) Stephen, R. C., (b) Thimann, Kenneth V.

References: [1] Cochrane, V. W. 1958. Physiology of fungi. J. Wiley and Sons, New York. p. 20. [2] Hawker, L. E. 1950. Physiology of fungi. Univ. London Press, London. p. 204. [3] Lilly, V. G., and H. L. Barnett. 1951. Physiology of the fungi. McGraw-Hill, New York. pp. 159-160. [4] Small, J. 1954. Modern aspects of pH. Baillière, Tindall, and Cox; London. pp. 214-216. [5] Thimann, K. V. 1955. The life of bacteria. Macmillan, New York. p. 144. [6] Wolf, F. A., and F. T. Wolf. 1949. The fungi. J. Wiley and Sons, New York. v. 2, p. 155.

149. OPTIMUM SOIL pH FOR GROWTH: PLANTS

With good management and if other factors are favorable, many of the plants listed will grow and develop satisfactorily outside the pH range indicated. Field crops and vegetables generally are not as sensitive to soil pH as are flowers and shrubs. Classification adapted from Engler and Diels, *Syllabus der Pflanzenfamilien*, 1936.

	Family and Species	pH	Reference
	(A)	(B)	(C)
	Gymnospermae		
	Ginkgoaceae		
1	*Ginkgo biloba*	5.5-7.0	6
	Taxaceae		
2	*Taxus* spp.	5.0-7.5	6
	Pinaceae		
3	*Abies* spp.	4.5-6.5	6
4	*Larix* spp.	4.5-7.5	6
5	*Picea* spp.	4.5-6.5	6
6	*P. pungens*	5.0-6.5	6
7	*P. sitchensis*	5.0-6.5	6
8	*Pinus* spp.	4.5-6.5	6
9	*P. palustris*	4.5-6.0	6
10	*P. resinosa*	5.0-6.0	4
11	*Pseudotsuga taxifolia*	5.0-6.5	6
12	*Tsuga canadensis*	4.5-6.0	6
	Taxodiaceae		
13	*Taxodium distichum*	6.0-7.5	6
	Cupressaceae		
14	*Chamaecyparis thyoides*	4.5-6.0	6
15	*Juniperus* spp.	5.5-7.5	6
16	*J. communis*	5.0-6.5	6
17	*J. communis saxatilis*	4.5-5.5	6
18	*J. virginiana*	5.0-8.0	6
19	*Thuja occidentalis*	6.0-7.5	4
	Angiospermae (Monocotyledoneae)		
	Gramineae		
20	*Agrostis alba*	5.0-6.5	6
21	*Avena sativa*	5.0-7.5	3,4
22	*Cynodon dactylon*	5.5-7.5	1
23	*Hordeum vulgare*	6.0-7.5	6
24	*Oryza sativa*	5.0-6.5	3,4
25	*Paspalum dilatatum*	6.0-7.0	1
26	*Phleum pratense*	6.0-8.0	4
27	*Poa pratensis*	5.5-7.5	3,4
28	*Saccharum officinarum*	6.0-8.0	3,4
29	*Secale cereale*	5.0-7.0	3,4
30	*Setaria italica*	5.0-6.5	3,4
31	*Sorghum vulgare*	5.5-7.5	3,4
32	*S. vulgare caffrorum*	6.0-7.5	3,4
33	*S. vulgare sudanense*	6.0-7.5	1
34	*Triticum aestivum*	5.5-7.5	3
35	*Zea mays*	5.5-7.5	3,4
	Bromeliaceae		
36	*Ananas comosus*	4.5-6.0	5
	Commelinaceae		
37	*Tradescantia virginiana*	5.0-7.5	4
	Liliaceae		
38	*Allium cepa*	6.0-7.5	6
39	*Asparagus officinalis*	6.0-8.0	4
40	*Hemerocallis* spp.	6.0-8.0	1
41	*Hyacinthus orientalis*	6.0-7.5	6
42	*Lilium longiflorum*	6.0-7.0	4
43	*Tulipa gesneriana*	6.0-7.5	6
	Amaryllidaceae		
44	*Narcissus* spp.	5.0-7.0	1
	Iridaceae		
45	*Gladiolus* spp.	6.0-8.0	1
46	*Iris* spp.	6.0-8.0	1
	Musaceae		
47	*Musa paradisiaca*	5.0-7.5	5
	Cannaceae		
48	*Canna indica*	6.0-8.0	4
	Angiospermae (Dicotyledoneae)		
	Salicaceae		
49	*Populus* spp.	5.5-7.5	6
50	*P. tremuloides*	4.5-5.5	6
51	*Salix* spp.	5.5-7.5	6
52	*S. repens*	4.5-6.0	6
	Juglandaceae		
53	*Carya ovata*	6.0-6.5	6
54	*Juglans* spp.	6.0-7.5	6
	Betulaceae		
55	*Alnus* spp.	6.0-7.5	6
56	*Betula lenta*	4.5-6.0	6
57	*Carpinus* spp.	6.0-7.5	6
58	*Ostrya virginiana*	6.0-7.0	6
	Fagaceae		
59	*Castanea dentata*	4.5-6.5	6
60	*C. pumila*	4.5-6.5	6
61	*Fagus grandifolia*	5.0-6.5	4
62	*F. sylvatica*	6.0-7.5	6
63	*Quercus* spp.[1]	4.5-6.5	6
64	*Q.* spp.[2]	4.5-5.0	6
65	*Q. alba*	6.0-8.0	1
66	*Q. palustris*	6.0-7.0	1
67	*Q. phellos*	4.5-6.5	6
68	*Q. prinus*	6.0-7.0	1
69	*Q. robur*	6.0-7.5	6
	Ulmaceae		
70	*Celtis* spp.	6.0-7.5	6
71	*Ulmus* spp.[3]	6.0-8.0	1
	Moraceae		
72	*Cannabis sativa*	6.0-7.5	6
73	*Morus* spp.	6.0-7.5	6
	Polygonaceae		
74	*Fagopyrum esculentum*	5.5-7.0	3,4
	Chenopodiaceae		
75	*Beta saccharifera*	6.5-8.0	4
76	*B. vulgaris*	6.0-7.5	4
77	*Spinacia oleracea*	6.0-7.5	4
	Caryophyllaceae		
78	*Dianthus caryophyllus*	6.0-7.5	4
	Ranunculaceae		
79	*Clematis* spp.	6.0-7.5	1
80	*Delphinium* spp.	6.0-8.0	1
	Magnoliaceae		
81	*Liriodendron tulipifera*	5.5-7.5	6
82	*Magnolia grandiflora*	5.0-7.0	1
	Cruciferae		
83	*Alyssum* spp.	6.0-8.0	1
84	*Brassica napobrassica*	5.0-7.5	2
85	*B. nigra*	6.0-7.5	4
86	*B. oleracea botrytis*	5.5-7.5	1
87	*B. oleracea capitata*	6.0-7.5	4
88	*B. oleracea gemmifera*	6.0-7.5	1
89	*B. oleracea italica*	6.0-7.0	4
90	*B. rapa*	5.5-7.0	1

/1/ Species include *coccinea, rubra, velutina*. /2/ Species include *falcata, laevis, marilandica, stellata*.
/3/ Species include *americana, parvifolia*.

continued

149. OPTIMUM SOIL pH FOR GROWTH: PLANTS

	Family and Species	pH	Reference
	(A)	(B)	(C)
	Angiospermae (Dicotyledoneae)		
	Cruciferae		
91	*Iberis* spp.	6.0-7.0	1
92	*Lepidium sativum*	6.0-7.0	4
93	*Matthiola incana*	6.0-7.5	4
94	*Raphanus sativus*	5.5-7.0	6
	Crassulaceae		
95	*Kalanchoe blossfeldiana*	6.0-7.5	4
	Hamamelidaceae		
96	*Liquidambar styraciflua*	5.0-6.5	6
	Platanaceae		
97	*Platanus* spp.	5.5-7.5	6
	Rosaceae		
98	*Amelanchier* spp.	5.0-7.5	6
99	*Fragaria* spp.	5.0-6.5	1,4
100	*Prunus cerasus*	6.0-7.0	4
101	*P. glandulosa*	6.0-7.5	6
102	*P. persica*	6.0-7.5	4
103	*P. virginiana*	6.0-7.5	6
104	*Pyrus communis*	6.0-7.5	4
105	*P. malus*	5.0-6.5	4
106	*Rosa hybrida*	5.5-7.0	4
107	*Rubus* spp.[4]	6.0-8.0	1
108	*Sorbus americana*	4.5-6.5	6
109	*S. aucuparia*	5.5-7.5	6
	Leguminosae		
110	*Acacia* spp.	6.5-8.0	6
111	*Anthyllis vulneraria*	5.5-8.0	2
112	*Arachis hypogaea*	5.0-6.5	4
113	*Cercis canadensis*	6.0-7.5	6
114	*Gleditsia triacanthos*	6.0-7.5	6
115	*Glycine soja*	6.0-7.5	6
116	*Gymnocladus dioicus*	6.0-7.5	6
117	*Lespedeza* spp.	5.0-6.5	1
118	*Medicago sativa*	6.2-7.8	3,4
119	*Melilotus alba*	6.0-7.5	6
120	*M. indica*	6.0-7.5	1
121	*Phaseolus limensis*	6.0-7.5	6
122	*P. vulgaris*	6.0-7.5	3,4
123	*Pisum sativum*	6.0-8.0	1
124	*Robinia* spp.	5.5-7.5	6
125	*Trifolium pratense*	6.0-7.5	3,4
126	*T. repens*	5.5-7.5	5
127	*Vicia* spp.	5.5-7.5	1
128	*V. faba equina*	6.0-7.0	4
129	*V. villosa*	5.0-7.0	4
130	*Vigna* spp.[5]	5.5-7.5	1
	Geraniaceae		
131	*Pelargonium domesticum*	6.0-8.0	1,4
	Tropaeolaceae		
132	*Tropaeolum majus*	5.5-7.5	4
	Linaceae		
133	*Linum usitatissimum*	5.0-7.0	3,4
	Rutaceae		
134	*Citrus limon*	6.0-7.5	4
135	*C. paradisi*	6.0-8.0	1
136	*C. sinensis*	6.0-7.5	4
	Simarubaceae		
137	*Ailanthus altissima*	6.0-8.0	6
	Euphorbiaceae		
138	*Ricinus communis*	6.0-7.5	4
	Buxaceae		
139	*Buxus sempervirens*	6.0-7.5	6
	Aquifoliaceae		
140	*Ilex aquifolium*	5.0-6.5	6
141	*I. cornuta*	6.0-7.5	1
142	*I. opaca*	4.5-6.0	6
143	*I. vomitoria*	5.5-7.5	1
	Aceraceae		
144	*Acer* spp.	5.5-7.5	6
145	*A. spicatum*	4.5-6.0	6
	Hippocastanaceae		
146	*Aesculus glabra*	6.0-7.5	6
147	*A. hippocastanum*	5.5-7.0	6
148	*A. pavia*	5.0-6.5	6
	Balsaminaceae		
149	*Impatiens balsamina*	6.0-7.5	4
	Vitaceae		
150	*Vitis* spp.	6.0-8.0	1
	Tiliaceae		
151	*Tilia* spp.	6.0-7.5	6
	Malvaceae		
152	*Althaea* spp.	6.0-8.0	1
153	*Gossypium hirsutum*	5.0-6.5	6
154	*Hibiscus esculentus*	6.0-7.5	1
155	*H. rosa-sinensis*	6.0-8.0	4
	Theaceae		
156	*Camellia japonica*	4.5-6.0	6
	Violaceae		
157	*Viola* spp.	6.0-7.5	1
	Begoniaceae		
158	*Begonia* spp.	5.5-7.0	6
	Nyssaceae		
159	*Nyssa sylvatica*	4.5-6.0	6
	Myrtaceae		
160	*Eucalyptus* spp.	6.5-8.0	6
	Oenotheraceae		
161	*Oenothera biennis*	6.0-8.0	4
	Araliaceae		
162	*Hedera helix*	6.0-8.0	4
	Umbelliferae		
163	*Apium graveolens dulce*	6.0-7.5	6
164	*Daucus carota*	5.5-7.0	4
165	*Petroselinum hortense*	5.0-7.0	4
	Cornaceae		
166	*Cornus florida*	5.0-6.5	6
	Ericaceae		
167	*Kalmia latifolia*	4.5-6.0	6
168	*Rhododendron obtusum amoenum*	4.5-6.0	4
169	*Vaccinium erythrocarpum*	4.5-6.0	4
	Oleaceae		
170	*Ligustrum* spp.	6.0-7.5	1
	Loganiaceae		
171	*Buddleia* spp.	6.0-8.0	1
	Convolvulaceae		
172	*Ipomoea batatas*	5.0-6.5	6
	Boraginaceae		
173	*Heliotropium* spp.	6.0-8.0	1
	Labiatae		
174	*Coleus blumei*	6.0-7.5	6
	Solanaceae		
175	*Capsicum annuum*	5.5-7.0	1
176	*Datura stramonium*	6.0-7.5	4
177	*Lycopersicon esculentum*	5.5-7.5	4
178	*Nicotiana tabacum*	5.5-7.5	3,4
179	*Petunia* spp.	6.0-8.0	1
180	*Solanum tuberosum*	5.0-6.5	3,4

/4/ Most varieties. /5/ Many varieties.

continued

149. OPTIMUM SOIL pH FOR GROWTH: PLANTS

	Family and Species	pH	Reference
	(A)	(B)	(C)
	Angiospermae (Dicotyledoneae)		
	Scrophulariaceae		
181	*Antirrhinum majus*	6.0-7.5	4
182	*Paulownia tomentosa*	5.5-7.5	6
	Bignoniaceae		
183	*Catalpa* spp.	6.0-7.5	6
	Gesneriaceae		
184	*Saintpaulia ionantha*	5.5-7.0	6
	Rubiaceae		
185	*Gardenia jasminoides*	5.0-7.0	1
	Caprifoliaceae		
186	*Abelia* spp.	6.0-8.0	1
	Cucurbitaceae		
187	*Citrullus vulgaris*	5.0-6.5	6
	Cucurbitaceae		
188	*Cucumis melo*	6.0-8.0	1
189	*C. sativus*	5.5-7.0	4
190	*Cucurbita maxima*	5.5-7.0	4
191	*C. pepo*	5.5-7.0	1
	Compositae		
192	*Calendula* spp.	6.0-8.0	1
193	*Callistephus chinensis*	6.0-7.5	6
194	*Chrysanthemum morifolium*	6.0-7.5	4
195	*Dahlia* spp.	6.0-8.0	1
196	*Gaillardia* spp.	6.0-8.0	1
197	*Helianthus annuus*	6.0-7.5	3,4
198	*H. tuberosus*	6.5-7.5	4
199	*Lactuca sativa*	6.0-7.5	6
200	*Zinnia* spp.	6.0-8.0	1

Contributors: (a) Walker, Richard B., (b) Wherry, Edgar T., (c) Bennett, W. F., (d) Thornton, M. K., (e) Larsen, Sigurd.

References: [1] Bennett, W. F. 1953. Texas Agr. Extension Service Leaflet L-164. [2] Dorph-Petersen, K. 1947. Tidsskr. Planteavl 51:1. [3] Ignatieff, V. 1949. Food and Agr. Organization U. N. Studies 9:108. [4] Spurway, C. H. 1941. Mich. State Coll. Agr. Expt. Sta. Spec. Bull. 396. [5] Sutton, C. D. Unpublished. Levington Research Station, Ipswich, England, 1962. [6] Wherry, E. T. Unpublished. Univ. Pennsylvania, Philadelphia, 1954.

150. EFFECT OF HYDROSTATIC PRESSURE ON EGG CELL DIVISION: VERTEBRATES AND INVERTEBRATES

	Phylum and Species	Temp. °C	Pressure		Result of Compression	Reference
			lbs per sq inch	atmospheres		
	(A)	(B)	(C)	(D)	(E)	(F)
	Chordata					
1	*Rana pipiens*	5	2000	135	Cleavage-inhibiting pressure increased with temperature	5, 6
2		10	2500	170		
3		15	3000	200		
4		20	3500	235		
5		25	4000	270		
6	*Ciona intestinalis*	.....	3000	200	Cleavage blocked	8
	Echinodermata					
7	*Arbacia amoebocytes*	.....	6000	400	Reversible regression of cleavage furrows; reversible solation of cortical plasmagel	2
8	*A. lixula*	10	2000	135	Cleavage-inhibiting pressure increased with temperature	5, 6
9		15	3000	200		
10		20	4000	270		
11		25	5000	330		
12	*A. punctulata*	10	3000	200	Cleavage-inhibiting pressure increased with temperature	3, 6
13		15	4000	270		
14		20	5000	330		
15		25	6000	400		
16		30	7000	470		
17	*A. pustulosa*	.....	<5000	<330	Cleavage blocked	8
18	*Echinarachnius parma*	5	3000	230	Cleavage-inhibiting pressure increased with temperature	1, 6
19		10	4000	270		
20		15	5000	330		
21		20	6000	400		
22	*Paracentrotus lividus*	Room	5000	330	Cleavage blocked	8

continued

150. EFFECT OF HYDROSTATIC PRESSURE ON EGG CELL DIVISION: VERTEBRATES AND INVERTEBRATES

	Phylum and Species	Temp. °C	Pressure		Result of Compression	Reference
			lbs per sq inch	atmospheres		
	(A)	(B)	(C)	(D)	(E)	(F)
	Echinodermata					
23	*Psammechinus microtuberculatus*	Room	<5000	<330	Cleavage blocked	8
24	*Sphaerechinus granularis*	Room	6000	400	Cleavage blocked	8
	Arthropoda					
25	*Drosophila melanogaster*	.....	5000-6000	330-400	Pole cell formation blocked	8
	Annelida					
26	*Chaetopterus pergamentaceus*	20	2000	135	Cleavage-inhibiting pressure increased with temperature	5, 6
27		25	2500	170		
28		30	3000	200		
	Echiuroidea					
29	*Urechis* sp.	.....	4500-6000	300-400	Reversible solation of spindles and asters; movements of chromosomes stopped	7
	Mollusca					
30	*Cumingia tellenoides*	Room	4000-5000	270-330	Cleavage blocked	8
31	*Planorbis* sp.	Room	3500	235	Cleavage blocked	8
32	*Solen siliqua*	Room	3000	200	Cleavage blocked	8
	Aschelminthes					
33	*Ascaris megalocephala* (univalens)	Room	>12,000	>800	Exceptionally resistant to pressure; division not inhibited	8
	Protozoa					
34	*Amoeba dubia*	.....	6000	400	Cleavage blocked; movement stopped	4, 8
35	*A. proteus*	.....	6000	400	Cleavage blocked; movement stopped	4, 8

Contributors: (a) Marsland, Douglas A., (b) Pease, Daniel C.

References: [1] Landau, J. V., and D. A. Marsland. 1950. Anat. Record 108:574. [2] Marsland, D. A. 1939. J. Cellular Comp. Physiol. 13:15. [3] Marsland, D. A. 1950. Ibid. 36:205. [4] Marsland, D. A., and D. E. S. Brown. 1936. Ibid. 8:167. [5] Marsland, D. A., and J. V. Landau. 1952. Anat. Record 113:582. [6] Marsland, D. A., and J. V. Landau. 1954. J. Exptl. Zool. 125:507. [7] Pease, D. C. 1941. Biol. Bull. 91:145. [8] Pease, D. C., and D. A. Marsland. 1939. J. Cellular Comp. Physiol. 14(suppl.):1.

XIII. GROWTH REGULATORS AND INHIBITORS

151. ORGANIC COMPOUNDS AFFECTING CELL DIVISION: ANIMALS AND PLANTS

Part I: EFFECT ON MITOSIS AND MEIOSIS

Phase (column D): I = interphase, T = telophase, M = metaphase, A = anaphase, P = prophase, NCP = not confined to one phase.

	Organism	Tissue	Substance	Cell Division		Reference
				Phase	Effect of Substance	
	(A)	(B)	(C)	(D)	(E)	(F)
1	*Mus* sp.	Epidermis	Glucose	I	Shortened	8
2		Intestine	Folic acid antagonists, hydroquinone, urethane	I	Pycnosis from preprophase damage	23,24
3		Tumor	Azaguanine	I	Initiation of prophase inhibited	66
4	*Rattus* sp.	Corneal epithelium	Nitrogen mustard	I	Initiation of prophase inhibited	26
5	*Oryctolagus cuniculus*	Fibroblast	Testosterone estrone	M	Abnormal chromosome orientation	60
6			Trypaflavin	A	Incomplete chromosome separation	6
7			Trypan blue	P	Spindle formation slowed	61
8			Urethane	P	Accelerated	7
9	*Gallus domesticus*	Fibroblast	Acridines	I	Initiation of prophase inhibited	37
10			Aureomycin	T	Cytoplasmic division suppressed	33
11			Thiourea	T	Nuclear reconstruction retarded	54
12		Osteoblast	Chloroacetophenone	T	Nuclear reconstruction retarded	32
13			Hypoxanthine	I	Shortened	31
14	*Rana* sp.	Sperm	Dyes	I	Initiation of prophase inhibited	5
15	*Arbacia punctulata*	Egg	Nitrophenols	P	Blocked	11
16			Phenylurethane	M	Monopolar mitotic figure induced	50
17			Purines	P	Reversion to interphase	14
18			Rotenone	T	Cytoplasmic division suppressed	53
19	*Echinarachnius parma*	Egg	Ryanodine	A	Incomplete chromosome separation	13
20	*Lytechinus variegatus*	Egg	Carbamates	T	Cytoplasmic division suppressed	12
21	*Tripneustes esculentus*	Egg	Carbamates	T	Cytoplasmic division suppressed	12
22	*Drosophila* sp.	Salivary glands	Urea	NCP	Chromosome dispersion and despiralization	51
23	*Tubifex* sp.	Egg	Quinone	T	Cytoplasmic division suppressed	38
24	*Clymenella torquata*	Regenerating tissue	Sulfhydryl	NCP	Chromosomes widened	30
25			Sulfoxide	NCP	Chromosomes widened	30
26	*Amoeba proteus*	Whole organism	Glutathione	P	Accelerated	10
27	Protozoa	Whole organism	Cysteine	NCP	Chromosome reduction induced	57
28	Saccharomycetaceae	....	Sulfhydryl compounds	T	Cytoplasmic division augmented	45
29	Spermatophyta	Cambium	Auxin	I	Shortened	58
30	*Allium cepa*	Root	Acenapthene	NCP	Chromosome breaks; centromere misdivision	18
31			Acridines	P	Reversion to interphase	16
32			Acridines	NCP	Chromosome breaks	16
33			Acridines	NCP	Pseudochiasmata	18
34			Alcohol	M	Nucleolus neoformation	59
35			Aminoacridine	NCP	Chromosome breaks	24
36			Aminobenzoate	NCP	Chromosome breaks	24
37			Antibiotics	NCP	Chromosome reduction induced	64
38			Aureomycin	P	Membrane dissolution delayed	64
39			*n*-Butyl gallate	NCP	Chromosome adhesion	40
40			Caffeine	A	Incomplete chromosome separation	42
41			Caffeine	T	Cytoplasmic division suppressed	29
42			Colchicine	M	Monopolar mitotic figure induced	27
43			Cortisone	I	Differentiated cell nuclei induced to divide	19
44			Coumarin	NCP	Chromosome breaks; pseudochiasmata	48
45			DDT	M	Nucleolus neoformation	59
46			Dichlorophenoxyacetic acid	P	Blocked	17

continued

151. ORGANIC COMPOUNDS AFFECTING CELL DIVISION: ANIMALS AND PLANTS

Part I: EFFECT ON MITOSIS AND MEIOSIS

	Organism	Tissue	Substance	Cell Division		Reference
				Phase	Effect of Substance	
	(A)	(B)	(C)	(D)	(E)	(F)
47	*Allium cepa*	Root	Diethyl bromacetyl carbamide	M	Multipolar spindle induced	49
48			Dyes	NCP	Chromosome adhesion	3
49			Ethoxycaffeine	NCP	Chromosome rearrangements	34
50			Indoleacetic acid	I	Differentiated cell nuclei induced to divide	19
51			Methyl naphthohydroquinone diacetate	M	Multipolar spindle induced	46
52			Methyl naphthoquinone	M	Abnormal chromosome orientation	46
53			Mustards	NCP	Chromosome rearrangements	20
54			Narcotics	M	Monopolar mitotic figure induced	49
55			Neotetrazolium	I	Pycnosis from preprophase damage	56
56			Nucleic acid	NCP	Chromosome reduction induced	1
57			Phenols	NCP	Chromosome breaks	39
58			Phenylacetic acid	I	Initiation of prophase inhibited	15
59			Streptomycin	M	Reversion to interphase	64
60			Sulfanilamide	T	Cytoplasmic division suppressed	4
61			Thallium acetate	M	Chromosome non-congregation	2
62			Theobromine	T	Cytoplasmic division suppressed	29
63			Trypaflavin	I	Destruction of interphase nucleus	52
64			Uracil	NCP	Chromosome breaks	22
65	*Triticum* sp.	Root	Diphenyl	M	Spindle rotation	28
66			Indoleacetic acid	M	Spindle rotation	9
67	*Zea mays*	Root	Protoanemonin	P	Blocked	25
68		Seedling	Ethylmercuric phosphate	M	Multipolar spindle induced	55
69	*Impatiens* sp.	Pollen mother cell	Ammonium thiocyanate	NCP	Chromosome dispersion and despiralization	36
70	*Nicotiana tabacum*	Anther	Nicotine	T	Cytoplasmic division suppressed	35
71		Pith	Indoleacetic acid	I	Chromosome doubling within nucleus	43
72	*Paeonia tenuifolia*	Bud	Urethane	NCP	Chromosome rearrangements	47
73	*Phaseolus* sp.	Internodes	Naphthaleneacetic acid	I	Differentiated cell nuclei induced to divide	19
74	*Pisum* sp.	Seedling	Nicotine	T	Spindle remnant persists	44
75	*P. sativum*	Root	Endothal	M	Chromosome non-congregation	65
76	*Tradescantia* sp.	Stamen hair	Ammonia	NCP	Chromosome dispersion and despiralization	62
77			Tropolones	P	Precocious chromosome split	63
78		Pollen mother cell	Mustard	NCP	Centromere misdivision	20
79	*Vicia faba*	Root	Epoxides	NCP	Chromosome rearrangements	41
80			Urethane	NCP	Chromosome breaks	21

Contributors: (a) Cornman, Ivor, (b) D'Amato, Francesco

References: [1] Allen, N. S., G. B. Wilson, and S. Powell. 1950. J. Heredity 41:159. [2] Avanzi, S. 1956. Caryologia 9:131. [3] Battaglia, E. 1950. Ibid. 2:223. [4] Bauch, R. 1949. Pharmazie 4:1. [5] Briggs, R. 1952. J. Gen. Physiol. 35:761. [6] Bucher, O. 1939. Z. Zellforsch. u. mikroskop. Anat. 29:283. [7] Bucher, O. 1949. Helv. Physiol. et Pharmacol. Acta 7:37. [8] Bullough, W. S. 1952. Biol. Revs. Cambridge Phil. Soc. 27:133. [9] Burström, H. 1942. Lantbruks-Högskol. Ann. 10:209. [10] Chalkley, H. W. 1951. Ann. N. Y. Acad. Sci. 51:1303. [11] Clowes, G. H. A. 1951. Ibid. 51:1409. [12] Cornman, I. 1950. J. Natl. Cancer Inst. 10:1123. [13] Cornman, I. 1951. Exptl. Cell Research 2:256. [14] Cornman, I. Unpublished, 1953. [15] D'Amato, F. 1949. Caryologia 1:109. [16] D'Amato, F. 1950. Ibid. 2:229. [17] D'Amato, F. 1950. Protoplasma 39:423. [18] D'Amato, F. 1950. Pubbl. staz. zool. Napoli 22(suppl.):158. [19] D'Amato, F. 1952. Caryologia 4:311. [20] Darlington, C. D., and P. C. Koller. 1947. Heredity 1:187. [21] Deufel, J. 1951. Chromosoma 4:239. [22] Deysson, M. 1952. Compt. rend. 234:650. [23] Dustin, P. 1947. Nature 159:794. [24] Dustin, P., Jr.

continued

Part I: EFFECT ON MITOSIS AND MEIOSIS

1950. Compt. rend. soc. biol. 144:1297. [25] Erickson, R. O., and G. U. Rosen. 1949. Am. J. Botany 35:317. [26] Friedenwald, J. S. 1951. Ann. N. Y. Acad. Sci. 51:1432. [27] Gaulden, M. E., and J. G. Carlson. 1951. Exptl. Cell Research 2:416. [28] Gavaudan, P. 1942. Compt. rend. soc. biol. 136:419. [29] Gosselin, A. 1940. Compt. rend. 210:544. [30] Hammett, F. S. 1934. Protoplasma 22:173. [31] Hopkins, F. G., and I. Simon-Reuss. 1944. Proc. Roy. Soc. (London), B, 132:253. [32] Hughes, A. F. W. 1950. Quart. J. Microscop. Sci. 91:251. [33] Keilova-Rodova, H. 1950. Experientia 6:428. [34] Kihlman, B. 1950. Exptl. Cell Research 1:135. [35] Kostoff, D. 1931. Bull. soc. botan. Bulgarie 4:87. [36] Kuwada, Y., N. Shinke, and G. Oura. 1938. Z. wiss. Mikroskop. 55:8. [37] Lasnitzki, I., and J. H. Wilkinson. 1948. Brit. J. Cancer 2:369. [38] Lehmann, F.-E. 1949. Exptl. Cell Research, Suppl. 1:156. [39] Levan, A., and J. H. Tjio. 1948. Hereditas 34:453. [40] Lopane, F. 1950. Caryologia 2:143. [41] Loveless, A. 1951. Nature 167:338. [42] Mangenot, G., and S. Carpentier. 1944. Compt. rend. soc. biol. 138:232. [43] Naylor, J., G. Sandor, and S. Skoog. 1954. Physiol. Plantarum 7:25. [44] Nemec, B. 1929. Protoplasma 7:99. [45] Nickerson, W. J., and J. W. van Rij. 1949. Biochim. et Biophys. Acta 3:461. [46] Nybom, N., and B. Knutsson. 1947. Hereditas 33:220. [47] Oehlkers, F., and H. Marquardt. 1950. Z. induktive Abstammungs.- u. Vererbungslehre 83:299. [48] Östergren, G. 1948. Botan. Notiser (4):376. [49] Östergren, G. 1950. Hereditas 36:371. [50] Painter, T. S. 1918. J. Exptl. Zool. 24:445. [51] Painter, T. S. 1944. Ibid. 96:53. [52] Resende, F. 1951. Bol. soc. Port. cienc. nat. 18:182. [53] Rogers, E. F., and I. Cornman. 1951. Biol. Bull. 101:227. [54] Rosin, A., E. Tenenbaum, and F. Doljanski. 1951. Anat. Record 111:239. [55] Sass, J. E. 1938. Am. J. Botany 25:624. [56] Sonnenblick, B. P., W. Antopol, and L. Goldman. 1950. Trans. N. Y. Acad. Sci., Ser. 2, 12:161. [57] Straub, J. 1951. Biol. Zentr. 70:24. [58] Thimann, K. V. 1938. Physiol. Revs. 18:524. [59] Vaarama, A. 1947. Hereditas 33:191. [60] Von Möllendorff, W. 1939. Z. Zellforsch. u. mikroskop. Anat. 29:706. [61] Von Möllendorff, W., and M. Ostrouch. 1939. Ibid. 29:323. [62] Wada, B. 1937. Cytologia (Tokyo), Fujii jubilaei vol. (2):785. [63] Wada, B. 1952. Ibid. 17:14. [64] Wilson, G. B., and C. C. Bowen. 1951. J. Heredity 42:251. [65] Wilson, S. M., A. Daniel, and G. B. Wilson. 1956. Ibid. 47:151. [66] Woodside, G. L., et al. 1951. Anat. Record 111:501.

Part II: METAPHASE BLOCKING AGENTS

	Organism	Tissue	Substance	Concentration	Reference
	(A)	(B)	(C)	(D)	(E)
1	Mammalia	Marrow	Benzene	....	10
2	*Homo sapiens*	Cell strain (culture)	Vincaleukoblastine	0.01 µg/ml	31
3	*H. sapiens* (embryo)	Connective (culture)	Vincaleukoblastine	0.01 µg/ml	31
4	*Mus* sp.	Ascites cells	Vincaleukoblastine	1.0 mg/kg	7
5	*Rattus* sp.	Bone marrow	Vincaleukoblastine	1.0 mg/kg	7
6	*Oryctolagus cuniculus*	Fibroblast	Nicotine	1/8000	2
7	*Gallus domesticus* (embryo)	Fibroblast	Aureomycin	100 ppm	20
8		Fibroblast	Dibenzanthracene	0.1%	25
9		Heart fibroblast	Epinephrine	0.01%	21
10		Iris epithelium	Morphine	10^{-4} M	37
11	*Arbacia punctulata*	Egg	Coumarin	0.1%	5
12			DDT	Saturated	32
13			Physostigmine	0.1%	1
14	*Echinarachnius parma*	Egg	Podophyllotoxin	10^{-4} mM	6
15	*Paracentrotus lividus*	Egg	*p*-Dichlorobenzene	Saturated	15
16			Ethyl-*p*-aminobenzoate	Saturated	15
17			Methyl anthranilate	Saturated	15
18			Sulfanilamide	....	38
19	*Sphaerechinus granularis*	Egg	Hexachlorocyclohexane	0.02%	4
20	*Strongylocentrotus lividus*	Egg	Phenylurethane	2×10^{3} M	30
21	*Tubifex* sp.	Egg	Naphthoquinone	0.5 M	18
22	*Chortophaga viridifasciata*	Neuroblast	Colchicine	10^{-5} M	13

continued

151. ORGANIC COMPOUNDS AFFECTING CELL DIVISION: ANIMALS AND PLANTS

Part II: METAPHASE BLOCKING AGENTS

	Organism	Tissue	Substance	Concentration	Reference
	(A)	(B)	(C)	(D)	(E)
23	*Drosophila melanogaster*	....	Acenaphthene	Vapor	42
24	*Allium cepa*	Root	Aureomycin	50 ppm	41
25			Colchicine	....	22
26			Coumarin	Saturated	29
27			DDT	Saturated	40
28			Ethyl-*p*-aminobenzoate	4×10^{-2} M	8
29			Naphthoquinone	10^{-3} M	28
30			Phenylurethane	0.02%	9
31			Physostigmine	0.05%	26
32			Podophyllotoxin	Saturated	36
33			Sulfanilamide	1/2000	35
34	*A. sativum*	Root	Benzene	Saturated	27
35	*Colchicum* sp.	Root	Acenaphthene	Saturated	23
36	*C. autumnale*	Root	Colchicine	20%	24
37	*Secale cereale*	Root	Dibenzanthracene	1.5 ppm	39
38	*Triticum vulgare*	Root	Apiol	Vapor	33
39			α-Bromonaphthalene	Vapor	14
40			*p*-Dichlorobenzene	Vapor	16
41	*Cucurbita pepo*	Root	Hexachlorocyclohexane	10^{-4} M	17
42	*Linum usitatissimum*	....	Methyl anthranilate	Vapor	34
43	*Nicotiana tabacum*	Bud	Nicotine	Vapor	19
44	*Tradescantia occidentalis*	Pollen tube	Epinephrine	1/100	11
45	*Vicia faba*	Root	Aurantia	4 ppm	12
46	*V. lutea*	Root	Morphine	0.1%	3

Contributors: (a) Cornman, Ivor, (b) D'Amato, Francesco, (c) Biesele, John J.

References: [1] Balzer, D. T., and C. A. Villee. 1951. Biol. Bull. 101:204. [2] Bucher, O. 1945. Bull. schweiz. Akad. med. Wiss. 1:252. [3] Carpio, D. A. 1949. Genet. iberica 1:41. [4] Chaix, P., and L. Lacroix. 1948. Biochim. et Biophys. Acta 2:86. [5] Cornman, I. Unpublished, 1953. [6] Cornman, I., and M. E. Cornman. 1951. Ann. N. Y. Acad. Sci. 51:1443. [7] Cutts, J. H. 1961. Cancer Research 21:168. [8] D'Amato, F. 1948. Caryologia 1:49. [9] Deysson, G. 1944. Compt. rend. 219:366. [10] Dustin, A.-P. 1931. Compt. rend. soc. biol. 107:1567. [11] Eigsti, O. J. 1940. Am. J. Botany 27 (suppl.):15. [12] Fischer, H. E. 1956. Z. Pflanzenzücht. 36:81. [13] Gaulden, M. E., and J. G. Carlson. 1951. Exptl. Cell Research 2:416. [14] Gavaudan, P., and N. Gavaudan. 1939. Compt. rend. soc. biol. 131:998. [15] Gavaudan, P., and N. Gavaudan. 1942. Ibid. 136:237. [16] Gavaudan, P., N. Gavaudan, and J.-F. Durand. 1939. Ibid. 130:1443. [17] Hopkins, H. T. 1952. Plant Physiol. 27:526. [18] Huber, W. 1945. Rev. suisse zool. 52:354. [19] Kostoff, D. 1931. Bull. soc. botan. Bulgarie 4:87. [20] Lépine, P., G. Barski, and J. Maurin. 1950. Proc. Soc. Exptl. Biol. Med. 73:252. [21] Lettré, H., and M. Albrecht. 1941. Hoppe-Seyler's Z. physiol. Chem. 271:200. [22] Levan, A. 1938. Hereditas 24:471. [23] Levan, A. 1940. Ibid. 26:262. [24] Levan, A., and E. Steinegger. 1947. Ibid. 33:552. [25] Lewis, M. R. 1935. Am. J. Cancer 25:305. [26] Mascré, M., and G. Deysson. 1944. Bull. soc. botan. France 91:206. [27] Meites, M. 1944. Mém. sec. sci. acad. sci. let. Montpellier, Ser. 3, 4. [28] Nybom, N., and B. Knutsson. 1947. Hereditas 33:220. [29] Östergren, G. 1948. Botan. Notiser (4):376. [30] Painter, T. S. 1918. J. Exptl. Zool. 24:445. [31] Palmer, C. G., et al. 1960. Exptl. Cell Research 20:198. [32] Rogers, E. F., and I. Cornman. 1951. Biol. Bull. 101:227. [33] Shmuck, A., and A. Gusseva. 1934. Compt. rend. acad. sci. U.R.S.S. 24:441. [34] Simonet, M., and G. Igolen. 1940. Compt. rend. 210:510. [35] Stoll, R. 1943. Compt. rend. soc. biol. 137:170. [36] Sullivan, B. J., and H. I. Wechsler. 1947. Science 105:433. [37] Taizo, K. 1939. Arch. exptl. Zellforsch. Gewebezücht. 23:253. [38] Thomas, J.-A. 1942. Compt. rend. soc. biol. 136:789. [39] Thomas, P. T., and R. Drew. 1943. Nature 152:564. [40] Vaarama, A. 1947. Hereditas 33:191. [41] Wilson, G. B., and C. C. Bowen. 1951. J. Heredity 42:251. [42] Zivin, M. O. 1946. Compt. rend. acad. sci. U.R.S.S. 52:351.

152. RELATIVE ACTIVITY OF GROWTH REGULATORS: PLANTS

Part I: CELL ELONGATION OF OAT COLEOPTILES

Elongation effect was determined by floating 15 apical sections (3 mm in length) of decapitated *Avena* coleoptiles, 90-92 hours old, on the surface of 25 ml of solution in a covered Petri dish, at 24°C for 24 hours. Where concentrations greater than 10^{-5} M were required for an elongation of 0.15 mm, the pH of the solutions was adjusted to 5.6 with NaOH. Activity Index = $\frac{\text{molar concentration of indole-3-acetic acid inducing an elongation of 0.15 mm}}{\text{molar concentration of growth regulator inducing an elongation of 0.15 mm}}$ x 100.

	Compound (A)	Activity Index (B)
	Indole acids	
1	Indole-3-acetic acid ($5 \cdot 10^{-8}$ M)	100
2	Indole-3-acetonitrile	250
3	4-Chloroindole-3-acetic acid	140
4	4,7-Dichloro-2-methylindole-3-acetic acid	0.1
5	5,7-Dichloro-2-methylindole-3-acetic acid	1.5
6	5-Fluoroindole-3-acetic acid	50
7	6-Fluoroindole-3-acetic acid	100
8	5-Hydroxyindole-3-acetic acid	0.5
9	2-Methylindole-3-acetic acid	1.5
10	Indole-3-butyric acid	15
11	Indole-3-propionic acid	1.5
	Phenoxy acids	
12	Phenoxyacetic acid	0.03
13	2-Acetylphenoxyacetic acid	0
14	3-Acetylphenoxyacetic acid	0.02
15	4-Acetylphenoxyacetic acid	0
16	3-Aminophenoxyacetic acid	0.005
17	4-Aminophenoxyacetic acid	0.02
18	2-Bromophenoxyacetic acid	0.1
19	3-Bromophenoxyacetic acid	2.5
20	4-Bromophenoxyacetic acid	1.5
21	2,4-Dibromophenoxyacetic acid	12.5
22	2,6-Dibromophenoxyacetic acid	0
23	2,4,6-Tribromophenoxyacetic acid	0
24	3-Carboxyphenoxyacetic acid	0
25	4-Carboxyphenoxyacetic acid	0
26	2-Chlorophenoxyacetic acid	0.06
27	3-Chlorophenoxyacetic acid	2
28	4-Chlorophenoxyacetic acid	5
29	2,4-Dichlorophenoxyacetic acid	50
30	2,6-Dichlorophenoxyacetic acid	0
31	3,5-Dichlorophenoxyacetic acid	0
32	2,4,5-Trichlorophenoxyacetic acid	25
33	2,4,6-Trichlorophenoxyacetic acid	0
34	2,4-Dichloro-6-methylphenoxyacetic acid	0
35	2,4-Dichloro-5-nitrophenoxyacetic acid	0.2
36	3-Cyanophenoxyacetic acid	0.02
37	4-Cyanophenoxyacetic acid	0
38	2-Ethyl-4-chlorophenoxyacetic acid	0
39	2-Fluorophenoxyacetic acid	0
40	3-Fluorophenoxyacetic acid	0.02
41	4-Fluorophenoxyacetic acid	5
42	2,4-Difluorophenoxyacetic acid	2
43	2-Trifluoromethylphenoxyacetic acid	0
44	3-Trifluoromethylphenoxyacetic acid	7
45	3-Pentafluorosulfurphenoxyacetic acid	1
46	3-Hydroxyphenoxyacetic acid	0.07
47	4-Hydroxyphenoxyacetic acid	0.01
48	2-Iodophenoxyacetic acid	0.1
49	3-Iodophenoxyacetic acid	7
50	4-Iodophenoxyacetic acid	0
51	2,4-Diiodophenoxyacetic acid	0
52	2-Isopropylphenoxyacetic acid	0
53	2-Methoxyphenoxyacetic acid	0
54	3-Methoxyphenoxyacetic acid	0.1
55	4-Methoxyphenoxyacetic acid	0.03
	Phenoxy acids	
56	2-Methylphenoxyacetic acid	0.2
57	3-Methylphenoxyacetic acid	0.07
58	4-Methylphenoxyacetic acid	0.05
59	2,4-Dimethylphenoxyacetic acid	0.5
60	2,5-Dimethylphenoxyacetic acid	0.2
61	3,5-Dimethylphenoxyacetic acid	0
62	2,4,6-Trimethylphenoxyacetic acid	0
63	2-Methyl-4-chlorophenoxyacetic acid	25
64	3-Methylsulfonylphenoxyacetic acid	0
65	2-Nitrophenoxyacetic acid	0
66	3-Nitrophenoxyacetic acid	0.2
67	4-Nitrophenoxyacetic acid	0.1
68	2,4-Dinitrophenoxyacetic acid	0
69	2-Phenylphenoxyacetic acid	0
70	4-Phenylphenoxyacetic acid	0
71	α-Methyl-γ-phenoxybutyric acid	0
72	γ-Phenoxybutyronitrile	0
73	α-Phenoxypropionic acid	0.5
	Phenyl compounds	
74	Phenylacetic acid	1
75	α-Aminophenylacetic acid	0
76	4-Aminophenylacetic acid	0.05
77	4-Chlorophenylacetic acid	1
78	3-Fluorophenylacetic acid	1.5
79	4-Fluorophenylacetic acid	1.5
80	2,5-Dihydroxyphenylacetic acid	0.02
81	3-Iodophenylacetic acid	10
82	4-Iodophenylacetic acid	0
83	2,4-Dimethylphenylacetic acid	0.5
84	3,5-Dimethylphenylacetic acid	0.5
85	2,4,6-Trimethylphenylacetic acid	0
86	4-Nitrophenylacetic acid	0
87	4-Phenylphenylacetic acid	0
88	Diphenylacetic acid	0
89	Phenylacetonitrile	2
90	γ-Phenylbutyric acid	1.5
91	*N*-Phenylglycine	0.05
92	4-Chlorophenylglycine	1
93	Phenylpropiolic acid	0
94	2-Chlorophenylpropiolic acid	0
95	3-Chlorophenylpropiolic acid	0
96	4-Chlorophenylpropiolic acid	0
97	β-Phenylpropionic acid	0
98	*S*-Phenylthioglycolic acid	0.07
99	4-Chlorophenylthioglycolic acid	0.5
	Benzoic acids	
100	Benzoic acid	0
101	2-Acetoxybenzoic acid	0
102	2-Aminobenzoic acid	0
103	2-Amino-3,5-diiodobenzoic acid	0
104	2-Bromobenzoic acid	0.1
105	3-Bromobenzoic acid	0
106	4-Bromobenzoic acid	0
107	2-Chlorobenzoic acid	0.05
108	3-Chlorobenzoic acid	0
109	4-Chlorobenzoic acid	0

continued

152. RELATIVE ACTIVITY OF GROWTH REGULATORS: PLANTS

Part I: CELL ELONGATION OF OAT COLEOPTILES

	Compound (A)	Activity Index (B)
	Benzoic acids	
110	2,4-Dichlorobenzoic acid	0
111	2,5-Dichlorobenzoic acid	1
112	2,6-Dichlorobenzoic acid	0.1
113	Pentachlorobenzoic acid	0
114	2-Chloro-4-fluorobenzoic acid	0
115	2-Chloro-6-fluorobenzoic acid	0.1
116	2-Chloro-5-nitrobenzoic acid	0
117	4-Ethyl-3-mercaptobenzoic acid	0
118	2-Fluorobenzoic acid	0
119	2,5-Difluorobenzoic acid	0
120	2-Fluoro-5-aminobenzoic acid	0
121	2-Fluoro-5-chlorobenzoic acid	0
122	2-Fluoro-3,5-dichlorobenzoic acid	0
123	2-Trifluoromethylbenzoic acid	0
124	2-Iodobenzoic acid	0
125	2,3,5-Triiodobenzoic acid	50
126	3,4,5-Triiodobenzoic acid	0
127	2,6-Dimethylbenzoic acid	0.05
128	2,6-Dimethyl-3-bromobenzoic acid	3
129	2,6-Dimethyl-3-chlorobenzoic acid	2
130	2,6-Dimethyl-3-iodobenzoic acid	2.5
131	2,6-Dimethyl-3-nitrobenzoic acid	0.1
132	2,4,6-Trimethylbenzoic acid	0
133	2-Nitrobenzoic acid	0.1
	Miscellaneous compounds	
134	Adamantine-1-acetic acid	0
135	Azulene-1-acetic acid	1
136	Azulene-1-acetonitrile	4

	Compound (A)	Activity Index (B)
	Miscellaneous compounds	
137	Azulene-1-carboxylic acid	0
138	Benzothiazyl-2-oxyacetic acid	0.5
139	Carboxymethyl dimethyldithiocarbamate	0.5
140	Ethoxycarbonylmethyl dimethyldithiocarbamate	1
141	Ethoxycarbonylmethyl diethyldithiocarbamate	0.1
142	Ethoxycarbonylmethyl dibutyldithiocarbamate	0
143	1-Cyclohexenylacetic acid	0.1
144	Δ-1-Cyclopentenylacetic acid	0
145	Ferroceneacetic acid	0
146	Ferrocenediacetic acid	0
147	Ferrocenepropionic acid	0
148	Gibberellic acid	100
149	5-Indanyloxyacetic acid	0
150	1-Naphthaleneacetic acid	50
151	1-Naphthaleneacetonitrile	100
152	1-Naphthoic acid	0
153	2-Naphthoxyacetic acid	0.7
154	2-Phenanthreneacetic acid	0
155	3-Pyridoxyacetic acid	0
156	3-Pyridylacetic acid	0.01
157	Quinoline-5-oxyacetic acid	0
158	Quinoline-6-oxyacetic acid	0
159	5-Chloroquinoline-6-oxyacetic acid	0
160	5-Chloroquinoline-8-oxyacetic acid	0
161	8-Chloroquinoline-5-oxyacetic acid	0

Contributor: Muir, Robert M.

References: [1] Muir, R. M., and C. Hansch. 1953. Plant Physiol. 28:218. [2] Muir, R. M., and C. Hansch. 1955. Ann. Rev. Plant Physiol. 6:157. [3] Muir, R. M., and C. Hansch. 1961. Proc. 4th Intern. Conf. Plant Growth Regulation, 1959, p. 249. [4] Muir, R. M., and C. Hansch. 1961. Nature 190:741. [5] Muir, R. M., C. Hansch, and J. Gally. 1961. Plant Physiol. 36:222.

Part II: STEM CURVATURE OF SPLIT PEA AND LEAF EXPANSION OF BEAN

	Compound (A)	Split Pea Stem Curvature[1] (B)	Bean Leaf Expansion[2] (C)
	Indole acids		
1	3-Indoleacetic acid	100	<18
2	β-(3-Indole)-propionic acid	....	<19
3	γ-(3-Indole)-butyric acid	190	<40
	Phenoxy compounds		
4	Phenoxyacetic acid	0	<11
5	2-Chlorophenoxyacetic acid	4	<19
6	2-Bromophenoxyacetic acid	....	<23
7	3-Chlorophenoxyacetic acid	....	<37

	Compound (A)	Split Pea Stem Curvature[1] (B)	Bean Leaf Expansion[2] (C)
	Phenoxy compounds		
8	4-Chlorophenoxyacetic acid	200	18,700
9	4-Bromophenoxyacetic acid	....	6160
10	2,4-Difluorophenoxyacetic acid	12	5360
11	2,4-Dichlorophenoxyacetic acid	200-1200	23,500
12	2,5-Dichlorophenoxyacetic acid	15	<69
13	2,6-Dichlorophenoxyacetic acid	3-4	137
14	3,5-Dichlorophenoxyacetic acid	<0.05	<44
15	2,4-Dibromophenoxyacetic acid	....	11,500

/1/ Expressed as percent of activity of 3-indoleacetic acid [4]. /2/ Activity expressed as reciprocal of dose (micromoles) causing 50% repression of leaf expansion [2].

continued

152. RELATIVE ACTIVITY OF GROWTH REGULATORS: PLANTS

Part II: STEM CURVATURE OF SPLIT PEA AND LEAF EXPANSION OF BEAN

	Compound	Split Pea Stem Curvature[1]	Bean Leaf Expansion[2]
	(A)	(B)	(C)
	Phenoxy compounds		
16	2,4-Diiodophenoxyacetic acid	....	344
17	4-Chloro-2-methylphenoxyacetic acid	500	513
18	2,4,5-Trichlorophenoxyacetic acid	500	<4740
19	2,4,6-Trichlorophenoxyacetic acid	0.4	294
20	2,4,6-Tribromophenoxyacetic acid	0.1	....
21	2,4,6-Trimethylphenoxyacetic acid	0	....
22	2,3,4,6-Tetrachlorophenoxy-acetic acid	1	....
23	DL-α-(2,4-Dichlorophenoxy)-propionic acid	600	16,800
24	D-α-(2,4-Dichlorophenoxy)-propionic acid	1200	....
25	β-(2,4-Dichlorophenoxy)-propionic acid	....	<47
26	γ-(2,4-Dichlorophenoxy)-butyric acid	....	18,500
27	*n*-Butyl 2,4-dichlorophenoxy-acetate	....	23,100
28	2,4-Dichlorophenoxyacetyl-chloride	....	19,900
29	2,4-Dichlorophenoxyacetamide	....	7760
30	2,4-Dichlorophenoxyacetanilide	....	30,800
31	2,4-Dichlorophenoxyethanol	....	22
32	2,4-Dichlorophenoxyethylamine	....	296
33	2,4-Dichlorophenoxythioacetic acid	....	20,300
	Phenyl acids		
34	Phenylacetic acid	3-6;10	<3
35	γ-Phenylbutyric acid	2	....
36	4-Bromophenylbutyric acid	15	....
37	2,4-Dichlorophenylacetic acid	15	....
38	*N*-(2,4-Dichlorophenyl)-glycine	....	2.04
39	*S*-(2,4-Dichlorophenyl)-thioglycolic acid	....	<47
40	2,4-Dinitrophenylacetic acid	0.1	<23
41	Phenylthioacetic acid	0	....
42	4-Chloro-2-methylphenylthio-acetic acid	200	....
	Benzoic acids		
43	2-Chlorobenzoic acid	....	<5
44	3-Chlorobenzoic acid	....	<15
45	4-Chlorobenzoic acid	....	<8
46	2,4-Dichlorobenzoic acid	0	<19
47	2,5-Dichlorobenzoic acid	....	204
48	3,4-Dichlorobenzoic acid	0	<19
49	2,3,5-Trichlorobenzoic acid	....	2130
50	2,3,6-Trichlorobenzoic acid	200	....
51	3,4,5-Trichlorobenzoic acid	....	<45
	Naphthalene compounds		
52	1-Naphthaleneacetic acid	250;370	<100
53	2-Naphthaleneacetic acid	100	<19
54	1-Naphthaleneacetamide	10	....
	Naphthoxy compounds		
55	1-Naphthoxyacetic acid	....	<40
56	2-Naphthoxyacetic acid	....	319
57	1-Naphthoxyacetamide	....	25
	Reference	1, 3-5	6

/1/ Expressed as percent of activity of 3-indoleacetic acid [4]. /2/ Activity expressed as reciprocal of dose (micromoles) causing 50% repression of leaf expansion [2].

Contributors: Brown, James W., and Weintraub, Robert L.

References: [1] Bonner, J. 1950. Plant biochemistry. Academic Press, New York. [2] Brown, J. W., and R. L. Weintraub. 1950. Botan. Gaz. 111:448. [3] Thimann, K. V. 1951. In F. Skoog, ed. Plant growth substances. Univ. Wisconsin Press, Madison. [4] Thimann, K. V. 1952. Plant Physiol. 27:392. [5] Thimann, K. V. Unpublished. Harvard Univ., Cambridge, 1953. [6] Weintraub, R. L., J. W. Brown, and J. A. Throne. Unpublished. Fort Detrick, Maryland, 1953.

	Endocrine Organ	Hormone Secreted	Chemical Nature	Target	Secretion Inhibited by (I) Stimulated by (S)
	(A)	(B)	(C)	(D)	(E)
1	Hypophysis Adenohypophysis	Follicle-stimulating hormone (FSH); thylakentrin	Protein (contains carbohydrate)	Ovarian follicles; seminiferous tubules	(I) Circulating estrogens and possibly androgens (S) Castration; menopause; low blood levels of estrogens or possibly androgens; hypothalamo-pituitary apparatus
2		Luteinizing hormone (LH); interstitial-cell-stimulating hormone (ICSH)	Protein	Maturing graafian follicles and interstitial cells (ovaries); interstitial cells of Leydig (testes)	(I) High levels of ovarian and testicular hormones (S) Intermediate levels of ovarian hormones; hypothalamo-pituitary apparatus
3		Lactogenic hormone (LTH); luteotropin; galactin; prolactin	Protein	Mammary glands; crop sac (pigeon); ovarian corpus luteum	(I) or (S) Effects of androgens, FSH, LH, and progesterone on target organs
4		Growth hormone (GH); somatotrophic hormone (STH)	Peptide	Bones, especially epiphyseal cartilage; most tissues	(S) Small doses of thyroid hormones, in absence of thyroid
5	Neurohypophysis	Oxytocin; oxytocic hormone; posterior-lobe principle	Octapeptide	Uterine and other smooth muscles; mammary glands	(S) Suckling
6	Thyroid	Thyroxin; tri-iodothyronine	Iodinated derivatives of tyrosine	All body cells; adenohypophysis	(I) Anti-thyroid drugs; thiouracil, thiourea, thiocyanate (S) Thyrotrophic hormone; stress
7	Parathyroid	Parathyroid hormone	Peptide	Bone; kidney; other soft tissues?	(I) High serum calcium? (S) Low serum calcium; high serum phosphate
8	Pancreas	Insulin	Protein	Muscle and adipose tissue; probably most other tissues except nervous tissue, erythrocytes and liver?	(I) Low blood glucose; low carbohydrate diet (S) Increase in blood glucose; excess growth hormone; excess adrenocortical hormones?
9	Adrenal cortex	Glucocorticoids	Steroid	Most or all tissues, especially those of mesenchymal origin	(S) ACTH
10	Ovaries Follicles & interstitial tissue	Estrogens (chiefly estradiol)	Steroid	All female secondary sex organs; mammary glands; mucous membranes; adenohypophysis	(S) LH; combined FSH and LH
11	Corpora lutea	Progesterone	Steroid	Endometrium of uterus; mammary gland lobules and alveoli; kidney tubules; adenohypophysis	(S) LTH
12	Testes (interstitial tissue)	Androgen (testosterone)	Steroid	All male secondary sex organs; hair follicles; bones; certain muscles, varying with species; adenohypophysis	(I) Sex steroids (S) ICSH
13	Placenta or chorion	Estrogens	Steroid	All female sex organs; mammary glands; adenohypophysis	
14		Progesterone	Steroid	Uterus; mammary glands; adenohypophysis	
15		Gonadotropin (HCG); prolan	Protein	Ovaries (during pregnancy)	(I) Sex steroids

Contributors: (a) Pritham, Gordon H., (b) Russell, Jane A.

References: [1] Emmens, C. W., ed. 1950. Hormone assay. Academic Press, New York. [2] Fieser, L., and 1949. Handbook of chemistry. Ed. 7. Handbook Publications, Sandusky, Ohio. [4] Means, J. H. 1948. The thyroid [6] Moulton, F. R., ed. 1944. The chemistry and physiology of hormones. American Association for the Advance- New York, v. 1. [8] Pincus, G., and K. V. Thimann. 1948. Ibid. v. 2. [9] Selye, H. 1949. Textbook of endocrin- and Febiger, Philadelphia. [11] Turner, C. D. 1960. General endocrinology. Ed. 3. W. B. Saunders, Philadelphia. ed. 1961. Sex and internal secretions. Ed. 3. Williams and Wilkins, Baltimore. [14] Zondek, H. 1944. Diseases

ON GROWTH: VERTEBRATES

Effects of: Deficiency	Effects of: Excess	Reference	
(F)	(G)	(H)	
Atrophy or immaturity of gonads; no maturation of ova or sperm	Growth of follicles (may be numerous); secretion of estrogen (FSH + LH); enlargement of tubules	7,8,10-12	1
Lack of ovulation and luteinization; little or no secretion of estrogen or androgen; atrophy of interstitial tissue in ovary and testis	Ovulation and luteinization of prepared follicles; increased secretion of estrogen (with FSH) and androgen; hypertrophy of Leydig tissue	5,7-11	2
Failure of lactation; deficient secretion of progesterone by corpus luteum	Initiation of lactation; development of crop glands (pigeon); maintenance of corpus luteum and secretion of progesterone; release of estrogen and progesterone by luteal tissue	5,7,8, 10,11	3
Cessation of growth of skeleton and of soft tissues; increased sensitivity to insulin	Giantism or acromegaly; increased protein anabolism	8-12	4
Delayed uterine contraction (pre- or postpartum); decreased milk flow	Contraction of uterus (especially if prepared by estrogen); increased milk flow	8,9,11, 12	5
Delayed maturation and growth; incomplete differentiation or metamorphosis; dwarfism	Acceleration of growth, of metabolic rate, and of maturation or metamorphosis	4,8-12, 14	6
Hypocalcemia; irritability of nervous system, convulsive seizures; retention of phosphate	Hypercalcemia, increased excretion of calcium and phosphate; renal calculi; increased osteoclastic activity in bone; decreased growth	5,7,9-11	7
Dwarfism; decreased response to growth hormone	Increased food intake; increased fat deposition; increased protein deposition	3,7,9-11	8
Decreased secondary sex characteristics; decreased growth in young	Inhibition of inflammatory responses and wound healing; decreased growth in young	1,6-10, 12	9
Immaturity or atrophy of accessory sex organs; lack of secondary sex characteristics and female behavior patterns	Precocious maturity; hypertrophy of accessory sex organs and mammary glands; estrus changes; deceleration of skeletal growth (premature closing of epiphyses)	1,2,7-13	10
Lack of normal cyclic changes and of development of endometrium for implantation and gestation	Progestational changes; prolongation of pregnancy; inhibition of uterine growth, especially endometrium	2,7-13	11
Immaturity or atrophy of accessory sex organs; lack of secondary sex characteristics and male behavior patterns	Precocious sex development; hypertrophy of accessory sex organs; increased growth of skeleton until closure of epiphyses; increased muscle mass; increased hirsutism	7-13	12
Immaturity or atrophy of accessory sex organs; lack of secondary sex characteristics and female behavior patterns	Precocious maturity; hypertrophy of accessory sex organs and mammary glands; estrus changes	3,5,7-9	13
Lack of normal cyclic changes and of development of endometrium for implantation and gestation	Progestational changes; prolongation of pregnancy	2,5,7-9,12, 14	14
Abortion	Toxemias of pregnancy	6,8,10-12	15

M. Fieser. 1949. Natural products related to phenanthrene. Ed. 3. Reinhold, New York. [3] Lange, N. A., ed.
and its diseases. Ed. 2. J. B. Lippincott, Philadelphia. [5] Merck Index. Ed. 7. 1960. Merck, Rahway, N. J.
ment of Science, Washington, D. C. [7] Pincus, G., and K. V. Thimann. 1948. The hormones. Academic Press,
ology. Ed. 2. Acta Endocrinologica, Montreal. [10] Soffer, L. J. 1951. Diseases of the endocrine glands. Lea
[12] Williams, R. H. 1962. Textbook of endocrinology. Ed. 3. W. B. Saunders, Philadelphia. [13] Young, W. G.,
of the endocrine glands. Ed. 4. Williams and Wilkins, Baltimore.

154. SEX HORMONES: THALLOPHYTES

Hormone (column B): NFC = hormone not fully characterized; PND = existence postulated but not demonstrated. The plus and minus symbols (columns C and D) indicate positively sexed mating groups.

Part I: ALGAE

For additional information, consult references 1, 16, 17-19, 23, 24, 29.

	Family and Species	Hormone	Source	Organ Affected	Specific Activity	Reference
	(A)	(B)	(C)	(D)	(E)	(F)
			Chlorophyta			
	Polyblepharidaceae					
1	*Dunaliella salina*	NFC	+ vegetative cells	- vegetative cells	Induces clumping	15
2		NFC	- vegetative cells	+ vegetative cells	Induces clumping	
	Chlamydomonadaceae					
3	*Chlamydomonas eugametos*	Glucoprotein	+ gametes	- gametes	Induces clumping	4,5,21
4		Glucoprotein	- gametes	+ gametes	Induces clumping	
5	*C. moewusii rotunda*	NFC	- gametes	+ gametes	Chemotaxis	26-28
6	*C. paupera*	PND	Sedentary gametes	Motile gametes	Chemotaxis	22
7	*C. reinhardii*	NFC	+ gametes	- gametes	Induces clumping	6
8		NFC	- gametes	+ gametes	Induces clumping	
	Tetrasporaceae					
9	*Tetraspora lubrica*	NFC	+ gametes	- gametes	Induces clumping	9
10		NFC	- gametes	+ gametes	Induces clumping	
	Hydrodictyaceae					
11	*Hydrodictyon reticulatum*	PND	Sedentary gametes	Motile gametes	Chemotaxis	20
	Ulvaceae					
12	*Ulva lactuca*	PND	+ gametes	- gametes	Induces clumping	8
13		PND	- gametes	+ gametes	Induces clumping	
	Sphaeropleaceae					
14	*Sphaeroplea* sp.	NFC	"Eggs"	"Sperm"	Chemotaxis	22
	Cladophoraceae					
15	*Cladophora suhrina*	PND	+ gametes	- gametes	Induces clumping	7
16		PND	- gametes	+ gametes	Induces clumping	
	Oedogoniaceae					
17	*Oedogonium* sp.	NFC	Oogonial mother cells	Androspores	Chemotaxis	18,25
18		NFC	Oogonial mother cells	Dwarf males	Directional growth	
19		NFC	Dwarf males	Oogonial mother cells	Cell division	
20		NFC	Oogonium	Sperm	Chemotaxis	
21	*O. cardiacum*	NFC	Oogonia	Sperm	Chemotaxis	13
	Dasycladaceae					
22	*Acetabularia mediterranea, A. wettsteinii*	"Fusion factors"; PND	+ gametes	- gametes	Active in chemotaxis, clumping, and copulation	10
23		"Clumping factors"; PND	- gametes	+ gametes		
24		"Attraction factors"; PND				
25	*Dasycladus claeviformis*	NFC	+ gametes	- gametes	Induces clumping	14
26		NFC	- gametes	+ gametes	Induces clumping	
			Phaeophyta			
	Ectocarpaceae					
27	*Ectocarpus siliculosus*	PND	♀ gametes	♂ gametes	Chemotaxis	11
28		PND	♂ gametes	♀ gametes	Induces sedentary habit	
	Cutleriaceae					
29	*Cutleria multifida*	NFC	♀ gametes	♂ gametes	Chemotaxis	12
	Fucaceae					
30	*Fucus serratus, F. spiralis, F. vesiculosis*	Chemotactic hydrocarbon substance	"Eggs"	"Sperm"	Chemotaxis	2,3

Contributors: (a) Machlis, Leonard, and Rawitscher-Kunkel, Erika, (b) Raper, John R.

References: [1] Coleman, A. W. 1962. In R. A. Lewin, ed. Physiology and biochemistry of algae. Academic Press, New York. p. 711. [2] Cook, A. H., and J. A. Elvidge. 1951. Proc. Roy. Soc. (London), B, 138:97.

continued

154. SEX HORMONES: THALLOPHYTES

Part I: ALGAE

[3] Cook, A. H., J. A. Elvidge, and I. Heilbron. 1948. Ibid., B, 135:293. [4] Forster, H., and L. Wiese. 1954. Z. Naturforsch. 9b:548. [5] Forster, H., and L. Wiese. 1955. Ibid. 10b:91. [6] Forster, H., L. Wiese, and G. Braunitzer. 1956. Ibid. 11b:315. [7] Foyn, B. 1934. Arch. Protistenk. 83:1. [8] Foyn, B. 1934. Ibid. 83:154. [9] Geitler, L. 1931. Biol. Zentr. 51:173. [10] Hammerling, J. 1934. Arch. Protistenk. 83:57. [11] Hartmann, M. 1934. Ibid. 83:110. [12] Hartmann, M. 1950. Publ. staz. zool. Napoli 22:120. [13] Hoffman, L. R. 1960. Southwestern Naturalist 5:111. [14] Kőhler, K. 1957. Arch. Protistenk. 102:209. [15] Lerche, W. 1937. Ibid. 88:236. [16] Lewin, R. A. 1954. In D. H. Weinrich, I. F. Lewis, and J. R. Raper, ed. Sex in microorganisms. American Association for the Advancement of Science, Washington, D. C. p. 100. [17] Linskens, H. 1954-60. Fortschr. Botan., Bd. 17-23. [18] Machlis, L. In press, 1962. Biology colloquium for 1961. Oregon State Univ., Corvallis. [19] Machlis, L., and E. Rawitscher-Kunkel. In press, 1962. Intern. Rev. Cytol. [20] Mainx, F. 1931. Arch. Protistenk. 75:502. [21] Moewus, F. 1933. Ibid. 80:469. [22] Pascher, A. 1931. Jahrb. wiss. Botan. 75:551. [23] Raper, J. R. 1952. Botan. Rev. 18:447. [24] Raper, J. R. 1957. Symposia Soc. Exptl. Biol. 11:143. [25] Rawitscher-Kunkel, E., and L. Machlis. 1962. Am. J. Botany 49:177. [26] Tsubo, Y. 1956. Botan. Mag. (Tokyo) 69:1. [27] Tsubo, Y. 1957. Ibid. 70:327. [28] Tsubo, Y. 1961. J. Protozool. 8:114. [29] Wiese, L. 1961. Fortschr. Zool. 13:119.

Part II: FUNGI

For additional information, consult references 14, 19, 34-37, 42.

	Family and Species	Hormone	Source	Organ Affected	Specific Activity	Reference
	(A)	(B)	(C)	(D)	(E)	(F)
	Phycomycetes					
	Blastocladiaceae					
1	*Allomyces* sp.	Sirenin; NFC	♀ gametes	♂ gametes	Chemotaxis	15-18
	Saprolegniaceae					
2	*Achlya bisexualis*,	A; NFC	♀ vegetative	♂ vegetative	Produces antheridial hyphae	3,8,26-33,38,40
3	*A. ambisexualis*	A_1; NFC	♂ vegetative	♂ vegetative	Augments A and A_1	
4	and, in part, in	A_2; NFC	♀ vegetative	♂ vegetative	Produces antheridial hyphae	
5	other species of	A_3; NFC	♂ vegetative	♂ vegetative	Inhibits A, A_1, A_2	
6	*Achlya* and *Thraustotheca*	B; NFC	♂ antheridial hyphae	♀ vegetative	Produces oogonial initials	
7		C; NFC	♀ oogonial initials	♂ antheridial hyphae	Attracts antheridial hyphae; causes delimitation of antheridia	
8		D; NFC	♂ antheridial hyphae	♀ oogonial initials	Causes oogonial delimitation and gametic differentiation	
	Rhipidiaceae					
9	*Sapromyces reinschii*	NFC	♀ vegetative	♂ vegetative	Produces antheridial hyphae	4
10		PND	♀ oogonial initials	♂ antheridial hyphae	Attracts antheridial hyphae	
	Mucoraceae					
11	*Mucor hiemalis*, *M. mucedo*, *Phycomyces blakesleeanus*, *Rhizopus nigricans*	+ progamone; NFC	+ mycelium	- mycelium	Induces production of - zygogenic hormone	2,7,9,10,21-25,39,41
12		- progamone; NFC	- mycelium	+ mycelium	Induces production of + zygogenic hormone	
13		- zygogenic hormone; NFC	+ mycelium	- mycelium	Induces - zygophores	
14		- zygogenic hormone; NFC	- mycelium	+ mycelium	Induces + zygophores	
15		+ zygotropic hormone; NFC	+ zygophores	- zygophores	Chemotropism	
16		- zygotropic hormone; NFC	- zygophores	+ zygophores	Chemotropism	

continued

154. SEX HORMONES: THALLOPHYTES

Part II: FUNGI

	Family and Species	Hormone	Source	Organ Affected	Specific Activity	Reference
	(A)	(B)	(C)	(D)	(E)	(F)
	Phycomycetes					
	Mucoraceae					
17	*Pilobolus crystallinus*	NFC	+ vegetative	- vegetative	Initiation and control of entire reaction prior to gametangial fusion	11,12
18		NFC	- progametangia	+ progametangia		
	Pezizaceae					
19	*Ascobolus stercorarius*	NFC	+ or - mycelia	Oidia	Suppresses vegetative development	5,6
20		NFC	+ mycelia	- oidia	Sexual activation	
21		NFC	- mycelia	+ oidia	Sexual activation	
22		NFC	+ oidia	- mycelium	Induces ascogonia	
23		NFC	- oidia	+ mycelium	Induces ascogonia	
24		NFC	Oidia	Trichogyne	Chemotropism	
25		NFC	Ascogonia	Ensheathing hyphae	Chemotropism	
	Ascomycetes					
	Melanosporaceae					
26	*Neurospora sitophila*	PND	Vegetative	Compatible vegetative	Inhibits conidial germination	1
27		PND	Conidia, spermatia	Trichogyne	Chemotropism	
	Sordariaceae					
28	*Bombardia lunata*	NFC	Spermatia	Trichogyne	Chemotropism	43
	Gnomoniaceae					
29	*Glomerella cingulata*	PND	Gametangial knot	Compatible vegetative	Chemotropism	20
	Saccharomycetaceae					
30	*Saccharomyces cerevisiae*	NFC	+ cells	- cells	Induces copulatory processes	13

Contributors: (a) Machlis, Leonard, and Rawitscher-Kunkel, Erika, (b) Raper, John R.

References: [1] Backus, M. P. 1939. Bull. Torrey Botan. Club 66:63. [2] Banbury, G. H. 1955. J. Exptl. Botany 6:235. [3] Barksdale, A. W. 1960. Am. J. Botany 47:14. [4] Bishop, H. 1940. Mycologia 32:505. [5] Bistis, G. 1956. Am. J. Botany 43:389. [6] Bistis, G. 1957. Ibid. 44:436. [7] Burgeff, H. 1924. Botan. Abhandl. 4:5. [8] Couch, J. N. 1926. Ann. Botany (London) 40:848. [9] Kehl, H. 1937. Arch. Mikrobiol. 8:379. [10] Köhler, F. 1935. Planta 23:358. [11] Krafczyk, H. 1931. Ber. deut. botan. Ges. 49:141. [12] Krafczyk, H. 1935. Beitr. Biol. Pflanz. 23:349. [13] Levi, J. D. 1956. Nature 177:753. [14] Linskens, H. 1954-60. Fortschr. Botan., Bd. 17-23. [15] Machlis, L. 1958. Nature 181:1790. [16] Machlis, L. 1958. Physiol. Plantarum 11:181. [17] Machlis, L. 1958. Ibid. 11:845. [18] Machlis, L. In press, 1962. Biology colloquium for 1961. Oregon State Univ., Corvallis. [19] Machlis, L., and E. Rawitscher-Kunkel. In press, 1962. Intern. Rev. Cytol. [20] McGahen, J. W., and H. E. Wheeler. 1951. Am. J. Botany 38:610. [21] Plempel, M. 1957. Arch. Mikrobiol. 26:151. [22] Plempel, M. 1960. Naturwissenschaften 47:472. [23] Plempel, M. 1960. Planta 55:254. [24] Plempel, M., and G. Braunitzer. 1958. Z. Naturforsch. 13b:302. [25] Plempel, M., and W. Dawid. 1961. Planta 56:438. [26] Raper, J. R. 1939. Am. J. Botany 26:639. [27] Raper, J. R. 1939. Science 89:321. [28] Raper, J. R. 1940. Am. J. Botany 27:162. [29] Raper, J. R. 1942. Ibid. 29:159. [30] Raper, J. R. 1942. Proc. Natl. Acad. Sci. U.S. 28:509. [31] Raper, J. R. 1950. Ibid. 36:524. [32] Raper, J. R. 1950. Botan. Gaz. 112:1. [33] Raper, J. R. 1951. Am. Scientist 39:110. [34] Raper, J. R. 1952. Botan. Rev. 18:447. [35] Raper, J. R. 1954. In D. H. Weinrich, I. F. Lewis, and J. R. Raper, ed. Sex in microorganisms. American Association for the Advancement of Science, Washington, D.C. p.42. [36] Raper, J. R. 1957. Symposia Soc. Exptl. Biol. 11:143. [37] Raper, J. R. 1960. Am. J. Botany 47:749. [38] Raper, J. R., and A. J. Haagen Smit. 1942. J. Biol. Chem. 143:311. [39] Ronsdorf, L. 1931. Planta 14:482. [40] Salvin, S. B. 1942. Am. J. Botany 29:674. [41] Verkaik, C. 1930. Proc. Koninkl. Akad. Wetenschap. Amsterdam 33:656. [42] Wiese, L. 1961. Fortschr. Zool. 13:119. [43] Zickler, H. 1937. Z. induktive Abstammungs.- u. Vererbungslehre 73:403.

APPENDIXES

Appendix I. ESTIMATED NUMBER OF SPECIES: ANIMAL AND PLANT KINGDOMS

Classification for animal kingdom adapted from Lord Rothschild, *A Classification of Living Animals*, 1961; classification for plant kingdom adapted from Engler, *Syllabus der Pflanzenfamilien*, I Band, 1954.

	Phylum and Class	No. of Species	Reference
	(A)	(B)	(C)
	Animal Kingdom		
1	Chordata	60,955	4, 8, 11, 12
2	Mammalia	4,500	11
3	Aves	8,590	8, 11
4	Reptilia	7,820	4
5	Amphibia	3,339	4
6	Pisces, Chondrichthyes, Agnatha	35,000	12
7	Cephalochordata[1]	13	11
8	Urochordata[1]	1,600	8, 11
9	Hemichordata[1]	91	11
10	Echinodermata	5,700	11
11	Ophiuroidea	1,900	6
12	Asteroidea	1,100	9
13	Echinoidea	850	6
14	Holothuroidea	1,100	6
15	Crinoidea	800	9
16	Pogonophora	43	11
17	Chaetognatha	50	11
18	Arthropoda	765,257	11
19	Tardigrada	280	11
20	Pentastomida	60	11
21	Pycnogonida	440	11
22	Arachnida	30,000	11
23	Merostomata	4	11
24	Crustacea	25,000	11
25	Insecta	700,000	11
26	Symphyla, Chilopoda, Diplopoda, Pauropoda	9,400	11
27	Onychophora	73	11
28	Annelida	7,000	8, 11
29	Echiuroidea	60	3, 8
30	Sipunculoidea	250	3, 8
31	Mollusca	81,000	10
32	Cephalopoda	675	10
33	Bivalvia	15,000	10
34	Scaphopoda	325	10
35	Gastropoda	64,200	10
36	Amphineura	800	10
37	Brachiopoda	260	3, 11
38	Phoronida	15	3, 9, 11
39	Polyzoa	4,000	11
40	Entoprocta	60	3, 8, 11
41	Acanthocephala	300	8, 11
42	Aschelminthes	11,995	11
43	Nematoda	10,000	11
44	Nematomorpha	250	11
45	Priapulida	5	8, 11
46	Echinoderida	100	11
	Aschelminthes		
47	Gastrotricha	140	11
48	Rotifera	1,500	8, 11
49	Nemertina	550	11
50	Platyhelminthes	9,000	3
51	Ctenophora	80	3, 11
52	Cnidaria	9,600	11
53	Porifera	4,500	3, 8
54	Mesozoa	50	8, 11
55	Protozoa	30,000	3, 8, 11
	TOTAL	990,725	
	Plant Kingdom		
56	Bacteria	1,600	2
57	Cyanophyta	1,400	5
58	Glaucophyta	12	5
59	Myxophyta	500	5
60	Euglenophyta	450	5
61	Pyrrophyta	1,100	5
62	Chrysophyta	10,000	5
63	Chlorophyta	6,500	13
64	Charophyta	250	13
65	Phaeophyta	1,500	5
66	Rhodophyta	4,000	5
67	Fungi	50,000	1
68	Archimycetes	120	1
69	Phycomycetes	1,400	1
70	Ascomycetes	15,000	1
71	Basidiomycetes	15,000	1
72	Fungi imperfecti	15,000	1
73	Lichenes	18,000	5
74	Bryophyta	23,315	5, 13
75	Hepaticae	8,800	13
76	Musci	14,515	5
77	Pteridophyta	10,238	5
78	Psilophytopsida	27	5
79	Lycopsida	1,166	5
80	Psilotopsida	5	5
81	Articulatae	40	5
82	Filices	9,000	5
83	Gymnospermae	750	5
84	Cycadopsida	100	5
85	Coniferopsida	555	5
86	Taxopsida	15	5
87	Chlamydospermae	80	5
88	Angiospermae	285,000	7
89	Monocotyledoneae	48,500	7
90	Dicotyledoneae	236,500	7
	TOTAL	414,615	

/1/ Subphylum.

Contributors: (a) Rothschild, Lord, (b) Kellogg, Remington, (c) Swallen, Jason R.

References: [1] Ainsworth, G. C. 1961. Dictionary of the fungi. Commonwealth Mycological Institute, Kew, England. [2] Breed, R. S., E. G. D. Murray, and N. R. Smith, ed. 1957. Bergey's Manual of determinative bacteriology. Ed. 7. Williams and Wilkins, Baltimore. [3] Buchsbaum, R., and L. J. Milne. 1960. The lower

continued

Appendix I. ESTIMATED NUMBER OF SPECIES: ANIMAL AND PLANT KINGDOMS

animals. Doubleday, Garden City, N. Y. [4] Cochran, D. M. Unpublished. U. S. Natl. Museum, Washington, D. C., 1962. [5] Engler, A. 1954. Syllabus der Pflanzenfamilien. Ed. 12. Gebrüder Bornträger, Berlin. [6] Fell, H. B. 1960. In W. H. Crouse, ed. McGraw-Hill encyclopedia of science and technology. McGraw-Hill, New York. [7] Jones, G. N. 1951. Sci. Monthly 72:289. [8] Mayr, E., E. G. Linsley, and R. L. Usinger. 1953. Methods and principles of systematic zoology. McGraw-Hill, New York. [9] Pratt, H. S. 1951. Manual of the common invertebrate animals. Blakiston, Philadelphia. [10] Rehder, H. A. Unpublished. U. S. Natl. Museum, Washington, D. C., 1962. [11] Rothschild, Lord. 1961. A classification of living animals. J. Wiley and Sons, New York. [12] Schultz, L. P., and E. M. Stern. 1962. The ways of fishes. Van Nostrand, New York. [13] Swallen, J. R. Unpublished. U. S. Natl. Museum, Washington, D. C., 1962.

Appendix II. SIGNIFICANT LEVELS OF t, F, AND X^2

In each block, upper value represents 5% level of significance, lower value 1% level. With only 1 degree of freedom for greater mean square, $F = t^2$; and for n_1 degrees of freedom, X^2 (chi-square) = n_1 x F ∞ degrees of freedom.

		n_1 = no. of degrees of freedom for greater mean square											
		1	2	3	4	5	6	8	10	12	15	20	50
n_2 = no. of degrees of freedom for lesser mean square	*t*	*F*											
1	12.7 63.7	161 4052	200 4999	216 5403	225 5625	230 5764	234 5859	239 5981	242 6056	244 6106	246 6156	248 6208	252 6302
2	4.3 9.9	18.5 98.5	19.0 99.0	19.2 99.2	19.2 99.2	19.3 99.3	19.3 99.3	19.4 99.4	19.4 99.4	19.4 99.4	19.4 99.4	19.4 99.4	19.5 99.5
3	3.2 5.8	10.1 34.1	9.6 30.8	9.3 29.5	9.1 28.7	9.0 28.2	8.9 27.9	8.8 27.5	8.8 27.2	8.7 27.0	8.7 26.9	8.7 26.7	8.6 26.4
4	2.8 4.6	7.7 21.2	6.9 18.0	6.6 16.7	6.4 16.0	6.3 15.5	6.2 15.2	6.0 14.8	6.0 14.5	5.9 14.4	5.9 14.2	5.8 14.0	5.7 13.7
5	2.6 4.0	6.6 16.3	5.8 13.3	5.4 12.1	5.2 11.4	5.0 11.0	5.0 10.7	4.8 10.3	4.7 10.0	4.7 9.9	4.6 9.7	4.6 9.6	4.4 9.2
6	2.4 3.7	6.0 13.7	5.1 10.9	4.8 9.8	4.5 9.2	4.4 8.8	4.3 8.5	4.2 8.1	4.1 7.9	4.0 7.7	3.9 7.6	3.9 7.4	3.8 7.1
8	2.3 3.4	5.3 11.3	4.5 8.6	4.1 7.6	3.8 7.0	3.7 6.6	3.6 6.4	3.4 6.0	3.3 5.8	3.3 5.7	3.2 5.5	3.2 5.4	3.0 5.1
10	2.2 3.2	5.0 10.0	4.1 7.6	3.7 6.6	3.5 6.0	3.3 5.6	3.2 5.4	3.1 5.1	3.0 4.8	2.9 4.7	2.8 4.6	2.8 4.4	2.6 4.1
12	2.2 3.1	4.8 9.3	3.9 6.9	3.5 6.0	3.3 5.4	3.1 5.1	3.0 4.8	2.8 4.5	2.8 4.3	2.7 4.2	2.6 4.0	2.5 3.9	2.4 3.6
15	2.1 2.9	4.5 8.7	3.7 6.4	3.3 5.4	3.1 4.9	2.9 4.6	2.8 4.3	2.6 4.0	2.6 3.8	2.5 3.7	2.4 3.5	2.3 3.4	2.2 3.1
20	2.1 2.8	4.4 8.1	3.5 5.8	3.1 4.9	2.9 4.4	2.7 4.1	2.6 3.9	2.4 3.6	2.4 3.4	2.3 3.2	2.2 3.1	2.1 2.9	2.0 2.6
50	2.0 2.7	4.0 7.2	3.2 5.1	2.8 4.2	2.6 3.7	2.4 3.4	2.3 3.2	2.1 2.9	2.0 2.7	2.0 2.6	1.9 2.4	1.8 2.3	1.6 1.9
100	2.0 2.6	3.9 6.9	3.1 4.8	2.7 4.0	2.5 3.5	2.3 3.2	2.2 3.0	2.0 2.7	1.9 2.5	1.8 2.4	1.8 2.2	1.7 2.1	1.5 1.7
∞	1.96 2.58	3.8 6.6	3.0 4.6	2.6 3.8	2.4 3.3	2.2 3.0	2.1 2.8	1.9 2.5	1.8 2.3	1.8 2.2	1.7 2.0	1.6 1.9	1.4 1.5
X^2 (chi-square)		3.8 6.6	6.0 9.2	7.8 11.3	9.5 13.3	11.1 15.1	12.6 16.8	15.5 20.1	18.3 23.2	21.0 26.2	25.0 30.6	31.4 37.6	67.5 76.0

Contributors: (a) Wadley, F. M., (b) Fortmann, Henry

References: [1] Fisher, R. A., and F. Yates. 1948. Statistical tables for biological, agricultural and medical research. Oliver and Boyd, Edinburgh. [2] Snedecor, G. W. 1946. Statistical methods. Ed. 4. Iowa State College Press, Ames.

Appendix III. GENETIC SEGREGATIONS AT 5% AND 1% PROBABILITY LEVELS

Columns B and C give the number of offspring required to obtain at least one desired individual among different genetic segregations at 5% and 1% probability levels.

	Mendelian Ratios	Probability Level at 5%	1%
	(A)	(B)	(C)
1	1:1	4	7
2	1:1:1:1, 3:1	10	16
3	15:1, 9:3:3:1, etc.	46	71
4	63:1, etc.	190	292
5	255:1, etc.	765	1176
6	2:1 (F_3)	7	11
7	8:1 (F_3)	25	39

Formula for calculating number *(n)* of required individuals at desired probability levels for all Mendelian ratios: $p = (\frac{e}{f})^n$

p = probability level desired
e = multiple dominant term of the numerator of a Mendelian fraction
f = common denominator of all the terms of the Mendelian fraction
n = number of required individuals needed to assure desired probability level

Example: How many individuals in a 15:1 Mendelian ratio are required to show at 5% probability that no double recessive is expected?

By substituting known values (p = 0.05, e = 15, f = 16) in the formula $p = (\frac{e}{f})^n$, n can be solved by transforming to logarithms:

$$(\log \frac{15}{16})^n = \log 0.05$$
$$n(\log 15 - \log 16) = \log 0.05$$
$$n = (1.17609 - 1.20412) = \bar{2}.69897 \text{ or } 8.69897 - 10$$
$$n = (-0.028029) = -1.30103$$
$$n = 46.4$$

Thus a population of 46 individuals is adequate to assure 1 phenotype or genotype out of 16 at a probability of 5%, if both gene pairs are segregating.

Rule of thumb for estimating n: At 5% probability, use 3 times the Mendelian denominator; at 1% probability, use 5 times the Mendelian denominator.

Contributors: (a) Poole, Charles F., (b) Mainland, Gordon B.

Appendix IV. CONSTANTS FOR USE IN BODY SURFACE AREA FORMULA: MAMMALS

K-values were derived from surface area values taken from extensive literature sources, using the formula $K = \frac{\text{area (sq cm)}}{\text{weight}^{2/3}\text{(g)}}$. Method (column D): M = mold, T = triangulation, S = skinning, I = surface integrator, P = perimeter, C = paper cover. Values in parentheses are ranges, estimate "c" for body weight (column E) and "d" for K-value (column F) (cf. Introduction).

	Order	Species	No. of Subjects	Method	Body Weight g	K-value (Constant)	Reference
	(A)	(B)	(C)	(D)	(E)	(F)	(G)
1	Primates	*Macaca mulatta*	6	M	2670(800-6600)	11.8(10.8-13.2)	2
2	Artiodactyla	*Antilope rupicapra*	1	T	6300	14.1	6
3		*Bos taurus* (Hereford-Shorthorn)	15	S	476,000(208,000-762,000)	9.3(8.1-10.8)	25
4			15[1]	S	375,000(163,000-641,000)	11.0(9.0-13.8)	25
5			10[1,2]	S	241,000(89,000-407,000)	9.9(9.3-10.5)	28
6			11[1,3]	S	315,000(78,000-493,000)	9.4(8.8-10.0)	28
7			7[1,4]	S	695,000(476,000-815,000)	7.6(7.3-7.9)	28
8		*Capra hircus*	1	T	15,100	10.5	6
9		*Ovis aries*	8	S	(21,800-29,100)	10.7	16
10			15	S	(3,780-50,400)	9.1	16
11			14	S	(23,600-37,700)	8.5	18
12			115	I	(2,200-68,000)	8.3	22
13		*Sus scrofa*	7	S	48,300(1,100-123,000)	9.9(8.6-12.4)	25
14			16	I	(25,000-330,000)	9.0	3
15			1	T	40,110	15.3	6
16	Perissodactyla	*Equus caballus*	8	S	(47,000-555,000)	10.5	26
17			11	I	(70,000-750,000)	(8.2-10.3)	3
18	Carnivora	*Canis familiaris*	6	S	1070(130-3650)	10.1(9.3-11.0)	27
19			1	S	1080	11.0	10
20			8	S & P	12,700(3,200-29,800)	11.6(10.2-12.5)	23
21			2	T	9,500(8,900-10,100)	9.9(9.85-9.90)	6
22			7	M	14,310(3,390-32,640)	11.2(10.3-12.1)	5
23			1	C	27,000	12.3	12
24		*Felis catus*	3	S	708(219-1389)	10.7(9.5-11.9)	27
25			2	S	100(84-116)	10.0(9.9-10.0)	27
26			2	T	1550(1500-1600)	8.7(8.6-8.9)	6
27		*Mustela foina*	1	T	1400	8.8	6
28		*Panthera leo*	1	T	64,200	12.3	6
29		*Vulpes vulpes*	2	T	6200(6100-6300)	13.0(12.9-13.2)	6
30	Cetacea	*Balaenoptera physalis*	3	P	160,000(115,000-220,000)	8.3(7.5-8.9)	19
31			1	P	43,000,000	11.1	19

/1/ Empty weight. /2/ Thin. /3/ Medium. /4/ Fat.

continued

Appendix IV. CONSTANTS FOR USE IN BODY SURFACE AREA FORMULA: MAMMALS

	Order	Species	No. of Subjects	Method	Body Weight g	K-value (Constant)	Reference
	(A)	(B)	(C)	(D)	(E)	(F)	(G)
32	Rodentia	*Cavia* spp.	6	S	206(123-269)	9.5(8.4-10.8)	21
33			3	S	157(123-191)	10.4(10.1-10.8)	21
34			3	S	256(235-269)	8.6(8.4-8.9)	21
35			3	S	373(148-650)	9.6(9.0-9.9)	8
36			13[5]	S	323(160-810)	8.9(7.9-9.6)	14
37			2	T	400(380-420)	7.1	6
38		*Clethrionomys gapperi*	1	S	22	7.1	20
39		*Marmota monax*	1	M	1236	9.3	2
40		*Microtus pennsylvanicus*	2	S	29(26-31)	6.9(6.5-7.2)	20
41		*Mus musculus* (albino)	12	S	16(10-22)	11.4(9.7-13.3)	21
42			11	S	15(6-27)	7.9	9
43			3	S	16(11-20)	10.5(10.4-10.5)	8
44			64[5]	S	13	6.9	21,24
45			13	M	(16-25)	9.0(8.4-9.4)	1
46		*Peromyscus* spp.	2	S	22	8.5	20
47		*Rattus norvegicus* (albino)	62	S	176(25-461)	11.4(9.6-13.0)	4
48			22	S	197(65-335)	10.5(9.0-12.7)	17
49			14	S	133(70-310)	11.6(10.9-12.1)	2
50			5	S	80(50-129)	9.9(9.6-10.4)	13
51			5	S	42(35-53)	10.5(10.1-10.8)	2
52			2	T	170(164-177)	7.15	6
53			72	M	(19-418)	9.0	15
54			56	M	125(24-366)	7.5(6.6-8.3)	7
55			14[5]	M	95(22-164)	7.6(7.3-8.8)	7
56	Lagomorpha	*Lepus cuniculus*	3[6]	S	32(26-40)	8.5	9
57			3[6]	S	560(70-925)	9.7	9
58			2	T	1130(1120-1140)	10.0(9.0-11.0)	6
59	Chiroptera	*Myotis lucifugus*	2	S	8.3(5.0-11.6)	44.5(44.0-45.0)	20
60	Insectivora	*Blarina brevicauda*	1	S	20	7.0	20
61		*Erinaceus europaeus*	1	S	200	7.5	10
62		*Sorex cinereus*	1	S	3.5	8.0	20
63	Marsupialia	*Didelphis didelphii*	4	S	1200(1000-1300)	11.3(10.5-11.8)	11

/5/ Starved animals. /6/ Surface area of one side of ear only.

Contributors: Morrison, Peter R., and Meyer, Marion P.

References: [1] Benedict, F. G. 1932. Yale J. Biol. and Med. 4:385. [2] Benedict, F. G. 1934. Ergeb. Physiol. u. exptl. Pharmakol. 36:300. [3] Brody, S., J. E. Comfort, and J. S. Matthews. 1928. Missouri Agr. Expt. Sta. Bull. 115. [4] Carman, G. G., and H. H. Mitchell. 1926. Am. J. Physiol. 76:380. [5] Cowgill, G. R., and D. L. Drabkin. 1927. Ibid. 81:36. [6] Custor, J. 1873. Arch. Anat. u. Physiol., Physiol. Abt., p. 478. [7] Diack, S. L. 1930. J. Nutrition 3:289. [8] Dreyer, G., and W. Ray. 1912. Trans. Roy. Soc. (London), B, 202:191. [9] Giaja, J. 1925. Ann. physiol. physicochim. biol. 1:597. [10] Giaja, J., and B. Males. 1928. Ibid. 4:884. [11] Gley, E., and A. O. De Almeida. 1924. Compt. rend. soc. biol. 90:467. [12] Hecker, C. 1894. Z. Veterinärk. 6:97. [13] Hill, A. V., and A. M. Hill. 1913. J. Physiol. (London) 46:81. [14] Kettner, H. 1909. Arch. Anat. u. Physiol., Physiol. Abt., p. 447. [15] Lee, M. O., and E. Clark. 1929. Am. J. Physiol. 89:24. [16] Lines, E. W., and A. W. Pierce. 1931. Australia Council Sci. and Ind. Research Bull. 55:21. [17] Mardones, G. 1931. Compt. rend. soc. biol. 108:118. [18] Mitchell, H. H. 1928. Ann. Rept. Illinois Agr. Expt. Sta. 317:155. [19] Parry, D. A. 1949. Quart. J. Microscop. Sci. 90:13. [20] Pearson, O. P. 1947. Ecology 28:127. [21] Pfaundler, M. 1916. Z. Kinderheilk. 14:69. [22] Ritzman, E. G., and N. F. Colovos. 1930. Univ. New Hampshire Agr. Expt. Sta. Circ. 32. [23] Rubner, M. 1883. Z. Biol. 19:553. [24] Rubner, M. 1902. Die Gesetze des Energieverbranches bei der Ernährung. F. Deuticke, Leipzig. [25] Seuffert, R. W., R. Giese, and R. Meyer. 1926. Beitr. Physiol. 3:203. [26] Seuffert, R. W., and F. Hertel. 1925. Z. Biol. 82:7. [27] Thomas, K. 1911. Arch. Anat. u. Physiol., Physiol. Abt., p. 9. [28] Trowbridge, P., C. Moulton, and L. Haigh. 1915. Missouri Agr. Expt. Sta. Research Bull. 18.

Appendix V. BODY SURFACE AREA FOR KNOWN WEIGHT AND HEIGHT: MAN

Values are square meters of body surface area, derived according to the method of Sendroy and Cecchini.

	Height	Weight, kg																		
	cm	5	10	15	20	25	30	35	40	45	50	55	60	65	70	75	80	85	90	95
1	20	0.18																		
2	30	0.20	0.35																	
3	40	0.23	0.36																	
4	50	0.26	0.38																	
5	60	0.29	0.41	0.54																
6	70	0.33	0.44	0.57																
7	80	0.37	0.48	0.60	0.68															
8	90	0.42	0.52	0.63	0.72	0.80														
9	100	0.48	0.57	0.67	0.76	0.84	0.92													
10	110	0.55	0.64	0.72	0.80	0.88	0.96	1.04	1.11											
11	120	0.62	0.69	0.77	0.85	0.93	1.01	1.08	1.15	1.23	1.30	1.37	1.44							
12	130		0.76	0.83	0.91	0.98	1.05	1.12	1.20	1.27	1.34	1.42	1.48	1.54	1.61	1.68	1.74	1.81	1.87	
13	140			0.89	0.97	1.03	1.10	1.17	1.25	1.32	1.39	1.46	1.52	1.58	1.65	1.72	1.78	1.84	1.90	1.97
14	150				1.03	1.09	1.16	1.23	1.30	1.37	1.44	1.50	1.57	1.63	1.70	1.76	1.82	1.88	1.94	2.01
15	160					1.15	1.22	1.29	1.36	1.43	1.49	1.55	1.62	1.68	1.75	1.81	1.86	1.92	1.98	2.05
16	170						1.28	1.35	1.42	1.48	1.54	1.61	1.67	1.73	1.80	1.86	1.91	1.97	2.03	2.09
17	180							1.42	1.48	1.54	1.60	1.67	1.73	1.79	1.85	1.91	1.96	2.02	2.08	2.14
18	190								1.55	1.61	1.67	1.73	1.79	1.85	1.91	1.96	2.02	2.07	2.13	2.18
19	200										1.74	1.80	1.85	1.91	1.96	2.02	2.07	2.13	2.18	2.24
20	210												1.92	1.97	2.02	2.07	2.13	2.18	2.24	2.30
21	220														2.08	2.13	2.18	2.24	2.30	2.36
22	230																2.25	2.31	2.36	2.42
23	240																			2.48

	Height	Weight, kg																	
	cm	100	105	110	115	120	125	130	135	140	145	150	155	160	165	170	175	180	185
13	140	2.03	2.10	2.17	2.23														
14	150	2.07	2.14	2.21	2.27	2.33	2.39	2.44	2.50	2.55	2.61	2.66	2.72	2.77					
15	160	2.12	2.18	2.24	2.30	2.36	2.42	2.47	2.53	2.58	2.63	2.69	2.74	2.80	2.86	2.91	2.96	3.01	3.06
16	170	2.16	2.22	2.28	2.33	2.39	2.45	2.51	2.56	2.62	2.67	2.73	2.78	2.83	2.89	2.94	2.99	3.04	3.09
17	180	2.20	2.26	2.32	2.38	2.43	2.49	2.54	2.60	2.66	2.71	2.77	2.83	2.88	2.93	2.98	3.03	3.08	
18	190	2.24	2.31	2.36	2.42	2.48	2.53	2.59	2.64	2.70	2.75	2.81	2.87	2.92	2.97	3.03	3.08		
19	200	2.30	2.35	2.41	2.47	2.53	2.58	2.63	2.69	2.74	2.80	2.86	2.92	2.97	3.02	3.07			
20	210	2.35	2.41	2.47	2.53	2.58	2.63	2.68	2.74	2.80	2.86	2.92	2.97	3.02	3.07				
21	220	2.41	2.47	2.53	2.58	2.63	2.69	2.75	2.81	2.87	2.92	2.97	3.03	3.08					
22	230	2.47	2.53	2.58	2.64	2.70	2.76	2.82	2.87	2.93	2.98	3.03	3.08						
23	240	2.54	2.60	2.65	2.71	2.77	2.83	2.88	2.93	2.98	3.04	3.09							
24	250			2.73	2.78	2.84	2.90	2.95	3.00	3.06									
25	260					2.93	2.97	3.02	3.08										

Contributor: Sendroy, Julius, Jr.

Reference: Sendroy, J., Jr., and L. P. Cecchini. 1954. J. Appl. Physiol. 7:1.

INDEX

It is suggested that the index be used in conjunction with the table of contents: the index to locate data for a specific organism, and the table of contents to determine the scope of the data for a particular topic. To facilitate identification, the index includes the taxonomic order for animals, and the family for plants.

† Class

† Class
†† Subphylum

† Class

†† Subphyllum

† Class

† Class

† Class

† Class

† Class

† Class

† Class
* Diagram

† Class

† Class

† Class

† Class

† Class

† Class
††† Subclass
* Diagram

† Class

† Class

† Class

† Class
†† Phylum

† Class

† Class

† Class

† Class

† Class

† Class

† Class
†† Phylum

†† Phylum

†† Phylum

† Class

† Class

† Class

† Class

† Class
†† Phylum

† Class

† Class

† Class

† Class

† Class

† Class

† Class